PSYCHOPATHOLOGY TODAY:
EXPERIMENTATION, THEORY AND RESEARCH

Experimentation, Theory
and Research

PSYCHOPATHOLOGY TODAY

William S. Sahakian

SUFFOLK UNIVERSITY

F. E. PEACOCK PUBLISHERS, INC. • ITASCA • ILLINOIS

Dedicated to my daughter

BARBARA JACQUELYN SAHAKIAN

whose effervescent personality
permeates any room with
joyous excitement

Preface

No field of psychology since World War II has had the vertical progress and development of that found in psychopathology. Research, especially in the area of schizophrenia, has enlisted the efforts of many able professionals in advancing our knowledge to a markedly higher level of sophistication heretofore unknown, with some researchers believing that the problem of schizophrenia will be resolved in our own lifetime!

Such rapid progress has had the effect of relegating the giants of the past (such as Freud) to the background, where their value has been diminished to historical worth for the most part. These new and significant developments in psychopathology, ordinarily reported in numerous journals published throughout the world, are now made available in a single volume to the reader who does not have these articles or journals at his disposal or who is not prepared to review voluminous material requiring research.

In order to integrate the diverse selections of the many writers representing varying schools of thought, an introduction to each chapter has been provided as a point of orientation. In this respect, the present text is the first book of its kind in psychopathology to be offered to the reading public.

WILLIAM S. SAHAKIAN

Beacon Hill
Boston, Massachusetts
January, 1970

Contents

CHAPTER I

Classification and Definition of Mental Disorders

PSYCHIATRY AND PSYCHOPATHOLOGY

P ERHAPS THE MAIN DISTINCTION between psychology and psychiatry is that the former is a science whose principal subject matter is the study of human behavior, whereas the latter is an applied science, the application of science to those persons afflicted with behavior disorders. Accordingly, psychopathology would then be defined as the science dealing with behavior disorders, while psychiatry is the practice, art, or technique of treating mental, emotional, or behavioral disorders (Jaspers, 1963; Silverman, 1963). Although the two may not overlap in theory, yet in fact or practice they do.

CLASSIFICATION OF MENTAL DISORDERS

The problem of the classification of mental disorders has posed a number of questions, such as: Which list of mental disorders should be adopted? Which diagnostic terms are preferable? Is it possible to classify mental disorders accurately, or is each case unique? Is the diagnosis and classification of mental disorder of a particular patient subjective on the part of the diagnostician?

One commonly accepted list of mental disorders is found in the *Diag-*

nostic and Statistical Manual: Mental Disorders, prepared by the Committee on Nomenclature and Statistics of the American Psychiatric Association (1965). A second one, adopted by the Nineteenth World Health Assembly is published by the World Health Organization (1967) in their *Manual of the International Statistical Classification of Diseases, Injuries, and Causes of Death.*

Lists, however, must be continually revised because of the emergence of new facts, theories, and findings. For example, some psychologists see more intelligence in distinguishing schizophrenia by the *process or reactive* distinction rather than by the simple, hebephrenic, catatonic, and paranoid types (Becker, 1959; Kantor, Wallner, & Winder, 1953; King, 1958). Mongolism is currently termed *Down's syndrome* (London & Rosenhan, 1968; Maher, 1966); and newer terms, concepts, and disorders are appearing, such as, noögenic neurosis (Frankl, 1958a, 1958b, 1959, 1962a, 1962b, 1966a, 1967a) and existential neurosis (Maddi, 1967).

DEFINITION OF MENTAL DISORDER

Albee (1959, pp. 9–10) does not consider a definition of mental illness difficult, and dismisses it as an "unusually persistent pattern of behavior over which the individual has little or no voluntary control; it differentiates him from his fellows; it incapacitates him; it interferes with his normal participation in life." This sweeping definition of mental disorder is too encompassing, for it includes many physical disorders such as heart disease, or no disorder whatever such as old age.

Lately, a fairly acceptable definition of psychosis has been a loss or distortion of one's contact with reality. This definition, however, would not include neurosis, subnormality, and some other disorders. To avoid the problem of distinguishing among mental disorders, Wishner (1953, 1955) proposes *efficiency* as the criterion of mental disorder, a decreased efficiency being the concomitant of the severer or graver mental disorders. But, again, efficiency is too broad a concept, one which would fail to distinguish between physical and mental disorders.

Efficiency is an inadequate criterion, for a definitive criterion would discriminate among sensory-perceptual anomalies, motor anomalies, and thought disorders. Even thought disorders would have to be subdivided into at least two categories: those relating to emotional problems and those disorders of logical thinking. Some work has been accomplished in this area by Von Domarus (1944), who explored the logical thought processes of the schizophrenic, while emotional and logical components of schizophrenic thinking have been investigated by Arieti (1955, 1959). The significance of words in schizophrenic thinking has been studied by

Chapman and Chapman (1965), while Payne (1961, 1962; Payne, Mattusek, & George, 1959; Payne, Caird, & Laverty, 1964) has been experimenting in the area of overinclusive thinking or thought disorder in schizophrenics. According to Bleuler, the thinking of some schizophrenics acquired a *negativism* (1912), while other schizophrenics developed an *autism* (1950). Sullivan (1953) has identified logical modes of experience, which he technically termed the prototaxic, parataxic, and syntaxic. In the prototaxic mode, the experience of an infant is lacking in serial connection and consists of an undifferentiated wholeness of experience between organism and environment; the parataxic mode is a slightly more mature stage of experience in which various experiences are differentiated. In the syntaxic, experience has reached its highest elevation of sophistication, one in which a person is capable of distinguishing logically and linguistically. Prototaxic and parataxic modes of experience are characteristic of psychotics.

Like Sullivan, Piaget (1928, 1929, 1930) studied the logical thought processes of children, and discovered many deficiencies in connection with abstract reasoning and class concepts, a mental state comparable to psychotic thinking. Gesell and Ilg (1949) report that the mind and behavior of the child grow in the direction of complex patterning processes. Mental life undergoes three levels of reality: "(1) *the vegetative functions* of respiration, alimentation, elimination; (2) *the world of things,* in time and space; (3) *the world of persons,* in home and community" (p. 20). The child, growing as a unit, develops as an integrated whole, and adjusts himself at all three levels of reality, but not on the "installment plan." Environmental factors do not beget progressions of development, but merely support them.

Recent reliable studies dealing with the thought processes of neurotics have been sparse. Freud (1963b, lecture 17) claims that the obsessional neurotic is "intellectually gifted above the average" as well as being highly ethical, overconscientious, and "more than usually correct." Horney (1942) sees neurotic thinking stemming from 10 neurotic needs which serve as drives that the neurotic vainly strives to fulfill.

CRITERIA OF NORMALITY AND MENTAL HEALTH

Consensus regarding positive mental health (or even mental abnormality) is far from unanimous (Knutson, 1963). Some identify the mentally ill as anyone who seeks to see a psychiatrist (or has visited one); at the other end of the spectrum there are those who view the mentally ill as those who hallucinate, lose or distort contact with reality, or wish to do away with themselves. The criterion for mental health thus is simply the absence of mental illness (Redlich, 1957). Jahoda (1958, p. 13) points out that *"evaluation of actions as sick, or normal, or extraordinary in a positive sense often depends largely on accepted social conventions."* Mead (1967) elaborates on this point further.

Kubie, whose definition of normality is unsatisfactory because it merely distinguishes between neurosis and psychosis, states that

. . . we are justified in calling "normal" any act in the determination of which the alliance of conscious and preconscious forces places the dominant role, that is, forces that are accessible on need; whereas on the same grounds we are justified in calling abnormal or unhealthy or neurotic an act in the determination of which unconscious processes are dominant (1954, pp. 184–185).

Redlich, also noting this deficiency in Kubie's definition, comments: "In stating his hypothesis he limits mental illness to essential differences between normal and neurotic. He does not consider abnormal behavior determined by organic causes or the problem of mental deficiency" (1957, p. 150). Allport, however, favors Kubie and regards normal motivation as "flexible, largely conscious, and 'at age,'" while neurotic motivation is "blind, largely unconscious, automatic, and disconnected from the remainder of life" (1961, p. 152).

When normality is used as a criterion for mental health, then it is usually defined either as statistical frequency or normatively in terms of the way a person ought to behave. Cultural relativism results from the statistical frequency definition, accordingly resulting in the justification of the cruel behavior of the Nazis during Hitler's regime. However, to define mental health as normality is to beg the question, "What is normality?" hence to become involved in a circular definition. Coleman synthesizes the cultural with the individual by defining normal behavior as the "optimal development and functioning of the individual consistent with the long-term well-being and progress of the group" (1964, p. 18).

Jahoda (1958) cites six criteria for positive mental health: (1) the attitudes of a person toward himself; these would include the ability of self-objectification (Allport, 1937, pp. 213–214) and of bringing the self to consciousness, i.e., being aware of one's motivations; the ability to see the self realistically and correctly as opposed to an ideal self (Cattell, 1957, p. 461; Horney, 1950, pp. 366–378); self-acceptance or the lack of ego-alien impulses; a sense of identity or Cattell's self-sentiment (1965, pp. 193–197; Cattell & Scheier, 1961). (2) A second criterion on positive mental health is growth, development, self-actualization, self-realization, or becoming (coming-to-be), i.e., the successful realization of one's potentialities, a view shared by a number of psychologists, especially Goldstein (1939, 1940) and Maslow (1954, 1967, 1968). (3) Integration as a criterion of mental health (Freud) includes the balance or equilibrium of psychic forces, a unifying philosophy of life, and a reasonable resistance or tolerance to stress and anxiety, i.e., a resiliency of character or ego, a frustration tolerance, or the ability to delay gratification (Allinsmith & Goethals, 1956). Shoben's model of integrative adjustment is "characterized by self-control, personal responsibility, social responsibility, democratic social interest, and ideals" (1957, p. 188). (4) Autonomy or a person's self-determination and relative independence from external influences (including internally regulating one's behavior and the independence of behavior) is also regarded as a criterion of mental health. (5) Still another criterion is the undistorted perception of reality, one free from need-distortion and from loss of contact with reality (Barron, 1955). (6) A sixth criterion for mental health is environmental mastery, one encompassing competency in problem-solving, adaptation or adjustment, adequate interpersonal relationships, a capacity for love, and efficiency in confronting situational requirements.

Approaching the question of mental illness from an operational point of view, Scott (1958) offers six definitions of mental illness: (1) exposure to psychiatric treatment; (2) maladjustment; (3) labeled mentally ill by psychiatric diagnosis; (4) the individual himself sensing that he is mentally ill or seeking assistance; (5) identified mentally ill by the outcome of psychological tests; and (6) the absence of mental health or positive striving for mental health.

Viewing the matter from a clinical psychologist's orientation, Dana (1966) lists five criteria for normality: (1) cultural-social; (2) legal, entailing the McNaghten and Durham rules; (3) statistical; (4) ideal (which includes adjustment to society and personality adjustment); and (5) clinical criterion (judgment of a clinician).

Scott's (1968) list contains the following criteria of normality: (1) general adaptive capacity; (2) capacity for self-gratification; (3) competence in interpersonal roles; (4) intellectual capacity; (5) emotional and motivational control; (6) wholesome attitudes toward people; (7) productivity; (8) autonomy; (9) mature integration; and (10) favorable attitudes toward self. Accompanying these main heads are a number of subheads.

STATISTICS ON MENTAL DISORDERS

According to the National Institute of Mental Health (1967), admissions of patients for the first time to state and county mental hospitals in the United States in 1965 are as follows: Of the 135,476 patients (representing 273 of 290 hospitals), 4,900 were diagnosed as having acute brain syndromes (3,500 of them as alcoholics); 30,952 with chronic brain syndromes (more than half with cerebral arteriosclerosis); 32,971 with psychotic disorders (23,861 of whom were schizophrenics); 245 with psychophysiologic autonomic and visceral disorders; 14,869 with psychoneurotic reactions; 33,662 with personality disorders (approximately half of them with alcoholic addiction); 4,957 with transient situational personality disturbance; 3,629 with mental deficiency; 7,544 with mental disorder undiagnosed; and 1,747 without any mental disorder.

The largest single group is comprised of schizophrenia, with alcoholic disorders running rather closely behind. The only other large segments are composed of those with cerebral arteriosclerosis and neurosis.

References to each "introduction" are found at the end of the final chapter.

1.

WORLD HEALTH ORGANIZATION

INTERNATIONAL CLASSIFICATION OF MENTAL DISORDERS

PSYCHOSES (290–299)

290   Senile and pre-senile dementia

290.0   *Senile dementia*
Dementia of old age
Senile imbecility
Senile:
  insanity
  psychosis NOS

290.1   *Pre-senile dementia*
Alzheimer's disease
Circumscribed atrophy of brain
Jacob-Creuzfeldt disease with dementia
Pick's disease of brain
Pre-senile:
  psychosis
  sclerosis

291   Alcoholic psychosis

291.0   *Delirium tremens*
Delirium alcoholicum

291.1   *Korsakov's psychosis (alcoholic)*
Alcoholic polyneuritic psychosis
Chronic alcoholic delirium

291.2   *Other alcoholic hallucinosis*
Alcoholic hallucinosis NOS

291.3   *Alcoholic paranoia*
Alcoholic psychosis, paranoid type

291.9   *Other and unspecified*
Alcoholic:
  dementia
  insanity
  mania
  psychosis

From World Health Organization, *Manual of the International Statistical Classification of Diseases, Injuries, and Causes of Death: Based on the Recommendations of the Eighth Conference, 1965, and Adopted by the Nineteenth World Health Assembly.* Vol. I. Geneva: World Health Organization, 1967. Pp. 141–155. Reprinted by permission.

(NOS or of any type not classifiable under 291.0-291.3)

292   Psychosis associated with intracranial infection
Includes: brain syndrome with psychotic reaction
  dementia
  psychosis (organic)
(due to or associated with the conditions indicated in categories 292.0-292.9)

292.0   *With general paralysis*
Any condition in 094.1

292.1   *With other syphilis of central nervous system*
Any condition in 090.4, 094.0, 094.9

292.2   *With epidemic encephalitis*
Any condition in 062-065

292.3   *With other and unspecified encephalitis*
Encephalitis:
  NOS
  following infection
  unknown cause (idiopathic)
Encephalomyelitis:
  NOS
  acute disseminated
Inflammation of brain NOS
Includes: postencephalitic psychosis NOS
Excludes: psychosis associated with traumatic encephalitis (293.5)

292.9   *With other and unspecified intracranial infection*
Abscess of brain
Meningitis
Tuberculosis of brain
Intracranial infection, other or unspecified

293   Psychosis associated with other cerebral condition
Includes: brain syndrome with psychotic reaction

dementia
psychosis (organic)
(due to or associated with the conditions
indicated in categories 293.0-293.9)

293.0 *With cerebral arteriosclerosis*
Any condition in 437
Includes: arteriosclerotic psychosis NOS

293.1 *With other cerebrovascular disturbances*
Any condition in 430-436, 438

293.2 *With epilepsy*
Any condition in 345

293.3 *With intracranial neoplasm*
Neoplasm (benign) (malignant):
  brain
  cerebral meninges
  intracranial NOS
Neoplasm (benign) (malignant):
  pineal gland
  pituitary gland

293.4 *With degenerative diseases of central nervous system*
Disease:
  Pelizaeus-Merzbacher
  Schilder's
Huntington's chorea
Multiple sclerosis
Sclerosis of brain
Degeneration of central nervous system, other or
  unspecified
Excludes: senile and pre-senile dementia (290)

293.5 *With brain trauma*
Any condition in:
  N800-N804 (Fracture of skull)
  N850-N854 (Intracranial injury, excluding
  those with skull fracture)
Birth injury to brain
Hypoxia (at birth)
Surgical injury to brain
Trauma to brain from electric current

293.9 *With other and unspecified cerebral condition*
Congenital anomalies of brain
Other or unspecified cerebral conditions

294   Psychosis associated with other physical condition
Includes: brain syndrome with psychotic reaction

dementia
psychosis (organic)
(due to or associated with the conditions
indicated in categories 294.0-294.9)

294.0 *With endocrine disorders*
Any condition in 240-258

294.1 *With metabolic and nutritional disorders*
Any condition in 260-279

294.2 *With systemic infections*
Acute rheumatic fever
Influenza
Malaria
Pneumonia
Septicaemia
Tuberculosis
Typhoid fever
Typhus
Systematic infection, other or unspecified
Excludes: psychosis associated with intracranial
  infection (292)

294.3 *With drug or poison intoxication*
Any condition in 304, N960-N979, N981-N989
Excludes: alcoholic psychosis (291)

294.4 *With childbirth*
Includes: puerperal:
          dementia NOS
          insanity NOS
      puerperal psychosis
          (any type classifiable to 299)
Excludes: psychosis of any type classifiable to
  295-298 arising during the puerperium

294.8 *With other physical conditions*

294.9 *With unspecified physical condition*
Includes: organic psychosis NOS
          postoperative psychosis NOS

295   Schizophrenia

295.0 *Simple type*
Schizophrenia, simple
Schizophrenia, simplex

295.1 *Hebephrenic type*
Hebephrenia
Schizophrenia, hebephrenic

295.2 *Catatonic type*
Catatonia
Schizophrenia, catatonic

295.3 *Paranoid type*
Schizophrenia, paranoid
Schizophrenia, paraphrenic

295.4 *Acute schizophrenic episode*
Acute schizophrenic NOS
Acute schizophrenia attack
Schizophrenic episode
Oneirophrenia
Excludes: conditions in 295.0-295.3 specified as
   acute (295.0-295.3)

295.5 *Latent schizophrenia*
Latent schizophrenic reaction
Pseudoneurotic schizophrenia
Pseudopsychopathic schizophrenia

295.6 *Residual schizophrenia*
Schizophrenic residual state (Restzustand)

295.7 *Schizo-affective type*
Mixed schizophrenic and affective psychosis
Schizo-affective psychosis

295.8 *Other*
Atypical forms of schizophrenia
Infantile autism
Schizophrenia, childhood type, NOS
Schizophrenia of specified type not classifiable
   under 295.0-295.7
Schizophreniform attack or psychosis

295.9 *Unspecified type*
Dementia praecox NOS
Schizophrenia NOS
Schizophrenic reaction NOS

296   **Affective psychoses**

296.0 *Involutional melancholia*
Agitated depression
Agitated melancholia
Climacteric insanity
Climacteric melancholia
Involutional depression
Menopausal melancholia
Excludes: involutional paraphrenic (297.1)

296.1 *Manic-depressive psychosis, manic type*
Hypomania NOS
Hypomanic psychosis
Mania NOS
Manic psychosis
Manic-depressive reaction:
   hypomanic
   manic

296.2 *Manic-depressive psychosis, depressed type*
Endogenous depression
Psychotic depression
Melancholia (senile)
Manic-depressive reaction, depressive

296.3 *Manic depressive psychosis, circular type*
Alternating insanity
Circular insanity
Cyclothymia
Manic-depressive reaction, circular

296.8 *Other*
Manic stupor
Unproductive mania

296.9 *Unspecified*
Affective psychosis NOS
Manic-depressive reaction NOS

297   **Paranoid states**
Excludes: acute paranoid reaction (298.3)
         paraphrenic schizophrenia (295.3)

297.0 *Paranoia*
Paranoiac psychosis

297.1 *Involutional paraphrenia*

297.9 *Other*
Paranoid reaction (chronic)
Paranoid state
Paraphrenia (late) NOS

298   **Other psychoses**

298.0 *Reactive depressive psychosis*
Psychogenic depressive psychosis
Reactive melancholia

298.1 *Reactive excitation*
Acute hysterical psychosis
Psychogenic excitation

298.2 *Reactive confusion*
Acute or sub-acute confusional state
Psychogenic confusion

298.3 *Acute paranoid reaction*
Bouffée délirante

298.9 *Reactive psychosis unspecified*
Psychogenic psychosis NOS
Reactive psychosis NOS

299   **Unspecified psychosis**
Dementia NOS

Exhaustion delirium
Insanity NOS
  confusional
  delusional
Mental deterioration NOS
Psychosis (involutional) NOS

NEUROSES, PERSONALITY DISORDERS AND OTHER NON-PSYCHOTIC MENTAL DISORDERS (300–309)

300   Neuroses
Excludes: when associated with physical conditions (309)

300.0   *Anxiety neurosis*
Anxiety:
  depression
  hysteria
Anxiety:
  reaction
  state (neurotic)
Panic state

300.1   *Hysterical neurosis*
Compensation neurosis
Conversion hysteria
Dissociative reaction
Functional paraplegia
Ganser's syndrome
Hysteria NOS
Hysterical manifestation (any)
Hystero-epilepsy

300.2   *Phobic neurosis*
Fear reaction
Phobia NOS
Phobic reaction

300.3   *Obsessive compulsive neurosis*
Neurosis:
  anankastic
  compulsive
  obsessional
Obsessional:
  phobia
  state
  syndrome

300.4   *Depressive neurosis*
Neurotic depression
Neurotic depressive state

300.5   *Neurasthenia*
Asthenic reaction

Fatigue neurosis
Nervous debility
Psychogenic:
  asthenia
  general fatigue

300.6   *Depersonalization syndrome*
Depersonalization
Derealization
Neurotic state with depersonalization episode

300.7   *Hypochondriacal neurosis*
Hypochondria
Hypochondriasis

300.8   *Other*
Occupational neurosis
Writer's cramp
Other specified neurosis

300.9   *Unspecified neurosis*
Nervous breakdown
Neurosis NOS
Psychoneurosis NOS

301   Personality disorders
Excludes: when associated with physical conditions (309)

301.0   *Paranoid*
Paranoid traits

301.1   *Affective*
Cyclothymic personality
Hyperthymic personality
Hypothymic personality

301.2   *Schizoid*

301.3   *Explosive*
Aggressive personality

301.4   *Anankastic*
Compulsive personality
Obsessive-compulsive personality
Obsessional personality

301.5   *Hysterical*
Histrionic personality
Labile personality

301.6   *Asthenic*
Inadequate personality
Passive personality
Passive-dependent personality

301.7   *Antisocial*
Asocial personality
Moral deficiency

301.8 *Other*
Immature personality NOS
Personality disorder of other specified type

301.9 *Unspecified*
Personality disorder NOS
Pathologic personality NOS

302 Sexual deviation
Excludes: when associated with physical conditions (309)

302.0 *Homosexuality*
Lesbianism
Sodomy

302.1 *Fetishism*

302.2 *Paedophilia*

302.3 *Transvestitism*

302.4 *Exhibitionism*

302.8 *Other*
Erotomania
Masochism
Narcissism
Necrophilia
Nymphomania
Sadism
Voyeurism

302.9 *Unspecified*
Pathological sexuality NOS
Sexual deviation NOS

303 Alcoholism
Excludes: alcoholic psychosis (291)
acute poisoning by alcohol (E860, N980)
when associated with physical conditions (309)

303.0 *Episodic excessive drinking*
Periodic drinking bouts

303.1 *Habitual excessive drinking*
Continual drinking to excess

303.2 *Alcoholic addiction*
Chronic alcoholism
Chronic ethylism
Dipsomania

303.9 *Other and unspecified alcoholism*
Alcoholism (acute) NOS
Ethylism (acute) NOS

304 Drug dependence
For drug dependence on specific substances under 304.0-304.9 see Alphabetical Index
Includes: addiction to
dependence on
chronic poisoning by
(the substances indicated in categories 304.0-304.9)
Excludes: psychosis associated with drug dependence (294.3)
when associated with physical conditions (309)

304.0 *Opium, opium alkaloids and their derivatives*

304.1 *Synthetic analgesics with morphine-like effects*

304.2 *Barbiturates*

304.3 *Other hypnotics and sedatives or tranquilizers*

304.4 *Cocaine*

304.5 *Cannabis sativa*

304.6 *Other psycho-stimulants*

304.7 *Hallucinogenics*

304.8 *Other*

304.9 *Unspecified*
Unspecified drug
Includes: drug:
addiction NOS
dependence NOS

305 Physical disorders of presumably psychogenic origin

305.0 *Skin*
Cutaneous neurosis
Pruritus:
neurogenic
psychogenic
Psychogenic:
dermatitis
eczema
skin reaction

305.1 *Musculoskeletal*
Musculoskeletal neurosis
Psychogenic disorder:
joint
limb
muscle

Psychogenic
  spasm
  torticollis
  tremor
  paralysis

305.2 *Respiratory*
Neurosis:
  larynx
  pharynx
  respiratory
Psychogenic air hunger
Psychogenic
  asthma
  cough
  hyperventilation
  respiratory disorder
  yawning

305.3 *Cardiovascular*
Cardiovascular neurosis
Cardiac neurosis
Da Costa's syndrome
Effort syndrome
Neurocirculatory asthenia
Soldier's heart
Psychogenic:
  cardiovascular disorder
  disturbance, heart rhythm
  heart disease (functional)

305.4 *Haemic and lymphatic*
Psychogenic disorder of blood or lymphatic system

305.5 *Gastro-intestinal*
Aerophagy
Cyclical vomiting
Gastric neurosis
Globus
Mucous colitis, psychogenic
Nervous:
  eructation
  diarrhoea
  dyspepsia
Psychogenic disorder, digestive system

305.6 *Genito-urinary*
Impotence (sexual)
Neurosis, bladder
Psychogenic disorder of:
  genito-urinary system
  micturition

Psychogenic
  disorder of sexual function
  dysmenorrhoea
  dyspareunia
  frigidity

305.7 *Endocrine*
Psychogenic disorder of endocrine system

305.8 *Organs of special sense*
Ocular neurosis

305.9 *Other*
Disorder:
  psychophysiologic NOS
  psychosomatic NOS
Psychogenic disorder of other or unspecified
  parts of the body

306   Special symptoms not elsewhere classified

This category is intended for use where an outstanding specific system is not manifestly part of a more fundamental classifiable condition.

306.0 *Stammering and stuttering*
Cluttering
Lalling
Stammering
Stuttering

306.1 *Specific learning disturbance*
Alexia
Specific learning defects (reading)
  (mathematics) (strephosymbolia)
Word blindness
Word deafness

306.2 *Tics*
Habit spasm

306.3 *Other psychomotor disorders*
Abasia
Astasia

306.4 *Specific disorders of sleep*
Hypersomnia
Insomnia
Nightmare
Sleep walking

306.5 *Feeding disturbances*
Anorexia nervosa

306.6 *Enuresis*
Enuresis

Incontinence of urine
            (of non-organic origin)
Excludes: when of unspecified cause (786.2)

306.7 *Encopresis*
Encopresis
Incontinence of faeces
            (of non-organic origin)
Excludes: when of unspecified cause (785.6)

306.8 *Cephalalgia*
Cephalalgia
Headache
            (of non-organic origin)
Tension headache
Excludes: headache of unspecified cause (791)

306.9 *Other*

307   Transient situational disturbances
Adjustment reaction of:
  adolescence
  late life
Adult situational reaction
Combat fatigue
Gross stress reaction

308   Behaviour disorders in childhood
Adjustment reaction of:
  infancy
  childhood
Jealousy
Masturbation
Tantrum
Truancy
            (of childhood)

309   Mental disorders not specified as psychotic associated with physical conditions
Includes: brain syndrome NOS
          acute
          chronic
        mental disorder:
          NOS
          non-psychotic:
              any type classifiable to 300-304
(due to or associated with the conditions
  indicated in categories 309.0-309.9)

309.0 *With intracranial infections*
Abscess of brain
Encephalitis
Inflammation of brain

Meningitis
Syphilis of central nervous system
Tuberculosis of brain
Intracranial infection, other or unspecified

309.1 *With drug, poison or systemic intoxication*
Acute rheumatic fever
Influenza
Intoxication by drug or poison
Malaria
Pneumonia
Septicaemia
Tuberculosis
Typhoid Fever
Typhus
Systemic intoxication, other or unspecified
Excludes: alcoholism (303)
            drug dependence (304)

309.2 *With brain trauma*
Any condition in:
  N800-N804 (Fracture of skull)
  N850-N854 (Intracranial injury, excluding
    those with skull fracture)
Birth injury to brain
Hypoxia (at birth)
Surgical injury to brain
Trauma to brain from electric current

309.3 *With circulatory disturbance*
Any condition in 393-458

309.4 *With epilepsy*
Any condition in 345

309.5 *With disturbance of metabolism, growth or nutrition*
Any condition in 240-279
Disturbance of metabolism, growth or nutrition,
  other or unspecified

309.6 *With senile or pre-senile brain disease*
Cerebral atrophy or degeneration, senile
Jakob-Creutzfeldt disease
Senile or pre-senile brain disease, other or unspecified

309.7 *With intracranial neoplasm*
Neoplasm (benign) (malignant)
  brain
  cerebral meninges
  intracranial NOS
Neoplasm (benign) (malignant)

pineal gland
pituitary gland

309.8 *With degenerative diseases of central nervous system*

Disease:
Pelizaeus-Merzbacher
Schilder's
Huntington's chorea
Multiple sclerosis
Sclerosis of brain
Degeneration of central nervous system, other or unspecified
Excludes: non-psychotic mental disorders associated with senile or pre-senile brain disease (309.6)

309.9 *With other or unspecified physical condition*

MENTAL RETARDATION (310–315)

The following fourth-digit sub-divisions may be used with categories 310-315:

.0 *Following infections and intoxications*
e.g. prenatal infections such as rubella, syphilis, toxoplasmosis
postnatal infections such as abscess of brain, encephalitis
intoxications such as kernicterus, lead poisoning, maternal toxaemia

.1 *Following trauma or physical agents*
e.g. mechanical injury or hypoxia at birth
postnatal injury or hypoxia

.2 *With disorders of metabolism, growth or nutrition*
e.g. cerebral lipoidosis
hepatolenticular degeneration (Wilson's disease)
hypothyroidism
phenylketonuria

.3 *Associated with gross brain disease (postnatal)*
e.g. acute infantile diffuse sclerosis (Krabbe's disease)
neurofibromatosis (von Recklinghausen's disease)
progressive subcortical encephalopathy (Schilder's disease)

spinal sclerosis (Friedreich's ataxia)
tuberous sclerosis

.4 *Associated with diseases and conditions due to (unknown) prenatal influence*
e.g. congenital anomaly of brain
craniostenosis
hypertelorism
microcephaly

.5 *With chromosomal abnormalities*
e.g. Down's disease
Klinefelter's syndrome

.6 *Associated with prematurity*
Prematurity without mention of other condition

.7 *Following major psychiatric disorder*

.8 *With psycho-social (environmental) deprivation*

.9 *Other and unspecified*
e.g. idiopathic
cause unknown

310   Borderline mental retardation
Backwardness
Borderline intelligence
Deficientia intelligenciae
Borderline mental deficiency or subnormality
IQ 68-85

311   Mild mental retardation
Feeble-mindedness
High-grade defect
Moron
Mild mental deficiency or subnormality
IQ 52-67

312   Moderate mental retardation
Imbecile, IQ 36-51
Moderate mental deficiency or subnormality
IQ 36-51

313   Severe mental retardation
Imbecile NOS
Severe mental deficiency or subnormality
IQ 20-35

314   Profound mental retardation
Idiocy
Profound mental deficiency or subnormality
IQ under 20

315   Unspecified mental retardation
Mental deficiency or subnormality NOS

2.

AMERICAN PSYCHIATRIC ASSOCIATION

DEFINITION OF MENTAL DISORDERS

DISORDERS CAUSED BY OR ASSOCIATED WITH IMPAIRMENT OF BRAIN TISSUE FUNCTION

These disorders are all characterized by a basic syndrome consisting of:

1. Impairment of orientation
2. Impairment of memory
3. Impairment of all intellectual functions (comprehension, calculation, knowledge, learning, etc.)
4. Impairment of judgment
5. Lability and shallowness of affect

This syndrome of organic brain disorder is a basic mental condition characteristic of diffuse impairment of brain tissue function from any cause. It may be mild, moderate, or severe, but most of the basic symptoms of the syndrome are generally present to a similar degree in any one patient at any one time. The severity of this basic syndrome is generally parallel to the severity of the impairment of brain tissue function.

This syndrome may be the only mental disturbance present or it may be associated with psychotic manifestations, neurotic manifestations, or behavioral disturbance. These associated reactions are not necessarily related in severity to the degree of the organic brain disorder or to the degree of brain damage; they are determined by inherent personality patterns, current emotional conflicts, the immediate environmental situation, and the setting of interpersonal relations, as well as by the precipitating organic disorder. These associated reactions are to be looked upon as being released by the organic brain disorder and superimposed upon

Committee on Nomenclature and Statistics of the American Psychiatric Association. *Diagnostic and Statistical Manual: Mental Disorders with Special Supplement on Plans for Revision.* (Special Printing —November, 1965.) Washington, D.C.: APA, 1965. Pp. 14–42. Reprinted by permission.

it. Since personality function depends greatly upon the integrity of brain function, various changes in personality reaction are to be expected with organic brain disorders. When these associated reactions are present to a significant degree, they are recognized by the addition of one of the qualifying statements listed (see Qualifying Phrases).

The organic brain disorders are separated into acute and chronic, because of the marked differences between these two groups in regard to prognosis, treatment, and general course of illness. The terms, "acute" and "chronic," refer primarily to the reversibility of brain pathology and its accompanying organic brain syndrome; and not to the etiology, onset, or duration of the illness. Since the same etiology may produce either temporary or permanent brain damage, a brain disorder which appears reversible, hence acute, at its beginning, may prove later to have left permanent damage and a persistent organic brain syndrome, which will then be diagnosed as chronic.

ACUTE BRAIN DISORDERS

These are the organic brain syndromes from which the patient recovers. They are the result of temporary, reversible, diffuse impairment of brain tissue function such as is present in acute alcoholic intoxication or "acute delirium." The basic disturbance of the sensorium may release other disturbances such as hallucinations, poorly organized, transient delusions, and behavior disturbances of varying degree. While a qualifying phrase may not ordinarily be needed with any diagnosis in this group, a qualifying phrase may be used when superimposed manifestations warrant such use by their severe modifications of the clinical picture.

These disorders are subclassified according to the cause of the impairment of brain tissue function.

15

009–100 *Acute Brain Syndrome associated with intracranial infection. Specify infection.* Here are to be classified those conditions due primarily to intracranial infection, such as encephalitis, epidemic and other, meningitis of all causes, and brain abscess, which appear to be temporary and reversible.

000–100 *Acute Brain Syndrome associated with systemic infection. Specific infection.* Here are to be classified those temporary, recoverable mental disturbances directly resulting from severe general systemic infections. Among the more common systemic infections producing such a reaction are pneumonia, typhoid fever, and acute rheumatic fever. Care must be taken to distinguish these reactions from other disorders, particularly manic depressive and schizophrenic reactions, which may be made manifest by even a mild attack of infectious disease.

000–3 . . *Acute Brain Syndrome, drug or poison intoxication. Specify drug or poison.* Drug: This category is intended for the inclusion of acute reversible brain syndromes due to drugs generally used in medical practices, such as bromides, barbiturates, opiates, or hormonal and similarly acting principles.

Poison: Here should be classified the acute brain syndromes associated with chemical action on the brain by substances not ordinarily used in medical practice, such as lead, other metals, gas, and other sources of intoxication (except alcohol) as listed in Category Three of the Standard Nomenclature of Diseases and Operations.

000–3312 *Acute Brain Syndrome, alcohol intoxication.* This group is given separate status from other intoxications for statistical purposes. Here will be classified the acute recoverable brain syndromes attributable to alcohol, notably delirium tremens and acute alcoholic hallucinosis. When simple alcoholic intoxication produces an acute brain syndrome requiring diagnosis, it will be classified here. Habitual alcoholism without brain syndrome should be diagnosed under Addiction. "Pathological Intoxication" may cause difficulty in proper diagnosis. When, without apparent preexisting mental disorder, there is a marked behavioral or psychotic reaction with an acute brain syndrome after minimal alcoholic intake, the case will be classified here. When a preexisting psychotic, psychoneurotic, or personality disorder is made more manifest after minimal alcoholic intake, the case will be classified under the diagnosis of the underlying condition.

000–4 . . *Acute Brain Syndrome associated with trauma. Specify trauma.* Here are to be classified those cases of acute brain syndrome developing immediately after head injury produced by external trauma of a gross physical nature, including surgery. Mental disturbances following injuries to other parts of the body are not to be classified here. Brain syndromes in which head trauma acts as a contributing or precipitating cause should be diagnosed under the proper etiological heading and not included in this group. This category does not include the chronic organic results of head injury.

000–5 . . *Acute Brain Syndrome associated with circulatory disturbance. (Indicate cardiovascular disease as additional diagnosis.)* Here are to be classified those acute recoverable brain syndromes occurring as a result of such circulatory disturbances as cerebral embolism, arterial hypertension, cardio-renal disease and especially cardiac disease, particularly in decompensation. Acute fluctuations in the chronic progressive course of circulatory disturbances such as cerebral arteriosclerosis will not be diagnosed here, but will be placed under the listing of Chronic Brain Syndrome.

000–550 *Acute Brain Syndrome associated with convulsive disorder. (Indicate manifestation by Supplementary Term.)* Under this heading will be classified only cases which show acute brain syndrome in connection with "idiopathic" epilepsy. Most common disturbance of this group is the epileptic clouded state occurring in those epileptics who develop, preceding or following convulsive attacks, or as equivalents of attacks, dazed reactions with deep confusion, bewilderment, and anxiety or excitement, with hallucinations, fears and violent outbreaks. Those cases in which the convulsive manifestations are symptomatic of other disease are to be classified under the headings for such other disease.

000–7 . . *Acute Brain Syndrome associated with metabolic disturbance. Specify.* Here will be classified those acute reversible brain syndromes resulting from metabolic disturbance, such as uremia, diabetes, hyperthyroidism, vitamin deficiency, and so forth.

000–8. . *Acute Brain Syndrome associated with intracranial neoplasm. (Indicate neoplasm as additional diagnosis.)* Here will be classified those acute reversible brain syndromes resulting from intracranial neoplasms, whether the neoplasm be primary or secondary. Reversibility of the pathological process underlying the acute brain syndrome (pressure, edema, etc.) is the basis of differentiation between acute and chronic syndromes of this category.

000–900 *Acute Brain Syndrome with disease of unknown or uncertain cause. (Indicate disease as additional diagnosis.)* Here will be classified those acute reversible brain syndromes resulting from diseases of unknown cause, such as multiple sclerosis. This diagnosis progressive disturbances of brain function.

This category differs from the one that follows, in that here the disease causing the acute brain syndrome is recognized and diagnosed although the etiology of the disease is unknown.

000–xx0 *Acute Brain Syndrome of unknown cause.* This category is intended for those acute brain syndromes whose cause cannot be recognized. It may also be used for acute brain syndromes of known cause, not elsewhere classifiable, in which case the causative disease will be separately diagnosed. Record librarians and statisticians may use this category for incomplete diagnoses.

CHRONIC BRAIN DISORDERS

The chronic organic brain syndromes result from relatively permanent, more or less irreversible, diffuse impairment of cerebral tissue function. While the underlying pathological process may partially subside, or respond to specific treatment, as in syphilis, there remains always a certain irreducible minimum of brain tissue destruction which cannot be reversed, even though the loss of function may be almost imperceptible clinically. The chronic brain syndrome may become milder, vary in degree, or progress, but some disturbance of memory, judgment, orientation, comprehension and affect persists permanently.

Other mental disturbances of psychotic, neurotic, or behavioral type may be superimposed on the chronic brain syndrome; when clinically significant, these will be recognized by addition of the appropriate qualifying phrase to the diagnosis (see Qualifying Phrases). When the chronic organic disorder is present during infancy and childhood, and results in significantly disturbed intellectual development, this may be recognized by addition of the qualifying phrase, .x4 with Mental deficiency.

These disorders are classified according to the cause of the impairment of brain function. Some of the diagnostic categories are identical with those of the acute brain syndromes; the differentiation is based on the permanent impairment of brain function in the chronic group.

009–0. ., 009–016, 009–071, 009–052, 009–050 *Chronic Brain Syndrome associated with congenital cranial anomaly, congenital spastic paraplegia, Mongolism, prenatal maternal infectious disease, birth trauma.* These categories are provided for the group of mental disturbances formerly diagnosed as secondary mental deficiency. Clinically, a general developmental defect of mentation is superimposed on the chronic brain syndrome, and when prominent may require the addition of the qualifying phrase .x4 Mental deficiency. The degree of defective intelligence will be specified as *mild, moderate,* or *severe,* and the current IQ rating will be added to the diagnosis (see Mental deficiency).

009–147.0 *Chronic Brain Syndrome associated with central nervous system syphilis (Meningoencephalitic).* Here will be classified the cases formerly diagnosed as general paresis. In addition to the organic brain syndrome, these cases show physical signs and symptoms of parenchymatous syphilis of the nervous system, and usually positive serology, including the paretic gold curve. The psychotic reaction, when such occurs, may simulate one of the "functional" psychoses but is to be classified here, with the Qualifying Phrase, .x1 with psychotic reaction.

004–147.0 *Chronic Brain Syndrome associated with central nervous system syphilis (Meningovascular).* The mental disturbance is that of the chronic brain syndrome, and is indistinguishable from the mental disturbance of Meningoencephalitic syphilis. A differential diagnosis may be possible in those cases in which the history, signs, and symptoms, including serology, suggest a primary and predominating involvement of the meninges and blood vessels rather than of the parenchyma of the nervous system. Suggestive of this type of syphilis (cerebral) rather than general paresis, are: comparatively early onset after infection, sudden onset of mental disturbance, focal signs, particularly cranial nerve palsy, apoplectiform seizures, very high spinal fluid cell count, positive blood and spinal fluid serology, and prompt response to general system antisyphilitic treatment. Cases showing mental disturbances on a basis of cerebral lesions from syphilitic vascular disease will be classified here rather than under the heading Chronic Brain Syndrome associated with disturbance of circulation.

0y0–147.0 *Chronic Brain Syndrome associated with other central nervous system syphilis.* Here will be classified the comparatively infrequent cases of chronic brain syndrome associated with syphilis of the central nervous system not covered in the previous groups, including intracranial gumma.

009–1...0 *Chronic Brain Syndrome associated with intracranial infection other than syphilis. Specify infection.* Here are to be classified chronic brain syndromes associated with intracranial infection other than syphilis. Many of these disorders will have been diagnosed acute brain syndrome early in the course of the illness. The case should be categorized here when it becomes apparent that there is diffuse, permanent damage to brain function. In addition to the primary diagnosis, many of these cases will require the use of a qualifying phrase; for example, encephalitides occurring in adolescence often develop a chronic brain syndrome with behavioral reaction.

009–300 *Chronic Brain Syndrome associated with intoxication. Specify.* In these two groups will be classified those chronic, organic reactions which remain permanently following toxic insult to the brain by such agents as lead, arsenic, mercury, carbon monoxide, illuminating gas, miscellaneous drugs and alcohol.

Chronic Brain Syndrome, alcohol intoxication, includes all degrees of permanent brain damage resulting from the use of alcohol, ranging from very mild up to and including severe. The latter may manifest itself by the type of chronic delirium formerly diagnosed as Korsakoff's psychosis. Under such conditions the psychosis will be recognized by the proper qualifying phrase.

Many of these reactions are ushered in with an acute brain reaction to the intoxicant. The case will be placed in the chronic category when it becomes apparent that permanent, irreversible damage to the brain has occurred.

009–400 *Chronic Brain Syndrome associated with brain trauma.* Here will be classified the post-traumatic chronic brain disorders, which produce impairment of mental function. Permanent brain damage which produces only neurologic changes because of its focal nature, without significant changes in the areas of sensorium and affect, will not be classified here. Generally, trauma producing a chronic brain syndrome would have to be diffuse and would have to leave permanent brain damage. Post-traumatic personality disorder associated with chronic brain syndrome will be placed in this group with the appropriate qualifying phrase.

If the brain injury occurs in early life, it may manifest itself primarily in a developmental defect of intelligence. Such cases will be qualified by the phrase .x4 Mental deficiency, and the current I.Q. included in the diagnosis.

A head injury may usher in, or expedite the course of, a chronic brain disease, especially cerebral arteriosclerosis. The differential diagnosis in such cases may be extremely difficult. If the case history shows symptoms of circulatory disturbance, particularly arteriosclerosis, before the injury, and the physical examination confirms the presence of arteriosclerosis, the case will be classified under Chronic Brain Syndrome associated with cerebral arteriosclerosis.

009–516 *Chronic Brain Syndrome associated with cerebral arteriosclerosis.* Here are to be classified those chronic, progressive, mental disturbances occurring in connection with cerebral arteriosclerosis. Clinical differentiation of the chronic brain syndrome associated with cerebral arteriosclerosis from that associated with senile sclerosis and presenile sclerosis may be impossible. Both underlying pathological changes may be present simultaneously. The age, history, and careful survey of the symptoms may assist in determining the predominate pathology. Commonly, the organic brain syndrome will be the only mental disturbance present. When significant psychotic, neurotic, or behavioral reactions are superimposed, the diagnosis will be qualified by the appropriate phrases (see Qualifying Phrases).

009–5.. *Chronic Brain Syndrome associated with circulatory disturbance other than cerebral asteriosclerosis. Specify.* Here are to be classified those chronic organic mental disturbances occurring in connection with circulatory disturbance other than cerebral arteriosclerosis, such as cerebral embolism, cerebral hemorrhages, arterial hypertension, and other chronic cardiovascular disease. Differentiation from the acute brain syndrome of like cause must be made on the irreversibility of the underlying brain damage. The circulatory disturbance will be specified.

009–550 *Chronic Brain Syndrome associated with convulsive disorder.* Here will be included only those cases which show chronic brain syndrome in connection with "ideopathic" epilepsy. Most of the etiological agents underlying chronic brain syndromes can and do cause convulsions. Convulsions are particularly common in the presence of syphilis, intoxication, trauma, cerebral arteriosclerosis, and intracranial neoplasm. When the convulsions are symptomatic of such other etiological agents, the chronic brain syndrome will be classified under the headings for those disturbances rather than here.

The most common type of case to be categorized here is seen in those epileptics who show a gradual development of mental dullness, slowness of associative thinking, impairment of memory and other intellectual functions, as well as apathy. Qualifying phrases are to be used when indicated.

009–79x *Chronic Brain Syndrome associated with senile brain disease.* This category is designed for the classification of organic brain syndrome occurring with senile brain disease, whether this be mild, moderate or severe. These cases vary from mild organic brain syndrome with self-centering of interest, difficulty in as-

similating new experiences, and "childish" emotionality, up to and including those so severely affected by senile brain disease as to require institutional care. Deterioration may be minimal or it may progress to a state of vegetative existence, with or without superimposed psychotic, neurotic, or behavioral reactions (see Qualifying Phrases).

009–700 *Chronic Brain Syndrome associated with other disturbance of metabolism, growth or nutrition (includes presenile, glandular, pellagra, familial amaurosis). Specify.* This category includes the chronic brain syndromes associated with disorders formerly classified separately, such as Alzheimer's disease, endocrine disorders, pellagra, and others of a similar nature.

In Alzheimer's disease, the brain pathology is characteristic. Clinically, the disorder may be suspected in severe progressive brain syndromes occurring at a comparatively early age period, as in the forties. The degree of brain atrophy, which is generalized, is usually severe, and can be demonstrated by pneumoencephalogram.

Chronic brain syndromes associated with complications of diabetes (not due to accompanying cerebral arteriosclerosis), disorders of the thyroid, pituitary, adrenals, and other disorders of metabolism, are to be classified under this heading. The majority of organic reactions occurring on a glandular or metabolic basis are acute and recoverable. They will be classified here only when there is evidence of permanent impairment of brain function.

Chronic brain syndromes associated with pellagra or other avitaminosis are included in this group. Cases developing pellagra or avitaminosis during the course of some other psychiatric disorder will not be classified under this heading, unless permanent brain damage occurs as a result of the avitaminosis.

009–8.. *Chronic Brain Syndrome associated with intracranial neoplasm. Specify neoplasm.* This category includes the chronic brain syndromes resulting from intracranial neoplasms, whether the neoplasm be primary or secondary. This category does not include reactions to new growths elsewhere in the body than in the cranium. Differentiation from the acute brain syndrome of like cause is made by the presence of irreversible brain damage.

009–900 *Chronic Brain Syndrome associated with the diseases of unknown or uncertain cause (includes multiple sclerosis, Huntington's chorea, Pick's disease and other diseases of a familial or hereditary nature.) Indicate disease by additional diagnosis.* Here will be classified those chronic brain syndromes associated with irreversible disruption of brain function by such disorders of unknown etiology as multiple sclerosis, Pick's disease, and Huntington's chorea.

This category differs from the one that follows (009–xx0), in that here the disease causing the chronic brain syndrome is recognized and diagnosed, although the etiology of the disease is unknown.

009–xx0 *Chronic Brain Syndrome of unknown cause.* This category is intended for those chronic brain syndromes whose cause cannot be recognized. It may also be used for chronic brain syndrome of known cause, not elsewhere classifiable, in which case the causative disease will be specified. Record librarians and statisticians may use this category for incomplete diagnoses.

MENTAL DEFICIENCY

009–x90 and 000–y90 *Mental deficiency.* Here will be classified those cases presenting primarily a defect of intelligence existing since birth, without demonstrated organic brain disease or known prenatal cause. This group will include only those cases formerly known as familial or "idiopathic" mental deficiencies. The degree of intelligence defect will be specified as *mild, moderate,* or *severe,* and the current I.Q. rating, with the name of the test used, will be added to the diagnosis. In general, *mild* refers to functional (vocational) impairment, as would be expected with I.Q.'s of approximately 70 to 85; *moderate* is used for functional impairment requiring special training and guidance, such as would be expected with I.Q.'s of about 50-70; *severe* refers to the functional impairment requiring custodial or complete protective care, as would be expected with I.Q.'s below 50. The degree of defect is estimated from other factors than merely psychological test scores, namely, consideration of cultural, physical and emotional determinants, as well as school, vocational and social effectiveness. The diagnosis may be modified by the appropriate qualifying phrase, when, in addition to the intellectual defects, there are significant psychotic, neurotic, or behavioral reactions.

DISORDERS OF PSYCHOGENIC ORIGIN OR WITHOUT CLEARLY DEFINED PHYSICAL CAUSE OR STRUCTURAL CHANGE IN THE BRAIN

PSYCHOTIC DISORDERS

These disorders are characterized by a varying degree of personality disintegration and failure to test and evaluate correctly external reality in various spheres. In addition, individuals with such disorders fail in their ability to relate themselves effectively to other people or to their own work.

000–796 *Involutional psychotic reaction.* In this category may be included psychotic reactions characterized most commonly by depression occurring in the involutional period, without previous history of manic depressive reaction, and usually in individuals of compulsive personality type. The reaction tends to have a prolonged course and may be manifested by worry, intractable insomnia, guilt, anxiety, agitation, delusional ideas, and somatic concerns. Some cases are characterized chiefly by depression and others chiefly by paranoid ideas. Often there are somatic preoccupations to a delusional degree.

Differentiation may be most difficult from other psychotic reactions with onset in the involutional period; reactions will not be included in this category merely because of their occurrence in this age group.

000–x10 AFFECTIVE REACTIONS

These psychotic reactions are characterized by a primary, severe, disorder of mood, with resultant disturbance of thought and behavior, in consonance with the affect.

000–x11—000–x13 *Manic depressive reactions.* These groups comprise the psychotic reactions which fundamentally are marked by severe mood swings, and a tendency to remission and recurrence. Various accessory symptoms such as illusions, delusions, and hallucinations may be added to the fundamental affective alteration.

Manic depressive reaction is synonymous with the term manic depressive psychosis. The reaction will be further classified into the appropriate one of the following types: manic, depressed, or other.

000–x11 *Manic depressive reaction, manic type.* This group is characterized by elation or irritability, with overtalkativeness, flight of ideas, and increased motor activity. Transitory, often momentary, episodes of depression may occur, but will not change the classification from the manic type of reaction.

000–x12 *Manic depressive reaction, depressed type.* Here will be classified those cases with outstanding depression of mood and with mental and motor retardation and inhibition; in some cases there is much uneasiness and apprehension. Perplexity, stupor or agitation may be prominent symptoms, and may be added to the diagnosis as manifestations.

000–x13 *Manic depressive reaction, other.* Here will be classified only those cases with marked mixtures of the cardinal manifestations of the above two phases (mixed type), or those cases where continuous alternation of the two phases occur (circular type). Other specified varieties of manic depressive reaction (manic stupor or unproductive mania) will also be included here.

000–x14 *Psychotic depressive reaction.* These patients are severely depressed and manifest evidence of gross misinterpretation of reality, including, at times, delusions and hallucinations. This reaction differs from the manic depressive reaction, depressed type, principally in (1) absence of history of repeated depressions or of marked cyclothymic mood swings, (2) frequent presence of environmental precipitating factors. This diagnostic category will be used when a "reactive depression" is of such quality as to place it in the group of psychoses (see 000–x06 Depressive reaction).

000–x20 SCHIZOPHRENIC REACTIONS

This term is synonymous with the formerly used term dementia praecox. It represents a group of psychotic reactions characterized by fundamental disturbances in reality relationships

and concept formations, with affective, behavioral, and intellectual disturbances in varying degrees and mixtures. The disorders are marked by strong tendency to retreat from reality, by emotional disharmony, unpredictable disturbances in stream of thought, regressive behavior, and in some, by a tendency to "deterioration." The predominating symptomatology will be the determining factor in classifying such patients into types.

000–x21 *Schizophrenic reaction, simple type.* This type of reaction is characterized chiefly by reduction in external attachments and interests and by impoverishment of human relationships. It often involves adjustment on a lower psychobiological level of functioning, usually accompanied by apathy and indifference but rarely by conspicuous delusions or hallucinations. The simple type of schizophrenic reaction characteristically manifests an increase in the severity of symptoms over long periods, usually with apparent mental deterioration, in contrast to the schizoid personality, in which there is little if any change.

000–x22 *Schizophrenic reactions, hebephrenic type.* These reactions are characterized by shallow, inappropriate affect, unpredictable giggling, silly behavior and mannerisms, delusions, often of a somatic nature, hallucinations, and regressive behavior.

000–x23 *Schizophrenic reaction, catatonic type.* These reactions are characterized by conspicuous motor behavior, exhibiting either marked generalized inhibition (stupor, mutism, negativism and waxy flexibility) or excessive motor activity and excitement. The individual may regress to a state of vegetation.

000–x24 *Schizophrenic reaction, paranoid type.* This type of reaction is characterized by autistic, unrealistic thinking, with mental content composed chiefly of delusions of persecution, and/or of grandeur, ideas of reference, and often hallucinations. It is often characterized by unpredictable behavior, with a fairly constant attitude of hostility and aggression. Excessive religiosity may be present with or without delusions of persecution. There may be an expansive delusional system of omnipotence, genius, or special ability. The systematized paranoid hypochondriacal states are included in this group.

000–x25 *Schizophrenic reaction, acute undifferentiated type*. This reaction includes cases exhibiting a wide variety of schizophrenic symptomatology, such as confusion of thinking and turmoil of emotion, manifested by perplexity, ideas of reference, fear and dream states, and dissociative phenomena. These symptoms appear acutely, often without apparent precipitating stress, but exhibiting historical evidence of prodromal symptoms. Very often the reaction is accompanied by a pronounced affective coloring of either excitement or depression. The symptoms often clear in a matter of weeks, although there is a tendency for them to recur. Cases usually are grouped here in the first, or an early, attack. If the reaction subsequently progresses, it ordinarily crystallizes into one of the other definable reaction types.

000–x26 *Schizophrenic reaction, chronic undifferentiated type*. The chronic schizophrenic reactions exhibit a mixed symptomatology, and when the reaction cannot be classified in any of the more clearly defined types, it will be placed in this group. Patients presenting definite schizophrenic thought, affect and behavior beyond that of the schizoid personality, but not classifiable as any other type of schizophrenic reaction, will also be placed in this group. This includes the so-called "latent," "incipient," and "prepsychotic" schizophrenic reactions.

000–x27 *Schizophrenic reaction, schizo-affective type*. This category is intended for those cases showing significant admixtures of schizophrenic and affective reactions. The mental content may be predominantly schizophrenic, with pronounced elation or depression. Cases may show predominantly affective changes with schizophrenic-like thinking or bizarre behavior. The prepsychotic personality may be at variance, or inconsistent, with expectations based on the presenting psychotic symptomatology. On prolonged observation, such cases usually prove to be basically schizophrenic in nature.

000–x28 *Schizophrenic reaction, childhood type*. Here will be classified those schizophrenic reactions occurring before puberty. The clinical picture may differ from schizophrenic reactions occurring in other age periods because of the immaturity and plasticity of the patient at the time of onset of the reaction.

Psychotic reactions in children, manifesting primarily autism, will be classified here. Special symptomatology may be added to the diagnosis as manifestations.

000–x29 *Schizophrenic reaction, residual type*. This term is to be applied to those patients who, after a definite psychotic, schizophrenic reaction, have improved sufficiently to be able to get along in the community, but who continue to show recognizable residual disturbance of thinking, affectively, and/or behavior.

000–x30 · PARANOID REACTIONS

In this group are to be classified those cases showing persistent delusions, generally persecutory or grandiose, ordinarily without hallucinations. The emotional responses and behavior are consistent with the ideas held. Intelligence is well preserved. This category does not include those reactions properly classifiable under Schizophrenic reaction, paranoid type.

000–x31 *Paranoia*. This type of psychotic disorder is extremely rare. It is characterized by an intricate, complex, and slowly developing paranoid system, often logically elaborated after a false interpretation of an actual occurrence. Frequently, the patient considers himself endowed with superior or unique ability. The paranoid system is particularly isolated from much of the normal stream of consciousness, without hallucinations and with relative intactness and preservation of the remainder of the personality, in spite of a chronic and prolonged course.

000–x32 *Paranoid state*. This type of paranoid disorder is characterized by paranoid delusions. It lacks the logical nature of systematization seen in paranoia; yet it does not manifest the bizarre fragmentation and deterioration of the schizophrenic reactions. It is likely to be of a relatively short duration, though it may be persistent and chronic.

000–xy0 PSYCHOTIC REACTION WITHOUT CLEARLY DEFINED STRUCTURAL CHANGE, OTHER THAN ABOVE

This classification is introduced primarily for the use of librarians and statisticians in those instances where the diagnosis has been left incomplete, and is not classifiable. This diagnosis is not intended for mixed reactions, which should be classified according to the predominant reaction.

PSYCHOPHYSIOLOGIC AUTONOMIC AND VISCERAL DISORDERS

This term is used in preference to "psychosomatic disorders," since the latter term refers to a point of view on the discipline of medicine as a whole rather than to certain specified conditions. It is preferred to the term "somatization reactions," which term implies that these disorders are simply another form of psychoneurotic reaction. These disorders are here given a separate grouping between psychotic and psychoneurotic reactions, to allow more accurate accumulation of data concerning their etiology, course, and relation to other mental disorders.

These reactions represent the visceral expression of affect which may be thereby largely prevented from being conscious. The symptoms are due to a chronic and exaggerated state of the normal physiological expression of emotion, with the feeling, or subjective part, repressed. Such long continued visceral states may eventually lead to structural changes.

This group includes the so-called "organ neuroses." It also includes some of the cases formerly classified under a wide variety of diagnostic terms, such as "anxiety state," "cardiac neurosis," "gastric neurosis," and so forth. Differentiation is made from conversion reactions by (1) involvement of organs and viscera innervated by the autonomic nervous system, hence not under full voluntary control or perception; (2) failure to alleviate anxiety; (3) physiological rather than symbolic origin of symptoms; (4) frequent production of structural changes which may threaten life. Differentiation is made from anxiety reactions primarily by predominant, persistent involvement of a single organ system.

Each diagnosis of this type of reaction will be amplified with the specific symptomatic manifestations, e.g., anorexia, loss of weight, dysmenorrhea, hypertension, and so forth.

001–580 *Psychophysiologic skin reaction.* This category includes such skin reactions as neurodermatoses, pruritus, atopic dermatitis, hyperhydrosis, and so forth, in which emotional factors play a causative role.

002–580 *Psychophysiologic musculoskeletal reaction.* This category includes musculoskeletal disorders such as "psychogenic rheumatism," backache, muscle cramps, myalgias (to include some cases of cephalagia, tension headaches) in which emotional factors play a causative role. In this group, differentiation from conversion reactions is of prime importance and at times is extremely difficult.

003–580 *Psychophysiologic respiratory reaction.* This category includes cases of bronchial spasm, some hyperventilation syndromes, sighing respirations, hiccoughs, and so forth, in which emotional factors play a causative role.

004–580 *Psychophysiologic cardiovascular reaction.* This category includes such types of cardiovascular disorders as paroxysmal tachycardia, hypertension, vascular spasms, migraine, and so forth, in which emotional factors play a causative role.

005–580 *Psychophysiologic hemic and lymphatic reaction.* Here may be included any disturbances in the hemic and lymphatic system in which emotional factors are found to play a causative role.

006–580 *Psychophysiologic gastrointestinal reaction.* This category includes such specified types of gastrointestinal disorders as peptic-ulcer-like reaction, chronic gastritis, ulcerative or mucous colitis, constipation, hyperacidity, pylorospasm, "heartburn," "irritable colon," "anorexia nervosa," and so forth, in which emotional factors play a causative role.

007–580 *Psychophysiologic genitourinary reaction.* This category includes some types of menstrual disturbances, dysuria, and so forth, in which emotional factors play a causative role.

008–580 *Psychophysiologic endocrine reaction.* This category includes endocrine disorders in which emotional factors play a causative role. Specify endocrine disturbance.

009–580 *Psychophysiologic nervous system reaction.* This category includes psychophysiologic asthenic reaction, in which general fatigue is the predominating complaint. There may be associated visceral complaints. The term includes many cases formerly called "neurasthenia." In some instances, an asthenic reaction may represent a conversion reaction; if so, it will be so classified, with asthenia as a manifestation.

In other instances it may be a manifestation of anxiety reaction and should be recorded as such.

Also included in this category are convulsive disorders not otherwise classifiable in which emotional factors play a causative role. Differentiation must be made from the convulsions of conversion reaction.

00x–580 *Psychophysiologic reaction of organs of special sense.* Here may be included any disturbances in the organs of special sense in which emotional factors are found to play a causative role and in which conversion reactions are excluded (see 000–x03).

PSYCHONEUROTIC DISORDERS

The chief characteristic of these disorders is "anxiety" which may be directly felt and expressed or which may be unconsciously and automatically controlled by the utilization of various psychological defense mechanisms (depression, conversion, displacement, etc.). In contrast to those with psychoses, patients with psychoneurotic disorders do not exhibit gross distortion or falsification of external reality (delusions, hallucinations, illusions) and they do not present gross disorganization of the personality. Longitudinal (lifelong) studies of individuals with such disorders usually present evidence of periodic or constant maladjustment of varying degree from early life. Special stress may bring about acute symptomatic expression of such disorders.

"Anxiety" in psychoneurotic disorders is a danger signal felt and perceived by the conscious portion of the personality. It is produced by a threat from within the personality (e.g., by supercharged repressed emotions, including such aggressive impulses as hostility and resentment), with or without stimulation from such external situations as loss of love, loss of prestige, or threat of injury. The various ways in which the patient attempts to handle this anxiety results in the various types of reactions listed below.

In recording such reactions the terms "traumatic neurosis," or "traumatic reaction" will not be used; instead, the particular psychiatric reaction will be specified. Likewise, the term "mixed reaction" will not be used; instead, the predominant type of reaction will be recorded, qualified by reference to other types of reactions as part of the symptomatology.

000–x01 *Anxiety reaction.* In this kind of reaction the anxiety is diffuse and not restricted to definite situations or objects, as in the case of phobic reactions. It is not controlled by any specific psychological defense mechanism as in other psychoneurotic reactions. This reaction is characterized by anxious expectation and frequently associated with somatic symptomatology. The condition is to be differentiated from normal apprehensiveness or fear. The term is synonymous with the former term "anxiety state."

000–x02 *Dissociative reaction.* This reaction represents a type of gross personality disorganization, the basis of which is a neurotic disturbance, although the diffuse dissociation seen in some cases may occasionally appear psychotic. The personality disorganization may result in aimless running or "freezing." The repressed impulse giving rise to the anxiety may be discharged by, or deflected into, various symptomatic expressions, such as depersonalization, dissociated personality, stupor, fugue, amnesia, dream state, somnambulism, etc. The diagnosis will specify symptomatic manifestations.

These reactions must be differentiated from schizoid personality, from schizophrenic reaction, and from analogous symptoms in some other types of neurotic reactions. Formerly, this reaction has been classified as a type of "conversion hysteria."

000–x03 *Conversion reaction.* Instead of being experienced consciously (either diffusely or displaced, as in phobias) the impulse causing the anxiety is "converted" into functional symptoms in organs or parts of the body, usually those that are mainly under voluntary control. The symptoms serve to lessen conscious (felt) anxiety and ordinarily are symbolic of the underlying mental conflict. Such reactions usually meet immediate needs of the patient and are, therefore, associated with more or less obvious "secondary gain." They are to be differentiated from psychophysiologic autonomic and visceral disorders. The term "conversion reaction" is synonymous with "conversion hysteria." Dissociative reactions are not included in this diagnosis.

In recording such reactions the symptomatic manifestations will be specified as anesthesia (anosmia, blindness, deafness), paralysis (paresis, aphonia, monoplegia, or hemiplegia), dyskinesis (tic, tremor, posturing, catalepsy).

000–x04 *Phobic reaction.* The anxiety of these patients becomes detached from a specific idea, object, or situation in the daily life and is displaced to some symbolic idea or situation in the form of a specific neurotic fear. The commonly observed forms of phobic reaction include fear of syphilis, dirt, closed places, high places, open places, animals, etc. The patient attempts to control his anxiety by avoiding the phobic object or situation.

In recording this diagnosis the manifestations will be indicated. The term is synonymous with the former term "phobia" and includes some of the cases formerly classified as "anxiety hysteria."

000–x05 *Obsessive compulsive reaction.* In this reaction the anxiety is associated with the persistence of unwanted ideas and of repetitive impulses to perform acts which may be considered morbid by the patient. The patient himself may regard his ideas and behavior as unreasonable, but nevertheless is compelled to carry out his rituals.

The diagnosis will specify the symptomatic expression of such reactions, as touching, counting, ceremonials, hand-washing, or recurring thoughts (accompanied often by a compulsion to repetitive action). This category includes many cases formerly classified as "psychasthenia."

000–x06 *Depressive reaction.* The anxiety in this reaction is allayed, and hence partially relieved, by depression and self-depreciation. The reaction is precipitated by a current situation, frequently by some loss sustained by the patient, and is often associated with a feeling of guilt for past failures or deeds. The degree of the reaction in such cases is dependent upon the intensity of the patient's ambivalent feeling toward his loss (love, possession) as well as upon the realistic circumstances of the loss.

The term is synonymous with "reactive depression" and is to be differentiated from the corresponding psychotic reaction. In this differentiation, points to be considered are (1) life history of patient, with special reference to mood swings (suggestive of psychotic reaction), to the personality structure (neurotic or cyclothymic) and to precipitating environmental factors and (2) absence of malignant symptoms (hypochondriacal preoccupation, agitation, delusions, particularly somatic, hallucinations, severe guilt feelings, intractable insomnia, suicidal ruminations, severe psychomotor retardation, profound retardation of thought, stupor).

000–x0y *Psychoneurotic reaction, other.* Under this classification will come all reactions considered psychoneurotic and not elsewhere classified. (Psychoneurotic manic reactions, etc.) This category is designed also for the use of record librarians and statisticians dealing with incomplete diagnosis. It does not include "mixed" reactions, which are to be diagnosed according to the predominant reaction.

PERSONALITY DISORDERS

These disorders are characterized by developmental defects or pathological trends in the personality structure, with minimal subjective anxiety, and little or no sense of distress In most instances, the disorder is manifested by a lifelong pattern of action or behavior, rather than by mental or emotional symptoms. Occasionally, organic diseases of the brain (epidemic encephalitis, head injury, Alzheimer's disease, etc.) will produce clinical pictures resembling a personality disorder. In such instances, the condition is properly diagnosed as a Chronic Brain Syndrome (of appropriate origin) with behavioral reaction.

The personality disorders are divided into three main groups with one additional grouping for flexibility in diagnosis (Special symptom reactions). Although the groupings are largely descriptive, the division has been made partially on the basis of the dynamics of personality development. The Personality pattern disturbances are considered deep seated disturbances, with little room for regression. Personality trait disturbances and Sociopathic personality disturbances under stress may at times regress to a lower level of personality organization and function without development of psychosis.

000–x40 PERSONALITY PATTERN DISTURBANCE

There are more or less cardinal personality types, which can rarely if ever be altered in their inherent structures by any form of therapy. Their functioning may be improved by prolonged therapy, but basic change is seldom accomplished. In some, "constitutional" features are marked and obvious. The depth of the psychopathology here allows these individuals little room to maneuver under conditions of stress, except into actual psychosis.

000–x41 *Inadequate personality.* Such individuals are characterized by inadequate response to intellectual, emotional, social, and physical demands. They are neither physically nor mentally grossly deficient on examination, but they do show inadaptability, ineptness, poor judgment, lack of physical and emotional stamina, and social incompatibility.

000–x42 *Schizoid personality.* Inherent traits in such personalities are (1) avoidance of close relations with others, (2) inability to express directly hostility or even ordinary aggressive feelings, and (3) autistic thinking. These qualities result early in coldness, aloofness, emotional detachment, fearfulness, avoidance of competition, and day dreams revolving around the need for omnipotence. As children, they are usually quiet, shy, obedient, sensitive and retiring. At puberty, they frequently become more withdrawn, then manifesting the aggregate of personality traits known as introversion, namely, quietness, seclusiveness, "shut-in-ness," and unsociability, often with eccentricity.

000–x43 *Cyclothymic personality.* Such individuals are characterized by an extratensive and outgoing adjustment to life situations, an apparent personal warmth, friendliness and superficial generosity, an emotional reaching out to the environment, and a ready enthusiasm for competition. Characteristic are frequently alternating moods of elation and sadness, stimulated apparently by internal factors rather than by external events. The individual may occasionally be either persistently euphoric or depressed, without falsification or distortion of reality. The diagnosis in such cases should specify, if pos-

sible, whether hypomanic, depressed or alternating.

000–x44 *Paranoid personality.* Such individuals are characterized by many traits of the schizoid personality, coupled with an exquisite sensitivity in interpersonal relations, and with a conspicuous tendency to utilize a projection mechanism, expressed by suspiciousness, envy, extreme jealousy and stubbornness.

000–x50 PERSONALITY TRAIT DISTURBANCE

This category applies to individuals who are unable to maintain their emotional equilibrium and independence under minor or major stress because of disturbances in emotional development. Some individuals fall into this group because their personality pattern disturbance is related to fixation and exaggeration of certain character and behavior patterns; others, because their behavior is a regressive reaction due to environmental or endopsychic stress.

This classification will be applied only to cases of personality disorder in which the neurotic features (such as anxiety, conversion, phobia, etc.) are relatively insignificant, and the basic personality maldevelopment is the crucial distinguishing factor. Evidence of physical immaturity may or may not be present.

000–x51 *Emotionally unstable personality.* In such cases the individual reacts with excitability and ineffectiveness when confronted by minor stress. His judgment may be undependable under stress, and his relationship to other people is continuously fraught with fluctuating emotional attitudes, because of strong and poorly controlled hostility, guilt, and anxiety.

This term is synonymous with the former term "psychopathic personality with emotional instability."

000–x52 *Passive-aggressive personality.* Reactions in this group are of three types, as indicated below, and the diagnosis can be further elaborated, if desired, by adding the specific type of reaction observed. However, the three types of reaction are manifestations of the same underlying psychopathology, and frequently occur interchangeably in a given individual falling in this category. For these reasons, the reactions are classified together. The clinical picture in such cases often has, superimposed upon it, anxiety reaction which is typically psychoneurotic (see Qualifying Phrases).

Passive-dependent type: This reaction is characterized by helplessness, indecisiveness, and a tendency to cling to others as a dependent child to a supporting parent.

Passive-aggressive type: The aggressiveness is expressed in these reactions by passive measures, such as pouting, stubbornness, procrastination, inefficiency, and passive obstructionism.

Aggressive type: A persistent reaction to frustration with irritability, temper tantrums, and destructive behavior is the dominant manifestation. A specific variety of this reaction is a morbid or pathological resentment. A deep dependency is usually evident in such cases. The term does not apply to cases more accurately classified as Antisocial reaction.

000–x53 *Compulsive personality.* Such individuals are characterized by chronic, excessive, or obsessive concern with adherence to standards of conscience or of conformity. They may be overinhibited, overconscientious, and may have an inordinate capacity for work. Typically they are rigid and lack a normal capacity for relaxation. While their chronic tension may lead to neurotic illness, this is not an invariable consequence. The reaction may appear as a persistence of an adolescent pattern of behavior, or as a regression from more mature functioning as a result of stress.

000–x5y *Personality trait disturbance, other.* This category is included to permit greater latitude in diagnosis. Instances in which a personality trait is exaggerated as a means to life adjustment (as in the above diagnoses), not classifiable elsewhere, may be listed here.

This category is designed also for the use of record librarians and statisticians dealing with incomplete diagnoses. It is not intended for use with "mixed" states, which are to be properly diagnosed according to the predominant trait disturbance.

000–x60 SOCIOPATHIC PERSONALITY DISTURBANCE

Individuals to be placed in this category are ill primarily in terms of society and of conformity with the prevailing cultural milieu, and not only in terms of personal discomfort and rela-

tions with other individuals. However, sociopathic reactions are very often symptomatic of severe underlying personality disorder, neurosis, or psychosis, or occur as the result of organic brain injury or disease. Before a definitive diagnosis in this group is employed, strict attention must be paid to the possibility of the presence of a more primary personality disturbance; such underlying disturbance will be diagnosed when recognized. Reactions will be differentiated as defined below.

000–x61 *Antisocial reaction.* This term refers to chronically antisocial individuals who are always in trouble, profiting neither from experience or punishment, and maintaining no real loyalties to any person, group, or code. They are frequently callous and hedonistic, showing marked emotional immaturity, with lack of sense of responsibility, lack of judgment, and an ability to rationalize their behavior so that it appears warranted, reasonable, and justified.

The term includes cases previously classified as "constitutional psychopathic state" and "psychopathic personality." As defined here the term is more limited, as well as more specific in its application.

000–x62 *Dyssocial reaction.* This term applies to individuals who manifest disregard for the usual social codes, and often come in conflict with them, as the result of having lived all their lives in an abnormal moral environment. They may be capable of strong loyalties. These individuals typically do not show significant personality deviations other than those implied by adherence to the values or code of their own predatory, criminal, or other social group. The term includes such diagnoses as "pseudosocial personality" and "psychopathic personality with asocial and amoral trends."

000–x63 *Sexual deviation.* This diagnosis is reserved for deviant sexuality which is not symptomatic of more extensive syndromes, such as schizophrenic and obsessional reactions. The term includes most of the cases formerly classed as "psychopathic personality with pathologic sexuality." The diagnosis will specify the type of the pathologic behavior, such as homosexuality, transvestism, pedophilia, fetishism and sexual sadism (including rape, sexual assaults, mutilation).

000–x64 *Addiction.* Addictions will be classified as defined below.

000–x641 *Alcoholism.* Included in this category will be cases in which there is well established addiction to alcohol without recognizable underlying disorder. Simple drunkenness and acute poisoning due to alcohol are not included in this category.

000–x642 *Drug addiction.* Drug addiction is usually symptomatic of a personality disorder, and will be classified here while the individual is actually addicted; the proper personality classification is to be made as an additional diagnosis. Drug addictions symptomatic of organic brain disorders, psychotic disorders, psychophysiologic disorders, and psychoneurotic disorders are classified here as a secondary diagnosis.

000–x70 SPECIAL SYMPTOM REACTIONS

This category is useful in occasional situations where a specific symptom is the single outstanding expression of the psychopathology. This term will not be used as a diagnosis, however, when the symptoms are associated with, or are secondary to, organic illnesses and defects, or to other psychiatric disorders. Thus, for example, the diagnosis Special symptom reaction, speech disturbance would be used for certain disturbances in speech in which there are insufficient other symptoms to justify any other definite diagnosis. This type of speech disturbance often develops in childhood. It would not be used for a speech impairment that was a temporary symptom of conversion hysteria or the result of any organic disease or defect.

The diagnosis should specify the particular "habit." (000–x71 Learning disturbance; 000–x72 Speech disturbance; 000–x73 Enuresis; 000–x74 Somnambulism; 000–x7y Other.)

TRANSIENT SITUATIONAL PERSONALITY DISORDERS

This general classification should be restricted to reactions which are more or less transient in character and which appear to be an acute symptom response to a situation without apparent underlying personality disturbance.

The symptoms are the immediate means used by the individual in his struggle to adjust to an overwhelming situation. In the presence of good adaptive capacity, recession of symptoms generally occurs when the situational stress diminishes. Persistent failure to resolve will indicate a more severe underlying disturbance and will be classified elsewhere.

000–x80 *Transient situational personality disturbance.* Transient situational disorders which cannot be given a more definite diagnosis in the group, because of their fluidity, or because of the limitation of time permitted for their study, may be included in this general category. This category is designed also for the use of record librarians and statisticians dealing with incomplete diagnoses.

000–x81 *Gross stress reaction.* Under conditions of great or unusual stress, a normal personality may utilize established patterns of reaction to deal with overwhelming fear. The patterns of such reactions differ from those of neurosis or psychosis chiefly with respect to clinical history, reversibility of reaction, and its transient character. When promptly and adequately treated, the condition may clear rapidly. It is also possible that the condition may progress to one of the neurotic reactions. If the reaction persists, this term is to be regarded as a temporary diagnosis to be used only until a more definitive diagnosis is established.

This diagnosis is justified only in situations in which the individual has been exposed to severe physical demands or extreme emotional stress, such as in combat or in civilian catastrophe (fire, earthquake, explosion, etc.). In many instances this diagnosis applies to previously more or less "normal" persons who have experienced intolerable stress.

The particular stress involved will be specified as (1) combat or (2) civilian catastrophe.

000–x82 *Adult situational reaction.* This diagnosis is to be used when the clinical picture is primarily one of superficial maladjustment to a difficult situation or to newly experienced environmental factors, with no evidence of any serious underlying personality defects or chronic patterns. It may be manifested by anxiety, alcoholism, asthenia, poor efficiency, low morale, unconventional behavior, etc. If untreated or not relieved such reactions may, in some instances, progress into typical psychoneurotic reactions or personality disorders. This term will also include some cases formerly classified as "simple adult maladjustment."

000–x83 *Adjustment reaction of infancy.* Under this term are to be classified those transient reactions in infants occurring on a psychogenic basis without organic disease. In most instances these will be outgrowths of the infant's interaction with significant persons in the environment or a response to the lack of such persons. Undue apathy, undue excitability, feeding and sleeping difficulties are common manifestations of such psychic disturbances in infants.

000–x84 *Adjustment reaction of childhood.* Under this heading are included only the transient symptomatic reactions of children to some immediate situation or internal emotional conflict. The more prolonged and definitive disturbances will be classified elsewhere.

Although the symptomatic manifestations are usually mixed, one type of manifestation may predominate. This group may be subclassified according to the most prominent manifestations as follows:

000–x841 *Habit disturbance.* When the transient reaction manifests itself primarily as a so-called "habit" disturbance, such as repetitive, simple activities, it may be subclassified here.

Indicate symptomatic manifestations under this diagnosis; for example, nail biting, thumb sucking, enuresis, masturbation, tantrums, etc.

000–x842 *Conduct disturbance.* When the transient reaction manifests itself primarily as a disturbance in social conduct or behavior, it will be classified here. Manifestations may occur chiefly in the home, in the school, or in the community, or may occur in all three. Conduct disturbances are to be regarded as secondary phenomena when seen in cases of mental deficiency, epilepsy, epidemic encephalitis, and other well-recognized organic diseases.

Indicate symptomatic manifestations under this diagnosis; for example, truancy, stealing, destructiveness, cruelty, sexual offenses, use of alcohol, etc.

000–x843 *Neurotic traits.* When the transient reaction manifests itself primarily as physical or emotional symptoms, it will be classified here. Care must be taken to differentiate these transitory situational responses from the psychoneurotic reactions.

Neurotic traits are closely related to habit disturbances and a distinction between the two is not always possible or desirable. Tics of organic origin should be classified under organic nervous disease.

Under this diagnosis indicate symptomatic manifestations; for example, tics, habit spasms, somnambulism, stammering, over-activity, phobias, etc.

000–x85 *Adjustment reaction of adolescence.* Under this diagnosis are to be included those transient reactions of the adolescent which are the expression of his emancipatory strivings and vacillations with reference to impulses and emotional tendencies. The superficial pattern of the behavior may resemble any of the personality or psychoneurotic disorders. Differentiation between transient adolescent reactions and deepseated personality trait disorders or psychoneurotic reactions must be made.

000–x86 *Adjustment reaction of late life.* Under this diagnosis will be included those transient reactions of later life which are an expression of the problems of physiological, situational, and environmental readjustment. Involutional physiological changes, retirement from work, breaking up of families through death, or other life situation changes frequently precipitate transient undesirable personality disturbances, or accentuate previous personality disorders. Such disturbances are to be differentiated from other psychogenic reactions and from reactions associated with cerebral arteriosclerosis, presenile psychosis, and other organic disorders.

3

NATIONAL INSTITUTE OF MENTAL HEALTH

STATISTICS ON MENTAL DISORDERS

Table 1.1 – ADMISSIONS WITH NO PRIOR ADMISSION TO ANY INPATIENT PSYCHIATRIC FACILITY, STATE AND COUNTY MENTAL HOSPITALS, BY MENTAL DISORDER, AGE AND SEX: UNITED STATES, 1965

MENTAL DISORDER AND SEX	ALL AGES	AGE (IN YEARS)									
		Under 15	15–24	25–34	35–44	45–54	55–64	65–74	75–84	85 and over	Age unknown
ACUTE BRAIN SYNDROMES ASSOC. WITH											
ALCOHOL INTOXICATION											
MALE	2,909	2	124	576	891	811	388	97	12	1	7
FEMALE	655	–	35	150	217	174	63	13	2	1	–
TOTAL	3,564	2	159	726	1,108	985	451	110	14	2	7
DRUG OR POISON INTOXICATION											
MALE	232	3	33	56	55	40	29	8	7	1	–
FEMALE	359	2	35	64	94	76	55	28	4	1	–
TOTAL	591	5	68	120	149	116	84	36	11	2	–
CONVULSIVE DISORDER											
MALE	60	4	11	13	15	9	6	1	1	–	–
FEMALE	31	1	11	7	4	4	–	2	2	–	–
TOTAL	91	5	22	20	19	13	6	3	3	–	–
ALL OTHER CONDITIONS											
MALE	387	6	36	34	59	81	90	52	24	2	3
FEMALE	267	3	23	25	43	62	69	26	14	2	–
TOTAL	654	9	59	59	102	143	159	78	38	4	3
TOTAL											
MALE	3,588	15	204	679	1,020	941	513	158	44	4	10
FEMALE	1,312	6	104	246	358	316	187	69	22	4	–
TOTAL	4,900	21	308	925	1,378	1,257	700	227	66	8	10
CHRONIC BRAIN SYNDROMES ASSOC. WITH											
DISEASES AND CONDITIONS DUE TO PRENATAL INFLUENCE											
MALE	104	40	29	11	9	6	6	2	–	1	–
FEMALE	64	24	16	5	4	9	5	1	–	–	–
TOTAL	168	64	45	16	13	15	11	3	–	1	–
MENINGOENCEPHALITIC SYPHILIS											
MALE	104	–	1	7	9	34	37	10	4	1	1
FEMALE	53	1	–	2	3	17	23	5	2	–	–
TOTAL	157	1	1	9	12	51	60	15	6	1	1
OTHER CNS SYPHILIS											
MALE	35	–	2	–	4	6	14	5	3	–	1
FEMALE	26	–	2	1	5	5	6	3	4	–	–
TOTAL	61	–	4	1	9	11	20	8	7	–	1
EPIDEMIC ENCEPHALITIS											
MALE	48	13	7	4	7	4	7	4	2	–	1
FEMALE	27	6	6	8	2	3	1	–	–	–	1
TOTAL	75	19	13	12	9	7	8	4	2	–	1
OTHER INTRACRANIAL INFECTIONS											
MALE	63	19	12	4	6	11	7	2	1	–	1
FEMALE	36	6	7	3	–	14	4	1	1	–	–
TOTAL	99	25	19	7	6	25	11	3	2	–	1
ALCOHOL INTOXICATIONS											
MALE	2,143	–	23	126	386	694	639	235	35	3	2
FEMALE	577	–	7	39	134	206	140	40	7	–	4
TOTAL	2,720	–	30	165	520	900	779	275	42	3	6
DRUG OR POISON INTOXICATION											
MALE	52	–	5	3	8	17	13	5	–	–	1
FEMALE	45	–	–	6	8	15	11	4	1	–	–
TOTAL	97	–	5	9	16	32	24	9	1	–	1
BIRTH TRAUMA											
MALE	172	23	60	29	23	19	11	3	3	–	1
FEMALE	68	14	26	12	10	3	2	–	1	–	–
TOTAL	240	37	86	41	33	22	13	3	4	–	1

Table 1.1 (CNTD) – ADMISSIONS WITH NO PRIOR ADMISSION TO ANY INPATIENT PSYCHIATRIC FACILITY, STATE AND COUNTY MENTAL HOSPITAL, BY MENTAL DISORDER, AGE AND SEX, UNITED STATES, 1965

MENTAL DISORDER AND SEX	ALL AGES	AGE (IN YEARS)									
		Under 15	15–24	25–34	35–44	45–54	55–64	65–74	75–84	85 and over	Age unknown
OTHER TRAUMA											
MALE	515	24	90	80	98	106	80	31	4	–	2
FEMALE	157	4	23	31	39	24	20	14	2	–	–
TOTAL	672	28	113	111	137	130	100	45	6	–	2
CEREBRAL ARTERIOSCLEROSIS											
MALE	8,378	–	–	–	3	153	1,107	2,856	3,343	875	41
FEMALE	7,339	–	–	–	2	102	832	2,491	2,998	892	22
TOTAL	15,717	–	–	–	5	255	1,939	5,347	6,341	1,767	63
OTHER CIRCULATORY DISTURBANCE											
MALE	713	1	9	4	21	82	195	198	165	36	2
FEMALE	527	2	2	2	16	61	125	156	140	19	4
TOTAL	1,240	3	11	6	37	143	320	354	305	55	6
CONVULSIVE DISORDER											
MALE	922	117	282	171	151	104	61	23	9	3	1
FEMALE	794	58	231	161	143	91	73	23	7	2	5
TOTAL	1,716	175	513	332	294	195	134	46	16	5	6
SENILE BRAIN DISEASE											
MALE	2,594	–	–	1	–	7	98	524	1,380	575	9
FEMALE	3,381	1	–	2	–	12	91	736	1,661	863	15
TOTAL	5,975	1	–	3	–	19	189	1,260	3,041	1,438	24
OTHER DISTURBANCE OF METABOLISM, GROWTH, AND NUTRITION											
MALE	183	3	–	6	5	35	77	29	18	8	2
FEMALE	214	1	2	9	13	39	100	32	12	5	1
TOTAL	397	4	2	15	18	74	177	61	30	13	3
INTRACRANIAL NEOPLASM											
MALE	45	–	1	8	3	12	12	7	2	–	–
FEMALE	48	1	3	3	6	15	13	7	–	–	–
TOTAL	93	1	4	11	9	27	25	14	2	–	–
DISEASES OF UNKNOWN CAUSE											
MALE	263	4	16	16	24	70	83	31	14	4	1
FEMALE	224	2	11	19	38	49	66	30	7	2	–
TOTAL	487	6	27	35	62	119	149	61	21	6	1
CHRONIC BRAIN SYNDROME OF UNKNOWN CAUSE											
MALE	648	81	78	31	56	101	158	80	50	9	4
FEMALE	390	38	30	20	31	58	116	53	30	11	3
TOTAL	1,038	119	108	51	87	159	274	133	80	20	7
TOTAL											
MALE	16,982	325	615	501	813	1,461	2,605	4,045	5,033	1,515	69
FEMALE	13,970	158	366	323	454	723	1,628	3,596	4,873	1,794	55
TOTAL	30,952	483	981	824	1,267	2,184	4,233	7,641	9,906	3,309	124
PSYCHOTIC DISORDERS											
INVOLUTIONAL PSYCHOTIC REACTION											
MALE	1,106	–	4	1	32	371	529	148	20	–	1
FEMALE	3,004	2	2	16	450	1,392	919	200	19	1	3
TOTAL	4,110	2	6	17	482	1,763	1,448	348	39	1	4
MANIC DEPRESSIVE REACTION											
MALE	566	3	49	85	122	151	104	42	7	–	3
FEMALE	832	1	81	145	216	191	132	53	11	–	2
TOTAL	1,398	4	130	230	338	342	236	95	18	–	5
PSYCHOTIC DEPRESSIVE REACTION											
MALE	959	9	102	162	220	206	172	65	16	4	3
FEMALE	1,787	7	232	416	446	287	253	123	16	2	5
TOTAL	2,746	16	334	578	666	493	425	188	32	6	8
SCHIZOPHRENIC REACTIONS											
MALE	11,475	423	3,457	3,155	2,393	1,328	517	129	19	14	40
FEMALE	12,386	283	2,735	3,564	3,166	1,737	676	157	27	9	32
TOTAL	23,861	706	6,192	6,719	5,559	3,065	1,193	286	46	23	72
PARANOID REACTIONS											
MALE	303	–	17	54	86	77	31	31	7	–	–
FEMALE	275	2	10	47	65	73	39	31	8	–	–
TOTAL	578	2	27	101	151	150	70	62	15	–	–
OTHER											
MALE	143	8	44	33	21	18	15	3	–	1	–
FEMALE	135	7	36	34	16	21	14	3	4	–	–
TOTAL	278	15	80	67	37	39	29	6	4	1	–
TOTAL											
MALE	14,552	443	3,673	3,490	2,874	2,151	1,368	418	69	19	47
FEMALE	18,419	302	3,096	4,222	4,359	3,701	2,033	567	85	12	42
TOTAL	32,971	745	6,769	7,712	7,233	5,852	3,401	985	154	31	89

Table 1.1 (CNTD) – ADMISSIONS WITH NO PRIOR ADMISSION TO ANY INPATIENT PSYCHIATRIC FACILITY, STATE AND COUNTY MENTAL HOSPITAL, BY MENTAL DISORDER, AGE AND SEX: UNITED STATES, 1965

MENTAL DISORDER AND SEX	ALL AGES	AGE (IN YEARS)									
		Under 15	15–24	25–34	35–44	45–54	55–64	65–74	75–84	85 and over	Age unknown
PSYCHOPHYSIOLOGIC AUTONOMIC AND VISCERAL DISORDERS											
MALE	109	3	15	25	26	19	10	4	6	1	–
FEMALE	136	7	17	28	25	36	10	7	4	2	–
TOTAL	245	10	32	53	51	55	20	11	10	3	–
PSYCHONEUROTIC REACTIONS											
MALE	5,422	132	936	1,391	1,231	966	560	168	28	6	4
FEMALE	9,447	91	1,857	2,798	2,170	1,353	793	327	45	7	6
TOTAL	14,869	223	2,793	4,189	3,401	2,319	1,353	495	73	13	10
PERSONALITY DISORDERS											
PERSONALITY PATTERN DISTURBANCE											
MALE	2,086	125	849	460	338	190	94	23	3	–	4
FEMALE	902	42	363	232	154	81	27	1	1	1	–
TOTAL	2,988	167	1,212	692	492	271	121	24	4	1	4
PERSONALITY TRAIT DISTURBANCE											
MALE	4,973	212	1,595	1,284	955	648	246	22	1	–	10
FEMALE	2,710	85	1,152	740	466	188	53	16	4	3	3
TOTAL	7,683	297	2,747	2,024	1,421	836	299	38	5	3	13
ANTISOCIAL REACTION											
MALE	1,811	41	1,028	467	173	61	27	7	–	2	5
FEMALE	415	14	248	98	43	9	2	–	–	1	–
TOTAL	2,226	55	1,276	565	216	70	29	7	–	3	5
DYSSOCIAL REACTION											
MALE	343	8	198	70	40	15	9	1	–	–	2
FEMALE	171	5	113	31	16	2	2	–	–	–	2
TOTAL	514	13	311	101	56	17	11	1	–	–	4
SEXUAL DEVIATION											
MALE	884	9	323	266	149	84	40	7	5	–	1
FEMALE	53	–	31	15	5	1	1	–	–	–	–
TOTAL	937	9	354	281	154	85	41	7	5	–	1
ALCOHOLISM ADDICTION											
MALE	14,242	6	457	2,471	4,604	4,253	2,011	381	37	3	19
FEMALE	2,395	3	93	415	915	699	229	35	3	1	2
TOTAL	16,637	9	550	2,886	5,519	4,952	2,240	416	40	4	21
DRUG ADDICTION											
MALE	2,071	2	918	722	298	72	47	9	1	1	1
FEMALE	581	–	143	180	138	82	24	13	–	1	1
TOTAL	2,652	2	1,061	902	436	154	71	22	1	1	2
SPECIAL SYMPTOM REACTION											
MALE	19	4	8	6	1	–	–	–	–	–	–
FEMALE	6	1	1	1	1	1	1	–	–	–	–
TOTAL	25	5	9	7	2	1	1	–	–	–	–
TOTAL											
MALE	26,429	407	5,376	5,746	6.558	5,323	2,474	450	47	6	42
FEMALE	7,233	150	2,144	1,712	1,738	1,063	339	65	8	6	8
TOTAL	33,662	557	7,520	7,458	8,296	6,386	2,813	515	55	12	50
TRANSIENT SITUATIONAL PERSONALITY DISTURBANCE											
MALE	2,783	894	1,323	181	124	99	62	62	22	8	8
FEMALE	2,174	407	1,113	260	178	75	71	41	17	5	7
TOTAL	4,957	1,301	2,436	441	302	174	133	103	39	13	15
MENTAL DEFICIENCY											
MALE	2,203	256	899	388	288	223	113	19	4	4	9
FEMALE	1,426	140	487	273	239	171	82	21	4	1	8
TOTAL	3,629	396	1,386	661	527	394	195	40	8	5	17
MENTAL DISORDER UNDIAGNOSED											
MALE	4,375	222	913	705	650	552	344	231	212	67	479
FEMALE	3,169	116	476	475	513	380	238	197	169	65	540
TOTAL	7,544	338	1,389	1,180	1,163	932	582	428	381	132	1,019
WITHOUT MENTAL DISORDER											
MALE	1,354	33	418	309	246	146	86	69	36	8	3
FEMALE	393	20	101	75	76	32	26	26	27	10	–
TOTAL	1,747	53	519	384	322	178	112	95	63	18	3
TABLE TOTAL 1/											
273 of 290 hospitals MALE	77,797	2,730	14,372	13,415	13,830	11,881	8,135	5,624	5,501	1,638	671
FEMALE	57,679	1,397	9,761	10,412	10,110	7,850	5,407	4,916	5,254	1,906	666
TOTAL	135,476	4,127	24,133	23,827	23,940	19,731	13,542	10,540	10,755	3,544	1,337

1/ See footnote at end of Tables

Table 1.2 — ADMISSIONS WITH NO PRIOR ADMISSION TO ANY INPATIENT PSYCHIATRIC FACILITY, STATE AND COUNTY MENTAL HOSPITALS, BY MENTAL DISORDER, SEX AND STATE, UNITED STATES, 1965

MENTAL DISORDER	TABLE TOTAL 1/ 273 of 290 hospitals			ALABAMA 2 of 2 hospitals			ALASKA 2 of 2 hospitals		
	TOTAL	MALE	FEMALE	TOTAL	MALE	FEMALE	TOTAL	MALE	FEMALE
ALL DIAGNOSES	135,476	77,797	57,679	2,372	1,332	1,040	192	107	85
ACUTE BRAIN SYNDROMES	4,900	3,588	1,312	83	66	17	16	12	9
ALCOHOL INTOXICATION	3,564	2,909	655	65	59	6	14	10	4
ALL OTHER CONDITIONS	1,336	679	657	18	7	11	2	2	-
CHRONIC BRAIN SYNDROMES	30,952	16,982	13,970	493	247	246	22	11	11
MENINGOENCEPHALITIC SYPHILIS	157	104	53	7	7	-	-	-	-
OTHER CNS SYPHILIS	61	35	26	5	2	3	-	-	-
ALCOHOL INTOXICATION	2,720	2,143	577	11	9	2	-	-	-
DRUG OR POISON INTOXICATION	97	52	45	-	-	-	-	-	-
CEREBRAL ARTERIOSCLEROSIS	15,717	8,378	7,339	260	125	135	9	4	5
OTHER CIRCULATORY DISTURBANCE	1,240	713	527	15	13	2	-	-	-
CONVULSIVE DISORDER	1,716	922	794	40	26	14	5	3	2
SENILE BRAIN DISEASE	5,975	2,594	3,381	105	44	61	4	3	1
ALL OTHER CONDITIONS	3,269	2,041	1,228	50	21	29	4	1	3
PSYCHOTIC DISORDERS	32,971	14,552	18,419	866	418	448	58	32	26
INVOLUTIONAL PSYCHOTIC REACTION	4,110	1,106	3,004	130	27	103	2	2	-
MANIC DEPRESSIVE REACTION	1,398	566	832	15	3	12	-	-	-
PSYCHOTIC DEPRESSIVE REACTION	2,746	959	1,787	17	8	9	1	-	1
SCHIZOPHRENIC REACTIONS	23,861	11,475	12,386	698	375	323	53	29	24
PARANOID REACTIONS	578	303	275	6	5	1	1	1	-
OTHER	278	143	135	-	-	-	1	-	1
PSYCHOPHYSIOLOGIC AUTONOMIC AND VISCERAL DISORDERS	245	109	136	-	-	-	1	1	-
PSYCHONEUROTIC REACTIONS	14,869	5,422	9,447	99	28	71	38	13	25
PERSONALITY DISORDERS	33,662	26,429	7,233	523	376	147	26	21	5
ALCOHOLISM ADDICTION	16,637	14,242	2,395	221	217	4	16	13	3
ALL OTHER	17,025	12,187	4,838	302	159	143	10	8	2
TRANSIENT SITUATIONAL PERSONALITY DISTURBANCE	4,957	2,783	2,174	27	17	10	6	3	3
MENTAL DEFICIENCY	3,629	2,203	1,426	95	59	36	7	2	5
MENTAL DISORDER UNDIAGNOSED	7,544	4,375	3,169	152	91	61	15	9	6
WITHOUT MENTAL DISORDER	1,747	1,354	393	34	30	4	3	3	-

*National Institute of Mental Health: Office of Program Planning and Evaluation, Biometry Branch, Survey and Reports Section, *Patients in Mental Hospitals,* Public Health Service Publication No. 1597 (Chevy Chase, Md.: NIMH, 1967).

Table 1.3 – FIRST ADMISSIONS TO PRIVATE MENTAL HOSPITALS, BY MENTAL DISORDER, AGE AND SEX, UNITED STATES, 1964

MENTAL DISORDER AND SEX	ALL AGES	UNDER 15	15-24	25-34	35-44	45-54	55-64	65-74	75-84	85 AND OVER	AGE UNKNOWN
ACUTE BRAIN SYNDROMES ASSOC. WITH											
ALCOHOL INTOXICATION											
MALE	544		7	35	148	172	126	48	3		5
FEMALE	258		2	42	75	72	43	10	12	1	1
TOTAL	802		9	77	223	244	169	58	15	1	6
DRUG OR POISON INTOXICATION											
MALE	53		5	14	12	9	10	2	1		
FEMALE	114		10	24	35	22	15	6	2		
TOTAL	167		15	38	47	31	25	8	3		
CONVULSIVE DISORDER											
MALE	23	1	6	4	3	2	3	4			
FEMALE	25		6	7	5	4		3			
TOTAL	48	1	12	11	8	6	3	7			
ALL OTHER CONDITIONS											
MALE	143		10	17	22	38	32	11	12		1
FEMALE	239	3	26	30	49	63	26	25	16	1	
TOTAL	382	3	36	47	71	101	58	36	28	1	1
TOTAL											
MALE	763	1	28	70	185	221	171	65	16		6
FEMALE	636	3	44	103	164	161	84	44	30	2	1
TOTAL	1,399	4	72	173	349	382	255	109	46	2	7
CHRONIC BRAIN SYNDROMES ASSOC. WITH											
DISEASES AND CONDITIONS DUE TO PRENATAL INFLUENCE											
MALE	8	4	3	1							
FEMALE	7		3	3		1					
TOTAL	15	4	6	4		1					
MENINGOENCEPHALITIC SYPHILIS											
MALE	3					1		1	1		
FEMALE	1					1					
TOTAL	4					2		1	1		
OTHER CNS SYPHILIS											
MALE	1					1					
FEMALE	4					2	1	1			
TOTAL	5					3	1	1			
EPIDEMIC ENCEPHALITIS											
MALE	4		4								
FEMALE	3	1	1	1							
TOTAL	7	1	5	1							
OTHER INTRACRANIAL INFECTIONS											
MALE	8	1	5			1			1		
FEMALE	7		2	1			1	3			
TOTAL	15	1	7	1		1	1	3	1		
ALCOHOL INTOXICATIONS											
MALE	161		2	14	32	54	36	18	4		1
FEMALE	99			13	27	32	19	8			
TOTAL	260		2	27	59	86	55	26	4		1
DRUG OR POISON INTOXICATION											
MALE	8		1		2	2	1	1	1		
FEMALE	33		2		17	5	6	3			
TOTAL	41		3		19	7	7	4	1		
BIRTH TRAUMA											
MALE	15	7	5		1	1	1				
FEMALE	19	2	7	6	3		1				
TOTAL	34	9	12	6	4	1	2				
OTHER TRAUMA											
MALE	39	2	9	8	6	3	7	1	3		
FEMALE	33	1	8	4	2	3	4	4	7		
TOTAL	72	3	17	12	8	6	11	5	10		
CEREBRAL ARTERIOSCLEROSIS											
MALE	505	1			1	5	58	184	206	50	
FEMALE	889		1			6	88	320	393	80	1
TOTAL	1,394	1	1		1	11	146	504	599	130	1

Table 1.3 (CNTD) — FIRST ADMISSIONS TO PRIVATE MENTAL HOSPITALS, BY MENTAL DISORDER, AGE AND SEX, UNITED STATES, 1964

MENTAL DISORDER AND SEX	ALL AGES	UNDER 15	15–24	25–34	35–44	45–54	55–64	65–74	75–84	85 AND OVER	AGE UNKNOWN
OTHER CIRCULATORY DISTURBANCE											
MALE	62			1		6	17	22	12	4	
FEMALE	91			1	1	13	15	23	30	8	
TOTAL	153			2	1	19	32	45	42	12	
CONVULSIVE DISORDER											
MALE	49	6	19	7	11	5		1			
FEMALE	65	5	22	6	13	7	2	6	3	1	
TOTAL	114	11	41	13	24	12	2	7	3	1	
SENILE BRAIN DISEASE											
MALE	400					31	60	176	98	32	3
FEMALE	454				2		17	107	256	70	2
TOTAL	854				2	31	77	283	354	102	5
OTHER DISTURBANCE OF METABOLISM, GROWTH, AND NUTRITION											
MALE	24	2	3	1	1	2	7	6	1	1	
FEMALE	36		5	1	3	4	12	3	6		2
TOTAL	60	2	8	2	4	6	19	9	7	1	2
INTRACRANIAL NEOPLASM											
MALE	16		1		4	1	6	3	1		
FEMALE	13			1	1	5	1	4	1		
TOTAL	29		1	1	5	6	7	7	2		
DISEASES OF UNKNOWN CAUSE											
MALE	28	4	1		3	7	6	7			
FEMALE	29	2	4	3	2	4	6	5	3		
TOTAL	57	6	5	3	5	11	12	12	3		
CHRONIC BRAIN SYNDROME OF UNKNOWN CAUSE											
MALE	107	14	7	1	5	16	21	30	11	2	
FEMALE	90	1	7	3	5	5	14	29	21	5	
TOTAL	197	15	14	4	10	21	35	59	32	7	
TOTAL											
MALE	1,438	41	60	33	66	136	220	450	339	89	4
FEMALE	1,873	12	62	43	76	88	187	516	720	164	5
TOTAL	3,311	53	122	76	142	224	407	966	1,059	253	9
PSYCHOTIC DISORDERS											
INVOLUTIONAL PSYCHOTIC REACTION											
MALE	446		4	7	30	125	200	71	8	1	
FEMALE	1,484		8	26	203	652	427	151	16	1	1
TOTAL	1,930		12	33	233	777	627	222	24	1	1
MANIC DEPRESSIVE REACTION											
MALE	635	3	53	107	152	145	115	47	10	1	2
FEMALE	1,270	2	123	254	330	264	181	94	19	1	2
TOTAL	1,905	5	176	361	482	409	296	141	29	2	4
PSYCHOTIC DEPRESSIVE REACTION											
MALE	712	5	55	118	159	153	122	85	14		1
FEMALE	1,469	1	115	263	321	296	265	173	33	2	
TOTAL	2,181	6	170	381	480	449	387	258	47	2	1
SCHIZOPHRENIC REACTIONS											
MALE	2,569	65	918	695	526	262	76	23	3	–	1
FEMALE	4,678	51	1,026	1,456	1,263	617	194	59	5	2	5
TOTAL	7,247	116	1,944	2,151	1,789	879	270	82	8	2	6
PARANOID REACTIONS											
MALE	275		28	62	82	40	33	17	8	1	4
FEMALE	418	3	36	102	108	90	47	27	5		
TOTAL	693	3	64	164	190	130	80	44	13	1	4
OTHER											
MALE	244	17	35	33	75	36	18	18	10	2	
FEMALE	515	9	73	99	151	75	59	32	14	3	
TOTAL	759	26	108	132	226	111	77	50	24	5	
TOTAL											
MALE	4,881	90	1,093	1,022	1,024	761	564	261	53	5	8
FEMALE	9,834	66	1,381	2,200	2,376	1,994	1,173	536	92	8	8
TOTAL	14,715	156	2,474	3,222	3,400	2,755	1,737	797	145	13	16

Table 1.3 (CNTD) – FIRST ADMISSIONS TO PRIVATE MENTAL HOSPITALS, BY MENTAL DISORDER, AGE AND SEX, UNITED STATES, 1964

MENTAL DISORDER AND SEX	ALL AGES	UNDER 15	15–24	25–34	35–44	45–54	55–64	65–74	75–84	85 AND OVER	AGE UNKNOWN
PSYCHOPHYSIOLOGIC AUTONOMIC AND VISCERAL DISORDERS											
MALE	53	3	10	12	12	13	2	1			
FEMALE	132	2	22	23	32	31	15	7			
TOTAL	185	5	32	35	44	44	17	8			
PSYCHONEUROTIC REACTIONS											
MALE	3,730	46	423	712	991	825	508	184	33	2	6
FEMALE	8,223	45	1,104	2,104	2,131	1,436	885	432	69	4	13
TOTAL	11,953	91	1,527	2,816	3,122	2,261	1,393	616	102	6	19
PERSONALITY DISORDERS											
PERSONALITY PATTERN DISTURBANCE											
MALE	412	23	138	87	79	46	29	5	2	–	3
FEMALE	469	12	163	124	79	59	19	10	2	–	1
TOTAL	881	35	301	211	158	105	48	15	4	–	4
PERSONALITY TRAIT DISTURBANCE											
MALE	650	48	179	118	163	85	46	5	2	–	4
FEMALE	800	15	254	202	191	92	31	13	1	–	1
TOTAL	1,450	63	433	320	354	177	77	18	3	–	5
ANTISOCIAL REACTION											
MALE	93	9	51	17	9	7		4			
FEMALE	74	4	29	21	7	7	2	4			
TOTAL	167	13	80	38	16	14	2	4			
DYSSOCIAL REACTION											
MALE	29	1	20	3	5						
FEMALE	36		12	13	7	1	1	2			
TOTAL	65	1	32	16	12	1	1	2			
SEXUAL DEVIATION											
MALE	55	2	19	20	11	2		1			
FEMALE	8		3	2	1	1	1	1			
TOTAL	63	2	22	22	12	3	1	1			
ALCOHOLISM ADDICTION											
MALE	1,579		27	185	432	554	279	69	9	2	22
FEMALE	642		6	72	202	216	109	25	5	1	6
TOTAL	2,221		33	257	634	770	388	94	14	3	28
DRUG ADDICTION											
MALE	139		27	25	29	30	19	5	1		3
FEMALE	118		11	30	34	24	13	5			1
TOTAL	257		38	55	63	54	32	10	1		4
SPECIAL SYMPTON REACTION											
MALE	40	2	4	8	10	10	4	2			
FEMALE	49	5	6	12	16	6	2	2			
TOTAL	89	7	10	20	26	16	6	4			
TOTAL											
MALE	2,997	85	465	463	738	734	377	87	14	2	32
FEMALE	2,196	36	484	476	537	406	178	61	8	1	9
TOTAL	5,193	121	949	939	1,275	1,140	555	148	22	3	41
TRANSIENT SITUATIONAL PERSONALITY DISTURBANCE											
MALE	396	78	240	30	18	12	12	5			1
FEMALE	481	64	271	57	50	15	9	8	6		1
TOTAL	877	142	511	87	68	27	21	13	6		2
MENTAL DEFICIENCY											
MALE	60	17	20	6	4	6	3	4			
FEMALE	46	13	12	7	4	3	5	2			
TOTAL	106	30	32	13	8	9	8	6			
MENTAL DISORDER, UNDIAGNOSED											
MALE	241	12	64	42	43	21	30	17	7	1	4
FEMALE	376	16	72	91	72	60	28	20	14	2	1
TOTAL	617	28	136	133	115	81	58	37	21	3	5
WITHOUT MENTAL DISORDER											
MALE	182	2	10	19	25	34	48	19	16	8	1
FEMALE	206	3	16	34	32	32	26	32	21	9	1
TOTAL	388	5	26	53	57	66	74	51	37	17	2
TABLE TOTAL [1]											
MALE	14,741	375	2,413	2,409	3,106	2,763	1,935	1,093	478	107	62
FEMALE	24,003	260	3,468	5,138	5,474	4,226	2,590	1,658	960	190	39
TOTAL	38,744	635	5,881	7,547	8,580	6,989	4,525	2,751	1,438	297	101

[1] Totals based on detailed schedules from 151 of 242 known private hospitals.

*National Institute of Mental Health: Office of Biometry, Survey & Reports Section, *Patients in Mental Institutions, 1964, Part III: Private Mental Hospitals and General Hospitals with Psychiatric Facilities*, Public Health Service Publication No. 1452 (Washington, D.C.: NIMH, 1966).

4.

GEORGE W. ALBEE

DEFINITION OF MENTAL ILLNESS AND
MENTAL HEALTH MANPOWER TRENDS

DEFINITION OF MENTAL HEALTH AND ILLNESS

Another project of the Joint Commission on Mental Illness and Health (Jahoda, 1958) has examined the requirements of a definition of mental health. The reader is referred to that report for a detailed discussion of the problems of definition.[1]

We should look briefly, however, at this subject because it determines who shall be considered to be relevant manpower in the field of mental health.

The definition of mental illness is not especially difficult, though a number of problems need to be considered in certain peripheral areas of breakdown in normal human behavior. Ordinarily, we think of mental illness as an unusually persistent pattern of behavior over which the individual has little or no voluntary control; it differentiates him from his fellows; it incapacitates him; it interferes with his normal participation in life. The mentally ill individual often is caught in the grip of forces making him dangerous to himself or to others. In the milder case he may simply be unable to compete in the normal struggle for the satisfaction of his needs, and in the extreme case he may be unaware of himself and his surroundings and may be driven to acts which society finds incomprehensible and strange beyond belief.

Although mental illness has been recognized and described by writers throughout history, there were no real institutions for the care of people with mental disorders until sometime around 1800. The deranged were driven from

Reprinted from pp. 9–13 of *Mental Health Manpower Trends* by George W. Albee, Monograph Series No. 3 of Joint Commission on Mental Illness and Health, © 1959 by Basic Books, Inc., Publishers, New York. Reprinted by permission.
[1]See next section.

place to place, locked in dungeons, and often left to starve or to die from exposure. Occasionally lone voices spoke out on behalf of these unfortunate people, but it was not until the end of the eighteenth century, when the French psychiatrist Philippe Pinel struck off their chains and brought them into the light, that any real concern was exhibited for their care or for the study of the causes of their condition. Progress has been slow until very recently and many of the old attitudes toward mental illness—fear, horror, and disgrace—still persist.

The large "insane asylums" that grew up to house the mentally disordered in the nineteenth century and the early years of this century too often have been looked upon with fear and distaste. Their very names have long been used to frighten children into obedience.

During the past seventy-five years progress has been made toward the understanding, description, and classification of mental illnesses. Although the older attitudes still persist, many believe that we are on the verge of tremendous discoveries which will go far to eliminate or prevent this age-old scourge.

Mental health is the positive side of the problem. Not only must our society be concerned with understanding and dealing with the problem of mental illness, but also it must become increasingly self-conscious about the positive mental welfare of its citizens.

We recognize that good mental health requires, in addition to the satisfaction of basic biological needs, as much freedom as possible from the unpredictable, capricious, and devastating blows of circumstance. To be mentally healthy, the human being requires a certain measure of both personal and extrinsic security, freedom from the threats of the devastation of war, depression, plague, and flood. He requires the positive rewards of appreciation, achievement, and self-realization. He needs some assurance that fate will not deal him an unexpected blow, plus the internal strength to survive such a blow if it falls and adaptability to avoid a second one if possible. He has come, in many parts of the civilized world, to expect education for his children, spiritual support from his religion, and protection from his government.

With the increased leisure time he has won, as a result of increasing productive efficiency, institutions and professions have come into existence which help to insure him against catastrophe and which help him achieve positive development of his interests and abilities.

The mental health professions, with which we will be chiefly concerned in this report, are psychiatry, psychology, social work, and psychiatric nursing.

These professions are of central importance to all those social institutions which have evolved to help the mentally disordered; to offer assistance to the needy, the inadequate, the incapacitated, and the unfortunate; to study the causes and the amelioration of suffering due to emotional disturbance; and to provide resources for research into all the complex problems of causation, treatment, and prevention of these disorders.

Kenneth E. Appel . . . 1954 president of the American Psychiatric Association, has defined mental health as ". . . the ability of people to meet and handle problems; to make choices and decisions; to find satisfaction in accepting tasks; to do jobs without avoiding them and without pushing them onto others; to carry on without undue dependency on others; to live effectively and satisfactorily with others without crippling complications; to contribute one's share in life; to enjoy life and to be able to love and be loved." He goes on to point out that "mental illness is the opposite side of the coin of mental health." . . . [2]

MANPOWER SHORTAGE TRENDS

Increasingly, there are signs that our society is

[2]Kenneth E. Appel, in R. H. Kurtz (ed.), *Social Work Yearbook* (National Association of Social Workers, 1957), p. 363.

ready to face the fact that a serious manpower crisis exists in a large number of specialized fields. Everything has been coming so easy for us for so long that, until recently, we have failed to notice that our system of education, upon which rests most of the achievement of our high standard of living, has been steadily changing its function in a direction that leads away from its original task of training the minds of our young in knowledge and its applications, and in techniques for the discovery of further knowledge.

Our society has grown so used to such a great variety of goods and services, to such a high level of technical productivity, and to the expectation of ready satisfaction of many of our health and welfare needs, that we have taken all of these blessings for granted. The time has now come for our discovery that such achievements do not occur by themselves, but are largely based on the effectively trained intelligence of our nation's brainpower.

The field of mental health faces a real manpower crisis. This seems paradoxical in view of the fact that our nation has many more trained mental health personnel per capita than any other nation in the world. Professional mental health services are available in some form to most of our citizens.

Shortages in many areas of living are largely a matter of aspiration. To the hungry man, there is only one shortage. To the society living on the verge of starvation, mental health personnel are a luxury far down its list of priorities. But in the industrial societies that have developed in Europe and the New World in the last century, services of many kinds have become important daily needs.

In a country with serious and widespread disease, whether it be malaria, yaws, tuberculosis, or typhoid fever, few voices are raised to demand that more psychiatrists be trained. But as, one by one, the plagues of mankind have been controlled in the West, the plague of mental disorder has been increasingly exposed to public view. Mental disorder is not an important cause of death. No one dies of schizophrenia. Schizophrenics die of pneumonia or of tuberculosis or of malnutrition or some other cause. While mental disorder is not an important cause of death, it is, in our society, the most important source of human incapacity and of manpower loss to the nation. Manpower in the mental health professions is insufficient to meet our society's current needs and demands. The prospect of the future, we shall see, is for more shortages.

5.

MARIE JAHODA

CRITERIA FOR POSITIVE MENTAL HEALTH

From an inspection of the diverse approaches uncovered, six major categories of concepts emerge.

1. There are several proposals suggesting that indicators of positive mental health should be sought in the *attitudes of an individual toward his own self.* Various distinctions in the manner of perceiving oneself are regarded as demonstrating higher or lower degrees of health.

2. Another group of criteria designates the individual's style and degree of *growth, development, or self-actualization* as expressions of mental health. This group of criteria, in contrast to the first, is concerned not with self-perception but with what a person does with his self over a period of time.

3. Various proposals place the emphasis on a central synthesizing psychological function, incorporating some of the suggested criteria defined in (1) and (2) above. This function will here be called *integration.*

The following three groups of criteria concentrate more exclusively than the preceding ones on the individual's relation to reality.

4. *Autonomy* singles out the individual's degree of independence from social influences as most revealing of the state of his mental health.

5. A number of proposals suggest that

mental health is manifested in the adequacy of an individual's *perception of reality.*

6. Finally, there are suggestions that *environmental mastery* be regarded as a criterion for mental health.

. . . . .

ATTITUDES TOWARD THE SELF AS CRITERIA FOR MENTAL HEALTH

A recurring theme in many efforts to give meaning to the concept of mental health is the emphasis on certain qualities of a person's self. The mentally healthy attitude toward the self is described by terms such as self-acceptance, self-confidence, or self-reliance, each with slightly different connotations. Self-acceptance implies that a person has learned to live with himself, accepting both the limitations and possibilities he may find in himself. Self-confidence, self-esteem, and self-respect have a more positive slant; they express the judgment that in balance the self is "good," capable, and strong. Self-reliance carries the connotation of self-confidence and, in addition, of independence from others and of initiative from within. However, the terms have become entrenched in everyday language in a manner leading to a large overlap in their connotations.

There exists also an overlap in meaning with other terms that indicate qualities of an attitude toward the self. Such terms are, for example, self-assertion, self-centeredness or egotism, and self-consciousness. These latter terms,

Reprinted from *Current Concepts of Positive Mental Health* by Marie Jahoda, Basic Books, Inc., Publishers, New York, 1958. Pp. 23–25, 30–32, 35–36, 45–46, 49, 53. Reprinted by permission.

however, have not been proposed as criteria for mental health.

A number of different dimensions or components appear to run through the various proposals. Those aspects of the self-concept that stand out most clearly are: (1) accessibility to consciousness, (2) correctness, (3) feeling about the self, and (4) sense of identity. Although not all of these components are made explicit by the writers who use attributes of the self as criteria for mental health, they are implicit in many of their contributions. Inevitably, there is a certain amount of overlap between these aspects.

· · · · ·

GROWTH, DEVELOPMENT, AND SELF-ACTUALIZATION AS CRITERIA FOR MENTAL HEALTH

A number of authors see the essence of mental health in an ongoing process variously called self-actualization, self-realization, growth, or becoming. The idea that the organism strives permanently to realize its own potentialities is old. Fromm (1947) credits Spinoza with having seen the process of development as one of becoming what one potentially is. "A horse would be as much destroyed if it were changed into a man as if it were changed into an insect," Spinoza said. Fromm continues: "We might add that, according to Spinoza, a man would be as much destroyed if he became an angel as if he became a horse. Virtue is the unfolding of the specific potentialities of every organism; for man it is the state in which he is most human."

The term self-actualization probably originated with Goldstein (1940). He spoke about the process of self-actualization as occurring in every organism and not only in the healthy one: "There is only one motive by which human activity is set going: the tendency to actualize oneself." The idea is echoed in Sullivan's dictum, "the basic direction of the organism is forward," and it also dominates the thinking of authors such as Carl Rogers, Fromm, Maslow, and Gordon Allport. Sometimes the term is used as implying a general principle of life,

holding for every organism; at other times it is applied specifically to mentally healthy functioning.

It is not always easy to distinguish these two meanings in the mental health literature. This lack of clarity probably has something to do with the controversial philosophical concept of Aristotelian teleology, to which the notion of realizing one's potentialities is related. The need for making the distinction in a discussion of mental health becomes urgent if one realizes that not only the development of civilization but also self-destruction and crime, from petty thievery to genocide, are among the unique potentialities of the human species.

Mayman (1955) is of the opinion that some of the proponents of self-actualization as a criterion of health have not succeeded in making the distinction. In a critical discussion of Rogers' use of the term, he says: "This position is insufficient in several respects: it presumes that this growth force is equally potent in all people; that if given the right of way, this force will inevitably assert itself for good; but most important of all it treats this force with almost religious awe rather than scientific curiosity. This urge to grow and be healthy is treated as an irreducible essence of life."

To make this life force an aspect of positive mental health requires that certain qualifications be introduced to distinguish its manifestations in healthy persons.

The process of self-actualization, as a rule, is described in rather global terms that make it difficult to identify constituent parts. Nonetheless, the various authors who regard it as a criterion of positive mental health seem to emphasize one or more of the following aspects: (1) self-concept (which has already been discussed and is mentioned here only to indicate the breadth of the term self-actualization); (2) motivational processes; and (3) the investment in living, referring to the achievements of the self-actualizing person as demonstrated in a high degree of differentiation, or maximum of development, of his basic equipment.

· · · · ·

INTEGRATION AS A CRITERION FOR MENTAL HEALTH

In the proposals suggesting certain qualities of the self-concept or self-actualization, or both, as criteria for mental health, there is as a rule, implicit or explicit, another criterion; this is generally called integration of the personality. Indeed, some writers clearly treat this additional criterion as part of either the self-concept or of self-actualization. Others single it out for special treatment. In view of its great importance to some, it will be treated here as a major category in its own right.

Integration refers to the relatedness of all processes and attributes in an individual. The coherence of personality, often referred to as the unity or continuity of personality, is an axiomatic assumption in much psychological thought. Indeed, psychological treatment of mental patients as a rule is predicated on the search for a unifying principle in terms of which the apparently most bizarrely inconsistent manifestations of personality can be understood to hang together. When integration is proposed as a criterion for positive mental health, something additional or different is implied. Some authors suggest that integration as a criterion for mental health refers to the inter-relation of certain areas of the psyche; others, that it lies in the individual's awareness of the unifying principle. Still others imply that there are distinctions in the degree or strength of the integrating factor. And some are silent on this point.

Integration as a criterion for mental health is treated, as a rule, with emphasis on one of the following aspects: (1) a balance of psychic forces in the individual, (2) a unifying outlook on life, emphasizing cognitive aspects of integration, and (3) resistance to stress.

. . . . .

AUTONOMY AS A CRITERION FOR MENTAL HEALTH

Many persons regard an individual's relation to the world as mentally healthy if it shows what is referred to variously as autonomy, self-determination, or i[...] these terms connot[...] vidual and environ[...] sion-making. In thi[...] conscious discrimin[...] environmental fact[...] reject. But occas[...] preted as a with[...] need for the stimu[...] or as a small degree of involvement in external matters.

Expositions of the criterion of autonomy deal with one or both of two aspects: (1) The nature of the decision-making process, emphasizing the regulation of behavior from within, in accordance with internalized standards; (2) The outcome of the decision-making process in terms of independent actions.

. . . . .

PERCEPTION OF REALITY AS A CRITERION FOR MENTAL HEALTH

Pervading many efforts to conceptualize mental health is the idea that the way an individual perceives the world around him supplies an important criterion for his mental health. As a rule, the perception of reality is called mentally healthy when what the individual sees corresponds to what is actually there. In the mental health literature, perception is discussed invariably as social perception, meaning that the conditions under which perception occurs or the object of perception, or both, involve other human beings. This has an implication for terminology. Even if it makes sense under different conditions to speak of perception as distinguishable from other cognitive processes such as attention, judgment, and thinking, social perception cannot be so isolated. The term perception will here be used as implying various modes of cognition.

Two aspects of reality perception are suggested as criteria for mental health: perception free from need-distortion, and empathy or social sensitivity.

. . . . .

MENTAL MASTERY AS A
ION FOR MENTAL HEALTH

aps no other area of human functioning s more frequently been selected as a criterion for mental health than the individual's reality orientation and his efforts at mastering the environment.

There are two central themes pervading the relevant literature: the theme of success and the theme of adaptation. As a rule the former is specified as achievement in some significant areas of living; the latter is a toned-down version of the former, implying appropriate functioning with the emphasis more often on the process than on its result.

In the mental health literature adaptation and environmental mastery are treated on different levels of specificity. Ordering these emphases roughly from most to least specific forms of human functioning, these aspects can be distinguished: (1) the ability to love; (2) adequacy in love, work and play; (3) adequacy in interpersonal relations; (4) efficiency in meeting situational requirements; (5) capacity for adaptation and adjustment; (6) efficiency in problem-solving.

CHAPTER II

Models for the Study of Psychopathology

$\mathbf{M}$ODELS USED in the understanding of psychopathological phenomena have been growing in number in recent years, owing to their heuristic value of producing pregnant and fertile ideas for a fuller grasp of this complicated field of study. Models serve as conceptualizations or analogues, enabling the psychologist to pattern his approach to psychopathological phenomena along lines which have proved successful in other areas of study, especially disciplines which have proved productive. Hopefully, with the employment of a good model borrowed from a prosperous discipline, comparable success is sought in psychopathological study. A model worthy of emulation will furnish a set of concepts, technical terminology, and laws or generalizations which can be appropriated, or conclusions extrapolated from the findings of another successful field of endeavor.

THE MEDICAL MODEL AND THE UNITARY CONCEPT OF MENTAL DISEASE

In the medical or disease model, psychopathological states are likened to ailments found in physical maladies with clusters of symptoms termed syndromes, each syndrome associated with its technical nomenclature identifying it. Research is then conducted in order to ascertain the etiology of the syndrome, since hopefully the cause of the ailment puts the researcher well on the way to detecting a cure. In the last chapter, numerous syndromes were enumerated and defined, almost exclusively from the standpoint of the medical model. Most psychiatrists, owing to their medical training, tend to view mental disorder from the medical model orientation. Much of the nosology employed in abnormal psychology consists of terms coined by psychiatrists.

In recent years the medical model has undergone a barrage of criticism initiated by Szasz (1960, 1961a, 1961b, 1963) and quickly supported by Mowrer (1960) and others. While Thorne (1966) saw fit to rebut Szasz, Ausubel (1961) defended the disease model as a valid concept.

Closely related to the medical model is the *unitary concept* of mental illness, a view championed by Menninger (1959, 1960; Menninger, Ellenberger, Pruyser, & Mayman, 1958). According to the unitary concept, the various mental disorders are regarded as essentially one and the same malady, differing merely in the dimension of quantity or severity, rather than in quality or kind.

THE MORAL MODEL

Szasz repudiated the medical model as sheer myth, viewing mental disorder as a problem in living, whereas Mowrer (1960, 1967a, 1967b) identified it with *sin*. Mowrer seeks to impute a greater degree of responsibility upon the neurotic than the medical model will allow. Actually, the medical model exculpates the neurotic from all guilt.

THE DYNAMIC MODEL

A model, called the *dynamic* because it seeks to explain mental phenomena in terms of the numerous psychodynamisms at work within the personality, is used extensively by the so-called "depth psychologists" or those who refer to the unconscious processes operative in the individual. The prototype of the dynamic, the Freudian or psychoanalytic (Freud, 1959, 1961, 1963; Fromm-Reichmann, 1949), resorts to psychic energy systems entailing unconscious, preconscious, and conscious mind; id, ego, and superego structure of personality; instinctual and libidinal urges of eros and thanatos; the ego's various mechanisms of defense; oral, anal, phallic, and genital stages of development; the oedipus complex, and other dynamisms.

Other psychodynamic systems include the individual psychology of Adler (1926, 1929, 1969), the analytic psychology of Jung (1924, 1928, 1953), the interpersonal theory of psychiatry of Sullivan (1947a, 1953), humanistic psychoanalysis of Fromm (1941, 1955), and the neo-Freudianism of Horney (1937, 1942, 1945).

Many of the current texts in abnormal psychology and psychiatry utilize the dynamic model to a greater or lesser extent, and Cameron (1963) has even subtitled his "a dynamic approach." White's *The Abnormal Personality* (1964) and Stern's *The Abnormal Person and His World* (1964) favor the dynamic approach.

BEHAVIORAL AND LEARNING THEORY MODEL

The learning theory model derives from those behavioral scientists who have made significant contributions in the field of psychology of learning. Principles of learning, motivation, individual differences, etc. have been extended and extrapolated to apply to psychopathology. One text which has accomplished this application with remarkable success has been Maher's *Principles of Psychopathology: An Experimental Approach* (1966), but other texts are beginning to incorporate the learning theory model into their texts as special chapters (Buss, 1966) or as portions of chapters (Ullmann & Krasner, 1969).

While Dollard and Miller (1950) have effectively synthesized Freud's dynamic model with that of learning theory, others have successfully related learning theory to some phase of psychopathology. Among them are: Rotter (1954, 1964), Phillips (1956; Phillips & Wiener, 1966), Eysenck (1959, 1965), and Mowrer (1953).

STATISTICAL MODEL

The statistical model is yet another approach to the study of psychopathology, one employing mathematical-statistical methods of measurement for ascertaining the nature, extent, and intensity of various human traits and characteristics. By so doing, one can discern the nature and degree of mental disorder as well as correlate such traits with those of persons who are healthy. Cattell (1966) has edited a handbook entirely devoted to this approach which he terms multivariate experimental psychology and has effectually applied the method to psychopathology, especially in measuring anxiety and neuroticism (1961, 1962, 1963). Cattell's trait factor technique was successfully applied to psychosis by Lorr (1968b).

Eysenck (1952, 1960), utilizing a dimensional approach within the statistical model, measured three dimensions of personality: introversion-extraversion, neuroticism, and psychoticism. Instead of classifying mental disorder according to the syndrome model, he was able to produce continuous measurements by his statistical technique.

Still another variation of the statistical model, the *typological* or *type-factor* approach, was offered by Guertin (1952, 1961a, 1961b,) and Zubin *et al.* (1961). These men applied factor analytic techniques to define behavior patterns and syndromes with a precision unobtainable by ordinary psychiatric methods. Zubin and his associates, interested in the prognostication of mental disorders, applied the factor-analytic model so as to identify factors that would enable one to predict the outcome of psychopathology in the light of the type of treatment employed.

THE ONTOANALYTIC OR EXISTENTIAL MODEL

According to the ontoanalytic or existential model, the singularly human characteristics of man's personality (*Dasein*) are emphasized. Man is seen as more than a human being (essence), he is seen as a human becoming (existence), that is, man exists in a state of continual process in which his innumerable possibilities are brought into existence by choice, freedom, and other peculiarly human qualities. By virtue of his freedom, man chooses himself, decides responsibly what he is to be and then brings it into existence. Owning the ability to transcend himself, man acquires for himself authentic selfhood through choice.

Originating as the philosophy of Martin Heidegger (1962) and Søren Kierkegaard (1941a), existential psychiatry and psychotherapy has penetrated deep into the field of psychopathology, even to the extent of its proponents publishing several journals.

Among the more prominent psychopathologists adhering to the existential model are Frankl (1967a, 1969), May (1959, 1961, 1967, 1969; Frankl, May, Angel, & Ellenberger, 1958), Boss (1962, 1963; Condrau & Boss, 1968), Strauss (1961, 1966), and Binswanger (1963). Maddi has recently (1967) contributed a paper treating existential neurosis, a concept initially developed by Frankl who termed it noögenic neurosis. Thorne (1963) has constructed an existential theory of anxiety.

OTHER MODELS

There are a number of other models, such as: the *endocrinological model* which was chiefly exploited by Hoskins (1946, 1954); the *psychopharmacological model*, investigated by Uhr and Miller (1960); and the *genetic model* which has commanded considerable attention in recent years, especially since through it psychopathologists have been able to comprehend mongolism. In the year 1959, Lejeune, Gautier, and Turpin (1959a, 1959b) in France; Jacobs, Baikie, Brown, and Strong (1959) in England; and Böök, Fraccaro, and Lindsten (1959) in Sweden were successful in deciphering the chromosomal configuration responsible for mongolism.

6.

THOMAS S. SZASZ

REPUDIATION OF THE MEDICAL MODEL

My aim in this essay is to raise the question "Is there such a thing as mental illness?" and to argue that there is not. Since the notion of mental illness is extremely widely used nowadays, inquiry into the ways in which this term is employed would seem to be especially indicated. Mental illness, of course, is not literally a "thing"—or physical object—and hence it can "exist" only in the same sort of way in which other theoretical concepts exist. Yet, familiar theories are in the habit of posing, sooner or later—at least to those who come to believe in them—as "objective truths" (or "facts"). During certain historical periods, explanatory conceptions such as deities, witches, and microorganisms appeared not only as theories but as self-evident *causes* of a vast number of events. I submit that today mental illness is widely regarded in a somewhat similar fashion, that is, as the cause of innumerable diverse happenings. As an antidote to the complacent use of the notion of mental illness—whether as a self-evident phenomenon, theory, or cause—let us ask this question: What is meant when it is asserted that someone is mentally ill?

In what follows I shall describe briefly the main uses to which the concept of mental illness has been put. I shall argue that this notion has outlived whatever usefulness it might have had and that it now functions merely as a convenient myth.

MENTAL ILLNESS AS A SIGN OF BRAIN DISEASE

The notion of mental illness derives its main support from such phenomena as syphilis of the brain or delirious conditions—intoxications, for

instance—in which persons are known to manifest various peculiarities or disorders of thinking and behavior. Correctly speaking, however, these are diseases of the brain, not of the mind. According to one school of thought, *all* so-called mental illness is of this type. The assumption is made that some neurological defect, perhaps a very subtle one, will ultimately be found for all the disorders of thinking and behavior. Many contemporary psychiatrists, physicians, and other scientists hold this view. This position implies that people *cannot* have troubles—expressed in what are *now called* "mental illnesses" —because of differences in personal needs, opinions, social aspirations, values, and so on. *All problems in living* are attributed to physico-chemical processes which in due time will be discovered by medical research.

"Mental illnesses" are thus regarded as basically no different than all other diseases (that is, of the body). The only difference, in this view, between mental and bodily diseases is that the former, affecting the brain, manifest themselves by means of mental symptoms; whereas the latter, affecting other organ systems (for example, the skin, liver, etc.), manifest themselves by means of symptoms referable to those parts of the body. This view rests on and expresses what are, in my opinion, two fundamental errors.

In the first place, what central nervous system symptoms would correspond to a skin eruption or a fracture? It would *not* be some emotion or complex bit of behavior. Rather, it would be blindness or a paralysis of some part of the body. The crux of the matter is that a disease of the brain, analogous to a disease of the skin or bone, is a neurological defect, and not a problem in living. For example, a *defect* in a person's visual field may be satisfactorily explained by correlating it with certain definite lesions in the nervous system. On the other

From Thomas S. Szasz, "The myth of mental illness." *American Psychologist*, 1960, *15*, 113–118. © 1960 by the American Psychological Association, and reproduced by permission.

hand, a person's *belief*—whether this be a belief in Christianity, in Communism, or in the idea that his internal organs are "rotting" and that his body is, in fact, already "dead"—cannot be explained by a defect or disease of the nervous system. Explanations of this sort of occurrence —assuming that one is interested in the belief itself and does not regard it simply as a "symptom" or expression of something else that is *more interesting*—must be sought along different lines.

The second error in regarding complex psychosocial behavior, consisting of communications about ourselves and the world about us, as mere symptoms of neurological functioning is *epistemological*. In other words, it is an error pertaining not to any mistakes in observation or reasoning, as such, but rather to the way in which we organize and express our knowledge. In the present case, the error lies in making a symmetrical dualism between mental and physical (or bodily) symptoms, a dualism which is merely a habit of speech and to which no known observations can be found to correspond. Let us see if this is so. In medical practice, when we speak of physical disturbances, we mean either signs (for example, a fever) or symptoms (for example, pain). We speak of mental symptoms, on the other hand, when we refer to a patient's *communications about himself, others, and the world about him.* He might state that he is Napoleon or that he is being persecuted by the Communists. These would be considered mental symptoms *only* if the observer believed that the patient was *not* Napoleon or that he was *not* being persecuted by the Communists. This makes it apparent that the statement that "X is a mental symptom" involves rendering a judgment. The judgment entails, moreover, a covert comparison or matching of the patient's ideas, concepts, or beliefs with those of the observer and the society in which they live. The notion of mental symptoms is therefore inextricably tied to the *social* (including *ethical*) *context* in which it is made in much the same way as the notion of bodily symptom is tied to an *anatomical* and *genetic context* (Szasz, 1957a, 1957b).

To sum up what has been said thus far: I have tried to show that for those who regard mental symptoms as signs of brain disease, the concept of mental illness is unnecessary and misleading. For what they mean is that people so labeled suffer from diseases of the brain; and, if that is what they mean, it would seem better for the sake of clarity to say that and not something else.

MENTAL ILLNESS AS A NAME FOR PROBLEMS IN LIVING

The term "mental illness" is widely used to describe something which is very different than a disease of the brain. Many people today take it for granted that living is an arduous process. Its hardship for modern man, moreover, derives not so much from a struggle for biological survival as from the stresses and strains inherent in the social intercourse of complex human personalities. In this context, the notion of mental illness is used to identify or describe some feature of an individual's so-called personality. Mental illness—as a deformity of the personality, so to speak—is then regarded as the *cause* of the human disharmony. It is implicit in this view that social intercourse between people is regarded as something *inherently harmonious*, its disturbance being due solely to the presence of "mental illness" in many people. This is obviously fallacious reasoning, for it makes the abstraction "mental illness" into a *cause*, even though this abstraction was created in the first place to serve only as a shorthand expression for certain types of human behavior. It now becomes necessary to ask: "What kinds of behavior are regarded as indicative of mental illness, and by whom?"

The concept of illness, whether bodily or mental, implies *deviation from some clearly defined norm*. In the case of physical illness, the norm is the structural and functional integrity of the human body. Thus, although the desirability of physical health, as such, is an ethical value, what health *is* can be stated in anatomical and physiological terms. What is the norm deviation from which is regarded as mental illness? This question cannot be easily answered. But whatever this norm might be, we can be certain of only one thing: namely, that it is a norm that must be stated in terms of *psychosocial, ethical,* and *legal* concepts. For example, notions such as "excessive repression" or "acting out an unconscious impulse" illustrate the use of psychological concepts for judging (so-called) mental health and illness. The idea that chronic hostility, vengefulness, or divorce are indicative of mental illness would be illustrations of the use of ethical norms (that is, the desirability of love, kindness, and a stable marriage relationship). Finally, the widespread psychiatric opinion that only a mentally ill person would commit homicide illustrates the use of a legal concept as a norm of mental health. The norm from which deviation is measured whenever one speaks of a mental illness is a *psychosocial and ethical one.* Yet, the remedy is sought in terms of *medical* measures which—it is hoped and assumed—are free from wide differences of ethical value. The definition of the disorder and the terms in which its remedy are sought are therefore at serious odds with one another. The practical significance of this covert conflict between the alleged nature of the defect and the remedy can hardly be exaggerated.

Having identified the norms used to measure deviations in cases of mental illness, we will now turn to the question: "Who defines the norms and hence the deviation?" Two basic answers may be offered: (*a*) It may be the person himself (that is, the patient) who decides that he deviates from a norm. For example, an artist may believe that he suffers from a work inhibition; and he may implement this conclusion by seeking help *for* himself from a psychotherapist. (*b*) It may be someone other than the patient who decides that the latter is deviant (for example, relatives, physicians, legal authorities, society generally, etc.). In such a case a psychiatrist may be hired by others to do something *to* the patient in order to correct the deviation.

These considerations underscore the importance of asking the question "Whose agent is the psychiatrist?" and of giving a candid answer to it (Szasz, 1956, 1958). The psychiatrist (psychologist or nonmedical psychotherapist), it now develops, may be the agent of the patient, of the relatives, of the school, of the military services, of a business organization, of a court of law, and so forth. In speaking of the psychiatrist as the agent of these persons or organizations, it is not implied that his values concerning norms, or his ideas and aims concerning the proper nature of remedial action, need to coincide exactly with those of his employer. For example, a patient in individual psychotherapy may believe that his salvation lies in a new marriage; his psychotherapist need not share this hypothesis. As the patient's agent, however, he must abstain from bringing social or legal force to bear on the patient which would prevent him from putting his beliefs into action. If his *contract* is with the patient, the psychiatrist (psychotherapist) may disagree with him or stop his treatment; but he cannot engage others to obstruct the patient's aspirations. Similarly, if a psychiatrist is engaged by a court to determine the sanity of a criminal, he need not fully share the legal authorities' values and intentions in regard to the criminal and the means available for dealing with him. But the psychiatrist is expressly barred from stating, for example, that it is not the criminal who is "insane" but the men who wrote the law on the basis of which the very actions that are being judged are regarded as "criminal." Such an opinion could be voiced, of course, but not in a courtroom, and not by a psychiatrist who makes it his practice to assist the court in performing its daily work.

To recapitulate: In actual contemporary social usage, the finding of a mental illness is made by establishing a deviance in behavior from certain psychosocial, ethical, or legal norms. The judgment may be made, as in medicine, by the patient, the physician (psychiatrist), or others. Remedial action, finally, tends to be sought in a therapeutic—or covertly medical—framework, thus creating a situation in which *psychosocial, ethical* and/or *legal deviations* are claimed to be correctible by (so-called) *medical action.* Since medical action is designed to correct only medical deviations, it seems logically absurd to expect that it will help solve problems whose very existence had been defined and established on nonmedical grounds. I think that these considerations may be fruitfully applied to the present use of tranquilizers and, more generally, to what might be expected of drugs of whatever type in regard to the amelioration or solution of problems in human living.

THE ROLE OF ETHICS IN PSYCHIATRY

Anything that people *do*—in contrast to things that *happen* to them (Peters, 1958)—takes place in a context of value. In this broad sense, no human activity is devoid of ethical implications. When the values underlying certain activities are widely shared, those who participate in their pursuit may lose sight of them altogether. The discipline of medicine, both as a pure science (for example, research) and as a technology (for example, therapy), contains many ethical considerations and judgments. Unfortunately, these are often denied, minimized, or merely kept out of focus; for the ideal of the medical profession as well as of the people whom it serves seems to be having a system of medicine (allegedly) free of ethical value. This sentimental notion is expressed by such things as the doctor's willingness to treat and help patients irrespective of their religious or political beliefs, whether they are rich or poor, etc. While there may be some grounds for this belief—albeit it is a view that is not impressively true even in these regards—the fact remains that ethical considerations encompass a vast range of human affairs. By making the practice of medicine neutral in regard to some specific issues of value need not, and cannot, mean that it can be kept free from all such values. The practice of medicine is intimately tied to ethics; and the first thing that we must do, it seems to me, is to try to make this clear and explicit. I shall let this matter rest here, for it does not concern us specifically in this essay. Lest there be any vagueness, however, about how or where ethics and medicine meet, let me remind the reader of such issues as birth control, abortion, suicide, and euthanasia as only a few of the major areas of current ethicomedical controversy.

Psychiatry, I submit, is very much more intimately tied to problems of ethics than is medicine. I use the word "psychiatry" here to refer to that contemporary discipline which is concerned with *problems in living* (and not with diseases of the brain, which are problems for neurology). Problems in human relations can be analyzed, interpreted, and given meaning only within given social and ethical contexts. Accordingly, it *does* make a difference—arguments to the contrary notwithstanding—what the psychiatrist's socioethical orientations happen to be; for these will influence his ideas on what is wrong with the patient, what deserves comment or interpretation, in what possible directions change might be desirable, and so forth. Even in medicine proper, these factors play a role, as for instance, in the divergent orientations which physicians, depending on their religious affiliations, have toward such things as birth control and therapeutic abortion. Can anyone really believe that a psychotherapist's ideas concerning religious belief, slavery, or other similar issues play no role in his practical work? If they do make a difference, what are we to infer from it? Does it not seem reasonable that we ought to have different psychiatric therapies—each expressly recognized for the ethical positions which they embody—for, say, Catholics and Jews, religious persons and agnostics, democrats and communists, white supremacists and Negroes, and so on? Indeed, if we look at how psychiatry is actually practiced today (especially in the United States), we find that people do seek psychiatric help in accordance with their social status and ethical beliefs (Hollingshead & Redlich, 1958). This should really not surprise us more than being told that practicing Catholics rarely frequent birth control clinics.

The foregoing position which holds that contemporary psychotherapists deal with problems in living, rather than with mental illnesses and their cures, stands in opposition to a currently prevalent claim, according to which mental illness is just as "real" and "objective" as bodily illness. This is a confusing claim since it is never known exactly what is meant by such words as "real" and "objective." I suspect, however, that what is intended by the proponents of this view is to create the idea in the popular mind that mental illness is some sort of disease entity, like an infection or a malignancy. If this were true, one could *catch* or *get* a "mental illness," one might *have* or *harbor* it, one might *transmit* it to others, and finally one could get *rid* of it. In my opinion, there is not a shred of evidence to support this idea. To the contrary, all the evidence is the other way and supports the view that what people now call mental illnesses are for the most part *communications* expressing unacceptable ideas, often framed, moreover, in an unusual idiom. The scope of this essay allows me to do no more than mention this alternative theoretical approach to this problem (Szasz, 1957c).

This is not the place to consider in detail the similarities and differences between bodily and mental illnesses. It shall suffice for us here to emphasize only one important difference between them: namely, that whereas bodily disease refers to public, physicochemical occurrences, the notion of mental illness is used to codify relatively more private, sociopsychological happenings of which the observer (diagnostician) forms a part. In other words, the psychiatrist does not stand *apart* from what he observes, but is, in Harry Stack Sullivan's apt words, a "participant observer." This means that he is *committed* to some picture of what he considers reality—and to what he thinks society considers reality—and he observes and judges the patient's behavior in the light of these considerations. This touches on our earlier observation that the notion of mental symptom itself implies a comparison between observer and observed, psychiatrist and patient. This is so obvious that I may be charged with belaboring trivialities. Let me therefore say once more than my aim in presenting this argument was expressly to criticize and counter a prevailing contemporary tendency to deny the moral aspects of psychiatry (and psychotherapy) and to substitute for them allegedly value-free medical considerations. Psychotherapy, for example, is being widely practiced as though it entailed nothing other than restoring the patient from a state of mental sickness to one of mental health. While it is generally accepted that mental illness has something to do with man's social (or interpersonal) relations, it is paradoxically main-

tained that problems of values (that is, of ethics) do not arise in this process.[1] Yet, in one sense, much of psychotherapy may revolve around nothing other than the elucidation and weighing of goals and values—many of which may be mutually contradictory—and the means whereby they might best be harmonized, realized, or relinquished.

The diversity of human values and the methods by means of which they may be realized are so vast, and many of them remain so unacknowledged, that they cannot fail but lead to conflicts in human relations. Indeed, to say that human relations at all levels—from mother to child, through husband and wife, to nation and nation—are fraught with stress, strain, and disharmony is, once again, making the obvious explicit. Yet, what may be obvious may be also poorly understood. This I think is the case here. For it seems to me that—at least in our scientific theories of behavior—we have failed to *accept* the simple fact that human relations are inherently fraught with difficulties and that to make them even relatively harmonious requires much patience and hard work. I submit that the idea of mental illness is now being put to work to obscure certain difficulties which at present may be inherent—not that they need be unmodifiable—in the social intercourse of persons. If this is true, the concept functions as a disguise; for instead of calling attention to conflicting human needs, aspirations, and values, the notion of mental illness provides an amoral and impersonal "thing" (an "illness") as an explanation for *problems in living* (Szasz, 1959). We may recall in this connection that not so long ago it was devils and witches who were held responsible for men's problems in social living. The belief in mental illness, as something other

---

[1] Freud went so far as to say that: "I consider ethics to be taken for granted. Actually I have never done a mean thing" (Jones, 1957, p. 247). This surely is a strange thing to say for someone who has studied man as a social being as closely as did Freud. I mention it here to show how the notion of "illness" (in the case of psychoanalysis, "psychopathology," or "mental illness") was used by Freud—and by most of his followers—as a means for classifying certain forms of human behavior as falling within the scope of medicine, and hence (by *fiat*) outside that of ethics!

than man's trouble in getting along with his fellow man, is the proper heir to the belief in demonology and witchcraft. Mental illness exists or is "real" in exactly the same sense in which witches existed or were "real."

CHOICE, RESPONSIBILITY, AND PSYCHIATRY

While I have argued that mental illnesses do not exist, I obviously did not imply that the social and psychological occurrences to which this label is currently being attached also do not exist. Like the personal and social troubles which people had in the Middle Ages, they are real enough. It is the labels we give them that concern us and, having labeled them, what we do about them. While I cannot go into the ramified implications of this problem here, it is worth noting that a demonologic conception of problems in living gave rise to therapy along theological lines. Today, a belief in mental illness implies—nay, requires—therapy along medical or psychotherapeutic lines.

What is implied in the line of thought set forth here is something quite different. I do not intend to offer a new conception of "psychiatric illness" nor a new form of "therapy." My aim is more modest and yet also more ambitious. It is to suggest that the phenomena now called mental illnesses be looked at afresh and more simply, that they be removed from the category of illnesses, and that they be regarded as the expressions of man's struggle with the problem of *how* he should live. The last mentioned problem is obviously a vast one, its enormity reflecting not only man's inability to cope with his environment, but even more his increasing self-reflectiveness.

By problems in living, then, I refer to that truly explosive chain reaction which began with man's fall from divine grace by partaking of the fruit of the tree of knowledge. Man's awareness of himself and of the world about him seems to be a steadily expanding one, bringing in its wake an even larger *burden of understanding* (an expression borrowed from Susanne Langer, 1953). *This burden*, then, *is to be expected and must not be misinterpreted.* Our only *rational* means for lightening it is *more understanding*, and appropriate *action* based on such understanding. The main alternative lies in acting as though the burden were not what in fact we perceive it to be and taking refuge in an outmoded theological view of man. In the latter view, man does not fashion his life and much of his world about him, but merely lives out his fate in a world created by superior beings. This may logically lead to pleading nonresponsibility in the face of seemingly unfathomable problems and difficulties. Yet, if man fails to take increasing responsibility for his actions, individually as well as collectively, it seems unlikely that some higher power or being would assume this task and carry this burden for him. Moreover, this seems hardly the proper time in human history for obscuring the issue of man's responsibility for his actions by hiding it behind the skirt of an all-explaining conception of mental illness.

CONCLUSIONS

I have tried to show that the notion of mental illness has outlived whatever usefulness it might have had and that it now functions merely as a convenient myth. As such, it is a true heir to religious myths in general, and to the belief in witchcraft in particular; the role of all these belief-systems was to act as *social tranquilizers*, thus encouraging the hope that mastery of certain specific problems may be achieved by means of substitutive (symbolic-magical) operations. The notion of mental illness thus serves mainly to obscure the everyday fact that life for most people is a continuous struggle, not for biological survival, but for a "place in the sun," "peace of mind," or some other human value. For man aware of himself and of the world about him, once the needs for preserving the body (and perhaps the race) are more or less satisfied, the problem arises as to what he should do with himself. Sustained adherence to the myth of mental illness allows people to avoid facing this problem, believing that mental health, conceived as the absence of mental illness, automatically insures the making of right and safe choices in one's conduct of life. But the facts are all the other way. It is the making of good choices in life that others regard, retrospectively, as good mental health!

The myth of mental illness encourages us, moreover, to believe in its logical corollary: that social intercourse would be harmonious, satisfying, and the secure basis of a "good life" were it not for the disrupting influences of mental illness or "psychopathology." The potentiality for universal human happiness, in this form at least, seems to me but another example of the I-wish-it-were-true type of fantasy. I do believe that human happiness or well-being on a hitherto unimaginably large scale, and not just for a select few, is possible. This goal could be achieved, however, only at the cost of many men, and not just a few being willing and able to tackle their personal, social, and ethical conflicts. This means having the courage and integrity to forego waging battles on false fronts, finding solutions for substitute problems—for instance, fighting the battle of stomach acid and chronic fatigue instead of facing up to a marital conflict.

Our adversaries are not demons, witches, fate, or mental illness. We have no enemy whom we can fight, exorcise, or dispel by "cure." What we do have are *problems in living*—whether these be biologic, economic, political, or sociopsychological. In this essay I was concerned only with problems belonging in the last mentioned category, and within this group mainly with those pertaining to moral values. The field

to which modern psychiatry addresses itself is vast, and I made no effort to encompass it all. My argument was limited to the proposition that mental illness is a myth, whose function it is to disguise and thus render more palatable the bitter pill of moral conflicts in human relations.

REFERENCES

HOLLINGSHEAD, A. B., & REDLICH, F. C. *Social class and mental illness.* New York: Wiley, 1958.

JONES, E. *The life and work of Sigmund Freud.* Vol. III. New York: Basic Books, 1957.

LANGER, S. K. *Philosophy in a new key.* New York: Mentor Books, 1953.

PETERS, R. S. *The concept of motivation.* London: Routledge & Kegan Paul, 1958.

SZASZ, T. S. Malingering: "Diagnosis" or social condemnation? *AMA Archives of Neurology and Psychiatry,* 1956, *76,* 432–443.

SZASZ, T. S. *Pain and pleasure: A study of bodily feelings.* New York: Basic Books, 1957. (a)

SZASZ, T. S. The problem of psychiatric nosology: A contribution to a situational analysis of psychiatric operations. *American Journal of Psychiatry,* 1957, *114,* 405–413. (b)

SZASZ, T. S. On the theory of psychoanalytic treatment. *International Journal of Psycho-Analysis,* 1957, *38,* 166–182. (c)

SZASZ, T. S. Psychiatry, ethics and the criminal law. *Columbia Law Review,* 1958, *58,* 183–198.

SZASZ, T. S. Moral conflict and psychiatry, *Yale Review,* 1959.

7.

DAVID P. AUSUBEL

MEDICAL OR DISEASE MODEL

In two recent articles in the *American Psychologist,* Szasz (1960) and Mowrer (1960) have argued the case for discarding the concept of mental illness. The essence of Mowrer's

From David P. Ausubel, "Personality disorder *is* disease," *American Psychologist, 61,* 1961, 69–74. © 1961 by the American Psychological Association, and reproduced by permission.

position is that since medical science lacks "demonstrated competence . . . in psychiatry," psychology would be wise to "get out" from "under the penumbra of medicine," and to regard the behavior disorders as manifestations of sin rather than of disease (p. 302). Szasz' position, as we shall see shortly, is somewhat more complex than Mowrer's, but agrees with the latter in emphasizing the moral as opposed to the psychopathological basis of abnormal behavior.

For a long time now, clinical psychology has both repudiated the relevance of moral judgment and accountability for assessing behavioral acts and choices, and has chafed under medical (psychiatric) control and authority in diagnosing and treating the personality disorders. One can readily appreciate, therefore, Mowrer's eagerness to sever the historical and professional ties that bind clinical psychology to medicine, even if this means denying that psychological disturbances constitute a form of illness, and even if psychology's close working relationship with psychiatry must be replaced by a new rapprochement with sin and theology, as "the lesser of two evils" (pp. 302–303). One can also sympathize with Mowrer's and Szasz' dissatisfaction with prevailing amoral and nonjudgmental trends in clinical psychology and with their entirely commendable efforts to restore moral judgment and accountability to a respectable place among the criteria used in evaluating human behavior, both normal and abnormal.

Opposition to these two trends in the handling of the behavior disorders (i.e., to medical control and to nonjudgmental therapeutic attitudes), however, does not necessarily imply abandonment of the concept of mental illness. There is no inconsistency whatsoever in maintaining, on the one hand, that most purposeful human activity has a moral aspect the reality of which psychologists cannot afford to ignore (Ausubel, 1952, p. 462), that man is morally accountable for the majority of his misdeeds (Ausubel, 1952, p. 469), and that psychological rather than medical training and sophistication are basic to competence in the personality disorders (Ausubel, 1956, p. 101), and affirming, on the other hand, that the latter disorders are genuine manifestations of illness. In recent years psychology has been steadily moving away from the formerly fashionable stance of ethical neutrality in the behavioral sciences; and in spite of strident medical claims regarding superior professional qualifications and preclusive legal responsibility for treating psychiatric patients, and

notwithstanding the nominally restrictive provisions of medical practice acts, clinical psychologists have been assuming an increasingly more important, independent, and responsible role in treating the mentally ill population of the United States.

It would be instructive at this point to examine the tactics of certain other medically allied professions in freeing themselves from medical control and in acquiring independent, legally recognized professional status. In no instance have they resorted to the devious stratagem of denying that they were treating diseases, in the hope of mollifying medical opposition and legitimizing their own professional activities. They took the position instead that simply because a given condition is defined as a disease, its treatment need not necessarily be turned over to doctors of medicine if other equally competent professional specialists were available. That this position is legally and politically tenable is demonstrated by the fact that an impressively large number of recognized diseases are legally treated today by both medical *and* non-medical specialists (e.g., diseases of the mouth, face, jaws, teeth, eyes, and feet). And there are few convincing reasons for believing that psychiatrists wield that much more political power than physicians, maxillofacial surgeons, ophthalmologists, and orthopedic surgeons, that they could be successful where these latter specialists have failed, in legally restricting practice in their particular area of competence to holders of the medical degree. Hence, even if psychologists were not currently managing to hold their own vis-à-vis psychiatrists, it would be far less dangerous and much more forthright to press for the necessary ameliorative legislation than to seek cover behind an outmoded and thoroughly discredited conception of the behavior disorders.

THE SZASZ-MOWRER POSITION

Szasz' (1960) contention that the concept of mental illness "now functions merely as a convenient myth" (p. 118) is grounded on four unsubstantiated and logically untenable propositions, which can be fairly summarized as follows:

1. Only symptoms resulting from demonstrable physical lesions qualify as legitimate manifestations of disease. Brain pathology is a type of physical lesion, but its symptoms properly speaking, are neurological rather than psychological in nature. Under no circumstances, therefore, can mental symptoms be considered a form of illness.

2. A basic dichotomy exists between *mental* symptoms, on the one hand, which are subjective in nature, dependent on subjective judgment and personal involvement of the observer, and referable to cultural-ethical norms, and *physical* symptoms, on the other hand, which are allegedly objective in nature, ascertainable without personal involvement of the observer, and independent of cultural norms and ethical standards. Only symptoms possessing the latter set of characteristics are genuinely reflective of illness and amenable to medical treatment.

3. Mental symptoms are merely expressions of problems of living and, hence, cannot be regarded as manifestations of a pathological condition. The concept of mental illness is misleading and demonological because it seeks to explain psychological disturbance in particular and human disharmony in general in terms of a metaphorical but nonexistent disease entity, instead of attributing them to inherent difficulties in coming to grips with elusive problems of choice and responsibility.

4. Personality disorders, therefore, can be most fruitfully conceptualized as products of moral conflict, confusion, and aberration. Mowrer (1960) extends this latter proposition to include the dictum that psychiatric symptoms are primarily reflective of unacknowledged sin, and that individuals manifesting these symptoms are responsible for and deserve their suffering, both because of their original transgressions and because they refuse to avow and expiate their guilt (pp. 301, 304).

Widespread adoption of the Szasz-Mowrer view of the personality disorders would, in my opinion, turn back the psychiatric clock twenty-five hundred years. The most significant and perhaps the only real advance registered by mankind in evolving a rational and humane method of handling behavioral aberrations has been in substituting a concept of disease for the demonological and retributional doctrines regarding their nature and etiology that flourished until comparatively recent times. Conceptualized as illness, the symptoms of personality disorders can be interpreted in the light of underlying stresses and resistances, both genic and environmental, and can be evaluated in relation to *specifiable* quantitative and qualitative norms of appropriately adaptive behavior, both cross-culturally and within a particular cultural context. It would behoove us, therefore, before we abandon the concept of mental illness and return to the medieval doctrine of unexpiated sin or adopt Szasz' ambiguous criterion of difficulty in ethical choice and responsibility, to subject the foregoing propositions to careful and detailed study.

MENTAL SYMPTOMS AND BRAIN PATHOLOGY

Although I agree with Szasz in rejecting the doctrine that ultimately some neuroanatomic or neurophysiologic defect will be discovered in *all* cases of personality disorder, I disagree with his reasons for not accepting this proposition. Notwithstanding Szasz' straw man presentation of their position, the proponents of the extreme somatic view do not really assert that the *particular nature* of a patient's disordered beliefs can be correlated with "certain definite lesions in the nervous system" (Szasz, 1960, p. 113). They hold rather that normal cognitive and behavioral functioning depends on the anatomic and physiologic integrity of certain key areas of the brain, and that impairment of this substrate integrity, therefore, provides a physical basis for disturbed ideation and behavior, but does not explain, except in a very gross way, the particular kinds of symptoms involved. In fact, they are generally inclined to attribute the *specific* character of the patient's symptoms to the nature of his pre-illness personality structure, the substrate integrity of which is impaired by the lesion or metabolic defect in question.

Nevertheless, even though this type of reasoning plausibly accounts for the psychological symptoms found in general paresis, various toxic deleria, and other comparable conditions, it is an extremely improbable explanation of *all* instances of personality disorder. Unlike the tissues of any other organ, brain tissue possesses the unique property of making possible awareness of and adjustment to the world of sensory, social, and symbolic stimulation. Hence by virtue of this unique relationship of the nervous system to the environment, diseases of behavior and personality may reflect abnormalities in personal and social adjustment, quite apart from any structural or metabolic disturbance in the underlying neural substrate. I would conclude, therefore, that although brain pathology is probably not the most important cause of behavior disorder, it is undoubtedly responsible for the incidence of *some* psychological abnormalities, *as well as* for various neurological signs and symptoms.

But even if we completely accepted Szasz' view that brain pathology does not account for any symptoms of personality disorder, it would still be unnecessary to accept his assertion that to qualify as a genuine manifestation of disease a given symptom must be caused by a physical lesion. Adoption of such a criterion would be arbitrary and inconsistent both with medical and lay connotations of the term "disease," which in current usage is generally regarded as including any marked deviation, physical, mental, or behavioral, from normally desirable standards of structural and functional integrity.

MENTAL VERSUS PHYSICAL SYMPTOMS

Szasz contends that since the analogy between physical and mental symptoms is patently fallacious, the postulated parallelism between physical and mental disease is logically untenable. This line of reasoning is based on the assumption that the two categories of symptoms can be sharply dichotomized with respect to such basic dimensions as objectivity-subjectivity, the relevance of cultural norms, and the need for personal involvement of the observer. In my opinion, the existence of such a dichotomy cannot be empirically demonstrated in convincing fashion.

Practically all symptoms of bodily disease involve some elements of subjective judgment—both on the part of the patient and of the physician. Pain is perhaps the most important and commonly used criterion of physical illness. Yet, any evaluation of its reported locus, intensity, character, and duration is dependent upon the patient's subjective appraisal of his own sensations and on the physician's assessment of the latter's pain threshold, intelligence, and personality structure. It is also a medical commonplace that the severity of pain in most instances of bodily illness may be mitigated by the administration of a placebo. Furthermore, in taking a meaningful history the physician must not only serve as a participant observer but also as a skilled interpreter of human behavior. It is the rare patient who does not react psychologically to the signs of physical illness; and hence physicians are constantly called upon to decide, for example, to what extent precordial pain and reported tightness in the chest are manifestations of coronary insufficiency, of fear of cardiac disease and impending death, or of combinations of both conditions. Even such allegedly objective signs as pulse rate, BMR, blood pressure, and blood cholesterol have their subjective and relativistic aspects. Pulse rate and blood pressure are notoriously susceptible to emotional influences, and BMR and blood cholesterol fluctuate widely from one cultural environment to another (Dreyfuss & Czaczkes, 1959). And anyone who believes that ethical norms have no relevance for physical illness has obviously failed to consider the problems confronting Catholic patients and/or physicians when issues of contraception, abortion, and preferential saving of the mother's as against the fetus' life must be faced in the context of various obstetrical emergencies and medical contraindications to pregnancy.

It should now be clear, therefore, that symptoms not only do not need a physical basis to qualify as manifestations of illness, but also that the evaluation of *all* symptoms, physical as well as mental, is dependent in large measure on subjective judgment, emotional factors, cultural-ethical norms, and personal involvement on the part of the observer. These considerations alone render no longer tenable

Szasz' contention (1960, p. 114) that there is an inherent contradiction between using cultural and ethical norms as criteria of mental disease, on the one hand, and of employing medical measures of treatment on the other. But even if the postulated dichotomy between mental and physical symptoms were valid, the use of physical measures in treating subjective and relativistic psychological symptoms would still be warranted. Once we accept the proposition that impairment of the neural substrate of personality can result in behavior disorder, it is logically consistent to accept the corollary proposition that other kinds of manipulation of the same neural substrate can conceivably have therapeutic effects, irrespective of whether the underlying cause of the mental symptoms is physical or psychological.

MENTAL ILLNESS AND PROBLEMS OF LIVING

"The phenomena now called mental illness," argues Szasz (1960), can be regarded more forthrightly and simply as "expressions of man's struggle with the problem of how he should live" (p. 117). This statement undoubtedly oversimplifies the nature of personality disorders; but even if it were adequately inclusive it would not be inconsistent with the position that these disorders are a manifestation of illness. There is no valid reason why a particular symptom cannot both reflect a problem in living *and* constitute a manifestation of disease. The notion of mental illness, conceived in this way, would not "obscure the everyday fact that life for most people is a continuous struggle . . . for a 'place in the sun,' 'peace of mind,' or some other human value" (p. 118). It is quite true, as Szasz points out, that "human relations are inherently fraught with difficulties" (p. 117), and that most people manage to cope with such difficulties without becoming mentally ill. But conceding this fact hardly precludes the possibility that some individuals, either because of the magnitude of the stress involved, or because of genically or environmentally induced susceptibility to ordinary degrees of stress, respond to the problems of living with behavior that is either seriously distorted or sufficiently

unadaptive to prevent normal interpersonal relations and vocational functioning. The latter outcome—gross deviation from a designated range of desirable behavioral variability—conforms to the generally understood meaning of mental illness.

The plausibility of subsuming abnormal behavioral reactions to stress under the general rubric of disease is further enhanced by the fact that these reactions include the same three principal categories of symptoms found in physical illness. Depression and catastrophic impairment of self-esteem, for example, are manifestations of personality disorder which are symptomologically comparable to edema in cardiac failure or to heart murmurs in valvular disease. They are indicative of underlying pathology but are neither adaptive nor adjustive. Symptoms such as hypomanic overactivity and compulsive striving toward unrealistically high achievement goals, on the other hand, are both adaptive and adjustive, and constitute a type of compensatory response to basic feelings of inadequacy, which is not unlike cardiac hypertrophy in hypertensive heart disease or elevated white blood cell count in acute infections. And finally, distortive psychological defenses that have some adjustive value but are generally maladaptive (e.g., phobias, delusions, autistic fantasies) are analogous to the pathological situation found in conditions like pneumonia, in which the excessive outpouring of serum and phagocytes in defensive response to pathogenic bacteria literally causes the patient to drown in his own fluids.

Within the context of this same general proposition, Szasz repudiates the concept of mental illness as demonological in nature, i.e., as the "true heir to religious myths in general and to the belief in witchcraft in particular" (p. 118) because it allegedly employs a reified abstraction ("a deformity of personality") to account in causal terms both for "human disharmony" and for symptoms of behavior disorder (p. 114). But again he appears to be demolishing a straw man. Modern students of personality disorder do not regard mental illness as a cause of human disharmony, but as a co-manifestation with it of inherent difficulties in personal adjustment and interpersonal relations; and in so far as I can accurately interpret the literature, psychopathologists do not conceive of mental illness as a cause of particular behavioral symptoms but as a generic term under which these symptoms can be subsumed.

MENTAL ILLNESS AND MORAL RESPONSIBILITY

Szasz' final reason for regarding mental illness as a myth is really a corollary of his previously considered more general proposition that mental symptoms are essentially reflective of problems of living and hence do not legitimately qualify as manifestations of disease. It focuses on difficulties of ethical choice and responsibility as the particular life problems most likely to be productive of personality disorder. Mowrer (1960) further extends this corollary by asserting that neurotic and psychotic individuals are responsible for their suffering (p. 301), and that unacknowledged and unexpiated sin, in turn, is the basic cause of this suffering (p. 304). As previously suggested, however, one can plausibly accept the proposition that psychiatrists and clinical psychologists have erred in trying to divorce behavioral evaluation from ethical considerations, in conducting psychotherapy in an amoral setting, and in confusing the psychological explanation of unethical behavior with absolution from accountability for same, *without* necessarily endorsing the view that personality disorders are basically a reflection of sin, and that victims of these disorders are less ill than responsible for their symptoms (Ausubel, 1952, pp. 392-397, 465-471).

In the first place, it is possible in most instances (although admittedly difficult in some) to distinguish quite unambiguously between mental illness and ordinary cases of immorality. The vast majority of persons who are guilty of moral lapses knowingly violate their own ethical precepts for expediential reasons—despite being volitionally capable at the time, both of choosing the more moral alternative and of exercising the necessary inhibitory control (Ausubel, 1952, pp. 465-471). Such persons, also, usually do not exhibit any signs of behavior disorder. At crucial choice points in facing the problems of living they simply choose the opportunistic instead of the moral alternative. They are not mentally ill, but they are clearly accountable for their misconduct. Hence, since personality disorder and immorality are neither coextensive nor mutually exclusive conditions, the concept of mental illness need not necessarily obscure the issue of moral accountability.

Second, guilt may be a contributory factor in behavior disorder, but is by no means the only or principal cause thereof. Feelings of guilt may give rise to anxiety and depression; but in the absence of catastrophic impairment of self-esteem induced by *other* factors, these symptoms tend to be transitory and peripheral in nature (Ausubel, 1952, pp. 362-363). Repression of guilt is more a consequence than a cause of anxiety. Guilt is repressed in order to avoid the anxiety producing trauma to self-esteem that would otherwise result if it were acknowledged. Repression per se enters the causal picture in anxiety only secondarily—by obviating "the possibility of punishment, confession, expiation, and other guilt reduction mechanisms" (Ausubel, 1952, p. 456). Furthermore, in most types of personality disorder other than anxiety, depression, and various complications of anxiety such as phobias, obsessions, and compulsion, guilt feelings are either not particularly prominent (schizophrenic reactions), or are conspicuously absent (e.g., classical cases of inadequate or aggressive, antisocial psychopathy).

Third, it is just as unreasonable to hold an individual responsible for symptoms of behavior disorder as to deem him accountable for symptoms of physical illness. He is no more culpable for his inability to cope with sociopsychological stress than he would be for his inability to resist the spread of infectious organisms. In those instances where warranted guilt feelings *do* contribute to personality disorder, the patient is accountable for the misdeeds underlying his guilt, but is hardly responsible for the symptoms brought on by the guilt feelings or for unlawful acts committed during his illness. Acknowledgment of guilt may be therapeutically beneficial under these circumstances, but punishment for the original misconduct should obviously be deferred until after recovery.

Lastly, even if it were true that all personality disorder is a reflection of sin and that people are accountable for their behavioral symptoms, it would still be unnecessary to deny that these symptoms are manifestations of disease. Illness is no less real because the victim happens to be culpable for his illness. A glutton with hypertensive heart disease undoubtedly aggravates his condition by overeating, and is culpable in part for the often fatal symptoms of his disease, but what reasonable person would claim that for this reason he is not really ill?

CONCLUSIONS

Four propositions in support of the argument for discarding the concept of mental illness were carefully examined, and the following conclusions were reached:

First, although brain pathology is probably not the major cause of personality disorder, it does account for *some* psychological symptoms by impairing the neural substrate of personality. In any case, however, a symptom need not reflect a physical lesion in order to qualify as a genuine manifestation of disease.

Second, Szasz' postulated dichotomy between mental and physical symptoms is untenable because the assessment of *all* symptoms is dependent to some extent on subjective judgment, emotional factors, cultural-ethical norms, and personal involvement of the observer. Furthermore, the use of medical measures in treating behavior disorders—irrespective of whether the underlying causes are neural or psychological—is defensible on the grounds that if inadvertent impairment of the neural substrate of personality can have distortive effects on behavior, directed manipulation of the same substrate may have therapeutic effects.

Third, there is no inherent contradiction in regarding mental symptoms both as expressions of problems in living *and* as manifesta-

tions of illness. The latter situation results when individuals are for various reasons unable to cope with such problems, and react with seriously distorted or maladaptive behavior. The three principal categories of behavioral symptoms—manifestations of impaired functioning, adaptive compensation, and defensive overreaction—are also found in bodily disease. The concept of mental illness has never been advanced as a demonological cause of human disharmony, but only as a co-manifestation with it of certain inescapable difficulties and hazards in personal and social adjustment. The same concept is also generally accepted as a generic term for all behavioral symptoms rather than as a reified cause of these symptoms.

Fourth, the view that personality disorder is less a manifestation of illness than of sin, i.e., of culpable inadequacy in meeting problems of ethical choice and responsibility, and that victims of behavior disorder are therefore morally accountable for their symptoms, is neither logically nor empirically tenable. In most instances immoral behavior and mental illness are clearly distinguishable conditions. Guilt is only a secondary etiological factor in anxiety and depression, and in other personality disorders is either not prominent or conspicuously absent. The issue of culpability for symptoms is largely irrelevant in handling the behavior disorders, and in any case does not detract from the reality of the illness.

In general, it is both unnecessary and potentially dangerous to discard the concept of mental illness on the grounds that only in this way can clinical psychology escape from the professional domination of medicine. Dentists, podiatrists, optometrists, and osteopaths have managed to acquire an independent professional status without rejecting the concept of disease. It is equally unnecessary and dangerous to substitute the doctrine of sin for illness in order to counteract prevailing amoral and nonjudgmental trends in psychotherapy. The hypothesis of repressed guilt does not adequately explain most kinds and instances of personality disorder, and the concept of mental illness does not preclude judgments of moral accountability where warranted. Definition of behavior disorder in terms of sin or of difficulties associated with ethical choice and responsibility would substitute theological disputation and philosophical wrangling about values for specifiable quantitative and qualitative criteria of disease.

REFERENCES

Ausubel, D. P. *Ego development and the personality*

disorders. New York: Grune & Stratton, 1952.

Ausubel, D. P. Relationships between psychology and psychiatry: The hidden issues. *American Psychologist*, 1956, *11*, 99–105.

Dreyfuss, F., & Czaczkes, J. W. Blood cholesterol and uric acid of healthy medical students under the stress of an examination. *AMA Archives of Internal Medicine*, 1959, *103*, 708.

Mowrer, O. H. "Sin," the lesser of two evils. *American Psychologist*, 1960, *15*, 301–304.

Szasz, T. S. The myth of mental illness. *American Psychologist*, 1960, *15*, 113–118.

8.

O. Hobart Mowrer

MORAL MODEL

Following the presentation of a paper on "Constructive Aspects of the Concept of Sin in Psychotherapy" at the 1959 APA convention in Cincinnati, I have repeatedly been asked by psychologists and psychiatrists: "But *why* must you use that awful word 'sin' instead of some more neutral term such as 'wrongdoing,' 'irresponsibility,' or 'immorality'?" And even a religious layman has reproached me on the grounds that "Sin is such a *strong* word." Its *strength*, surely, is an asset, not a liability; for in the face of failure which has resulted from our erstwhile use of feebler concepts, we have very heavy work for it to do. Besides, sin (in contrast to its more neutral equivalents) is such a handy *little* word that it would be a pity to let it entirely disappear from usage. With Humpty-Dumpty, we ought to expect words to be "well-behaved" and to mean what *we* want them to!

A few years ago I was invited to teach in the summer session at one of our great Pacific Coast universities; and toward the end of the

term, a student in my class on Personality Theory said to me one day: "Did you know that near the beginning of this course you created a kind of scandal on this campus?" Then he explained that I had once used the word "sin" without saying "so-called" or making a joke about it. This, the student said, was virtually unheard-of in a psychology professor and had occasioned considerable dismay and perplexity. I did not even recall the incident; but the more I have thought about the reaction it produced, the more frequently I have found myself using the term—with, I hope, something more than mere perversity.

Traditionally, sin has been thought of as whatever causes one to go to Hell; and since Hell, as a place of otherworldly retribution and torment, has conveniently dropped out of most religious as well as secular thought, the concept of sin might indeed seem antiquated and absurd. But, as I observed in the Cincinnati paper, Hell is still very much with us in those states of mind and being which we call neurosis and psychosis; and I have come increasingly, at least in my own mind, to identify anything that carries us toward these forms of perdition as *sin*. Irresponsibility, wrongdoing, immorality, sin: what

From O. Hobart Mowrer, " 'Sin,' the lesser of two evils," *American Psychologist*, *15*, 1960, 301–304. © 1960 by the American Psychological Association, and reproduced by permission.

do the terms matter if we can thus understand more accurately the nature of psychopathology and gain greater practical control over its ramified forms and manifestations?

But now the fat is in the fire! Have we not been taught on high authority that personality disorder is not one's own "fault," that the neurotic is *not* "responsible" for his suffering, that he has done nothing wrong, committed no "sin?" "Mental illness," according to a poster which was widely circulated a few years ago, "is no disgrace. It might happen to anyone." And behind all this, of course, was the Freudian hypothesis that neurosis stems from a "too severe superego," which is the product of a too strenuous socialization of the individual at the hands of harsh, unloving parents and an irrational society. The trouble lay, supposedly, not in anything wrong or "sinful" which the individual has himself *done,* but in things he merely *wants* to do but cannot, because of *repression.*

The neurotic was thus not sinful but *sick,* the helpless, innocent victim of "the sins of the fathers," and could be rescued only by a specialized, esoteric form of *treatment.* Anna Russell catches the spirit of this doctrine well when she sings in "Psychiatric Folksong,"

At three I had a feeling of
  Ambivalence toward my brothers,
And so it follows naturally
  I poisoned all my lovers.
But now I'm happy; I have learned
  The lesson this has taught;
That everything I do that's wrong
  Is someone else's fault.

Freud saw all this not only as a great scientific discovery but also as a strategic gain for the profession which had thus far treated him so indifferently. It was, one may conjecture, a sort of gift, an offering or service which would place medicine in such debt to him that it could no longer ignore or reject him. In his *Autobiography,* Freud (1935) puts it thus:

My medical conscience felt pleased at my having arrived at this conclusion [that neurosis has a sexual basis]. I hoped that I had filled up a gap in medical science, which, in dealing with a function of such great biological importance, had failed to take into account any injuries beyond those caused by infection or by gross anatomical lesions. The medical aspect of the matter was, moreover, supported by the fact that sexuality was not something purely mental. It had a somatic side as well . . . (p. 45).

In his book on *The Problem of Lay Analysis,* Freud (1927) later took a somewhat different position (see also Chapter 9 of the third volume of Jones' biography of Freud, 1957); but by this time his Big Idea had been let loose in the world and was no longer entirely under his control.

Psychologists were, as we know, among the first of the outlying professional groups to "take up" psychoanalysis. By being analyzed, we not only learned—in an intimate, personal way—about this new and revolutionary science; we also (or so we imagined) were qualifying ourselves for the practice of analysis as a form of therapy. Now we are beginning to see how illusory this all was. We accepted psychoanalytic theory long before it had been adequately tested and thus embraced as "science" a set of presuppositions which we are now painfully having to repudiate. But, more than this, in accepting the premise that the neurotically disturbed person is basically *sick,* we surrendered our professional independence and authenticity. Now, to the extent that we have subscribed to the doctrine of mental *illness* (and tried to take part in its "treatment"), we have laid ourselves open to some really very embarrassing charges from our friends in psychiatry.

In 1954 the American Psychiatric Association, with the approval of the American Medical Association and the American Psychoanalytic Association, published a resolution on "relations between medicine and psychology," which it reissued (during the supposed "moratorium") in 1957. This document needs no extensive review in these pages; but a few sentences may be quoted to indicate what a powerful fulcrum the sickness conception of neurosis provides for the aggrandizement of medicine.

For centuries the Western world has placed on the medical profession responsibility for the diagnosis and treatment of illness. Medical practice acts have been designed to protect the public from unqualified practitioners and to define the special responsibilities assumed by those who practice the healing art. . . . Psychiatry is the medical speciality concerned with illness that has chiefly mental symptoms. . . . Psychotherapy is a form of medical treatment and does not form the basis for a separate profession. . . . When members of these [other] professions contribute to the diagnosis and treatment of illness, their professional contributions must be coordinated under medical responsibility (pp. 1–2).

So long as we subscribe to the view that neurosis is a bona fide "illness," without moral implications or dimensions, our position will, of necessity, continue to be an awkward one. And it is here I suggest that, as between the concept of sin (however unsatisfactory it may in some ways be) and that of sickness, sin is indeed the lesser of two evils. We have tried the sickness horn of this dilemma and impaled ourselves upon it. Perhaps, despite our erstwhile protestations, we shall yet find sin more congenial.

We psychologists do not, I believe, object *in principle* to the type of authority which psychiatrists wish to exercise, or to our being subject to other medical controls, if they were truly functional. But authority and power ought to go with demonstrated competence, which medicine clearly has in the physical realm but, equally clearly, does not have in "psychiatry." Despite some pretentious affirmations to the contrary, the fact is that psychoanalysis, on which modern "dynamic" psychiatry is largely based, is in a state of virtual collapse and imminent demise. And the tranquilizers and other forms of so-called chemotherapy are admittedly only ameliorative, not basically curative. So now, to the extent that we have accepted the "illness" postulate and thus been lured under the penumbra of medicine, we are in the ungraceful maneuver of "getting out."[1]

But the question remains: Where do we *go*, what do we *do*, now? Some believe that our best policy is to become frankly agnostic for the time being, to admit that we know next to nothing about either the cause or correction of psychopathology and therefore ought to concentrate on *research*. This is certainly a safe policy, and it may also be the wisest one. But since this matter of man's total adjustment and psychosocial survival does not quickly yield up its innermost secrets to conventional types of scientific inquiry, I believe it will do no harm for us at the same time to be thinking about some frankly ideological matters.

For several decades we psychologists looked upon the whole matter of sin and moral accountability as a great incubus and acclaimed our liberation from it as epoch-making. But at length we have discovered that to be "free" in this sense, i.e., to have the excuse of being "sick" rather than *sinful*, is to court the danger of also becoming *lost*. This danger is, I believe, betokened by the widespread interest in Existentialism which we are presently witnessing. In becoming amoral, ethically neutral, and "free," we have cut the very roots of our being; lost our deepest sense of self-hood and identity; and, with neurotics themselves, find ourselves asking: Who *am* I? What is my *destiny*? What does living (existence) *mean*?

In reaction to the state of near-limbo into which we have drifted, we have become suddenly aware, once again, of the problem of *values* and of their centrality in the human enterprise. This trend is clearly apparent in the programs at our recent professional meetings, in journal articles, and, to some extent already, in our elementary textbooks. Something very basic is obviously happening to psychologists and their "self-image."

In this process of moving away from our erstwhile medical "entanglements," it would be a very natural thing for us to form a closer and friendlier relationship than we have previously had with religion and theology. And something of this sort is unquestionably occurring. At the APA Annual Convention in 1956 there was, for the first time in our history I believe, a symposium on religion and mental health; and each ensuing year has seen other clear indications of a developing rapprochement.

However, here too there is a difficulty—of a

---

[1] Thoughtful psychiatrists are also beginning to question the legitimacy of the disease concept in this area. In an article entitled "The Myth of Mental Illness" which appeared after this paper went to press, Thomas S. Szasz (1960) is particularly outspoken on this score. He says: ". . . the notion of mental illness has outlived whatever usefulness it might have had and . . . now functions merely as a convenient myth . . . mental illness is a myth, whose function it is to disguise and thus render more palatable the bitter pill of moral conflicts in human relations" (p. 118). Szasz' entire article deserves careful attention.

most surprising kind. At the very time that psychologists are becoming distrustful of the sickness approach to personality disturbance and are beginning to look with more benign interest and respect toward certain moral and religious precepts, religionists themselves are being caught up in and bedazzled by the same preposterous system of thought as that from which we psychologists are just recovering. It would be possible to document this development at length; but reference to such recent "theological" works as Richard V. McCann's *Delinquency: Sickness or Sin?* (1957) and Carl Michalson's *Faith for Personal Crises* (1958, see especially Chapter 3) will suffice.

We have already alluded to Anna Russell's "Psychiatric Folksong" and, in addition, should call attention to Katie Lee's 12-inch LP recording "Songs of Couch and Consultation." That entertainment and literary people are broadly rejecting psychoanalytic froth for the more solid substance of moral accountability is indicated by many current novels and plays. It is not without significance that Arthur Miller's *Death of a Salesman*," written in the philosophical vein of Hawthorne's great novel *The Scarlet Letter,* has, for example, been received so well.

How very strange and inverted our present situation therefore is! Traditionally clergymen have worried about the world's entertainments and entertainers and, for a time at least, about psychology and psychologists. Now, ironically, the entertainers and psychologists are *worrying about the clergymen.* Eventually, of course, clergymen will return to a sounder, less fantastic position; but in the meantime, we psychologists can perhaps play a socially useful and, also, scientifically productive role if we pursue, with all seriousness and candor, our discovery of the essentially moral nature of human existence and of that "living death" which we call psychopathology. This, of course, is not the place to go deeply into the substantive aspects of the problem; but one illustration of the fruitfulness of such exploration may be cited.

In reconsidering the possibility that sin must, after all, be taken seriously, many psychologists seem perplexed as to what attitude one should take *toward the sinner.* "Nonjudgmental," "non-punitive," "nondirective," "warm," "accepting," "ethically neutral": these words have been so very generally used to form the supposedly proper therapeutic imago that reintroduction of the concept of sin throws us badly off balance. *Our* attitudes, as would-be therapists or helping persons, toward the neurotic (sinner) are apparently less important than his attitude *toward himself;* and, as we know, it is usually—in the most general sense—a rejecting one. Therefore, we have reasoned, the way to get the neurotic to accept and love himself is for us to love and accept *him,* an inference which flows equally from the Freudian assumption that the patient is not really guilty or sinful but only fancies himself so and from the view of Rogers that we are all inherently good and are corrupted by our experiences with the external, everyday world.

But what is here generally overlooked, it seems, is that recovery (constructive change, redemption) is most assuredly attained, not by helping a person reject and rise above his sins, but by helping him *accept them.* This is the paradox which we have not at all understood and which is the very crux of the problem. Just so long as a person lives under the shadow of real, unacknowledged, and unexpiated guilt, he *cannot* (if he has any character at all) "accept himself"; and all *our* efforts to reassure and accept him will avail nothing. He will continue to hate himself and to suffer the inevitable consequences of self-hatred. But the moment he (with or without "assistance") begins to accept his guilt and his sinfulness, the possibility of radical reformation opens up; and with this, the individual may legitimately, though not without pain and effort, pass from deep, pervasive self-rejection and self-torture to a new freedom, of self-respect and peace.

Thus we arrive, not only at a new (really very old) conception of the nature of "neurosis" which may change our entire approach to this problem, but also at an understanding of one of the most fundamental fallacies of Freudian psychoanalysis and many kindred efforts at psychotherapy. Freud observed, quite accurately, that the neurotic tortures himself; and he conjectured that this type of suffering arose from the irrationality and overseverity of the superego.

But at once there was an empirical as well as logical difficulty which Freud (unlike some of his followers) faithfully acknowledged. In the *New Introductory Lectures on Psychoanalysis* (1933), he said:

The superego [paradoxically] seems to have made a one-sided selection [as between the loving and the punitive attitudes of the parents], and to have chosen only the harshness and severity of the parents, their preventive and punitive functions, while their loving care is not taken up and continued by it. If the parents have really ruled with a rod of iron, we easily understand the child developing a severe superego, but, contrary to our expectations, experience shows that the superego may reflect the same relentless harshness even when the up-bringing has been gentle and kind (p. 90).

And then Freud adds, candidly: "We ourselves do not feel that we have fully understood it." In this we can fully agree. For the only way to resolve the paradox of self-hatred and self-punishment is to assume, not that it represents merely an "introjection" of the attitudes of others, but that the self-hatred is realistically justified and will persist until the individual, by radically altered attitude *and action*, honestly and realistically comes to feel that he now deserves something better. As long as one remains, in old-fashioned religious phraseology, hard-of-heart and unrepentant, just so long will one's conscience hold him in the vise-like grip of "neurotic" rigidity and suffering. But if, at length, an individual confesses his past stupidities and errors and makes what poor attempts he can at restitution, then the superego (like the parents of an earlier day—and society in general) forgives and relaxes its stern hold; and the individual once again is free, "well" (Mowrer, 1959).

But here we too, like Freud, encounter a difficulty. There is some evidence that human beings do not change radically unless they first acknowledge their sins; but we also know how hard it is for one to make such an acknowledgment unless he has *already changed*. In other words, the full realization of deep worthlessness is a severe ego "insult"; and one must have some new source of strength, it seems, to endure it. This is a mystery (or is it only a mistaken observation?) which traditional theology has tried to resolve in various ways—without complete success. Can we psychologists do better?

REFERENCES

AMERICAN PSYCHIATRIC ASSOCIATION, Committee on Relations between Psychiatry and Psychology. Resolution on relations of medicine and psychology. *American Psychiatric Association Mail Pouch,* October, 1954.

FREUD, S. *The problem of lay analysis.* New York: Brentano, 1927.

FREUD, S. *New introductory lectures on psychoanalysis.* New York: Norton, 1933.

FREUD, S. *Autobiography.* New York: Norton, 1935.

JONES, E. *The life and work of Sigmund Freud.* Vol. 3. New York: Basic Books, 1957.

McCANN, R. V. *Delinquency: Sickness or sin?* New York: Harper, 1957.

MICHALSON, C. *Faith for personal crises.* London: Epworth, 1958.

MOWRER, O. H. Changing conceptions of the unconscious. *Journal of Nervous and Mental Disease,* 1959, *129*, 222–234.

SZASZ, T. S. The myth of mental illness. *American Psychologist,* 1960, *15*, 113–118.

9.

FRIEDA FROMM-REICHMANN

DYNAMIC MODEL

Before attempting any discussion of recent advances in psychoanalysis a brief review should be given of some basic concepts of classical psychoanalysis versus its modifications in recent modern dynamic psychoanalytic conceptual thinking, so that a useful frame of reference may be established.

Advances achieved in psychoanalysis in recent years are in relation to these conceptions, to the method and technique of therapy, and to the types of patients who can be treated by psychoanalytic psychotherapy. (1)

BASIC PSYCHOANALYTIC CONCEPTS

Psychoanalysis understands the functioning of the human mind as the result of the dynamic interaction between mental operations on various levels and with different qualities of awareness. (Freud: Conscious, preconscious, unconscious.) Thoughts and feelings which are incompatible with the standards of a person himself, with those of significant people in his environment or of his culture at large may be barred from awareness and recall ("repressed," "dissociated") because of the effect of anxiety they would produce were they to remain in awareness. Unknown to the person, these repressed experiences remain alive in his mind and influence his thoughts, feelings, and actions. At times, this is the reason for people expressing things which are seemingly not meaningful. As psychoanalysts have learned to realize that their origin is on other levels of awareness, hence qualitatively different from those in which the person communicates, they have learned to understand that all mental and emotional manifestations are meaningful and, at least potentially, understandable.

This dynamic conception of the modes of operation of the human mind is in contrast to the preanalytic, descriptive, psychiatric approach to an understanding of the working of the mind as a static entity. Poets and philosophers, of course, have known for centuries about the functional dichotomy of the human mind. It is the scientific discovery of its application to psychiatry and to psychology, and more specifically in the context of this paper, of its medical application to psychiatry, to psychotherapy, and to medicine at large (psychosomatic medicine), that I am discussing here.

To gain an understanding of human personality as characterized by psychoanalytic dynamic psychiatry, its functioning must be explored and understood genetically, that is, from its total history. The early developmental history of infancy and childhood plays a predominant role in the formation of character and personality and especially in the formation of patterns of human interrelationships. This early history is understood in terms of three elements complementing one another. They are: constitution, or that which a person brings with him, the influences of external circumstances at large, and, most of all, the specific important interpersonal experiences of the infant and young child with the significant people of his early environment. The latter play a portentous role, due to the length of time and the extent of the biological and psychological dependence of the human.

Unknown to the person, this pattern formation and its reappearance hold true also for the early traumatic interpersonal experiences which have been subjected to the process of dissociation or repression. Because they have been dissociated there can be no participation of such experiences in the growth and maturation

From Frieda Fromm-Reichmann, "Recent advances in psychoanalysis," *Journal of the American Medical Women's Association*, 1949, 4, 320–326. Reprinted by permission.

of the rest of the personality. It is their reflection in the interpersonal experiences of later life which is the salience of many distorted evaluations of and responses to these experiences throughout life, on the one hand, and of the mental patient's unwitting, compulsive search for their repetition, on the other. Whether the connection of these early, unclarified interpersonal experiences is with love, hatred, pain, anxiety, or other feelings and emotions, their transference to the people of one's later life plays a very important role in all relationships.

So much, in brief, about the generally accepted basic psychoanalytic concepts of the functioning of the human mind and personality. I shall endeavor now to outline briefly a few highlights of the various psychoanalytic conceptions of human developmental history because they form the frame of reference for all genetically oriented psychoanalytic psychotherapy.

DEVELOPMENTAL HISTORY

The early developmental history as conceived by Freud is psychosexual in nature. (2, 3, 4, 5) He understands the various phases of a person's development to be the outcome of a response to the lust obtainable and the interpersonal expression available by means of the bodily zones of food intake and elimination. Consequently, Freud speaks of an oral, anal, and phallic state of one's pregenital psychosexual development, all of which precede the ability of a person to feel genital lust. The sexual energy manifesting itself in these psychosexual pregenital and genital interests and activities, Freud calls libido. He conceives the course of character development and personality in its ultimate mentally healthy outcome to be the result of this libidinal energy having run a complete and uninterrupted course, from the early oral state to the time at which the human gains the ability to feel primarily genital lust in relation to another person of the opposite sex.

According to Freud, a person matures as he learns to take care of the desexualization of his pregenital libido by means of sublimation,

reaction formation, over-compensation, etc. Subsequently he develops the ability for orgastic genital experiences with a mature person of the opposite sex.

OEDIPUS COMPLEX

This is done first in terms of the Oedipus complex, the situation in which the genitalization of libido is felt in connection with a tender and sexual affection for the parent of the opposite sex and concomitant feelings of rivalry and hatred for the parent of the same sex. The Oedipus constellation in the mentally healthy is resolved by the child's tendency to use the parent of the same sex as a model for its own further developmental patterns and ideal formations, and the parent of the opposite sex as a person through whom it learns to develop friendly interpersonal relationships.

The ability to amalgamate feelings of emotional tenderness and of sexual attraction toward one and the same person is considered another evidence of matureness. Freud views love as an outcome and a concomitant feeling of sexual attraction to another person.

In the course of neurotic character development, according to Freud's concepts, the progress of libidinal energy from oral to genital primacy is interrupted and incomplete. The libidinal charge is fixated or attached emotionally to one of the pregenital levels of the psychosexual development. Also, the neurotic person has not succeeded in overcoming the early conflicts of the original Oedipus constellation. According to Freud, these early conflicts constitute one universally valid reason for the later development of neurotic disorders.

The doctrine of the ubiquitousness and of the sexual nature of the Oedipus complex has been revised by many psychoanalytic authors and cultural anthropologists. (Boehm [6], Fromm [7], Malinowski [8], Mullahy [9], *et al.*). They would demonstrate, first, that in matriarchal societies it may not be the father but an uncle who is the target for the little boy's hatred; second, that the boy's hatred against the father, where encountered, is much more frequently based upon his resentment of the authoritative prerogatives of the father figure and/or his envy of the interpersonal intimacy between the father and mother, than upon a sexual origin.

Sullivan viewed the various phases of developmental history in terms of the interpersonal experiences characteristic of each of these phases of development. (10) He referred to the period of infancy, the childhood period, the juvenile era, preadolescence, and, as a last developmental phase, adolescence.

The period of infancy he refers to as the time during which the human is in contact with the mothering one by empathic linkage, the state of non-verbal contact through non-sensory channels which is characteristic of the early mother-infant relationship. In varying degrees, empathy may operate in people throughout their lives. It is the quality due to which non-verbalized, meaningful, communication is frequently successful and its operation becomes therapeutically important in the psychiatrist's dealings with his mental patients, especially with mute or inarticulate ones.

The childhood period, Sullivan characterizes by the development of mutual, verbalized communication, contentment in a communal life with authoritarian adults, and the more or less personalized pets, toys, and other objects.

The juvenile era is characterized by maturation of the need for compeers and of one's talents for such interpersonal phenomena as co-operation, competition, and compromise.

Preadolescence is a time during which the need for a chum to love is a predominant interpersonal factor. Love, as defined by Sullivan and Fromm, (11) is the state of relatedness in which a person is as interested in the loved one's well-being, satisfaction, and security, growth, and maturation, as he is in his own.

Adolescence is the period that is characterized by the process of puberty, gradually producing a maturing sense of self-realization. This is the time when there is a need to break away from the authoritative people of childhood in a rather dramatic way, via the detour of exchanging them for dependence upon and admiration for one's heroes and heroines. In this way the ability to form independent evaluational judgments is finally gained and ultimately the capacity is developed for establishing durable relationships of intimacy.

PSYCHIATRY—THE SCIENCE OF INTERPERSONAL RELATIONSHIPS

This interpersonal concept of the developmental history is an illustrative part of Sullivan's total doctrine of psychiatry as being the art and science of interpersonal relationships, which means that human personality functions and can be understood only in terms of a person's actual or phantasy relationships and through the medium of a person's contacts and exchange with others.

The emotional importance of the bodily zones of intake and elimination and of their functions during early life is not denied, of course, by any of the modern psychoanalytic psychiatrists. (Fromm [12], Horney. [13]) However, many of them do not believe that character and personality trends can be understood as the outcome of various forms of desexualization, as has been described in the review of the basic classical psychoanalytic concepts. Fromm, for instance, sees the fundamental basis of character formation in the specific kind of relatedness of a person to the world as it is molded in childhood by the family, the psychic agent of society. His concept of a receptive, exploitative, hoarding, and marketing character versus a productive character who is able "to use his powers and to realize the potentialities inherent in him," in a positive, life-furthering sense are illustrative of his approach.

We see from these concepts, then, that modern developmental psychoanalytic theory is characterized by the maintenance of the paramount significance of the total developmental history and by the negation of its classical psychosexual interpretation.

Freud's conception of the emotional significance of immediate environmental influences for the understanding of human personality and for the treatment of human psychopathology has been broadened in the direction of the inclusion of cultural influences on a general scale versus his otherwise predominantly biological approach to human psychopathology.

The concepts of Fromm (12, 14), Horney (13, 15), Kardiner (16), Sullivan (10, 17), *et al.*, on the Oedipus constellation, may serve as an example for this development.

PSYCHOANALYTIC CONCEPTS OF ANXIETY

Another expression of the changes and advances in psychoanalytic thinking and therapy is with regard to some mental symptoms, among them the most outstanding one: anxiety. The study of the concepts of anxiety as developed in the various schools of psychoanalytic thinking is of greatest importance for any student and practitioner in the field, since the understanding and adequate handling of the patient's anxiety plays a crucial role in all psychopathology, hence in all psychoanalytic psychotherapy.

Freud has defined anxiety in his early writings as the correlate of repressed libidinal strivings. Later he saw it as a person's fear at the realization of culturally inacceptable inner strivings. (18) This definition is similar to the one Sullivan gives in his interpersonal frame of reference. (10, 19) In Sullivan's definition, anxiety is the discomfort which the child learns to feel in the presence of the disapproval of the significant adult who first uses the arousal of this discomfort as a tool while training the child to abide by the basic requirements of acculturation. With great variations as to the threshold of endurance, anxiety remains effective throughout people's lives in response to disapproval from important people which interferes with a person's security and prestige. Sullivan has taught the understanding of all mental disorders as an expression of and an attempt at warding off anxiety. Horney speaks of four principal modes of defense against anxiety: affection, submissiveness, power, withdrawal. She teaches that the craving for affection, for power, and for control plays a paramount role in the development of neuroses and neurotic personalities.

Where there is anxiety there is insecurity; where there is insecurity there is lack of self-respect; where there is lack of self-respect there is lack of respect for others. Anxiety causes impairment of relatedness to others, fear of friendliness in giving and taking, loneliness and hostility, all well-known symptoms in mental patients.

This brief outline of psychoanalytic concepts may suffice as a background for the following discussion of the recent advances in the method and technique of psychoanalytic psychotherapy and the types of patients who may be treated by modern, dynamic psychoanalytic psychotherapy.

ETIOLOGY OF MENTAL DISORDER

In the light of the dynamic and genetic conceptions of the working of the mind, human psychopathology is understood by all dynamic psychiatrists as the outcome of early warp, thwarting experiences, and severe frustrations in relation to a significant person in the infant's or child's environment. In the upbringing of our present day, circumscribed as it is by family life, as a rule, it is a parent who is responsible for warping experiences, the threat of which is too great to be offset by other benign influences. The type of emotional disturbance which a person develops will depend upon the timing of the first decisive blow of a set of such traumatic experiences and from the presence or absence of other benign or malignant interpersonal influences. Many emotional experiences of his later life will be undergone, actually or by his interpretation, as if they were really repetitions of the original traumata in the childhood setting.

In other words, whenever a person who has undergone too severe or too frequent early traumatic experiences is exposed to later life experiences engendering pain, hostility, anxiety, etc., he has to cope not only with the actual experience as such, but in addition with its repetitional validity. This repetitional aspect stems from his early dissociated, therefore never satisfactorily integrated, traumatic experiences with all their immature misevaluation and their concomitant anxiety.

In order to avoid misunderstanding, I wish to state at this point, that in discussing the psychopathological effects of keeping emotional experiences from awareness, I do not mean to say that all dissociative or repressed processes are psychopathological in nature. The contrary is true. Man depends upon successful dissociations and processes of selective inattention for the mastery of his psychobiological existence. It is the surplus of painful and anxiety-rousing emotional experience, whose barring from awareness creates psychopathological problems. If a patient's original traumatic material is brought to awareness in psychotherapy, it can be submitted to revaluation on the present level of the patient's matureness, anxiety can be relieved and recent traumatic experience can be freed from the additional weight stemming from non-integrated previous experience. Hence, the bringing to awareness and the subsequent evaluation of repressed material must be an integral part of the psychotherapeutic process just as will the investigation of those feelings, the reflection of which will be transferred to the people of one's later life.

PSYCHOANALYTIC PSYCHOTHERAPY

In the situation of psychoanalytic psychotherapy these feelings, unknown to the patient himself, will be transferred to the psychotherapist and so they can be studied *in statu nascendi* by psychiatrist and patient. Otherwise, treatment must be directed toward resolving psychopathological repression and dissociation and understanding the patient's difficulties in terms of his developmental history. This aim is attained in using the following psychotherapeutic tools: collecting data from the patient regarding biographical and historical facts which the patient is able to offer; his presenting problems, previous problems and crises situations; biographical data especially regarding his developmental history; his private mental experiences, such as dreams and daydreams, hallucinatory and delusional experiences.

The means for collecting the data are listening intelligently, as a participant observer, to all that the patient has to say; asking simply meaningful and pertinent questions; encourag-

ing associative thinking; and picking up marginal thoughts and physical sensations, where direct information is failing. Further therapeutically valid material presents itself in the repetition and reactivation, during treatment, of the powers which originally motivated the patient's dissociative procedures. As mentioned before, this also takes place, and is of the essence for therapeutic use in the vicissitudes of the doctor-patient relationship, in its real and in its distorted, "parataxic," aspects—in classical terminology, in the patient's "transference" experiences. Once the pertinent data is carefully collected, interpretative collaboration between the patient and the psychotherapist follows, with regard to the understanding of the hidden meaning of the previously dissociated material, as to its genetics, dynamics, and content.

INTERPRETATION

Interpretation means translating into the language of awareness, and thereby bringing into the open, that which the patient communicates, without being conscious of its contents, dynamics, revealing connections with other experiences or of various implications pertaining to its factual or emotional background.

At the present state of development in psychoanalytic psychotherapy, special interpretative attention is given to the clarification of the dynamic significance of the defense mechanisms, the security operations which the anxious mental patient uses, wittingly or unwittingly, in his dealings with his fellow men, including the psychotherapist. These security operations are directed against anxiety producing, real or alleged, threats to the patient's safety and prestige which he expects from the people of his environment. This makes it advisable that great attention be paid to the actual interpersonal experiences of the patient in his everyday life, both previous to and during the treatment situation, and that special attention be paid to the crises which may have precipitated his entering treatment, and as they recur while he is undergoing psychotherapy. (15, 10, 29)

Part of the previously hidden meaning of the

patient's material reveals itself and part of his dissociations resolve themselves by the mere process of relating the data to the doctor, that is, by bringing his hitherto private covert experiences into contact with outward reality. Another part gets clarified in the course of the interpretative investigation of the patient's security operations. Only what remains unclarified by these two devices should be uncovered and revalued by direct interpretation of content. By and large, content interpretation, *per se,* is not considered as important today as it was in the early years of psychoanalysis, and it is used with ever-increasing thriftiness, caution, and discrimination.

No cure is accomplished according to present classical and modified psychoanalytic knowledge by any single, one-time understanding of any single symptom or any single previously dissociated experience. All emotional experiences which are made accessible to the patient's awareness and mature emotional judgment have to be recognized and accepted ("worked through") repeatedly in various contexts. In doing so, psychiatrist and patient should be guided by what gradually transpires as the patient's central problem. Working through should be continued until the time is reached when the intellectual understanding of this problem, its previously dissociated causes and its various interlocking mental and emotional ramifications are gradually transformed into real creative emotional insight.

FREE ASSOCIATIONS

The encouragement of the patient's "free associations" is considered to be a backbone of classical psychoanalytic therapy. It is designed to eliminate the patient's conscious control over his mental productions, thus bringing out previously repressed and dissociated material.

Since the psychoanalytic doctrine and method were first conceived, an impressive body of knowledge and experience as to the modes of operation and expression used in interpersonal processes which are outside of awareness has been collected. Therefore, many modern dynamic psychotherapists do not feel

the indiscriminate use of the so-called method of "free association" to be a basic requirement in psychoanalytic therapy. This marks another change in psychoanalytic therapy.

Many psychoanalysts feel that a sufficient amount of recognizable dissociated material comes to the surface and may arise into awareness in more directed psychotherapeutic interchange and directed focused associative thinking.

DREAM INTERPRETATION

Scientific dream interpretation continues to be considered an important means of understanding many thoughts and feelings that the patient cannot express while awake, because of the fact that, during sleep, control and censorship of his mental processes are eliminated or at least greatly reduced. The extent to which dream interpretation may be used in any single psychotherapeutic process depends upon the therapeutic usefulness of both the nature of a patient's dreams and the understanding and interpretative skill of the psychotherapist.

DIDACTIC PSYCHOANALYSIS

In this connection, emphasis may be placed upon the fact that the extent and nuance of the use of the various psychotherapeutic tools in each course of treatment will, of necessity, be co-determined by the assets and liabilities of both persons concerned, the patient and the doctor as participant observer. This being so, a personal psychoanalysis is among the training requirements for any psychiatrist who wishes to do psychoanalytic psychotherapy.

SET-UP IN PSYCHOANALYTIC PSYCHOTHERAPY

The trend toward more therapeutic attention being paid to the actual realities in the patient's life is responsible for several practical changes in the set-up of the treatment situation. Among these recent trends is the relinquishment, by many psychoanalysts, of the binding rule that the patient must lie on the couch, the doctor seated invisibly behind him. As is now understood by many psychoanalytic psychotherapists, this arrangement interfered, for quite a number of patients, with an experience of reality and spontaneity in the exchange between patient and doctor. This feeling of reality and a spontaneous interchange should be encouraged, notwithstanding the maintenance of the strictly professional character of the doctor-patient relationship. Present arrangements of many psychoanalysts allow for patients to sit or to lie down, depending upon the way it appears to work best with each patient. With some patients this may be decided upon at once for the entire course of treatment, with others changes of position once or repeatedly may be advisable during the course of the treatment.

BRIEF PSYCHOTHERAPY–GROUP PSYCHOTHERAPY

Other recent changes in psychoanalytic psychotherapy stem from research and practical endeavor directed toward shortening the psychoanalytic process with a carefully selected group of patients. Important work in that direction is under way at one of the leading psychoanalytic training centers in this country, the Chicago Psychoanalytic Institute. (20, 21) The successful introduction of psychoanalytic concepts into group psychotherapy as it has been developed in many psychotherapy centers during and after the last war should also be mentioned in this connection. (22, 23, 24)

PSYCHOSOMATIC MEDICINE

The technique of psychoanalytic psychotherapy was originally created for the special application to psychoneuroses. Treatment of physical symptoms was in terms of an interpretative approach to the "conversion symptoms" of the hysteric. (2, 3, 4, 5) Modern developments in psychosomatic medicine are mainly due to psychoanalytic research. (25, 26, 27) Two sets of results, which have become of great significance for practically all branches of modern medicine, stem from this advance in psychoanalytic development. One is the psychotherapeutic approach to the emotional roots of the etiological factors of somatic symptomatology, where previously symptoms and syndromes were approached in terms of their clinical appearance. The other is the finding of certain laws governing the correlation between certain types of psychoneurotic personalities and their choice of bodily disturbances. The psychosomatic significance of high blood pressure, gastric ulcers, and the various types of colitis, asthma, and hay fever is by now known to every physician as representative of these findings.

PSYCHOSES

There is one more important progressive step in psychoanalytic psychotherapy, which is signified by a modification in the technique of psychoanalysis for the application to the psychoses. (28, 30) An early attempt at doing classical psychoanalysis with a manic depressive was made by Abraham. (31) Recently research and therapeutic endeavor focused around the manic depressive group has been done in England. (32) In this country, severely disturbed schizophrenics have been approached with modified psychoanalytic techniques. This became possible in line with the previously described recent changes in psychoanalytic technique and as a result of the two aforementioned great discoveries of psychoanalytic psychiatry: that all mental manifestations, including those of the mentally disordered, are potentially meaningful; and that there is interpersonal interaction between any two people who meet, including the mentally disturbed patient and the psychotherapist.

Out of this grew the psychopathologically significant insight: that the difference between healthy, neurotic, and psychotic people is much more one of degree than one in kind; that the mentally handicapped may have assets which may not be found in the healthy, and that the healthy may have liabilities not duplicated in the mentally disturbed. (32) In brief, that we are all "Much more simply human than otherwise." (10)

Some psychoanalytic psychiatrists hope that

it is not too optimistic to harbor the dream that this psychiatric insight may in time develop into a small contribution toward improving the mutual understanding between the people of the disturbed world of today.

REFERENCES

1. FROMM-REICHMANN, F. Recent advances in psychoanalytic psychotherapy, *Psychiatry*, May, 1941, *4*, 161–164.
2. FREUD, S. *A general introduction to psychoanalysis.* New York: Boni & Liveright, 1920.
3. BRILL, A. A. *The basic writings of Sigmund Freud.* New York: Modern Library, 1938.
4. HENDRICKS, I. *Facts and theories of psychoanalysis.* New York: Alfred Knopf, 1939.
5. FENICHEL, O. *Outline of clinical psychoanalysis,* New York: W. W. Norton, 1934.
6. BOEHM, F. *Intern. Ztschr. Psychoanalyse,* 1926, *12,* 66–79. Not translated.
7. FROMM, E., in *The family, its function and destiny, a synthesis,* Anshen, Ruth Nanda (Ed.), Chapters XVII, XIX. New York: Harper & Brothers, 1949.
8. MALINOWSKI, B. *Sex and repression in savage society,* New York: Harcourt, London: K. Paul, Trenck Trubner & Co., 1927.
9. MULLAHY, P. *Oedipus myth and complex.* New York: Hermitage Press, Inc., 1948 (offers orientation on the attitude of all psychoanalytic schools to the problem).
10. SULLIVAN, H. S. Conceptions of modern psychiatry; William Alanson White Memorial Lectures, *Psychiatry,* 1940, *3,* 1–117. Reprinted as monograph. The William Alanson White Psychiatric Foundation, Washington, D.C., 1947.
11. FROMM, E. Selfishness and self-love, *Psychiatry,* 1939, *2,* 507–523.
12. FROMM, E. *Escape from freedom.* New York and Toronto: Farrar and Rhinehart, Inc., 1941.
13. HORNEY, K. *The neurotic personality of our time.* New York: W. W. Norton, 1937.
14. FROMM, E. *Man for himself; and inquiry into the psychology and ethics.* New York: Rhinehart, 1947.
15. HORNEY, K. *New ways in psychoanalysis,* New York: W. W. Norton, 1939.
16. KARDINER, A. *The individual and his society.* New York: Columbia University Press, 1939.
17. SULLIVAN, H. S. A note on the implications of psychiatry, the study of interpersonal relations, for investigations in the social sciences, *American Journal of Sociology, 43,* 848–861.
18. FREUD, S. *The problem of anxiety.* New York: W. W. Norton, 1936.
19. SULLIVAN, H. S. The meaning of anxiety in psychiatry and in life, *Psychiatry,* 1948, *1,* 1–13.
20. ALEXANDER, F., FRENCH, T. M. & others. *Psychoanalytic therapy.* New York: Ronald Press, 1946.
21. Proceedings of the Psychotherapy Council, Chicago Psychoanalytic Institute, 1946.
22. ABRAHAM, J. Group psychotherapy; remarks on its basis and application. *Medical Annals of the District of Columbia,* 1947, *16,* 612–616.
23. ACKERMAN, N. W. Dynamic patterns in group psychotherapy, *Psychiatry,* 1944, *7,* 341–348.
24. SLAVSON, S. R. *An introduction to group therapy,* London, Oxford: Commonwealth Fund, 1943.
25. *The Journal of Psychosomatic Medicine,* The Williams and Wilkins Company, Baltimore, Md.
26. DUNBAR, H. F. *Emotions and bodily changes.* New York: Columbia University Press, 1938.
27. WEISS, E., & ENGLISH, O. S. *Psychosomatic medicine.* Philadelphia and London: W. B. Saunders Co., 1943.
28. SULLIVAN, H. S. Environmental factors in etiology and course under treatment of schizophrenia, *Medical Journal and Record,* 1931, *133,* 19–22.
29. SULLIVAN, H. S. Therapeutic investigations in schizophrenia, *Psychiatry,* 1947, *10,* 121–125.
30. FROMM-REICHMANN, F. Notes on the development of treatment of schizophrenics by psychoanalytic psychotherapy, *Psychiatry,* 1948, *11,* 263–273.
31. ABRAHAM, K. *Selected Papers.* International Psychoanalytical Library, No. 13, p. 473 ff.
32. KLEIN, M. A contribution to the psychogenesis of manic-depressive states, *International Journal of Psycho-analysis,* 1935, *16,* 145–174.

10.

H. J. Eysenck

LEARNING THEORY MODEL

It would probably be true to say that the present position in the psychiatric treatment of neurotic disorders is characterized by the following features. (1) With the exception of electroshock, the only method of treatment at all widely used is psychotherapy. (2) In practically all its manifestations, psychotherapy is based on Freudian theories. (3) With the exception of intelligence testing, psychological contributions consist almost entirely in the administration and interpretation of projective tests, usually along psycho-analytic lines. I have argued in the past, and quoted numerous experiments in support of these arguments, that (1) there is little evidence for the practical efficacy of psychotherapy, whether strictly Freudian or "eclectic" (8, 17); (2) that Freudian theories are outside the realm of science because of their failure to be consistent, or to generate testable deductions (10); and (3), that projective tests are so unreliable and lacking in validity that their use, except in research, cannot be defended (16). I shall not here argue these points again; the evidence on which these views are based is quite strong, and is growing in strength every year. I shall instead try to make a somewhat more constructive contribution by discussing an alternative theory of neurosis, an alternative method of treatment, and an alternative way of using the knowledge and competence of psychologists in the attempted cure of neurotic disorders. It need hardly be emphasized that the brief time at my disposal will make it inevitable that what I have to say will sound much more dogmatic than I would like it to be; I have to ask your indulgence in this respect, and request you to bear in mind all the obvious qualifying clauses

which, if included in this paper, would swell it to three times its present size.

Few psychiatrists are likely to deny that all behaviour ultimately rests on an inherited basis, but even fewer would be prepared to assert that environmental influences played no part in the genesis and modification of behaviour. Once we are agreed that learning and conditioning are instrumental in determining the different kinds of reaction we may make to environmental stimulation, we will find it very difficult to deny that neurotic reactions, like all others, are *learned* reactions, and must obey the laws of learning. Thus, I would like to make my first claim by saying that modern learning theory (24), and the experimental studies of learning and conditioning carried out by psychologists in their laboratories (38) are extremely relevant to the problems raised by neurotic disorders (41). If the laws which have been formulated are not necessarily true, but at least partially correct, then it must follow that we can make deductions from them to cover the type of behaviour represented by neurotic patients, construct a model which will duplicate the important and relevant features of the patient, and suggest new and possibly helpful methods of treatment along lines laid down by learning theory. Whether these methods are in fact an improvement over existing methods is, of course, an empirical problem; a few facts are available in this connection and will be mentioned later. It is unfortunate that insistence on empirical proof has not always accompanied the production of theories in the psychiatric field—much needless work, and many heart-breaking failures, could have been avoided if the simple medical practice of clinical trials with proper controls had always been followed in the consideration of such claims.

How, then, does modern learning theory look

From H. J. Eysenck."Learning theory and behaviour therapy."*Journal of Mental Science*, 1959, *105*, 61–75. Reprinted by permission.

upon neurosis? In the first place, it would claim that neurotic symptoms are *learned patterns of behaviour* which for some reason or other are *unadaptive*. The paradigm of neurotic symptom formation would be Watson's famous experiment with little Albert, a nine months old boy who was fond of white rats (44). By a simple process of classical Pavlovian conditioning Watson created a phobia for white rats in this boy by standing behind him and making a very loud noise by banging an iron bar with a hammer whenever Albert reached for the animal. The animal was the conditioned stimulus in the experiment, the loud fear-producing noise was the unconditioned stimulus. As predicted, the unconditioned response (fear) became conditioned to the C.S. (the rat), and Albert developed a phobia for rats, and indeed for all furry animals. This latter feature of the conditioning process is of course familiar to all students as the generalization gradient (38); an animal or a person conditioned to one stimulus also responds, although less and less strongly, to other stimuli further and further removed from the original one along some continuum.

The fear of the rat thus conditioned is unadaptive (because white rats are not in fact dangerous) and hence is considered to be a neurotic symptom; a similarly conditioned fear of snakes would be regarded as adaptive, and hence not as neurotic. Yet the mechanism of acquisition is identical in both cases. This suggests that chance and environmental hazards are likely to play an important part in the acquisition of neurotic responses. If a rat happens to be present when the child hears a loud noise, a phobia results; when it is a snake that is present, a useful habit is built up!

The second claim which modern learning theory would make is this. People and animals differ in the speed and firmness with which conditioned responses are built up (39). Those in whom they are built up particularly quickly and strongly are more likely to develop phobias and other anxiety and fear reactions than are people who are relatively difficult to condition (15). Watson was lucky in his choice of subject; others have banged away with hammers on metal bars in an attempt to condition infants, but not always with the same success. Individual differences must be taken into account in considering the consequences of any course of attempted conditioning. Nor is the degree of conditionability the only kind of individual variability with which we are concerned. Learning theory tells us that the amount of reinforcement following any action determines in part the amount of conditioning that takes place (43). Thus the louder the noise, the greater the fright of the infant, and the greater the fright, the stronger the phobia. But different children have different types of autonomic systems, and the same amount of noise produces quite unequal amounts of autonomic upheaval in different children. Consequently, autonomic reactivity must also be considered; the more labile or reactive the child, the more likely he is to produce strongly conditioned fear reactions, anxieties, and phobias. The individual differences in autonomic reactivity and in conditionability have been conceptualized as giving rise to two dimensions of personality, namely neuroticism and introversion respectively (11). The more autonomically reactive, the more prone will the individual be to neurotic disorders. The more easily he forms conditioned responses, the more introverted will his behaviour be. Combine introversion and neuroticism, and you get the dysthymic individual, the person almost predestined to suffer from anxieties, conditioned fears and phobias, compulsions and obsessions, reactive depressions and so forth.

But this is only part of the story. Many conditioned responses are unadaptive, and consequently may embarrass the individual and even drive him into a mental hospital if sufficiently intense. Yet other conditioned responses are obviously necessary and desirable; indeed, many of them are indispensable for survival. It has been argued very strongly that the whole process of socialization is built up on the principle of conditioning (35); the overt display of aggressive and sexual tendencies is severely punished in the child, thus producing conditioned fear and pain responses (anxiety) to situations in which the individual is likely to display such tendencies. He consequently refrains from acting in the forbidden manner, not because of some conscious calculus of hedonic pleasure which attempts to equate the immediate pleasure to be gained from indulgence with the remote probability of later punishment, but because only by not indulging, and by physically removing himself can he relieve the very painful conditioned anxiety responses to the whole situation. Anxiety thus acts as a mediating drive, a drive which may be exceedingly powerful by virtue of its combination of central, autonomic, skeletal, and hormonal reactions. This mediating role of anxiety, and its capacity to function as an acquired drive, have been subjected to many well conceived experimental studies, and the consensus of opinion appears to leave little doubt about the great value and predictive capacity of this conception (34).

Let us now consider an individual who is deficient in his capacity to form quick and strong conditioned responses. He will be all the less likely to be subject to phobias and other anxieties, but he will also be less likely to form useful conditioned responses, or to become a thoroughly socialized individual. When this lack of socialization is combined with strong autonomic drive reactions (high neuroticism), such an individual is likely to show the neurotic symptomatology of the psychopath or the hysteric, and indeed, in our experimental work we have found that, as predicted, dysthymic patients and normal introverts are characterized by the quick and strong formation of conditioned responses, while psychopaths and normal extraverts are characterized by the weak and slow formation of conditioned responses (12, 14, 15). Thus the deviation from the average in either direction may prove disastrous—too strong conditioning easily leads to dysthymic reactions, too weak conditioning easily leads to psychopathic and hysterical reactions. The logic of this whole approach leads me to postulate two great classes of neurotic symptoms which between them exhaust in principle all the possible abnormal reactions with which you are all familiar. On the one hand we have *surplus conditioned reactions*, i.e., reactions acquired along the lines I have adumbrated, and where the reaction is unadaptive, even though originally it may have been well suited to circumstances. On the other hand we

have *deficient conditioned reactions*, i.e., reactions normally acquired by most individuals in society, which are adaptive, but which because of defective conditioning powers have not been acquired by a particular person. It is necessary to emphasize that surplus conditioned reactions and deficient conditioned reactions are due to an interplay between such individual factors as conditionability and autonomic lability, on the one hand, and environmental conditions on the other. There will be no socialization for an individual who cannot form conditioned responses at all, but conversely, there will be no socialization for a person growing up on a desert island, however powerful his conditioning mechanism may happen to be. In this paper I have no time to deal with differences in the conditioning forces of the environment, and their relation to such factors as social class, but they should certainly not be forgotten.

Many other testable deductions, apart from the differential conditionability of dysthymics and hysterics, follow from such a formulation. Some of these deductions can be tested in the laboratory, and examples have been given in my book, *The Dynamics of Anxiety and Hysteria*. But others can be tested clinically, and for the sake of an example I shall give just one of these. I have shown how psychopathic reactions originate because of the inability of the psychopath, due to his low level of conditionability, to acquire the proper socialized responses. But this failure is not absolute; he conditions much less quickly and strongly than others, but he does condition. Thus where the normal person may need 50 pairings of the conditioned and the unconditioned stimulus, and where the dysthymic may need 10, the psychopath may require 100. But presumably in due course the 100 pairings will be forthcoming, although probably much later in life than the 10 of the dysthymic, or the 50 of the normal person, and then he will finally achieve a reasonable level of socialization. If this chain of reasoning is correct, it would lead us to expect that the diagnosis "psychopath" would by and large be confined to relatively young people, say under thirty years of age; after thirty the course of life should have brought forth the required 100 pairings and thus produced the needed amount of socialization. As far as I can ascertain, clinical psychiatric opinion is in agreement with this prediction.

How does our theory compare with the psychoanalytic one? In the formation of neurotic symptoms, Freud emphasizes the traumatic nature of the events leading up to the neurosis, as well as their roots in early childhood. Learning theory can accommodate with equal ease traumatic single-trial learning, for which there is good experimental evidence (26), but it can also deal with repeated sub-traumatic pain and fear responses which build up the conditioned reaction rather more gradually (42). As regards the importance of childhood, the Freudian stress appears to be rather misplaced in allocating the origins of *all* neuroses to this period. It is possible that many neurotic symptoms find their origin in this period, but there is no reason at all to assume that neurotic symptoms cannot equally easily be generated at a later period provided conditions are arranged so as to favour their emergence.

The point, however, on which the theory here advocated breaks decisively with psychoanalytic thought of any description is in this. Freudian theory regards neurotic symptoms as adaptive mechanisms which are evidence of repression; they are "the visible upshot of unconscious causes" (37). Learning theory does not postulate any such "unconscious causes," but regards neurotic symptoms as simple learned habits; there is no neurosis underlying the symptom, but merely the symptom itself. *Get rid of the symptom and you have eliminated the neurosis.* This notion of purely symptomatic treatment is so alien to psychoanalysis that it may be considered the crucial part of the theory here proposed. I would like to explore its implications a little further later on.

From the point of view of learning theory, treatment is in essence a very simple process. In the case of surplus conditioned responses, treatment should consist in the extinction of these responses; in the case of deficient conditioned responses, treatment should consist in the building up of the missing stimulus-response connections. Yet this apparent simplicity should not mislead us into thinking that the treatment of neurotic disorders offers no further problems.

It is often found in scientific research that the solution of the problems posed by applied science is as complex and difficult as is the solution of the problems posed by pure science; even after Faraday and Maxwell had successfully laid the foundations of modern theories of electricity it needed fifty years and the genius of Edison to make possible the actual application of these advances to the solution of practical problems. Similarly here; a solution in principle, even if correct, still needs much concentrated and high-powered research in the field of application before it can be used practically in the fields of cure, amelioration, and prophylaxis.

What are the methods of cure suggested by learning theory? I shall give two brief examples only, to illustrate certain principles; others have been given by H. G. Jones (29). One method of extinguishing the neurotic response X to a given stimulus is to condition another response R to S, provided that R and X are mutually incompatible. This method, called "reciprocal inhibition" by Wolpe (45, 46), harks back to Sherrington (40) of course, and may be illustrated by returning to our rat phobic little boy. Essentially what Watson had done was to condition a strong sympathetic reaction to the sight of the rat. If we could now succeed in establishing a strong parasympathetic reaction to the sight of the animal, this might succeed in overcoming and eliminating the sympathetic response. The practical difficulty arises that, to begin with at least, the already established conditioned response is of necessity stronger than the to-be-conditioned parasympathetic response. To overcome this difficulty, we make use of the concept of stimulus gradient already mentioned. The rat close by produces a strong conditioned fear reaction; the rat way out in the distance produces a much weaker reaction. If we now feed the infant chocolate while the rat is being introduced in the far distance the strong parasympathetic response produced by the chocolate-munching extinguishes the weak sympathetic response produced by the rat. As the conditioned parasympathetic response grows in strength, so we can bring the rat nearer and nearer, until finally even close proximity does not produce sympathetic reactions. The sympathetic reaction has been extinguished; the phobia has been cured. This is in fact the method which was used experimentally to get rid of the experimentally induced fear (27), and it has been used successfully by several workers in the field of child psychiatry. More recently Herzberg (23) in his system of active psychotherapy, and more particularly, Wolpe (46) in his psychotherapy by reciprocal inhibition, have shown that these principles can be applied with equal success to the severe neuroses of adult men and women—substituting other methods, of course, for the chocolate-munching, which is more effective with children than with adults!

As an example of the cure of deficient conditioned responses, let me merely mention *enuresis nocturna*, where clearly the usual conditioned response of waking to the conditioned stimulus of bladder extension has not been properly built up. A simple course of training, in which a bell rings loudly whenever the child begins to urinate, thus activating an electric circuit embedded in his bedclothes, soon establishes the previously missing connection, and the extremely impressive list of successes achieved with this method, as compared with the very modest success of psychotherapeutic methods, speaks strongly for the correctness of the theoretical point of view which gave rise to this conception (36).

We thus have here, I would suggest, an alternative theory to the Freudian, a theory which claims to account for the facts at least as satisfactorily as does psychoanalysis, and which in addition puts forward quite specific suggestions about methods of treatment. I have called these methods "behaviour therapy" to contrast them with methods of psychotherapy.[1]

This contrast of terms is meant to indicate two things. According to psychoanalytic doctrine, there is a psychological complex, situated in the unconscious mind, underlying all the manifest symptoms of neurotic disorder. Hence the necessity of therapy for the psyche. According to learning theory, we are dealing with unadaptive behaviour conditioned to certain classes of stimuli; no reference is made to any underlying disorders or complexes in the psyche. Following on this analysis, it is not surprising that psychoanalysts show a preoccupation with psychological methods involving mainly *speech*, while behaviour therapy concentrates on actual *behaviour* as most likely to lead to the extinction of the unadaptive conditioned responses. The two terms express rather concisely the opposing viewpoints of the two schools. Table 2.1 presents, in summary form, a tabulation of the most important differences between Freudian psychotherapy and behaviour therapy.

What kind of answer would we expect from the Freudians? I think their main points would be these. They would claim, in the first place, that conditioning therapy has frequently been tried, but with very poor results; aversion therapies of alcoholism are often mentioned in this connection. They would go on to say that even where symptomatic treatments of this kind are apparently successful, as in enuresis, the symptom is likely to return, or be supplanted by some other symptom, or by an increase in anxiety. And, in the third place, they would claim that even, if in some cases the therapies suggested might be successful, yet in the great majority of cases psychoanalysis would be the only method to produce lasting cures. Let me deal with these points one by one.

There is no doubt that conditioning treat-

[1] The growth of the theoretical concepts and practical methods of treatment subsumed in the term behaviour therapy" owes much to a large number of people. Apart from Pavlov and Hull, who originated the main tenets of modern learning theory, most credit is probably due to Watson, who was among the first to see the usefulness of the conditioned paradigm for the explanation of neurotic disorders; to Miller and Mowrer, who have done so much to bring together learning theory and abnormal human behaviour; to Spence, whose important contributions include the detailed analysis of the relation between anxiety and learning; and to Wolpe, who was the first to apply explicitly some of the laws of learning theory to the large

scale treatment of severe neurotics. If there is any novelty in my own treatment of these issues it lies primarily: (1) in the pulling together of numerous original contributions into a general theory and (2) in the introduction into this system of the concepts of neuroticism and extraversion/introversion as essential parameters in the description and prediction of behaviour. I would like to emphasize, however, that this contribution could not have been made had the ground work not been well and truly laid by the writers quoted above and by many more, only some of whom are quoted in the bibliography.

TABLE 2.1

Freudian Psychotherapy	Behaviour Therapy
1. Based on inconsistent theory never properly formulated in postulate form.	Based on consistent, properly formulated theory leading to testable deductions.
2. Derived from clinical observations made without necessary control observation or experiments.	Derived from experimental studies specifically designed to test basic theory and deductions made therefrom.
3. Considers symptoms the visible upshot of unconscious causes ("complexes").	Considers symptoms as unadaptive conditioned responses.
4. Regards symptoms as evidence of *repression*.	Regards symptoms as evidence of faulty learning.
5. Believes that symptomatology is determined by defence mechanism.	Believes that symptomatology is determined by individual differences in conditionability and autonomic lability, as well as accidental environmental circumstances.
6. All treatment of neurotic disorders must be *historically* based.	All treatment of neurotic disorders is concerned with habits existing at *present*; their historical development is largely irrelevant.
7. Cures are achieved by handling the underlying (unconscious) dynamics, not by treating the symptom itself.	Cures are achieved by treating the symptom itself, i.e. by extinguishing unadaptive C.R.s and establishing desirable C.R.s
8. Interpretation of symptoms, dreams, acts, etc. is an important element of treatment.	Interpretation, even if not completely subjective and erroneous, is irrelevant.
9. Symptomatic treatment leads to the elaboration of new symptoms.	Symptomatic treatment leads to permanent recovery provided autonomic as well as skeletal surplus C.R.s are extinguished.
10. Transference relations are essential for cures of neurotic disorders.	Personal relations are not essential for cures of neurotic disorder, although they may be useful in certain circumstances.

ment of alcoholism has often been tried, and that it has often failed. I have no wish to take refuge in a *tu quoque* argument, by pointing out that alcoholism has been particularly difficult to treat by any method whatever, and that psychoanalytic methods also have been largely unsuccessful. I would rather point out that learning theory is an exact science, which has elaborated quite definite rules about the establishment of conditioned reflexes; it is only when these rules are properly applied by psychologists with knowledge and experience in this field that the question of success or failure arises. Thus it is quite elementary knowledge that the conditioned stimulus must precede the unconditioned stimulus if conditioning is to take place; backward conditioning, if it occurs at all, is at best very weak. Yet some workers in the field of alcoholism have used a method in which the unconditioned stimulus regularly preceded the conditioned stimulus; under these conditions learning theory would in fact predict the complete failure of the experiment actually reported! Again, the time relation between the application of the conditioned stim-

ulus and the unconditioned stimulus is a very important one; it is controlled to very fine limits of hundredths of a second in psychological experimentation, and it has been universally reported that conditioning in which any but the optimal time relation is chosen is relatively ineffective. Taking eye-blink conditioning as an example, it is found that a time interval of about ½ second is optimal, and that with intervals of 2½ seconds no conditioning at all takes place (31, 32). No attention seems to have been paid to these points by most workers on alcoholism, who apply the conditioned and unconditioned stimuli in such a vague way that it is often impossible to find out what the actual time relations were. This lack of rigour makes it quite impossible to adduce these so-called experiments as evidence either in favour of or against conditioning therapy (19).

How about the return of symptoms? I have made a thorough search of the literature dealing with behaviour therapy with this particular point in view. Many psycho-analytically trained therapists using these methods have been specially on the lookout for the return of symptoms, or the emergence of alternative ones; yet neither they nor any of the other practitioners have found anything of this kind to happen except in the most rare and unusual cases (35). Enuresis, once cured by conditioning therapy, remains cured as a general rule; relapses occur, as indeed one would expect in terms of learning therapy under certain circumstances, but they quickly yield to repeat treatment. So certain of success are the commercial operators of this method that they work on a "money back if unsuccessful" policy; their financial solvency is an adequate answer to the psychoanalytic claim. Nor would it be true that alternative symptoms emerge; quite the contrary happens. The disappearance of the very annoying symptom promotes peace in the home, allays anxieties, and leads to an all-round improvement in character and behaviour. Similar results are reported in the case of major applications of behaviour therapy to adults suffering from severe neurotic disorders; abolition of the symptom does not leave behind some mysterious complex seeking outlet in alternative symptoms (35). Once the symptom is removed, the patient is cured; when there are multiple symptoms, as there usually are, removal of one symptom facilitates removal of the others, and removal of all the symptoms complete the cure (46).

There is one apparent exception to this rule which should be carefully noted because it may be responsible for some of the beliefs so widely held. Surplus conditioned reactions may themselves be divided into two kinds, autonomic and motor. Anxiety reactions are typical of the autonomic type of surplus conditioned reactions, whereas tics, compulsive movements, etc., are typical of motor conditioned reactions. What has been said about the complete disappearance of the symptom producing a complete disappearance of the neurosis is true only as far as the autonomic conditioned reactions are concerned. Motor reactions are frequently activated by their drive-reducing properties *vis-à-vis* the historically earlier conditioned autonomic responses (35); the extinction of the motor response without the simultaneous extinction of the conditioned autonomic response would only be a very partial cure and could not be recommended as being sufficient. As pointed out at the end of the previous paragraph, "removal of *all* the symptoms completes the cure," and clearly removal of the motor conditioned response by itself, without the removal of the autonomic conditioned response is only a very partial kind of treatment. Behaviour therapy requires the extinction of all non-adaptive conditioned responses complained of by the patient, or causally related to these symptoms.

But how frequently does this type of treatment result in cures? Again I have made a thorough search of the literature, with the following outcome. G. P. treatment, not making use of psychotherapy in any of its usual forms, results in a recovery of about two seriously ill neurotics out of three (4). Eclectic psychotherapy results in a recovery of about two seriously ill neurotics out of three (8). Psychotherapy by means of psychoanalysis fares slightly worse, but results are at a comparable level (17). Results of behaviour therapy of seriously ill neurotics, as reported by Wolpe, are distinctly superior to this, over 90 per cent recovering (46). This difference is highly significant statistically, and it should be borne in mind that the number of sessions required by behaviour therapy is distinctly smaller than that required by psychotherapy, whether eclectic or psychoanalytic. (Wolpe reports an average of about 30 sittings for his cases.)

These results are encouraging, but of course, they must not be taken too seriously. Actuarial comparisons of this kind suffer severely from the difficulty of equating the seriousness of disorders treated by different practitioners, the equally obvious difficulty of arriving at an agreed scale for the measurement of "recovery," and the impossibility of excluding the myriad chance factors which may effect gross behaviour changes of the kind we are here considering. I would not like to be understood as saying that behaviour therapy has been *proved* superior to psychotherapy; nothing could be further from my intention. What I am claiming is simply that as far as they go—which is not very far—available data do not support in any sense the Freudian belief that behaviour therapy is doomed to failure, and that only psychoanalysis or some kindred type of treatment is adequate to relieve neurotic disorders. This Freudian belief is precisely this—a belief; it has no empirical or rational foundation. I have no wish to set up a counter-belief, equally unsupported, to the effect that psychotherapy is doomed to failure, and that only behaviour therapy is adequate to relieve neurotic disorders. What I would like to suggest is simply that a good case can be made out, both on the theoretical and the empirical level, for the proposition that behaviour therapy is an effective, relatively quick, and probably lasting method of cure of some neurotic disorders. This case is so strong that clinical trials would appear to be in order now to establish the relative value of this method as compared with other available methods, such as psychoanalysis, or electroshock treatment. Even more important, I think the evidence would justify psychiatrists in experimenting with the method, or rather set of methods, involved, in order to come to some preliminary estimate of their efficiency. I have noted with some surprise that many psychotherapists have refused to use such methods as conditioning therapy in enuresis, not on empirical grounds, but on *a priori* grounds, claiming that such mechanical methods simply could not work, and disregarding the large body of evidence available. Even in long-established sciences *a priori* considerations carry little weight; in such a young discipline as psychology they are quite out of place. Only actual use can show the value of one method of treatment as opposed to another.

There is one point I would like to emphasize. Freud developed his psychological theories on the basis of his study of neurotic disorders, and their treatment. Behaviour therapy, on the contrary, began with the thorough experimental study of the laws of learning and conditioning in normal people, and in animals; these well-established principles were then applied to neurotic disorders. It seems to me that this latter method is in principle superior to the former; scientific advance has nearly always taken the form of making fundamental discoveries and then applying these in practice, and I can see no valid reason why this process should be inverted in connection with neurosis. It may be objected that learning theorists are not always in agreement with each other (24), and that it

is difficult to apply principles about which there is still so much argument. This is only very partially true; those points about which argument rages are usually of academic interest rather than of practical importance. Thus reinforcement theorists and contiguity theorists have strong differences of view about the necessity of reinforcement during learning, and different reinforcement theorists have different theories about the nature of reinforcement. Yet there would be general agreement in any particular case about the optimum methods of achieving a quick rate of conditioning, or extinction; these are questions of fact, and it is only with the interpretation of some of these facts that disagreements arise. Even when the disputes about the corpuscular or wavular nature of light were at their height, there was sufficient common ground between contestants regarding the facts of the case to make possible the practical application of available knowledge; the same is true of learning theory. The 10 per cent, which is in dispute should not blind us to the 90 per cent, which is not—disagreements and disputes naturally attract more attention, but agreements on facts and principles are actually much more common. Greater familiarity with the large and rapidly growing literature will quickly substantiate this statement (38).

It is sometimes said that the model offered here differs from the psychoanalytic model only in the terminology used, and that in fact the two models are very similar. Such a statement would be both true and untrue. There undoubtedly are certain similarities, as Mowrer (35) and Miller and Dollard (5) have been at pains to point out. The motivating role of anxiety in the Freudian system is obviously very similar in conception to the drive-producing conditioned autonomic responses of learning theory, and the relief from anxiety produced by hysterical and obsessional symptoms in Freudian terminology is very similar to the conditioned drive-reducing properties of motor movements. Similarly, a case could be made out in favour of regarding the under-socialized, non-conditionable psychopathic individual as being Id-dominated, and the dysthymic, over-conditionable individual as being Super-Ego dominated. Many other similarities will occur to the reader in going through these pages, and indeed the writer would be the first to acknowledge the tremendous service that Freud has done in elucidating for the first time some of these dynamic relationships, and in particular in stressing the motivating role of anxiety.

Nevertheless, there are two main reasons for not regarding the present formulation as simply an alternative differing from the psychoanalytic one only in the terminology used. In the first place, the formulation here given differs from the Freudian in several essential features, as can be seen most clearly by studying Table 2.1. Perhaps these differences are most apparent with respect to the deductions made from the two theories as to treatment. Psychoanalytic theory distrusts purely symptomatic treatment and insists on the removal of the underlying complexes. Behaviour theory on the other hand stresses the purely symptomatological side of treatment and is unconvinced of the very existence of "complexes." It might, of course, be suggested that there is some similarity between the Freudian "complex" and the "conditioned surplus autonomic reaction" posited by behaviour therapy. That there is some similarity cannot be denied, but no one familiar with psychoanalytic writings would agree that the Freudian complex was not in essence a very different conception from the conditioned autonomic response, both from the point of view of its origins, as well as from the point of view of the appropriate method of extinction.

This brings me to the second great difference between the two models. What the Freudian model lacks above all is an intelligible objectively testable *modus operandi* which can be experimentally studied in the laboratory, which can be precisely quantified, and which can then be subjected to the formulation of strict scientific laws. The stress on such a mechanism, namely that of conditioning, is the most noteworthy feature of the model here advocated. It is entirely due to the great body of research which has been done in connection with the elaboration of laws of modern learning theory that we are enabled to make fairly precise deductions resulting in different methods of treatment for patients suffering from neurotic dis-

orders, and it is with respect to this feature of the model that the relevant case histories and accounts of treatment should be read (28, 33, 47).

It has sometimes been suggested that the criticisms which I have levelled against the psychotherapeutic schools because of their failure to provide adequate control groups to validate their claims regarding the curative properties of their methods, could justifiably be levelled against the accounts given by those who have used behaviour therapy and reported upon the effects achieved. Such a criticism would not be justified for two reasons. In the first place the cases quoted are *illustrative of methods*, not *proofs of psychotherapeutic efficacy*; the only case in which claims regarding relative efficacy have been made contains a statistical comparison with the effects of psychoanalytic treatment of similar cases (46). In the second place the concept of "control" in scientific experiments is somewhat more than simply the provision of a control *group*; the control in an experiment may be *internal*. As an example, consider the experiment reported by Yates (47) on the extinction of four tics in a female patient by means of a rather novel and unusual method, namely that of repeated voluntary repetition of the tic by massed practice. Precise predictions were made as to the effects that should follow, and these predictions were studied by using the fate of some of the tics as compared to the fate of other tics submitted to dissimilar treatment. Thus, practice for two tics might be discontinued for a fortnight, while practice on the other two would go on. By showing that the predictions made could thus be verified, and the *rate of extinction* of the tics varied at will in accordance with the experimental manipulation for such variables as massing of practice, a degree of control was achieved far superior to the simple assessment of significance produced in the comparison of two random groups submitted to different treatments. It is by its insistence on such experimental precision and the incorporation of experimental tests of the hypotheses employed, even during the treatment, that behaviour theory differs from psychotherapy.

There is one further method of pointing up

the differences between the two theories and of deciding between them; I mention this matter with some hesitation because to many psychiatrists it seems almost sacrilegious to use animal experimentation in the consideration of human neurosis. However, Fenichel himself (18, p. 19) has quoted "experimental neuroses" as support for the Freudian conception of neurotic disorders, and it is with respect to these experiments that the contrast between the psychoanalytic and our own model may be worked out most explicitly. Fenichel maintains that the model of psychoneurosis "is represented by the artificial neuroses that have been inflicted upon animals by experimental psychologists. Some stimulus which had represented pleasant instinctual experiences or which had served as a signal that some action would now procure gratification is suddenly connected by the experimenter with frustrating or threatening experiences, or the experimenter decreases the difference between stimuli which the animal had been trained to associate with instinct gratification and threat respectively; the animal then gets into a state of irritation which is very similar to that of a traumatic neurosis. He feels contradictory impulses; the conflict makes it impossible for him to give in to the impulses in the accustomed way; the discharge is blocked, and this decrease in discharge works in the same way as an increase in influx; it brings the organism into a state of tension and calls for emergency discharges.

"In psychoneuroses some impulses have been blocked; the consequence is a state of tension and eventually some 'emergency discharges.' These consist partly in unspecific restlessness and its elaborations and partly in much more specific phenomena which represent the distorted involuntary discharges of those very instinctual drives for which a normal discharge has been interdicted. Thus we have in psychoneuroses, first a defense of the ego against an instinct, then a conflict between the instinct striving for discharge and the defensive forces of the ego, then a state of damming up and finally the neurotic symptoms which are distorted discharges as a consequence of the state of damming up—a compromise between the opposing forces. The symptom is the only step in this development that becomes manifest; the conflict, its history, and the significance of the symptoms are unconscious."

Hebb (22) has laid down certain requirements for attempting to demonstrate that experimental neurosis occurs in animals and Broadhurst (2, 3) has examined the literature, and particularly that referred to by Fenichel, from this point of view. Here is his summary.

How does the large body of American work stand up to such an assessment? For the purposes of a recent review (3), the available literature was examined in the light of Hebb's criteria. Noteworthy among this is the work of the group headed by Liddell . . ., one of the pioneers of conditioning methodology in the United States, who has used principally the sheep as his experimental subject; of Gantt (20), whose long term study of the dog "Nick" is well known; and of Masserman (30), who has done extensive work using cats. This is not the place to enter into the details of this evaluation, which is reported elsewhere (3), but the overall conclusion which was reached was that there are few instances in all this work of any cases of experimentally induced abnormalities of animal behaviour which meet all of Hebb's criteria. Let us take, for example, the work of Masserman, whose theoretical interpretation of abnormal behaviour need not concern us here except to note that it was the basis upon which he designed his experiments to produce "conflict" between one drive and another. What he did was this. He trained hungry cats to respond to a sensory signal by opening a food box to obtain food. Then he subjected them to a noxious stimulus, a blast of air, or electric shock, just at the moment of feeding. The resulting changes in behaviour—the animals showed fear of the situation and of the experimenter, and refused to feed further—he identified as experimental neurosis. But the behaviour observed fails to fulfil more than one or two of Hebb's criteria, and, moreover, certain deficiencies in the design of his experiments make it impossible to draw any satisfactory conclusions from them. Thus Wolpe (45) repeated part of Masserman's work using the essential control group which Masserman had omitted—that is, he gave the cats the noxious stimulus alone, without any "conflict" between the fear motivation thus induced, and the hunger which, in Masserman's animals, operated as well—and found that the same behaviour occurred. It hardly needs to be said that a fear response to a threatening stimulus is not abnormal and cannot be regarded as an experimental neurosis.

It is clear from the studies cited that Fenichel is quite wrong in claiming that "experimental neurosis" is in any way analogous to the Freudian model of human neurosis. It appears, therefore, that in so far as these studies are relevant at all they can be regarded as demonstrating nothing but simple conditioned fear responses of the kind called for by our theory. It is perhaps worthy of note that the failure of psychoanalysis to use control groups in the human field has extended to their work with animals, as in the case of Masserman quoted above. Fenichel's easy acceptance of data congruent with his hypothesis is paralleled by his failure to mention data contrary to the psychoanalytic viewpoint. Taking into account all the data it seems more likely that a correct conclusion will be reached.

I would now like to return to some of the points which I raised at the beginning of this paper. I argued then that the special knowledge and competence of psychologists in mental hospitals was largely wasted because of concentration on, and preoccupation with, Freudian theories and projective types of test. I would now like to make a more positive suggestion and maintain that by virtue of their training and experience psychologists are (or should be) experts in the fields of conditioning and learning theory, laboratory procedures, and research design. In suitable cases, surely their help would be invaluable in diagnostic problems, such as ascertaining a given patient's speed of conditioning, in the theoretical problem of constructing a model of his personality dynamics, and in the practical problem of designing a suitable course of behaviour therapy which would take into account all the available information about the case. I am not suggesting that psychologists should themselves necessarily carry out this course of treatment; it would appear relatively immaterial whether the therapy is carried out by one person or another, by psychologist or psychiatrist. Both types of procedure have been experimented with, and both have shown equally promising results. Indeed, certain aspects of the therapy can obviously be carried out by less senior and experienced personnel, provided the course of treatment is reviewed periodically by the person in charge. Psychoanalysis lays much stress on what is sometimes called "transference," a devil conjured up only to be sent back to his usual habitat with much expenditure of time and energy (18). Behaviour therapy has no need of this adjunct, nor does it admit that the evidence for its existence is remotely adequate at the present time. However that may be, relinquishing the personal relationship supposed to be indispensable for the "transference" relation allows us to use relatively unqualified help in many of the more time-consuming and routine parts of behaviour therapy. In certain cases, of course, personal relationships may be required in order to provide a necessary step on the generalization gradient; but this is not always true.

From a limited experience with this kind of work, carried out by various members of my department, I can say with confidence two things. The direct application of psychological theories to the practical problem of effecting a cure in a particular person, here and now, acts as a very powerful challenge to the psychologist concerned, and makes him more aware than almost anything else of the strengths and weaknesses of the formulations of modern learning theory. And the successful discharge of this self-chosen duty serves more than almost anything else to convince his psychiatric colleagues that psychology can successfully emerge from its academic retreat and take a hand in the day-to-day struggle with the hundred-and-one problems facing the psychiatrist. It seems to me that the tragic fratricidal struggle between psychiatrists and psychologists, which has so exacerbated relations between them in the United States, could easily be avoided here by recognizing the special competence of the psychologist in this particular corner of the field, while acknowledging the necessity of keeping the general medical care of the patient in the hands of the psychiatrist. I believe that most psychiatrists are too well aware of the precarious state of our knowledge in the field of the neurotic disorders to do anything but welcome the help which the application of learning theory in the hands of a competent psychologist may be able to bring.

REFERENCES

1. ANDERSON, O. P., & PARMENTER, A. A long-term study of the experimental neurosis in the sheep and dog, *Psychosomatic Medicine Monograph*, 1941, 2, (3, 4) 1–150.

2. BROADHURST, P. L. The contribution of animal psychology to the concept of psychological, normality-abnormality, *Proceedings of the XIII International Congress of Applied Psychology*, 1958.

3. BROADHURST, P. L. Abnormal animal behaviour. In H. J. Eysenck (Ed.). *Handbook of abnormal psychology*. London: Pitman, 1959.

4. DENKER, P. G. Results of treatment of psychoneuroses by the general practitioner. A follow-up study of 500 cases, *New York State Journal of Medicine*, 1946, 46, 2164–2166.

5. DOLLARD, J., & MILLER, V. G. *Personality and psychotherapy*. New York: McGraw-Hill, 1950.

6. ESTES, W. K. *et al. Modern learning theory*. New York: Appleton-Century, 1954.

7. EYSENCK, H. J. *Dimensions of personality*. London: Routledge & Kegan Paul, 1947.

8. EYSENCK, H. J. The effects of psychotherapy: an evaluation, *Journal of Consulting Psychology*, 1952, 16, 319–324.

9. EYSENCK, H. J. *The scientific study of personality*. London: Routledge & Kegan Paul, 1952.

10. EYSENCK, H. J. *Uses and abuses of psychology*. London: Pelican, 1953. (a)

11. EYSENCK, H. J. *The structure of human personality*. London: Methuen, 1953. (b)

12. EYSENCK, H. J. Zur Theorie der Persönlichkeitsmessung, *Ztchr. f. diag. Psychol. u. Persönlichkeitsforschung*, 1954, 2, 87–101, 171–187.

13. EYSENCK, H. J. *Psychology and the foundation of psychiatry*. London: H. K. Lewis, 1955.

14. EYSENCK, H. J. Los principios del condicionamiento y la teoria de la personalidad, 1957, 12, 655–667. (Revista Mexicana De Psicología).

15. EYSENCK, H. J. *Dynamics of anxiety and hysteria*. London: Routledge & Kegan Paul, 1957.

16. EYSENCK, H. J. Personality tests: 1950–1955. In G. W. T. H. Fleming (Ed.), *Recent progress in psychiatry*. London: J. and A. Churchill, 1959.

17. EYSENCK, H. J. The effects of psychotherapy. H. J. Eysenck (Ed.), *Handbook of abnormal psychology*. London: Pitman, 1959.

18. FENICHEL, O. *The psychoanalytic theory of neurosis*. London: Kegan Paul, 1945.

19. FRANKS, C. M. Alcohol, alcoholics and conditioning: a review of the literature and some theoretical considerations, *Journal of Mental Science*, 1958, 104, 14–33.

20. GANTT, W. H. Experimental basis for neurotic behaviour, *Psychosomatic Medicine Monograph*, 1944, 3, 1–211.

21. GLOVER, E. *The technique of psychoanalysis*. London: Baillièr, 1955.

22. HEBB, D. O. Spontaneous neurosis in chimpanzees: theoretical relations with clinical and experimental phenomena, *Psychosomatic Medicine*, 1947, 9, 3–16.

23. HERZBERG, A. Short treatment of neuroses by graduated tasks, *British Journal of Medical Psychology*, 1941, 19, 36–51.

24. HILGARD, G. A. *Theories of learning*. New York: Appleton-Century, 1956.

25. HILGARD, E. A., & MARQUIS, D. G. *Conditioning and learning*. New York: Appleton-Century, 1940.

26. HUDSON, B. B. One-trial learning in the domestic rat, *Genetic Psychology Monograph*, 1950, 41, 94–146.

27. JERSILD, A. T., & HOLMES, F. B. Methods of overcoming children's fears, *Journal of Psychology*, 1935, 1, 25–83.

28. JONES, H. G. The application of conditioning and learning techniques to the treatment of a psychiatric patient, *Journal of Abnormal and Social Psychology*, 1956, 52, 414–420.

29. JONES, H. G. Neurosis and experimental psychology, *Journal of Mental Science*, 1958, 104, 55–62.

30. MASSERMAN, J. K. *Behaviour and neurosis*. Chicago: University of Chicago Press, 1943.

31. McALLISTER, W. R. Eyelid conditioning as a function of the CS-UCS interval, *Journal of Experimental Psychology*, 1953, 45, 412–422.

32. McALLISTER, W. R. The effect on eyelid conditioning of shifting the CS-UCS interval, *Journal of Experimental Psychology*, 1953, 45, 423–428.

33. MEYER, V. The treatment of two phobic patients on the basis of learning principles, *Journal of Abnormal and Social Psychology*, 1957, 55, 261–266.

34. MILLER, V. G. Learnable drives and rewards. In S. S. Spencer (Ed.), *Handbook of experimental psychology*. New York: Wiley, 1951.

35. MOWRER, O. H. *Learning theory and personality dynamics*. New York: Ronald Press, 1950.

36. MOWRER, O. H., & MORER, W. A. Enuresis: A method for its study and treatment, *American Journal of Orthopsychiatry*, 1938, 8, 436–447.

37. MUNROE, R. L. *Schools of psychoanalytic thought*. New York: Dryden Press, 1955.

38. OSGOOD, C. E. *Method and theory in experimental psychology*. London: Oxford University Press, 1953.

39. PAVLOV, I. P. *Conditioned reflexes*. London: Oxford University Press, 1927.

40. SHERRINGTON, C. S. *The integrative action of the central nervous system*. London: Oxford University Press, 1926.

41. SHOBEN, E. J. Psychotherapy as a problem in learning theory, *Psychological Bulletin*, 1949, 46, 366–392.

42. SOLOMON, R. L., KAMIN, L. J., & WYNNE, L. C. Traumatic avoidance learning, *Journal of Ab-*

normal and Social Psychology, 1953, *48,* 291–302.

43. SPENCE, K. G., HAGGARD, P. F., & ROSS, L. G. UCS intensity and the associated (habit) strength of the eyelid CR, *Journal of Experimental Psychology,* 1958, *95,* 404–411.

44. WATSON, J. B., & RAYNOR, R. Conditioned emotional reaction, *Journal of Experimental Psychology,* 1920, *3,* 1–4.

45. WOLPE, J. Experimental neurosis as learned behaviour, *British Journal of Psychology,* 1952, *43,* 243–268.

46. WOLPE, J. *Psychotherapy by reciprocal inhibition.* Stanford, Calif.: Stanford University Press, 1958.

47. YATES, A. The application of learning theory to the treatment of tics, *Journal of Abnormal and Social Psychology,* 1958, *56,* 175–182.

11.

KARL MENNINGER

UNITARY CONCEPT OF MENTAL ILLNESS

Among the devices employed by mankind to enable his frail intelligence to cope with the infinitude of the phenomena of the universe, that of classification has always been prominent. Certain things seem to be clearly related to and yet distinct from each other, showing the characteristics of discontinuity and specificity: animals, plants, crystals. Others, such as colors, tones and ocean waves, manifest connectedness and continuity. Epistemologists traditionally distinguish two types of classifications, natural and artificial, the former reflecting an "order of things" inherent in Nature, the latter complying with man's need for order or thought economy.

To which type of classification does medical nosology belong? Are our taxonomies man-made artifacts useful chiefly for communication? Or do diseases constitute entities, which can be identified and classified in natural systems, as Sydenham asserted in the 17th century when he introduced the principle of specificity into medicine? The development of bacteriology 200 years later seemed to justify his stand, although the modern trend is away from it. Psychiatric illnesses can *rarely* be related to anything so definite as a bacterial invasion. Have they the specificity and relatedness which our older nosologies imply?

A prodigious number of psychiatric classifications have been elaborated in the course of the centuries, becoming progressively more complicated. The height of complexity was reached in the 18th century with the school of the "systematists" who attempted to introduce Sydenham's principle into psychiatry, using quite arbitrary criteria. The physician and botanist, Boissier de Sauvages, classified all diseases into ten classes with 295 genera and about 2,400 species. One of these ten classes included the bulk of mental disease and it was divided into four orders and 23 genera. One genus, melancholia, was subdivided into 14 species!

Toward the end of the 18th century a tendency toward simpler classifications appeared. In 1798 Pinel published his large, extremely sophisticated and complicated classification, similar to those of Boissier de Sauvages and his imitators. But three years later Pinel published a revised classification as simple as the former one had been complex (1). All mental illnesses had been reduced to four basic types. His contemporary in Italy, Chiarugi, identified only three types, and his successor, Esquirol, extended this merely to five.

However, the trend toward the multiplication of psychiatric disease entities revived, and the 19th century was a flourishing period for new classifications. The nosological labors of such men as Kahlbaum, Morel and Kraepelin became

Karl Menninger (with Henri Ellenberger, Paul Pruyser, and Martin Mayman)."The unitary concept of mental illness."*Bulletin of the Menninger Clinic,* 1958, *22,* 4–12. Reprinted by permission.

historic. The delineation of general paralysis as an entity (by Bayle, 1822) whetted the appetite of investigators and resulted in attempts to isolate and designate new disease entities, such as hebephrenia (1864), catatonia (1874), and later dementia praecox (1896) and manic-depressive psychosis (1899).

But the 19th century was also marked by an undercurrent of rebellion against nosological distinctions. The trend toward simplification reappeared. In 1820 Georget (2), one of Esquirol's pupils, declared mental illness to be an "idiopathic affection of the brain" which could be manifest in a variety of ways which were not independent disease entities. This was the first modern enunciation of the unitary concept of mental illness.

Following Georget, Guislain (5) (1797-1860) in Belgium contended that the various mental diseases were nothing but the successive transformations of what he called the *phrenopathias*. The basis for them all was *phrenalgia*, *i.e.*, "pain of the mind," occurring with various degrees of intensity. These ideas of Guislain's were repeated and expanded in Germany by Zeller, Griesinger, Neumann and Arndt.

Zeller considered the various mental illness syndromes as successive *Zustandsbilder* in a single fundamental pathological process. Sometimes the illness was restricted to the first stage, *Schwermut;* sometimes it evolved through the successive stages of *Tollheit* (mania) and *Vernücktheit* (paranoia) to the last stage of *Blödsinn* (dementia).

Wilhelm Griesinger (6) (1817-1868), the first director of the famous Burghölzli Hospital, proclaimed that "Mental diseases are brain diseases." He held that psychiatric syndromes should be classified according to their underlying brain lesions, but because of the undeveloped science of pathology one must be content provisionally with a "functional" classification.

But it was Heinrich Neumann (7), a great pioneer who is too much neglected and forgotten today, who was most definite and thoroughgoing in his development of the unitary concept. "Diagnosis," said he, "is not simply the designation of a group of symptoms but the key to the comprehension of the case . . . We consider any classification of mental illness to be artificial, and therefore unsatisfactory, (and) we do not believe that one can make progress in psychiatry until one has resolved to throw overboard all classifications and to declare with us: *there is only one kind of mental illness. . . ."* (italics ours.)

Neumann felt strongly that psychiatric classifications of the kinds he knew were not only artificial and illusory, but directly dangerous. "Rather no classification," he said, "than a false one. The lack of any classification at least leaves free space for investigation, whereas a false classification leads directly into errors!" (Quoted by Llopis [3].)

Neumann's wise words might well be engraved on the staff conference rooms of all psychiatric hospitals! But for all their eloquence and wisdom, the battle for simplicity was again —if only temporarily—lost. During the second half of the 19th century the discoveries of bacteriology, pathological anatomy and genetics seemed to bring irrefutable confirmation of Trousseau's famous declaration: "The principle of specificity dominates all medicine" (8). The unitary concept in psychiatry was forgotten. The problem became, rather, how many disease entities actually exist and how can one group and classify them in the most logical fashion.

But with the dawn of the 20th century the unitary principle reappeared. By that time the realization had dawned that *names* do not create illness forms; they only comfort the doctors and impress the relatives. If a patient is poor, said Janet with tongue in cheek, he is committed to a public hospital as "psychotic"; if he can afford the luxury of a private sanitarium, he is put there with the diagnosis of "neurasthenia"; if he is wealthy enough to be isolated in his own home under constant watch of nurses and physicians, he is simply an indisposed "eccentric." Janet (9) devoted an entire chapter to a sharp criticism of the current psychiatric classifications. He, himself, distinguished only two large groups: the organic and the functional. Sometimes, he said, a car stops because the machinery is broken, sometimes because it is out of gasoline. Essentially Janet was a unitarian.

Freud, of course, while adhering to conventional designations in his scientific reports, abandoned most of the old landmarks to devote himself to the common substructure of psychological disturbances (as Gregory Zilboorg [10] has pointed out). Freud was never much concerned with names.

The most consistent effort in the direction of modern unitary concepts in Europe has been by Henri Ey (11). "A powerful movement has arisen," he wrote, "against the idea that a mental disease should be purely and simply identified with the somatosis which constitutes its known or hypothetical organic 'substratum.'" Mental diseases—he went on to say—appear to us less and less as disease entities, more and more as "syndromes" or "pathological reactions" resulting from a multiplicity of factors. Ey considers the various clinical syndromes as the expression of various degrees of "dissolution" in Hughlings Jackson's terms.

Ey's position is very similar to our own. A similar concept is being developed by Bartolomé Llopis (3) of Madrid who has recently contributed a history of the unitary concept. Llopis (4) does not distinguish, as does Ey, between acute and chronic conditions but has elaborated a "psychic frame" in which one dimension is the "state of consciousness" and the other the "content of consciousness."

In this review of the changing concepts of mental illness, we may not leave Europe without mentioning the outstanding work of Manfred Bleuler and of Jakob Wyrsch, both of Switzerland: for it Eugen Bleuler had already laid the groundwork. Contemporary with him was another Swiss, Adolph Meyer, who fostered in America the Kraepelinian classification, which tended strongly in the direction of specificity. Meyer soon became dissatisfied with it and somewhat dismayed at its "success" in his adopted country. (Like Freud, Meyer never quite comprehended the epidemiology of new ideas in America.) Meyer reverted (or as we prefer to think, progressed!) to a nonspecific, essentially unitary concept of mental illness. The various classical syndromes he considered to be various reaction types, various patterns of misdirected energy. His "ergasia" concept was based on a holistic personality theory, and

was supported by the eloquent psychoanalytic and psychiatric leader William Alanson White.

These two systems developed in American psychiatry side by side—the specific entity concept with which Kraepelin worked and the unitary concept which Meyer developed. The former prevailed. Each worker considered his to be a natural classification, the other an artificial one.

During the first World War, Ernest Southard of Harvard proposed a simplification of the official nosology of the day into eleven major groups. During World War II my brother, William Menninger, developed another reformulation reducing the basic groups of mental illness to five, and emphasizing Freudian and Meyerian principles of psychodynamics. This classification was adopted in the United States by the medical departments of our military forces and by the Veterans Administration, although it was clearly recognized by all that various inconsistencies had been retained as a matter of practical compromise. A very similar classification, prepared by a committee under Dr. George Raines, was subsequently adopted by the American Psychiatric Association.

Looking back, then, to the days of Hippocrates and since, we see how psychiatric nosology, after modest beginnings, gradually expanded in size and increased in differentiation; then contracted; then expanded to a great maximum; and in these latter days is again contracting toward simpler, more holistic and process-oriented concepts. Psychiatry was only lately joined to medicine and science; many of our classical designations were practical, administrative descriptions or fanciful "explanatory" terms rather than scientific concepts. But it is difficult to free ourselves from the misleading implications that have become attached historically to the various labels not necessarily by their originators, but by their users. This is true even when the old label is replaced with a new model or the concept revised. "Madness" became "lunacy," "lunacy" became "insanity," "insanity" became "psychosis," and now many psychiatrists (in the United States at least) feel that the word "psychosis" should be abandoned. A hundred names have been applied throughout the ages to conditions which were, by a later generation, called *délire onirique* or "hebephrenia" or "catatonia," and by the following generation called "dementia praecox," and by the next generation called "schizophrenia."

And finally we have the eloquent testimony of Manfred Bleuler (14), whose most assiduous and scholarly investigation of changes in the concept of schizophrenia led him to declare:

The main characteristic of research in schizophrenia in the past decade has been . . . the collapse of speculations and prejudices which used to be inextricably bound up with the concept of schizophrenia . . . for example that it is a disease entity . . . inherited, physically conditioned . . . and so on. . . . Most investigators no longer consider schizophrenia a disease entity, an inherited disorder, an expression of a somatic disease or a disorder susceptible to a specific somatic treatment.

The fact remains, however, that in the minds of many young doctors and in the minds of vast numbers of laymen, mental illness and particularly schizophrenia is a definite, specific, evil thing which invades the unsuspecting like a fungus or a tapeworm. The word schizophrenia becomes a damning designation. To have it once applied to a young man can be to ruin a career, despite all evidence of subsequent healthiness. A name implies a concept; and if this concept is unsound, the diagnosis can ruin the treatment; the very naming it can damage the patient whom we essay to help. Nathanial Hawthorne in *The House of the Seven Gables* told us what we psychiatrists should well know: "The sick in mind . . . are rendered more darkly and hopelessly so by the manifold reflection of their disease, mirrored back from all quarters in the deportment of those about them; they are compelled to inhale the poison of their own breath, in infinite repetition."

It was these considerations among others which stirred the beginning of our studies some twenty years ago. Speaking as the senior author, I recall how it once seemed to me of the utmost importance to make a sharp distinction between the various types of what we called dementia praecox, or between them and some otherwise labeled syndrome. Today it seems to me most important that we *not* do that. Have I changed so much? Or is it the times and concepts that have changed? It is not that we decry classifica-

tion as such; we recognize it as a useful scientific tool. But it is dangerous when it leads to reification of terms.

My interest in this developed from my experiences in teaching psychiatrists, some hundreds of whom are or have been enrolled in the Menninger School of Psychiatry for varying periods of time. The concepts gained in their medical schooling are, naturally, carried over by the young doctors into the field of psychiatry, but often these concepts handicap them. They seek specific therapies instead of ways to help their psychiatric patients to better modes of living, to better social adjustment, to greater utilization of latent powers. We would have them think of the patient, not as one afflicted with a certain *disease* which they must *name* and then battle with and attempt to dispel, but rather as a human being, one somewhat isolated from his fellows, one whose interactive relationships with them have become mutually unsatisfactory and disturbing; to this he has reacted in various ways, all *intended* to salvage the situation and insure survival, even at the cost of social acceptance.

Suppose that instead of putting so much emphasis on different kinds of illness we tried to think of all mental illness as being essentially the same in quality, and differing, rather, quantitatively. This is what we mean when we say that we all have mental illness of different degrees at different times, and that sometimes some of us are much worse or much better. If one sets up a scale of well-being—in other words, a scale for the successfulness of an individual-environment adaptation—at one end of it would be health, happiness, success, achievement and the like and at the other end misery, failure, crime, delirium and so forth. On such a continuum one could mark some practical stages. We can say that some people are relatively healthy, that some are relatively sick, and that the latter are either mildly, moderately or extremely sick. These would vary, of course, depending upon the culture in which one lives and the duration of the particular episode of maladjustment and many other things.

Modern organismic theory conceives of systems and subsystems relating themselves to one another in the interests of homeostasis, the steady state of the open system, as defined by von Bertalanffy (15). Pressures from instinctual urges, from somatic needs, from environmental threats, losses and excitations, from the culture and from the conscience *all* bear upon the ego, whose task it is to effect a reconciliation of them in order to maintain a steady state at the best possible level. The effectiveness *and* the cost of the reconciliatory efforts determine the degree of mental healthiness of the individual. Inadequate resolution of the conflicting pressures results in increased tension, a warning of danger to the organism which evokes compensatory shifts. If an imbalance continues despite these warnings and shifts, there comes reduced function, more pain, "sickness" and even death. Successful resolution, on the other hand, insures the continuation of constructive activity and organismic growth.

Mental illness, then, is seen by us as an impairment in self-regulation whereby comfort, production and growth are temporarily surrendered for the sake of survival at the best level possible, and at the cost of emergency coping devices which may be painful. Psychiatrists are apt to look upon mental illness as an indication of ego failure. But now this "failure" acquires a different meaning. Beset by a variety of stresses, the ego tries to insure survival and optimal adaptation at the least cost, and in this it has *succeeded.*

We believe it possible to construct an empirical series of the regulatory moves or efforts of the ego progressively more urgent, more adventitious, more symptomatic. Ours is a combined dynamic-economic scale. First come those mild symptoms regarded by the layman as "nervousness"; a Second Order of devices would include neurotic phenomena; the Third Order embraces episodic and explosive discharges, and the Fourth Order various syndromes of more persistent and severe disorganization. Our emphasis is on the *degree of disorganization and its course* or trend of development; the factors determining this trend are the keys to rational therapy.

Such an approach does not preclude the administrative usefulness of recognizing the well-known psychopathologic syndromes to which various conventional designations have been applied. *Of course* one can describe a "manic" or a "depressed" or a "schizophrenic" constellation of symptoms, but what is most important about this constellation in each case? Not, we think, its curious external form, but rather what it indicates in regard to the process of organization, disorganization and reorganization of the personality in a state of attempted adjustment to environmental reality. Is the imbalance increasing or decreasing? To what is the stress related? What psychological factors are accessible to external modification? What latent capacities for satisfaction in work, play, love, creativity are discoverable for therapeutic exploitation? Is a restoration or reconstruction of adjustment patterns developing? Can this be fostered by discriminating medical intervention? This is what we conceive of as rational therapeutic planning.

In summary, reverting to the topic of classification with which we began, we believe that the natural "class" in psychiatry must be either the disturbed individual or all mankind in trouble. There are no natural mental disease entities. An ordering of clinical phenomena on the basis of the economics of adaptation such as we have proposed does justice to the essential unity of sickness and health; at the same time it leaves room for recognizing the latent potentials of every individual. It transcends the distinction between natural and artificial classification, the question raised in our opening paragraphs. The trend toward a unitary concept of mental illness is clearly apparent in psychiatric history, and it seems to us to follow modern trends in other fields of science. It spares us some grievous errors and offenses against our patients. It enables rational therapeutic programming. Hence it is our continuing aim to see the unity in diversity of psychiatric symptomatology as reflecting, from the side of the individual, the nature of an organism-environment interaction, and the basic continuity of the conditions labeled health and sickness of various degrees.

REFERENCES

1. PINEL, P. *Traité médico-philosophique sur l'aliénation mentale ou la manie.* Paris: Richard, Caille et Ravier, 1801.

2. GEORGET, E. *De la folie*. Paris: Chevot, 1820.
3. LLOPIS, B. La psicosis unica. *Archivos de Neurobiologia*, 1954, *17*, 1–39.
4. LLOPIS, B. La psicosis pelagrosa. Barcelona: Editorial Cientifico Medica, 1946, pp. 47–67.
5. GUISLAIN, J. *Traité des phrenopathies*. Bruxelles: Etablissement Encyclographique, 1833.
6. GRIESINGER, W. *Die Pathologie und Therapie der psychischen Krankheiten*. Stuttgart: Krabbe, 1861.
7. NEUMANN, H. *Lehrbuch der Psychiatrie*. Erlangen: F. Enke, 1859, pp. 75–76, 167.
8. TROUSSEAU, A. *Clinique médicale de l'Hotel-Dieu de Paris* (ed. 5). Paris: Ballière, 1877.
9. JANET P. *La force et la faiblesse psychologiques*. Paris: Maloine, 1932.
10. ZILBOORG, G. Freud's fundamental psychiatric orientation, *International Journal of Parapsychology*, 1954, *35*, 90–94.
11. EY, H. *Etudes Psychiatriques*, Vol. 3. Paris: Desclée de Brouwer & Cie, 1954.
12. LAIGNEL-LAVASTINE: *La méthode concentrique dans l'étude des psychonévroses*. Paris: Chahine, 1928.
13. LECONTE, M., & DAMEY, A. *Essai critique des nosographies psychiatriques actuelles*. Paris: Doin, 1949.
14. BLEULER, M. Research and changes in concepts in the study of schizophrenia, 1941–1950. English tr., in *Bulletin of the Isaac Ray Medical Library*, 1955, *3*, 1–132.
15. BERTALANFFY, L. VON. An outline of general systems theory, *British Journal for the Philosophy of Science*, 1950, *1*, 134–165.

12.

ROLLO MAY

EXISTENTIAL MODEL

There are several endeavors in this country to systematize psychoanalytic and psychotherapeutic theory in terms of forces, dynamisms, and energies. The existential approach is the opposite of these attempts. We do not deny dynamisms and forces; that would be nonsense. But we hold that they have meaning only in the context of the existing, living being —if I may use a technical word, only in the *ontological* context.

If we are to have a science adequate to serve as a basis for psychotherapy, several guiding principles are required. First, *the science must be relevant to the distinguishing characteristics of what we are trying to understand, in this case the human being*. It must be relevant, that is, to the distinctive qualities and characteristics that constitute the human being as *human*. These are the characteristics that constitute the self as self, without which this being would not be what he is: a human being.

A second guiding principle is in opposition to the assumption in conventional science that we explain the more complex by the more simple. This is generally taken on the model of evolution: the organisms and activities higher on the evolutionary scale are explained by those lower. But this is only half the truth. It is just as true that when a new level of complexity emerges (such as self-consciousness in man), this level becomes decisive for our understanding of all previous levels. The principle here is, *the simpler can be understood and explained only in terms of the more complex*. This point is particularly important for psychology and is discussed more fully later in this chapter with the topic of self-consciousness.

A third guiding principle is this: our fundamental unit of study in psychotherapy is not a "problem" that the patient brings in, such as impotence; or a pattern, such as a neurotic pattern or sadomasochism or a diagnostic category of sickness, such as hysteria or phobia, ad infinitum; or a drive or pattern of drives. Our unit of study is, rather, *two-persons-existing-in-a-world, the world at the moment being represented by the consulting room of the therapist.* To be sure, the patient brings in all his problems, his "illness," his past history, and every thing else simply because it is an integral part of him. But what is important is that the one datum that has reality at the time is that he creates a certain world in the consulting room, and it is in the context of this world that some understanding of him may emerge. This world and the understanding of it is something in which both persons, patient and therapist, participate. Our point here has far-reaching implications not only because it bears directly on our research and practice in psychotherapy, but also because it suggests the guiding lines of an existential approach to science.

Here is a patient, Mrs. Hutchens, who comes into my office for the first time, a suburban woman in her middle thirties. She tries to keep her expression poised and sophisticated. But no one could fail to see in her eyes something of the terror of a frightened deer or a lost child. I know, from what her neurological specialists have already told me, that her presenting problem is hysterical tenseness of the larynx, as a result of which she can talk only with a perpetual hoarseness. I have been given the hypothesis from her Rorschach that she has felt all her life, "If I say what I really feel, I'll be rejected; under these conditions it is better not to talk at all." During this first hour with her, I also get some hints of the genetic *why* of her problem as she tells me of her authoritarian relation with her mother and grandmother and of *how* she learned to guard firmly against telling any secrets at all. But if I am chiefly pondering these *why's* and *how's* of her problem, I will grasp everything except the most important fact of all, namely, the living, existing person here in the room with me.

I propose, then, that we begin with the one real datum that we have in the therapeutic situation, namely, the existing person sitting in the consulting room with a therapist. Let us ask: What are the essential characteristics that constitute this patient as an existing person, that constitute this self as a self? I wish to propose six characteristics, which I shall call

processes, that I find in my work as a psychotherapist. They can as well be called *ontological characteristics.* Though these are the product of a good deal of thought and experience with many cases, I shall illustrate them with episodes from the case of Mrs. Hutchens.

First, Mrs. Hutchens, like every existing person, *is centered in herself, and an attack on this center is an attack on her existence itself.* This is a characteristic that we human beings share with all living beings; it is self-evident in animals and plants. I never cease to marvel how, whenever we cut the top off a pine tree on our farm in New Hampshire, the tree sends up a new branch from heaven knows where to become a new center. But our principle has a particular relevance to human beings and gives a basis for the understanding of sickness and health, neurosis and mental health. Neurosis is not to be seen as a deviation from our particular theories of what a person should be. *Is not neurosis, rather, precisely the method the individual uses to preserve his own center, his own existence?* His symptoms are ways of shrinking the range of his world (so graphically shown in Mrs. Hutchens' inability to let herself talk) in order that the centeredness of his existence may be protected from threat, a way of blocking off aspects of the environment so that he may then be adequate to the remainder.

Mrs. Hutchens had gone to another therapist for half a dozen sessions a month before she came to me. He told her, in an apparently ill-advised effort to reassure her, that she was too proper, too controlled. She reacted with great upset and immediately broke off the treatment. Now, technically he was entirely correct; existentially he was entirely wrong. What he did not see, in my judgment, was this very properness, this overcontrol, far from being things that Mrs. Hutchens wanted to get over, were part of her desperate attempt to preserve what precarious center she had. As though she were saying, "If I opened up, if I communicated, I would lose what little space in life I have." We see here, incidentally, how inadequate is the definition of neurosis as a failure of adjustment. *An adjustment is exactly what neurosis is; and that is just its trouble. It* is a necessary adjustment by which centeredness can be preserved; a way of accepting *nonbeing*, if I may use this term, in order that some little *being* may be preserved. And in most cases it is a boon when this adjustment breaks down.

This is the only thing we can assume about Mrs. Hutchens, or about any patient, when she comes in: she, like all living beings, requires centeredness, and this has broken down. At a cost of considerable turmoil she has taken steps, that is, come for help. Our second process, thus, is: every existing person *has the character of self-affirmation, the need to preserve its centeredness*. The particular name we give this self-affirmation in human beings is "courage." Paul Tillich's emphasis on the "courage to be" is very important, cogent, and fertile for psychotherapy at this point. He insists that in man, being is never given automatically, as it is in plants and animals, but depends upon the individual's courage; and without courage one loses being. This makes courage itself a necessary ontological corollary. By this token, I as a therapist place great importance upon expressions of the patients that have to do with willing, decisions, choice. I never let such little remarks the patient may make as "maybe I can," "perhaps I can try" slip by without my making sure he knows I have heard him. It is only a half truth to say that the will is the product of the wish; I emphasize rather the truth that the wish can never come out in its real power except with will.

Now as Mrs. Hutchens talks hoarsely, she looks at me with an expression of mingled fear and hope. Obviously a relation not only exists between us here but has already existed in anticipation in the waiting room and ever since she thought of coming. She is struggling with the possibility of participating with me. The third process is, thus: *all existing persons have the need and possibility of going out from their centeredness to participate in other beings*. This always involves risk; if the organism goes out too far, it loses its own centeredness, its identity—a phenomenon that can easily be seen in the biological world. If the neurotic is so afraid of loss of his own conflicted center that he refuses to go out and holds back in rigidity,

living in narrowed reactions and shrunken world space, his growth and development are blocked. This is the pattern in neurotic repressions and inhibitions, the common neurotic forms in Freud's day. But it may well be in our day of conformity and the outer-directed man, that the most common neurotic pattern takes the opposite form, namely, the dispersing of one's self in participation and identification with others until one's own being is emptied.

At this point we see the rightful emphasis of Martin Buber in one sense and Harry Stack Sullivan in another, that the human being cannot be understood as a self if participation is omitted. Indeed, if we are successful in our search for these ontological processes of the existing person, it should be true that the omission of any one of the six would mean that we do not then have a human being.

Our fourth principle is: *the subjective side of centeredness is awareness*. Such awareness is present in forms of life other than human; it is certainly observable in animals. Howard Liddell has pointed out how the seal in its natural habitat lifts its head every ten seconds even during sleep to survey the horizon lest an Eskimo hunter with poised bow and arrow sneak up on it. This awareness of threats to being in animals Liddell calls *vigilance*, and he identifies it as the primitive, simple counterpart in animals of what in human beings becomes anxiety.

The first four characteristic processes are shared by the existing person with all living beings; they are biological levels in which human beings participate. The fifth process refers now to a distinctively human characteristic: self-consciousness. *The uniquely human form of awareness is self-consciousness.* Awareness and consciousness should not be identified. I associate awareness, as Liddell indicates, with vigilance. This is supported by the derivation of the term "aware," coming as it does from the Anglo-Saxon *gewaer, waer*, meaning knowledge of external dangers and threats. Its cognates are *beware* and *wary*. Awareness certainly is what is going on in an individual's neurotic reaction to threat, in, for example, Mrs. Hutchens' experience in her first hours that I am also a threat to her.

Consciousness, however, is not simply my awareness of threat from the world but *my capacity to know myself as the one being threatened, my experience of myself as the subject who has a world*. Consciousness, to use Kurt Goldstein's terms, is man's capacity to transcend the immediate concrete situation, to live in terms of the possible. It underlies the wide range of possibility that man has in relating to his world, and it constitutes the foundation of psychological freedom. Thus, human freedom has its ontological base and I believe must be assumed in all psychotherapy.

In his book *The Phenomenon of Man*, the paleontologist Pierre Teilhard de Chardin brilliantly describes how awareness is present, including the form of tropism, in all forms of evolutionary life from amoeba to man. But in man a new function arises, namely self-consciousness. Teilhard de Chardin undertakes to demonstrate something that I have always believed, that when a new function emerges, the whole previous pattern of the organism changes. The total gestalt shifts; thereafter the organism can be understood only in terms of the new function. That is to say, it is only a half truth to hold that the organism is to be understood in terms of the simpler elements below it on the evolutionary scale. The other half of the truth is more crucial for us, namely every new function forms a new complexity that reorganizes all the simpler elements in this organism. As I previously said, *the simple can be understood only in terms of the more complex*.

This is what self-consciousness does in man. All the simpler biological functions must now be understood in terms of this new function. No one would, of course, deny for a moment the old functions, or anything in biology that man shares with less complex organisms. Take sexuality, for example, which we obviously share with all mammals. Given self-consciousness, sex becomes a new gestalt, as is demonstrated in therapy all the time. Sexual impulses are then conditioned by the *person* of the partner; what we think of the other male or female, in reality or fantasy or even repressed fantasy, can never be ruled out. The fact that the subjective person of the other to whom we relate sexually makes least difference in *neurotic* sexuality, say in patterns of compulsive sex or prostitution, only proves our point the more firmly, for these situations require precisely the blocking off, the checking out, and the distorting of self-consciousness. Thus, when we discuss sexuality in terms of sexual objects, as Kinsey does, we may garner interesting and useful statistics; but we simply are not talking about human sexuality.

Nothing in what I am saying here should be taken as anti-biological in the slightest; on the contrary, I think it is only from this approach that we *can* understand human biology without distorting it. As Kierkegaard aptly put it, "The natural law is as valid as ever." I argue only against the uncritical acceptance of the assumption that the organism is to be understood only in terms of those elements below it on the evolutionary scale, an acceptance that has led us to overlook the self-evident truth that what makes a horse a horse are not the elements it shares with the dog but what constitutes distinctively, "horse." Now, *what we are dealing with in neurosis are those characteristics and functions that are distinctively human*. It is these that have gone awry in disturbed patients. The condition for these functions is self-consciousness—which accounts for what Freud rightly discovered, that the neurotic pattern is characterized by repression and blocking off of consciousness.

It is the task of the therapist, therefore, not only to help the patient become aware, but even more significantly, to help him *transmute this awareness into consciousness*. Awareness is his knowing that something is threatening from outside in his world—a condition that may, as in paranoids and their neurotic equivalents, be correlated with much acting-out behavior. But self-consciousness puts this awareness on a quite different level; it is the patient's seeing that *he is the one who is threatened,* that he is the being who stands in this world which threatens, that he is the subject who *has* a world. And this gives him the possibility of *in-sight,* of "inward sight," of seeing the world and his problems in relation to himself. And thus it gives him the possibility of doing something about his problems.

To come back to our too-long silent patient: After about twenty-five hours of therapy Mrs. Hutchens had the following dream. She was searching room by room for a baby in an unfinished house at an airport. She thought the baby belonged to someone else, but the other person might let her take it. Now it seemed that she had put the baby in a pocket of her robe (or her mother's robe), and she was seized with anxiety that it would be smothered. Much to her joy, she found that the baby was still alive. Then she had a strange thought, "Shall I kill it?"

The house was at the airport where she, at about the age of twenty, had learned to fly solo, a very important act of self-affirmation and independence from her parents. The baby was associated with her youngest son, whom she regularly identified with herself. Permit me to omit the ample associative evidence that convinced both her and me that the baby stood for herself, and specifically for consciousness of herself. The dream is an expression of the emergence and growth of self-consciousness, a consciousness that she is not yet sure is hers and a consciousness that she considers killing in the dream.

About six years before her therapy, Mrs. Hutchens had left the religious faith of her parents, to which, by way of them, she had had a very authoritarian relation. She had then joined a church of her own belief. But she had never dared tell her parents of this. Instead, when they came to visit, she attended their church in great tension lest one of her children let the secret out. After about thirty-five sessions, when she was considering writing her parents to tell them of this change of faith, she had, over a period of two weeks, spells of partially fainting in my office. She would become suddenly weak, her face would go white, she would feel empty and "like water inside" and would have to lie down for a few moments on the couch. In retrospect, she called these spells "grasping for oblivion."

She then wrote her parents informing them once and for all of her change in faith and assuring them it would do no good to try to dominate her. The following session, she asked in considerable anxiety whether I thought she

would become psychotic. I responded that whereas anyone of us might at some time have such an episode, I saw no more reason why she should than any of the rest of us; and I asked whether her fear of becoming psychotic was not rather anxiety arising out of her standing against her parents, as though genuinely being herself, she felt to be tantamount to going crazy. (I have noted several times that patients experience this anxiety at being themselves as tantamount to psychosis.) This is not surprising, for consciousness of one's own desires and affirming them involves accepting one's originality and uniqueness. It implies that one must be prepared not only to be isolated from those parental figures upon whom one has been dependent but at that instant to stand alone in the entire psychic universe as well.

We see the profound conflicts of the emergence of self-consciousness in three vivid ways in Mrs. Hutchens, whose chief symptom, interestingly enough, was the denial of that uniquely human capacity based on consciousness, talking. These conflicts are shown in (1) the temptation to kill the baby; (2) the grasping at oblivion by fainting, as though she were saying, "If only I did not have to be conscious, I would escape this terrible problem of telling my parents"; and (3) the psychosis anxiety.

This brings us to the sixth and last characteristic of the existing person: *anxiety*. Anxiety is the state of the human being in the struggle against that which would destroy his being. It is, in Tillich's phrase, the state of a being in conflict with nonbeing, a conflict that Freud mythologically pictured in his powerful and important symbol of the death instinct. One wing of this struggle will always be against something outside the self. But even more portentous and significant for psychotherapy is the inner battle, which we saw in Mrs. Hutchens; namely, the conflict within the person as he confronts the choice of whether and how far he will stand against his own being, his own potentialities.

Thus, I take very seriously, if metaphorically, this temptation to kill the baby, or kill her own consciousness, as expressed in these forms by Mrs. Hutchens. I neither water it down by calling it "neurotic" and the product merely of sickness, nor do I slough over it by reassuring her, "Okay, but you don't need to do it." If I did these, I would be helping her adjust at the price of surrendering a portion of her existence, that is, her opportunity for fuller independence. The self-confrontation that is involved in the acceptance of self-consciousness is anything but simple: it involves, to identify some of the elements, accepting of the hatred of the past, her mother's hatred of her and hers of her mother; accepting her present motives of hatred and destruction; cutting through rationalizations and illusions about her behavior and motives, and the acceptance of the responsibility and aloneness that this implies; the giving up of childhood omnipotence, and acceptance of the fact that although she can never have absolute certainty about her choices, she must choose anyway.

But all these specific points, easy enough to understand in themselves, must be seen in the light of the fact that *consciousness itself implies always the possibility of turning against one's self, denying one's self.* The tragic nature of human existence inheres in the fact that con-

sciousness itself involves the possibility and temptation at every instant to kill itself. Dostoevsky and our other existential forebears were not indulging in poetic hyperbole or expressing the after effects of too much vodka the night before when they wrote of the agonizing burden of freedom.

I trust that the fact that existential psychotherapy places emphasis on these tragic aspects of life does not at all give the impression that it is pessimistic. Quite the contrary. The confronting of genuine tragedy is a highly cathartic experience psychically, as Aristotle and others through history have reminded us. Tragedy is inseparably connected with man's dignity and grandeur and is the accompaniment, as illustrated in such dramas as Oedipus and Orestes, of the human being's moment of great insight.

In my judgment, the analysis of characteristics of the existing being—these ontological characteristics that I have tried to point out—can give us a structural base for our psychotherapy. It can also give us a base for a science of man that will not fragmentize and destroy man's humanity as it studies him.

13.

MARGARET MEAD

SOCIO-CULTURAL MODEL

One of the most challenging tasks the anthropologist has to perform is to see our own period and our own lives in the perspective of history and of the human race. Today's world is certainly filled with tension and frustration. But it is difficult to say whether it's filled with more tension and frustration than life in a little New Guinea village. In such a village you don't know where next month's meal is coming from —and there are even greater uncertainties. If

From Margaret Mead. "The changing world of living." *Diseases of the Nervous System*, 1967, *28* suppl., 5–11. Reprinted by permission.

you wrap a little bit of leaf around a sore, you had better put the leaf away very carefully afterwards, or someone will get it and sorcerize you. In such a village, too, your principal reason for existence is to act as headhunting material for the next village. So it's an open question whether we live under more tension than these simple villagers.

But this much is certain. They never heard of the concept of tension; they wouldn't discuss it; they wouldn't worry about it; and they couldn't possibly do anything about it.

And I think that this is the most striking

difference, really, between ourselves and the sorts of people that I work with in the field —people who represent a partial version of our own history, anything from 2,000 to 10,000 years back, depending upon our ethnic origins. (China has a longer record, and the Middle East has the longest.) What occurs to me when I compare the tensions of people of this sort and those we experience, is that we think we can do something about it.

I would take the number of people who are in mental hospitals today, not as an index that the society we live in is so much more difficult than other societies, but as an index of hope —an index of the fact we really think we can do something about it. Whether we are working with psychotherapies that do or do not use various sorts of milieu therapy or drug therapy, we are nevertheless living in a world where, when somebody shows signs of a breakdown, a large proportion of their friends and relatives say: "You should do something about it. This isn't necessary. It isn't inevitable."

You have to be in a pretty protected environment to get away with a tic today in New York City. And you have to be awfully good. A magnificent secretary with a tic may be retained in a protected environment, but on the whole, most large companies wouldn't want a receptionist with a tic. It would worry them. Yet you can go into small towns anywhere in the United States, and find tics all over the place; and people say: "Oh, you know, but the Smiths always have tics." And they don't worry.

Now, this difference—difference between the expectation today of what is treatable and what should be treated, as compared with the past—is very, very striking. I want to talk this morning about the extent to which the whole rest of the community, including the physician, are involved in any case of mental illness. They are involved in the standard of treatment, the standard of expectation, and the standard of condemnation that exists in the community. The physician serves as the representative of what can be done, shares in a very large degree in the beliefs of the rest of the community and teaches the rest of the community what can be done. This involvement is an essential component of mental illness itself.

We may look very briefly at some other societies. If you live in a small community all your life, as you grow up and show peculiar traits, such as undue irascibility, or a tendency to withdraw, everybody learns about them. In a community of 300 people, you know who is likely to hit you, and you dodge.

Now, we have some experiences of this sort that are a little trying for the anthropologist. An anthropologist friend of mine, for instance, was all alone in his little hut in the village, when a man started running toward him across the village, holding a spear ready to strike. There were several children around who promptly climbed up a tree and cried: "Don't hurt him. He'll be all right tomorrow." But such information can be very unreassuring when a man is coming toward you with a spear. And while all this was going on, somebody ran to get his father's sister, because she could always calm down the temporarily mad attacker.

The only unusual element in this situation was the anthropologist, who hadn't climbed a tree in time. We have the same thing happening in small communities today. There are people who are dangerous when drunk. Other people know it and watch them, and perhaps take a knife away from them, or they give them a wide berth—and so no one is killed.

I lived in one village in Bali where we had a man—a hard worker and a perfectly respectable member of the community, married, with children—who just didn't like people to borrow his machete. People in Bali today are always borrowing each other's machetes. People often do not have a machete when they want one, and so they borrow somebody else's. So people would ask to borrow this man's machete, and about every hundredth time that somebody asked to borrow it, he tried to cut them with it.

They didn't stop borrowing his machete. They were sufficiently wary so they usually managed to jump away. Once in the course of the period I was there, somebody got a very deep cut in his arm. But nobody thought anyone could do anything about it. This was just the way he did things, and the community was adjusted to it.

We have very good records of a tribe in the

New Guinea highlands (1) where if a man has taken on more than he can manage, something might well happen to him. Using our corporation life as an analogy, he might be promoted to the head of a department when he was getting on quite well in a subordinate position or he might be moved from one department to another that required quite different traits, salesmanship rather than administration or administration rather than salesmanship and suddenly break down. We don't know what to do with such people, and they often end up in the psychiatrist's office. In the center of New Guinea they go into a terrific, wild piece of "insane" behavior. They run around and steal everybody's property, collecting everything, and then they run away to the bush. After a while, people persuade them to come back and return everything, and assign them a lower position in the society. It is a device for shifting gears inside society when you have taken on more than you should have taken on.

In every society such illustrations could be multiplied. They could also be demonstrated in terms of different kinds of small communities in the United States. Every society has a limit, a general setting within which they will tolerate abnormal behavior. If the behavior goes beyond that point they then will have some method of treating it. One such method is to put pressure on the individual manifesting the unfortunate behavior to do something about it. Thus, the therapeutic situation stems from a collaboration between the community, the physician, and the patient.

The patient wants to be treated, and goes a little bit further than anybody will tolerate. By doing so he comes within purview, very often, first of the general practitioner and later of either police authorities or psychiatrists.

Erik Erikson relates the case of a little boy who ate paper. Nobody, however, paid any attention to him. He ate more and more paper. Still nobody cared. So finally he ate the theatre tickets, and then he received treatment!

One of the ways of looking at symptomatology at any period in any society is: What is the point where you eat the theatre tickets? We had quite an interesting case brought to the Menninger Clinic of a girl who really

didn't need treatment herself, although her parents did. They lived in a house with one bathroom. She used to lock the door and take a three-hour bath. In time, the parents brought her to a psychiatrist, and then she was able to get them treated.

These devices for going beyond the limits in the particular society are very important. When patients come into a physician's office for the first time, it is essential to find out who sent them there, what sort of pressure got them there. Was it the desperation they felt, while alienating other people more and more that brought them there? Or did their families send them there because they couldn't tolerate their behavior any more?

We had a good study done several years ago in terms of looking at the family structure of hospital patients, and finding out whether they were key people in their families. Those who were the key breadwinners in the family were brought to the hospital later than the others. Obviously one puts up with the man who is bringing in the money a lot longer than one puts up with a man who isn't bringing in the money (2). So these patients were likely to be sicker when they arrived.

The same study by Dr. Muriel Hammer also brought out some very interesting ways in which "mental illness" serves as a path of adjustment for rural southern Negro migrants to New York, who hadn't learned where to fight, when to fight, or how to get drunk, and so were very likely to overstep the limits of the new urban community they lived in. As a consequence, they would be brought into a mental institution once (a rather grim initiation into New York) and they learned that this is what happened if they did the particular thing that brought them there. In very large measure, they stopped doing it.

So we have to realize also that our crowded mental institutions are in one way educational institutions for kinds of education we might wish we didn't have to give, but do.

One other factor that I think we have to take into account is that we have alive today so many more vulnerable people. It is worthwhile considering what happens in a society with an infant death rate sometimes as high as 50 per cent. For example, I have never seen an autistic child in a savage community. What would you do with an autistic child? I have never seen a seriously depressed infant. A seriously depressed infant won't eat. Where infants are breast-fed, women, as biological creatures, want to have milk for their babies, want to feed them, and want them to grow. Such women are much like obstetricians and pediatricians, who also want infants to get fat, or at least reach the right weight. If a baby that is breast-fed doesn't gain weight, its mother loses milk. So it gains less, she loses more milk, and the baby slowly dies of malnutrition. In such a setting we don't have the type of psychoses that we see in young children here. We simply don't have them in primitive societies.

I have never seen a congenitally blind individual survive in a primitive society. But I have seen the congenitally deaf survive, because the adults did not realize early enough that they were deaf. So a really tough, lively deaf baby has a pretty good chance of surviving, if people don't find out until they have learned to enjoy the baby and to like it.

But today we save individuals with an enormous range of sensitivities, and they are types of sensitivities that nobody ever treated before. Even our medical training is not yet keyed to the kinds of people we now have to treat—the sort of people that Karl Menninger discussed in his last book (3). You simply can't tell what's wrong with these people, because they have so many things wrong with them on a small scale, and do not suffer from some major and identifiable disease.

So another thing we have to consider today, in thinking about those whom we label as mentally ill and those who first crowd the offices of the general practitioner and later, crowd our mental hospitals, is that we are keeping a lot more vulnerable people alive—although we ourselves are not keyed to handling that vulnerability. The physician, after all, although he is so specially trained and knows so much more than the general public, nevertheless is trained at a given period of medical sophistication. Perhaps the most striking example of this is the disappearance in most parts of the United States of simple hysterical symptoms.

But in World War I we had a very large number of gross hysterias—such as hysterical blindness and hysterical deafnesses—among enlisted men. This type of disorder was particularly characteristic for enlisted men. A large number of people escaped active service by these symptoms, which of course were inarticulate and unconscious. The physicians who treated these conditions did not yet know that they were psychologically motivated. So if you were hysterically blind, you were put in a ward for the blind, and you weren't expected to fight any more.

In recent years I have talked to young doctors who have never seen a case of classical hysteria. And why? First, the physicians learned what we learned by the end of World War I—what these hysterias were and how they could be treated. The general public also learned, and the interaction between the physicians and the general public, back and forth, is such that patients don't develop such symptoms today.

They have much more obscure diseases today, usually of the gastrointestinal tract, that are less easy to identify. These were characteristic of World War II. So the total community—the physician within the community, and the patients themselves—are a collaborating group in deciding what is a mental illness. They also collaborate in deciding what symptoms will be regarded as meaning that a person is mentally ill, what symptoms a general practitioner will treat, and what symptoms will prompt a family to force one of its members to have treatment.

The very interesting thing that has been happening in the United States—especially in the last decade or so with the use of psychotherapeutic drugs, particularly—has been the expectation that a great deal of mental illness is treatable. There are parts of the world where there is still no belief that a hospitalized mental illness is treatable. I remember asking in a big mental hospital in a Mediterranean country, with 2,000 patients: "What is the rate of discharge?" They looked at me, and they said: "There is no discharge. No one who comes in here ever goes out again." That was characteristic of some of our mental institutions—not completely, but to a very large extent—just a very few years ago.

We suddenly have the notion that things are

treatable. We furthermore have the notion (I say "notion" because I don't want to label it as a theory or a hypothesis, or anything of the sort) that has spread with the use of psychotherapeutic drugs, that it is possible to treat many conditions that we used to think we couldn't treat, and that it is possible to treat them very early in the onset of the pathological disease.

One of the characteristics of Americans is that they have no tolerance at all of anybody putting up with anything. You see, we believe that whatever is going wrong, ought to be fixed. During World War II there was a lovely instance in which I was in a little, tiny, miserable spot where women volunteers were serving 2,000 cups of coffee a day to G. I.'s, and I was being taken around by an Englishwoman and an American man.

The Englishwoman said: "Aren't they wonderful! Think of these women who are coping with this terrible little bar and giving coffee to 2,000 G. I.'s a day!"

And the American said: "Isn't it ridiculous!"

In general, we feel that anything you can fix, you ought to fix. This is very sharply delineated in our attitude towards cosmetic surgery. We have no sympathy anymore with people with awful birthmarks or girls with enormous noses and no chins. We think they ought to take a piece off the nose and put it on the chin, and look like people.

And as we begin to believe—and this is the kind of belief that has been growing—that you don't have to be depressed, that when the secretary starts weeping into her typewriter, it's not only disagreeable or uncomfortable for the company, but it isn't necessary, then we say, "Why doesn't she do something about it?"

We don't put up with people who become suddenly violent and start throwing the telephone across the office. A hundred years ago there were a lot of things you could throw across a room, and it didn't make much difference, but it's very bad for the telephone, and we don't approve of it.

Our tolerance of aberrant behavior has gone down and down, as we have found new methods of dealing with it, so that there are now strong pressures in the society to seek help for people

who are anxious or depressed. (On the other hand pathological ebullience which leads to shopping sprees is objected to only by husbands.)

Two things we won't tolerate much now are too much anxiety and too much depression, and we feel we have ways of dealing with both. Superficially, one might think this is a little cruel. We deny people the sorts of comfortable depression that they were allowed to have for hundreds of years. We don't approve of the woman who has had two children and retires to a sofa for the rest of her life—behavior which used to be a very good upper class solution to the population problem.

We object to all of these things. We are less tolerant. But it is also worth recognizing that we are living in a world where it is necessary for people to have just the right level of anxiety. If you have too much, you don't cross the street at all; if you have too little, you get run over. You have got to be right in the middle. You have to have what some people called "good" anxiety which is kind of a contradiction in terms.

But you mustn't be what my Balinese secretary called our second kitchen boy: too happy: He broke too many dishes.

We are living in a world that calls for a certain continuous alert apprehensiveness. It calls for a capacity to meet strangers all day long in most urban environments, and behave. The strangers are not supposed to know that when a given individual they meet loses his temper, he pulls a knife out of his pocket. People have got to behave in a more predictable way.

But this lowered tolerance goes together with our greater capacity to deal with these things, and it goes together hopefully, with much earlier diagnosis. We spot smaller and smaller deviances from normal behavior. When a wife notes that for three days in a row her husband puts no sugar in his coffee although he normally uses sugar, but simply glares at her, she is likely to say: "Dear, you better see a psychiatrist."

Now, you may feel this is overdone. I think it's often very overdone to send such a person to a psychiatrist. We don't have enough psychiatrists, and they have more serious problems to deal with. But I don't think it's overdone to say: "You better see your doctor." And it isn't overdone for that doctor to be sufficiently alert to know that when people deviate from their expected behavior in the eyes of their employers, their family, or their friends, something is beginning to go wrong that probably could be righted. This is one of the most exciting things about our present decade—that the community will not tolerate things that would have been tolerated in a small town in another age. The physician, therefore, gets another kind of patient. And the physician has at his disposal methods that he did not have before. So, hopefully, we will be able to diagnose difficulty much earlier and be able to restore people to the community, instead of incarcerating them in mental institutions.

REFERENCES

1. NEWMAN, P. "Wild men" behavior in New Guinea Highlands community, *American Anthropologist,* February, 1964, *66*(1), 1–19.
2. HAMMER, M. An analysis of social networks as factors influencing the hospitalization of mental patients, Ph.D. thesis, New York: Columbia University, 1961.
3. MENNINGER, K. A. *Vital balance.* New York: Viking, 1963.

CHAPTER III

Neuroses

Neurosis (including the term psychoneurosis, which is used interchangeably with it) lacks a common definition among psychologists. An attempt at a definition of this term often is predicated upon one's theory of neurosis, that is to say, some learning theorists regard a neurotic as merely a person who is victimized by some bad habits, while psychoanalysts view him as an early substage of the psychotic.

Despite the variety of views and the discrepancies involved in the nature and definition of neurosis, there nevertheless exists some consensus regarding the issue. However, agreement exists regarding the functional nature of neurosis, its absence of lesions or organic disease, its chief characteristic symptom being anxiety. Furthermore, the neurotic maintains conscious contact with external reality relatively free from any major falsification of it, his personality organization remaining intact, hence distinguishing him from the psychotic. Moreover, it is unlikely that the neurotic would resort to violent behavior.

NEUROTIC DEPRESSION AND ENDOGENOUS DEPRESSION

Kiloh and Garside (1963) have demonstrated a decisive difference between neurotic depression and endogenous depression, an important distinction from the standpoint of treatment as well as accurate prognostication.

Since the varieties of neuroses accompanied by their definitions have been enumerated in Chapter I, we need not reiterate the matter here, but use the space more advantageously to cite diverse contending views espoused by contemporary authorities.

ANXIETY THEORY OF NEUROSIS

An anxiety theory of neurosis, viewing neurosis as the upshot of a person's struggle for security and rooted in self-preservation, is offered by R. W. White (1964). The warped outcome of the struggle is neurosis, the only assurance of safety offered the neurotic whose security is threatened. The neurotic's characteristics or symptoms are defensive measures, the purpose of which is to cope with his anxiety. The fundamental postulate of Keiser's book, *The Traumatic Neurosis,* is that "all types of psychiatric illness may develop as a manifestation of traumatic neurosis" (1968, p. 42).

LEARNING THEORY OF NEUROSIS

The learning theorist view of neurosis as a functional disturbance produced through experience and learning has been championed by Dollard and Miller (1950), who see the main factors of neurosis as conflict, stupidity, and misery with symptoms. While conflict produces misery, and repression causes stupidity, symptoms reduce conflict slightly. In any case, neurosis obeys the laws of learning. For example, Freud's pleasure principle is merely the learning theorist's principle of reinforcement; repression is the inhibition of cue-producing responses; transference is generalized responses occurring in the therapeutic experience; and inhibition and restraint serve in place of repression and suppression.

Miller later (1959) postulated a gradient of avoidance explaining fear, anxiety, or conflict according to the following theory: "the tendency to avoid a feared stimulus is stronger the nearer the subject is to it." According to Miller's gradient model, "the strength of avoidance increases more rapidly with nearness than does that of approach." Furthermore, "the strength of tendencies to approach or avoid varies directly with the strength of the drive upon which they are based." In case two incompatible responses conflict, then the stronger one will take precedence.

Miller (1966) reported that since barbiturates reduce fear and since fear reduction acts as a reward, then this finding corroborates that of the clinicians that potent fear, guilt, and other aversive drives tend to heighten the probability that persons will become addicted to barbiturates. In the same report he cites how differing social conditions produce differing learned responses. Two children through social learning can acquire different types of psychosomatic responses to stress.

O. H. Mowrer, who is also committed to learning theory, seeks to revise Freudian postulates to harmonize with those of learning theory, especially his own two-factor theory of learning. According to Mowrer (1953), neurosis is a problem understood in the light of solution learning and sign learning; the id is viewed as a primary drive, the superego as the result of sign learning or social conditioning, and the ego as that aspect of the personality dealing with solution learning. Symptoms of neurosis manifest themselves as the result of habits (repressions) being devised as solutions to a conflict ensuing between primary drives (id forces) and secondary drives (fears), a conflict caused by social conditioning or discipline.

According to Mowrer (1960), the neurotic is not a person who is ill, nor is he a person who is to be excused for his behavior, but he is one who is entangled in sin. His inability to escape his predicament is due to his neurotic paradox (1948, 1952), that is, despite unfavorable consequences ensuing from the neurotic's behavior, he nevertheless perpetuates this senseless pattern, whereas a normal man or even animal would avoid behavior whose net effect is undesirable. Mowrer suggests that neurosis might better be viewed as an "identity crisis" or "sociosis," because the neurotic is not abnormal, but ab-normal, a deviant from "the established *norms* of the individual's reference group" (1966, p. 448). Accordingly, the neurotic is not superego-dominated, but a social deviant, for if he were superego-dominated as Freud contended, then he would not be neurotic, but socially well integrated and comfortably in conformity with his society (1967b). Psychotherapy based on amorality rather than curing personality disorder is likely to cause personality deviation (1961). Psychotherapy must be a social re-integration (1964), accomplished through "integrity therapy" (1966, 1967b).

LEARNING THEORY AND FACTOR ANALYSIS OF NEUROSIS

Eysenck's (1950, 1952) approach to neurosis is via learning theory and factor analysis. Isolating three factors in his dimensional approach to personality (neuroticism, psychoticism, and extraversion-introversion) and utilizing his criterion analysis, Eysenck finds the cause of neurosis in two types of anxiety, one stemming from an inherited autonomic lability and the second from a conditioned anxiety (1957).

Buss (1962, 1966) and Hamilton (1959) corroborate the findings of Eysenck to the extent that anxiety neurosis displays two patterns, somatic symptoms on the one hand, and cognitive-motor ones on the other. They found one factor dominated by autonomic reactions and one predominated by motor and cognitive aspects of anxiety. According to Eysenck, neurotic syndromes also vary according to extraversion-introversion, hysterics tending toward extraversion, and introverts toward dysthymia, i.e., anxiety, obsession-compulsion, etc.

As a learning theorist, as well as a factor analyst, Eysenck insists that neurotic symptoms are merely learning habits. Inasmuch as neurotic symptoms are unadaptive forms of learned patterns of behavior, "get rid of the symptom and you have eliminated the neurosis" (1959, 1965). The symptom *is* the neurosis; replace the maladaptive habit causing the symptom, and you have a neurotically-free individual with adaptive habits.

In America, factor analysis or multivariate experimental psychology, as it is coming to be called, has been championed by Cattell who edited a handbook in the field (1966). Cattell's interest is in measuring neuroticism and the various traits associated with the neurotic (1965). In recent years, he has been interested in measuring anxiety and neuroticism (1957, 1962, 1963; Cattell & Scheier, 1961) by means of variables that are their manifestations, and comparing them with personality factors recognized as dimensions within the normal individual.

TAYLOR MANIFEST ANXIETY SCALE

The measurement of anxiety was also conducted by Janet Taylor (1951, 1953), producing the well-known Taylor Manifest Anxiety Scale (MAS). Consisting of factors indicative of manifest anxiety, the scale is a technique in studying human motivation relevant to anxiety. A correlation exists between internal anxiety and drive level. The relationship between the intensity of manifest anxiety of patients and anxiety-scale scores of normal persons is ascertained. K. W. Spence also shared in some of these studies with Taylor (1951, 1953) and with Farber also (1953).

BYRNE REPRESSION-SENSITIZATION SCALE

Studies in neurotic patterns of avoidance were accelerated by the introduction of Byrne's Repression-Sensitization Scale (1961). Stimulated by studies in perceptual defense by Eriksen (1954) and Lazarus (1954), Byrne arrived at a concept of behavior dimension consisting of psychological defenses from repression at one end and sensitization at the other. The R-S Scale serves as a measure of defensive behavior, as a measure of adjustment (Byrne, Golightly, & Sheffield, 1965), and as a dimension of personality (Byrne, 1964).

PSYCHOANALYSIS

With the exception of advancements in psychosomatic medicine, progress in classical psychoanalysis has failed to keep pace in recent years at a comparable rate to that set by learning theorists and other schools of psychopathology. Psychoanalysts have not significantly advanced beyond Freud's original discoveries. Their efforts have fructified in stimulating other schools of thought to launch their own investigations. Similar observations may be made of certain offshoot schools whose founders were one-time associates of Freud, e.g., that of Jung. Noteworthy new ideas of major significance (comparable to those sired by other schools of thought) are wanting in psychoanalytically oriented circles despite the prevalence of journals devoted to these schools. Psychoanalysis presented and re-presented is virtually the same position that existed 20, 30, or more years ago. It is not to be implied that these journals have lost their usefulness or that they no longer contain current articles of urgent or novel import, for they contain numerous significant contributions by "outsiders" and by those within the "camp" with worthwhile contributions in fields not strictly aligned with the purpose of the journal in question. For example, a thinker of the magnitude of Viktor Frankl is presently without an organ devoted to the dissemination of contributions to logotherapy, hence utilizes periodicals devoted to other schools in order to keep the world abreast of his contributions.

The most comprehensive and authoritative treatment of psychoanalytical theory of neurosis was contributed by Fenichel (1945), but even that is a quarter of a century old, yet unrivalled. A book of more than 700 pages, it is merely a reformulation of Freudianism, granting only minor concessions to the cultural or neo-Freudians. Nevertheless, novel advances in psychoanalysis have been made by the culturalists, environmentalists, and interpersonalists, such as, Horney (1937, 1945, 1950), Sullivan (1953, 1956), Fromm-Reichmann (who synthesizes Freud and Sullivan; 1950), and Fromm (1941, 1947, 1955). Fromm later sought to integrate psychoanalysis with Zen Buddhism (Suzuki, Fromm, & DeMartino, 1960).

Fromm-Reichmann (1949), reporting on recent advances in psychoanalysis, cites the developments by Fromm, Horney, Kardiner, and Sullivan with respect to cultural factors; and revisions of the Oedipus complex by Boehm, Fromm, Malinowski, and Mullahy. Contrary to Freud, Fromm-Reichmann sees certain dissociative or repressed processes as desirable, for "man depends upon successful dissociations and processes of selective inattention for the mastery of his psychobiological existence" (1949, p. 323). Predicated upon this important observation, Whitaker and Malone (1953) constructed an experiential theory of psychotherapy. For the sake of enhancing the experience of reality, some psychoanalysts have relinquished the regulation which binds them to utilize the couch in therapy. Perhaps the greatest innovation in psychoanalysis is the trend toward more abbreviated forms of therapy. Another important advance has been the deep interest by some members in psychosomatic medicine and its recent illuminating experiments, especially by Alexander (1959, 1962) and his associates (1961).

EXISTENTIAL NEUROSIS

Existential neurosis is one of the newer psychopathologies to be recognized, and it is regarded as a concomitant of our present day existence. Just as sexual neurosis dominated the neuroses of a few generations ago, owing to sex repression which was prevalent at the time, today existential neurosis is emerging as the disturbance emanating from our cultural and personal mode of existence.

The development of our knowledge of existential neurosis has been proponed by Frankl (1958a, 1958b, 1959, 1962a, 1962b, 1966, 1967a, 1967b), but recently Maddi (1967) has lent his support. Existential neurosis, or as Frankl often refers to it "noögenic neurosis," stems from a void or "existential vacuum" (Frankl), that is a sense of meaninglessness or "existential frustration." Existential neurosis emanates from spiritual conflicts, mental aimlessness, ennui, and ethical perplexities, a wrestling within a human being seeking for a meaningful life. Logotherapy is the most effective form of treatment for this peculiar type of neurosis. Logotherapy entails more than psychology, it includes philosophy as well (Fabry, 1968).

Maslow's (1967) contribution to the advancement of our knowledge of neurosis is in terms of neurosis as a failure of personal growth. Neurosis is the inability to achieve self-actualization, that is, to gain "full humanness"; instead, the neurotic is in a state of "human diminution" or a "not-yet-actualization of human capacities and possibilities." Inasmuch as man's psychological nature is innately good, then normal is equated with healthy and happy while interrupted growth is unhealthy (1968). Not too distant from Maslow's general attitude toward neurosis is that of Angyal's (1965) "holistic theory." For Angyal, neurosis is a way of life inherently destined to failure. Neurosis, a making of the real self, prevents the real or better self from emerging and assuming its proper role.

Kelly (1955), too, sees the neurotic in an improper role, with his personal constructs failing him. Anxiety is the result of the failure of personal construction; and threat, the upheaval of one's core structure. Guilt emerges when a person is dislodged from his role.

The social roles that a person plays and their relevancy to mental health have been scored by Adler (1939) and in recent years by the social learning theorists such as Rotter (1954, 1964). The social learning theorist sees behavior as goal directed. A person prefers behavior from which he has learned to acquire the greatest satisfaction under given situations. A person possesses "need potentials," i.e., a set of behaviors that are goal-directed. By his "freedom of movement" (expectancies that his behavior leads to a set of goals), he achieves his "need value," the worth of the goals of reinforcements. Maladaptive behavior ensues from a low freedom of movement and a high need value. The ill-adapted person fails to learn how to achieve his goals; rather he is learning how to avoid failure and experiences concomitant frustration.

The superiority of the social learning theorists over the usual brand of learning theorists is the level of sophistication to which they have elevated learning theory. While ordinary learning theorists concentrate their experiments and extrapolate their information from animal behavior, social learning theorists derive their information from human beings and from qualities peculiarly human. Predicated on this distinction (which is also Rotter's; 1964), this author favors social learning theory, interpreting neurotic behavior from that point of view. Subhuman neurosis is never quite the same as human neurosis, owing particularly to man's higher mental processes and his interpersonal relationships or social atmosphere. Furthermore man has extra-animal needs (Fromm, 1955, p. 25) and a self-awareness that renders his neurosis much more complex and different from animal neurosis. Although experimental neurosis lends insight into human neurosis, it is only a partial explanation at best. Man's sense of responsibility heightens his sense of guilt and even complicates it in such a manner as to compound the human sense of guilt. Social intercourse as such does not create guilt (as Freud supposed), but it does point the direction or cite that about which a person may sense a feeling of guilt. If I were devoid of guilt feeling, then my society could never make me feel guilty about any matter, but being constructed in a manner so that guilt is part of my constitution, then through social learning I may be directed toward that mode of behavior which issues in guilty feelings. Once I am victimized by a drive which directs me to behavior that is socially reprehensible, then both the behavior and the sense of accompanying guilt become conditioned as part of my trait makeup. If I am conditioned to believe that punitive or catastrophic results are the outcome of guilt, then I associate guilt with anxiety, or I become anxiety-ridden with the sense of guilt (Sahakian, 1969a).

14.

OTTO FENICHEL

PSYCHOANALYTIC THEORY OF NEUROSIS

Mental functions should be approached from the same angle as the functions of the nervous system in general. They are manifestations of the same basic function of the living organism —irritability. The basic pattern which is useful for the understanding of mental phenomena is the reflex arc. Stimuli from the outside world or from the body initiate a state of tension that seeks for motor or secretory discharge, bringing about relaxation. However, between stimulus and discharge, forces are at work opposing the discharge tendency. The study of these inhibiting forces, their origin and their effect on the discharge tendency, is the immediate subject of psychology. Without these counterforces there would be no psyche, only reflexes. . . .

With such a starting point, it is apparent that psychoanalytic psychology attempts more than mere description. It explains mental phenomena as the result of the interaction and counteraction of forces, that is, in a *dynamic* way. A dynamic explanation is also a *genetic* one, since it examines not only a phenomenon as such but the forces that brought it about as well. It does not examine single acts; it examines the phenomena in terms of processes of development, of progression or regression.

The idea of looking at mental phenomena as a result of interacting forces certainly was not derived merely by transferring the concept of energy from the other natural sciences to psychology. Originally it happened the other way around: the everyday assumption that one understands mental reactions when one understands their motives has been transferred to physics.

One special kind of mental phenomena, instinctual drives, is directly experienced as an

"urging energy." Certain perceptions have a provocative character: they press for immediate action; one feels oneself impelled by forces of various intensities. In connecting this experience with the reflex pattern, it may be assumed that the instinctual impulses have the general tendency to lower the excitation level by the discharge of tensions that have been brought about by exciting stimuli. Counterforces, to be investigated later, oppose this, and the struggle so created constitutes the basis of the realm of mental phenomena.

This certainly does not mean that psychoanalytic psychology assumes all mental phenomena to be instinctual in nature. It only means that noninstinctual phenomena have to be explained as the effects of external stimuli on biological needs. The noninstinctual part of the human mind becomes understandable as a derivative of the struggle for and against discharge, created by the influence of the external world. Nor does the cell theory maintain that all living substance is made up only of cells; its position remains justified as long as it succeeds in proving that the noncellular components of living substance, like tendons, hair, or intercellular material, are parts or products of cells. The same holds true for psychoanalytic psychology as long as it can prove that the noninstinctual mental phenomena are derivatives of more primitive instinctual ones. Therefore Freud's short paper, "On Negation" . . . , is of principal importance, for therein he shows how the seemingly very remote function of judgment is derived from instincts.

However, the expression *Trieb* which Freud uses does not signify exactly the same thing as the English expression *instinct*, as it is customarily translated. Inherent in the concept of instinct is the idea that it represents an inherited and unchangeable pattern; in the German concept of *Trieb* this unchangeability is by no means implied. On the contrary, the *Triebe* obviously are changed in aim and object under influences stemming from the environment, and Freud was even of the opinion that they originated under the same influence . . . This incorrect equating of *instinct* and *Trieb* has created serious misunderstandings.

The assumption has been made in various forms by many biologists that there is a basic vital tendency to abolish tensions that have been brought about by external stimulation and to return to the energy state that was effective before the stimulation. The most fruitful conception in this respect is Cannon's formulation of the principle of "homeostasis." . . . "Organisms, composed of material which is characterized by the utmost inconstancy and unsteadiness, have somehow learned the methods of maintaining constancy and keeping steady in the presence of conditions which might reasonably be expected to prove profoundly disturbing." The word homeostasis "does not imply something set and immobile, a stagnation"; on the contrary, the living functions are extremely flexible and mobile, their equilibrium being disturbed uninterruptedly, but being re-established by the organism equally uninterruptedly.

It was the same basic principle Fechner had in mind when he spoke about the "principle of constancy," . . . and for which Freud, following Barbara Low, often used the expression "Nirvana principle." . . . It seems more appropriate to see the ultimate goal for all these equalization tendencies as the aim of maintaining a certain level of tension characteristic for the organism, of "preserving the level of excitation," as Freud put it very early, . . . rather than the aim of the total abolition of all tension. . . .

It can be seen everywhere that this principle of homeostasis does not remain unopposed. Some behavior seems to be directed not toward getting rid of tensions but rather toward creating new tensions, and the main task of psychology is to study and understand counterforces that tend to block or to postpone immediate discharge.

However, this understanding will never be arrived at if an attempt is made to differentiate a "homeostatic instinct" from other "nonhomeostatic instincts." . . . Homeostasis is, as a

principle, at the root of all instinctual behavior; the frequent "counterhomeostatic" behavior must be explained as a secondary complication, imposed upon the organism by external forces.

＊ ＊ ＊

Thus the forces whose interaction is supposed to explain the actual mental phenomena have definite *directions*—toward motility or away from motility. The impulses toward discharge are representative of a primary biological tendency; the opposite impulses are brought into the organism by influences from the outside.

＊ ＊ ＊

When tendencies to discharge and tendencies to inhibit are equally strong, there is externally no evidence of activity; but energy is consumed in an internal hidden struggle. Clinically this is manifested by the fact that individuals subject to such conflicts show fatigue and exhaustion without doing perceptible work.

MENTAL ECONOMICS

With this example we find ourselves in the field that Freud has called psycho-economics. . . . The above-mentioned persons were tired because they were consuming energy in a struggle between inner forces. When a person suppresses an irritation and subsequently in another situation reacts violently to an insignificant provocation, it must be assumed that the first quantity of irritation, which was suppressed, was still at work in him as a readiness to discharge, later seizing the first possible opportunity. The energy of the forces behind the mental phenomena is displaceable. Strong impulses demanding discharge are more difficult to restrain than weak ones; however, they can be restrained if the counterforces are equally strong. What quantity of excitation can be borne without discharge is an economic problem. There is a "mental energy exchange," an economic distribution of the energy at hand between intake, consumption, and output. Another example of the usefulness of the economic concept is seen in the fact that neuroses frequently break out at puberty and at the climacterium. The person affected was able to withstand a certain amount of undischarged instinctual excitation; however, when physical changes increased the absolute quantity of this excitation, the countermeasures no longer sufficed. Countless other examples exist which bring home the importance of the economic point of view for the understanding of factually observed phenomena. The person who was tired after having done nothing represents but a special type of general inhibitions due to silent internal tasks. Those who have inner problems to solve must apply a great deal of their energy to them, and there remains little for other functions.

The concept of a "quantity" of mental energy is exactly as justifiable or unjustifiable as the introduction of other scientific working concepts that have proved practical. It is regrettable that this quantity cannot be measured directly; it may be measured indirectly by its physiological manifestations.

CONSCIOUS AND UNCONSCIOUS

In the exposition of the dynamics and economics of the mental organization, nothing has been stated as yet about the significance of whether a given phenomenon is conscious or unconscious. This is due to the fact that the differentiation is initially purely descriptive, not quantitative. Posthypnotic suggestion demonstrates the existence of a psychic unconscious before our very eyes. The forgetting of a name makes us feel it subjectively. One knows that one knows the name and still one does not know it.

When the dynamic and the economic points of view are applied, the problem of conscious or unconscious should be put in the following way: Under what circumstances and through what energies does the condition of consciousness arise? It is in these terms that all mental qualities should be examined. Too, the feelings of pleasure and pain as qualities are describable only; to "explain" them means to determine under what dynamic and economic conditions they are experienced.

This way of putting the problem would find a simple justification if a direct correlation could be found between fundamental quantities and the definite qualities that appeared only

with them: for example, if Fechner's hypothesis—that every increase in mental tension is felt as displeasure and every decrease as pleasure—could be confirmed. Many facts are in accordance with such a viewpoint, but unfortunately there are contradictory facts, too. . . . There are pleasurable tensions, like sexual excitement, and painful lacks of tension, like boredom or feelings of emptiness. Nevertheless, Fechner's rule is valid in general. That sexual excitement and boredom are secondary complications can be demonstrated. The pleasure of sexual excitement, called forepleasure, turns immediately into displeasure if the hope of bringing about a discharge in subsequent end pleasure disappears; the pleasure character of the forepleasure is tied up with a mental anticipation of the end pleasure. The displeasure of boredom turns out, on closer inspection, not to correspond to a lack of tension but rather to an excitement whose aim is unconscious. . . . A further discussion of the problem at this point would lead us too far astray. . . . It was brought up in order to demonstrate that attempts to coordinate quantitative factors and qualitative phenomena are warranted.

Returning to the quality "conscious," the fact whether or not an impulse is conscious reveals nothing of its dynamic value. Conscious phenomena are not simply stronger than unconscious ones; nor is it true that everything unconscious is the "real motor" of the mind, and everything conscious merely a relatively unimportant side issue. The many memory traces that can be made conscious by a simple act of attention are "unimportant" though unconscious (they are called preconscious). Other unconscious phenomena, however, must be imagined as intense forces striving for discharge but kept in check by an equally strong force, which manifests itself as "resistance." Unconscious material under such high pressure has only one aim: discharge. Its freely floating energy is directed according to the "primary process"; that is, it is unburdened by the demands of reality, time, order, or logical considerations; it becomes condensed and displaced, following only the interests of increased possibilities of discharge. This mode of functioning of the archaic mind remains effective in the realm of the unconscious; in the more differentiated parts of the mind it gradually becomes supplanted by the organized "secondary process." . . .

THE MENTAL STRUCTURE

Mental phenomena are to be regarded as the result of the interplay of forces pressing respectively toward and away from motility. The organism is in contact with the outside world at the beginning and at the end of its reaction processes, which start with the perception of stimuli and end with motor or glandular discharge. Freud looks at the mental apparatus as modeled after an organism floating in water. . . . Its surface takes up stimuli, conducts them to the interior, whence reactive impulses surge to the surface. The surface is differentiated gradually with respect to its functions of stimulus perception and discharge. The product of this differentiation becomes the "ego." The ego proceeds selectively in its reception of perceptions as well as in its allowing impulses to gain motility. It operates as an inhibiting apparatus which controls, by this inhibiting function, the position of the organism in the outside world. Alexander in his "vector analysis" regards all mental tendencies as combinations of intake, retention, and elimination. . . . We add: living begins with intake; but with the initial intake the first urge to eliminate appears; retention, however, arises later under complicating influences.

The ego develops abilities with which it can observe, select, and organize stimuli and impulses: the functions of judgment and intelligence. It also develops methods of keeping the rejected impulses from motility by the use of energy quantities kept ready for this purpose; that is, it blocks the tendency toward discharge and changes the primary process into the secondary process. . . . All this takes place by means of a special organization which aims to fulfill its different tasks with a minimum of effort (principle of multiple function). . . .

Underneath the organized periphery of the ego lies the core of a dynamic, driving chaos of forces, which strive for discharge and nothing else, but which constantly receive new stimulations from external as well as internal perceptions, influenced by somatic factors that determine how the perceptions are experienced. . . . The organization proceeds from the surface to the depth. The ego is to the id as the ectoderm is to the endoderm. The ego becomes the mediator between the organism and the outer world. As such it has to provide protection against hostile influences from the environment as well as enforcement of gratification even against a restricting outside world. There is no reason to assume that the ego, created for the purpose of ensuring the gratification of the organism's impulses, is in any way primarily hostile to the instincts.

What does the differentiation of ego and id have to do with the qualities of conscious and unconscious? It would be simple if ego and conscious, id and unconscious could be coordinated. But unfortunately things are more complicated. That which takes place in consciousness consists of (corresponding to "intake" and "discharge") perceptions and impulses. We may regard imagery as consisting of impulses with a weaker cathexis. . . . However, not all impulses and perceptions are conscious. There are "below threshold" stimuli which can be proved to have been perceived without ever having been conscious. . . . Further, there are repressed perceptions, in hysterical blindness, for example, where the effectiveness of unconscious perceptions can be observed. There is also unconscious motility, as in somnambulism. Unconscious perceptions and movements have specific peculiarities which differentiate them from the conscious ones. All living organisms must maintain exchanges with the outside world through the basic functions of perception and motility—this is true even before there is any differentiation of an ego, and in the same way that nourishment and breathing must be performed by each living cell even before there is a differential development of a multicellular respiratory and metabolic apparatus. Before a systematic conception of reality can be developed there must of necessity exist a certain unsystematic perception.

Consciousness comes into being at some point in the process of systematization. . . .

This process depends on the ability to utilize memories. Memory traces are remnants of perceptions; they apparently arise on a second level below that of the perceptions themselves. . . . The ego broadens out from the layer of these memory traces, called the preconscious. The differentiation of the ego is a gradual process. There are deeper layers of the ego which are unconscious. The transition from ego to id is a gradual one and is only sharp at those points where a conflict exists. However, where such conflict does arise, even highly differentiated forces of the ego become unconscious again.

The portion of the unconscious that is best known is the "repressed"—that which is unconscious because strong, dynamic forces hinder its becoming conscious. The repressed pushes toward consciousness and motility; it consists of impulses seeking outlets. In this seeking activity it tends to produce "derivatives," that is, to displace its cathexes onto associatively connected ideas that are less objectionable to the conscious ego. In psychoanalysis, preconscious derivatives are encouraged and caught by the patient's attention; this is the way repressed content gradually becomes known. The repressed consists, first of all, of the ideas and conceptions connected with the aim of the warded-off impulses which, by being warded off, have lost their connection with verbal expression; by regaining verbalization, unconscious ideas become preconscious. . . . But it is also meaningful to talk about unconscious sensations, feelings, or emotions. Certainly the qualities of feelings come into being only by being felt. But there are tensions in the organism which, were they not hindered in their discharge and development by blocking counter-cathexes, would result in specific sensations, feelings, or emotions. They are unconscious "dispositions" toward these qualities, unconscious "longings for affects," strivings toward development of affects that are held in check by opposing forces, while the individual does not know that he has such readiness toward rage or sexual excitement or anxiety or guilt feeling or whatever it may be. . . . Of course, such "unconscious dispositions toward affects" are not theoretical constructions but may be

observed clinically in the same way that unconscious ideas may be observed: they, too, develop derivatives, betray themselves in dreams, in symptoms, and in other substitute formations, or through the rigidity of the opposing behavior, or, finally, merely in general weariness.

The mental apparatus, however, does not consist only of an ego and an id. Its further development brings a further complication.

Previously it was stated that the question as to the nature of the forces blocking discharge was the basic one of all psychology. In the main, these forces were thrust upon the mind by the environment. It is the consideration of reality that keeps the ego from immediately complying with the discharge drive of the impulses. However, such inhibiting tendencies, which according to the definition are derived from the ego, are not in all respects the opposite of "instinctual drives." Often, for example in ascetics or moral masochists, the anti-instinctual behavior betrays all the characteristics of an instinct. This contradiction can be explained genetically. The energy with which the ego carries out its instinct-inhibiting activities is drawn from the instinctual reservoir of the id. A portion of the instinctual energy is changed into counterinstinctual energy. A certain part of the ego which inhibits instinctual activity develops on the one hand closer to the instincts and on the other hand is in conflict with other parts of the ego that are hungry for pleasure. This part, which has the function (among others) of deciding which impulses are acceptable and which are not, is called the superego. While the ego is also a representative of the outside world, here again we have a special representative of the outside world within the first representative.

DEFINITION OF NEUROSIS

After bringing forth the dynamic, economic, and structural points of view, an initial attempt will be made to clarify what takes place in a neurosis. Is there any common denominator in the manifold neurotic phenomena that may be utilized for comprehending the essential nature of neuroses?

In all neurotic symptoms something happens which the patient experiences as strange and unintelligible. This something may be involuntary movements, other changes of bodily functions and various sensations, as in hysteria; or an overwhelming and unjustified emotion or mood, as in anxiety spells or depressions; or queer impulses or thoughts, as in compulsions and obsessions. All symptoms give the impression of a something that seems to break in upon the personality from an unknown source —a something that disturbs the continuity of the personality and that is outside the realm of the conscious will. But there are also neurotic phenomena of another kind. In "neurotic characters" the personality does not appear to be uniform or disturbed only by one or the other interrupting event, but openly so torn or deformed and often so involved in the illness that one cannot say at what point the "personality" ends and the "symptom" begins. But different as "symptom neuroses" and "character neuroses" seem to be, both have this in common: the normal and rational way of handling the demands of the external world as well as the impulses from within is substituted by some irrational phenomenon which seems strange and cannot be voluntarily controlled. Since the normal functioning of the mind is governed by a control apparatus that organizes, leads, and inhibits deeper archaic and more instinctual forces—in the same way that the cortex organizes, leads, and inhibits impulses of the deeper and more archaic levels of the brain—it can be stated that the common denominator of all neurotic phenomena is an insufficiency of the normal control apparatus.

The simplest way to "control" stimuli is to discharge by motor reactions the excitation they arouse. Later the immediate discharge is replaced by more complicated control mechanisms of counterforces. This control consists in a distribution of counterenergies in an adequate economic stability between incoming stimuli and outgoing discharges.

All neurotic phenomena are based on insufficiencies of the normal control apparatus. They can be understood as involuntary emergency discharges that supplant the normal ones. The insufficiency can be brought about in two ways.

One way is through an increase in the influx of stimuli: too much excitation enters the mental apparatus in a given unit of time and cannot be mastered; such experiences are called traumatic. The other is through a previous blocking or decrease of discharge which has produced a damming up of tensions within the organism so that normal excitations now operate relatively like traumatic ones. These two possible ways are not mutually exclusive. A trauma may initiate an ensuing blocking of discharge; and a primary blocking, by creating a state of being dammed up, may cause subsequent average stimuli to have a traumatic effect.

A model of the first type can be seen in irritations that everyone experiences after little traumata, like a sudden fright or some smaller accident. The person feels irritated for a certain time, cannot concentrate because inwardly he is still concerned about the event and has no energy free for attention in other directions. He repeats the event in his thoughts and feelings a few times—and after a short while his mental stability is re-established. Such a little traumatic neurosis can be explained as flooding of the organism by amounts of unmastered excitation and as attempts at a belated mastery. The severe traumatic neuroses must be looked at from the same angle.

A model of the second type of neurosis, characterized by a previous blocking of discharge and called psychoneurosis, is represented by the artificial neuroses that have been inflicted upon animals by experimental psychologists. Some stimulus which had represented pleasant instinctual experiences or which had served as a signal that some action would now procure gratification is suddenly connected by the experimenter with frustrating or threatening experiences, or the experimenter decreases the difference between stimuli which the animal had been trained to associate with instinct gratification and threat respectively; the animal then gets into a state of irritation which is very similar to that of a traumatic neurosis. He feels contradictory impulses; the conflict makes it impossible for him to give in to the impulses in the accustomed way; the discharge is blocked, and this decrease in discharge works in the same way as an increase in influx: it brings the organism into a state of tension and calls for emergency discharges.

In psychoneuroses some impulses have been blocked; the consequence is a state of tension and eventually some "emergency discharges." These consist partly in unspecific restlessness and its elaborations and partly in much more specific phenomena which represent the distorted involuntary discharges of those very instinctual drives for which a normal discharge has been interdicted. Thus we have in psychoneuroses, first a defense of the ego against an instinct, then a conflict between the instinct striving for discharge and the defensive forces of the ego, then a state of damming up, and finally the neurotic symptoms which are distorted discharges as a consequence of the state of damming up—a compromise between the opposing forces. The symptom is the only step in this development that becomes manifest; the conflict, its history, and the significance of the symptoms are unconscious.

NEUROTIC SYMPTOMS

These considerations of the essence of the neuroses call forth an objection that should not be overlooked. Much of the given characterization of neurotic phenomena seems valid also for a category of very normal mental phenomena, namely, of affective or emotional spells.

Actually a search for a common denominator for all sudden outbursts of affect reveals a close relationship between outbursts of this kind and neurotic phenomena.

Affective spells consist of (a) movements and other physiological discharges, especially changes in the muscular and glandular functions, and (b) emotional feelings. Both the physical and the mental phenomena are specific for any given affect—and in particular the correlation of both phenomena is specific. Emotional spells occur without the consent or even against the will of the individual; persons who undergo emotional spells have "lost control." Apparently something of a more archaic nature is substituted for the normal ego—there is no doubt that children and infantile personalities are more unstable emotionally.

Such spells occur as a response to (a) extraordinarily intense stimuli, the quantity of which explains the temporary insufficiency of the normal control apparatus of the ego; in this case the emotional spells seem to be a kind of emergency control supplanting the normal ego control; or (b) to ordinary stimuli when certain conditions obtain in the organism. The simplest example is displaced rage. A slight precipitating factor evokes a fit of anger if there was a readiness for it in the organism rooted in a previous experience that afforded this tendency no means of expression. In general the organism tends toward emotional regressions if it is in a state of tension. This is why an unduly intense emotional reaction generally can be regarded as a "derivative" of something that was previously suppressed. In summary, emotional spells occur when the normal ego control has been rendered relatively insufficient by (a) too much influx of excitation, or (b) a previous blocking of the efflux.

This definition is identical with that given for neurotic symptoms. The neurotic symptoms, too, are discharge phenomena that occur without the consent of the ego; and if their precipitating factors, too, are analyzed, either an increased influx of excitation (traumatic neuroses) is found or defense activities of the ego that had previously blocked discharges and thus brought the organism into a state of tension (psychoneuroses). Thus the causation of emotional spells and of neurotic symptoms is essentially the same: a relative insufficiency of ego control because of either increased influx or blocking of discharge. Both emotional spells and neurotic symptoms are partial substitutes, of a more archaic nature, for the normal ego motility. Neurotic symptoms could be called a kind of "personally structured" affective spells. The difference lies in the nature of what is substituted. In neurosis the substitute is subjectively determined in the history of the individual. In affect the substitute is objectively determined; the syndrome is more or less the same in different individuals and is caused by chemically induced nervous reactions—just where it comes from, we do not know. The impression that there is a general similarity between neurotic and emotional spells impelled Freud, after having discovered the historical determination of the hysterical fit, to look for a historical determination of the anxiety syndrome also. . . .

The similarity between neurotic symptoms and emotional spells seems less striking in the case of compulsive symptoms. However, the compulsive symptom is less primitive than other neurotic symptoms; it is not a simple breaking through of the repressed forces. Similarly, not all affects have the character of sudden spells; the compulsive symptoms may be compared to tension affects like grief. If a conversion symptom corresponds to an outburst of intractable sexual excitement or of rage, then the compulsive symptom is paralleled by the more gradual work of mourning. Both compulsion and mourning represent a secondary elaboration of the original tendency toward stormy discharge.

The psychoneuroses are essentially the result of a conflict between instinctual demands and defensive forces of the ego. This knowledge shows how best to organize a theory of neurosis. To be studied are (a) the defending ego and its development, (b) the instincts and their development, (c) the types of conflicts between the two, their motives, methods and manifestations, and (d) the consequences of the conflicts, the neuroses proper.

15.

O. H. MOWRER

THE NEUROTIC PARADOX

On an earlier occasion, I have presented a paper before this Association entitled "Learning Theory and the Neurotic Paradox" (3). Here I propose to take up again the thesis of that paper and, so to say, bring it up to date.

I. THE NEUROTIC PARADOX

In the earlier paper, attention has been called to the fact that neurosis, or at least the modern conception of neurosis, involves a paradox. It is today very generally believed that neurosis presents a *learning excess* and that, more specifically, this excess consists of fears which are no longer warranted by the individual's life situation but which persist in spite of their unrealistic nature. Where physical traumata, such as

From O. H. Mowrer, "Symposium, 1952: The Therapeutic Process; III. Learning Theory and the Neurotic Fallacy." *American Journal of Orthopsychiatry,* 1952, *22,* 679–689. Copyright, the American Orthopsychiatric Association, Inc. Reproduced by permission.

those of war or natural catastrophe, cannot be demonstrated, it is common to assume that the individual who later becomes neurotic must, in childhood, have been treated with unusual harshness by his parents or parent substitutes and must in this way have developed, as Freud was wont to say, "an excessively severe superego." Such a superego, or conscience, reflecting the overseverity and strictness of parents, has been assumed by Freud and his followers to impede the free and healthy expression of the "instincts" and thus to generate anxiety and the varied attempts to deal therewith which we call neurotic "symptoms."

Now in "Learning Theory and the Neurotic Paradox," it was pointed out that laboratory learning studies have repeatedly demonstrated that fears, however powerful, always disappear eventually if there is a change in circumstances which makes such fears genuinely unrealistic, genuinely nonfunctional. It may take several repetitions of the stimulus, or situation, which was previously associated with danger to bring about full extinction of the fear reaction; but sooner or later the subject becomes convinced of the safety of the situation and reacts accordingly (8). In light of these facts, one is moved to ask: What is it, then, that in neurosis we have fears which appear to have long outlived any real justification but which stubbornly persist or which may even augment to the point of seriously incapacitating the individual?

It can, of course, be pointed out, quite properly, that the learning laboratory is not the same as life and that principles demonstrated in the former may or may not hold in the wider experience of the individual. Yet the dilemma just described seemed sufficiently real and important to prompt Freud to make numerous attempts to resolve it. These took the form of speculations regarding "erotic fixation," the "timelessness of the repressed," the "repetition compulsion," the "death instinct," constitutional variables, and the "racial unconscious." But Freud himself was never fully content with any of his attempted resolutions of this paradox, and on more than one occasion expressed his uncertainties and misgivings on this score. Perhaps his most extended comment in this connection and surely an eloquent one—is the following:

Why are not all neuroses merely episodes in the individual's development which become a closed chapter when the next stage of development is reached? Whence comes the element of permanency in these reactions to danger? Whence springs the preference over all other affects which the affect of anxiety seems to enjoy in alone evoking reactions which we distinguish from others as abnormal and which in their inexpediency obstruct the stream of life? In other words, we find ourselves abruptly confronted once again by the oft-repeated riddle: What is the source of neurosis, what is its ultimate, its specific, underlying principle? After decades of analytic effort this problem rises up before us, as untouched as at the beginning (2, p. 20).

II. PROPOSED RESOLUTION OF THE NEUROTIC PARADOX

In the earlier paper, an extended review of the writings of Freud and numerous other investigators in this field led to the conclusion that the neurotic paradox arises because of a false premise: namely, the premise that the neurotic is suffering from excessive and unrealistic fears. This conclusion, that the neurotic paradox is a spurious one because based upon a false premise, was stated and interpreted as follows:

As defined at the outset of this paper, the neurotic paradox lies in the fact that human behavior is sometimes indefinitely perpetuated despite the fact that it is seriously self-defeating. Freud's major attempt to resolve this paradox involves the assumption that in neurosis there are acts and feelings which have been appropriate at one stage of the individual's life history but are no longer so. More specifically, Freud believed that it was the superego which, as a result of too zealous childhood training, retained its overseverity into adult life despite altered circumstances and in this way produced the distressing, hampering effects seen in neurosis. But this approach to the problem goes counter to one of the best-established principles in the psychology of learning, which is that all learning tends to undergo extinction unless it is at least periodically reinforced.

Recognizing this difficulty in Freud's formulations, Horney and others have sought to rectify it by positing that the wasteful, self-defeating habits and attitudes which constitute neurosis do indeed become periodically reinforced through the operation of so-called vicious circles. But here again neurosis is conceived as a *learning excess,* and it is assumed that if one can but stop the cyclic sequence of events which keeps this learning reinforced, neurosis will be self-correcting.

Against these and similar attempts to resolve the neurotic paradox, we have posited the view that neurosis is not a learning excess but a *learning deficit.* Because of resistance which the infantile ego sets up against the socializing forces and because of the opposition which it later exerts against the internalized agent of these forces, namely, the superego, the ego remains immature, asocial, id-dominated.

That such an ego continues to experience anxiety is in no way surprising since it is still at war with the superego, which is constantly being kept alive and vigorous by the very nature of the social realities which it represents. We do not ask why the criminal continues to be a fearful individual. There is the ever-present danger that he will be apprehended and punished for his rebellious, antisocial behavior. And much the same is true of the neurotic. It is not that he is suffering from unreal or "childish" fears. He, too, faces a real danger, the danger of having his immaturities and "delinquencies" discovered—the danger, as one patient expressed it, of being "unmasked"—and of having to resume the painful task of renouncing the pleasure principle of infancy and accepting the reality principle of adulthood.

The problem, then, is not to explain why the neurotic does not *unlearn;* it is rather to account for the fact that he does not *learn*. We have already touched upon some of the reasons why small children resist primary socialization and why in later life the ego of the neurotic continues to fight with the superego. And we have also seen the way in which this intrapsychic struggle again becomes externalized in therapy and to what extent the transference behavior is essentially defensive, defensive in the sense of trying to avert the learning involved in further "growing up."

Having thus established the thesis that the neurotic is an "underdone" human being, in some respects not unlike the criminal, rather than an overdone, superhuman sort of creature, we must now turn and make an important modification of an earlier statement. We have repeatedly characterized the neurotic as a victim of underlearning, immaturity, ignorance; but this underlearning is of a special kind and is vouchsafed by what is, in one respect, "overlearning." Preston [9] has remarked that mental health is a matter of attitudes, and it is with respect to *attitudinal learning* that the neurotic is most deficient. To say that an individual is neurotic is not to say that there is anything deficient about his problem-solving learning ability. Indeed, it is the very fact that he has been so skillful in parrying the early attempts of his elders, and later of his conscience, to socialize him that has kept him neurotic. The essence of the difficulty is precisely that, through problem-solving learning, or the primitive pleasure principle, he has learned how to keep from learning in the sense of being conditioned, i.e., changed emotionally and attitudinally. To put this matter somewhat paradoxically but succinctly, the neurotic is an individual *who has learned how not to learn*. . . .

When we see the development of human personality in this light, not only is the neurotic paradox formally resolved; we are also enabled to conceive the task of therapy, not as that of attempting to stay or actually reverse the process whereby the human animal is converted into a full-fledged member of his society; rather do we see therapy as the more promising venture of reinstituting and, if possible, in some measure completing the education of the laggard learner.

At the time it was written, some four years ago, the above excerpt represented the best statement I could then make of my view of neurosis and its origin. This view still stands, but further experience as a therapist and certain related developments in behavior theory now make it possible to be more concrete and, it is hoped, more cogent and convincing with respect to this argument. In what follows an attempt will therefore be made to give the stated position greater precision and to develop its logical implications along some previously unexplored lines.

III. THE NEUROTIC FALLACY AND ITS PROFESSIONAL ACCEPTANCE

In the preceding section it is pointed out that the neurotic paradox, as I have called it, arises because of a debatable assumption: the assumption that the neurotic is excessively and unrealistically fearful. We have seen that although Freud was well aware of the paradoxical implications to which this assumption leads, he nevertheless continued to hold to it; and a recent review of current theorizing in respect to neurosis and its treatment (5) shows that acceptance of this assumption is still very widespread in the professions most concerned with these matters.

Now it is surely arresting and perhaps also instructive to discover that this same assumption is very widely held by neurotics themselves. This assumption takes myriad forms. One of the commonest of these is the tendency on the part of neurotics to see others—especially parents and "society"—as responsible for their difficulties. Having persuaded themselves of the baleful influence which these "significant others," to borrow Sullivan's phrase, have had upon them, patients are full of self-vindication and resentment. Certainly their view of the situation is that they have been grievously wronged and mistreated.

If a therapist uses the approach that neurosis results from inhibition of sexual and aggressive instincts by an unreasonable, overly severe superego (which reflects the irrationality and malevolence of parents and "society"), he is sure to get a strong "positive transference" from patients. Here at last, they feel, is a person who understands them and who is willing and, they hope, able to help them on their own terms (6, Chap. 18). Then, when this "honeymoon" ends and disillusionment begins to develop in the patient, his reactions are said to represent "negative transference," and one settles down comfortably to "analyze" it for two or three years.

If one wishes to see the same forces at work in a different setting, then let him proceed on the assumption that what is repressed in the neurotic is not so much the forces of the id as those of conscience. Promptly and emphatically the patient will point out that his problems arise precisely because he is *too conscientious,* and in support of this thesis he will again tell you of symptoms which might appear to make of him a veritable monster of morality, a victim of such scruples as one can hardly imagine.

Surely these are suspicious circumstances! It is one thing to say that a therapist must take the patient's "point of view" if by this we mean being willing to listen long and carefully to what he says. But a therapist whose conception and philosophy of neurosis does not differ perceptibly from that of persons who have themselves fallen victim of this disorder can hardly be expected to provide either the conceptual leadership or the curative efficiency of which we are in such need in this field.

In fairness let us grant that a therapist with the orientation which is here under scrutiny will not *wholly* agree with his patients. He will, for example, be the first to tell you that whereas the patient believes or, at some crucial point in the past, has believed in the strategy of resolving psychic conflicts by denial and repression, he, the therapist, stands for a policy of facing conflicts and resolving them without repression; and to this end the therapist will try, by interpretation of dreams, symptoms, slips, etc., to bring back into consciousness those impulses which, in the interests of psychological peace, have been pushed into "the unconscious."

But even here such a therapist is playing into the patient's hands and sharing with him the neurotic fallacy. He is basing his interpretations, his campaign for reality-facing, upon an assumption which the patient would like to believe is true but which, it seems, rarely is. The patient is only too ready to believe that he suffers because of inhibited lust and hostility and is willing to spend much time, effort and money trying to root out these fear-induced barriers to a better life. But if, in point of fact, the patient's dissociative strategies have worked in another way, i.e., if he has repressed not sex and aggression but instead the forces of his own conscience, all the allegiance in the world to the "reality principle" and the utmost belief in the im-

portance of making the unconscious conscious will not achieve the desired end.

Is it, then, too cynical a view to suggest that a therapist who follows the traditional Freudian line or some currently popular variation of it agrees with the patient in areas where the patient is almost certainly wrong and that in those areas where the therapist *disagrees* with the patient, he is, in effect, accusing the patient of something which the patient actually has not done? We are often charged with basing our theories of personality too much upon our experience with "the abnormal." Certainly the insights of those who make a specialty of studying "only normal people" have not been very helpful or profound. But we cannot easily escape the suspicion that those clinicians who have taken the neurotic patient as their standard have been more victimized in this respect than is commonly recognized.

IV. A CASE ILLUSTRATION

During the course of her college career, Margaret L became increasingly tense, developed rashes, and entered into a full-blown anxiety state. At this point she went to a clinic and was referred to a woman therapist. However, Margaret obtained no relief from this contact and soon entered into a suicide pact with the young man with whom she was currently involved. Following the suicide attempt, both of these young people had to be hospitalized for a few days, but their physical recovery was rapid and they were soon discharged. Margaret was now assigned to a male therapist who took the following view of her problems. He told her that her basic difficulty was that she "hated men" and supported this pronouncement as follows. Margaret, he said, obviously had exorbitant guilt in connection with sex, and since she perceived her father as the stricter of her two parents, it was he that Margaret blamed and hated most for the irrational and unfair way in which she had been trained. Her hatred of her father generalized, said this therapist, to all men and thus prompted Margaret's need to kill her lover, as well as herself.

Upon entering therapy a third time, Margaret was still chanting, "I hate men," which she said

Dr. K had told her was her trouble; and she was trying to believe this was true but that it had not seemed to help very much. She said that she had been so terrorized by her experiences of the past year and was so afraid of the future that no sacrifice would be too great if she could only be relieved of her suffering.

During the course of the first seven interviews with this patient, it became apparent that it was not so much "men" as herself that she hated and that the basis of her self-reproaches was likewise not so much the illicit sexual activities in which she had been engaged as the fact that she was borrowing money from her parents to complete her education and while presenting a picture of great industry and ambition to them was actually spending most of her time and energy seeking solace from her anxiety in one love affair after another.

At the eighth interview Margaret announced that she had an opportunity to drive to her home in a nearby city over the week end and that she had about decided to do so and have a "talk" with her father. She said that it seemed that she was not going to have any peace until she told her parents, particularly her father, what the real state of affairs was; but she said she felt she could not do this unless she said her therapist had *told* her to. Margaret was advised not to undertake this enterprise until she was herself convinced of its soundness and was able to take full responsibility for it. She made the trip, with results which are given in the following excerpts from the ninth interview. After some preliminary comments, Margaret said:

"Uh—Up until the time that I started talking to my folks I was feeling pretty good. I—just the usual uh—amount of tension; but I wasn't feeling any particular anxiety. And uh—pretty soon after I got up I told my folks that uh—I was still nervous and uh—uh—I was—My father said, 'Why don't you take some shots?' I said, 'No, Dad, they're—the nervousness I'm talking about is neurotic nervousness. You notice I'm talking as loud as—I'm racked with nervousness, I'm feeling anxiety.' And he said, 'About what? About the money we owe you?' [This was a slip; she should have said, ". . . the money you owe us?"] And I said, no, I didn't think it

was that. And I felt that—uh—it was more a question of the way I acted; it was more a question of the fact that I wanted to be more honest; I wanted to talk to them. And throughout the conversation with my father he would go off on another vein and try to get me off the subject, but I kept with it. Ah-h-h [big sigh]. It ended up that I seemed to make it more impersonal. At first, when I was losing my nerve about talking I started to talk about neurotic behavior and the value of psychology and what is nervousness and all that sort of thing. On the other hand, my father just—it was just as well that I did that because he was all set to tell once again that I needed vitamin pills and so forth. Uh—we started talking about honesty, as I said, and I asked him if—if he thought sex was evil. And he said, no, he didn't think so, not in the right time and place; and—and then my mother broke in and said—and—and said, 'Oh, well, don't bother talking like this.' And I said, no, I was going to, and then I said uh—well, I had always gotten the impression, I think, from him that he felt it was. And he said, no, he didn't; he thought that I had a lot of impressions about things that he thought [which] he didn't have. And I asked him if he—'Do you want me to go out on dates? Do you want me to get married?' and he said, 'Yes, of course I want you to do all those things.' And uh—then I said, 'Well, Dad, do you object to the fact that I've had love affairs with men?' He said, 'Well, one thing at a time. You're in school now and don't bother with love affairs.' And I realized then that he thought that I meant by that just going together and being serious about getting married. And he said, 'Never mind about being uh—being serious about someone.' And I said to him, 'Well, I am serious and I have been.' And he said, 'Well, never mind about that. One thing at a time. If those fellows want to get married, let 'em—have him come and talk to me.'

"At which time my mother said, 'That isn't done any more.' And then I completely lost my nerve. I uh—I felt as if someone was tightening a band around my head and I was feeling a *great* deal of anxiety. And I wanted very much to tell them what I meant by 'love affairs,' but I started to open my mouth and it just—nothing came out; I couldn't do it. So I sat around a long time and I thought about it and thought about it and thought about it and tried to get up some nerve, and then I called up Jerry, who drove me to my home this week end. I was whining on the phone to him, 'This is all so foolish. I don't want to do this. I'm just hurting my father. You come over and tell him.' He said—I said, 'I don't know what to say to him.' And I said, uh—'This is just some silly experiment and I don't—I don't want to do it.' He said to me, 'Well, you're either going to do it now or in the future—take your choice.' And then I tried to—I—I tried to make him say —make me say to hi—make him say to me that I didn't have to do it. I used every trick I knew. I said, 'This is going to make a big difference in our friendship. I'm liable to feel guilty about a whole lot of things and—and so forth.' But he stuck to his guns and he said, 'You have to tell it, it's better for you.' And he said, 'You want to feel anxiety or do you want to tell them?' And I said, 'I want to feel the anxiety!' And he said, 'Just go in there and tell them!'

"So I want back and—and uh—I said—by that time my father was listening to the radio, and I said uh—'Look, Dad, I don't—I don't think we understand each other by what we mean by love affairs.' And then my nerve was gone again and I started to hem and haw. And I said—and then he said to me, 'Are you talking about intercourse?' And I said, 'Yes, I am.' And he said uh—'Well—' He just sat there for a minute. And I said, 'Yes, Dad, that's exactly what I'm talking about.' But I never said it myself; I couldn't bring myself to do it. I couldn't say, 'Yes, I have had love affairs, including intercourse, with men.' It was he that said it, and I just sat there and agreed with him on the fact that that's what I was talking about. I was very relieved when he said it. And uh—I said, 'You see, Dad, I've gotta make a decision here whether I'm going to feel extreme nervousness or whether I'm going to tell you about these things and—and it's uh—I've made a decision that I'm going to tell you this that I have—that uh—' I don't remember how I worded that—oh, I just went that far and he said, 'Well, that's all right.' He said uh—'Everything in its place

though. You're in school now.' And he said, 'If those—don't let anyone give you a line.' And I said, no, no one had given me a line. My mother said something to the effect of Tom, who is the fellow I used to go with. My dad said, 'Oh, Tom's a liar.' What he meant by that I don't know. Probably he thought that Tom had talked me into this situation and then didn't want to marry me. And I said no, that wasn't true.

"And I said, 'Well, then, you don't reject me on this score.' He said, 'No, I don't.' And then he said, 'I want you to go to school and when you get out of school, make your decisions about anything. Don't do thinking about other things now.' I said, 'Don't you uh—you just told me you didn't care if I went out on dates.' And he said, 'Well, better just go to school now.' By that time I was really feeling physically ill. So I could—I wanted to say more at that point, but I managed to say that I want to make some decisions of my own. And he said, 'Decisions about what?' And then I just regressed into my childlike behavior. I—I started talking to my mother and kidding with her and then later on I told her. I said, 'Well, I do want to make my own decisions; I want to be captain of my own ship or get to the point where I can be.' He said, 'Well, that's all right; that's fine; that's what you should do.' And when I left I felt better than I ever have in a year—a year and a half.

"And yesterday I felt a great deal different. . . . It was just like a miracle how much better I felt. But I didn't, I really didn't think I'd ever make it through towards the—and I—it just kept going through my head what was said about—I kept wanting to leave it at the word love affairs. Maybe he understood and maybe he didn't. And I wa-—I was trying to talk myself into the fact that oh, he probably did. And I realized that he really didn't. And it—it took a great deal for me to go on with it after that. I didn't think I'd make it. That's the first time that I've *ever* said anything to my father, in any sense of the word, about sex. And then to come out with *all* of this and I—I know he felt very strangely.

"I kept thinking after that, after how much better I felt, that maybe lots of things that

Dr. K said were wrong. I just don't feel those things at all. [Pause.] I still feel I have a long way to go; I—but I've—I've certainly developed different—[long pause]. . . .

"But again, I must say, I certainly felt different after Sunday. I felt a great deal relieved. [Long pause.] Oh, I certainly don't feel entirely at ease or entirely confused or unconfused rather, or entirely sure of what I want to do in the future. But I know—this is for sure—that it was a very wise thing for me to do, and I'm certainly very happy that I did it."

As this girl herself realizes, there is still work to be done before she achieves a fully integrated personality; but she has taken a significant step toward recovery and, barring unforeseen events, her progress should now be swift and sure. One case does not, to be sure, prove a theory; but growing experience indicates that by following precepts delineated in the foregoing pages it is possible to achieve in 30 to 70 interviews results which seem to be more satisfactory than those obtained after hundreds of hours of orthodox Freudian analysis (5).

V. SOME CONCLUDING COMMENTS AND REJOINDERS

1. If the conception of neurosis which has been presented in this paper is sound, then the contemporary scene would seem to reflect more of an attempt to devise a theory and a therapy which will be popular with neurotics than to devise a theory and a therapy which will fit facts and produce results. This inference—that the "neurotic fallacy" has been widely accepted in those professions which are most concerned with these matters—may in some measure account for the generally backward nature of both treatment and prevention of personality disorder in our time.

2. Confusion with respect to masculinity and femininity (i.e., the tendency toward "homosexuality," unmanliness, unwomanliness) is a common feature of neurosis. How can this fact be related to the assumption that neurosis is more a matter of faulty and perverted problem-solving by the patient than of mistraining and malconditioning by others? Freudian theory

makes character development contingent upon libidinal development. The present approach puts matters differently. Psychosexual development and orientation are features—one can almost say, by-products—of general character development (4, Chap. 21); and if one sees the neurotic with "homosexual" trends as a person who is trying to avoid full adulthood in the manner appropriate to one's particular sex, as a person who, like Achilles of old, hides from manly duty and danger among the women, active therapeutic movement replaces the slow and questionable results produced by Freudian "analysis" of such problems.

3. It is sometimes inferred that personal consistency demands absolute social conformity, and conformity is assumed to mean an end to "creativity" and "progress." The resolution of this seeming dilemma consists merely of *taking consequences.* One can be as much of a non-conformist or innovator as one wishes and remain mentally healthy, *provided* one does not "cheat," i.e., does not try to have the advantages of conformity and nonconformity simultaneously.

4. How can one hold to a scientific conception of human motivation and behavior and yet see the neurotic as in any way "responsible" for his difficulties? Here we encounter another aspect of the "neurotic fallacy." Neurotics commonly complain of the meaningless and mechanistic nature of human life; they speak of fate and predestination; and they report being haunted by the feeling of helplessness in the face of causal determinism. This is a large issue which will not be settled philosophically or logically in a few words. Clinically, however, the matter is often resolved for all practical purposes by the discovery that the patient has, in the manner of Faust, bartered his sense of freedom to the devil for the dubious comfort of feeling no responsibility, no guilt. As many writers, especially older writers such as Kierke-gaard, have pointed out, to be free is to be responsible, capable of guilt. To the extent that our professional efforts are directed toward banishing guilt, not in the sense of helping the patient become guiltless but in the sense of diminishing his capacity for guilt, may we not be leading him further into the kind of help-

lessness, isolation and enslavement of which the neurotic so often complains?

5. We are beginning to hear a good deal about the implications of "information" or "communication" theory for mental disorder and health. Mind, we are told, is a system, an organization which is built and depends upon communication, particularly communication of the feedback or "servo" variety. In both deception and dissociation there is a distortion, as impairment of "communication." As Professor Deutsch (1) has observed, there is a loss of "openness." If mind is so composed, small wonder, then that in neurosis the patient feels he is "losing his mind." More literally, he is destroying it, destroying it, paradoxically enough, in an attempt to preserve it; i.e., he is trying to eliminate contradiction and strain within himself; but he does so, not integratively, communicatively, constructively, but by "cutting connections." The neurotic, in the interest of easy solution and avoiding consequences, first cuts "connections" between himself and other persons (evasion, duplicity); and when there is self-reproach on this account, he then begins to deny, dissociate, cut off from the main body of the self-system those segments which are producing undesirable internal consequences. "Thou shalt not bear false witness" and "Know thyself," *know*, acknowledge, communicate with yourself, may yet guide us to surer ground in our quest for psychological healing and wholeness (7).

REFERENCES

1. DEUTSCH, K. M. Communication theory and social science, *American Journal of Orthopsychiatry*, 1952, 22, 469–483.
2. FREUD, S. *The problem of anxiety.* New York: Norton, 1936.
3. MOWRER, O. H. Learning theory and the neurotic paradox, *American Journal of Orthopsychiatry*, 1948, *18*, 571–610.
4. MOWRER, O. H. *Learning theory and personality dynamics.* New York: Ronald Press, 1950.
5. MOWRER, O. H. Neurosis: A Disorder of Conditioning or Problem Solving?" In E. J. Kempf (Ed.), *Comparative Conditioned Neuroses in Human and Other Animals* (in press).
6. MOWRER, O. H. (Ed.). *Theory and research in psychotherapy.* New York: Ronald Press (in press).
7. MOWRER, O. H. Neurosis and its treatment as learning phenomena. In D. Brower and L. B. Abt (Eds.), *Progress in clinical psychology.* New York: Grune & Stratton, 1952.
8. MOWRER, O. H. *A note on methodology and interpretation in certain types of animal experimentation* (in preparation).
9. PRESTON, G. H. *Psychiatry for the curious.* New York: Rinehart, 1940.

16.

ABRAHAM H. MASLOW

NEUROSIS AS A FAILURE OF PERSONAL GROWTH

. . . The frame of reference which all in this symposium have taken for granted considers the neurosis to be, from *one* aspect, a describable, pathological state of affairs which presently exists, a kind of disease or sickness or illness, on the medical model. But we have learned to see it also in a dialectical fashion, as simultaneously a kind of moving forward, a clumsy groping forward toward health and toward fullest humanness, in a kind of timid and weak way, under the aegis of fear rather than of courage, and *now* involving the future as well as the present.

From Abraham H. Maslow,"Neurosis as a failure of personal growth." *Humanitas*, 1967, *3*, 153–169. Institute of Man symposium on *Neurosis and Personal Growth*, November 18, 1966. Reprinted by permission.

All the evidence that we have (mostly clinical evidence, but already some other kinds of research evidence) indicates that it is reasonable to assume in practically every human being, and certainly in almost every newborn baby, that there is an active will toward health, an impulse toward growth, or toward the actualization of human potentialities. But at once we are confronted with the very saddening realization that so few people make it. Only a small proportion of the human population gets to the point of identity, or of selfhood, full humanness, self-actualization, etc., even in a society like ours which is relatively one of the most fortunate on the face of the earth. This is our great paradox. We all have the impulse towards full development of humanness. Then why is it that it does not happen more often? What blocks it?

This is our new way of approaching the problem of humanness, i.e., with an appreciation of its high possibilities and simultaneously, a deep disappointment that these possibilities are so infrequently actualized. This attitude contrasts with the "realistic" acceptance of whatever happens to be the case, and then of regarding that as the norm, as, for instance, Kinsey did, and as the TV pollsters do today. We tend then to get into the situation that Dr. Barton pointed out to us this morning in which normalcy from the descriptive point of view, from the value-free science point of view—that this normalcy or averageness is the best we can expect, and that therefore we should be content with it. From the point of view that I have outlined, normalcy would be rather the kind of sickness or crippling or stunting that we share with everybody else and therefore don't notice. I remember an old textbook of abnormal psychology that I used when I was an undergraduate, which was an awful book, but which had a wonderful frontispiece. The lower half was a picture of a line of babies, pink, sweet, delightful, innocent, lovable. Above that was a picture of a lot of passengers in a subway train, glum, grey, sullen, sour. The caption underneath was very simply, "What happened?" This is what I'm talking about.

In studying healthy people, self-actualizing people, etc., there has been a steady move from the openly normative and the frankly personal, step by step, toward more descriptive, objective words, to the point at which there is today a standardized test of self-actualization (16). Self-actualization can now be defined quite operationally, as intelligence used to be defined, i.e., self-actualization is what that test tests. It correlates well with external variables of various kinds, and keeps on accumulating additional correlational meanings. As a result, I feel heuristically justified in *starting* with my "determined naivete." Most of what I was able to see intuitively, directly, personally is being confirmed now with numbers and tables and curves.

FULL-HUMANNESS AND FUSION-WORDS

I would like to suggest a further step toward the fusion-word "fully-human," a concept which is still more descriptive and objective (than the concept "self-actualization") and yet retains everything that we need of normativeness. This is in the hope of moving from intuitive heuristic beginnings toward more certainty, greater reliability, more and more external validation, which in turn means more scientific and theoretical usefulness of this concept. This phrasing and this way of thinking was suggested to me about fifteen or so years ago by the axiological writings of Robert Hartman (3) who defined "good" as the degree to which an object fulfills its definition or concept. This suggested to me that the conception of humanness might be made, for research purposes, into a kind of quantitative concept. For instance, full humanness can be defined in a cataloguing fashion, i.e., full humanness is the ability to abstract, to have a grammatical language, to be able to love, to have values of a particular kind, to transcend the self, etc., etc., etc. The complete cataloguing definition could even be made into a kind of check list.

We might shudder a little at this thought, but it could be very useful if only to make the theoretical point for the researching scientist that the concept *can* be descriptive and quantitative—and yet also normative, i.e., this person is closer to full humanness than that other person. Or we could even say: This person is *more* human than that one. This is a fusion-word in the sense that I have mentioned above; it is really objectively descriptive because it has nothing to do with my wishes and tastes, my personality, my neuroses. Moreover, my unconscious wishes or fears, anxieties or hopes are far more easily excluded from the conception of full humanness than they are from the conception of psychological health.

If you ever work with the concept of psychological health—or any other kind of health, or normality—you will discover what a temptation it is to project your own values and to make it into a self-description or perhaps a description of what you would like to be, or what you think people *should* be like. You'll have to fight against it all the time, and you'll discover that, while it is *possible* to be objective in such work, it is certainly difficult. And even then, you cannot be really sure. Have you fallen into sampling error? After all, if you select persons for investigation on the basis of your personal judgment and diagnosis, such sampling errors are more likely than if you select by some more impersonal criterion (6).

Clearly, fusion-words are a scientific advance over more purely normative words, while also avoiding the trap of believing that science *must* be *only* value-free, and non-normative, i.e., non-human. Fusion-concepts and words permit us to participate in the normal advance of science and knowledge from its phenomenological and experiential beginnings on toward greater reliability, greater validity, greater confidence, greater exactness, greater sharing with others and agreement with them (11).

Other obvious fusion-words are: problem, task, duty, mature, evolved, developed, stunted, crippled, fully-functioning, graceful, awkward, clumsy, and the like. There are many more words which are less obviously fusions of the normative and the descriptive. One day we may even have to get used to thinking of fusion-words as paradigmatic, as normal, usual and central. Then the more purely descriptive words and the more purely normative words would be thought of as peripheral and excep-

tional. I believe that this will come as part of the new humanistic Weltanschauung which is now rapidly crystallizing into a structured form.[1]

HUMAN DIMINUTION

One consequence of the usage of "full-humanness" rather than "psychological health" is the corresponding or parallel use of "human diminution," instead of "neurosis," which is a totally obsolete word anyway. Here the key concept is the loss or not-yet-actualization of human capacities and possibilities, and obviously this is also a matter of degree and quantity. Furthermore, it is closer to being externally observable, i.e., behavioral, which of course makes it easier to investigate than, for example, anxiety or compulsiveness or repression. Also it places on the same continuum all the standard psychiatric categories, all the stuntings, cripplings and inhibitions that come from poverty, exploitation, maleducation, enslavement, etc., and also the newer value pathologies, existential disorders, character disorders that come to the economically privileged. It handles very nicely the diminutions that result from drug-addiction, psychopathy, authoritarianism, criminality, and other categories that cannot be called "illness" in the same medical sense as, for example, brain tumor.

This is a radical move away from the medical model, a move which is long overdue. Strictly speaking, neurosis means an illness of the nerves, a relic we can very well do without today. In addition, using the label "psychological illness" puts neurosis into the same universe of discourse as ulcers, lesions, bacterial invasions, broken bones, or tumors. By now, we have learned very well that it is better to consider neurosis as related rather to spiritual disorders, to loss of meaning, to doubts about the goals of life, to grief and anger over a lost love, to seeing life in a different way, to loss of courage or of hope, to despair over the future, to

---

[1] I consider the "degree of humanness" concept to be more useful also than the concepts of "social competence," "human effectiveness" and similar notions.

dislike for oneself, to recognition that one's life is being wasted, or that there is no possibility of joy or love, etc., etc.

These are all fallings away from full-humanness, from the full blooming of human nature. They are losses of human possibility, of what might have been and could perhaps yet be. Physical and chemical hygiene and prophylaxes certainly have some place in this realm of psychopathogenesis, but are nothing in comparison with the far more powerful role of social, economic, political, religious, educational, philosophical, axiological and familial determinants.

SUBJECTIVE BIOLOGY

There are still other important advantages to be gained from moving over to this psychological-philosophical-educational-spiritual usage. Not the least of these, it seems to me, is that it encourages the *proper* conceptual use of the biological and constitutional base which underlies any discussion of Identity or of The Real Self, of growth, of uncovering therapy, of full-humanness or of diminution of humanness, of self-transcendence, or any version of these. Briefly, I believe that helping a person to move toward full-humanness proceeds inevitably via awareness of one's identity (among other things). A very important part of this task is to become aware of what one *is*, biologically, temperamentally, constitutionally, as a member of a species, of one's capacities, desires, needs, and also of one's vocation, what one is fitted for, what one's destiny is.

To put it bluntly and unequivocally, one absolutely necessary aspect of this self-awareness is a kind of phenomenology of one's own inner biology, of that which I have called instinctoid (10), of one's animality and specieshood. This is certainly what psychoanalysis tries to do, i.e., to help one to become conscious of one's animal urges, needs, tensions, depressions, tastes, anxieties. So also for Horney's distinction between a real self and a pseudo-self. Is this also not a subjective discrimination of what one truly is? And what *is* one truly if not first and foremost one's own

body, one's own constitution, one's own functioning, one's own specieshood? (I have very much enjoyed *qua theorist*, this pretty integration of Freud, Goldstein, Sheldon, Horney, Cattell, Frankl, May, Rogers, Murray, *et al.* Perhaps even Skinner could be coaxed into this diverse company, since I suspect that a listing of all his "intrinsic reinforcers" for his human subjects might very well look much like the "hierarchy of instinctoid basic needs and metaneeds" that I have proposed!)

I believe it is possible to carry through this paradigm even at the very highest levels of personal development, where one transcends one's own personality (9). I hope to make a good case soon for accepting the probable instinctoid character of one's highest values, i.e., of what might be called the spiritual or philosophical life (12). Even this personally discovered axiology I feel can be subsumed under this category of "phenomenology of one's own instinctoid nature" or of "subjective biology" or "experiential biology" or some such phrase.

Think of the great theoretical and scientific advantages of placing on one single continuum of degree or amount of humanness, not only all the kinds of sickness the psychiatrists talk about but also all the additional kinds that existentialists and philosophers and religious thinkers and social reformers have worried about. Not only this, but we can also place on the same single scale all the various degrees and kinds of *health* that we know about, plus even the health-beyond-health of self-transcendence, of mystical fusion, and whatever still higher possibilities of human nature the future may yet disclose.

INNER SIGNALS

Thinking in this way has had for me at least the one special advantage of directing my attention sharply to what I called at first "the impulse voices" but which could be called more generally something like the "inner signals" (or cues or stimuli). I had not realized sufficiently that in most neuroses, and in many other disturbances as well, the inner signals become weak or even disappear entirely (as in the severely obsessional person) and/or are not "heard" or *cannot* be heard. At the extreme we have the experientially-empty person, the zombie, the one with empty insides. Recovering the self *must*, as a *sine qua non*, include the recovery of the ability to have and to cognize these inner signals, to know what and whom one likes and dislikes, what is enjoyable and what is not, when to eat and when not to (Schachter), when to sleep, when to urinate, when to rest.

The experientially-empty person, lacking these directives from within, these voices of the real self, must turn to outer cues for guidance, for instance eating when the clock tells him to, rather than obeying his appetite (he has none). He guides himself by clocks, rules, calendars, schedules, agenda, and by hints and cues from other people.

In any case, I trust that the particular sense in which I suggest interpreting the neurosis as a failure of personal growth must be clear by now. It is a falling short of what one could have been, and even one could say, of what one *should* have been, biologically speaking, that is, if one had grown and developed in an unimpeded way. Human and personal possibilities have been lost. The world has been narrowed, and so has consciousness. Capacities have been inhibited. I think for instance of the fine pianist who couldn't play before an audience of more than a few, or the phobic who is forced to avoid heights or crowds. The person who can't study, or who can't sleep, or who can't eat many foods has been diminished as surely as the one who has been blinded. The cognitive losses, the lost pleasures, joys, and ecstasies, the loss of competence, the inability to relax, the weakening of will, the fear of responsibility —all these are diminutions of humanness.

I have mentioned some of the advantages of replacing the concepts of psychological illness and health with the more pragmatic, public and quantitative concept of full or diminished humanness, which I believe is also biologically and philosophically sounder. But before I move on, I would like to note also that diminution can, of course, be either reversible or irreversible, for example, we feel far less hopeful about

the paranoid person than we do about say a nice, lovable hysterical. And, of course, diminution is also dynamic, in the Freudian style. The original Freudian schema spoke of an intrinsic dialectic between the impulse and the defenses against this impulse. In this same sense, diminution leads to consequences and processes. It is only rarely a completion or a finality in a simple descriptive way. In most people these losses lead not only to all sorts of defensive processes which have been well described by Freudian and other psychoanalytic groups, for instance, to repression, denial, conflict, etc. They also lead to coping responses as I stressed long ago (13).

Conflict itself is of course a sign of relative health, as you would know if you ever met really apathetic people, hopeless people, people who have given up hoping, striving and coping. Neurosis is by contrast a very hopeful kind of thing. It means that a man who is frightened, who does not trust himself, who has a low self-image, etc., reaches out for the human heritage and for the basic gratifications to which every human being has a right, simply by virtue of being human. You might say it's a kind of *timid* and ineffectual striving toward self-actualization, toward full humanness.

Diminution can of course be reversible. Very frequently, simply supplying the need gratifications can solve the problem, especially in children. For a child who has not been loved enough, obviously the treatment of first choice is to love him to death, to just slop it all over him. Clinical and general human experience is that it works—I don't have any statistics, but I would suspect nine out of ten times. So is respect a wonderful medicine for counteracting a feeling of worthlessness. Which of course brings up the obvious conclusion that, if "health and illness" on the medical model are seen as obsolete, so also must the medical concepts of "treatment" and "cure" and the authoritative doctor be discarded and replaced.

THE JONAH SYNDROME

In the little time I have left, I would like to turn to one of the many reasons for what Angyal (1) called the evasion of growth. Certainly everybody in this room would like to be better than he is. All of us have an impulse to improve ourselves, an impulse toward actualizing more of our potentialities, toward self-actualization, or full humanness, or human fulfillment, or whatever term you like. Granted this for everybody here, then what holds us up? What blocks us?

One such defense against growth, which I'd like to speak about especially because it hasn't received much notice, I shall call the Jonah syndrome.

In my own notes I had at first labelled this defense the "fear of one's own greatness" or the "evasion of one's destiny" or the "running away from one's best talents." I had wanted to stress as bluntly and sharply as I could the non-Freudian point that we fear our best as well as our worst, even though in different ways. It is certainly possible for most of us to be greater than we are in actuality. We all have unused potentialities or not fully developed ones. It is certainly true that many of us evade our constitutionally suggested vocations (call, destiny, task in life, mission). So often we run away from the responsibilities dictated (or rather suggested) by nature, by fate, even sometimes by accident, just as Jonah tried —in vain—to run away from *his* fate.

We fear our highest possibilities (as well as our lowest ones). We are generally afraid to become that which we can glimpse in our most perfect moments, under the most perfect conditions, under conditions of greatest courage. We enjoy and even thrill to the godlike possibilities we see in ourselves in such peak moments. And yet we simultaneously shiver with weakness, awe and fear before these very possibilities.

I have found it easy enough to demonstrate this to my students simply by asking, "Which of you in this class hopes to write the great American novel, or to be a Senator, or Governor, or President? Who wants to be Secretary-General of the United Nations? Or a great composer? Who aspires to be a saint, like Schweitzer, perhaps? Who among you will be a great leader?" Generally everybody starts giggling, blushing, and squirming until I ask, "If not you, then who else?" Which of course is the truth. And in this same way, as I push my graduate students toward these higher levels of aspiration, I'll say, "What great book are you now secretly planning to write?" And then they often blush and stammer and push me off in some way. But why should I not ask that question? Who else will write the books on psychology except psychologists? So I can ask, "Do you not plan to be a psychologist?" "Well, yes." "Are you in training to be a mute or an inactive psychologist? What's the advantage of that? That's not a good path to self-actualization. No, you must want to be a first-class psychologist, meaning the best, the very best you are capable of becoming. If you deliberately plan to be less than you are capable of being, then I warn you that you'll be deeply unhappy for the rest of your life. You will be evading your own capacities, your own possibilities."

Not only are we ambivalent about our own highest possibilities. We are also in a perpetual and I think universal—perhaps even *necessary*—conflict and ambivalence over these same highest possibilities in other people, and in human nature in general. Certainly we love and admire good men, saints, honest, virtuous, clean men. But could anybody who has looked into the depths of human nature fail to be aware of our mixed and often hostile feelings toward saintly men? Or toward very beautiful women or men? Or toward great creators? Or toward our intellectual geniuses? It is not necessary to be a psychotherapist to see this phenomenon—let us call it "counter-valuing." Any reading of history will turn up plenty of examples, or perhaps I could even say that any such historical search might fail to turn up a single exception throughout the whole history of mankind. We surely love and admire all the persons who have incarnated the true, the good, the beautiful, the just, the perfect, the ultimately successful. And yet they also make us uneasy, anxious, confused, perhaps a little jealous or envious, a little inferior, clumsy. They usually make us lose our aplomb, our self-possession and self-regard. (Nietzsche is still our best teacher here.)

Here we have a first clue. My impression so far is that the greatest people, simply by their presence and by being what they are, make us feel aware of our lesser worth, whether or not they intend to. If this is an unconscious effect, and we are not aware of why we feel stupid or ugly or inferior whenever such a person turns up, we are apt to respond with projection, i.e., we react as if he were *trying* to make us feel inferior, as if we were the target (5). Hostility is then an understandable consequence. It looks to me so far as if conscious awareness tends to fend off this hostility. That is, if you are willing to attempt self-awareness and self-analysis of your *own* counter-valuing, i.e., of your unconscious fear and hatred of true, good, beautiful people, you will most likely be less nasty to them. I am willing also to extrapolate the guess that if you can learn to love more purely the highest values in others, this might make you love these qualities in yourself in a less frightened way.

Allied to this dynamic is the awe before the highest, of which Rudolf Otto (15) has given us the classical description. Putting this together with Eliade's insights (2) into sacralization and desacralization, we become more aware of the universality of the fear of direct confrontation with a god or with the godlike. In some religions death is the inevitable consequence. Most preliterate societies also have places or objects that are taboo because they are too sacred and *therefore too dangerous*. In the last chapter of my *Psychology of Science* (11), I have also given examples mostly from science and medicine of desacralizing and re-sacralizing and tried to explain the psychodynamics of these processes. Mostly it comes down to awe before the highest and best (I want to stress that this awe is intrinsic, justified, *right,* suitable, rather than some sickness or failing to get "cured of").

But here again my feeling is that this awe and fear need not be negative alone, need not be something to make us flee or cower. These are also desirable and enjoyable feelings capable of bringing us even to the point of highest ecstasy and rapture. Conscious awareness, insight and "working through," à la Freud, is the answer here too I think. This is the best path I know to the acceptance of our highest powers, and whatever elements of greatness or goodness or wisdom or talent we may have concealed or evaded.

A helpful sidelight for me has come from trying to understand why peak-experiences are ordinarily transient and brief (7). The answer becomes clearer and clearer. *We are just not strong enough to endure more!* It is just too shaking and wearing. So often people in such ecstatic moments say, "It's too much," or "I can't stand it," or "I could die." And as I get the descriptions, I sometimes feel, "Yes, they *could* die." Delirious happiness cannot be borne for long. Our organisms are just too weak for any large doses of greatness, just as they would be too weak to endure hour-long sexual orgasms, for example.

The word "peak-experience" is more appropriate than I realized at first. The acute emotion must be climactic and momentary and it *must* give way to nonecstatic serenity, calmer happiness, and the intrinsic pleasures of clear, contemplative cognition of the highest goods. The climactic emotion can not endure, but B-Cognition *can* (9, 11).

Does this not help us to understand our Jonah syndrome? It is partly a justified fear of being torn apart, of losing control, of being shattered and disintegrated, even of being killed by the experience. Great emotions after all can in *fact* overwhelm us. The fear of surrendering to such an experience, a fear which reminds us of all the parallel fears found in sexual frigidity, can be understood better I think through familiarity with the literature of psychodynamics and depth psychology, and of the psychophysiology and medical psychomatics of emotion.

There is still another psychological process that I have run across in my explorations of failure to actualize the self. This evasion of growth can also be set in motion by a fear of paranoia. Of course this has been said in more universal ways. Promethean and Faustian legends are found in practically any culture. For instance, the Greeks called it the fear of *hubris*. It has been called "sinful pride," which is of course a permanent human problem. The person who says to himself, "Yes, I will be a great philosopher and I will rewrite Plato and do it better," must sooner or later be struck dumb by his grandiosity, his arrogance. And especially in his weaker moments, will say to himself, "Who? Me?" and think of it as a crazy fantasy or even fear it as a delusion. He compares his knowledge of his inner private self, with all its weakness, vacillation, and shortcomings, with the bright, shining, perfect, and faultless image he has of Plato. Then, of course, he will feel presumptuous and grandiose. (What he fails to realize is that Plato, introspecting, must have felt just the same way about himself, but went ahead anyway, overriding his own doubts about self.)

For some people this evasion of one's own growth, setting low levels of aspiration, the fear of doing what one is capable of doing, voluntary self-crippling, pseudo-stupidity, mock-humility are in fact defenses against grandiosity, arrogance, sinful pride, hubris. There are people who cannot manage that graceful integration between humility and pride which is absolutely necessary for creative work. To invent or create you must have the "arrogance of creativeness" which so many investigators have noticed. But, of course, if you have *only* the arrogance without humility, then you are in fact paranoid. You *must* be aware not only of the godlike possibilities within, but also of the existential human limitations. You must be able simultaneously to laugh at yourself and at all human pretensions. If you can be amused by the worm trying to be a god (17), then in fact you may be able to go on trying and being arrogant without fearing paranoia or bringing down upon yourself the evil eye. This is a good technique.

May I mention one more such technique that I saw at its best in Aldous Huxley, who was certainly a great man in the sense I have been discussing, one who was able to accept his talents and use them to the full. He managed it by perpetually marvelling at how interesting and fascinating everything was, by wondering like a youngster at how miraculous things are, by saying frequently, "Extraordinary! Extraor-

inary!" He could look out at the world with wide eyes, with unabashed innocence, awe and fascination, which is a kind of admission of smallness, a form of humility, and then proceed calmly and unafraid to the great tasks he set for himself.

Finally, may I refer you to a paper of mine (8) relevant in itself, but also as the first in a possible series. Its name, "The need to know and the fear of knowing," illustrates well what I want to say about *each* of the intrinsic or ultimate values that I call Values of Being (B-Values). I am trying to say that these ultimate values, which I think are also the highest needs (or metaneeds, as I'm calling them (12) in a forthcoming publication) fall, like all basic needs, into the basic Freudian schema of impulse *and* defense against that impulse. Thus it is certainly demonstrable that we need the truth and love and seek it. And yet it is just as easy to demonstrate that we are also simultaneously *afraid* to know the truth. For instance, certain truths carry automatic responsibilities which may be anxiety-producing. One way to evade the responsibility and the anxiety is simply to evade consciousness of the truth.

I predict that we will find a similar dialectic for each of the intrinsic Values of Being, and I have vaguely thought of doing a series of papers on, for example, "The love of beauty and our uneasiness with it," "Our love of the good man and our irritation with him," "Our search for excellence and our tendency to destroy it." Of course these counter-values are stronger in neurotic people, but it looks to me as if all of us must make our peace with these mean impulses within ourselves. And my impression so far is that the best way to do this is to transmute envy, jealousy, *ressentiment,* and nastiness into humble admiration, gratitude, appreciation, adoration, and even worship via conscious insight and working through (14). This is the road to feeling small and weak and unworthy and *accepting* these feelings instead of needing to protect a spuriously high self-esteem by striking out (4).

Again I think it is obvious that understanding this basic existential problem should help us to embrace the B-Values not only in others, but also in ourselves, thereby helping to resolve the Jonah syndrome.

REFERENCES

1. ANGYAL, A. *Neurosis and treatment: A holistic theory.* New York: Wiley, 1965.
2. ELIADE, M. *The sacred and the profane.* New York: Harper & Row, 1961.
3. HARTMAN, R. The science of value. In A. H. Maslow, *New knowledge in human values.* New York: Harper & Row, 1959.
4. HORNEY, K. *Neurosis and human growth.* New York: W. W. Norton, 1950.
5. HUXLEY, L. *You are not the target.* New York: Farrar, Straus & Co., 1963.
6. MASLOW, A. H. Some frontier problems in mental health. In A. Combs (Ed.), *Personality theory and counseling practice.* Gainesville, Fla.: University of Florida Press, 1961.
7. MASLOW, A. H. Lessons from the peak-experiences, *Journal of Humanistic Psychology,* 1962, 2, 9–18.
8. MASLOW, A. H. The need to know and the fear of knowing, *Journal of General Psychology,* 1963, 68, 111–125.
9. MASLOW, A. H. *Religions, values, and peak-experiences.* Columbus, Ohio: Ohio State University Press, 1964.
10. MASLOW, A. H. Criteria for judging needs to be instinctoid. In M. R. Jones (Ed.), *Human motivation: A symposium.* Lincoln, Nebr.: University of Nebraska Press, 1965, pp. 33–47.
11. MASLOW, A. H. *The psychology of science: A reconnaissance.* New York: Harper & Row, 1966.
12. MASLOW, A. H. A theory of metamotivation: The biological rooting of the value-life. *Journal of Humanistic Psychology,* 1967, in press.
13. MASLOW, A. H., & MITTLEMAN, B. *Principles of abnormal psychology.* New York: Harper & Row, 1941.
14. MASLOW, A. H., RAND, H., & NEWMAN, S. Some parallels between the dominance and sexual behavior of monkeys and the fantasies of patients in psychotherapy, *Journal of Nervous & Mental Disease,* 1960, 131, 202–212.
15. OTTO, R. *The idea of the holy.* London: Oxford University Press, 1958.
16. SHOSTROM, E. Personal orientation inventory (POI). Educational and Industrial Testing Service, 1963.
17. WILSON, C. *The stature of man.* Boston: Houghton Mifflin, 1959.

17.

SALVATORE R. MADDI

EXISTENTIAL NEUROSIS

This is an attempt to clarify existential literature by distinguishing among the relevant behavioral manifestations those that are psychopathological and those that signify mental health. Existential neurosis emerges as chronic meaninglessness, apathy, and aimlessness. The premorbid identity out of which this neurosis may come involves definition of self as nothing more than an embodiment of biological needs and a player of social roles. The premorbid identity can be undermined, producing existential neurosis, by stresses such as threat of imminent death, social upheaval, and acute awareness of superficiality. Discussion of the premorbid identity leads to postulation of the ideal identity as expressive of not only the biological and social sides of man,

From Salvatore R. Maddi, "The existential neurosis," *Journal of Abnormal Psychology,* 72, 1967, 311–325. © 1967 by the American Psychological Association, and reproduced by permission.

but the psychological side as well. The psychological side includes symbolization, imagination, and judgment. Developmental hypotheses for premorbid and ideal identities are presented, and general implications of the position are discussed.

Social critics, philosophers, sociologists, and psychotherapists are raising the cry that alienation and the problems of existence form the sickness of our times. Even though a significant proportion of the statements has been vague and polemical, more and more people are hanging on every word. I do not think this is merely the new fad. There is too much insistence and desperation in people's attempts to understand the commentaries that have been made in some terms that will make a difference in their lives.

It is too hard to overlook the evidence that people seeking psychotherapy do so in ever increasing numbers because they are deeply dissatisfied with the nature and bases of their living. It is too obvious that even those who do not seek psychotherapy often feel alone and empty.

* * *

A MODEL FOR NEUROSIS

At the outset we need a model for neurosis that can serve as a heuristic device, a thread of Ariadne, lest we lose our way in the labyrinth of words that has been created. The model I suggest we adopt represents fairly standard thinking in the area, happily enough. It starts with the notion of a neurosis as a set of symptoms that can be distinguished not only from mental health but also from other psychopathological states. So the hysterical neurosis, for example, can be described as a set of cognitive and motor symptoms that are absent not only in the healthy state, but also in other classes of illness, like psychosis, and other neuroses, like obsessive-compulsiveness. When we discuss the existential neurosis, then, we will be searching for a set of relevant symptoms that are clearly different both from whatever we consider to be mental health and from other forms of psychopathology.

Further, the model distinguishes between the neurosis itself and the premorbid personality out of which the neurosis may come through a process of breakdown. For example, if you are working within a psychoanalytic framework, you would say that the obsessive-compulsive neurosis represents the breakdown of the anal character type. While the anal character type bears some strong resemblances to the obsessive-compulsive neurosis (e.g., the reliance upon defense mechanisms of intellectualization, isolation, and undoing), the latter includes symptoms (e.g., obsessions and compulsions) that are considered pathological and that appear in only minimal form in the former. The premorbid personality is within the category of normality, though like the neurosis it can be distinguished from other types of premorbid personality. As there is an anal character type, so also are

there phallic and oral character types. The differences between the premorbid personalities define predispositions to different kinds of neuroses. The significance of all this for discussion of the existential neurosis is that we will want to define a premorbid personality for which the neurosis itself is a believable breakdown product.

Premorbid personalities define predispositions to particular neurotic manifestations because they incorporate invulnerabilities to particular kinds of stress. The next aspect of the model, stress, is best considered to be something objectively describable, whether originating inside or outside the person, that represents a comprehensive enough threat to the personality to disrupt the premorbid balance or adjustment. Obviously, stress has to be defined with the characteristics of premorbid personality in mind. Loss of a strong loved one may be especially stressful to the person with an oral character, because in that character satisfaction of dependency is especially important for adequate functioning. Stress can be a sudden occurrence, or an accumulation of undermining events, as long as what is called stress is reasonably specifiable.

The model states that neurosis is some joint function of premorbidity and stress. Without attempting to state the exact nature of the function, some facets of the relationship are apparent. If there is zero stress, there should be no neurosis. Further, the amount of stress necessary to precipitate a neurosis should depend upon the intensity of the vulnerability constituted by the premorbid characteristics. But it should be kept in mind that the stress must match the nature of the vulnerability if undermining of the premorbid adjustment is to be possible. In considering the existential neurosis, I will try to identify the kinds of stress that are relevant, though it will be very difficult to make any qualitative statements about how much stress is too much.

Any model which involves the notion of premorbidity, or that which predisposes to illness, also involves the notion of what the ideal personality would be. What I am saying is not very mysterious or new. In psychoanalytic thinking, the ideal is genital personality, whereas in

Rogerian thinking, the ideal is the fully functioning person. The ideal personality is usually a null class, which nonetheless has the very important theoretical function of permitting specification of what it is about the premorbid personality that predisposes to illness. In discussing the existential neurosis, we should expect to understand at least those aspects of the ideal personality that insure against the likelihood of that disorder. It may, in addition, be possible to gain an even more comprehensive sense than that of what is ideal.

The rest of the model refers to development. There is first ideal development, or that series of early life experiences that culminate in the ideal personality. Second, there is what might be called deviant development—a series of life experiences leading to premorbidity. It should be possible to specify the particular developmental deviancy that accounts for particular premorbid personalities. It will be important in this article to consider the developmental vicissitudes producing the premorbid state out of which the existential neurosis may come, and, in this consideration, a sense of what would be developmentally more ideal will necessarily be gained.

Without a doubt there are vexing questions that can be raised concerning this model. But rather than raise them here, let me encourage you to consider the general outlines of the model as no more than an interesting and plausible heuristic device. In that spirit, let us plunge in.

THE SYMPTOMS CALLED EXISTENTIAL NEUROSIS

Like all neuroses, we should expect the existential neurosis to have cognitive, affective, and actional components. Once we have accepted the heuristic notion that there are existential manifestations some of which are neurotic and some of which are not, we have already begun to find the road to clarity. The cognitive component of the existential neurosis is meaninglessness, or chronic inability to believe in the truth, importance, usefulness, or interest value of any of the things one is engaged in or can imagine doing. The most characteristic features of affective tone are blandness and boredom,

punctuated by periods of depression which become less frequent as the disorder is prolonged. As to the realm of action, activity level may be low to moderate, but more important than amount of activity is the introspective and objectively observable fact that activities are not chosen. There is little selectivity, it being immaterial to the person what if any activities he pursues. If there is any selectivity shown, it is in the direction of ensuring minimal expenditure of effort and decision making.

It is important to recognize that the syndrome described above refers to a chronic state of the organism. I do not refer to stabs of doubt, in the cognitive domain, or occasional indifference and passivity, in the affective and actional domains. Rather, I refer to the settled state of meaninglessness, apathy, and aimlessness, such that contradictory states of commitment, enthusiasm, and activeness are the exception rather than the rule. The temporary state of doubt, though an existential manifestation, is not here defined as part of the existential neurosis. Indeed, doubt is a by-product of vigorous mental health, I shall argue later, no matter how painful it may be.

If my model is to be served, the existential neurosis must be distinguished from other forms of illness. I take it that the obviousness of its difference from such psychotic states as schizophrenia and senile psychosis, such character disorders as homosexuality and psychopathy, and such neuroses as obsessive-compulsiveness and hysteria, is clear without further attention. Of the traditional states of psychopathology, the existential neurosis probably most nearly resembles neurasthenia and depression. It is from these two disorders that distinctions are important. The major difference between neurasthenia and the existential neurosis is that the dreadful lack of energy and somatic decrepitude of the former is not present in the latter. There is certainly listlessness in existential neurosis, but it is not experienced as a primarily somatic disability. In addition, the cognitive state of meaninglessness is virtually absent in neurasthenia.

The distinction between depression and the existential neurosis is harder to make, specifically because the latter state sometimes includes sadness, and usually includes low activity level. But in existential neurosis, depressive affect is the exception rather than the rule, with apathy—an actual absence of strong emotion—being the usual state. Apathy is not typical of depression, though it may occur occasionally in that disorder. In traditional terms, what I am calling the existential neurosis might actually be called depression, but this would involve an unwarranted stretching of the latter concept, taking some such form as inferring depressive affect hidden by defenses such that apathy was the visible resultant. But once we have decided that traditional terminology is not necessarily exhaustive in describing psychopathology, the syndrome I have called the existential neurosis is very likely to emerge as discriminably different from depression.

The way I have defined it, the existential neurosis is characterized by the belief that one's life is meaningless, by the affective tone of apathy and boredom, and by the absence of selectivity in actions. This symptom cluster is, to judge from the writing of many psychotherapists, sociologists, and social critics (e.g., Fromm, 1955; Josephson & Josephson, 1962; May, Angel, & Ellenberger, 1958; Sykes, 1964), rampant in contemporary life. It may seem as if what I am talking about as existential neurosis is much closer to alienation from self, than it is to alienation from society. But on reflection, it should be clear that the existential neurotic would be separated from deep interaction with others as well as from his own personal vitality. Therefore, I find the existential neurotic to be alienated both from self and from society. Indeed, the notions of self-alienation and societal alienation represent little more to me than biases reflecting whether the theorist considers the individual or the group to be the most important unit of analysis.

Nonetheless, it is true that traits sometimes considered under the rubric of alienation are not covered by my definition of the existential neurosis. Such things as anguish, rebelliousness, acute dissatisfaction, and civil disobedience are sometimes considered evidence of alienation. Alienation in such cases is usually taken to be from society and not at all from self. First, I should affirm that such traits are not to be considered part of the existential neurosis. The symptoms of the neurosis all point to a rather comprehensive psychological death, where there is no longer even anguish or anger to remind the person that he is a person, and a very dissatisfied one at that. But what can be said in understanding these traits that I have excluded? Sometimes, what is meant is doubt of the kind that I will later argue is quite healthy. Even when this is not the case, I have difficulty understanding why the traits are considered evidence of alienation in the first place. After all, a person acutely dissatisfied with society, and actively trying to change it through his own actions, is hardly alienated in any important sense. He is accepting the importance of society by the stance that it is worth changing, and feeling perhaps even more powerfully than most of us that he can produce a change. There is little here of the meaninglessness and powerlessness that are supposed to characterize alienation. The person with these traits may well have some psychological malady, but unless his social protest masks an underlying tendency toward meaninglessness, apathy, and aimlessness, the malady bears little relationship to either existential neurosis or what has been called alienation.

The character of Meursault in Camus' (1946) *The Stranger* is a perfect example of the existential neurotic. He frequently says, and even more frequently implies, that he believes life to be meaningless and his activities to be arbitrary. He is virtually always bored and apathetic He never imagines or daydreams. He has no goals. He makes only the most minimal decisions, doing little more than is necessary to keep a simple job as a clerk. He walks in his mother's funeral cortege and makes love to a woman with the same apathy and indifference. He frequently says, "It's all the same to me." His perceptions are banal and colorless. The most difference anything makes is to be mildly irritating. He has this reaction, for example, to the heat of the sun, but then does nothing about it. Although it might seem remarkable that a novel about such a person could have any literary power at all, it is precisely because of the omnipresence of the symptom cluster we have been calling existential neurosis that the reader is intrigued and shocked. When Meursault finally murders a man without any emotional provocation or reaction, without any premeditation or reason, without any greater decision than is involved in resolving to take a walk, the reader is not even surprised. Anything is possible for Meursault, specifically because nothing is anything of importance. His is a vegetative existence that amounts to psychological death. Some writers have called this a state of nonbeing (e.g., May *et al.*, 1958; Sartre, 1956).

THE PREMORBID PERSONALITY

Turning to the premorbid personality out of which the existential neurosis can come through a process of breakdown precipitated by appropriate stress, I find that the concept of central importance is that of *identity*. I define identity in phenomenological terms, as that which you consider yourself to be. Although a person's identity is not necessarily expressed in verbal terms at any given time, it can be so stated if the person reflects upon the question of what he thinks he is. In focusing upon identity, therefore, I am not implying something that is barred from awareness.

Theorists having recourse to this kind of concept of identity or self have frequently considered of importance the discrepancy between one's sense of identity and one's natural potentialities as a human being. In following that lead, I would say that the premorbid personality corresponding to the existential neurosis is one in which the identity includes only some of the things that express the true nature of man. I will not discuss the true nature of man until the section of this paper on the ideal personality. It will suffice for initial purposes to say that the premorbid identity can be considered overly *concrete* and *fragmentary*. These are certainly ideas that are, in one form or another, common enough in the existential literature (e.g., Fromm, 1955; Kierkegaard, 1954; May *et al.*, 1958). But to say this and nothing more is to fall short of the precision really necessary for adequate understanding of the etiology of existential neurosis. We must ask in what ways is the

premorbid identity overly concrete and fragmentary?

The best way to summarize the problem is that the premorbid identity stresses qualities of man that are, among those he has, the ones least unique to him both as opposed to other species and to other men. In other words, the identity is insufficiently humanistic. For our society at this point in time, it is easy to say what an insufficiently humanistic identity looks like. Such an identity leads the person to consider himself to be nothing more than *a player of social roles and an embodiment of biological needs*. I must stress that the difficulty is not so much that man is not these two things, but that what he is in addition to them finds little representation in identity. Considering yourself to be an embodiment of biological needs certainly does not set you apart from other species. Neither does the view of yourself as a player of social roles, for most subhuman species have social differentiation of at least a rudimentary sort. And there is little in either of the two components of identity that permits much sense of difference between individual men, except in the trivial sense that the particular social roles played this moment may be different for me than for you, and the biological needs that I have right now may happen to be different than those you have. But tomorrow, or an hour from now, the situation may change, and we may not even have that small basis for distinguishing ourselves from one another. The overarching fact of life for a person with the premorbid personality I have described is that all men play a small number of social roles and all men embody a few biological needs, and that is that.

Consider what it means to view yourself as a player of social roles. First, you accept the idea that the social system—a set of interrelated institutions operating according to a different group of laws than those that govern individual existence—is a terribly real and important force in living. Second, you believe that the way you presently perceive the social system and have been taught it to be is its real and unchangeable nature. Finally, you consider it not only inevitable, but proper, that you conform to the pressures of the social system. A major aim in life becomes playing the roles that are necessarily yours as well as you can.

Also imagine what it means to consider yourself an embodiment of biological needs. First, you believe that such needs as that for food, water, and sex are terribly important and real forces in living. Second, you are convinced that an important gauge of the adequacy of the life is the degree to which these needs are satisfied. Finally, you believe that any alternative to direct expression of these needs, if an alternative were possible, would be unwise because it would constitute a violation of the true nature of man. All this means that a major aim in life becomes biological survival and satisfaction.

A person who has only these two themes represented in his identity would feel powerless in the face of social pressures from without, and powerless in the face of biological pressures from within. Both social and biological pressures would be considered independent variables, that is, variables that influence the behavior of the person without themselves being influenced by him. Naturally he tries to play his social roles well and to insure physical satisfaction and survival. Indeed, he *is* his social roles and biological needs. In other words, his identity is overly concrete. The goals of serving social roles and biological needs often lead in different, if not incompatible, directions. Generally speaking, the person will try to serve social and biological pressures at different times, or in different places, keeping possible incompatibilities from the eyes of others and from direct confrontation in his own awareness. In other words, this kind of identity is overly fragmentary.

For vividness, consider further the cognitive and affective state of the person with the premorbid personality under discussion. In the cognitive realm, the person would be rather consistently pragmatic and materialistic in his outlook on life. The pragmatism would come primarily from accepting the necessity of playing certain social roles. How often one hears that the world is the way it is, so one might as well be practical about it! The materialism would come primarily from the view that man is an embodiment of biological needs. The pursuit of material things is given the status of a natural

process. How often one hears that narrow self-interest is the only real motivating force outside of society! Superimposed upon the fairly consistent pragmatism and materialism would be more transitory states of fatalism, cynicism, and pessimism. These transitory cognitive states would presumably mirror the moment-to-moment economy of social system and biological rewards and punishments. There is a final implication contained in the premorbid personality that is extremely important. If you consider yourself bound by certain rules of social interaction, on the one hand, and in need of certain material goods for satisfaction and survival, on the other hand, relationships between yourself and other people will be made on contractual grounds, rather than on the grounds of tradition or intimacy. The person with a premorbid personality will tend to look upon relationships as serving some specific social or biological end. His view of relationship will be rather cold-blooded.

Turning to the affective realm, the person with a premorbid identity would tend to worry about such things as whether he is considered by others to be conscientious, whether he is seen to be a nice person, whether he is admired, whether people can guess the animal lusts within him, whether he can satisfy his needs without interfering too much with social role playing. His predominant affective states would be fear and anxiety, and these would be only aggravated by the frequent incompatibility between serving other-directed social aims and self-interested biological aims. The other affective states typical of the premorbid state stem from the continual emphasis upon contractual relationships. Since relationships are defined in terms of limited, specific goals, and in terms of the economic considerations of who is getting what out of interaction, social life will be rather structured and superficial. Contractual relationships are devoid of intimacy, commitment, and spontaneity because of the preemptiveness of role playing and need expression. Thus, important affective states associated with premorbidity would be loneliness and disappointment. On the one hand, the person feels anxious and afraid a good deal of the time, while on the other hand, he feels alone and as if something were missing from his life.

You will have recognized in the discussion of the premorbid personality many of the features common in writings on alienation. There is much in what I have said that is reminiscent of Fromm's (1955) marketing personality and Sartre's (1956) idea of bad faith, to name only two sources. I want to encourage you to think of the premorbid personality not as a sickness in itself, but rather as a predisposition to sickness of an existential sort. What I have described as premorbidity is simply too common and livable to be considered frank neurosis, though it is a state with its own characteristic sufferings and limitations. The premorbid person is still too much enmeshed in the problems of his living, still too much concerned with having a successful life, to be considered existentially neurotic, given the implications of detachment from life included in that idea.

PRECIPITATING STRESS

For the person with a premorbid identity, life may go on in a rather empty, though superficially adequate, way for a long time. He may even be reasonably successful in objective terms, keeping his vague dissatisfactions and anxieties to himself. But he may also be precipitated into an existential neurosis if he encounters stress of the right content and sufficient intensity to be undermining.

The stresses that will be effective are those that have content that strikes at the vulnerabilities inherent in defining yourself as nothing more than a player of social roles and an embodiment of biological needs. The stronger this self-definition the weaker can the stress be and still produce breakdown. In speaking of precipitating stress, I do not mean the things that merely make the person worry. The threat of social censure or biological deprivation are potent sources of concern for the premorbid personality we are discussing, but these things do not ordinarily cause the kind of comprehensive breakdown involved in the existential neurosis. *The stresses that can produce the neurosis are ones that disconfirm the premorbid identity by forcing recognition of its overly concrete, fragmentary, and nonhumanistic nature.*

Three stresses come readily to mind, though there are bound to be others as well. Perhaps the most effective of them is the concrete threat of imminent death. It is my impression that this threat must be to your own life in order to be very effective. Even the threatened death of someone reasonably close to you may not have the force I am about to describe. Perhaps those of you who have faced the threat of death to yourself and to others will know what I mean. If the threat of death actually does lead to death, people with the premorbid identity tend to die *The Death of Ivan Ilyich*, in the great novella by Tolstoi (1960). Ilyich knows he is dying of a horrible disorder, and this colors all his perceptions and judgments. Most of the visitors to his bedside are business associates who, he comes to realize, are only performing what they experience as a distasteful obligation of their social role. Then he realizes that the same thing is true of his own family! None of these people is deeply touched by his drift toward death, for theirs is a contractual rather than intimate relationship to him. And even more horrible, he realizes the appropriateness of their behavior because he too has thought of and experienced them only in contractual superficial terms. The triviality and superficiality of their materialism and social conformity—and his own—are thrown into sharp relief by the threat of death. He becomes acutely aware of his wasted life and can tell himself nothing that will permit a peaceful death. He realizes that he has always felt deprived of intimacy, love, spontaneity, and enthusiasm. By renouncing himself and the people around him, he is finally able to feel truly human and alive just at the point where he dies physically. This story is didactically and literarily powerful because this is a tragic way to die. What bankruptcy when it is death that frees us from the impoverishing shackles of social conformity and biological needs!

If the person with a premorbid identity who is faced with the threat of imminent death should actually recover rather than die he is likely to experience an existential neurosis. Before he dies, Ilyich is certainly a good example of this. If the threat of death disconfirms your previous identity, then you have no identity to work with, and in an adult this is virtually the same as psychological death. The adequacy of recovery from the existential neurosis will be determined by whether the person can use, or be helped to use, the knowledge gained through facing death to build a more comprehensive, abstract, humanistic identity.

The second stress that can precipitate existential neurosis is gross disruption of the social order, through such things as war, conquest, and economic depression, leading to disintegration of social roles and even of the institutionalized mechanisms for satisfying biological needs. Such catastrophe has two effects on people with the premorbid identity. First, it makes it difficult to continue to obtain the usual rewards for playing social roles and expressing biological needs. Second, and more important, disruption of the social order demonstrates the relativity of society to someone who has been treating it as absolute reality. The premorbid person is left without much basis for living and an existential neurosis may well ensue. Thinking along very similar channels, Durkheim (1951) saw social upheaval, or anomie, as a factor increasing suicide rates.

The final stress is difficult to describe because it is less dramatic than threat of death and social upheaval. Not only is this stress less dramatic, but it is usually an accumulation of events rather than something that need happen only once. And yet, this final stress is probably the most usual precipitating factor in the existential neurosis. The stress I mean is the repeated confrontation with the limitation on deep and comprehensive experiencing produced by the premorbid identity. These confrontations usually come about through other people's insistence on pointing out the person's existential failures. The aggressive action of other people is more or less necessary because the person with the premorbid identity usually avoids self-confrontation. But let there be a close relative who is suffering because of the person's premorbidity, and confrontations will be forced.

A good example of this kind of stress and its effects is to be found in Arthur Miller's (1964) *After the Fall*. During the first two-thirds of the play, Quentin discovers that his is what I would call a premorbid identity. The discovery is a terribly painful stress. It begins when his first wife, working up the courage for a separation and divorce, tries, after a long period of docility, to force him to recognize the limitations in their relationship and her deep dissatisfaction with him. In listening to his own attempts to answer her charges, and in considering her attacks, he begins to recognize that his has been little more than a contractual commitment to her. He has been merely conforming to social roles in being husband and father. Under her scrutiny, he begins to recognize his superficial sexuality—a biological need—as well. He feels at fault for his limitations, but can do little about them, instead asking pathetically for understanding. His wife is also important in forcing recognition that his offer to defend his old law professor in court is not out of deep affection, or intimacy, or even loyalty, but rather out of an attempt to convince people that he feels these ways toward this man. Frightened and distraught by what he is learning about himself, Quentin finally begins to envy his wife for her ability to experience deeply and know what she wants.

After the breakup of his first marriage, Quentin moves impulsively into a second. His second wife, Maggie, idealizes him, and he feels reassured about himself, though he has not really changed much. It is only after they have been married for some time that Quentin begins to appreciate Maggie's extraordinary neediness and lack of differentiation as a person. Her adulation of him can no longer serve to reassure him, and to make matters worse, he has new evidence of his superficiality in his inability to reach her in any significant way. He must stand by and let her commit suicide, having decided that the most he can do is to save his own life! Whatever depth of personality could have saved her in a husband, he simply did not have.

After Maggie's death, Quentin spends 2 years or so in a state of meaninglessness, apathy, and aimlessness. He does not work, he does not relate to people, he merely drifts. This period is clearly one of existential neurosis, and can be seen as precipitated by a person's being forced repeatedly to confront the limitations on living produced by social conformity and expression of biological need.

THE IDEAL PERSONALITY

From the discussion of the premorbid personality, it will come as no surprise that the ideal identity from my point of view is abstract, unified, and humanistic.

* * *

First, let us assume that there are three sides to man's nature—social, biological, and psychological. The social side refers to interpersonal relationships, the biological side to physical survival and satisfaction, and the psychological side to mental processes, primarily symbolization, imagination, and judgment. Assume further that all three sides are of equal importance for successful living, and that curtailment of expression of any of them sets up some kind of premorbidity.

When you express your psychological side fully and vigorously, you generate symbols that represent concrete experiences in the general form that makes clear their similarities to and differences from other experiences. You also have an active and uninhibited imagination, which you use as a guide rather than substitute for action. In other words, you let your imagination reveal what you want your life to be, and then attempt to act on that knowledge. The psychological faculty of judgment functions as a check upon the validity of your imagination. When you act upon imagination, you can evaluate the nature of your ensuing experience in order to determine whether it is really what you seem to want. Does the action lead to satisfaction, or is it frightening or boring? Hence the knowledge gained through exercising judgment is also used as a guide to living.

Of the psychological, biological, and social sides of man, it is the psychological side that is most human. All subhuman species have biological requirements for survival and satisfaction, and these requirements are generally acted upon in a straightforward and simple manner. Most subhuman species have patterned social relationships. Indeed, sometimes subhuman society is quite complex and extensive. But even

then it tends to be rigidly organized and characterized by social roleship. Only in man is it reasonable to consider the psychological side of life to be of much importance. Indeed, when social and biological behavior is unusually subtle and complex in man it is because of his most human, or psychological, side.

Let me make my position more vivid by contrasting the lives of people with premorbid and ideal identities. Whereas both premorbid and ideal identities involve expression of the social and biological sides of man, only the ideal identity shows much representation of the psychological side. Because the premorbid person does not have available to him the generalizing, unifying, humanizing effect of psychological expression, encompassing as it does symbolization, imagination, and judgment, he achieves only the most obvious, common, superficial forms of social and biological expression. He accepts social roles as given, tries to play them as well as he can, and sees himself quite literally as the roles he plays. He accepts biological needs as given and acts on them in a way that is isolated and unreflective, however straightforward it may be. The best example of such biological expression is with regard to the sexual need. The premorbid person considers sexuality to be no more than an animalistic urge, and satisfies it as simply as possible, with little consideration of relationship, affection, or even comprehensiveness of attraction. Little wonder that though he seems very social, he frequently feels insecure, lonely, and without intimacy, and that though he seems very active in expressing biological needs, he frequently feels incompletely satisfied. The loneliness and incomplete satisfaction are signs that he is deprived of psychological expression.

As the premorbid person does not rely upon the processes of symbolization, imagination, and judgment, favoring instead the view that life is determined by social and biological considerations, he not only feels powerless to influence his actions, but also does indeed lead an existence that is rather stereotyped and unchanging. As no human being is completely without psychological expression, the premorbid person often has a glimmer of awareness that his life is not what it might be. This accumulated sense of missed opportunity is what May *et al.* (1958, pp. 37–91) have called ontological guilt.

With vigorous psychological expression, would come social and biological living that is more unified, subtle, deep, and rewarding than that I have described above. The person with the ideal identity would not feel powerless in the face of social and biological pressures, because he puts heavy reliance in living on his own processes of symbolization, imagination, and judgment. He would perceive many alternatives to simple role playing and isolated biological satisfaction. Because he sees himself to be the "fountain of power," to use Emerson's excellent phrase, his social and biological living transcend the concrete instance and involve anything that he can imagine and anything that is evaluated by him as worthwhile.

So, if contractual relationships leave him unsatisfied, he can choose to relate otherwise, such as on the basis of shared personal experience. He can even make a start on this by talking with others about his dissatisfaction with merely playing social roles. Once he does this, he will undoubtedly find some people who will be encouraged to share their own feelings of loneliness with him, and the road to more subtle, myriadly rewarding social relations has already been found. If simple, unreflective expression of biological urges leaves him unsatisfied, he can choose to explore other forms of expression. For example, instead of merely seeking food, he can make hunger the basis for more comprehensive satisfaction by cooking especially tasty dishes, or by eating in the company of people with whom he feels intimate. And the same with sex. He can make sexual expression a subtle, complex, changing thing, indulged in with people toward whom he feels intimate and affectionate on other than simply sexual grounds. There will be many more parts to the life of the person with an ideal identity, and the parts will achieve much closer integration than is true for the premorbid person.

One important consequence of reliance upon his imagination and judgment as guides to living is that the ideal person is not a conformist. Some critics of my position would argue that it amounts to advocating the unleashing of monsters on the world. What is to stop a person

from murdering, or robbing, if he feels so free to put his imagination into operation? Psychologists like Rogers (1961) would answer this criticism by contending that there is nothing basic to the organism that would lead in the direction of such monstrosities. As the individual is oriented toward survival, so too does his natural functioning support the survival of his species. One can easily develop an evolutionary argument for this position. Rogers would believe that only an imagination already perverted by psychopathogenic social pressures would lead the person in the direction of terrible aggressions toward his fellow men. I have considerable sympathy for this position, but would like to add to it the notion that judgment is a maturing supplement to imagination. Your imagination might even include the bases for catastrophic action, perhaps at a time when someone has hurt you badly, and still you might not act on the imagination if judgment provided some balance. I sincerely feel that although the ideal person might well make mistakes in life, he will not be a monster simply because he does not conform to the most obvious societal pressures.

It should be remembered that Emerson's (Atkinson, 1940, p. 148) conclusion that "whosoever would be a man must be a nonconformist" is echoed by many of the world's finest thinkers. If a critic responds by claiming that this kind of thinking permits such abominations as Hitler, I would suggest that he was a badly twisted man who showed less imagination than repetitive, compulsive preoccupations, and less judgment than megalomanic overconfidence. It is only by losing the usual standards of what is meant by imagination and judgment that Hitler and the ideal identity can be discussed in the same breath! But a secondary argument could be made that the position I am taking makes it at least possible for some twisted person like Hitler to gain dangerous power because those around him believe enough in imagination and judgment as guides to living that they may not see that he is only a pseudo-example of this in time to do anything about it. This is a terribly weak argument. Indeed, it is much more likely that people who define themselves as social role players and embodiments of biological needs will not recognize or be able to stop a man like Hitler. It is to the point that Hannah Arendt (1964) subtitled her treatise on the enacting of the final solution to the "Jewish problem" *a report on the banality of evil*. To judge from reports, the rank-and-file Germans were simply following rules when they gassed people!

Another consequence of relying upon imagination and judgment as guides to action is that the life of the ideal person will be a frequently changing, unfolding thing. New possibilities will be constantly developing, though it is unlikely that the process of change will be without pattern or continuity. The reliance upon judgment insures that there will be values and principles represented in the personality, and these would be slow to change. But more concrete experiential possibilities would change, presumably in an orderly fashion, due to the abstract view of experience and the play of imagination. The person with an ideal identity would not, then, be beset by boredom or by ontological guilt. Indeed, he would feel emotions deeply and spontaneously, be they pleasant or unpleasant. He would be enthusiastic and committed.

But his life would not be quite that rosy. When you are in a rather continual process of change, you cannot predict what existential outcomes will be. Interestingly enough, we find that doubt (Frankl, 1955), or existential anxiety (May *et al.*, 1958, pp. 37–91) is a necessary concomitant of the ideal identity. When you stop to think about it, it is quite understandable that someone who is his own standard of meaning would be unsure and anxious at times when he was changing.

Looked at in this way, doubt (existential anxiety) is actually a sign of strength, rather than illness. This is precisely what was meant by Camus (1955) when he said, "I cherish my nights of despair," and Tillich (1952) when he designated doubt to be the "god above God." Powerful expression to doubt as an aspect of humanism, and therefore strength, is given by Frankl (1955) when he says:

Challenging the meaning of life can . . . never be taken as a manifestation of morbidity or abnor-mality; it is rather the truest expression of the state of being human, the mark of the most human nature in man. For we can easily imagine highly developed animals or insects—say ants or bees—which in many aspects of their social organization are actually superior to man. But we can never imagine any such creature raising the question of the meaning of its own existence, and thus challenging this existence. It is reserved for man alone to find his very existence questionable, to experience the whole dubiousness of being. More than such faculties as power of speech, conceptual thinking, or walking erect, this factor of doubting the significance of his own existence is what sets man apart from animal [p. 30].

On logical grounds alone, nothing so basic to man's nature as doubt could ever be defined as psychopathological, for to do so would be to call everyone sick by virtue of his true nature. This logical argument is made more psychologically compelling by recognizing that when one is one's own standard of meaning, that will entail accepting and even valuing doubt because it is the necessary concomitant of the uncertainty produced by personal change. To avoid doubt is to avoid change and to give over the power in living to social and biological considerations. This is too big a price to pay for comfort alone. In avoiding the tragedies, you also lose the potentiality of triumphs.

PRECIPITATING STRESS AND THE IDEAL PERSONALITY

If the ideal identity is truly an improvement over the premorbid identity, then the stresses that precipitate breakdown in the latter should be ineffective in the former. You will recall that the three stresses mentioned earlier are the threat of imminent death, social upheaval, and the accumulated sense of failure in living deeply and committedly.

The ideal person would be so actively and enthusiastically enmeshed in living socially, biologically, and psychologically that the therapeutic effect of threat of imminent death would be markedly diminished. You simply do not need the threat of death to remind you to take life seriously and live in the immediate moment, if you are already doing these things. To the ideal person, such a threat could be frightening to some degree, but it would not be helpful. A definite implication of my saying this is the belief that the emphasis on death as what makes life important, which appears in one form or another in so much existential writing, is only of relative importance. Only when you think in terms of premorbidity as the true nature of man and the world, do you celebrate the purifying effects of threat of imminent death.

If the ideal person actually does come to the point of death, he will die a much more graceful death than that of Ivan Ilyich. Death for the ideal person will be no more than a very unfortunate interruption of an intense and gratifying life process. I contend that someone who is living well will more easily face death than someone who senses that he has not even lived at all. In any event, it seems clear that the threat of imminent death will hardly precipitate an existential neurosis in a person with the ideal identity.

*   *   *

Rather than constituting a stress, social upheaval may well be a boon for the person with the real identity.

Finally, there is the matter of an accumulated sense that your life is a failure in terms of depth and committedness of experience. Actually, I am speechless here. It is simply incomprehensible that a person with an ideal identity would ever experience the painful course of self-revelation leading to existential neurosis seen in Arthur Miller's Quentin. The person with an ideal identity will certainly make mistakes, and suffer for them, but will not go for as long as Quentin with no cognizance for his superficiality and attendant frustration, and, hence, will not be in the position of condemning his life.

IDEAL AND DEVIANT DEVELOPMENT

It is natural at this point to raise the question of how ideal and premorbid identities develop. But before launching into considerations of early experience and their effects on later personality, one obviously relevant and thorny problem should be raised. It is the problem of free will.

Some of you may have long since decided that I have left the scientific fold with all this emphasis upon the person himself as the "fountain of power." Does this not mean, you will ask, that according to me man's actions are not determined by anything but his own will? And is this not a view antithetical to science? Let me try to explain why I think what I am saying is quite scientific. *I am explicating the way in which a particular set of beliefs about oneself and the nature of the world can lead to actions that are more varied, active, and changeable than is true when that set of beliefs is absent.* In the psychologist's terms, I am focusing upon proactive and reactive behavior, and attempting to explain the differences between them on the basis of differences in sense of identity. The functioning of the ideal person is well summarized by the concept of proactive behavior, with its emphasis on the person as an influence on his environment. In contrast, reactive behavior, which is influenced by the environment, is very descriptive of the premorbid person. But just because proactive behavior is more varied, flexible, and original is no reason to presume it is not caused in a scientifically specifiable way. In my view, proactive behavior is caused by the characteristics of the ideal personality, namely, the humanistic belief in oneself as the fountain of power, and the associated preparedness to exercise fully the psychological as well as social and biological sides of man. Further, the ideal personality is not a mysterious implant of God, like the concept of soul. The ideal personality, like the premorbid personality, is formed out of early life experiences. I propose to sketch these experiences in the paragraphs that follow. Clearly, my position assumes that all action is determined in a specifiable scientific way. My approach amounts to availing oneself of the value in recognizing that some behavior is active while some is passive without assuming anything about a soul, or divine inspiration, or mysterious freedom.

In developing an ideal identity it certainly helps to start out with a minimum of average intelligence, but once having this, the rest depends upon the parent-child relationship, and the supplementation of this in later relationships that are significant. Even relationship of child to teacher needs to be considered. One route to ideal development is for the person to experience in his relationships with significant people in his life what Rogers (1959) has called unconditional positive regard. This means that the person is appreciated as a human being and knows it. With such appreciation, the person comes to value his own humanness, and is able to act without fear and inhibition from all three sides of himself. But unconditional positive regard is not enough. There must be something better suited to point the young person in particular directions rather than others. The people around him must value symbolization, imagination, and judgment and encourage and support the child when he shows evidence of these psychological processes. But in this, the emphasis must be upon the child's own psychological processes, rather than on his parroting those of others. In addition, the child's range of experience must be broad, so that the generalizing function of symbolization, and the ordering function of judgment will have raw material with which to work. A broad range of experience may also have the secondary value of firing the imagination. Finally, it is crucial that the significant people in the child's life recognize the importance of social and biological functioning as well, so that they can encourage him in such expression. Their encouragement, however, should not be in the service of accepting social roles and animalistic urges, so much as in the conviction that social and biological living is what you make it, and, in the final analysis, these two sides of man are not so separate from each other and from the life of the mind.

From this brief statement, it is easy to see what would be deviant development leading to premorbidity. All you need to develop a premorbid identity is to grow up around people in significant relationship to you who value only some aspects of you, who believe in social roles and biological needs as the only defining pressures of life, and who are either afraid of active symbolization, imagination, and judgment, or see no particular relevance of these processes to living. Have these significant people act on their views in interactions with the child, and he will develop a premorbid identity.

While my brief remarks may seem somewhat flippant, I urge you to recognize that the two kinds of identity are almost that simply caused.

CONCLUDING REMARKS

If I have succeeded in my purpose, you should have a clearer, potentially research-oriented sense of existential disorder, its precursors, and its opposite, than you did before. In addition, you should have found documented here aspects of your own life and those of the people you know well.

If I have drawn the outlines of premorbid identity at all well, you will have recognized its great frequency in our contemporary Western world. While one can point to a set of early experiences in explaining the development of premorbidity, this does not help very much in understanding why this type of personality should be so prevalent these days. Inevitably, the question is raised of why so many parents and significant people in the life of modern-day youngsters instill in them the seeds of premorbidity. This question requires an answer concerning the general cultural milieu in which both adult and child exist. It is as products of their culture that adults influence the young.

Much has been written about the cultural causes of conformity, materialism, and shallow living, and I do not intend to review that literature here. But I would like to point to three broad views, of special interest to psychologists, that have gone far toward creating a cultural climate congenial to premorbidity. The men usually associated with these views are Darwin, Weber, and Freud.

Darwin argued a kinship between all animals, and this view has been sloppily interpreted by many to mean that man is very little different from lower animals. Any characteristics of man that do not seem amply represented in lower animals must be epiphenomenal, or reducible to simpler, animalistic things. Inevitably, such a view undercuts the importance of psychological processes and humanistic doctrines. And that is just what happened. I would like to point out, however, that there is nothing in the concept of a phylogenetic scale that justifies overlooking the importance of characteristics that seem to emerge at one level, having appeared in what may be only minimal prototypical form at lower levels. Add this to the reasonable view that man is really quite far on the scale from his next lower kin, and you have a form of Darwinism that is not so incompatible with my view of the ideal identity, and that would not be a cultural seed for the existential neurosis. To those psychologists who have rashly made what Murray (1954, p. 435) calls "the audacious assumption of species equivalence" between man and white rat I would say that a meaningful comparative psychology is as much interested in the differences as the similarities between species.

The sociologist Weber was certainly among the first to formally specify that modern, industrial society is necessarily bureaucratic in nature. This view has been considered to mean that the social roles a person is delegated are the most important things about him. Indeed, many a modern sociologist will define personality as the sum total of the social roles played by a person. Anyone who accepts such a view of himself without looking more deeply into the matter will very likely either be on the road to premorbidity himself, or be the kind of parent that breeds premorbidity in his children. In trying to show that there is an alternative to this view, let me agree that all behavior can be analyzed as social role playing, but point out that this does not necessarily mean that the social system is unchangeable and an irresistible shaper of individual living. The first step in convincing yourself of this is recognizing that there are different types of social roles. Social roles differ in their rigidity, preemptiveness, status, initiative requirements, and even in the degree to which they involve the person in changing existing social roles. The import of all this is that some social roles encourage the expression of symbolization, imagination, and judgment. Clear examples are roles of leadership, power, and aestheticism. The second step in convincing yourself that the social system is not necessarily the prime mover of individual life is to ask yourself the question of how any person comes to play certain types of roles as opposed to others. In any society that does not restrict competition for roles, the roles that a person actually does come to play will be determined in part by his view of the good life and his sense

of personal identity. The person with the ideal identity will gravitate toward roles involving symbolization, imagination, and judgment, while the person with the premorbid identity will avoid these roles. Indeed, the sense of powerlessness and despair pointed to by Marx in people playing social roles that are inhuman may be a psychological problem as much as a sociological one.

Finally, we come to Freud. It may not have escaped your recognition that Freud, in classical libido theory, gives expression to the belief that life represents a compromise between the necessity of playing social roles and of expressing biological needs. He makes what I have called premorbidity the ideal! Further, for Freud the psychological processes are defensive in nature, reflecting at most no more than a pale shadow of the truth. It is not hard to believe that our current-day outlook that thought processes are not to be trusted and that man's self-interested sexual needs to be checked by society was given great impetus by Freud's theory. Interestingly enough, his theory may well have served as a necessary corrective in his day, when thought had become arid through neglect of the biological side of man and too heavy in emphasis upon judgment to the detriment of imagination. But because his theory was a corrective rather than something more comprehensively adequate, its acceptance into the general culture has contributed to setting the stage for a new emphasis in psychopathology, namely, the existential neurosis.

REFERENCES

ARENDT, H. *Eichmann in Jerusalem—a report on the banality of evil.* New York: Viking, 1964.

ATKINSON, B. (Ed.) *The selected writings of Ralph Waldo Emerson.* New York: Modern Library, 1940.

CAMUS, A. *The stranger.* New York: Knopf, 1946.

CAMUS, A. *The myth of Sisyphus and other essays.* (Trans. by J. O'Brien) New York: Knopf, 1955.

DURKHEIM, E. *Suicide.* Glencoe, Ill.: Free Press, 1951.

FRANKL, V. *The doctor and the soul.* (Trans. by R. Winston & C. Winston) New York: Knopf, 1955.

FROMM, E. *The sane society.* New York: Rinehart, 1955.

JOSEPHSON, E., & JOSEPHSON, M. (Eds.) *Man alone.* New York: Dell, 1962.

KIERKEGAARD, S. *The sickness unto death.* (Trans. by W. Lowrie) New York: Doubleday, 1954.

MAY, R., ANGEL, E., & ELLENBERGER, H. F. (Eds.), *Existence.* New York: Basic Books, 1958.

MILLER, A. *After the fall.* New York: Viking, 1964.

MURRAY, H. A. Toward a classification of interaction. In T. Parsons & E. A. Shils (Eds.), *Toward a general theory of action.* Cambridge, Mass.: Harvard University Press, 1954. Pp. 435 ff.

ROGERS, C. R. A theory of therapy, personality, and interpersonal relationships, as developed in the client-centered framework. In S. Koch (Ed.), *Psychology: A study of a science.* Vol. 3. New York: McGraw-Hill, 1959. Pp. 184–256.

ROGERS, C. R. *On becoming a person.* Boston: Houghton, Mifflin, 1961.

SARTRE, J. P. *Being and nothingness.* (Trans. by H. Barnes) New York: Philosophical Library, 1956.

SYKES, C. (Ed.) *Alienation.* New York: Braziller, 1964.

TILLICH, P. *The courage to be.* New Haven: Yale University Press, 1952.

TOLSTOI, L. *The death of Ivan Ilyich.* New York: Signet, 1960.

18.

WILLIAM S. SAHAKIAN

SOCIAL LEARNING THEORY OF OBSESSIONAL NEUROSIS

ABSTRACT

This paper seeks to explain the obsessional neuroses from a base established by social learning theory, humanistic psychology, and ontoanalytic or existential psychology. From needs and a nature that are singularly human, man through social learning can develop obsessional behavior characteristics.

The premise on which this paper rests is that man, though like subhuman species, possesses characteristics or qualities that are singularly human, a fact implicit in social learning theory where the human model rather than the animal is used (Rotter, 1964, p. 82). Furthermore, human existence is differentiated from animal existence in the existentialist sense (Heidegger, 1962) as possessing consciousness, freedom, guilt, self-consciousness. Man, owning a "super-animal" existence, identified by Frankl (1959, 1962a, 1962b, 1966, 1967, pp. 73-74) as noōgenic, or that purely human domain of existence (Fabry, 1968, pp. 19-20), must be studied from the standpoint of his peculiarly human nature as well as his animal being. Maslow's (1949) accusation that man's animal na-

From William S. Sahakian, "A social learning theory of obsessional neurosis," *Israel Annals of Psychiatry and Related Disciplines,* 1969, 7, 70–75.

ture is maligned may be a valid observation of psychology of a pre-Darwinian vintage, but the mainstream of current experimental and physiological psychology seems to have resulted in the converse and maligned man's human existence, assuming that his nature has indeed been aspersed at all.

A synthesis of man's animality and humanity has been aptly described by Fromm (1955, p. 25):

The animal is content if its physiological needs—its hunger, its thirst and its sexual needs—are satisfied. Inasmuch as man is *also* animal, these needs are likewise imperative and must be satisfied. *But inasmuch as man is human, the satisfaction of these instinctual needs is not sufficient to make him happy; they are not even sufficient to make him sane. The archimedic point of the specifically human dynamism lies in this uniqueness of the human situation; the understanding of man's psyche must be based on the analysis of man's needs stemming from the conditions of his existence.*

Scheler, with perceptive insight, noted "man can be either more or less than animal, but never *an animal*" (1961, p. 29). We know that aspect of man which is lower than the animal—a perverted, sadistic, and belligerent being—but we know also that aspect which is more than animal, a self-conscious, moral being who is aware of values. Or, as Nietzsche put it, "man is an animal that can make promises." It is true that the animal is in possession of consciousness which is devoid in the plant, but the animal lacks self-consciousness, as Leibnitz observed. Man alone can make himself an object of his thoughts, transcend himself, understand his world in scientific terms, possesses a capacity for humor and irony, experience sympathy and empathetic love, identify with his fellow man, choose that which is within himself that ought to be realized, choose external goals and values that he feels obliged to realize, understand his life and world in teleological terms, think in terms of logical and mathematical abstractions, appreciate both tangible and abstract (poetry) beauty, be creative (Berdyaev, 1962), deny physical needs and pleasures, reduce the world and man to a system of ideas, defy or suppress his urges by choosing an ascetic existence or through sublimation, and numerous other human capabilities absent in animal existence. The remainder of this paper is predicated on the foregoing view of man.

A second point requiring clarification is the term *obsessional neurosis,* of which for present purposes White's (1964, p. 259) definition has been adopted: "An obsession is an idea or desire which forces itself persistently into the patient's mind in what he experiences as an irrational fashion." In this paper a compulsion is regarded as an act which the individual is psychologically compelled to execute, while an obsession is limited solely to the realm of thought. Obsessional thoughts of the neurotic are ordinarily antisocial with violent or harmful consequences if carried into action, such as, slitting a friend's throat, arson, strangling a child, or suicide by some violent means. Although in compulsive neurosis the victim may be obsessed with thoughts which are relieved only when some harmless ritual is performed, such as checking the gas stove in order to be sure that the jet is turned off, it is not to be confused with pure obsessional neurosis (as the term is being used in this paper), which is limited to troublesome thoughts. The fusion of these two types of neuroses is common today

as is found in Stone and Stone (1966, p. 193).

Experimental neurosis, that performed on animals, is never quite the same as human neurosis, due not merely to man's higher mental processes (Dollard & Miller, 1950, ch. 6, 11) or to man's two-factor learning ability (Mowrer, 1953, pp. 140-149), but to his other human characteristics, such as those listed above, plus his interpersonal relationships. Man's poignant sense of guilt is heightened by his social environment, self-consciousness, sense of responsibility, value consciousness, and other factors which have an intensifying effect on one's guilt-feelings. Not that these things create guilt nor that guilt is a mere superego or its concomitant, the product of our culture as Freud (1949, pp. 16-18, 121-122) surmised. Guilt, as a human experience, may be modified or directed toward specific objects through social learning, but it is neither instilled in man nor can it be eradicated from human experience.

However, as learning theorists maintain, guilt and anxiety can function as drives (Miller, 1966; Mowrer, 1939), just as sex (Freud, 1957) and inferiority (Adler, 1926) do, and so they operate as drives in this fashion in neurosis. Utilizing Mowrer's moral model (1960) and his neurotic paradox (1948) or the neurotic "stupidity" concept of Dollard and Miller (1950, pp. 14, 20), significant insights into the mental modus operandi of neurotic thought processes can be gained.

An obsessional neurosis is not the result of a single experience, regardless of how intensive the isolated experience may have been traumatically. It is the product of a repetition compulsion (Freud, 1950), an act which is repeated because it is drive generated; but in the obsessional neurotic it is an act that lacks the sanction of the individual committing it. That is to say, the neurotic is driven to continue behavior which he deplores morally, yet which is continued because it is overwhelmingly compelling and intensely satisfying in some manner. For example, autistic thinking (Murphy, 1947, pp. 341 ff.), feelings of inferiority (Adler), and sexual urges (Freud), etc. act as potent drives, and their strength is compounded when they function conjunctively with one another.

An obsessional neurosis develops as the result of a mental conflict in which the neurotic vainly resists an overwhelming drive—not once, but repetitively—if not invariably, then at least with a degree of regularity. Actually, he is undergoing a state of conditioning of which he is not aware, amounting to the establishment of a mental habit of doing things that he chooses not to do. When a neurotic reaches the point where the conditioned response is confirmed ("I do things that I do not want to do"), he is plagued with the obsessive thought that he is susceptible to doing things which he abhors and which are against his will. Through the gradient of generalization (Dollard & Miller, 1950), the obsessional neurotic's mind associates or transfers (Thorndike & Woodworth, 1901) this conditioned mental state to other acts which the neurotic loathes.

The obsessional neurotic's problem is that his mind is left in a state of conflict with the feeling that he is losing control of his mind and self, when actually what is taking place is a displacement (Freud, 1963, lec. 23) of that which underwent conditioning initially, owing to generalization and transfer.

The foregoing theory is corroborated by clinical case studies and a logotherapeutic technique which Frankl (1960, 1966, 1969) terms *paradoxical intention,* a technique successfully utilized by Gerz (1966) and others.

Consider a typical case of neurosis perpetuated by sex and guilt such as that cited by Mowrer (1964, ch. 7) concerning a minister who was given to masturbation from adolescence and to other sex-related acts that were repugnant to his moral sensitivities. In a number of cases that the author has counseled in which sex is a compulsion—such as compulsive masturbatory practices—the drive is intensified and perpetuated by autistic experiences, reveries or visions entertained by the mind concurrently with the sex act. The strength of the drive may be augmented further by the reveries containing fancies of power (Adler); or as one client (with a severe sense of inferiority) put it: "I do not enjoy sex unless I can feel that I am deflowering the girl." The potency of this man's sex drive lay in his autistic imageries

generated by compelling aggression (Buss, 1966) and inferiority feelings.

Whether the minister cited by Mowrer was driven similarly is a moot question, but many neurotics have been so enmeshed. It is well known that the sex drive, expressed for any period of time in such a manner that guilt ensues, will fructify in a neurosis, probably initially one of anxiety states. It is also obvious that a neurotic, once becoming aware that his morally sanctioned practices are related to his states of anxiety or guilt, will want to terminate such practices. Yet, owing to the intensity of the drive motivating these practices, their regular occurrence or repetition compulsion, the neurotic rationalizes and succumbs to them, as happened repeatedly in the case cited by Mowrer.

But what is not commonly known is that a principle of social learning is taking effect. In one case of obsessional neurosis which appeared following a fairly extended period of anxiety states and depression, the neurotic (feeling guilt on the conclusion of masturbatory practices) would promise himself that he would never again reduce himself to such a depraved practice. However, with the insurgency and overwhelming intensity of the drive, he would succumb. Not once, but again and again, he would yield, each time promising himself solemnly that he would abandon the practice; yet, finding himself impotent to pursue his determined course of abstinence. In effect, he had conditioned himself unwittingly to believe that "I do crazy things that are against my will." Once this conditioning process is established (and the neurotic is not aware of what has been transpiring, or conscious of the conditioned response established), he is left with the disquieting feeling and conviction that he commits outrageous deeds despite his resolute will to do otherwise. The assumption that the obsessional neurotic has the subconscious desire to do that which he fears seems to be a mistake; on the contrary, the obsessional has no desire whatever to do that which he fears, but is terrified because his sense of determination or will has been demoralized and he no longer trusts himself.

The reason why logotherapeutic techniques of paradoxical intention and dereflection work in obsessional cases is that the conditioning process is being reversed (Gerz, 1966) and the obsessional is undergoing experimental extinction (Dollard & Miller, 1950). Wolpe's (1958, 1961, 1969) psychotherapy by reciprocal inhibition is capable of desensitizing the strength of obsessional neurosis by counteracting the initial conditioning process responsible for obsessional neurosis.

REFERENCES

ADLER, A. *The neurotic constitution: Outlines of a comparative individualistic psychology and psychotherapy.* New York: Dodd, Mead, 1926.

BERDYAEV, N. *The meaning of the creative act.* New York: Collier, 1962.

BUSS, A. H. The effect of harm on subsequent aggression, *Journal of Experimental Research in Personality*, 1966, *1*, 249–255.

DOLLARD, J., & MILLER, N. E. *Personality and psychotherapy: an analysis in terms of learning, thinking, and culture.* New York: McGraw-Hill, 1950.

FABRY, J. B. *The pursuit of meaning: logotherapy applied to life.* Boston: Beacon, 1968.

FRANKL, V. E. The spiritual dimension in existential analysis and logotherapy, *Journal of Individual Psychology*, 1959, *15*, 157–165.

FRANKL, V. E. Paradoxical intention: a logotherapeutic technique, *American Journal of Psychotherapy*, 1960, *14*, 520–535.

FRANKL, V. E. Psychiatry and man's quest for meaning, *Journal of Religion and Health*, 1962, *1*, 93–103. (a)

FRANKL, V. E. *Man's search for meaning: An introduction to logotherapy* (Rev. ed.). Boston: Beacon, 1962. (b)

FRANKL, V. E. *The doctor and the soul: From psychotherapy to logotherapy* (Rev. ed.). New York: Knopf, 1966.

FRANKL, V. E. *Psychotherapy and existentialism.* New York: Washington Square, 1967.

FRANKL, V. E. Logotherapy. In W. S. Sahakian (Ed.), *Psychotherapy and counseling: Studies in technique.* Chicago: Rand McNally, 1969.

FREUD, S. *An outline of psychoanalysis.* New York: W. W. Norton, 1949.

FREUD, S. *Beyond the pleasure principle.* London: Hogarth, 1950.

FREUD, S. Instincts and their vicissitudes. In *The collected papers of Sigmund Freud.* New York: Basic, and London: Hogarth, 1957.

FREUD, S. *A general introduction to psycho-analysis.* London: George Allen and Unwin, 1963.

FROMM, E. *The sane society.* New York: Holt, Rinehart, & Winston, 1955.

GERZ, H. O. Experience with the logotherapeutic technique of paradoxical intention in the treatment of phobic and obsessive-compulsive patients, *American Journal of Psychiatry*, 1966, *123*, 548–553.

HEIDEGGER, M. *Being and time.* New York: Harper, 1962.

MASLOW, A. H. Our maligned animal nature, *Journal of Psychiatry*, 1949, *28*, 273–278.

MILLER, N. E. Experiments relevant to learning theory and psychopathology, *Proceedings of the International Congress of Psychology*, 1966. In W. S. Sahakian (Ed.), *Psychopathology today.* Itasca, Ill.: F. E. Peacock Publishers, Inc., 1970.

MOWRER, O. H. A stimulus-response analysis of anxiety and its role as a reinforcing agent, *Psychological Review*, 1939, *46*, 553–565.

MOWRER, O. H. Learning theory and the neurotic paradox, *American Journal of Orthopsychiatry*, 1948, *18*, 571–610.

MOWRER, O. H. *Psychotherapy: theory and research.* New York: Ronald Press, 1953.

MOWRER, O. H. "Sin," the lesser of two evils, *American Psychologist*, 1960, *15*, 301–304.

MOWRER, O. H. *The new group therapy.* New York: D. Van Nostrand, 1964.

MURPHY, G. *Personality: A biosocial approach to origins and structure.* New York: Harper, 1947.

ROTTER, J. B. *Clinical psychology.* Englewood Cliffs, N.J.: Prentice Hall, 1964.

SCHELER, M. *Man's place in nature.* New York: Noonday, 1961.

STONE, A. A., & STONE, S. S. *The abnormal personality through literature.* Englewood Cliffs, N.J.: Prentice-Hall, 1966.

THORNDIKE, E. L., & WOODWORTH, R. S. The influence of improvement in one mental function upon the efficiency of other functions, *Psychological Review*, 1901, *8*, 247–261, 384–395, 553–564.

WHITE, R. W. *The abnormal personality* (3rd ed.). New York: Ronald Press, 1964.

WOLPE, J. *Psychotherapy by reciprocal inhibition.* Stanford: Stanford University Press, 1958.

WOLPE, J. The systematic desensitization treatment of neurosis, *Journal of Nervous and Mental Diseases*, 1961, *132*, 189–203.

WOLPE, J. Psychotherapy by reciprocal inhibition. In W. S. Sahakian (Ed.), *Psychotherapy and counseling: Studies in technique.* Chicago: Rand McNally, 1969.

19.

Neal E. Miller

EXPERIMENTS RELEVANT TO LEARNING THEORY
AND PSYCHOPATHOLOGY

First I want to say how especially honored and pleased I am to be asked by my eminent colleagues in the Soviet Union to speak to this Congress. I am especially glad that some of the experiments I shall report will show that a great difference which some people have assumed exists between the mechanisms of the classical conditioning of glandular and visceral responses studied so brilliantly in the Soviet Union and those of the instrumental learning of skeletal responses studied in my own country does not, in fact, exist. As we get to understand each other better, may some of the other differences between our two great nations prove illusory instead of real!

At this Congress we have all seen how scientists from all nations of the world can work together to increase mutual understanding. This inspiring example of mutual respect and cooperation must be extended to other aspects of national life. Modern science has the potential to give a better life to all peoples of all nations. This enormous power must not be used for war which can only bring destructive misery to everyone, but for peace which will bring constructive happiness to all mankind!

Tonight I am going to describe a variety of different experiments in the hope that each of you will find something of especial interest. The focus of this research is on motivation and learning. Some of the problems come from psychopathology and some of the techniques from Physiology and Biochemistry. I hope that this work will emphasize the fact that science is not limited to the artificial boundaries of the

disciplines found in the average university department, and that it is interesting and fruitful to cross such boundaries.

Thirty years ago in the Institute of Human Relations at Yale University, a group of us from different disciplines—Experimental Psychology, Psychiatry, Sociology, and Anthropology—were trying to work together to lay the foundation for a unified science of man's behavior. We found that a knowledge of the scientific laws of learning, as developed by Pavlov, Ebbinghaus, Thorndike, and others who continued their work, is essential to understanding behavior. However, knowing the laws alone is not enough; one must also know the conditions. Thus if you release a wooden ball, the laws of Physics will not predict how it will move unless you know also the conditions—whether it is freely falling in a vacuum, rolling down an inclined plane, or being released under water, so that it will float up to the surface. Similarly, in studying an animal the laws of learning will not allow you to predict its behavior unless you know also conditions, such as what the relevant stimuli are and which responses will be rewarded and which punished. In the human learning involved in the development of personality, most of the crucial conditions are social. Therefore, a knowledge of society, as scientifically studied by the anthropologists and sociologists, is essential for understanding human behavior (44).

Clinical studies conducted by insightful psychiatrists provide detailed natural-history observations of individuals struggling to learn to adapt to the conditions of their social environment. These observations have emphasized the importance of strong drives and of conflicts between responses to different drives. In more recent years, great advances in physiology and biochemistry have given us powerful new tools

Read in somewhat condensed form as Invited Evening Lecture at the XVIII International Congress of Psychology, Moscow, 1966. Additional experiments on visceral learning have been summarized in N. E. Miller, "Learning of visceral and glandular responses." *Science*, 1969, *163*, 434–445. Printed by permission of Neal E. Miller.

for studying the physical basis for such drives and indeed may soon enable us to discover the physical basis for memory and learning— a problem on which I am now working.

In the early days at the Yale Institute, an attempt to make a more rigorous interpretation of Freud's (14) clinical observations led Hobart Mowrer (46) to the hypothesis that fear functions as a drive and that a sudden reduction in its strength acts as a reward to reinforce instrumental learning. Figure 3.1 shows the apparatus in which I performed the experiment verifying this hypothesis (23). If rats are placed in this apparatus with the door between the two compartments open, they wander aimlessly about showing no particular motivation to get to any particular side.

matic persistence of the response of running, or has a drive been conditioned to the left side?

To answer this question the door between the two compartments is closed. The rats cannot escape to the other side. Their tension, agitation, urination and defecation indicate strong fear. They perform a variety of motor responses. If switches are set so that one of these responses, that of turning the little wheel above the door, causes it to drop open so that they can escape to the other side, most of the rats eventually will happen to perform this response of turning the wheel and, as Figure 3.2 shows, those that do will learn it. We can see that the escape from the fear-producing situation has reinforced the learning of one particular response, turning a wheel. The learning is the same as if the drive had been hunger, instead of fear, and the reward food instead of a sudden reduction in the strength of fear.

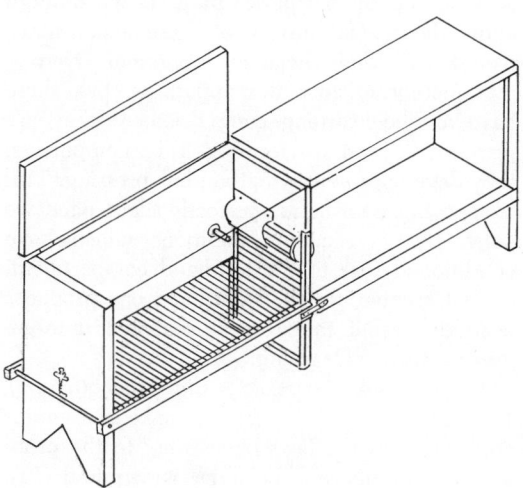

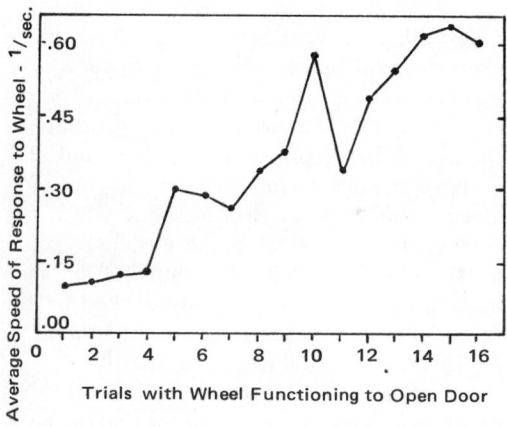

FIGURE 3.1. Apparatus for proving the rewarding effect of a reduction in the strength of fear. From Miller (23) ·

FIGURE 3.2. Learning the first new habit during trials without electric shock. From Miller (23) .

If they are given a number of trials during which they are dropped into the left-hand side of the apparatus and given an electric shock through the grid floor, they rapidly learn to escape by running through the open door to the right side. Even after the shock is turned off they continue to run. Is this the mere auto-

Figure 3.3 shows that, if the switches are changed so that turning the wheel no longer opens the door that allows the rat to escape, but pressing a bar will open it, the first habit of turning the wheel will extinguish and a second new one of pressing the bar will be learned.

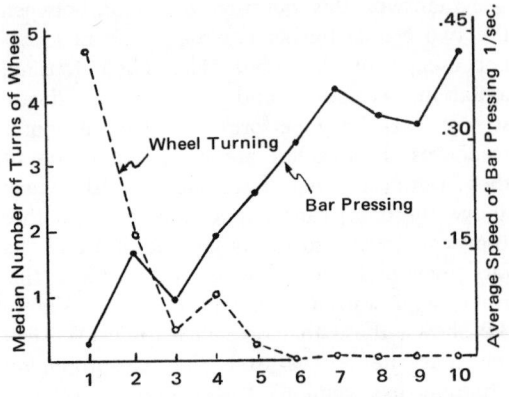

FIGURE 3.3. Extinguishing the habit of wheel-turning and learning the new habit of bar pressing rewarded by a reduction in fear. From Miller (23).

Two different types of learning situations are involved in this experiment. First there is classical conditioning, the scientific study of which was initiated by Pavlov (51). The conditioned stimulus of being placed in the left-hand side of the apparatus is followed by the unconditioned stimulus of an electric shock which has an innate tendency to elicit the specific response of fear. As the result of a number of such presentations, the fear originally elicited by the electric shock is conditioned to the stimuli in the left-hand side of the apparatus (24).

After shock is turned off and the door is closed, we have an example of instrumental learning, the scientific study of which was initiated by Thorndike (63), and which is also called trial-and-error learning, Type II conditioning, or operant conditioning. The reinforcing event, often called the reward, is escape from fear. It does not have any innate tendency to elicit the specific response of turning the wheel, but has the property of being able to strengthen any immediately preceding response. Thus the same reinforcement can be used to strengthen quite different responses, such as turning the wheel or pressing the bar. In instrumental learning these same two responses could be strengthened also by a different reward, such

as food when hungry or water when thirsty. Since any reward can strengthen any response, the possibilities for reinforcement are considerably more flexible with instrumental learning than they are with classical conditioning, where the reinforcement is limited to an unconditioned stimulus that is able to elicit the response to be learned.

Later in this paper we shall return to the fascinating problem of whether classical conditioning and instrumental learning are merely two different types of learning situations, or whether they represent two fundamentally different types of learning mechanisms which obey different laws and involve different parts of the nervous system.

An important thing about fear as a strong drive is that it can be conditioned to new stimuli so that its occurrence can depend upon previous conditions of learning. If we did not know the special history of these animals, we would find their behavior abnormal. Normal rats merely explore the apparatus, but these have a wheel-turning compulsion. If they are prevented from performing this compulsion, they develop a new symptom, bar pressing. This bizarre behavior is all perfectly clear once we know the antecedent conditions which have conditioned fear to the left-hand compartment, so that escape into the right-hand one produces a sudden relief that serves as a reward to reinforce further learning.

In our book *Personality and Psychotherapy*, John Dollard and I tried to make a rigorous application of the laws of learning to the problem of how neurotic behavior is acquired (11). We came to the conclusion that fear is one (but not necessarily the only one) of the important drives motivating such behavior and that escape from fear is one of the rewards reinforcing it. Explaining the successful use of barbiturates in the therapy of certain neuroses, especially combat neuroses in which the role of fear is particularly clear, we assumed that in an approach-avoidance conflict, these barbiturates reduce the fear motivating the avoidance more than the drive motivating the approach. Subsequently my students and I have performed many experiments studying the details of conflict behavior (28) and confirming this particular hypothesis about the effect of barbiturates (35).

Figure 3.4 presents the results of one of these experiments. Hungry rats were first trained to press a bar which caused food to be delivered to them. After they had thoroughly learned this, they were given increasingly strong electric shocks whenever they pressed the bar until they stopped performing that response. After this, the electric shocks were turned off permanently, so that the fear inhibiting pressing the bar was no longer realistic.

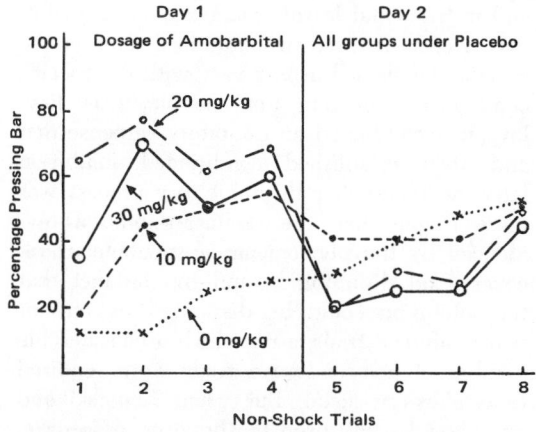

FIGURE 3.4. On Day 1, the amobarbital reduces the fear that is preventing the hungry rats from pressing a bar to get food, but on Day 2 this effect fails to transfer to the non-drugged state. From Miller (39).

In this kind of a situation, as in psychotherapy, one of the problems is to get the subject to perform the response that has been inhibited by fear so that he is exposed to a situation in which the fear can be unlearned by experimental extinction and by counterconditioning and so that the approach response can be strengthened by reward.

In this experiment we used the fear-reducing effects of a barbiturate, amobarbital, to reduce the fear of pressing the bar. As you can see from Figure 3.4, the rats with this drug did indeed press the bar sooner and more frequently, with

the 20 mg/kg dose being optimal, presumably because the largest dose was strong enough to interfere with the rat's ability to move. These results confirm the hypothesis that this drug produces a differential reduction in the strength of fear.

It should be noted, however, that the shift from the drug to the non-drug condition produced a stimulus generalization decrement which caused the beneficial effects to be lost (39). More recent work in our laboratory suggests that this loss may possibly be reduced by withdrawing the drug gradually, but additional work on this problem is needed.

If the drug does indeed reduce fear promptly, then we will expect that frightened animals will be rewarded for learning a response, such as pressing a bar, to give themselves a dose of the drug. In order to test this, Dr. Jack Davis and I devised an apparatus in which, when the rat pressed a bar, a suitable dose of drug was delivered via a chronic catheter into the rat's jugular vein (7). As Figure 3.5 shows, rats which were subjected to pain and fear from brief inescapable shocks once every sixty seconds, learned to press the bar to secure a moderately rapidly acting barbiturate, amobarbital, and learned even better to secure a more rapidly acting barbiturate, hexobarbital. Furthermore, rats which did not receive electric shocks did not learn to press a bar to receive these drugs. These results confirm the prediction made on the basis of previous experiments showing that barbiturates reduce fear and that fear reduction acts as a reward. They fit in with the clinical observation that strong fear, guilt, and other aversive drives increase the probability that a person will become addicted to barbiturates.

In other studies on this same general topic, we have found that it is possible to train animals to resist pain and fear by introducing electric shocks gradually into a situation in which they will be rewarded for persisting in spite of receiving the shocks. Mere exposure to painful electric shocks is not efficient; the animals must be specifically rewarded for persisting in spite of the shocks (29, 12).

We also have found it possible to train rats to respond to fear-evoking situations with the

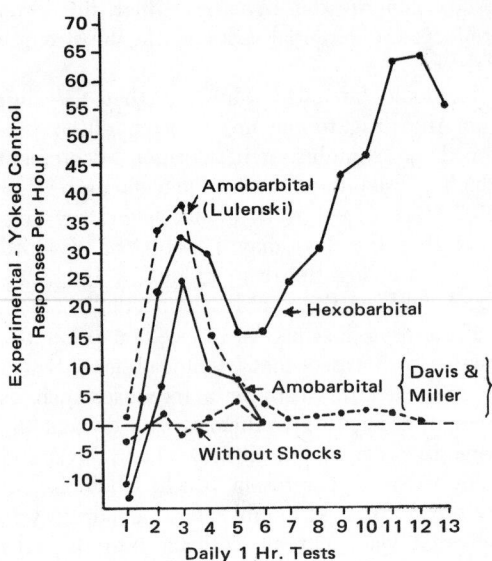

FIGURE 3.5. Rats subjected to brief inescapable electric shocks learn to press a bar to receive intravenous injections of a fear-reducing barbiturate; without shocks they do not learn. The faster-acting drug, hexobarbital, produces better learning. From (7) with new data from the author's laboratory.

passive pattern of freezing or the opposite one of becoming more active, and that training in one of these two patterns will transfer to new situations to affect subsequent learning in them. Furthermore, animals which are still growing gain less weight if they are trained to freeze than they do if they are trained to be active.

We have explored some of the implications of the idea that fear can be conditioned to new situations in which it then serves as a drive to motivate the instrumental learning and performance of any responses rewarded by a sudden reduction in its strength. Let us now return to the problem of whether classical conditioning and instrumental learning are two basically different types of learning, involving different parts of the nervous system.

Many distinguished learning theorists, such as Professors Konorski, Skinner, Mowrer, Sol-

omon, and many others believe that there is a fundamental difference (21, 57, 47, 48, 17, 58, 18). They believe that, while skeletal responses of the striped muscles under the control of the somatic nervous system can be modified by instrumental learning, glandular and visceral responses under the control of the automatic nervous system can be modified only by classical conditioning. If true, this difference has deep implications for theories of learning and its neurophysiological basis, as well as for psychosomatic medicine.

I always have been impressed by the similarity between the laws of classical conditioning and instrumental learning (28, 25, 44, 45). But, within each of these two situations some of the specific details of learning vary with the specific conditions of learning. For example, when Pavlov (52) conditioned an excitatory response first and then established conditioned inhibition later, he found that the inhibitory process was more fragile than the excitatory one, as evidenced by the phenomena of spontaneous recovery and disinhibition and by the fact that the inhibition could be dissipated by one or two reinforced trials, after which a considerable number of non-reinforced trials were required to establish it again. But when Konorski and Szwejkowska (22) used the opposite procedure, of conditioning the inhibition first and then conditioning excitation later, they secured different phenomena; the excitatory process was more fragile than the inhibitory one. To give another example, Terrace (62) has found in an instrumental learning situation that some of the phenomena of discrimination learning are quite different if the non-reinforced negative stimulus is introduced very gradually by starting it at a sub-threshold intensity and then very slowly increasing its strength over a series of trials until its intensity equals that of the positive one. In both examples some of the phenomena of learning·varied, or in other words interacted, with the conditions of learning. But in neither case does it seem plausible to assume that we are dealing with two fundamentally different types of learning involving grossly different parts of the nervous system. I believe that it is probable that all of the allegedly fundamental differences between classical conditioning and instrumental learning will turn out to be effects of different conditions of learning, analogous to those in the previous examples, rather than effects of fundamentally different mechanisms of learning.

Let us return now to one of the most important alleged differences—the assertion that the instrumental learning of visceral responses is impossible. Recently I have sharply and specifically challenged this particular assertion (31, 33, 34, 36). And at about this same time, but perhaps as a parallel development independent of my articles, a number of experimental studies have begun to appear seeming to show that changes in the heart rate, in the galvanic skin response and in vasomotor responses, can be produced in human subjects by instrumental training procedures (53, 13, 19, 20, 55). It is known, however, that such changes can be produced indirectly as reflex results of certain skeletal responses, such as tensing the muscles of the diaphragm or changing the rate of breathing, and it seems reasonable that such indirect mediation is more likely with human subjects. For this reason, I had decided to do my experiments on animals.

Published reports of research are written with the wisdom of hindsight. They leave out the initial blind groping and fumbling, to save journal space (and perhaps also to save face), and exclude almost all of those attempts that are abandoned as failures. Therefore, they present a misleading picture, which is far too orderly and simple, of the actual process of trying to extend the frontiers of science into unknown territory. I shall try to mention a few of my fumbles, but shall not have time to do them justice.

In 1958 Melissa Lewis and I used a balloon on the end of a chronic catheter into the stomach to record and try to reward stomach contractions. Our techniques were rather crude and the results were slightly encouraging, but very far from being conclusive. The fact that we were unable to find any evidence for classically conditioned changes in stomach contractions to signals for delivery of food to hungry animals discouraged us because it meant that negative results on instrumental learning would be inconclusive; perhaps stomach contractions could not be modified by any form of learning. When

Melissa Lewis had to leave, this line of work lapsed.

In 1960, I had an undergraduate, Mr. Khachadourian, try to test the effects of rewarding a hungry dog with food whenever his heart rate slowed down. He did get an apparent learning curve of decreasing heart rate, but this could have been an artifact of habituation to the situation, and Mr. Khachadourian graduated before more decisive tests could be made (34).

In 1961, a graduate student of mine, Mr. Robert Fromer, started to see whether the vasomotor responses in the ears of hungry rabbits could be modified by giving them food as a reward. The results were somewhat encouraging, but it was difficult to be absolutely sure that the rabbits had not cheated by changing the pressure of their necks against the opening in the restraining box or by performing some other skeletal response that had a vasomotor effect (34). We decided to try to eliminate this possible source of artifacts by paralyzing all skeletal muscles with curare, but we ran into difficulties in keeping rabbits alive for a series of training days. Since the initial development and subsequent refinement of a reliable recording technique had already taken so much time, Mr. Fromer had to shift to a safer project for his Ph.D. dissertation, and I found it difficult to get any students to take time from the other interesting projects in my laboratory to devote to this harebrained one.

At last, a complete experiment was carried out with the help of a graduate student, Alfredo Carmona, and a technician, Mrs. Jennie M. Lewis (42). The subjects were thirsty dogs with their parotid salivary glands cannulated by a system developed by Dr. Sheffield (56) so that a plastic tube could be connected to a tiny, stainless steel one projecting from the cheek. This tube was connected to an entirely hydraulic system, eliminating the inevitable lag whenever air is in the system. An electronic relay counted highly standardized drops.

We first established the fact that moderately thirsty dogs would show spontaneous salivation, and that there was no apparent unconditioned response to the delivery of water which they drank from a dish. As a further control on any possible unconditioned effects of the water used as a reward, half of the dogs were rewarded for bursts of spontaneous salivation, and the other half for the opposite response of pauses without salivation. Dogs salivating so much that they could not increase their rate or so little that they could not decrease it, were discarded before the training began. Two groups of three each were matched on the basis of preliminary tests for spontaneous salivation, and then the random flip of a coin determined which group would be rewarded for salivating and which for not salivating.

The average results are shown in Figure 3.6. Each of the three dogs rewarded for increasing salivation showed a statistically reliable increase, while each of the dogs rewarded for not salivating showed a statistically reliable decrease. Additional experiments showed similar differences.

FIGURE 3.6. Instrumental learning of a glandular response, salivation, in thirsty dogs rewarded by water. From (42).

The results are clear-cut, but the interpretation is not. While the dogs were not making any obvious skeletal responses, such as chewing or panting, it is conceivable that they made more subtle ones which we failed to observe. In some of the dogs, we recorded breathing and heart rate, and in others the EEG, or so-called brain-wave, electrical potentials from the

surface of the cortex. There was a positive correlation between the number of breaths in a test session and the amount of salivation, but there was not enough difference in the breathing between the two groups to account for all of the difference in salivation. Heart rate did not seem to be an appreciable factor. But the dogs rewarded for increased salivation seemed to be much more alert, showing also fast, low-voltage EEG records, while those rewarded for not salivating seemed to be more relaxed and drowsy, showing an EEG record with more high-voltage waves resembling brain waves during sleep. Therefore, it is possible that the difference in salivation was a part of a general difference in the state of arousal vs. drowsiness.

Encouraged by the results of this experiment, we proceeded to try to design one that would be more rigorously unequivocal. The best way to rule out the effects of skeletal responses seemed to be to use curare, which blocks the motor end-plates of nerves to skeletal muscles and paralyzes them, without blocking glandular or visceral responses. Unfortunately, however, curare produces a copious secretion of unusually viscous saliva, so it seemed desirable to turn to another response, the heart rate.

The next experiment was performed by a graduate student, Jay Trowill, who showed great perseverance, ingenuity and courage in working for his Ph.D. dissertation with me on this problem (64). In the brief time available, my account of Trowill's three years of work will not do his perseverance, ingenuity and courage the justice it richly deserves. After he had spent a great deal of time working on this problem, I lost considerable sleep worrying that I had sent him up a blind alley, but he had much more at stake than I did.

To present a greatly shortened and simplified account, he started using the heart rate of curarized dogs because Black, Carlson, and Solomon (3) had already shown that this response could be classically conditioned. Since the possibilities of rewarding an animal paralyzed by curare are somewhat limited, we decided to use escape from a mild electric shock, but found that the unconditioned increase in heart rate elicited by the electric shock in dogs was so great and persistent that there seemed to be little possibility of modifying it by learning.

The most feasible other strong reward for curarized animals seemed to be direct electrical stimulation of rewarding areas of the brain (50). Since the dog's skull is so irregular, and since little work had been done on the rewarding effects of electrical stimulation of different areas of its brain, we decided to change to the rat. It was necessary to perfect a face mask and techniques for respirating the rat, to discover that simple peritoneal injections were as good as or better than the intravenous ones which had always been used with this drug before but are difficult with the rat, to work out dose-response relationships for curare, to find the level of respiration at which the heart rate remained stable at an intermediate range.

Finally, there was the problem of recording heart rate and designing circuits to trigger reward when the rate changed. The electrical potential generated by the heart muscle, or in other words the EKG, was fed into the preamplifier of a Grass polygraph, and the amplified signal was used to operate both a recording pen and a relay which was activated by the large spike of each heart beat. The relay operated predetermining counters which could be set so that reward was delivered whenever the number of beats in a given period of approximately a second exceeded a certain number, if the rat was rewarded for a fast rate, or was below a certain number if the rat was rewarded for a slow one.

First, rats with chronic electrodes implanted in the medial forebrain bundle of the lateral hypothalamus were tested to determine the rewarding effect of electrical stimulation via these electrodes. If they learned to press a bar to secure a half-second of stimulation by approximately 50 microamperes of 60 cycle alternating current, such stimulation was considered to be rewarding. After the rats had learned to press a bar for this stimulation, they were given two more days of training to get them used to a schedule in which each rewarded bar press was followed by an 8-second time-out period during which bar presses did not deliver reward.

On a later day they were injected intraperitoneally with a dose of d-tubo-curarine chloride (24 units/kg), sufficient to completely paralyze their striped musculature for approximately three hours. A face mask was put over the snout and the respirator adjusted to a level which had been found to maintain a heart rate within the normal range of approximately 300 to 500 beats per minute which would remain stable in control rats during a one-hour experimental period. In order to be sure preliminary adjustments could not introduce unconscious experimenter bias into the results, the decision whether the rat was to be rewarded for fast or slow heart rate was made randomly after all adjustments had been completed; no further ones were made after this decision.

Trowill found that 15 out of 19 rats rewarded for a faster heart rate showed increases, while 15 out of 17 rewarded for a slower one showed decreases. Although the group differences in each direction were highly reliable statistically, they were quite small, amounting to a change of only approximately 5% in each direction. Therefore, it seemed highly desirable to repeat this experiment and to try to secure larger differences.

Greatly encouraged by Trowill's results, a postdoctoral student, Leo DiCara, helped me with this replication, which involved the following improvements in procedure on the basis of Trowill's experience. In order to allow more complete recovery from the preceding brain stimulation, the time-out period was lengthened from 8 to 20 seconds. In order to make the conditions more clear-cut, a tone and light were present for the time-in period during which responses were rewarded and absent during the time-out period for both preliminary training in the bar-pressing situation and the final training of heart rate under curare. After the rat had learned to get reward by making a small change in heart rate, the task was made progressively more difficult by changing the criterion settings so that progressively faster rates were required for the one group, and slower ones for the other, before reward would be delivered. In this way it was found possible to "shape" the rats to produce either increases or decreases of approximately 20% in heart rate (43).

Figure 3.7 shows the results. It can be seen that during the 90-minute training period the

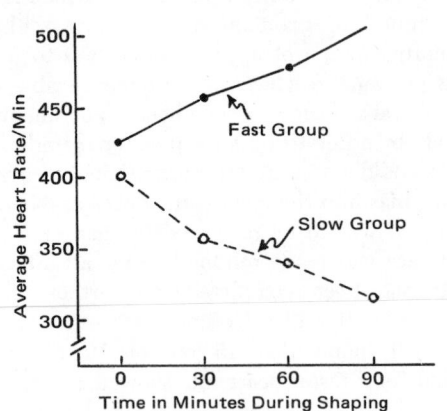

FIGURE 3.7. Instrumental learning by curarized rats rewarded for fast or for slow rates of heartbeat. From (43).

rats rewarded for fast heart rates showed a progressive increase, while those rewarded for slow ones showed a progressive decrease. The results were highly reliable not only for the group, but also for practically every one of the individual rats. Eleven out of the 12 rats rewarded for fast rates showed increases, each of which would be expected by chance less than one time in a hundred, while 10 out of the 11 rats rewarded for slow rates showed decreases, each of which would be expected by chance less than one time out of a hundred. In each group one rat showed no reliable changes.

A cardiologist, Dr. A. V. N. Goodyer, who examined the details of the electrocardiogram of rats rewarded for slowing down, reported that during the latter part of their training the reduction in the amplitude of the P-wave and the increased interval between it and the R-wave indicated that the heart was being inhibited by impulses from the vagal nerve.

Most of the learning shown in Figure 3.7 was in the form of an overall increase or decrease in rate. In other words, relatively little of the effect was specific to the time-in stimulus which indicated when reward could be achieved.

After we had convinced ourselves that general changes in heart rate could be learned, we began holding some of the rats at the most difficult criterion for an additional 45 minutes to see if they could learn to respond more specifically to the time-in stimulus. The results on one of these rats is shown in Figure 3.8. This rat has already slowed down from 530 to 230 beats per minute by the beginning of the discrimination training, which is shown in the top record. It can be seen that there is no appreciable change in the heart rate that is specific to the time-in stimulus, and that a considerable time elapses between the onset of this stimulus and the moment at which the rat achieves the criterion and receives the reward.

At the end of discrimination training, as is shown in the bottom record, the overall rate during time-out remains approximately the same, but the rat slows down when the time-in stimulus occurs, and achieves the reward much faster after the onset of this stimulus than he did at the beginning of this training. In short, he has learned the discrimination of responding to the time-in stimulus.

The 8 fast and 6 slow rats given this part of the training showed roughly similar results, which are summarized in Figure 3.9. You can see that the rate of criterion responses achieved during the time-out period does not change appreciably during this training, but that the rate (based on speed) of achieving the criterion after the time-in stimulus is turned on shows progressive improvement. This improvement, shown by the fact that the two curves are farther apart at the end than at the beginning of training, is of a size that would be expected by chance less than one time in a thousand. Thus it is clear that in curarized rats heart rate can be modified by reward, and that a specific change in heart rate can be learned as a response to a specific stimulus.

In order to increase our confidence in the generality of our results, we have initiated experiments with a considerably different type of visceral response, namely the contraction of the smooth muscles in the large intestine. This work has been done with the help of a graduate student, Mr. Ali Banuazizi (41). We have used a small balloon on the end of a piece of hypo-

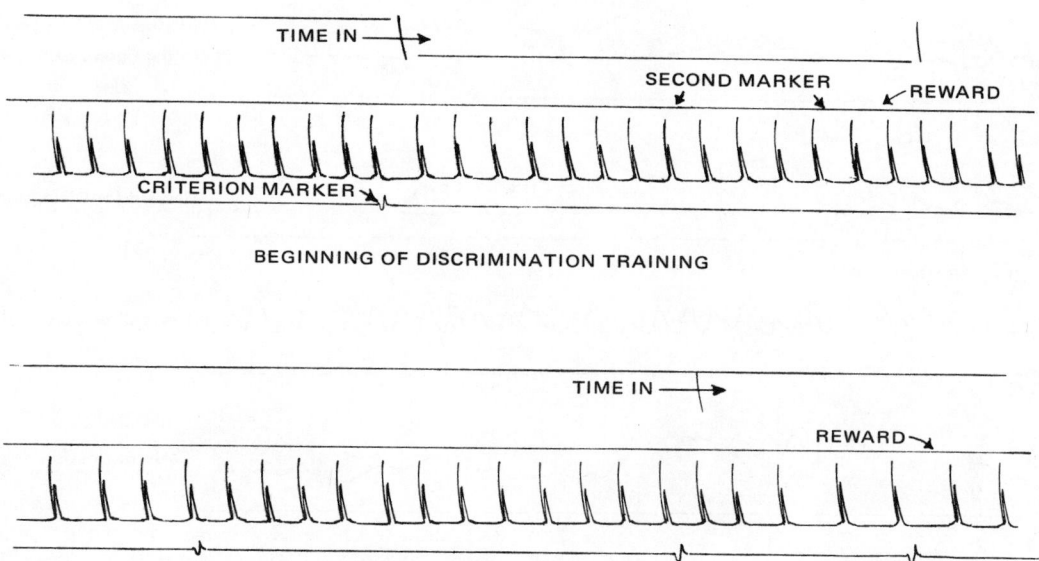

FIGURE 3.8. Electrocardiogram showing learning of a discriminative response to the time-in stimulus by a curarized rat rewarded for slow heart rate. From Miller and DiCara (43).

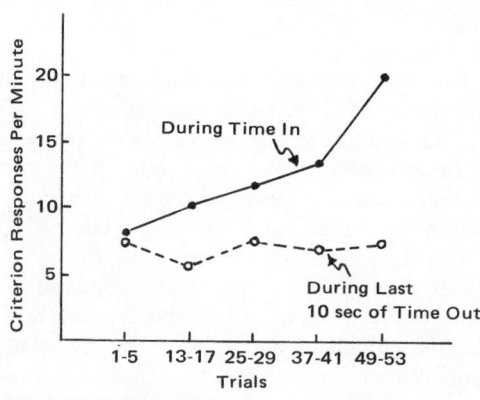

FIGURE 3.9. Learning the discrimination of making the heart-rate response specifically to the time-in stimulus. From (43).

dermic needle tubing, thrust up into the large intestine. This balloon is filled with water and the tubing is connected to a transducer yielding an electrical output proportional to the pressure. The implantation of electrodes, pretraining of the rat, curarization, and artificial respiration are similar to the procedures in the preceding experiment.

Figure 3.10 shows the results of an experiment. The top record is of initial spontaneous contractions. The next record shows the reduced contractions after 45 minutes of training during which rewards are given only when the record is below the lower line. The next record shows the opposite effect, of increased contractions after 45 minutes of rewarding the opposite response of contracting the intestine enough to raise the recording above the upper line. The next record shows the reduced level of responding after 10 minutes of experimental extinction

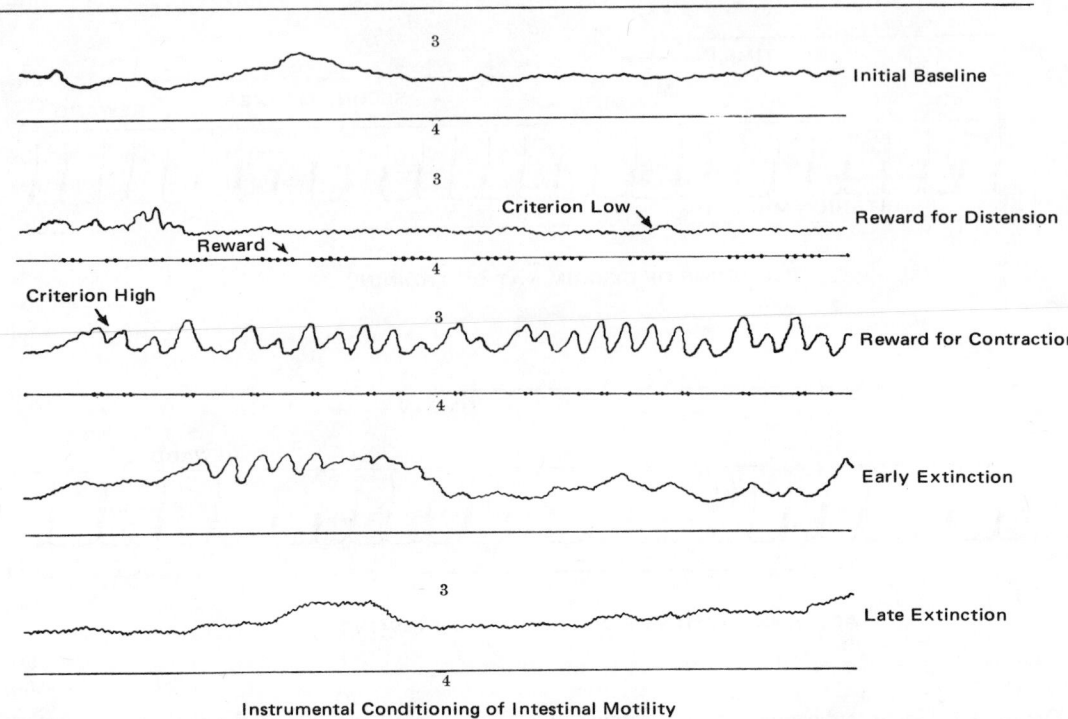

FIGURE 3.10. Instrumental learning of intestinal responses by curarized rats. When rewarded for distension, the number of contractions decreases; when rewarded for contraction, it increases; when the reward is withdrawn, the learned response extinguishes. From Miller and Banuazizi (41).

without any rewards, and the bottom record shows the level after 20 minutes of extinction.

Figure 3.11 presents a more detailed graph of the average results on a different rat, showing that the foregoing sample records were indeed representative of the results. Statistical analysis shows that all of the effects in both rats were reliable beyond the .01 level. We have similar results on 10 rats, some of which were run in the opposite sequence, being rewarded for contractions first and for distension second.

We also have results indicating that vasomotor responses, recorded by a photoelectric plethismograph, can be changed by rewarded training and that escape (and avoidance) of electric shock may be used as a reward for the instrumental learning of visceral responses.

You have just seen that experiments on the salivary glands, the cardiovascular system, and the large intestine all indicate that responses of these organs, which are under the control of the autonomic nervous system, are indeed subject to instrumental learning reinforced by a reward, such as brain stimulation. This refutes the traditional view that such responses are subject only to classical conditioning and hence that the autonomic and spinal parts of the nervous system are subject to different laws of learning. It removes an argument for a fundamental difference in the neurophysiological mechanisms involved in classical conditioning and in instrumental learning and suggests instead a fundamental unity in the learning process.

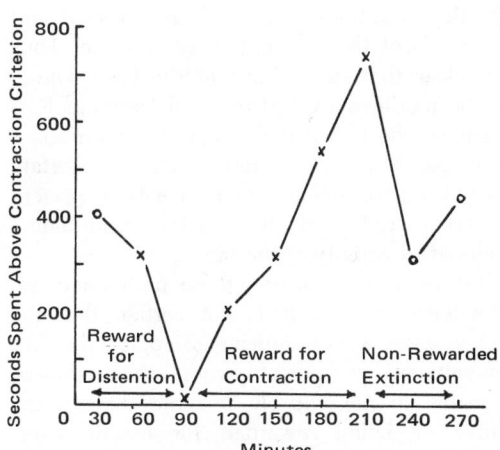

FIGURE 3.11. Average results on a second typical curarized rat, first rewarded for distending the large intestine and then for contracting it. From Miller and Banuazizi (41).

These results have possible implications also for the origin of psychosomatic symptoms, allowing them the more flexible possibilities of instrumental reinforcement by rewards which do not have to be limited to those stimuli eliciting the particular symptom as a specific unconditioned response. Suppose two children are extremely frightened about an examination in school which they feel they are likely to fail. Before leaving for school on the day of the examination, both of them react to fear with a variety of symptoms which are quite common as responses to that drive. Let us suppose that the mother of one child is particularly worried about cardiovascular symptoms, while the mother of the other child is particularly worried about gastrointestinal ones. This difference in social conditions may produce differences in the response learned.

When the first child complains of mild stomach and intestinal distress, his complaints will be ignored, but when he looks pale and shows signs of fainting, his mother will say: "You are sick and should stay home from school!" This announcement will give the child a sudden relief from fear. But as we have seen from the first experiment in this paper, a sudden reduction in fear serves as a powerful reward; and from the immediately preceding experiments, this reward will be expected to strengthen the cardiovascular responses responsible for fainting.

Conversely, if the second child is ignored when he shows symptoms of fainting, but rewarded by escape from the fear-inducing examination when he shows symptoms of gastrointestinal disturbance, he should learn to produce the latter kind of symptoms. In this way the two children may learn different kinds of psychosomatic reactions to stress. Our experiments have shown the possibility for such learning; it remains for further work to demonstrate the degree to which the appropriate social conditions for rewarding such learning actually occur in various societies.

It also remains to be seen whether or not, in normal animals and people, the homeostasis achieved by innate regulatory mechanisms is improved upon by the additional mechanism of instrumental visceral learning, as I suspect to be the case.

According to the foregoing analysis, there are two ways in which a psychosomatic symptom could be acquired. First, conditions of learning can produce a strong drive which tends to elicit the symptom as an innate response to the drive (34). This is illustrated by the first experiment, in which the symptoms of urination and defecation were elicited by the fear conditioned to the left-hand compartment. Secondly, specific glandular and visceral responses that are promptly rewarded by events, such as a marked reduction in fear, are strengthened in the same instrumental way as were the skeletal responses of turning the wheel or pressing the bar in the first experiment. Of course, the responses elicited in the first way are among those which can be further strengthened by the second.

According to the foregoing analysis, symptoms produced in either way could be cured by eliminating the strong drive, also called an emotion. But symptoms, especially those produced in the second way, might be eliminated also by immediately and specifically rewarding either their non-occurrence or any reduction occurring in their magnitude. It remains to be seen how ingeniously this second method can be applied to clinical cases.

We have just seen that glandular and visceral responses are subject to instrumental learning. How much farther can the domain of such learning be extended?

You will remember that, when Carmona and I were rewarding some dogs for salivating and others for not salivating, we seemed also to be affecting their general level of arousal. Is there some more direct way of rewarding a general level of arousal or relaxation?

It is known that during sleep, slow high-voltage brain waves can be recorded from the surface of the cortex, while when the animal is aroused, the record is characterized by fast, low-voltage activity. What would be the effect of differentially rewarding these two electrical indices of brain activity? Alfredo Carmona is now working with me on this problem, using rats with chronically implanted electrodes and rewarded for different voltages of brain waves by direct electrical stimulation of rewarding areas in the brain (40, 5). The skeletal muscles of these rats are paralyzed by curare and their breathing is maintained by artificial respiration.

Figure 3.12 shows the results of such training. You can see that in the group rewarded for high-voltage waves, the frequency of such waves increases, while in the group rewarded for not showing high-voltage waves, the frequency of such waves decreases. In a later test, the conditions of reward are reversed and the trends of the learning curves reverse. Thus it is clear that the voltage of the brain waves can be modified by instrumental learning. Furthermore, the fact that the rat's skeletal muscles were paralyzed by curare rules out certain possibilities for artifacts that have been present in earlier studies of the classical conditioning of electrical activity of the brain.

But we must interpret these preliminary results with caution. It is not certain that the high-voltage waves indicate sleep, or that the low-voltage ones indicate arousal. Nevertheless, it seems to me entirely possible that in the course of being rewarded for certain overt activities, some people may learn a high level of arousal, while others may learn a low level. It might be profitable to discover more about the best ways of teaching different levels of arousal.

To summarize this portion of our talk, we have seen that instrumental learning is not limited to overt skeletal responses. At least some, and perhaps all, glandular and visceral responses can be modified by instrumental learning reinforced by a suitable reward. Of course, pioneering experimental work in the Soviet Union has already shown that many such responses can be modified by classical conditioning (4, 1, 52, 53). Yet other internal responses, such as the brain waves, may be modified by instrumental training. Fear may be used as a drive to motivate instrumental learning and a sudden reduction in the strength of fear may be used as a reward to reinforce such learning. You have seen animals learn to rotate a wheel or press a bar to secure the reward of escaping from a fear-evoking situation; they will also learn to give themselves an injection of a drug that reduces fear. In brief, the important thing is not how afraid one is, but whether one has learned adaptive or maladaptive responses to fear.

The foregoing experiments, and others which I have not had time to mention (9), have emphasized the roles of drives and rewards in learning. I want to close with a brief descrip-

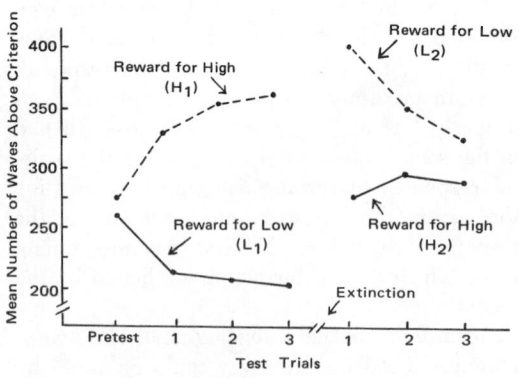

FIGURE 3.12. Instrumental learning by curarized rats rewarded for high-voltage or for low-voltage waves recorded from the cerebral cortex. From Carmona (5).

tion of how advances in Physiology and Biochemistry are helping us to understand more
about the mechanisms of certain drives. One
of these advances is the use of chronically implanted electrodes which allow one to stimulate
or record from the brains of normal, unanesthetized animals. We have already seen the use of
such electrodes to stimulate rewarding areas
of the brain. Stimulation of certain areas can also
elicit drive. Twelve years ago, at the Fourteenth
International Congress of Psychology in Montreal, I gave a paper and showed a film describing experiments proving that electrical stimulation of certain areas of the brain had all of
the behavioral properties of normally elicited
pain and fear; it could motivate the learning
and performance of new instrumental responses,
and escape from such central stimulation could
serve as a reward to reinforce learning (26,
10). I have been looking for, but have not yet

found, areas of the brain where electrical
stimulation will inhibit fear.

Subsequent experiments in my laboratory
have shown that stimulation of a different area,
the lateral hypothalamus, can not only elicit
eating, as has long been known, but also motivate the learning and performance of food-
seeking habits (27, 32), and have various other
properties of normal hunger.

There is only time to describe one recent
experiment of this kind, in which, with the help
of a graduate student, Eric Stone, we showed
that the motivation elicited by such stimulation
was strong enough to overcome the normal food-
regulatory mechanism so that a rat could be
stimulated to overeat greatly and become fat
(59). Figure 3.13 shows the results on one
such rat. You see the moderate amount eaten
and relatively slow rate of weight gain before
electric stimulation was started. While the rat

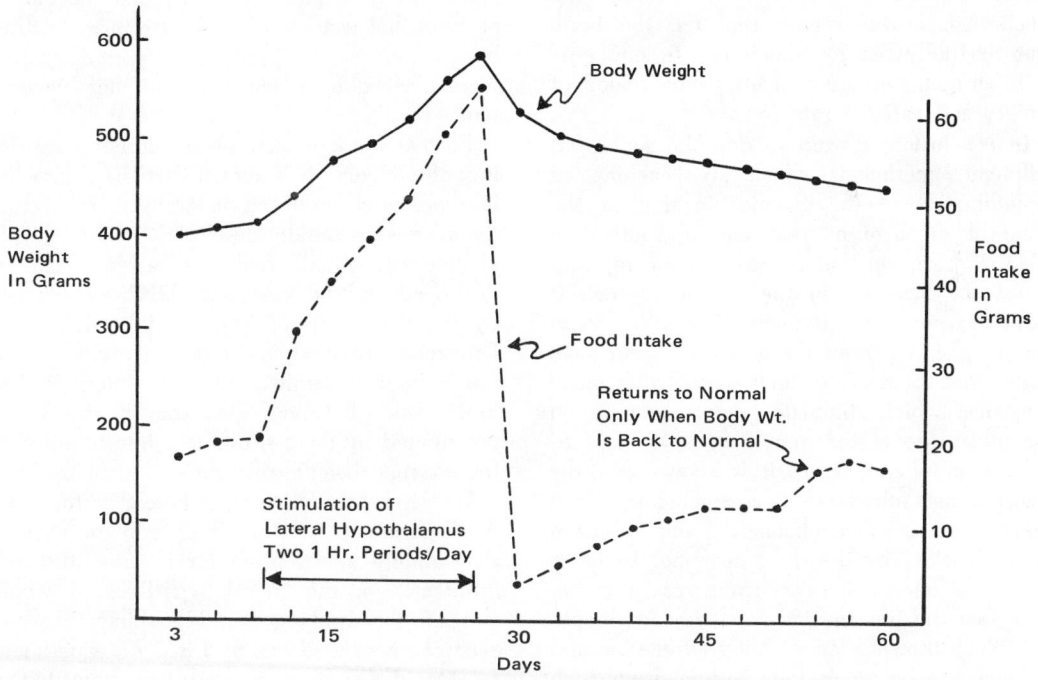

FIGURE 3.13. Increased food intake and obesity produced by two one-hour periods of electrical
stimulation of the lateral feeding area in the rat hypothalamus. From (59)

was stimulated for two one-hour periods each day with progressively increasing strengths of current, his food intake was greatly increased and he gained weight equivalent to a 150-pound man gaining 60 pounds (or 27 kilos) in 19 days. When this regime of electrical stimulation was stopped, the rat virtually stopped eating and did not return to normal food consumption until his weight had returned to approximately what it would have been at the end of this number of days of normal growth. Control experiments show that this stopping eating was the result of the overeating and not an after-effect of the electrical stimulation.

This last result agrees with those of workers in other laboratories who have forced rats to overeat by injections of insulin or by inserting abnormal amounts of liquid diet into their stomachs via stomach tube (6, 61). It shows that the brain has some way of knowing when the body has considerably more fat than it needs. We are now seeking to discover the mechanism of the signals that tell the brain that the body has too much fat. In one type of experiment we are exchanging the blood of hungry and satiated rats (8).

In conclusion, I want to describe somewhat different experiments which are teaching us something about the chemical coding in the brain of mechanisms that control motivation (38). It is known that transmission of impulses across the synapses in the nervous system is different from that in the nerve fibers. Studies in the peripheral part of the nervous system have shown that the nerve endings secrete a chemical substance which stimulates the membrane on the other side of the minute synaptic gap. In certain peripheral nerves it is known that the transmitting substance is acetylcholine. Such transmission is called cholinergic and is known to be blocked by the drug atropine. In other peripheral nerves there is strong reason to believe that the transmitting agent is norepinephrine. Such transmission is called adrenergic and is known to be blocked by certain drugs such as ethomoxane.

Do these peripherally-studied transmitter substances also work centrally in the brain?

As some of you may know, one of my students, Sebastian P. Grossman, recently studied the effects in injecting minute amounts of such substances directly into the brain via chronically implanted cannulae (15). At my suggestion, he tried the "feeding-drinking" area in the hypothalamus of the rat since we had already studied this area by electrical stimulation. He found that the injections of the cholinergic substance, acetylcholine, or of a similar synthetic substance, carbachol, would cause satiated rats to drink or to work at pressing a bar that delivered water. When injected into exactly the same place via exactly the same cannula, minute amounts of the adrenergic substances, norepinephrine or epinephrine, would cause hungry rats to eat or to work at pressing a bar that delivered food.

Suitable control tests with a variety of other substances showed that these effects were not due to osmotic pressure, pH, vasoconstriction or vasodilatation. The most convincing evidence that these effects were due to the transmitter action of these substances was that the effects of carbachol were blocked by atropine, but not by ethomoxane, while those of norepinephrine were blocked by ethomoxane but not by atropine (16).

Further work has supplied another powerful link of evidence. It is known that the acetylcholine normally produced in transmission across the synapse is rapidly destroyed by the enzyme cholinesterase, and that this enzyme can be destroyed by the substance DFP, or blocked by the drug eserine. Thus, if the effects that Grossman observed mean that acetylcholine is the normal transmitter in this system in the brain, we will expect such transmission to be potentiated by these substances interfering with the enzyme that destroys the acetylcholine.

We have found that such indeed is the case. An experiment by Mrs. Chien and me showed that minute injections of eserine into the preoptic area or the lateral hypothalamus would increase the drinking of mildly thirsty rats and even cause satiated rats to drink. An experiment by David Quartermain and me showed that similar effects could be produced by DFP, but that this effect lasted much longer, as would be expected from the nature of the action of that drug. These results are especially important because they make use of the acetylcholine normally present in the brain. They strongly suggest that transmission in the thirst system is chemically coded with an acetylcholine-like substance being the transmitter (38).

On the other hand, one might argue that we are not stimulating the thirst system directly, but stimulating nerves that inhibit the secretion of antidiuretic hormones so that the kidneys stop reabsorbing the water and lose more of it as urine. Such water loss could activate the thirst mechanism in the normal manner, but would not be a direct effect of chemostimulation of thirst mechanisms in the brain.

In order to test this possibility, Mrs. Chien and I studied the effect on the secretion of urine of direct chemical stimulation of the brain with doses of carbachol of the size which my previous dose-response studies showed were optimal for eliciting drinking. Instead of increasing the secretion of urine, we found that such doses decreased it (38). This ruled out the type of indirect effect that has just been described, and indicated that we were stimulating a general system for dealing with deficiencies of water. This system has the physiological effect of eliciting the secretion of the antidiuretic hormone that causes the kidney to reabsorb water and prevent it from being wasted. At the same time, it has the behavioral effect of motivating the animal to perform water-seeking habits, and to drink water when he finds it. These results beautifully illustrate an intimate interrelationship between physiological and behavioral means of preserving homeostasis, which I have pointed out elsewhere (37). In the present experiment the physiological-behavioral system is activated by direct chemostimulation by the transmitter, acetylcholine, or the similar synthetic substance, carbachol. Under normal circumstances, the system is activated by signals of water deficiency.

What is the source of these signals? Andersson (2) has found that injections into a region near the third ventricle of the brain of a solution that is slightly more salty than the normal body fluids will cause satiated goats to drink. This result was repeated by Melissa Lewis and me in cats, and as Figure 3.14 shows, we have further found that minute injections of water in this region will cause thirsty cats to drink less (30). This effect of pure water is especially

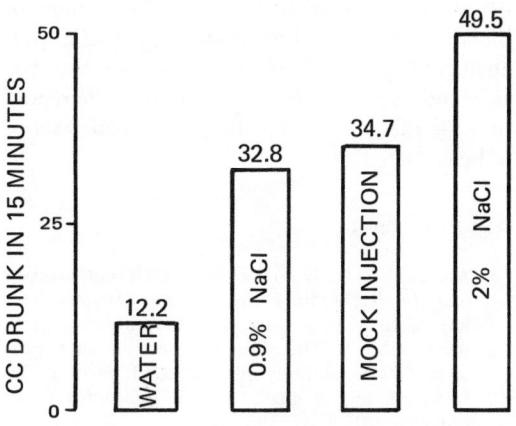

FIGURE 3.14. In moderately thirsty cats, minute injections into the ventricle of the brain reduce thirst if they are hypotonic and increase it if they are hypertonic. From (30).

significant because hypertonic saline can directly stimulate nerves, so that Andersson's experiment could have been interpreted as such an effect. Thus the brain seems to have osmo-receptors that respond to the increased salinity of the blood when the body is dehydrated and the decreased salinity when the water balance is restored. Work in my laboratory by Donald Novin (49), who has measured the concentration of saline by its effect on electrical conductivity, and by Edward Stricker (60), who has made direct chemical analyses of the blood and various tissues, has shown that at least one other factor is involved also. This is the volume of fluid in the vascular system. Reducing this volume can induce thirst. We are now trying to find the receptors that monitor volume and to learn how they work.

Much remains to be done, but I hope I have shown you how the use of physiological and biochemical techniques is increasing our understanding of the mechanism of drives that have important effects on behavior.

Putting the first part of my talk together with this last part, I hope it is clear that many different disciplines contribute to the scientific understanding of behavior and that psychologists occupy a central position among these disciplines so that it is especially fitting for them to cross the boundaries separating psychology from the social sciences on the one side and the biological ones on the other, and to take the lead in creating a unified science of behavior (37).

REFERENCES

1. AIRAPETJANTZ, E. S. *Die höhere Nerventätigkeit und die Rezeptionen der inneren Organe.* Berlin: Veb. Verlag Volk und Gesundheit, 1956.
2. ANDERSSON, B. The effect of injections of hypertonic NaC1 solutions into different parts of the hypothalamus of goats. *Acta Physiologica Scandinavica,* 1953, *28,* 188–201.
3. BLACK, A. H., CARLSON, N. J., & SOLOMON, R. L. Exploratory studies of the conditioning of autonomic responses in curarized dogs. *Psychological Monographs,* 1962, *76,* (29).
4. BYKOV, K. M. *The cerebral cortex and the internal organs.* (Ed. and Trans. by W. H. Gantt). New York: Chemical Publishing Co., 1957.
5. CARMONA, A. Instrumental learning of amplitude changes in cortical EEG. (Ph.D. dissertation), in preparation.
6. COHN, C., & JOSEPH, D. Body weight and fat of "normal" lean and obese rats. *Yale Journal of Biology and Medicine,* 1962, *34,* 598–607.
7. DAVIS, J. D., & MILLER, N. E. Fear and pain: Their effect on self-injection of amobarbital sodium by rats. *Science,* 1963, *141,* 1286–1287.
8. DAVIS, J. D., & MILLER, N. E. A technique for mixing the blood of unanesthetized rats. *Journal of Applied Psychology,* in press.
9. DEBOLD, R. C., MILLER, N. E., & JENSEN, D. D. Effect of strength of drive determined by a new technique of classical conditioning of rats. *Journal of Comparative and Physiological Psychology,* 1965, *59,* 102–108.
10. DELGADO, J. M. R., ROBERTS, W. W., & MILLER, N. E. Learning motivated by electrical stimulation of the brain. *American Journal of Physiology,* 1954, *179,* 587–593.
11. DOLLARD, J., & MILLER, N. E. *Personality and psychotherapy.* New York: McGraw-Hill, 1950.
12. FEIRSTEIN, A. R., & MILLER, N. E. Learning to resist pain and fear: effects of electric shock before versus after reaching goal. *Journal of Comparative and Physiological Psychology,* 1963, *56,* 797–800.
13. FOWLER, R. L., & KIMMEL, H. D. Operant conditioning of the GSR. *Journal of Experimental Psychology,* 1962, *63,* 563–567.
14. FREUD, S. *The problem of anxiety.* New York: Norton, 1936.
15. GROSSMAN, S. P. Direct adrenergic and cholinergic stimulation of hypothalamic mechanism. *American Journal of Physiology,* 1962, *202,* 872–882.
16. GROSSMAN, S. P. Effects of adrenergic and cholinergic blocking agents on hypothalamic mechanisms. *American Journal of Physiology,* 1962, *202,* 1230–1236.
17. KELLER, F. S., & SCHOENFELD, W. N. *Principles of psychology.* New York: Appleton-Century-Crofts, 1950.
18. KIMBLE, G. A. *Hilgard and Marquis' conditioning and learning.* New York: Appleton-Century-Crofts, Inc., 1961.
19. KIMMEL, E., & KIMMEL, H. D. A replication of operant conditioning of the GSR. *Journal of Experimental Psychology,* 1963, *65,* 212–213.
20. KIMMEL, H. D., & HILL, F. A. Operant conditioning of the GSR. *Psychological Reports,* 1960, *7,* 555–562.
21. KONORSKI, J., & MILLER, S. Further remarks on two types of conditioned reflex. *Journal of General Psychology,* 1937, *17,* 405–407.
22. KONORSKI, J., & SZWEJKOWSKA, G. Chronic extinction and restoration of conditioned reflexes. *Acta Biologiae Experimentalis,* 1952, *16,* No. 7.
23. MILLER, N. E. Studies of fear as an acquirable drive: I. Fear as motivation and fear-reduction as reinforcement in the learning of new responses. *Journal of Experimental Psychology,* 1948, *38,* 89–101.
24. MILLER, N. E. Learnable drives and rewards. In S. S. Stevens (Ed.), *Handbook of Experimental Psychology.* New York: Wiley, 1951, pp. 435–472.
25. MILLER, N. E. Comments on multiple-process conceptions of learning. *Psychological Review,* 1951, *58,* 375–381.
26. MILLER, N. E. Drive, drive reduction and reward. *Proceedings of the XIV International Congress of Psychology,* Montreal, 1954.
27. MILLER, N. E. Experiments on motivation: Studies combining psychological, physiological and pharmacological techniques. *Science,* 1957, *126,* 1271–1278.
28. MILLER, N. E. Liberalization of basic S-R concepts: Extensions to conflict behavior, motivation and social learning. In S. Koch (Ed.), *Psychology: A study of a science,* Study 1, Vol. 2. New York: McGraw-Hill, 1959.
29. MILLER, N. E. Learning resistance to pain and fear: effects of overlearning, exposure and rewarded exposure in context. *Journal of Experimental Psychology,* 1960, *60,* 137–145.
30. MILLER, N. E. Learning and performance motivated by direct stimulation of the brain. In D. Sheer (Ed.), *Electrical stimulation of the brain.*

Austin, Tex.: University of Texas Press, 1961.

31. MILLER, N. E. Integration of neurophysiological and behavioral research. *Annals of the New York Academy of Science*, 1961, 92, 830–839.

32. MILLER, N. E. Some experiments on the mechanisms of motivation. *Voprosy Psikhologii*, Academy Pedagogical Sciences, Moscow, USSR, 1961, No. 4, 143–146.

33. MILLER, N. E. Some reflections on the law of effect produce a new alternative to drive reduction. *Nebraska symposium on motivation, 1963*. Lincoln, Nebr.: University of Nebraska Press, 1963.

34. MILLER, N. E. Animal experiments on emotionally-induced ulcers. *Proceedings of World Congress of Psychiatry, June 4–10, 1961, Montreal*. Canada: University of Toronto Press, 1963.

35. MILLER, N. E. The analysis of motivational effects illustrated by experiments on amylobarbitone sodium. In Ciba Foundation, *Animal behavior and drug action*. London: J. & A. Churchill, 1964.

36. MILLER, N. E. Some implications of modern behavior theory for personality change and psychotherapy. In P. Worchel & D. Byrne (Eds.), *Personality change*. New York: Wiley, 1964, pp. 149–175.

37. MILLER, N. E. Physiological and cultural determinants of behavior. In *The scientific endeavor*. New York: Rockefeller Institute Press, 1964. Also, *Proceedings of the National Academy of Sciences*, 1964, 51, 941–954.

38. MILLER, N. E. Chemical coding of behavior in the brain, *Science*, 1965, 148, 328–338.

39. MILLER, N. E. Some animal experiments pertinent to the problem of combining psychotherapy with drug therapy. *Comprehensive Psychiatry*, 1966, 7, 1–12.

40. MILLER, N. E. Extending the domain of learning. *Science*, 1966, 152, 676 (abstract).

41. MILLER, N. E., & BANUAZIZI, A. Instrumental learning of a specific visceral response, intestinal or cardiac, by curarized rats. *Journal of Comparative and Physiological Psychology*, 1968, 65, 1.

42. MILLER, N. E., & CARMONA, A. Modification of a visceral response, salivation in thirsty dogs, by instrumental training with water reward. *Journal of Comparative and Physiological Psychology* (in press).

43. MILLER, N. E., & DiCARA, L. Instrumental learning of heart-rate changes in curarized rats: shaping, and specificity to discriminative stimulus. *Journal of Comparative and Physiological Psychology* (in press).

44. MILLER, N. E., & DOLLARD, J. *Social learning and imitation*. New Haven: Yale University Press, 1941.

45. MILLER, N. E., & MILES, W. R. Effect of caffeine on the running speed of hungry, satiated and frustrated rats. *Journal of Comparative and Physiological Psychology*, 1935, 20, 397–412.

46. MOWRER, O. H. A stimulus-response analysis of anxiety and its role as a reinforcing agent. *Psychological Review*, 1939, 46, 553–565.

47. MOWRER, O. H. On the dual nature of learning—A reinterpretation of "conditioning" and "problem solving." *Harvard Educational Review*, 1947, 17, 102–148.

48. MOWRER, O. H. *Learning theory and personality dynamics*. New York: Ronald Press, 1950.

49. NOVIN, D. The relation between electrical conductivity of brain tissue and thirst in the rat. *Journal of Comparative and Physiological Psychology*, 1962, 55, 145–154.

50. OLDS, J., & MILNER, P. Positive reinforcement produced by electrical stimulation of septal area and other regions of rat brain. *Journal of Comparative and Physiological Psychology*, 1954, 47, 419–427.

51. PAVLOV, I. P. Sur la sécrétion psychique des glands salivaires (phénomènes nerveux complexes dans le travail des glands salivaires) *Archives Internationales de Physiologie et de Biochimie*, 1904, 1, 119–135.

52. PAVLOV, I. P. *Conditioned reflexes*. G. V. Anrep (Trans.) London: Oxford University Press, 1927. Reprinted by Dover Publications, New York, 1960.

53. RAZRAN, G. The observable unconscious and the inferable conscious in current Soviet psychophysiology: Interoceptive conditioning, semantic conditioning and the orienting reflex. *Psychological Review*, 1961, 68, 81–147.

54. SHAPIRO, D., CRIDER, A. B., & TURSKY, B. Differentiation of an autonomic response through operant reinforcement. *Psychonomic Science*, 1964, 1, 147–148.

55. SHEARN, D. W. Operant conditioning of heart rate. *Science*, 1962, 137, 530–531.

56. SHEFFIELD, F. D. Salivary conditioning in dogs. *Yearbook of the American Philosophical Society*, 1957, 284–287.

57. SKINNER, B. F. *The behavior of organisms*. New York: Appleton-Century, 1938.

58. SOLOMON, R. L., & WYNNE, L. C. Traumatic avoidance learning: The principles of anxiety conservation and partial irreversibility. *Psychological Review*, 1954, 61, 353–385.

59. STEINBAUM, E. A., & MILLER, N. E. Obesity from eating elicited by daily stimulation of hypothalamus. *American Journal of Physiology*, 1965, 208, 1–5.

60. STRICKER, E. M. Extracellular fluid volume and thirst. *American Journal of Physiology*, 1966, 211, 232–238.

61. TEITELBAUM, P. Motivational correlates of hypothalamic activity. In *Proceedings of the XXII*

International Congress Physiological Sciences,
Vol. 1, Part II. Amsterdam: Excerpta Medica
Foundation, 1962.
62. TERRACE, H. S. Stimulus control. In W. K.
Honig (Ed.), *Operant behavior: Areas of re-
search and application.* New York: Appleton-
Century-Crofts, 1966.
63. THORNDIKE, E. L. Animal intelligence: An ex-

perimental study of the associative processes in
animals. *Psychological Review, Monographs,
Supplement,* 1898, 2.
64. TROWILL, J. A. Instrumental conditioning of
the heart rate in the curarized rat. *Journal of
Comparative and Physiological Psychology* (in
press).

20.

JANET A. TAYLOR

MANIFEST ANXIETY SCALE

A series of recent studies (3, 4, 5, 6, 7, 9, 10)
has shown that performance in a number of
experimental situations, ranging from simple
conditioning and reaction time to a "therapy"
situation involving experimentally induced
stress, is related to the level of anxiety as revealed on a test of manifest anxiety. Most of
these investigations were concerned with the
role of drive or motivation in performance,
drive level being varied by means of selection
of subjects on the basis of extreme scores made
on an anxiety scale rather than by experimental
manipulation (e.g., electric shock, stress-pro-
ducing instructions, etc.). The use of the anxiety scale in this connection was based on two
assumptions: first, that variation in drive level
of the individual is related to the level of internal anxiety or emotionality, and second, that
the intensity of this anxiety could be ascertained
by a paper and pencil test consisting of items
describing what have been called overt or manifest symptoms of this state.

Since the scale has proved to be such a useful device in the selection of subjects for experimental purposes, a description of the construction of the test and the normative data that
have been accumulated in connection with it

may be of interest to other investigators in the
field of human motivation.

DEVELOPMENT OF THE SCALE

The manifest anxiety scale was originally constructed by Taylor (6) for use in a study of
eyelid conditioning. Approximately 200 items
from the Minnesota Multiphasic Personality Inventory were submitted to five clinicians, along
with a definition of manifest anxiety that followed Cameron's (2) description of chronic
anxiety reactions. The judges were asked to
designate the items indicative of manifest anxiety according to the definition. Sixty-five
items on which there was 80 per cent agreement or better were selected for the anxiety
scale. These 65 statements, supplemented by
135 additional "buffer" items uniformly classified by the judges as non-indicative of anxiety,
were administered in group form to 352 students in a course in introductory psychology.
The measures ranged from a low anxiety score
of one to a high score of 36, with a median of
approximately 14. The form of the distribution
was slightly skewed in the direction of high
anxiety.

Subsequently, the scale went through several modifications.[1] At present it consists of 50

From Janet A. Taylor, "A personality scale of
manifest anxiety," *Journal of Abnormal and Social
Psychology,* 48, 1953, 285–290. © 1953 by the
American Psychological Association, and reproduced
by permission.

[1]J. L. Hedlund, I. E. Farber, and H. P. Bechtoldt, "Normative characteristics of the Manifest

TABLE 3.1

ITEMS INCLUDED ON THE MANIFEST ANXIETY SCALE AND RESPONSES SCORED AS "ANXIOUS" ITEMS ARE NUMBERED AS THEY APPEAR IN THE COMPLETE BIOGRAPHICAL INVENTORY

4. I do not tire quickly. (False)
5. I am troubled by attacks of nausea.* (True)
7. I believe I am no more nervous than most others.* (False)
11. I have very few headaches. (False)
13. I work under a great deal of tension.* (True)
14. I cannot keep my mind on one thing. (True)
16. I worry over money and business. (True)
18. I frequently notice my hand shakes when I try to do something. (True)
24. I blush no more often than others.* (False)
25. I have diarrhea once a month or more.* (True)
26. I worry quite a bit over possible misfortunes.* (True)
27. I practically never blush. (False)
33. I am often afraid that I am going to blush. (True)
35. I have nightmares every few nights. (True)
36. My hands and feet are usually warm enough. (False)
37. I sweat very easily even on cool days. (True)
38. Sometimes when embarrassed, I break out in a sweat which annoys me greatly.* (True)
41. I hardly ever notice my heart pounding and I am seldom short of breath.* (False)
43. I feel hungry almost all the time. (True)
44. I am very seldom troubled by constipation.* (False)
48. I have a great deal of stomach trouble. (True)
51. I have had periods in which I lost sleep over worry.* (True)
54. My sleep is fitful and disturbed.* (True)
56. I dream frequently about things that are best kept to myself.* (True)
66. I am easily embarrassed. (True)
67. I am more sensitive than most other people.* (True)
77. I frequently find myself worrying about something.* (True)

82. I wish I could be as happy as others seem to be.* (True)
83. I am usually calm and not easily upset. (False)
86. I cry easily. (True)
87. I feel anxiety about something or someone almost all the time.* (True)
94. I am happy most of the time. (False)
99. It makes me nervous to have to wait. (True)
100. I have periods of such great restlessness that I cannot sit long in a chair.* (True)
103. Sometimes I become so excited that I find it hard to get to sleep. (True)
107. I have sometimes felt that difficulties were piling up so high that I could not overcome them.* (True)
112. I must admit that I have at times been worried beyond reason over something that really did not matter.* (True)
117. I have very few fears compared to my friends.* (False)
123. I have been afraid of things or people that I know could not hurt me. (True)
136. I certainly feel useless at times. (True)
138. I find it hard to keep my mind on a task or job. (True)
145. I am unusually self-conscious.* (True)
152. I am inclined to take things hard.* (True)
153. I am a high-strung person.* (True)
163. Life is a strain for me much of the time.* (True)
164. At times I think I am no good at all. (True)
168. I am certainly lacking in self-confidence.* (True)
183. I sometimes feel that I am about to go to pieces.* (True)
187. I shrink from facing a crisis or difficulty.* (True)
190. I am entirely self-confident.* (False)

*Statements rewritten for subsequent revision.

of the original 65 items that showed a high correlation with the total anxiety scores in the original group tested. Furthermore, the buffer items have been changed so that the total test, which has been lengthened from 200 to 225 items, includes most of the items from the *L*, *K*, and *F* scales of the MMPI and 41 items that represent a rigidity scale developed by Wesley (10). The 50 anxiety items are reproduced in Table 3.1, along with the responses to these

Anxiety Scale." Unpublished paper. This statistical analysis, along with most of the data collected with the scale, was carried out under the direction of H. P. Bechtoldt at the State University of Iowa.

items considered as "anxious" and the ordinal numbers of the statements as they appear in the present form of the test.

NORMATIVE DATA

Under the innocuous title of *Biographical Inventory*, the test in its present form has been administered to a total of 1971 students in introductory psychology at the State University of Iowa during five successive semesters from September, 1948 to June, 1951. The distribution for this sample is presented in Figure 3.15. As can be seen by inspection, the distribution shows a slight positive skew, as did the original

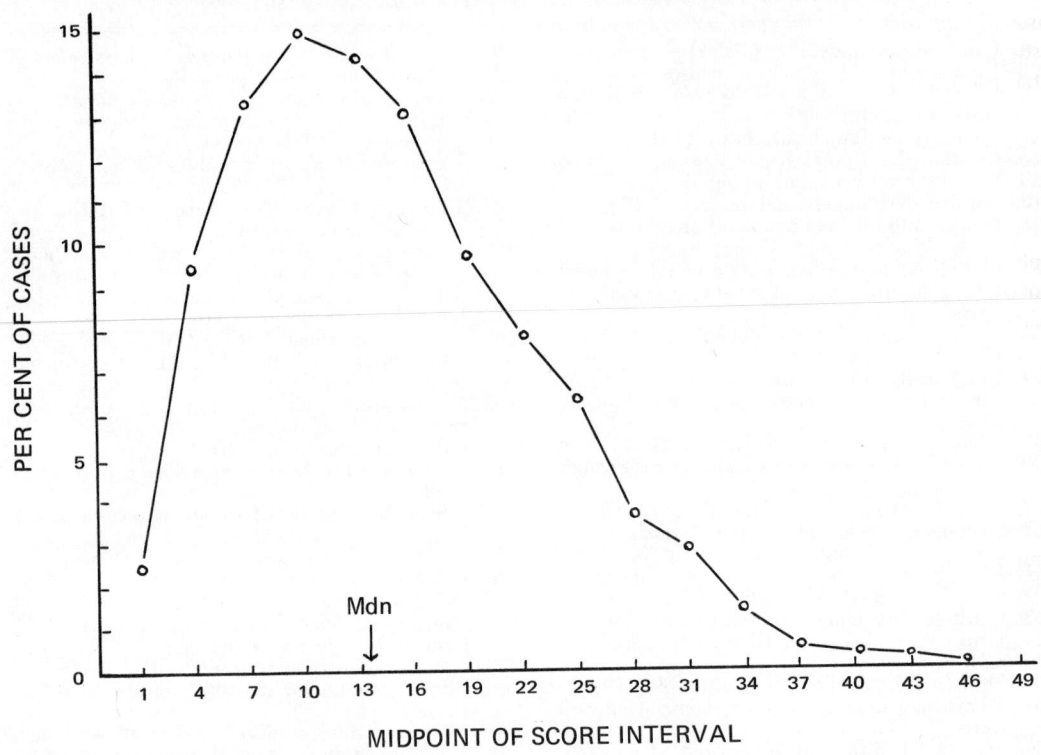

FIGURE 3.15. Frequency polygon showing per cent of the 1971 university students receiving the indicated scores on the Manifest Anxiety Scale.

scale. The fiftieth percentile falls at about 13, the eightieth at about 21, and the twentieth at about 7. The mean of the distribution is 14.56.

SEX DIFFERENCES

A comparison of the scores of males and females in this total sample revealed that the mean score of the women was somewhat higher. The difference between the two means however was not statistically significant. For this reason, both sexes have been included in a single distribution.

DIFFERENT POPULATIONS

Scores on the scale are also available for samples drawn from somewhat different populations. Distributions for 683 airmen tested at the beginning of basic training at Lackland Air Force Base and for 201 Northwestern University night-school students of introductory psychology show essentially the same form as the group reported above, while the quartiles are in close agreement.

CONSISTENCY OF SCORES

In order to determine the stability of the anxiety scores over time, groups of individuals have been retested on the scale after various intervals. In one instance, the results of retesting 59 students in introductory psychology after a lapse of three weeks yielded a Pearson product-moment coefficient of .89. In a second test-retest study,[2] the scale was given to 163

―――――――――――――
[2]*Ibid.*

students in an advanced undergraduate psychology course who had previously taken the test as introductory students. For 113 of these cases 5 months had elapsed since the first testing, while an interval of 9-17 months had intervened for the remaining 50. The test-retest coefficient was found to be .82 over 5 months and .81 for the longer period. Furthermore, no systematic change, upwards or downwards, was found in these distributions, i.e., the means of each of the three sets of scores remained essentially the same after retesting. Thus, for all groups tested, both the relative position of the individual in the group and his absolute score tended to remain constant over relatively long periods of time.

RELATIONSHIP OF THE BIOGRAPHICAL
INVENTORY TO THE MMPI

Since it might be desired to obtain anxiety scores for individuals who have been given the complete MMPI rather than the Biographical Inventory, it is necessary to consider the effects of the different sets of filler items on the 50 anxiety statements. There is some evidence[3] to suggest that the distribution of anxiety scores given in the form of the MMPI will differ significantly from that obtained from the Biographical Inventory. The Biographical Inventory was administered to 282 freshman males, and approximately 18 weeks later the group MMPI was given to the same students. The correlation between the two sets of measures, obtained by determining the scores on the 50 anxiety items on each test, was .68. This, it will be noted, is a slightly lower figure than that obtained by test-retest on the Inventory after a comparable length of time. In addition, the forms of the distributions were statistically different, as indicated by a chi-square test of homogeneity. Since the initial scores of this group, obtained from the Biographical Inventory, were similar to those found with other groups, the discrepancy of the results between the Inventory and the MMPI suggests that the radical change in filler items may exert a definite influence on the anxiety scores. Before anxiety scores obtained from the MMPI can

be evaluated it would appear to be necessary to have more normative data concerning the scale scores obtained from this form.

REVISION OF THE SCALE

A further revision of the scale is now being carried out by the writer. This variation represents an attempt to simplify the vocabulary and sentence structure of some of the anxiety items that appear to be difficult to comprehend, especially for a noncollege population. Toward this end, the 50 anxiety items were first submitted to 15 judges who were instructed to sort them into four piles according to comprehensibility, the first position representing the simplest to understand and the fourth the most difficult. It was found that 28 of the items had a mean scale value of 2.00 or more. These 28 items were selected for revision and rewritten in at least two alternate forms.[4] Each set of alternatives was then ranked by a different set of 18 judges, first for ease of understanding and then for faithfulness of meaning to the original statement. For most of the items, the alternative judged to be simplest was also chosen as being closest in meaning to the original item and was therefore selected for the new scale. For those items in which discrepancy occurred, faithfulness of meaning was chosen over simplicity. However, in every case, the new statement selected for inclusion on the scale was judged simpler than the original. These 28 rewritten items are shown in Table 3.2.

RELATIONSHIP BETWEEN THE OLD AND NEW
VERSIONS OF THE SCALE

To demonstrate the relationship between the old and new versions of the test, both forms were administered to students in introductory psychology at Northwestern University College. A sample was selected from the college population for this purpose since it was thought that this group would show the least confusion

---

[3]See footnote 1.

[4]In rewriting the items, the Thorndike word count (9) was consulted. These counts primarily determined substitution of words within an item whenever this was done.

TABLE 3.2

THE 28 ITEMS REWRITTEN FOR THE REVISED FORM OF THE MANIFEST ANXIETY SCALE AND RESPONSES
SCORED AS "ANXIOUS"

(Items are numbered as they appear in the Biographical Inventory.)

5. I am often sick to my stomach. (True)
7. I am about as nervous as other people. (False)
13. I work under a great deal of strain. (True)
24. I blush as often as others. (False)
25. I have diarrhea ("the runs") once a month or more. (True)
26. I worry quite a bit over possible troubles. (True)
38. When embarrassed I often break out in a sweat which is very annoying. (True)
41. I do not often notice my heart pounding and at a time (True)
44. Often my bowels don't move for several days at a time. (True)
51. At times I lose sleep over worry. (True)
54. My sleep is restless and disturbed. (True)
56. I often dream about things I don't like to tell other people. (True)
67. My feelings are hurt easier than most people. (True)
77. I often find myself worrying about something. (True)
82. I wish I could be as happy as others. (True)

87. I feel anxious about something or someone almost all of the time. (True)
100. At times I am so restless that I cannot sit in a chair for very long. (True)
107. I have often felt that I faced so many difficulties I could not overcome them. (True)
112. At times I have been worried beyond reason about something that really did not matter. (True)
117. I do not have as many fears as my friends. (False)
145. I am more self-conscious than most people. (True)
152. I am the kind of person who takes things hard. (True)
153. I am a very nervous person. (True)
163. Life is often a strain for me. (True)
168. I am not at all confident of myself. (True)
183. At times I feel that I am going to crack up. (True)
187. I don't like to face a difficulty or make an important decision. (True)
190. I am very confident of myself. (False)

---

in interpreting the original versions of the difficult items and, therefore, better demonstrate the comparability of the two forms than less verbally sophisticated individuals. Scores obtained from 59 students showed a Pearson product-moment correlation of .85 between the old and new versions, the latter being administered three weeks after the initial testing. This figure is quite comparable to the test-retest coefficient found for the previous form of the scale after a similar time interval. Considering only the 28 rewritten items, the correlation becomes .80.

While the correlation coefficient shows the high degree of relationship between the old and revised forms, the question still remains as to whether rewriting the 28 items has reduced the difficulty level of these statements so as to minimize confusion and misinterpretation. In an attempt to determine this, the scores of the 59 students given both versions were analyzed into two components: that for the 28 difficult items and that for the 22 items left intact. For each form, scores on the 28 items were correlated with the remaining 22. It was reasoned

that if the original forms of the 28 items were confusing, then the rewritten items, if attempts to simplify were successful, would show a higher correlation with the 22 items left intact than would the original statements. The actual correlations obtained in this manner were .81 for the old version and .83 for the new. Although the difference between the coefficients was in the desired direction, a *t* test indicated that it was statistically insignificant. However, a significant difference in correlations might be obtained with subjects of lesser educational attainment since misinterpretation of the 28 original items would be more likely to occur with such a group.

NORMATIVE CHARACTERISTIC OF THE
NEW SCALE

To determine further characteristics of the distribution of scores on the new version, 229 students in introductory psychology were given only the revised form of the scale (1). It was found that the shape of the distribution and the values of the quartiles did not differ significantly from those obtained with the previous form.

Retest scores are also available for 179 individuals from the sample described above. A product-moment correlation of .88 was found after an interest interval of four weeks. However, while the position of the individuals in the group tended to remain the same, a downward shift in the absolute scores of the entire distribution was noted from test to retest. The difference between means (14.94 vs. 12.92) was significant at the .01 level of confidence, as indicated by a *t* test.

RELATIONSHIP OF THE ANXIETY SCALE TO OTHER MEASURES

The anxiety scale was developed for, and has been used exclusively as, a device for selecting experimental subjects, without regard to the relationship of the scores to more common clinical definitions (e.g., clinical observation). While defining degree of anxiety in terms of the anxiety-scale scores is a perfectly legitimate operational procedure, determining the relationship between this definition and clinical judgments might extend the applicability of both the scale and the experimental results found in the studies utilizing the scale.

In order to determine the relationship between the scale and clinical judgments, it would be necessary to have ratings made by trained observers for a large, randomly selected group of individuals and to correlate these with the anxiety-scale scores. Such an investigation has not yet been carried out. However, some indirect evidence on this point is provided by the anxiety scores of patients undergoing psychiatric treatment.[5] The anxiety scale used with these patients is essentially the same as the unrevised Biographical Inventory except that it is being administered in an individual form.

Anxiety scores are available for 103 neurotic and psychotic individuals, drawn from both an in- and outpatient population. As can be seen from Figure 3.16, the distribution of scores is highly skewed toward the low anxiety end of the scale. The median score is approximately

34, a score equivalent to the 98.8 percentile of the normal subjects shown in Figure 3.15. Thus the distributions of scores for the patient and the normal group are markedly different.

On the assumption that psychiatric patients will tend to exhibit more manifest anxiety symptoms (as determined by direct observation) than do normal individuals, this difference between the two groups appears to indicate that there is some relationship between the anxiety-scale scores and clinical observation of manifest anxiety.

SUMMARY

A manifest anxiety scale, consisting of items drawn from the Minnesota Multiphasic Personality Inventory judged by clinicians to be indicative of manifest anxiety, was developed as a device for selecting subjects for experiments in human motivation.

After statistical analysis the original 65-item scale was reduced to the 50 most discriminating statements. These items, supplemented by 225 statements nonindicative of anxiety, are given under the title of the Biographical Inventory. Normative data and test-retest correlations found with scale scores taken from the Biographical Inventory are presented.

A further revision of the scale was undertaken in which certain items were rewritten in an attempt to simplify their vocabulary and sentence structure. Characteristics of the scores obtained from this revised version were found to be similar to those of the previous form.

In an attempt to determine the relationship between the anxiety-scale scores and manifest anxiety as defined and observed by the clinician, the anxiety scores for groups of normal individuals and psychiatric patients were compared.

---

[5]These data are obtained from a study currently being conducted by the writer and K. W. Spence investigating the role of anxiety in neurotic and psychotic disorders by means of an eyelid conditioning technique.

REFERENCES

1. AHANA, E. A study on the reliability and internal consistency of a manifest anxiety scale. Unpublished master's thesis, Northwestern University, 1952.
2. CAMERON, N. *The psychology of behavior disorders: A bio-social interpretation.* Boston: Houghton Mifflin, 1947.
3. LUCAS, J. D."The interactive effects of anxiety, failure, and intraserial duplication." *American Journal of Psychology,* 1952, 65, 59–66.

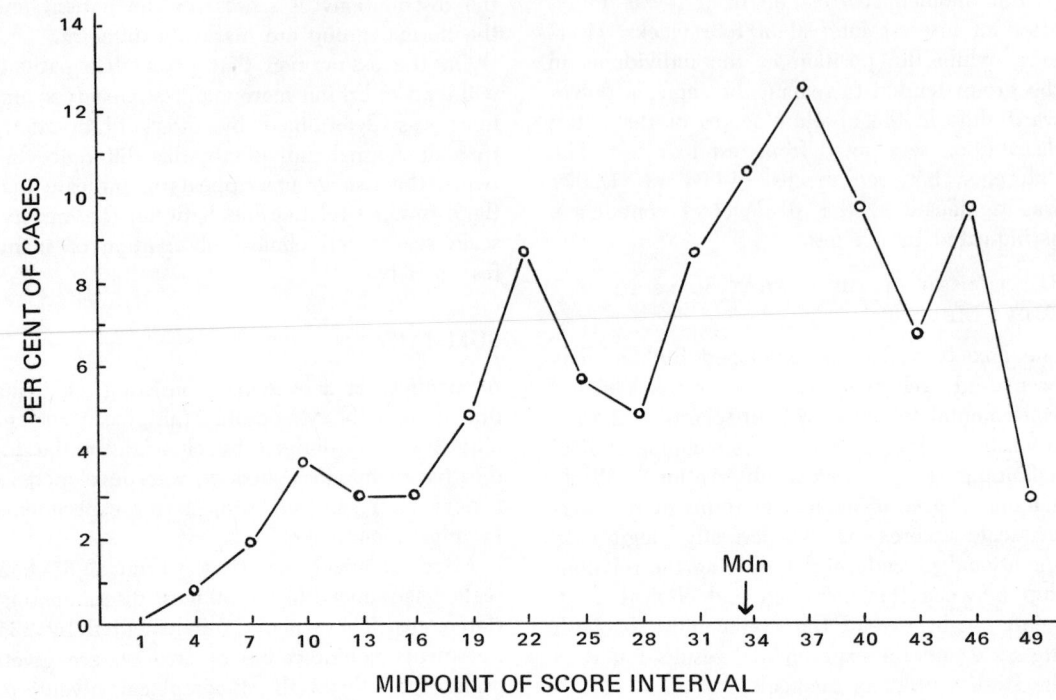

FIGURE 3.16. Graph of the frequency distribution of Manifest Anxiety Scores received by 103 psychiatric patients.

4. PECK, R. The influence of anxiety upon effectiveness of counseling. Unpublished doctor's dissertation, State University of Iowa, 1950.

5. SPENCE, K. W., & TAYLOR, JANET. Anxiety and strength of the UCS as determiners of the amount of eyelid conditioning. *Journal of Experimental Psychology*, 1951, *42*, 183–188.

6. TAYLOR, J. A. The relationship of anxiety to the conditioned eyelid response. *Journal of Experimental Psychology*, 1951, *41*, 81–92.

7. TAYLOR, J. A., & SPENCE, K. W. The relationship of anxiety to performance in serial learning.

Journal of Experimental Psychology, 1952, *44*, 61–64.

8. THORNDIKE, E. L., & LORGE, I. *Teacher's word book of 20,000 words.* New York: Teachers College, Columbia University, 1941.

9. WENAR, C. Reaction time as a function of manifest anxiety and stimulus intensity. Unpublished doctor's dissertation, State University of Iowa, 1950.

10. WESLEY, E. L. Perseverative behavior in a concept formation task. Unpublished doctor's dissertation, State University of Iowa, 1950.

21.

Raymond B. Cattell

MEASUREMENT OF NEUROTICISM AND ANXIETY

The techniques for unitary trait research can now be illustrated by focusing them on a single concept—the measurement of anxiety. The naive approach to research on anxiety has been to set up an arbitrary questionnaire that is validated by its ability to distinguish neurotics from normals. By contrast the factor analyst, alert to Francis Bacon's dictum about the tyranny of words, first asks two questions: (1) are there several anxieties or only one, as the single word anxiety might cajole us into believing, and (2) what are the behavioral measures that will give a relatively pure measure of this factor(s) suitable for investigating laws about anxiety?

When Scheier and Cattell experimented with this problem some six or seven years ago, the realm of questionnaire responses that covered *immediate introspective experience in anxiety* (and many other fields besides) had already been factor-analytically structured by the Sixteen Personality Factor (P.F.) Questionnaire and the Child Personality Questionnaire (Porter and Cattell, 1960). At first the inspection of 16 P.F. item content seemed to indicate that no fewer than five or six of these factors could be interpreted as forms of anxiety. A carefully planned factor-analytic experiment with 16 P.F. measurements on a large sample showed that those very same six primaries that on the meaning of their content would be considered anxiety are also united in *a single second-order factor* structurally. This structure is shown in Table 3.3, along with the structure of some other second-order factors for comparison.

From Raymond B. Cattell. Advances in the measurement of neuroticism and anxiety in a conceptual framework of unitary-trait theory. *Annals of the New York Academy of Sciences*, 93, Art. 20, 815–839; October 25, 1962. © The New York Academy of Sciences; 1962; Reprinted by permission. This paper was the first of three presented at a meeting of the Division of Psychology on January 15, 1962. This excerpt begins with p. 817.

What we call a factor structure, as shown in Table 3.3, is nothing more than the correlations of the second-order factors with the primaries, and, as usual, we cannot from correlational evidence alone decide the direction of causation. However, if we adopt the hypothesis that those primaries are sources of anxiety flowing into a total pool constituted by the second-order factor, the agreement of these findings with psychoanalytic conceptions is quite striking. The second-order structure here revealed would say, in effect, that high undischarged drive tension—the ergic tension or Q_4 factor in the 16 P.F.—together with O, high guilt, and C($-$), ego weakness, are the main sources of anxiety.

Scheier's article in this *Annals* will discuss interpretation, and, therefore, my treatment can be confined to a more complete survey of the factual evidence for anxiety as a functional unity. Proceeding beyond the evidence for questionnaire, introspective sources we turn next to the new realm of objective, *behavioral* tests of anxiety. Practically every measurable variable that a responsible investigator has ever claimed to be a manifestation of anxiety has now been included in the series of factor-analytic experiments covering this problem (Cattell and Scheier, 1961). The approximately 800 variables included hand tremor, blood pressure, behavioral lack of confidence in untried performances, parameters of voice quality, emotionality of comment, electrical skin resistance, digit span in memory, tendency to slips and errors, etc.

The verdict of such analyses over both normal and abnormal subject groups is now clear. A *single* general factor of anxiety, which we have indexed as Universal Index (U.I.) 24, covers, and is responsible for, most of these manifestations. It is true that a second factor covering somewhat different variables and requiring investigation as a possible factor of

TABLE 3.3

ANXIETY IN QUESTIONNAIRE RESPONSE PATTERNS

Factor II in Second-Order Rating and Questionnaire Factors: Average* Estimate From Available Researches of Loadings of First-Order Questionnaire and Rating Factors on Second-Order Factors

First-Order Factor	Second-Order Factor I Introversion-Extraversion or Invia-exvia			First-Order Factor	Second-Order Factor II Anxiety			First-Order Factor	Second-Order Factor III Pathemia (Affectivity) vs. Corticalertia			First-Order Factor	Second-Order Factor IV Promethean Will vs. Resignation		
	Adult† Trait	Adult State	Child‡ Trait		Adult Trait	Adult State	Child Trait		Adult Trait	Adult State	Child Trait		Adult Trait	Adult State	Child Trait
A–	–42	–38	–49	Q_4+	+67	+44	+44	I+	+44	+50	+19	N+	+32	+21	
F–	–40	–44	–44	O+	+60	+20	+50	N–	–37	–50		E+	+28	+52	+28
H–	–35	–22	–43	Q_3–	–53	–51	–33	A+	+28	+18	+60	Q_1+	+27	+12	
Q_2	+32	+39	+06	C–	–49	–53	–40	Q_3–	–21	–04	–02	J–	+14		–37
M+	+26	+36		L+	+45	+08		C–	–17	–08	–05	F+	–01	+17	+20
Q_1+	+19	+20		H–	–32	–06	–57	O+	+17	(–13)§	+07	Q_3+	+43	–07	–24
L+	+14	+12		M+	+30	+18						D+			+09
				Q_2+		+30						C–	–15	(+02)	–01
				D+			+43								

*In combining loadings from separate studies to arrive at an average, equal weights were usually used, but these were sometimes modified slightly according to size of N in the study, goodness of measurement of the factor in that study, etc.

†The state is a pattern of change-through-time for a given individual or set of individuals, whereas the trait is a pattern referring to interindividual differences at any given occasion of measurement.

‡From 6 to 15 years of age.

§Parentheses emphasize reversals from expected, consistent direction of association.

"bound anxiety" (U.I. 28) turned up. But setting this aside, the main U.I. 24 factor of unbound anxiety is what both laymen and professional psychologists talk about as anxiety, as witnessed by (1) the content of its variables, (2) its correlation with anxiety as independently rated by different psychiatrists, and, finally, (3) by a very neat coincidence of this objective, test factor with the second-order questionnaire factor that we have already tied down. The crucial experiment to see whether the questionnaire and the objective test factors of anxiety are the same was made when a large enough group could be found to undergo the five hours of testing necessary to include both areas of response. The results, shown in Table 3.4, bring together both a representative set of variables known to load the *objective* factor and the *questionnaire* primaries, the loadings on which have just the pattern required for the second-order questionnaire factor as found independently in Table 3.3.

TABLE 3.4
ANXIETY AS A TRAIT IN OBJECTIVE TESTS*

Highest Loaded Objective Test Variables	Approx. Mean Loading over 16 Experiments
High susceptibility to annoyance....	0.5
Readiness to confess unworthiness...	0.4
Lack of confidence in untried performance	0.3
Tendency to agree (test response set)	0.3
High emotionality of comment......	0.3
Restrained reading preferences.....	0.3
Fewer friends recalled............	0.3
Logical inconsistency in attitude responses	0.3
Low handwriting pressure	0.3
High ratio hard-headed to sentimental attitudes	0.3
High ratio of later to initial in novel performance	0.2
Cold pressor and startle response (pulse)	0.7†
C–, Low ego strength	0.4†
H–, High threctia (responsiveness to threat)	0.3†
L, High protension (paranoid).....	0.3†
O, Guilt proneness..............	0.5†
Q₃– Low self integration..........	0.6†
Q₄, High ergic tension............	0.6†

*Indexed as U.I. 24.
†Two experiments only.

The research up to this point supplies us with an objective and unambiguous basis for validating anxiety measures that we have taken advantage of by constructing the Objective-Analytic (O.A.) battery (Cattell, 1955) and the eight parallel-form battery (Scheier, 1960), but it still leaves much room for discussion of the *interpretation* of the anxiety pattern. Here the critical thinker will notice that the definition of the factor derives only from individual difference studies. That is to say the research asks what behaviors go together in anxiety as a *trait*. Theoretical interests urge us next to ask whether anxiety as a *state* is conceptually identical with anxiety as a *trait*. R-technique factor-analytic experiments, yielding a weighting pattern that is known to be correct for what characterologically *distinguishes different people*, strictly define a common *trait* pattern. To check whether the pattern for anxiety as a state or mood is similar to or different from the trait we have two possible methods—P-technique and Incremental R-technique (Cattell, 1957). I shall not discuss the statistical properties of these methods but shall point out that they study correlations of measurements made over time with regard to a set of variables that would be hypothesized to vary together with changing stimulation and internal condition as manifestations of a single underlying anxiety factor. More generally viewed, these techniques are capable of objectively revealing the *independent dimensions of human mood change* and of isolating the functional unities that operate as broad response patterns. A series of experiments (Cattell, 1957; Cattell and Scheier, 1961) using both psychological and physiological measures showed good mutual agreement in again indicating a single anxiety factor across objective tests and questionnaire primaries. As shown in Table 3.5, the pattern unmistakably has the same general character as that obtained by R-technique. However, there are also some interesting modifications from the trait pattern, which piques further and finer research. For example, raised systolic blood pressure is more strongly associated with anxiety as a state than as a trait.

These P-technique and incremental R-technique analyses of mood not only give a check

TABLE 3.5

ANXIETY AS A STATE*

Objective test variable

Total anxiety factor score (composite score from all previously known anxiety trait markers in this battery 0.72
High willingness to admit common faults 0.58
High susceptibility to annoyance 0.46
Fast rate of respiration 0.45
High plasma 17-OH in blood 0.43
High level of anxiety (questionnaire responses only) 0.37
Faster heart rate 0.30
Much lack of confidence in skill in untried performances 0.22
High level of psychiatrically-evaluated anxiety 0.20

Other purely physiological variables found associated with the anxiety-state factor†

Increase in systolic pulse pressure (4 studies)
Increase in heart rate (4 studies)
Increase in respiration rate (2 studies)
Increase in basal and current metabolic rate
Increase in phenyl hydracrylic acid in urine
Decrease in electrical skin resistance (2 studies)
Increase in hippuric acid in urine
Increase in 17-OH ketosteroid excretion (4 studies)
Decrease in alkalinity of saliva (2 studies)
Decrease in cholinesterase in serum
Decrease in neutrophils and, less clearly, eosinophils (2 studies)
Increase in phenylalanine, leucine, glycine, and serine
Increase in histidine in urine
Decrease in urea concentration (2 studies)
Decrease in glucuronidase in urine and in serum

*Data from Cattell and Scheier, 1961.
†The second set are listed in approximate order of degree of association and degree of confidence in confirmation. At lower levels of association and/or with less confidence, we can add to the above: Increase in body temperature, general corticosteroid excretion, sodium in serum, red cell count, volume of saliva secreted, and, possibly, palmar sweat. Decrease in blood glutathione, alkalinity of urine, phosphorus and potassium in serum, and staff neutrophils in white corpuscle count. Increase of hand tremor and of tension in trupezius (EMG), but decrease in involuntary muscle tension in arm and in handwriting pressure exerted.

on the agreement of the state and trait concepts of anxiety and yield a clear measurement basis for a battery of repeated anxiety-level observations, but also reveal some interesting relationships between anxiety as a state and other mood dimensions. Actually, some *nine* dimensions of mood-state change have so far been revealed by factor analysis and perhaps six of them, including elation-depression, excitement-torpor, and diurnal fatigue, have sufficiently clear loading patterns for us to

have constructed a state battery to measure them (Cattell, 1962). The main finding that is of importance to this present topic, however, is the existence of a new, additional pattern of *stress response* that is quite different from that of anxiety. This pattern, which we have called *effort stress* (because effort, rather than anxiety, is the central feature), has some relation to the first stage of Selye's general adaptation syndrome (Selye, 1953).

Much of the confusion and contradiction of findings that has prevailed during the past decade over both psychological associations and physiological effects of anxiety arise, we believe, from the inability of prefactorial research to recognize that two distinct factors are at work. These factors differ not only in their response pattern but also in their occasion and setting. The anxiety appears when the individual evades a reality demand and suffers internal conflict, whereas the effort stress appears when he forcefully grapples with reality. Such a theory of function would require a moderate —but significant—negative correlation of stress and anxiety in any person over time, and this in fact occurs, as shown in Figure 3.17, which places anxiety and stress in a second-order analysis of state factors.

Granted certain assumptions, it follows from this inverse relation of anxiety and stress in any one person over time that the person who gives more stress responses also gives fewer anxiety responses. . . . It is possible that a higher emotional lability is common to individuals with either high stress or high anxiety responsiveness, but otherwise they are opposite types and in this respect the psychosomatic should not be considered a neurotic.

* * *

The third part of Table 3.6, using data from the recent book on "The Meaning and Measurement of Neuroticism and Anxiety" (Cattell and Scheier, 1961), shows the magnitudes of the differences between neurotics and normals measured on sixteen of the eighteen then known general personality factors. The first part compares a group of major criminals, from a well-known high-security prison, with normals. In relation to theories of "oversocialization" we

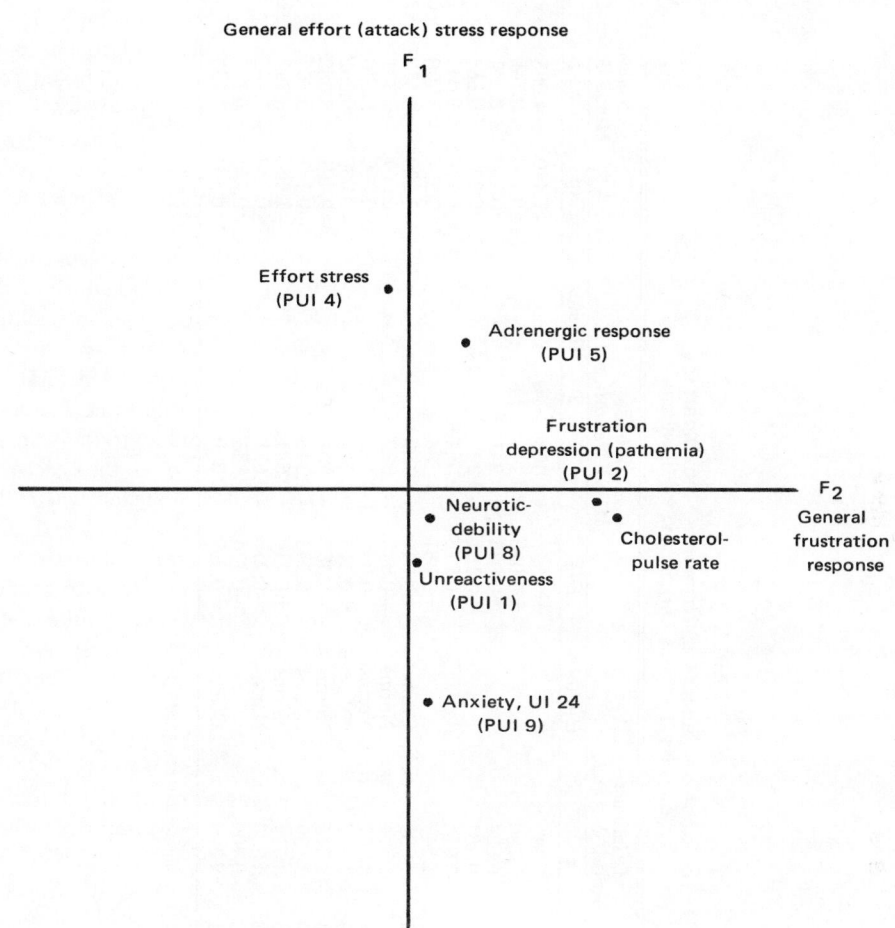

General effort (attack) stress response

F_1

Effort stress
(PUI 4)

Adrenergic response
(PUI 5)

Frustration
depression (pathemia)
(PUI 2)

F_2

Neurotic-
debility
(PUI 8)

Cholesterol-
pulse rate

General
frustration
response

Unreactiveness
(PUI 1)

Anxiety, UI 24
(PUI 9)

FIGURE 3.17. Effort stress and anxiety as opposites on an attack-retreat continuum (interrelation of state factors in second-order action).

should note that in some factors the neurotics and delinquents deviate in the *same* direction and in others they deviate in the *opposite*. For example, both are more anxious and less realistic than normals, but neurotics deviate oppositely from criminals in regard to higher comention, the factor most connected with moral behavior, and to rigid superego or asthenia.

Confining discussion here to clinical neurotics one notes that no fewer than six out of the eighteen factors here tried actually distinguish neurotics from normals beyond the one-per-cent level of confidence! The clinician is naturally interested in the individual meaning of these factors, but for the moment I want to show only that in practical effectiveness a very high diagnostic validity is implied. These factors are practically uncorrelated, so that statistically each contributes an essentially new kind of information. Thus a multiple correlation or discriminant function based on these measures might be expected to yield a very powerful separation of neurotics and normals. Actually, as shown in Figure 3.18, almost com-

TABLE 3.6

DIFFERENCES OF CRIMINALS, NEUROTICS, AND NORMALS ON PERSONALITY FACTORS OBJECTIVELY MEASURED

Factor Index	Source Trait	Criminals Minus Normals				Criminals Minus Neurotics				Neurotics Minus Normals			
		Diff.	t	P*	Higher	Diff.	t	P	Higher	Diff.	t	P	Higher
U.I. 16	Unbound ego	−0.059	−0.527			+1.381	+4.003	xx	Crims	−1.440	−4.068	xx	Norms
U.I. 17	Inhibition	+0.227	+1.760			+0.033	+0.146			+0.194	+0.749		
U.I. 18	Hypomania	+0.214	+0.824			+0.085	+0.241			+0.129	+0.441		
U.I. 19	Promethean will	+0.107	+0.431			−0.121	−0.399			+0.228	+0.884		
U.I. 20	Comention	+0.003	−0.014			−0.173	−0.584			+0.170	+0.641		
U.I. 23	Mobilization	−0.473	−1.848			+0.381	+1.194			−0.854	−3.500		Norms
U.I. 24	Anxiety	+1.262	+4.988	xx	Crims	+0.040	+0.120			+1.222	+4.577	xx	Neurots
U.I. 25	Composed realism	−1.309	−4.804	xx	Norms	−0.642	−2.032	x	Neurots	−0.667	−2.951	xx	Norms
U.I. 26	Self-control	−0.646	−2.401	x	Norms	−0.056	−0.189			−0.590	−2.576	xx	Norms
U.I. 27	Frustration-rejection	+0.479	+1.717			+0.515	+1.561			−0.036	−0.152		
U.I. 28	Rigid super ego	−0.786	−3.275	xx	Norms	−0.382	−1.504			−0.404	+2.082	x	Neurots
U.I. 30	Frustration accepting	−0.539	−2.130	x	Norms	−0.398	−1.345			−0.141	−0.557		
U.I. 32	Extraversion	−0.848	−3.519	xx	Norms	+0.216	+0.641			−1.064	−3.746	xx	Norms
U.I. 33	Dourness	−0.588	−2.380	x	Norms	−0.245	−0.671			−0.343	−1.132		
U.I. 34	Autism	−0.113	−0.409			−0.334	−0.888			+0.221	+0.752		
U.I. 35	Disillusionment	+0.561	+2.504	x	Crims	+0.097	+0.330			+0.464	+1.725		

*In P Column, xx = significant at < 0.01 level and x = significant at < 0.05 level.

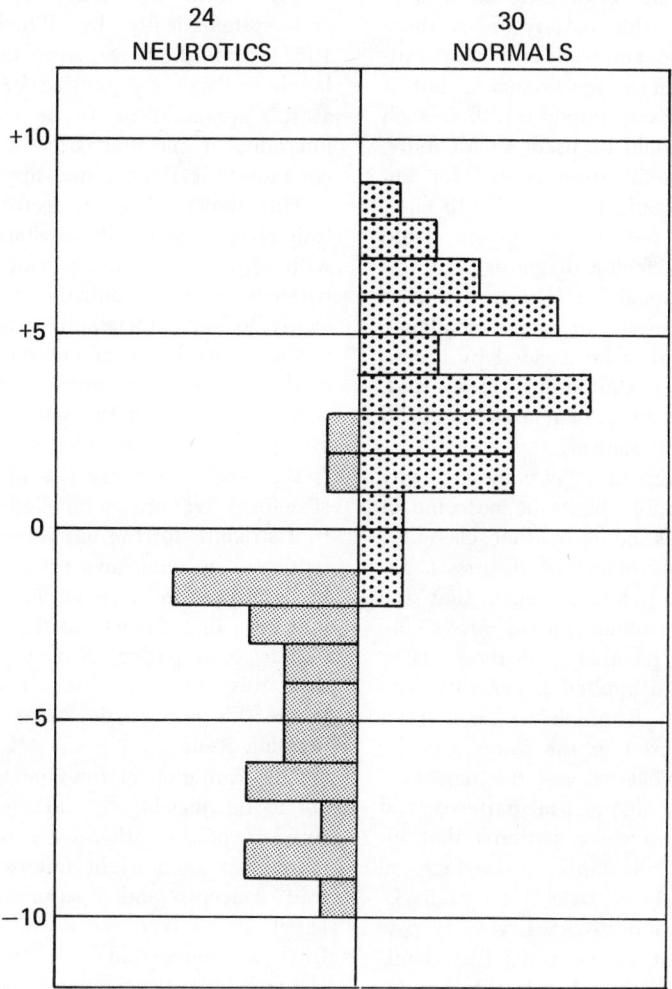

FIGURE 3.18. Diagnostic separation of normals and neurotics achieved by the O-A battery. Frequency histogram of the linear discriminant function for 30 normal and 24 neurotic subjects on objective test personality factors. A discriminant function analysis (Cattell and Scheier, 1961, pp. 181, 246–248) was carried out on the mean factor differences on all factors, between 30 normals and 24 neurotics in the R9-Ta study (see chapter 5 and appendix I, Cattell and Scheier, 1961). The diagram shows the actual distributions of the compound measurement in the two groups tested. The maximum likelihood cut-off point of —0.69 misclassifies two normals and two neurotics or only about 7 per cent of these subjects. Thus, the correct classification of over 90 per cent would seem to be appreciably higher (even allowing for shrinkage on subsequent samples) than that obtained by most current diagnostic techniques.

The above analysis was performed by Owen White, Research Assistant, The Laboratory of Personality Assessment and Group Behavior, University of Illinois.

plete separation of neurotics and normals is obtained. Of course, this battery takes three hours of testing time and demands more administrative skill than a questionnaire, but if reliability of diagnosis is important then such objective batteries should be used. Incidentally, in the interests of stimulating regard for improved diagnosis it would be a service to clinical psychology if a sort of tournament could be planned between factor diagnosis and traditional diagnosis through such instruments as the Rorschach. The results of such a challenge would, of course, need to be decided by a neutral party in neither contending camp and, perhaps on 50 varied types of neurotics and 50 control cases, by blind analysis.

Though an experimental psychologist may have virtually no doubt about the outcome of this challenge, let us be clear that classification is not the whole object of diagnosis. Indeed, it is on this point, perhaps, that the greatest failure of communication arises between the research factorist and those using traditional methods in applied personality psychology. By explicit definition a factor is a *common* trait, measured in the same way for all people. The clinician, if not the personnel man, is interested in *unique* trait patterns, and it is in his regard for these patterns that his apparently irrational reluctance to use factored measures is ultimately rooted. But certain issues have not been understood. Let every psychometrist admit that source traits like dominance, intelligence, or schizothymia obtained by R-technique are common traits with a form that is a sort of "greatest common measure" of all individual forms. An assigned score on the dominance factor is an average across levels on an agreed important set of common areas of expression and says nothing about the special areas in which that individual, for reasons of personal history and situation, is most given to expressing his dominance. Parenthetically, factor analysis *is* capable, by its various techniques (Cattell, 1957; Williams, H. V., 1954; Williams, J. R., 1959), of expressing the uniqueness of the individual. Even by R-technique it can express that uniqueness by designating for each person a unique combination of common traits. But it does so more completely and systematically by P-technique (Cattell, 1957). Here, however, since P-technique would be clinically very expensive, let us look squarely at this weakness or, to be exact, this explicit limitation, if one must use the ordinary unitary common-trait P-technique approach.

This limitation to measuring the common-trait form is especially obvious and discussable with respect to dynamic traits. Factor analysis happens to have contributed a great deal recently to our understanding of personality dynamics, notably by giving positive evidence as to the number and nature of drives and on the typical structure of the self (Cattell and Horn, 1963; Sweney and Cattell, 1961; Williams, J. R., 1959). In every one of these discovered structures we are compelled to measure the trait strength for the individual with a *common* battery. The clinician's response to this is that he is happy to have an instrument that tells him, say, that the narcissistic component of the sex drive in patient X is unusually high, but that this concerns him less than knowing *where* X's narcissistic drive is peculiarly expressing itself.

This limitation of the common-trait system is not to be questioned, and such measures need supplementation, therefore, in the consulting room. But an outright failure to use common-trait concepts and measurement for this alleged reason betokens some misunderstanding. It shows conceptual inability to perceive how common-trait measurements actually contribute to more reliable treatment of the unique individual. Perhaps a glance at an older field of therapy, physical medicine, can be helpful in clarifying this point. In psychotherapy, because of the poorness of his diagnostic instruments, the practitioner has got into the habit of prolonging his diagnosis into the treatment period, and he therefore tends to forget that essential logical sequence of diagnosis and therapy about which physical medicine is less obscure. Parenthetically, even if diagnosis has to be prolonged, it could be improved by explicit use of tests, as Scheier in his following paper shows in regard to repeated anxiety measures in conjunction with consulting-room incidents. However, the main point to note about physical measurement is that in taking a measure of blood pressure, or of glucose in the urine or basal metabolic rate, the physician is making a *common-trait* measurement, i.e., something that is the exact equivalent of a measure on our general personality factor levels measured similarly for everyone. The physician then comprehends the nature of the unique individual problem from a collection of common-trait measures—and the psychotherapist is missing considerable opportunities if he does not similarly avail himself of common-trait diagnostic information.

For example, if the factor indexed as U.I. 36 is ego strength, then it is important to have as exact a measure as possible of the neurotic's degree of weakness on this factor, both initially and throughout the course of treatment. The actual steps that the therapist undertakes to remedy a weak ego structure may have to do with working out all kinds of specific conflicts noted in the individual's past experience and in his present situation, all of which are truly unique to the individual. But the main evidence as to the success of therapy resides in the extent to which such unique dynamic restructuring and relearning finally results in significant changes on these common-trait measurements, such as ego strength and anxiety, that we definitely know distinguish the neurotic from the non-neurotic person.

* * *

REFERENCES

CATTELL, R. B. *The objective analytic (O-A) personality factor batteries.* Champaign, Ill.: The Institute for Personality and Ability Testing, 1955.

CATTELL, R. B. *Personality and motivation structure and measurement.* New York: Harcourt, World and Brace, 1957.

CATTELL, R. B. *The IPAT seven factor state battery: A research instrument.* Champaign, Ill.: The Institute for Personality and Ability Testing, 1962.

CATTELL, R. B., & SCHEIER, I. H. *The meaning and measurement of neuroticism and anxiety.* New York: Ronald Press, 1961.

PORTER, R. B., & CATTELL, R. B. *Handbook for the IPAT children's personality questionnaire.* Champaign, Ill.: The Institute for Personality and Ability Testing, 1960.

SCHEIER, I. H., & HORN, J. L. Objective test factor U.I. 23: Its relation to clinically judged neuroticism. *Journal of Clinical Psychology,* 1960, *16,* 135–145.

SELYE, H. The general adaptation syndrome, etc. In A. Weider (Ed.), *Contributions toward medical psychology.* New York: Ronald Press, 1953.

WILLIAMS, H. V. A determination of psychosomatic functional unities in personality by means of P-technique. *Journal of Social Psychology,* 1954, *39,* 25–45.

WILLIAMS, J. R. A test of the validity of the P-technique in the measurement of internal conflict. *Journal of Personality,* 1959, *27,* 418–437.

22.

DONN BYRNE

REPRESSION-SENSITIZATION SCALE

For over a decade, work in the area of perceptual defense has generated widespread interest and a deluge of empirical data. Since the Harvard studies in the late forties (Bruner &

From Donn Byrne, "The repression-sensitization scale: rationale, reliability, and validity." *Journal of Personality,* 1961, *29,* 334–349. Reprinted by permission of the author and the journal.

Postman, 1947a; Bruner & Postman, 1947b; Postman, Bruner, & McGinnies, 1948), articles dealing with this topic have been primarily of three varieties: the demonstration of differential recognition thresholds for matched pairs of neutral and emotionally-toned stimuli, attempts to explain (or explain away) these data, and the investigation of the correlates of individual differences in responding to such tachistoscopic tasks. While articles of the first two varieties have been the focus of a good deal of controversy, the third has involved a consistent and steadily growing body of evidence. The relevance of these findings to personality theory and their freedom from the earlier criticisms of work on perceptual defense has periodically been stressed (Eriksen, 1954b; Lazarus, 1954).

REPRESSION-SENSITIZATION AS A BEHAVIOR DIMENSION

Though terminology has varied somewhat across experiments, results with many different response measures suggest that individuals fall along a continuum with respect to the characteristic way in which they respond to threatening stimuli. At one extreme of his continuum are behavior mechanisms of a predominantly avoiding (denying, repressing) type, while at the other extreme are predominantly approaching (intellectualizing, obsessional) behaviors. Research utilizing differential recognition thresholds for emotionally-toned vs. neutral stimulus material has frequently employed the terms represser and sensitizer to describe representatives of the respective ends of this dimension. Individuals in the former category are defined as those exhibiting a relatively elevated threshold for emotional material (defense, disruption) and in the latter as those exhibiting a relatively lowered threshold for such material (vigilance, facilitation).

In several studies, a relationship was found between differential threshold scores and other behavior. Compared with sensitizers, individuals who respond repressively in a perceptual task also tend to be identified as represser on the basis of case history and interview material (Lazarus, Eriksen, & Fonda, 1951), to be classified by psychiatrics personnel as internalizers (Shannon, 1955), to remember successes better than failures in a scrambled-sentence task (Eriksen, 1952a), to forget an anxiety-arousing Blacky picture (Perloe, 1960), to prefer avoidance and forgetting defenses on the Blacky Defense Preference Inquiry (Nelson, 1955), to express less sexuality and hostility on a sentence-completion test (Lazarus *et al.*, 1951), to respond to a sentence-completion test with blocking, avoidance, denial, and cliches (Carpenter, Wiener, & Carpenter, 1956), to give evidence of inhibition and constriction on the Rorschach and a figure-drawing task (Kissin, Gottesfeld, & Dickes, 1957), and to give fewer TAT stories with aggressive themes (Eriksen, 1951). Negative results were reported by Kurland (1954) who found no relationship between therapist ratings of defense mechanisms and differential threshold scores.

Another series of studies dealing with this behavior dimension has utilized response measures other than threshold determination. In contrast to behavior which could be labeled repressing, sensitizing defenses are suggested by behavior in which individuals tend to recall failures and material associated with painful shock (Lazarus & Longo, 1953), to recall incompleted tasks in a threatening situation and learn affective words as easily as neutral ones (Eriksen, 1952b), to be able to verbalize the pattern of electric shock applied during a learning task and to be able to avoid the punished responses deliberately (Eriksen & Kuethe, 1956), to have a shorter latency for aggressive and succorant words on a word-association test and to accept such concepts on the Rorschach (Eriksen & Lazarus, 1952), to give more emotional words in response to appropriate TAT cards and to give more Rorschach responses (Ullmann, 1958), to respond to a sentence-completion test with admission of inadequacy and failure, rationalization, intellectualization, and humor (Wiener, Carpenter, & Carpenter, 1956), and to be sharpeners rather than levelers in a neutral psychophysical task (Holzman & Gardner, 1959).

An implicit assumption with a personality variable such as repression-sensitization is that individuals are consistent in their defensive reactions to threatening stimuli over a period of time. Attempts to establish intra-individual consistency have met with both success (Stein, 1953) and failure (Spence, 1957.) However, because almost every *E* devises his own methodology and seldom pauses to investigate the reliability of his measuring devices (Byrne & Holcomb, in press), negative findings are not as damaging as they might be.

Most of the evidence is positive and indicates that repression-sensitization is a meaningful behavior dimension. A series of hypotheses, involving this dimension both as an independent and as a dependent variable, have emerged from work in this area. In order to further this line of research, it would be helpful to have an easily administered, reliable, valid method by which these defenses could be measured. While several possibilities (including differential perceptual thresholds, Rorschach, TAT, Blacky, sentence completion test, and behavior ratings) have been utilized in the investigations just discussed, an MMPI approach seemed to meet the criteria most effectively.

AN MMPI SCALE TO MEASURE REPRESSION-SENSITIZATION

MMPI Defense Indicators. From time to time various scales of the MMPI have been used to measure defenses. Sensitizing behavior has been found to be characteristic of Ss scoring low on K and L (Page & Markowitz, 1955), high on the F minus K index (Ullmann, 1958), low on Hy (Eriksen, 1954a; Mathews & Wertheimer, 1958), low on the Hy denial scale (Carlson, 1954; Gordon, 1957; Gordon, 1959), high on the Hy admission scale (Gordon, 1959), low on the Hy minus Pt index (Eriksen & Davids, 1955; Truax, 1957), high on Pt (Carlson, 1954; Eriksen, 1954a; Eriksen & Browne, 1956; Eriksen & Davids, 1955; Eriksen, Kuethe, & Sullivan, 1958), and high on the MAS (Eriksen & Davids, 1955; Gordon, 1959). Repressive behavior is indicated by scores which lie in the opposite direction. In addition, a clinical interpretation of the total profile has been successfully used as an index of repression (LaForge, Leary, Naboisek, Coffey, & Freedman, 1954).

The Repression-Sensitization Scale. In a recent paper, Altrocchi, Parsons, and Dickoff (1960) report the use of a defense measure which was made up of a combination of six MMPI scales. Their measure of the repression-sensitization dimension was an index, representing the common theme of many previous measures of the dimension, in which the total of the D plus Pt plus Welsh Anxiety scores was subtracted from the L plus K plus Hy denial total.

High positive scores were defined as indicative of repressive behavior while high negative scores were defined as sensitization.

Several potential measurement difficulties arise with this measure because of item overlap among the six MMPI scales which are combined in it. For example, item 32 contributes to D, Pt, and Welsh Anxiety scores, thereby giving it an arbitrary weight of three. More confusing possibilities also arise. For example, item 30 contributes to D *and* to L, K, and Hy denial; thus, it is included in opposing halves of the index with a net weight of two for repression. While such differential item weights could conceivably prove to be the optimum ones, their accidental nature in this instance is clear.

To overcome these possible deficiencies, the author substituted a repression-sensitization scoring system in which each of the items comprising the six scales is scored only once; in addition, all inconsistently scored items were eliminated. In this new scale, high scores indicate sensitization and low scores repression. The items and scoring are given in Table 3.7.

TABLE 3.7
SCORING OF THE MMPI ITEMS (GROUP FORM) IN THE REPRESSION-SENSITIZATION SCALE

Items Scored True: 5, 6, 10, 12, 15, 22, 26, 32, 41, 43, 45, 52, 60, 67, 71, 75, 76, 86, 90, 93, 94, 102, 104, 105, 106, 109, 120, 124, 129, 130, 134, 135, 136, 138, 141, 142, 147, 148, 150, 158, 159, 162, 165, 170, 171, 172, 180, 182, 183, 189, 193, 195, 201, 213, 217, 225, 234, 236, 238, 255, 259, 265, 266, 267, 278, 279, 288, 289, 290, 292, 301, 304, 305, 316, 321, 322, 336, 337, 340, 342, 343, 344, 345, 346, 349, 351, 352, 356, 357, 358, 359, 360, 361, 362, 374, 382, 383, 384, 389, 396, 397, 398, 406, 411, 414, 418, 431, 443, 461, 465, 499, 502, 511, 518, 544, 555.
Items Scored False: 2, 3, 8, 9, 18, 36, 46, 51, 57, 58, 64, 80, 88, 95, 96, 98, 107, 122, 131, 145, 152, 153, 154, 155, 164, 178, 191, 207, 208, 233, 241, 242, 248, 253, 263, 270, 271, 329, 353, 379.

In order to establish the reliability and validity of this scale for a college population, a questionnaire was designed which contained all 182 items of the six original scales in the order in which they appear in the MMPI. The questionnaire consists of 156 scorable and 26 buffer items.

Reliability and Norms

Coefficient of internal consistency. To determine the split-half reliability of the scale, the test booklet was administered to 133 students (60 males, 73 females) enrolled in introductory psychology courses at the University of Texas. Scores on odd and even items constituted the two halves of the test. The coefficient of internal consistency was found to be .88, corrected by the Brown-Spearman formula.

Coefficient of stability. Another sample of students from the same population was utilized to establish the stability of the score over time. The test was administered to a group of 75 students (37 males, 38 females) and then readministered six weeks later. The coefficient of stability was also found to be .88. These two reliability estimates are of sufficient magnitude to warrant the further use of this scale in research.

Norms. Because the most immediate research contemplated with the test involves the use of college students as Ss, the normative data obtained up to the present time are limited to this group. It is quite unlikely that these norms would be appropriate for other populations such as neuropsychiatric patients. In addition, to the extent that introductory psychology students at the University of Texas represent a special group, the reported figures may be inappropriate for other college populations.

With these limitations in mind, the material presented in Table 3.8 consists of summary data for the total of 624 Ss to whom the test has been administered. The difference between the mean scores of male and female Ss is not statistically significant.

TABLE 3.8

NORMATIVE DATA FOR REPRESSION-SENSITIZATION SCALE

	Frequency Distribution	
	Males	*Females*
110–119	2	1
100–109	9	2
90–99	31	6
80–89	35	25
70–79	51	39
60–69	72	48
50–59	100	53
40–49	66	40
30–39	26	13
20–29	1	3
10–19	1	—
Mean	63.08	61.80
Standard deviation	17.71	16.20
N	394	230

CONCURRENT AND CONSTRUCT VALIDITY

The studies described below involve a correlational approach to test validation. Since there is no definitive criterion measure of the repression–sensitization behavior dimension, each of the studies is best conceptualized as relevant to the establishment of concurrent and/or construct validity. The purpose of this research was not to test hypotheses growing out of a theory of defensive behavior. Rather there was an effort to determine whether or not scores obtained on the R–S scale are (*a*) consistent with scores on an instrument designed to measure a similar behavior dimension and (*b*) related to various response measures in a manner consistent with previously reported indices of repression–sensitization.

ULLMANN'S FACILITATION–INHIBITION SCALE

Background. Shannon (1955) defined three types of defensive reaction as internalization (avoidance of anxiety by denial), externalization (avoidance of anxiety by projecting the motivation onto others), and acting-out (avoidance of anxiety by immediate expression of the conflict in verbal or nonverbal behavior). With neuropsychiatric patients classified according to these definitions, he found a highly significant relationship between defensive behavior as judged by hospital personnel and defensive behavior as measured by a tachistoscopic task. Internalizers responded to sexual, aggressive, and dependency stimuli with perceptual repression while externalizers and acters-out responded with perceptual sensitization. In subsequent work with Shannon's defense categories, the latter two defensive reactions are usually grouped together as facilitators in contrast to inhibitors (internalizers). On the basis of the perceptual differences, inhibition–facilitation appears to correspond with repression–sensitization.

Following up Shannon's investigation, Ullmann (1958) devised a reliable scale for rating case history records for these types of behavior mechanisms. In order to increase the objectivity of measurement and to obtain a more economical measuring system, he developed (Ullmann, 1960) an empirical MMPI scale to measure facilitation-inhibition. With case history ratings as the criterion, 43 cross-validated MMPI items were found to discriminate patients in the two defense categories and to constitute a reliable test.

The origin of Ullmann's scale suggests that it is measuring the same behavior dimension as the R–S scale. Since the two tests are scored in the opposite direction, it is hypothesized that they will be negatively correlated.

Procedure. A total of 64 students (40 males, 24 females) were given the R-S scale and the Facilitation-Inhibition scale several weeks apart.

Results. A difficulty arises in correlating the two sets of scores because both scales utilize MMPI items and 20 of these are common to both instruments. Thus, simply ascertaining the relationship between the total scores should yield a spuriously high coefficient. On the other hand, removing the common items from both instruments would shorten each, decrease the reliability of measurement, and probably yield a spuriously low correlation. There are also intermediate possibilities in which the overlapping items are removed from one scale and not the other. The results of each of these types of comparison are reported in Table 3.9. There is a statistically significant negative relationship between scores obtained on the two scales, whether or not the overlapping items are excluded. The hypothesized relationship was confirmed.[1]

TABLE 3.9

RELATIONSHIP BETWEEN FACILITATION–INHIBITION SCALE AND R–S SCALE

Variables	r	p
F–I scale and R–S scale	−.76	<.01
Abridged F–I scale* and R–S scale	−.71	<.01
F–I scale and abridged R–S scale*	−.81	<.01
Abridged F–I scale* and abridged R–S scale*	−.71	<.01

*Minus overlapping items.

[1] Dr. Ullmann (personal communication) has carried out a similar correlational study, using a population of 64 male hospitalized patients. He found that the Facilitation-Inhibition scale correlates −.94 with the R–S scale (both scales unabridged). Greater variability in defensive behavior within the

SELF-IDEAL DISCREPANCY

Background. The degree of congruency between an individual's description of himself as he is and as he would like to be has frequently been used as a measure of psychological adjustment. However, a person who characteristically utilizes repressive defense mechanisms might be considerably less likely to verbalize negative self descriptions (to himself or to E) than a person whose defenses are characteristically sensitizing. And, on at least one such measuring instrument —Worchel's (1957) Self Activity Inventory—the self–ideal discrepancy score is primarily a function of differences in self descriptions. With a sample of 57 students, the author found that negative self descriptions on the test correlated .74 ($p < .01$) with the discrepancy score while negative ideal–self descriptions correlated −.08 (n.s.). Therefore, defense mechanisms should be expected to influence self scores (and hence discrepancy scores) but not ideal-self scores.

There is some evidence that repressing individuals tend to describe themselves more positively on Leary's Interpersonal Check List (Altrocchi *et al.*, 1960) and in a Q-sort task (Block & Thomas, 1955; Chodorkoff, 1954) than do individuals who utilize sensitizing defenses. On the basis of these studies, it is hypothesized that the R–S scale is positively related to negative self descriptions, positively related to the degree of discrepancy between descriptions of self and ideal–self, and unrelated to negative ideal–self descriptions.

Procedure. In two independent investigations, students enrolled in introductory psychology courses at the University of Texas were given the R–S scale and Worchel's SAI on different days by different Es. The SAI is a measure of self-ideal discrepancy which consists of 51 statements describing hostile, achievement-oriented, sexual, and dependency behavior. S indicates on a five-point scale the degree to which the statement describes him as he is and the degree to which it describes the sort of person he would like to be. The discrepancy score consists of the total absolute difference between

hospital group probably accounts for the greater magnitude of the correlation coefficient in Ullmann's study. Using a sample of 132 psychiatric patients, Ullmann also found that 72 of the 156 R–S scale items significantly differentiate facilitators and inhibitors identified on the basis of case history material.

self and ideal ratings for each item. In the first study, Ss consisted of 98 students (48 males, 50 females) for whom only the discrepancy scores from the SAI were available. In the second, Ss consisted of 57 students (37 males, 20 females) for whom self, ideal-self, and discrepancy scores were available.

Results. In the first sample, repression–sensitization correlated .62 ($p < .01$) with self–ideal discrepancy. In the second sample, the R–S scale correlated .55 ($p < .01$) with self–ideal discrepancy, .66 ($p < .01$) with self description, and .25 (n.s.) with ideal–self description. Again, the hypothesized relationships were confirmed.

AUTHORITARIANISM

Background. Individuals high on the authoritarian dimension have been described (Adorno, Frenkel-Brunswick, Levinson, & Sanford, 1950) as repressers who do not accept their own sexual and aggressive impulses, avoid introspection and insight, and are unaware of their hostility toward parental figures. Conversely, nonauthoritarians have been described as intellectualizers who manifest a greater readiness to become aware of their unacceptable tendencies and impulses, to ruminate about their weaknesses, to experience anxiety, and to admit ambivalent feelings toward parental figures.

Additional support for these formulations was supplied by Kogan (1956). He obtained auditory recognition scores for sexual, aggressive and neutral sentences. The ratio between sex recognition scores and neutral recognition scores were negatively correlated with F scales scores; the same relationship was found between authoritarianism and the aggressive/neutral ratio. If the R–S scale is measuring the same behavior dimension as Kogan's perceptual task, this scale should also be negatively related to authoritarianism.

Procedure. A ten-item F scale was constructed in which five of the items were the reversed ones developed by Couch and Keniston (1960) and five were conventional F scale items (Numbers 1, 8, 13, 18, and 42 from Forms 45 and 40). Thus, total score was not confounded with any response set to agree or disagree. This measure of authoritarianism and the R–S scale were administered by different Es several weeks apart. A total of 73 students (36 males, 37 females) were given each test.

Results. The correlation between this F scale and the R–S scale was found to be $- .40$ ($p < .01$). The hypothesis was confirmed.

SEX, AGGRESSION, AND EMOTIONALITY ON THE TAT

Background. Eriksen (1951) has argued that the patterns of defensive responses which are elicited by perceptual tasks should be reflected in projective test responses. Using male neuropsychiatric patients, he found that Ss with low recognition thresholds for aggressive stimuli gave more TAT stories with aggression as a main theme than did Ss with high recognition thresholds for such stimuli. Ullmann (1958) made a similar argument with respect to inhibitors and facilitators. Classifying male neuropsychiatric patients on the basis of case history material, he found that facilitators responded to appropriate TAT cards with more emotional words than did inhibitors.

Several assumptions were tentatively made in planning the following investigation. It was assumed that the R–S scale measures a general tendency to approach or avoid threatening stimuli; that sexual, aggressive, and emotional responses represent some degree of threat to almost everyone in our culture; and that individual differences in defensive behavior are sufficiently great in a normal population to yield differences in fantasy productions comparable to those found in hospital populations. If these assumptions are tenable, Ss with high scores on the R–S scale should respond to TAT cards with more sexuality and aggression and with a greater proportion of emotional words than Ss with low scores.

Procedure. From a total group of 213 introductory psychology students whose R–S scores were available, 29 with high scores (78 to 110) and 24 with low scores (18 to 47) were selected. In groups of 2 to 15, they were shown nine TAT cards (20, 12BG, 14, 6GF, 6BM, 18GF, 7BM, 3BM, 13MF) according to Atkinson's (1958, pp. 836–837) administration procedure. Without knowledge of each S's R–S score, the protocols were scored for sexual content[2] (Mussen & Scodel, 1955), aggressive content (Feshbach, 1955), and the number of emotional words (Ullmann, 1957). Scoring by two independent judges resulted in correlation of .94, .87, and .998 which indicates high interscorer reliability for each scoring system.

[2] Card 18GF was not scored for sex because Mussen and Scodel used only the other eight cards.

Results. For the three sets of scores, the data were examined for males and females separately to compare sensitizers and repressers. In Table 3.10 the means and standard deviations are shown. A series of t tests were computed in order to compare the two defense groups for each TAT score. Neither the aggression score nor the percentage of emotional words were found to be related to the defense measure. However, the male sensitizers had significantly higher sexual scores than the male repressers $(t = 2.86, df = 38, p < .01)$. Sex scores for the female sensitizers and repressers differed in the same direction, and the magnitude of the difference was slightly greater than for male Ss. However, the difference was not statistically significant $(t = 1.42, df = 11, p < .20)$. It should be noted that there were only 13 female Ss in contrast to 40 males.

In brief, the hypothesis relating sexual fantasy productions and defenses was partially confirmed, those concerning aggressive fantasy and the use of emotional words were not.

DEVIANT RESPONSE BIAS

Background. Berg (1955) has proposed that deviant response patterns (responses which differ from the modal response of the group) constitute a general personality characteristic. Therefore, the tendency to respond deviantly to any stimulus should be related to the tendency to engage in any deviant behavior, including those which we label abnormal. A considerable amount of evidence has been presented to support this contention (e.g., Berg, 1955; Berg, 1958).

Following Berg's lead, Grigg and Thorpe (1960) used Gough's Adjective Check List and established modal and deviant responses for university freshmen. They then constructed a scale made up of the 33 most commonly and 39 least commonly checked adjectives. The deviant response score equals the number of the latter words checked plus the number of the former words not checked. It was found that the mean deviant response score of students seeking psychiatric and personal counseling was significantly higher than that of unselected students and those seeking vocational counseling.

If deviant response set on this instrument is a general measure of maladjustment, the R–S scale should be related to it in a curvilinear fashion. However, if defense mechanisms are operative in influencing the checking of adjectives, it would be hypothesized that a positive, linear relationship exists between defense scores and deviant response scores.

Procedure. In two separate investigations, students in introductory psychology courses were given both the R–S scale and the 72-item Adjective Check List. In the first study a group of 50 males and in the second a group of 63 Ss (40 males, 23 females) were given the two tests on separate testing sessions.

Results. In both instances, a positive correlation between the two sets of scores was found with no evidence of curvilinearity. For the first group the correlation was .42 $(p < .01)$ and for the second .33 $(p < .01)$. The second of the two hypotheses was thus confirmed. There seems to be a small but statistically significant tendency for the most deviant responses to be made by sensitizers and for the most repressive Ss to make modal responses.

TABLE 3.10
TAT SCORES FOR SEX, AGGRESSION, AND EMOTIONAL WORDS

	Males				Females			
	Repressers ($N = 18$)		Sensitizers ($N = 22$)		Repressers ($N = 6$)		Sensitizers ($N = 7$)	
	M	SD	M	SD	M	SD	M	SD
Sex	4.39	3.13	7.91	4.39	1.50	3.57	5.29	5.58
Aggression	1.70	.48	1.89	.61	1.76	.69	1.74	.56
Percentage of Emotional Words	8.88	4.15	9.62	2.30	9.18	1.84	9.77	2.32

INTELLIGENCE

Background. In investigating construct validity, the absence of a relationship with a theoretically irrevelant construct can be as important as the presence of predicted relationships. In the case of the repression–sensitization dimension and intelligence, neither theory nor empirical findings would lead to the postulation of a relationship.

Procedure. Two separate studies, using different measures of intelligence, were carried out. In the first, 132 students (60 males, 72 females) were given the R–S scale and the Shipley-Hartford scale. In the second, 26 males were given the R–S scale, and their standard scores (based on a University of Texas freshman population) on a college entrance test were obtained.

Results. In neither study was a relationship found between repression–sensitization and a measure of intellectual ability. Correlation with the Shipley-Hartford was − .15 (n.s.) and with the entrance test scores .25 (n.s.).

INDEPENDENCE OF SAMPLES

In this portion of the paper, dealing with validity, nine different studies were reported. It should be noted, however, that it was not possible to secure nine independent samples of Ss. Actually, students were drawn by a variety of Es from three distinct subject pools. In the first, 132 Ss participated in the first IQ study, and 98 of these individuals also took part in the first SAI study. In the second, 50 Ss were drawn for the first deviant-response-bias investigation, and 26 of them also took part in the second IQ study. In the third, 127 Ss participated in the work on the remaining five studies. Of these Ss 48 participated in only one study (25 for Authoritarianism, 21 for the TAT, and one each for the Ullmann and second deviant-response-bias investigations) while 13 took part in all five. Of the remaining Ss in this pool, in various combinations, four of the tests were given to 21 Ss, three to 27 Ss, and two to 18 Ss.

Even though the use of nine different populations would have been a preferred procedure, it is well to remember that four of the six reported relationships were replicated on independent samples.

DISCUSSION

The body of findings reported here lend support to the propositions that the R–S scale is a reliable measuring instrument and that it is a measure of defense mechanisms as defined by previous work in the area.

Also, some additional problems have been touched upon. Two proposed measures of maladjustment (self–ideal discrepancy and deviant-response bias) were found to be positively related to the repression–sensitization dimension. There appears to be a strong possibility that psychodiagnostic instruments which rely on self-ratings in one form or another tend to identify as maladjusted those who respond to stress with sensitizing mechanisms while overlooking the repressing individuals. An alternate possibility is that scores on the repressing end of this dimension represent optimum adjustment.

The lack of relationship between the defense measure and aggressive and emotional TAT responses points up the difficulty in generalizing across populations as different as hospitalized patients and university freshmen. Perhaps the positive results reported by Eriksen (1951) and Ullmann (1958) with neuropsychiatric patients depended on the degree of anxiety evoked by such cues as emotionally disturbed individuals. The fact that the sexual responses did yield positive results in this study for the male Ss is possibly a function of a greater degree of anxiety arousal by sexual than by aggressive and emotional cues in a college population. In addition, female Ss might well be found to yield similar results if (*a*) a female E is used to decrease the possible tendency of female sensitizers to suppress sexual responses deliberately and (*b*) a larger sample is used.

In future work, an attempt will be made to refine the R–S scale in order to increase its reliability as a measuring device. It seems likely that in a college population many of the MMPI items are inappropriate. One approach to increasing the reliability of this instrument will be that of an item analysis in which the goal will be greater homogeneity of the scale. Additional research plans call for a presentation of theoretical and empirical material dealing with (*a*) the antecedent childhood conditions which result in individual differences in defensive behavior, (*b*) defensive response tendency as an intervening variable in a number of stimulus-response relationships, and (*c*) the possibility of bringing about either permanent or temporary changes in defense mechanisms.

SUMMARY

Work in the area of perceptual defense has led to the concept of a behavior dimension comprising psychological defenses ranging from repression to sensitization. Several scales of the MMPI have been found to be related to this dimension, and the present test consists of a combination of six of these scales. In a college population, the coefficient of internal consistency was found to be .88, and the coefficient of stability was also .88. Normative data were presented.

A series of studies were undertaken in order to contribute to the establishment of concurrent and construct validity for the repression–sensitization scale. It was found that the R–S scale is negatively correlated with Ullmann's Facilitation–Inhibition scale; positively correlated with self–ideal discrepancy and with negative self description but unrelated to ideal–self descriptions; negatively correlated with the California F scale; positively related to the expression of sexual responses on the TAT for male Ss only and unrelated to the expression of aggression and emotionality for either sex; positively correlated with deviant-response bias on an Adjective Check List; and unrelated to measures of intellectual ability.

Thus, the R–S scale appears to be a reliable test, and, with minor exceptions, the evidence suggests that it is a measure of defensive behavior.

REFERENCES

ADORNO, T. W., FRENKEL-BRUNSWIK, E., LEVINSON, D. J., & SANFORD, R. N. *The authoritarian personality.* New York: Harper, 1950.

ALTROCCHI, J., PARSONS, O. A., & DICKOFF, H. Changes in self-ideal discrepancy in repressors and sensitizers. *Journal of Abnormal and Social Psychology,* 1960, *61*, 67–72.

ATKINSON, J. W. (Ed.). *Motives in fantasy, action, and society.* Princeton: D. Van Nostrand, 1958.

BERG, I. A. Response bias and personality: The Deviation Hypothesis. *Journal of Psychology,* 1955, *40*, 61–72.

BERG, I. A. The unimportance of test item content. In B. M. Bass & I. A. Berg (Eds.), *Objective approaches to personality assessment.* New York: Van Nostrand, 1958. Pp. 83–99.

BLOCK, J., & THOMAS, H. Is satisfaction with self a measure of adjustment? *Journal of Abnormal and Social Psychology,* 1955, *51*, 254–259.

BRUNER, J. S., & POSTMAN, L. Emotional selectivity in perception and reaction. *Journal of Personality,* 1947, *16*, 69–77. (a)

BRUNER, J. S., & POSTMAN, L. Tension and tension-release as organizing factors in perception. *Journal of Personality,* 1947, *15*, 300–308. (b)

BYRNE, D., & HOLCOMB, J. The reliability of response measure: Differential recognition-threshold scores. *Psychological Bulletin* (in press).

CARLSON, V. R. Individual differences in the recall of word-association-test words. *Journal of Personality,* 1954, *23*, 77–87.

CARPENTER, B., WIENER, M., & CARPENTER, J. T. Predictability of perceptual defense behavior. *Journal of Abnormal and Social Psychology,* 1956, *52*, 380–383.

CHODORKOFF, B. Self-perception, perceptual defense, and adjustment. *Journal of Abnormal and Social Psychology,* 1954, *49*, 508–512.

COUCH, A., & KENISTON, K. Yeasayers and naysayers: Agreeing response set as a personality variable. *Journal of Abnormal and Social Psychology,* 1960, *60*, 151–174.

ERIKSEN, C. W. Some implications for TAT interpretation arising from need and perception experiments. *Journal of Personality,* 1951, *19*, 282–288.

ERIKSEN, C. W. Defense against ego-threat in memory and perception. *Journal of Abnormal and Social Psychology,* 1952, *47*, 230–235. (a)

ERIKSEN, C. W. Individual differences in defensive forgetting. *Journal of Experimental Psychology,* 1952, *44*, 442–446. (b)

ERIKSEN, C. W. Psychological defenses and "ego-strength" in the recall of completed and incompleted tasks. *Journal of Abnormal and Social Psychology,* 1954, *49*, 45–50. (a)

ERIKSEN, C. W. The case for perceptual defense. *Psychological Review,* 1954, *61*, 175–182. (b)

ERIKSEN, C. W., & BROWNE, C. T. An experimental and theoretical analysis of perceptual defense. *Journal of Abnormal and Social Psychology,* 1956, *52*, 224–230.

ERIKSEN, C. W., & DAVIDS, A. The meaning and clinical validity of the Taylor anxiety scale and the hysteria-psychasthenia scales from the MMPI. *Journal of Abnormal and Social Psychology,* 1955, *50*, 135–137.

ERIKSEN, C. W., & KUETHE, J. L. Avoidance conditioning of verbal behavior without awareness: A paradigm of repression. *Journal of Abnormal and Social Psychology*, 1956, 53, 203–209.

ERIKSEN, C. W., KUETHE, J. L., & SULLIVAN, D. F. Some personality correlates of learning without verbal awareness. *Journal of Personality*, 1958, 26, 216–228.

ERIKSEN, C. W., & LAZARUS, R. S. Perceptual defense and projective tests. *Journal of Abnormal and Social Psychology*, 1952, 47, 302–308.

FESHBACH, S. The drive-reducing function of fantasy behavior. *Journal of Abnormal and Social Psychology*, 1955, 50, 3–11.

GORDON, J. E. Interpersonal predictions of repressors and sensitizers. *Journal of Personality*, 1957, 25, 686–698.

GORDON, J. E. The stability of the assumed similarity response set in repressors and sensitizers. *Journal of Personality*, 1959, 27, 362–373.

GRIGG, A. E., & THORPE, J. S. Deviant responses in college adjustment clients: A test of Berg's Deviation Hypothesis. *Journal of Consulting Psychology*, 1960, 24, 92–94.

HOLZMAN, P. S., & GARDNER, R. W. Leveling and repression. *Journal of Abnormal and Social Psychology*, 1959, 59, 151–155.

KISSIN, B., GOTTESFELD, H., & DICKES, R. Inhibition and tachistoscopic thresholds for sexually charged words. *Journal of Psychology*, 1957, 43, 333–339.

KOGAN, N. Authoritarianism and repression. *Journal of Abnormal and Social Psychology*, 1956, 53, 34–37.

KURLAND, S. H. The lack of generality in defense mechanisms as indicated in auditory perception. *Journal of Abnormal and Social Psychology*, 1954, 49, 173–177.

LAFORGE, R., LEARY, T. F., NABOISEK, H., COFFEY, H. S., & FREEDMAN, M. B. The interpersonal dimension of personality: II. An objective study of repression. *Journal of Personality*, 1954, 23, 129–153.

LAZARUS, R. S. Is there a mechanism of perceptual defense? A reply to Postman, Bronson, & Gropper. *Journal of Abnormal and Social Psychology*, 1954, 49, 396–398.

LAZARUS, R. S., ERIKSEN, C. W., & FONDA, C. P. Personality dynamics and auditory perceptual recognition. *Journal of Personality*, 1951, 19, 471–482.

LAZARUS, R. S., & LONGO, N. The consistency of psychological defense against threat. *Journal of Abnormal and Social Psychology*, 1953, 48, 495–499.

MATHEWS, ANNE, & WERTHEIMER, M. A "pure" measure of perceptual defense uncontaminated by response suppression. *Journal of Abnormal and Social Psychology*, 1958, 57, 373–376.

MUSSEN, P. H., & SCODEL, A. The effects of sexual stimulation under varying conditions on TAT sexual responsiveness. *Journal of Consulting Psychology*, 1955, 19, 90.

NELSON, S. E. Psychosexual conflicts and defenses in visual perception. *Journal of Abnormal and Social Psychology*, 1955, 51, 427–433.

PAGE, H. A., & MARKOWITZ, GLORIA. The relationship of defensiveness to rating scale bias. *Journal of Psychology*, 1955, 40, 431–435.

PERLOE, S. I. Inhibition as a determinant of perceptual defense. *Perceptual and Motor Skills*, 1960, 11, 59–66.

POSTMAN, L., BRUNER, J. S., & McGINNIES, E. Personal values as selective factors in perception. *Journal of Abnormal and Social Psychology*, 1948, 43, 142–154.

SHANNON, D. T. The effects of ego-defensive reactions on reported perceptual recognition. Unpublished doctoral dissertation, Stanford University, 1955.

SPENCE, D. P. A new look at vigilance and defense. *Journal of Abnormal and Social Psychology*, 1957, 54, 103–108.

STEIN, K. B. Perceptual defense and perceptual sensitization under neutral and involved conditions. *Journal of Personality*, 1953, 21, 467–478.

TRUAX, C. B. The repression response to implied failure as a function of the hysteria-psychasthenia index. *Journal of Abnormal and Social Psychology*, 1957, 55, 188–193.

ULLMANN, L. P. Productivity and the clinical use of TAT cards. *Journal of Projective Techniques*, 1957, 21, 399–403.

ULLMANN, L. P. Clinical correlates of facilitation and inhibition of response to emotional stimuli. *Journal of Projective Techniques*, 1958, 22, 341–347.

ULLMANN, L. P. An empirically derived MMPI scale that measures facilitation—inhibition of recognition of threatening stimuli. *Res. Rep. of VA Palo Alto*, No. 10, 1960.

WIENER, M., CARPENTER, B., & CARPENTER, JANETH T. Determination of defense mechanisms for conflict areas from verbal material. *Journal of Consulting Psychology*, 1956, 20, 215–219.

WORCHEL, P. Adaptability screening of flying personnel: Development of a self-concept inventory for predicting maladjustment. SAM, USAF, Randolph AFB, Texas, No. 56–62, 1957.

CHAPTER IV

Psychosomatic and
Stress Disorders

Cases in which emotional or psychic disturbances are responsible for organic or physical disorders are termed *psychosomatic*. Occasionally psychosomatic disorders are regarded as the counterpart of ailments which are physically based yet possess psychical concomitants; these latter are termed somatopsychic disorders (White, 1964, p. 391). Pope and Scott restrict the term psychosomatic to those disorders in which "somatic and psychological signs and symptoms may both be expressions of a single pathological process" (1967, p. 276).

Essential hypertension, bronchial asthma, ulcerative colitis, migraine headaches, arthritis, peptic and duodenal ulcers are examples of the psychosomatic, while encephalitis, head injury, and tuberculosis exemplify the somatopsychic. Stern (1964) adds still a third category in which the psychic plays a part in all ailments. The above-mentioned ailments do not exhaust the list of psychosomatic disturbances for authorities have extended the list to cover a great number including: hypo- and hyper-thyroidism (Lidz, 1954); diabetes mellitus (Lidz, 1954); sexual dysfunctions (Gutheil, 1959; Benedek, 1959); diarrhea (Stokvis, 1957); obesity (Maslow & Mittelmann, 1951); skin diseases, such as, dermatitis factitia, neurodermatitis, urticaria, rosacea, psoriasis, and alopecia areata as reported by Seitz (1954); plantar warts (Yalom, 1964). Silverman (1968) adds fever, chills, hematemesis, cough, vertigo, itching ears, dyspnea, chest pain, eye trouble, constipation, sore throat, biliary symptoms, abdominal cramps, and mouth lesions. Dunbar (1954) carries the list even further, adding sterility and numerous others. Mitscherlich (1961) links even Parkinsonism to a psychosomatic base.

THEORIES OF PSYCHOSOMATIC DISORDER

The *specific emotion hypothesis* of Alexander (1939a, 1939b, 1950) theorizes that at the base of each psychosomatic disorder there lies a corresponding specific emotional constellation. "Just as the nature of the chronic unrelieved emotional state varies, so also will the corresponding vegetative disturbance vary" (1943). Thus, there exists a "specific correlation between the emotional state and its physiological concomitants" (Alexander & Szasz, 1952); or each emotional conflict has its peculiar accompanying physical disorder as a counterpart.

Dunbar (1942, 1943) advanced her *personality-type hypothesis*, claiming that individuals possessing identical psychosomatic difficulties also share in common certain personality traits. Consequently, certain personality types are conducive or predisposed to particular kinds of psychosomatic disorders. A person with a given psychosomatic profile is susceptible to an "associated illness syndrome, and is likely to contract it when subjected to particular stress and strain in his specific sphere of major difficulty" (1942, p. 907).

The *symptom-symbol hypothesis,* earlier offered by Deutsch (1939) and later by Garma (1950a, 1950b), is a psychoanalytic rendition of psychosomatic disorders. Garma theorized that the introjected psychic image of the mother (who is symbolized as food which is digested with difficulty) later acquires a harmful oral attitude capable of producing an ulcer. The liberation of the patient from his mother during therapy is achieved by psychically associating the food as a "good object" so that food assimilation becomes positive in character rather than negative. Predisposition to ulcers is traced to the oral stage of libidinal development.

Another contending psychosomatic theory, *locus minoris resistentiae,* somatic weakness, or "weak organs" hypothesis, theorizes that the organ which is constitutionally vulnerable is the one which is the body's "weakest link," that is, the organ that puts up the least resistance is the one most likely to break down under stress (Draper, Dupertius, & Caughey, 1944; Katz, 1962; Wolff, 1947, 1950a, 1950b, 1962). According to Wolff, psychosomatic dysfunctions are protective reactions against psychogenic stress and are not too expensive adjustments that grant one security and tranquillity. Similar reactive patterns are common to given families, hence psychosomatic disorders are hereditarily constitutional and cultivated in childhood, but appear during periods in which the individual is threatened. According to Katz, emotional disturbances affect the weakened organ, so that an inherited weak stomach is disturbed by emotional upheaval and consequently the target of psychosomatic disorder; the same holds true for respiratory infection making the lungs and nasal passages susceptible to psychosomatic disorders of bronchitis or asthma.

Grace and Graham (1952; Graham, Stern, & Winokur, 1958; D. T. Graham, F. K. Graham, & Kabler, 1960; D. T. Graham, Kabler, & F. K. Graham, 1962; D. T. Graham, Lundy, Benjamin, Kabler, Lewis, Kunish, & F. K. Graham, 1962b) have offered a *specific attitude hypothesis,* a theory that is related to the specificity hypothesis. According to these two physicians, each psychosomatic disorder is a physiological change that is specific to the corresponding conscious attitude. As attitudes alter, there is a concomitant change in symptoms. The theory stated by its authors is that a specific relation exists

between the *attitude* that a patient develops toward the life situation disturbing him and the diseases or symptoms he develops in response to it. . . . On the basis of the plausible assumption that a different physiological process underlies each disease, the hypothesis also implies that each attitude is associated with its own specific set of physiological changes. . . . The differences between patients who develop different psychosomatic disturbances in response to disturbing life situations lie in the attitudes they develop toward these situations. Similarly, the explanation of the difference in symptoms a person may develop at different times is to be found in a difference in his attitude toward the situations responsible for the various symptoms (Graham, Stern, & Winokur, 1958, p. 446).

According to Ruesch's (1948, 1951, 1959) *communication theory,* psychosomatic disorders stem from a communication failure in childhood interpersonal relationships. Immature and socially isolated persons, unable to cope with adult communication succumb to psychosomatic symptoms because the body is fundamentally an instrument of communication. Disease is disruptive to the communication instrument, and a disturbance of communication function produces disease. For example, two men conversing at cross purposes and unable to communicate become animated and resort to gestures until the emotional heat generated affects the visceral organs. But psychosomatic symptoms disappear where communication is restored to a proper social field.

Margolin's (1951, 1953, 1954; Macleod, Wittkower, & Margolin, 1954) *regression hypothesis* theorizes that psychosomatic disorders are throwbacks to earlier stages of development in instances with which the organism is incapable of coping. They are a retreat to earlier stages of development, learning patterns, and experiences, but differ markedly from schizophrenia in that only portions—not the entire organism—regress, and do so in varying degrees only. Such an individual is mosaic with elements of his personality in differing states of regression. From the psychosomatic standpoint, "the same syndrome may be identifiable at different levels of psychophysiological regression, and the principle of correlating the syndrome with the development level involved is necessary. . . . Psychosomatic symptoms are seen as regressive psychophysiological states" (Macleod, Wittkower, & Margolin, 1954, p. 22).

From the social psychological point of view, Halliday (1938, 1943a, 1943b, 1945a, 1945b, 1948) has developed a *cultural hypothesis* correlating psychosomatic disorder with social or cultural changes. Rapid cultural changes play a role in the increased prevalence and the high incidence of chronic recurrent psychosomatic illnesses such as peptic ulcer, rheumatism, etc., owing to the deterioration of parent-child relationships, and the rapid and rigid pace of 20th-century living in which the individual becomes lost. Psychosomatic illnesses increase as the birthrate decreases. Thus, in a sense, it is society that is ill.

According to Grinker's *field theory*, a comprehensive approach entailing the complete organismic-environmental transactional field from the standpoint of a variety of disciplines (psychology, sociology, physiology), that is, the entire gamut of behavioral sciences is utilized to the end of gaining some insight into the psychosomatic question as a total field of investigation. " 'Psychosomatic' connotes more than a kind of illness; it is a comprehensive approach to the totality of an integrated process of transactions among many systems: somatic, psychic, social, and cultural" (1953, p. 188).

An *anxiety hypothesis*, developed by Mahl (1949, 1950, 1952) from the standpoint of learning theory, traces psychosomatic disorders to unrelieved chronic anxiety that is, for example, capable of producing gastric hydrochloric acid, resulting in peptic ulcer.

A *stress hypothesis* advanced by Selye (1946, 1955, 1956a, 1956b) views psychosomatic and other disorders as diseases of adaptation or adaptive responses to stress, instead of the deleterious effects of germs, poisons, or other external agents. Hence psychosomatic ailments are essentially diseases of adaptation. Stress, more than the rate of wear and tear, is "the state manifested by a specific syndrome which consists of all the nonspecifically induced changes within a biologic system" (1956b, p. 423), but is without a specific cause and is manifested by the stress-syndrome, i.e., general adaptation syndrome (G.A.S.). Evolving in three specific stages (alarm reaction, stage of resistance, stage of exhaustion), the general adaptation syndrome becomes fully developed. Dunbar, agreeing with the stress thesis, writes: "It can no longer be doubted that many latent maladies within the body await activation by some stressor. . . . It is well known that the *milieu intérieur* is subject to change with stress" (1959, p. 12).

According to Groen's (1957, 1964) *substitution theory* of psychosomatic disorders, disturbances are viewed as a form of substituted behavior. The hypothesis essentially is that "when psychopathic or psychoneurotic re-action patterns to frustration are thus inhibited from discharge, *somatic* reaction patterns are substituted in an increased intensity and duration, so that they are called diseased" (1964, p. 301). The rationale of psy-chosomatic disorder is that the public views somatic disorder with sym-pathy and concern, but regards neurotic symptomatology with irritation, amusement, or disdainful pity; and sociopathic behavior with "moral indignation." Even physicians, once ascertaining the neurotic background in a patient with ulcerative colitis or asthma, for example, alter their attitude and attention toward the patient in question. Accordingly, "in-hibitions enforced on the social behaviour of the individuals by cultural patterns may block sociopathic or psychoneurotic discharges and thereby favour the occurrence of psychosomatic syndromes" (1964, p. 307).

Later, Groen with Welner added that "psychosomatic disturbances are . . . pathological deviations of originally physiological, adaptive feedback mechanisms" (1966, p. 141). In his adaptation to environment, the psychosomatic, employing the same automatic behavior patterns of the normal, does so with pathological exaggeration. Intensely inhibited neuromuscular discharges (owing to the character of our contemporary culture or society) cause harm to the visceral organs when these are enforced in intensity and duration. Psychosomatic specificity is explained by the factors of personality and stress, that is, the nature of one's per-sonality and what strikes him as particularly stressful in interpersonal and other environmental situations.

Stern offers a *pluralistic hypothesis* or eclectic theory of psychosomatic disorders, claiming that the following conditions are responsible for their onset (1964, p. 127):

1. A vulnerable or sensitized organ or organ system ("somatic com-pliance");

2. The presence of some illness involving the organ system in a relative ("psychic exposure");

3. The symbolic meaning to the patient of a given organ system;

4. Overall psychic vulnerability ("readiness to regress");

5. The nature and severity of the situational stress.

DISTINCTION BETWEEN PSYCHOSOMATIC
AND HYSTERIC DISORDERS

Psychosomatic disorders may be distinguished from systemic diseases by the presence of psychological factors, but differ from neuroses, especially conversion hysteria, in at least four respects. They are: (*a*) the presence of lesions in psychosomatic disorders (ulcers), and the absence of them in hysterical symptoms; (*b*) psychosomatic ailments do not alleviate anxiety as do hysterical symptoms; (*c*) the adherence of psychosomatic disorders to physiological laws, and the failure of hysterical symptoms so to behave; (*d*) whereas psychosomatic disorders are mainly affected by those organs under the control of the autonomic nervous system, hysterical symptoms are responsive to those regions of the body that respond to the central nervous system. In psychoanalysis, however, conversion as the mechanism explaining somatic disorder continues to maintain a central position (Engel, 1968).

23.

Roy R. Grinker and John P. Spiegel

COMBAT STRESS

NEUROTIC REACTIONS TO SEVERE COMBAT STRESS

. . . We described the reactions of men who were unsuited to combat flying because of previous emotional disorders or because of some personality defect rendering them peculiarly susceptible to combat stress. The defect, whether apparent or hidden, led to the appearance of marked inefficiency after exposure to what for the average combat crewman constituted minimal or slight stress. We now come to the much larger group of individuals in whom inefficiency appears only after very severe stress. Psychological difficulties in these men are due less to internal weakness than to the specific ways in which they were harassed by external events. Again, after the ego's strength has been weakened by constant pounding under stress, it is possible in some cases to detect details of the individual's past history which should have indicated the limit to the amount of psychological tension which he could stand. Yet no one has been able to achieve maturity without some psychological scarring, some crack in the psychosomatic equipment with which he faces the world. Everyone has a limit to the amount of stress which he can withstand. In this realm the airman's difficulties are merely seen in an enlarged focus as Everyman's struggles with a harsh reality, ending in some cases with continued strength and mastery of the circumstances, in others with a neurotic compromise and partial defeat.

The neurotic compromise, in these circumstances, consists in a breakdown of an otherwise normal individual's ability to deal with his mounting anxiety and hostility in an efficient manner. Fear and anger in small doses are

From *Men Under Stress* by R. R. Grinker and J. P. Spiegel. Copyright, 1945, McGraw-Hill, Inc. Used with permission of McGraw-Hill Company.

stimulating and alert the ego, increasing its efficiency. But, when stimulated by repeated psychological traumata, the intensity of the emotion heightens until a point is reached at which the ego loses its effectiveness and may become altogether crippled. . . . Here we wish to present the clinical picture which manifests itself as control is lost and the ego gives way under increasing pressure. The observable clinical symptoms, the anxieties, the phobic reactions, the host of physical and psychological responses to battle stress, should be considered as manifestations of this loss of control. The particular symptom which develops, although of great theoretical interest, is not so important as its intensity and its relation to the individual's ability to perform his job. Free anxiety may be tolerated for long periods of time without destroying efficiency, yet an equal intensity of anxiety which leads to vomiting or diarrhea may become immediately incapacitating.

The clinical description of the neurotic reactions to severe combat stress is thus a passing parade of every type of psychological and psychosomatic symptom, and of unadaptive behavior. For convenience and to avoid stigmatizing the flier unduly, these reactions are roughly grouped under the undiagnostic term of "operational fatigue." It is important, however, for all medical personnel to understand that this term signifies a reactive state in which the ego loses its power to control intense anxieties and hostilities in the given situation, and to maintain its functional efficiency. In many cases the ego readily regains its functional efficiency when the individual is removed from the precipitating situation. In others, a more serious psychological wound has been inflicted and recovery from the symptoms takes place only after a long time or after vigorous psychotherapy. Because the symptoms merely reflect the dynamic struggles of the ego in handling its overwhelming anxieties and hostilities in some manner, they do not fall into clear-cut diagnostic categories. Mixtures of anxiety, depression and psychosomatic reactions color almost every case. In addition, one of the most characteristic traits of neurotic reactions to battle is the manner in which the symptoms alter with the lapse of time, change of geographical setting, distance from the combat scene and progress or lack of treatment. What begins as a severe anxiety reaction in the combat area may end up as a severe depression in a rear area or at home. Nevertheless, we have attempted to present the following clinical cases in five categories based upon the chief presenting symptom. These include *free anxiety states* of various intensities, *phobic states, conversion states, psychosomatic reactions* and *depressions.*

It is a rare thing not to see some degree of free anxiety intermixed with any of the other categories mentioned above. It is almost impossible to remain for any length of time in active combat without experiencing anxiety. The *free anxiety states,* however, are distinguished by the great intensity of this feeling, by the manner in which progressively greater portions of the combat environment become associated with it and by the accompanying weakening of the ego. As the ego becomes fatigued, it is unable either to suppress fear or to undertake capably the manipulative functions involved in flying. If the process becomes extensive, good judgment is lost and finally all power of intelligent action. Thus, one may speak of mild anxiety states in which the subjective and motor signs of anxiety are present but function is not yet interfered with. The flier may have a tremor and feel constantly jittery and apprehensive or display severe tension and fear over the target area, and still be able to carry on his tasks in flying. In moderate anxiety states, the same symptoms may have progressed to the point where the flier makes mistakes in flying and now has his own incapacity to fear as well as the other conscious and unconscious sources of anxiety. This is the most common neurotic reaction among flying personnel. Severe anxiety states, with much regression of the ego, confusion in regard to the environment, mutism and

stupor, are not seen in fliers but only in ground combat personnel who are submitted to more prolonged, continuous and severe punishment.

In the free anxiety states, insight varies considerably. Some men are well aware of their own fear and its origin. In general, good insight is likely to be accompanied by larger amounts of depression. Those with poor insight tend to develop psychosomatic or conversion symptoms. In the latter case, the anxiety will disappear as the conversion symptoms develop. An occasional individual with poor insight will develop an unusually unrealistic, slap-happy attitude and will insist upon flying, when it is obvious to all that he is completely incapable of so doing because of anxiety. The degree of insight varies somewhat with the activities and attitudes of the unit medical officers, who have the first opportunity to deal with these reactions. Since they are the first line of medical defense, their efforts are of the greatest importance in increasing the fliers' insight as well as in aiding them in their control of objective and subjective symptoms.

These symptoms are the psychosomatic expressions of anxiety. The drawn and haggard faces give the young fliers the appearance of old men. The anxiety which can be seen in their faces in the daytime pursues them at night, interfering with sleep either through continued wakefulness and tension or by producing nightmares of combat. The constant tension numbs their appetites, and as a consequence they lose weight. Changes in personality are less common than the other signs of disturbance and are usually manifested by increased irritability. Little arguments rapidly lead to explosive rages far in excess of the demands of the disagreement. As sensitivity increases, many men withdraw from their former close contact with their buddies, and, although they do not brood and are not depressed, they feel better when they are alone. Others temper their reactions to suit the times, and, refusing to think about either the past or the future, live only for the moment. They throw themselves vigorously, sometimes too vigorously, into whatever amusement or distraction they can find. Athletic activity in the daytime gives way to drinking and card parties at night, often carried to such an excess that no one gets any sleep. Of all the symptoms, however, whether of personality or mood, whether physical or psychological, the most important are those that the fliers experience while actually exposed to the combat situation.

* * *

NARCOSYNTHESIS

The indications for the use of pentothal in the treatment of returnees are largely concerned with time. In almost all cases the same material and the same emotional release can be obtained by psychiatric interviews while the patient is fully conscious. This has been adequately proven in our work with large numbers of patients. In the brief period available for therapy in the military setting, the uncovering of anxieties and conflicts and the production of adequate abreactions require the aid of some shortcut to overcome resistances. Since the military psychiatrist is short of time for individual treatment, sodium pentothal is frequently utilized for the diagnosis and treatment of our patients.

It is difficult to specify definite time relationships for the administration of pentothal. Like every other part of psychiatric procedure, timing is a skill or art based on the therapist's intuition or "feeling" for the particular problem. As a general rule pentothal should be first used only when the utmost has been obtained from the conscious patient—when the physician feels that the pathogenic material is not conscious and knows from experience that the subsequent insight will take a large amount of time. When resistances occur, pentothal may be used at that point. Probably only half of our patients require the drug.

The technique of administering the drug is the same as that employed overseas. . . . A 2.5 or 5.0 per cent solution is slowly injected intravenously until the appropriate stage of narcosis is reached, while the patient relaxes quietly on a couch. The quantity varies for each person. More is necessary when the patient is anxious or tense, but the usual dose varies from 0.3 to 0.5 Gm. Rapid injection frequently results in failure, for the patient may go to sleep quickly and awaken suddenly, passing rapidly through the optimum stage just between sleep

and awakening. Alcoholics require excessive doses, rarely have a good response and cannot remember what transpires, so that drinking is prohibited at least twenty-four hours before the treatment. The patient is given the drug until his counting aloud ceases and he begins to take deep, stertorous breaths. A trifle more is then given. The needle should be held in the vein until it is certain that the patient has reached and maintains the proper responsiveness. If not, more may be given in the midst of the interview.

Under pentothal the various forces within the personality seem to dominate the trend of associations at different times. A patient may start talking in an overcompensatory aggressive manner, denying fear, and only later break down into a weeping longing for home and mother. He may begin by expressing superego self-punishing attitudes, followed by unconscious hostile feelings toward a comrade for whose death he blames himself.

The depth of the narcosis may determine which part of the personality is concerned in the responses, very similarly to the way in which various aspects of dreams are related to the depth of sleep. Our experience, however, indicates that the time under narcosis is a more important factor, since the deeper levels of the personality speak later in the pentothal interview after resistances are overcome, even though the narcosis is then lighter.

No patient is given pentothal treatment without adequate preliminary interviews, until a good grasp is obtained of the factual material regarding combat and past life, or until a good transference relationship has been established by the physician. The patient is given a crucial verbal stimulus to start him talking, one that deals with a traumatic experience or, if possible, a situation associated with his emotional disturbances. Sometimes a specific harrowing mission is chosen to start up his associations. Actually the beginning is not too important, for the patient will eventually talk about his important isolated memories and emotions.

The best method is to start the patient talking and let him continue uninterrupted in spite of associations leading him far from the subject of war. He should be urged to continue if he hesitates to recount severely traumatic incidents or if he blocks by repeating, like a broken record, details preceding a crucial experience. If silences last too long or if the patient seems to have gone to sleep, he may be stimulated anew. In other words, resistances occur under pentothal as well as in the conscious state and the therapist must put the patient under pressure to overcome them. Psychiatrists accustomed to the method of free association, and not disturbed by silences, have no difficulty in following this method. Younger medical officers cannot endure silences and in spite of frequent admonitions break into the patient's stream of thought with questions directed by their own curiosity and associations. This is not good technique. Especially is this true for returnees, in whom the relationship of combat experiences and past life is so important for subsequent therapy.

There are certain specific differences between the results that we obtained in this country, working with returnees, and those previously reported in the battle zone. They may be enumerated as follows:

1. The material is frequently recited in the past tense, although, when the emotion becomes intense, the patient not only speaks in the present tense, but also vividly lives out the situation with all the excitement and tenseness of that time.

2. The patient is often fully oriented and aware that there is a doctor in the room, to whom he sometimes directs his remarks. In the height of emotion this fixity to the environment is lost and he acts as if he were in his plane, the doctor becoming the copilot or another gunner.

3. The abreaction is achieved with much more hostility, when present, than we ever heard overseas, where fear dominated the material. Here, the hostile resentful attitudes toward specific individuals, especially officers, and toward the army are freely expressed.

4. The material is not restricted to combat situations or scenes, but associations from the patient's past, his childhood, his family life and the current life setting are freely intermingled. The relationship between combat stress, interpersonal problems, past difficulties and current problems clearly indicates their dynamic ties.

5. Quantitative values of interacting trends can be estimated as they are expressed in the same session. The relationship between regressive dependent needs and self-respecting ego forces and even overcompensations often becomes quite clear as the different portions of the personality are expressed in associations. Likewise, hostilities and superego punishment because of guilty feelings may appear clearly in relation to each other.

After the pentothal has worn off, the patient is pressed to recapitulate, while conscious, the material which he abreacted or remembered while under narcosis. He frequently states that he cannot remember what he has said but with pressure most of the associations can be recalled. In many cases no urging is necessary. For other patients gaps in the material must be filled in by the therapist to the astonishment of the patient, who surprisedly asks: "Did I say that?" It is often necessary to give pentothal more than once, sometimes three and four times, when there is a great quantity of buried material. Sometimes a single treatment is completely effective. We often use pentothal to verify our impression that nothing more of importance is repressed or isolated, or to discover the effect of therapy on the underlying attitudes and emotional trends.

We have stated many times that the emotional expressions evoked under the influence of pentothal must be considered usually as an abreaction, which is rarely curative in itself but is the necessary beginning to the attainment of insight. Subsequent interviews, interpretations and "working through" are necessary in almost every case. For this purpose the patient should be able to remember, or to recall to memory by persuasion or forcing, at the same session or at later interviews, his emotional abreaction. Otherwise the episode has been only an eruption or explosion of tension, which is certain to rebuild, and it is therefore of only temporary benefit. For this reason the faculties necessary for memory or recall must be intact. Abreactions spontaneously lived through under alcohol are nontherapeutic, as we have learned from our patients who, while drunk, explode terrific hostilities in neighboring bars. For the same reason, the method of using ether to facilitate abreaction has no lasting value. Ether or alcohol narcosis may make the patient more susceptible to hypnotic suggestion, but not to insight.

It was not the property of inducing an affective abreaction that led to the use of the term "narcosynthesis" to describe the effect of pentothal. It was the fact that under the influence of the drug and during the process of abreaction, although not fully conscious, the ego, devoid of the stress of anxiety, synthesizes some and often much of the important isolated and pathogenic material into its main body. It is as if the emotions or the memories had been separated from the active ego forces as in a hysterical dissociation, because they had been too threatening to the ego's stability or productive of terrifying and unendurable anxiety. Under pentothal the ego can accept the relatively smaller doses of anxiety, decreased by the sedative effect of the drug, especially since the emotions are not primary but "relived." The ego is supported by the therapist and his strength (transference), and under the quieting effect of the sedation does not react to the emotional reliving as if it were so very dangerous. For all these reasons the ego-alien abreacted emotional experiences can be synthesized and reaccepted by the ego. It is as a result of this phenomenon that certain patients after a single session under pentothal, followed by very little or no interpretation, and apparently amnesic for their abreaction, make a complete recovery in that they lose their symptoms and feel well again. . . .

But narcosynthesis is not only the process of recapture by the ego of alienated ideas and emotions. It is also the synthesis of related feelings that have been separated by the process of dissociation. Thus, under pentothal, hostility and fear may be recombined as derivatives of a reaction to the same stress. The patient becomes aware that his anger is due to his being left unprotected in a fearful situation.

* * *

CASE OF PENTOTHAL TREATMENT UNEARTHING
THE RELATIONSHIP OF A SPECIFIC INCIDENT
IN COMBAT TO A CONVERSION SYMPTOM

A 23 year old Sergeant was overseas for ten months and completed fifty missions. The second mission was very difficult; on it he lost two good friends. He developed nightmares and dreams of combat but he stifled his desire to see his Flight Surgeon. He entered our hospital depressed and restless with no interest in anything, complaining of a peculiar black spot before his eyes in the shape of a plane. The patient was worried about his future and scared of flying. He had a phobia for flying with green crews.

Under the first pentothal treatment he told about a difficult raid and then complained that his eyes were burning. He told about his brother in the marines and his buddies who were killed. A great deal of envious hostility toward the brother was loosened. Following is the second pentothal abreaction:

"I'm goin' over Bremen. We've knocked out of formation. We lost an engine going over France and one engine over the target when the fighters hit us.

"I'm no good—throw me out. I can't see. We're still over Bremen. Something happened. Something in front of my eyes. He's going to crack. He's going to crash into us." ("Who?") "An ME 109. Get the hell out! Just get out of his way. George, you'd better come back and take over for me." ("Where are you going?") "Gettin' the hell out of here. I'm no good. I can't see a thing. I can see a little now. They're coming in again. There he goes, George. There go the pieces. Flames. There's more of them. Wish I could focus my eyes. That flak. Something just blew. The whole tunnel's apart." (The patient's eyes were troubling him from their first mention.) "They blew all the plexiglass out. My God! My eyes are leaving." ("Don't you have your goggles on?") "Yes! I'll get them on as soon as I clear my eyes. We'll never make it back today. We won't get to London after all, George. There's one coming after you, George. He just peeled off. They're coming in low—watch me, Gus. Fred, look out—there're ten of them lined up. Oh my God! My eyes are O.K. now, Doc. I can see as good as ever. I thought I was going blind. That burst was too much for me. I suppose I'm going to be grounded now, g— d—. My hands are O.K., George. Doc said I'd be grounded for three weeks. Here's your ship—it's all shot to hell but we got 'er back. Hope we don't have to go over that place again. Three times is too much.

"Whoever said a B-24 couldn't get back on two engines. I've got thirteen missions, fellow. We just got back on two engines. Tell him, George. Tell this ignorant s— o— b—, George. I'm one of the original crews. You get the air medal for five missions. I got thirteen. Now go peddle your s—t somewhere else. Don't scare these green crews. Let me hit him just once more, George. When he gets a few under his belt, he'll wise up.

"You know, George, my eyes never cleared up. I see spots and think they're fighters but when I aim at them they're gone. I don't trust them any more. I'm no damned good now. Sure, I know guns. I can't pick out fighters. What the hell good am I? I'll get on another crew. You guys are too far gone to bother with me. O.K. I'll sleep it off and we'll talk about it tomorrow. You're stickin' your necks out. You're a swell bunch of fellows or you're crazy. O.K. Good night."

The patient was asked about his blind spell in an effort to determine the cause. Although the plexiglass was blown out, it was doubtful whether it injured his eyes. The patient had a definite feeling of guilt about this, blamed himself and worried about whether or not his eye trouble would come back again. The fact that he was tail gunner made him worry for the safety of his crew even more. He told nobody about it. "I shouldn't have done it. I was afraid to go to the Flight Surgeon after that and tell him I was scared."

The next day the blind spell was discussed. The plexiglass that blew out apparently did not touch the patient. He was worried about his capacity to carry on as a tail gunner and was afraid to tell the Flight Surgeon that he was scared. The incident happened just as an ME 109 made an attack on the ship and patient was afraid it would crash into him. He said that since then he had had a "spot" before his eyes which resembled a plane. The Flight Surgeon had told him it was probably a piece of flak. When he realized that the scotoma was related to fear of the attacking enemy plane, he lost his depression and became interested in his surroundings and active in the convalescent program. He also lost his visual difficulty and was returned to flying duty.

The peculiar conversion symptom of spots before the eyes that looked like planes was found to be related to a specific threatening incident in combat. This was fixed in his mind by the unwise treatment by his Flight Surgeon. Yet the patient within himself knew of his conflict based on fear and felt depressed because of his sense of failure. Rapid recovery ensued after the relationship between the stimulus and the symptom was discovered. Subsequent psychotherapy allayed the patient's depression.

24.

HANS SELYE

GENERAL ADAPTATION SYNDROME OR STRESS SYNDROME

. . . When we were first confronted with the "alarm reaction," the idea that presented itself most vividly was that the very tangible and accurately measurable morphologic character-

From Hans Selye, "Stress and disease." *Science*, 1955, *122*, 625–631. Reprinted by permission.

istics of this first stage of the stress response might give us a key to the objective scientific analysis of systemic, nonspecific reactions. The enlargement of the adrenal cortex and the atrophy of the thymus and lymph nodes, for example, were changes that could be expressed in strictly quantitative terms, and they were certainly not specific, since any agent that caused systemic damage or stress elicited them.

A multitude of questions presented themselves immediately. Which among the manifestations of this alarm reaction are useful for the maintenance of health and which are merely signs of damage? How does an injury to a limited area of the body reach the various internal organs that are eventually affected during the alarm reaction? For instance, how does a trauma to one limb eventually influence such distant structures as the adrenal cortex or the thymus? Which organ change is the cause and which the consequence of another structural alteration? For instance, does the disintegrating thymus tissue liberate substances that stimulate the adrenals or does the enlarged adrenal cortex secrete hormones that affect the thymus?

It was quite evident, of course, that to answer these questions would take much time and probably long series of often monotonous stereotypic experiments, using various stressors on various species of animals. Nevertheless, a general blueprint for the dissection and clinical utilization of the stress syndrome presented itself immediately. In particular, we asked ourselves five questions, which we thought would now be amenable to experimental analysis: (i) What are the changes characteristic of stress as such? (ii) How does the stress response evolve in time? (iii) What are the pathways through which stress reaches various organs? (iv) Are there "diseases of adaptation," that is, maladies principally the result of errors in the adaptation syndrome? (v) To what extent are the animal experiments on stress applicable to clinical medicine?

None of these questions has been fully answered, and, indeed, the complete clarification of biologic problems is hardly an attainable aim. However, partial answers have been obtained to all of these basic questions, and—most important of all—it appears that they have been so formulated that further progress is now largely a matter of time.

We have learned, for instance, that acute involution of the lymphatic organs, diminution of the blood eosinophiles, enlargement and increased secretory activity of the adrenal cortex,

and a variety of changes in the chemical constitution of the blood and tissues are truly nonspecific and characteristic of stress as such. It has also become evident that they represent a syndrome, in that they are closely correlated with one another, both in time and in intensity. Whenever dissociations among them tend to occur, it can usually be shown that these are attributable to one of the following two reasons: (i) either the specific actions of the evocative agent are superimposed upon the stress syndrome and thus obscure some of the nonspecific manifestations (for example, if insulin is used as a stressor, the glycemic response is masked by the hypoglycemic effect of the hormone); or (ii) one of the pathways through which stress acts in the organism is deranged (for example, stress causes no thymus involution after adrenalectomy).

No agent produces only stress. Hence, in actual experimentation, the stress response is invariably complicated by certain superimposed specific changes, and in every species—indeed, in every individual—one or the other pathway is more or less functional than the rest. These factors tend to mask or deform the typical stress response, and failure to recognize them was undoubtedly the principal handicap to clear characterization of the stress response in the past. Let us now return to our five basic problems and enumerate at least the most important facts about them that have come to light during these 20 years of research on stress.

CHANGES CHARACTERISTIC OF STRESS

In attempting to answer the question, "What are the changes characteristic of stress as such?" the first problem was, of course, to define *stress*, at least as accurately as definitions can be formulated in biology. The word, especially when it is used with its mate *strain*, has long been in everyday usage, but its significance in biology had never been defined. The layman speaks, for instance, of *eyestrain* or *mental stress* in referring to rather specific complaints. Cannon, the great student of homeostasis, also used the terms *stresses* and *strains* in connection with specific reactions. He emphasized, for instance, that the stresses and strains of oxygen lack, hemorrhage, and starvation elicit totally different and specific homeostatic reactions. Conversely, it is a characteristic of the stress syndrome, as we understand it, that it is always the same, no matter what happens to elicit it. For over-all responses, which include specific and nonspecific features—and this is even more true of purely specific responses—the term now used would be *reaction* (not *stress*) and the eliciting agent would be called a *stimulus* (not a *stressor* or *alarming stimulus*). Such specific reactions are precisely the part of the over-all response that we must subtract to arrive at our stress syndrome.

To make this distinction clear, we always used the term *nonspecific stress* in our early publications. Later, unfortunately, it became customary to omit the adjective, for brevity's sake. To avoid confusion, we then pointed out that in the sense in which we use the term, stress may be defined as a nonspecific deviation from the normal resting state; it is caused by function or damage and it stimulates repair.

Here, the nonspecific causation of the change has been selected as its most characteristic feature. However, even the term *specific* had been used somewhat loosely in medicine; we therefore defined a nonspecific change as one that can be produced by many or all agents, as opposed to a specific change, which is elicited only by one or few agents. Correspondingly, a nonspecific agent acts on many targets, a specific one acts on few targets, and a stressor is an agent that causes stress.

Of course, we realized from the outset that these, like all biologic definitions, are imperfect, but trying to formulate them helped us to impart precision to our own concepts of *stimulus, stressor, stress, specific,* and *nonspecific.* Among other things, these considerations brought out with particular clarity the fact that stress is not necessarily the result of damage but can be caused by physiologic function and that it is not merely the result of a nonspecific action but also comprises the defense against it. These are cardinal facts, as we shall see later when we consider the relationship between stress and disease.

In our efforts to identify the characteristics of stress, our main problem was to eliminate all specific manifestations that are typical either of the agent or of the reacting organism. Hence, a large number of animal species had to be studied, following exposure to a great variety of essentially different stimuli, to compare the resulting structural, chemical, and functional changes. This made it possible to determine which are the responses common to all types of exposure, and only these could be considered to be truly nonspecific—that is, the result of stress as such. The residue that remained after subtraction of all the specific changes is the general-adaptation syndrome.

In this response, every part of the body is involved, but the two great integrators of activity, the hormonal and the nervous systems, are especially important. The facts known today may lead us to believe that the anterior pituitary and the adrenal cortex play the cardinal roles in coordinating the defense of the organism during stress. This view is probably distorted by the fact that the syndrome has been studied primarily by endocrinologists, and investigations concerning the participation of the nervous system are handicapped by the greater complexity of the required techniques. It is considerably easier to remove an endocrine gland and to substitute for its hormones by the injection of extracts than it is to destroy minute individual nervous centers selectively and then restore their function to determine the role they may play during stress.

STRESS RESPONSE IN TIME

To establish the evolution of the stress response in time, animals had to be repeatedly exposed to stressors (cold, forced muscular exercise, bloodletting, and drugs) of a constant intensity over long periods of time. It was found that, after a while, the same agent does not continue to produce the same nonspecific response. For instance, treatment with a drug that initially causes discharge of adrenocortical lipid granules will later actually promote accumulation of lipids in the adrenal cortex, after the animals have become more resistant to the damaging effects of the agent. Upon still more continued exposure, sooner or later, this acquired adaptation is invariably lost; then the animals again show signs of damage, and their adrenal cortices again discharge their lipid granules.

These adrenal changes are taken as only one example among the many characteristics of the general-adaptation syndrome that show such a triphasic pattern (for example, glycemia, chloremia, and body weight). In fact the whole syndrome is essentially triphasic; thus its manifestations depend as much on the stressor effect of the eliciting agent as on the time elapsed since the organism was first exposed to it.

The three stages of the stress syndrome are (i) the alarm reaction, in which adaptation has not yet been acquired; (ii) the stage of resistance, in which adaptation is optimum; and (iii) the stage of exhaustion, in which the acquired adaptation is lost again.

The physicochemical basis of the curious terminal loss of acquired adaptation is still quite obscure. Exhaustion cannot be fully compensated, either by changes in the caloric intake or by any known hormonal substitution therapy. The term *adaptation energy* has been suggested to designate the adaptability that is gradually consumed during exposure, but despite much research we have learned nothing about the nature of this "energy."

Many of the changes characteristic of the stage of exhaustion are strikingly similar to those of senility. It is tempting to view the general-adaptation syndrome as a kind of accelerated aging. It appears as though, because of the greater intensity of stress, the three major periods of life—infancy (in which adaptation has not yet been acquired), adulthood (in which adaptation has been acquired to the usual stresses of life), and senility (in which the acquired adaptation is lost again)—are here telescoped into a short space of time.

However, these will remain sterile speculations until some ingenious mind can devise new experimental procedures with which to analyze them in quantitative terms. It is only to stimulate thought along these lines that I venture even to mention these problems here. I hope that some talented young mind, still sufficiently uninhibited by textbook knowledge to see a new approach, will follow this trail. To me it seems more promising of truly great progress

in the understanding of life and adaptability than any other aspect of stress research.

PATHWAYS OF STRESS

To clarify the pathways through which stress reaches various organs, it was merely necessary to use the classic procedures of experimental medicine—namely, the destruction of suspected relay stations and, wherever possible, their restoration (for example, removal of an endocrine gland and substitution therapy with extracts containing its hormones.) Figure 4.1 helps to summarize the principal data that have come to light in this respect.

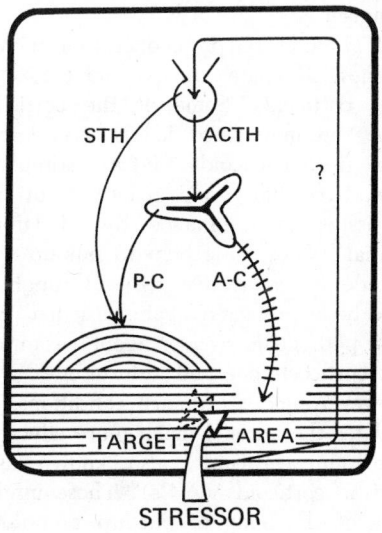

FIGURE 4.1. Diagram illustrating the principal pathways of the stress response. [After Selye (1).]

All agents that act on the body or any of its parts exert dual effects: (i) specific actions, with which we are not concerned in this review, except insofar as they modify the nonspecific actions of the same agents and (ii) nonspecific or stressor effects, whose principal pathways (as far as we know them today) are illustrated in Figure 4.1. The stressor acts on the target (the body or some part of it) directly (thick arrow) and indirectly by way of the pituitary and the adrenal. Through some unknown pathway (labeled by a question mark), the "first mediator" travels from the directly injured target area to the anterior pituitary. It notifies the latter that a condition of stress exists and thus induces it to discharge adrenocorticotrophic hormone (ACTH).

It is quite possible that this first mediator of hormonal defense is not always the same. In some instances, it may be an adrenaline discharge, in others a liberation of histaminelike toxic tissue metabolites, a nervous impulse, or even a sudden deficiency in some vitally important body constituent (such as glucose or an enzyme). During stress it is rarely the lack of adrenal corticoids that stimulates ACTH secretion, through a self-regulating "feed-back" mechanism.

ACTH, alone or in cooperation with other hormones, stimulates the adrenal cortex to discharge corticoids. Some of the cortical hormones, the mineralocorticoids, also known as prophlogistic corticoids (P-Cs), stimulate the proliferative ability and reactivity of connective tissue; they enhance the "inflammatory potential." Thus, they help to put up a strong barricade of connective tissue through which the body is protected against further invasion by the pathogenic stressor agent (examples are desoxycorticosterone and aldosterone).

However, under ordinary conditions, ACTH stimulates the adrenal much more effectively to secrete glucocorticoids, also known as antiphlogistic corticoids (A-Cs). These inhibit the ability of the body to put up granulomatous barricades in the path of the invader; in fact, they tend to cause involution of connective tissue with pronounced depression of the inflammatory potential. Thus they can suppress inflammation, but, by this same token, they open the way to the spreading of infection (examples are cortisol and cortisone).

Certain recent experiments suggest that, depending on the conditions, ACTH may cause a predominant secretion of one or the other type of corticoid. However, be this as it may, the "growth hormone," or somatotrophic hormone (STH), of the pituitary increases the inflammatory potential of connective tissue very much as the prophlogistic corticoids do; hence, it can sensitize the target area to the actions of the prophlogistic corticoids.

It is possible that the hypophysics also secretes some special corticotrophin that induces the adrenal to elaborate predominantly prophlogistic corticoids; indeed, STH itself may possess such effects, but this has not yet been proved. Probably the electrolyte content of the blood can also regulate mineralocorticoid production. In any event, even if ACTH were the only corticotrophin, the actions of the corticoids produced under its influence can be vastly different, depending on "conditioning factors" (such as STH) that specifically sensitize the target area for one or the other type of corticoid action. Actually, conditioning factors could even alter the response to ACTH of the adrenal cortex itself, so that its cells would produce more antiphlogistic or prophlogistic corticoids. Thus, during stress, one or the other type of effect can predominate.

As work along these lines progressed, it became increasingly more evident that the actions of all the "adaptive hormones" (corticoids, ACTH, STH) are so largely dependent on conditioning factors that the latter must be considered to be equally as important, in determining the final outcome of a reaction to stress, as the hormones themselves. It will be rewarding, therefore, to discuss this topic thoroughly.

Conditioning of Hormone Actions. Heredity, age, previous exposure to stress, nervous stimuli, the nutritional state, and many other factors can affect both the production of the adaptive hormones and their effect on individual target organs. The action of mineralocorticoids on most of their target tissues is augmented, and that of glucocorticoids is diminished, by an excess of dietary sodium. However, stress during the secretion of adaptive hormones is perhaps the most effective and most common factor capable of conditioning their actions. Thus systemic stress augments the antiphlogistic, lympholytic, catabolic, and hyperglycemic actions of antiphlogistic corticoids. Furthermore, one of the salient effects of the adaptive hormones, that of modifying the course of inflammation, naturally cannot manifest itself unless some "topical stressor" (for example, a nonspecific irritant acting on a circumscribed tissue region) first elicits an inflammatory response.

A few words about the recently introduced concept of the "permissive actions" of corticoids may be in order here. This hypothesis assumes that the corticoids do not themselves affect the targets of stress but merely permit stressors to act on them. Thus the presence or absence of corticoids could only allow or disallow a stress reaction but could not vary its intensity. To illustrate this concept, one might compare the production of light by an electric lamp to the biologic reaction and the switch to the permissive factor. The switch cannot produce light or regulate the degree of its intensity, but unless it is turned on the lamp will not function. Correspondingly, the functional signs—generally considered to be characteristic of overproduction of corticoids during stress—would result not from any actual increase in corticoid secretion but from the extra-adrenal actions of the stressors themselves. The presence of corticoids would be necessary only in a "supporting capacity" to maintain the vitality and reactivity of tissues (2).

Actually, it is precisely in the specific and not in the nonspecific (stress) reactions that the corticoids play a purely permissive role of this type. Here they are necessary only to prevent stress and collapse, thus keeping the tissues responsive. For instance, adrenalectomized rats will not respond to injected STH with somatic growth or to sexual stimulation with mating without a minimal-maintenance corticoid treatment. However, these are specific reactions; they are not characteristic either of stress or of the corticoids and could not be duplicated in the absence of the specific stimulus (STH and sexual stimulation), even with the highest doses of corticoids.

The characteristics of antiphlogistic corticoid overproduction that we see in the alarm reaction (for example, atrophy of the lymphatic organs; catabolism, and inhibition of inflammation) are also impeded by adrenalectomy; they are also restored even by mere maintenance doses of antiphlogistic corticoids in the presence of stress, because the latter sensitizes, or conditions, the tissues to them.

The fundamental difference is, however, that —unlike specific actions—these nonspecific effects can be duplicated, even in the absence of any stressor, if large doses of antiphlogistic corticoids are given.

The importance of such conditioning influences is particularly striking in the regulation of stress reactions, because, in the final analysis, they are the factors that can actually determine whether exposure to a stressor will be met by a physiologic adaptation syndrome or cause "diseases of adaptation." Furthermore, in the latter instance, these conditioning factors can even determine the selective breakdown of one or the other organ. We are led to believe that differences in predisposition, caused by such factors, might explain why the same kind of stressor can cause diverse types of diseases of adaptation in different individuals.

"Buffering Action" of the Adrenals. It has long been noted that it is much more difficult to obtain overdosage with either glucocorticoids or mineralocorticoids in the presence than in the absence of the adrenals. Thus, for instance, cortisol exerts its typical actions (for example, on inflammation, body weight, and the thymicolymphatic organs) at much lower dose levels in intact rats than it does in adrenalectomized rats. This is largely, if not entirely, the result of the absence of mineralocorticoids, for it proved possible to restore the glucocorticoid resistance of the adrenalectomized rat to normal by treatment with small doses of mineralocorticoids (desoxycorticosterone and aldosterone). Even a mere excess of dietary sodium can, (at least partially, substitute for the adrenal in such experiments; hence it is reasonable to assume that here the mineralocorticoids antagonize the glucocorticoids, as a direct result of their effect upon mineral metabolism.

These experiments definitely disproved the so-called "unitarian theory" of adrenocortical function, which was still held by some of the most distinguished adrenal physiologists a short while ago. It is clear not only that the cortex produces more than one kind of corticoid but that the mineralocorticoids and the glucocorticoids are mutually antagonistic in many respects, as postulated by the "corticoid balance theory."

However, several observations still did not seem to be consonant with our concept of corticoid antagonism. For instance, in the presence of the adrenals, both in experimental animals and in man, it proved extremely difficult to stimulate inflammatory reactions much above normal, even with very large doses of mineralo-corticoids. On the other hand, glucocorticoids always succeed in overcoming the buffering action of an intact adrenal, as long as the dosage is sufficiently high.

It is only quite recently that the cause of this apparent exception to the concept of adrenal hormone antagonism has been clarified by the demonstration that the corticoids act in accordance with the "law of intersecting dose-effect curves."

Law of Intersecting Dose-Effect Curves." When a solution containing fixed proportions of cortisol acetate and desoxycorticosterone acetate (DCA) is administered to adrenalecto-mized rats, the cortisol action (catabolism, thymolysis, and inhibition of inflammation) predominates at low, and the opposite, desoxy-corticosterone type of activity, predominates at high dose levels. This was ascribed to the fact that the DCA activity rises rapidly to its optimum level, but then a "ceiling" is reached, and raising the dose further will not increase the effect. The cortisol type of activity, on the other hand, rises more slowly but does not flatten out until it far exceeds the ceiling of its antagonist (Figure 4.2).

The relationship between the two types of corticoids explains why it is readily possible to overcome the adrenal buffer with appropriate doses of cortisol-like hormones, whereas even the highest doses of DCA cannot inhibit this effect. In the presence of the adrenals the normal level of mineralocorticoid production is usually already at its optimum of efficacy. This may also explain the frequently made observation that in adrenalectomized animals and man —where the starting point is below the mineralo-corticoid ceiling—desoxycorticosterone stimulates inflammatory phenomena (for example, arthritis), and this can be antagonized by concurrent treatment with cortisol.

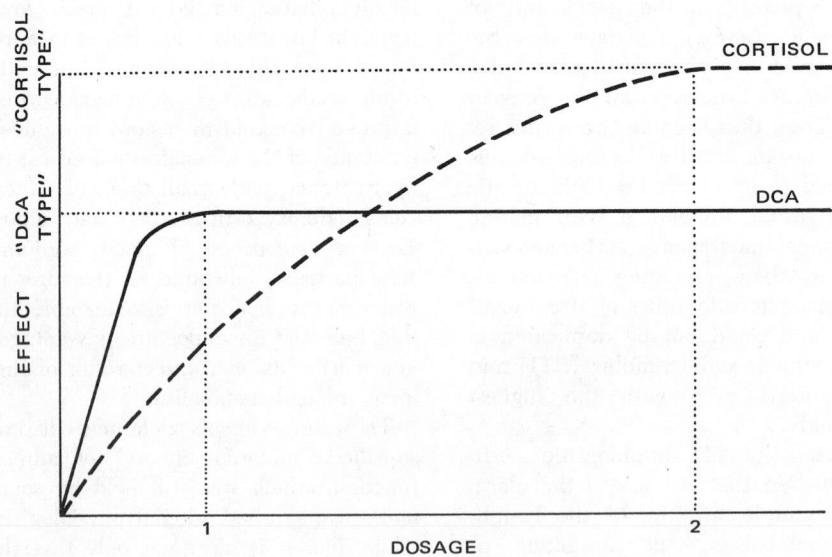

FIGURE 4.2. Effect of varying the dose while the cortisol/desoxycorticosterone is kept constant. Difference in the slopes results in intersecting dose-effect curves. [After Selye and Bois (4).]

However, in certain respects, the desoxy-corticosterone action does not appear to have a definite ceiling. Thus, in the rat, the production of renal damage by desoxycorticosterone is quite proportional to the amount given, within a very wide dose range.

Exceptional Position of the Kidney among the Targets of Corticoid Activity. Numerous observations show that there exists a rather special relationship between the corticoids and the kidney, a relationship that clearly distinguishes renal tissue from other targets of corticoid activities.

Thus, the renal damage (nephrosclerosis) produced with high doses of desoxycorticosterone, in the rat, is not antagonized but is actually aggravated by concurrent treatment with cortisol. In other words, here there is no mineralo-corticoid-glucocorticoid antagonism.

Furthermore, the kidney-damaging effect of various agents (for example, cold, foreign proteins, large doses of STH-preparations, and methylandrostenediol) can be prevented by adrenalectomy, while their extrarenal effects (including, for instance, the influence of STH and methylandrostenediol upon inflammation) are not markedly affected.

The cause of this exceptional reactivity of renal tissue to corticoids is not yet known. However, two factors undoubtedly play an important role here: (i) glucocorticoids and mineralocorticoids are not strictly antagonistic (and may even be synergistic) in their actions on the kidney; (ii) the inability of mineralocorticoids to produce more than a limited effect on extra-adrenal tissues (no matter how much the dose is raised) does not apply to the kidney.

In the preceding discussion we have just barely mentioned the "topical stressors," but now we shall have to consider these a little more carefully before we turn our attention to the diseases of adaptation.

Concept of the Local-Adaptation Syndrome. In Figure 4.1 we have indicated that nonspecific damage to a limited tissue area can influence the pituitary-adrenal system and consequently initiate systemic reactions to stress. It has long been known, furthermore, that many local responses to injury are nonspecific; it has been observed, for instance, that a variety of topical stressors (burns, microbes, drugs) share the power of producing local nonspecific tissue damage and/or inflammation. However, it is only recently that the close relationship between the systemic and local types of nonspecific reactions has been more clearly established. While the characteristic response of the body to systemic stress is the general-adaptation syndrome, which is characterized by manifold morphologic and functional changes throughout the organism, topical stress elicits a local adaptation syndrome, the principal repercussions of which are confined to the immediate vicinity of the eliciting injury. They consist, on the one hand, of degeneration, atrophy, and necrosis and, on the other hand, of inflammation, hypertrophy, hyperplasia, and, under certain conditions, even of neoplasia.

At first sight, there appears to be no striking similarity between the systemic and the local reaction types. A patient in traumatic shock furnishes a characteristic example of the general-adaptation syndrome and, in particular, of its earliest stage, the shock phase of the general alarm reaction. On the other hand, an abscess formed around a splinter of wood represents a typical example of the local-adaptation syndrome and, in particular, of its stage of resistance, during which the defensive inflammatory phenomena predominate. On the surface, these two instances of disease reveal no striking similarities; yet more careful study shows them to be closely related: (i) both are nonspecific reactions, comprising damage and defense; (ii) both are triphasic (with systemic or local alarm, resistance, and exhaustion); (iii) both are singularly sensitive to the adaptive hormones (ACTH, STH, and corticoids); (iv) if the two reactions develop simultaneously in the same individual, they greatly influence each other—that is, systemic stress markedly alters tissue reactivity to local stress and vice versa.

The fundamental reaction pattern to topical stressors is a local-adaptation syndrome; to systemic stressors the fundamental reaction pattern is the general-adaptation syndrome. Various modifications of these two basic responses constitute the essence of most of the diseases known today.

ARE THERE DISEASES OF ADAPTATION?

By diseases of adaptation, we mean maladies that are caused principally by errors in the adaptation syndrome. Thus we arrived at the conclusion that the pathogenicity of many systemic and local stressors depends largely on the function of the hypophysis-adrenocortical system. The latter may either enhance or mitigate the body's defense reactions against stressors. We think that derailments of this adaptive mechanism are the principal factors in the production of certain maladies, which we consider, therefore, to be essentially diseases of adaptation (3).

It must be kept in mind that such diseases of adaptation do not necessarily become manifest during exposure to stress. This is clearly demonstrated by the observation that temporary overdosage with desoxycorticosterone can initiate a self-sustaining hypertension, which eventually leads to death, long after hormone administration has been discontinued. Here, we speak of "metacorticoid" lesions. The possibility that a temporary excess of endogenous mineralocorticoids could induce similar delayed maladies deserves serious consideration.

Among the derailments of the general-adaptation syndrome that may cause disease, the following are particularly important: (i) an absolute excess or deficiency in the amount of adaptive hormones (for example, corticoids, ACTH, and STH) produced during stress; (ii) an absolute excess or deficiency in the amount of adaptive hormones retained (or "fixed") by their peripheral target organs during stress; (iii) a disproportion in the relative secretion (or fixation) during stress of various antagonistic adaptive hormones (for example, ACTH and antiphlogistic corticoids, on the one hand, and STH and prophlogistic corticoids, on the other hand); (iv) the production by stress of metabolic derangements, which abnormally alter the target organ's response to adaptive hormones (through the phenomenon of "conditioning"); and (v) finally, we must not forget that, although the hypophysis-adrenal mechanism plays a prominent role in the general-adaptation syndrome, other organs that participate in the latter (for example, nervous system, liver, and kidney) may also respond abnormally and become the cause of disease during adaptation to stress.

With this in mind it may be convenient for investigative purposes to classify as "diseases of adaptation" those maladies in which an inadequacy of the adaptation syndrome plays a particularly important role. This means that the term should be used only when the maladaptation factor appears to be more important than the eliciting pathogen itself. No disease is purely a disease of adaptation, anymore than it could be purely a disease of the heart or an infectious disease, without overlap with other nosologic groups. Conversely, there is no disease in which adaptive phenomena play no part.

It is undoubtedly useful to realize, however, that some agents are virtually "unconditional pathogens," in that their influence on the tissues is so great that they cause damage almost irrespective of any sensitizing or adaptive factors (for example, immediate effect of x-rays or of severe thermal and mechanical injuries, and the actions of certain micro-organisms to which everybody is susceptible).

Most disease-producing agents, however, are to a greater or lesser extent "conditionally acting pathogens"; that is, their ability to produce illness is largely dependent on our adaptive reactions to them. Here, correct adaptation may prevent disease (for instance, a focus of tuberculosis perfectly held in check by an appropriate inflammatory barricade), but insufficient or excessive adaptive reactions may themselves be what we experience as illness (excessive and unnecessary inflammation around an otherwise harmless allergen).

APPLICATION OF ANIMAL EXPERIMENTS TO CLINICAL MEDICINE

Since most of the fundamental work on stress had been performed on laboratory animals, it was reasonable to question its applicability to problems of clinical medicine. It may now be said, however, that although there are certain differences in the stress response of every species, the general pattern of reaction is essentially the same in the various kinds of experimental animals and in man. Furthermore, a good deal of evidence has accumulated in support of the view that the experimental similes of spontaneous diseases produced in animals by exposure to stress, or by overdosage with certain adaptive hormones, are closely related to the corresponding maladies of man.

Let us merely mention a few of the most striking similarities in the responses to stress and to adaptive hormones of animals and man.

Morphologic and Functional Adreno-cortical Changes during Stress. There can be no doubt that, during intense stress (for example, severe mechanical or thermal injuries and massive infections), the adrenal cortex of man, just as that of laboratory animals, shows morphologic changes characteristic of hyperactivity. At the same time, there is a demonstrable increase in the blood concentration and urinary excretion of corticoids and their metabolites. The other manifestations (morphologic, functional, and chemical) of the stress syndrome also failed to exhibit any fundamental dissimilarity in the reaction patterns of animals and man.

Corticoid Requirements during Stress. During stress, the corticoid requirements of all mammals are far above normal. After destruction of the adrenals by disease (as after their surgical removal), the daily dose of corticoids, necessary for the maintenance of well-being at rest, is comparatively small, but it rises sharply during stress (for example, cold, intercurrent infections, and hemorrhage), both in experimental animals and in man.

Anti-inflammatory Effects of Corticoids. The same antiphlogistic corticoids (cortisone and cortisol) that were shown to inhibit various types of experimental inflammations in laboratory animals exert similar effects in a human being afflicted by inflammatory diseases (for example, rheumatoid arthritis, rheumatic fever, and allergic inflammations).

Sensitivity to Infection after Treatment with Antiphlogistic Corticoids. In experimental animals, the suppression of inflammation by antiphlogistic hormones is frequently accompanied by an increased sensitivity to infection, presumably because the encapsulation of microbial foci is less effective and perhaps partly also because serologic defense is diminished. Thus, even a species naturally resistant to the human type of tuberculosis, such as the rat, can contract this disease during overdosage with ACTH or cortisone. Similarly, in patients undergoing intense treatment with antiphlogistic hormones (for example, for rheumatoid arthritis), a previously latent tuberculous focus may suddenly spread. It is a well-known fact that in patients suffering from tuberculosis the disease is especially readily aggravated by exposure to any kind of stress situation. Rest cures have long been practiced in view of this. It is perhaps not too farfetched to consider the possibility that an increased ACTH and cortisol secretion during stress may play an important part in the development of clinical tuberculosis.

Sensitization to Mineralocorticoids by Sodium and the Buffering Effect of the Adrenals. In experimental animals, mineralocorticoids tend to raise the blood pressure and to cause vascular and renal damage (nephrosis and nephrosclerosis) often with edema. This effect is aggravated by simultaneous treatment with sodium chloride and becomes particularly severe after adrenalectomy. Similarly, in man on a high sodium intake, and especially after adrenalectomy, otherwise nontoxic doses of desoxycorticosterone will produce hypertension and edema. Apparently, in man as in the laboratory animal, sodium acts as a conditioning factor for mineralocorticoids, while the adrenal exerts a buffering effect.

This may also explain why, in many cases of clinical hypertension, bilateral adrenalectomy exerts a beneficial effect, as long as only cortisone or cortisol is used for substitution therapy, while treatment with desoxycorticosterone restores or further aggravates the hypertensive disease. Apparently, the adrenals of these patients produce some desoxycorticosteronelike factor that plays at least an adjuvant role in the pathogenesis of hypertension.

In patients suffering from rheumatoid arthritis, adrenalectomy has also been reported to exert a beneficial influence if only glucocorticoids are used for maintenance. Furthermore desoxycorticosterone tends to elicit arthritic changes only in the adrenal-deficient but not in the intact patient. This effect of desoxycorticosterone is, in turn, corrected by simultaneous cortisone treatment.

Finally, let us point out that, both in man and in animals, the various characteristic effects of cortisone are also obtained at especially low dose levels after adrenalectomy.

Psychological and Psychiatric Effects of Corticoid Overdosage. Considerable attention has been given of late to the possible mental effects of stress and of the adaptive hormones. It would be beyond the scope of this article (and certainly outside my competence) to discuss these in detail, but a few remarks based on our experimental observations may be in order.

It has long been noted that various steroids —including desoxycorticosterone, cortisone, progesterone, and many others—can produce in a variety of animal species (even in primates such as the rhesus monkey) a state of great excitation followed by deep anesthesia. It has more recently been shown that such steroid anesthesia can also be produced in man, and, of course, the marked emotional changes (sometimes bordering on psychosis) that may occur in predisposed individuals during treatment with ACTH, cortisone, and cortisol are well known. Several laboratories reported furthermore that the electroshock threshold of experimental animals and their sensitivity to anesthetics can be affected by corticoids.

Thus, it appears very probable that corticoids secreted during stress also have an important influence on nervous and emotional reactions. Conversely, it is now definitely established that nervous stressors (pain and emotions) are particularly conducive to the development of the somatic manifestations of the stress syndrome; thus stress can both cause and be caused by mental reactions.

In conclusion, let us reemphasize that no illness is exclusively a disease of adaptation, but considerable evidence has accumulated in favor of the view that stress, and particularly the adaptive hormones produced during stress, exert an important regulating influence on the development of numerous maladies.

It is virtually certain that our concepts concerning the role of pituitary and corticoid hormones in the pathogenesis of certain diseases of adaptation will have to undergo modifications as more facts become known. However this is true with every theory. The same was true, for instance, of the original theory that related diabetes to a simple hypoinsulinism, when the role of the anterior pituitary was discovered. Yet, the realization of some pathogenic relationship between insulin and diabetes was an almost indispensable step in the subsequent development of this field.

The best theory is that which necessitates the minimum number of assumptions to unite the maximum number of facts, since such a theory is most likely to possess the power of assimilating new facts from the unknown without damage to its own structure. Our facts must be correct; our theories need not be if they help us to discover new facts, even if these discoveries necessitate some changes in the structure of the theory.

Meanwhile, the stress theory, as outlined in this article, permits us to correlate the known facts and furnishes a concrete plan for the systematic development of this field through planned investigation rather than through the mere empirical collection of chance observations.

OUTLOOK

Pasteur, Koch, and their contemporaries introduced the concept of specificity into medicine, a concept that has proved to be of the greatest heuristic value up to the present time. Each individual, well-defined disease, they held, has its own specific cause. It has been claimed by many that Pasteur failed to recognize the importance of the "terrain," because he was too preoccupied with the pathogen (microorganism) itself. His work on induced immunity shows that this is incorrect. Indeed, at the end of his life he allegedly said, "Le microbe n'est rien, le terrain est tout."

The theory that directed the most fruitful investigations of Pasteur and his followers was that the organism can develop specific adaptive reactions against individual pathogens and that by imitating and complementing these, whenever they are short of optimal, we can treat many of the diseases that are caused by specific pathogens.

To my mind, the general-adaptation syndrome represents, in a sense, the negative counterpart, or mirror image, of this concept. It holds that many diseases have no single cause, no specific pathogen, but are largely due to nonspecific stress and to pathogenic situations that result from inappropriate responses to such nonspecific stress.

Our blueprint of the pathways through which stress acts may be partly incorrect; it is certainly quite incomplete. But in it we have a basis for the objective scientific dissection of such time-honored, but hitherto rather vague, concepts as the role of "reactivity," "constitution and resistance," or "nonspecific therapy," in the genesis and treatment of disease.

If I may venture a prediction, I would like to reiterate my opinion that research on stress will be most fruitful if it is guided by the principle that we must learn to imitate—and if necessary to correct and complement—the body's own autopharmacologic efforts to combat the stress factor in disease.

REFERENCES

1. INGLE, D. J. *Recent progress in hormone research.* New York: Academic Press, 1951, Vol. 6, p. 159.
2. SELYE, H. *The story of the adaptation syndrome.* Montreal: Acta, 1952.
3. SELYE, H. *Journal of Clinical Endocrinology,* 1946, *6,* 117.
4. SELYE, H., & BOIS, P. *Fourth annual report on stress,* H. Selye and G. Heuser (Eds.) Montreal: Acta, 1954, pp. 533–552.

25.

JOSEPH V. BRADY, ROBERT W. PORTER, DONALD G. CONRAD, AND JOHN W. MASON

ULCERS IN "EXECUTIVE" MONKEYS

Observations in our laboratory over the past year or more have revealed the development of extensive gastrointestinal lesions in a series of some 15 monkeys restrained in chairs and subjected to a variety of prolonged behavioral conditioning and/or intracerebral self-stimulation experiments (1). The behavioral studies focused upon emotional conditioning procedures of the "fear" or "anxiety" type, and upon avoidance of noxious electric shocks to the feet. Intracerebral self-stimulation through chronically implanted electrodes involved various limbic-system structures. While the program for each animal in this initial series varied considerably, all were subjected to intensive experimental

From Joseph V. Brady, Robert W. Porter, Donald G. Conrad, and John W. Mason, "Avoidance behavior and the development of gastroduodenal ulcers," *Journal of the Experimental Analysis of Behavior,* 1958, *1,* 69–72. Copyright 1958 by the Society for the Experimental Analysis of Behavior, Inc. Reprinted by permission of the society.

study for at least 2 to 8 weeks. Five control monkeys, subjected only to restraint in the chair for similar periods, however, showed no gastrointestinal complications.

The present report describes the results of an experiment designed to define some of the more specific behavioral factors contributing to the etiology of this lethal pathological picture. Eight rhesus monkeys, restrained in chairs . . . were divided into pairs and conditioned according to a "yoked-chair" avoidance procedure. Each pair of monkeys received brief electric shocks (5 milliamperes, 60-cycle AC, for 0.5 second) to the feet from a common source every 20 seconds unless the experimental animal of the pair pressed a lever which delayed the shock another 20 seconds for both animals (3). Inactivation of the lever available to the control animal insured an equal number and temporal distribution of shocks to both monkeys ("physical trauma"), while providing the avoidance contingency for only the experimental animal. Each pair of monkeys received 6-hour sessions on this procedure, alternating with 6-hour "off-periods" (no shocks) 24 hours each day for periods up to 6 or 7 weeks. A red light was illuminated in plain view of both animals during the 6-hour "avoidance" periods, and was turned out during the 6-hour off-periods. The experimental procedure was programmed and the animals' behavior recorded automatically by timers, magnetic counters, cumulative-work recorders, and associated relay circuits. Lever responses and shocks were recorded continuously for all animals, and separate counts were maintained for the avoidance periods and for the off-periods. Throughout the entire experiment, urine was collected continuously from all animals in 24- or 48-hour samples for 17-hydroxycorticosteroid determinations.

The avoidance behavior was trained initially during two preliminary daily sessions of 2 to 4 hours. The training procedure involved the use of a short 5-second interval between shocks in the absence of a lever response (the "shock-shock" or "S-S" interval) and a 20-second interval between lever responses and shocks (the "response-shock" or "R-S" interval). At the outset, a lever response by either animal of a given pair delayed the shock for both animals and no further "shaping" of the behavior was attempted. Within the first preliminary session, however, one monkey of each pair was observed to develop avoidance lever-pressing before its partner and was selected as the experimental animal. At this point in the preliminary training procedure, both the "shock-shock" and the "response-shock" intervals were set at 20 seconds and the control monkey's lever was made ineffective with respect to avoiding shocks for the remainder of the experiment.

Within a few hours after the initiation of the alternating 6-hour sessions, the experimental animals of each pair had developed stable avoidance lever-pressing rates (Figure 4.3) which showed little change throughout the experiment. Responses during the 6-hour off-periods in the absence of the red light rapidly dropped to a low level, as shown in Figure 4.3, and also remained there throughout the experiment. Since the lever-pressing rates for the experimental animals during the 6-hour avoidance periods approximated 15 to 20 responses per minute, the behavior effectively prevented all but an occasional shock for both animals throughout the alternating 6-hour "on-off" cycles of any given 24-hour period. The shock rates never exceeded 2 per hour during the 6-hour avoidance periods, and typically averaged less than 1 per hour. For the most part, only somewhat variable "operant levels" of lever-pressing were maintained by the control animals of each pair, although one of these animals did appear to develop what might be termed a "superstitious avoidance" rate during the 3-week alternating procedure. From an initial rate not exceeding 1 response per hour during the first few days on the procedure this control monkey gradually increased his output to 2 responses per minute by the 10th day, and ultimately reached a peak of 5 responses per minute on the 20th day. During the succeeding 5-day period, however, his rate again gradually declined to relatively high levels of considerably less than 1 response per minute. Throughout this entire period, the experimental animal of this pair maintained a lever-pressing response rate of almost 20 responses per minute.

Measurement of the urinary excretion of total 17-hydroxycorticosteroids (17-OH-CS) at selected stages during the experiment revealed slight increases in the 24-hour 17-OH-CS output in both monkeys of each pair during the initial phases of avoidance conditioning. Otherwise, the samples tested in subsequent phases of the experiments showed no evidence of increased adrenal cortical activity, as judged by the 24-hour 17-OH-CS excretion. Fluctuations outside the normal range which may have occurred within individual 6-hour avoidance or rest periods cannot, however, be excluded by the data on 24-hour urine portions.

With the first pair of monkeys, the death of the avoidance animal after 23 days terminated the experiment during one of the 6-hour avoidance periods. With the second pair, the avoidance monkey again expired during one of the 6-hour "on-periods," this time 25 days after the start of the experiment. With the third

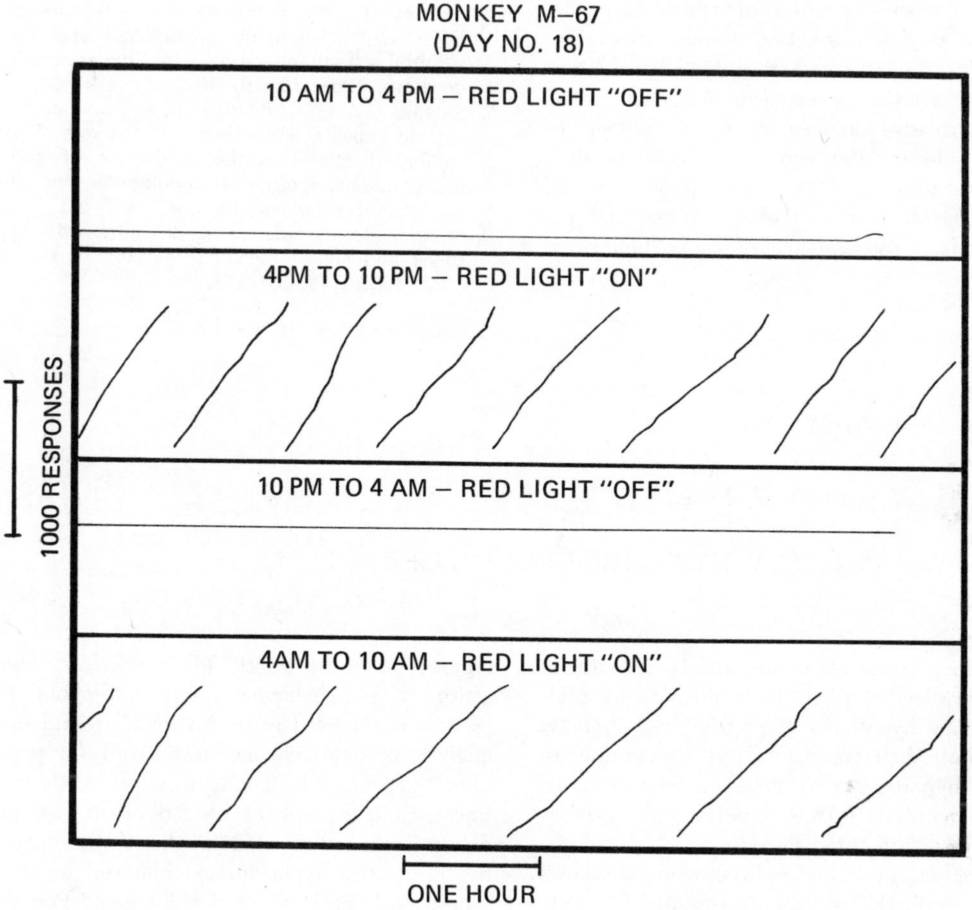

MONKEY M–67
(DAY NO. 18)

10 AM TO 4 PM – RED LIGHT "OFF"

4PM TO 10 PM – RED LIGHT "ON"

1000 RESPONSES

10 PM TO 4 AM – RED LIGHT "OFF"

4AM TO 10 AM – RED LIGHT "ON"

ONE HOUR

FIGURE 4.3. A sample cumulative-response curve showing one 24-hour session (alternating 6-hour "on-off" cycles) for experimental "avoidance" monkey M-67 on day No. 18. The oblique "pips" on the record indicate shocks.

pair in this series, the death of the experimental animal again terminated the experiment during one of the avoidance cycles, this time only 9 days after initiation of the alternating 6-hour on-off procedure. And the experimental animal of the fourth pair of monkeys was sacrificed in a moribund condition after 48 days on the avoidance procedure. In all instances, gross and microscopic analysis revealed the presence of extensive gastrointestinal lesions with ulcera-

tion as a prominent feature of the pathological picture in the experimental animals. However, none of the control animals sacrificed for comparison with their experimental partners and subjected to complete post-mortem examination, showed any indications of such gastrointestinal complications.

The results obtained with this technique, while consistent with previous reports of experimentally produced "psychosomatic" conditions

(2), must be considered only as the initial findings of a programmatic effort to systematically define the variables of which this phenomenon may be a function. Follow-up studies, presently in progress, strongly suggest that selection criteria for experimental and control animals, relative degrees of "social contact" or isolation during the experiment and possibly even constitutional factors may play a critical role in the development of gastrointestinal pathology as a consequence of such "behavioral stress."

REFERENCES

1. PORTER, R. W., BRADY, J. V., CONRAD, D. G., & MASON, J. W. Occurrence of gastrointestinal lesions in behaviorally conditioned and intracerebral self-stimulated monkeys. Federation Proceedings, 1957, *16*, 101–102.
2. SAWREY, W. L., CONGER, J. J., & TURRELL, E. S. An experimental investigation of the role of psychological factors in the production of gastric ulcers in rats. *Journal of Comparative and Physiological Psychology*, 1956, *49*, 457–461.
3. SIDMAN, M. Avoidance conditioning with brief shock and no exteroceptive warning signal. *Science*, 1953, *118*, 157–158.

26.

GEORGE F. MAHL

ANXIETY HYPOTHESIS OF ULCER

This paper reconsiders an anxiety hypothesis of peptic ulcer etiology, its relation to an oral-dependency hypothesis of peptic ulcer etiology, recent published comments (8) concerning an anxiety hypothesis and its experimental basis, and it cites some further experimental observations relevant to this problem.

Substantial direct and indirect evidence shows that increased HCl secretion is essential in peptic ulcer etiology (9) and Wolf and Wolff (9) and others have shown how local vascular changes and mechanical factors might play a contributory role in this disorder. There is, however, no conclusive evidence as to the emotional processes that are positively associated with these important physiologic changes.

The most explicitly formulated viewpoint expressed in the literature is that of Alexander (1, 2, 3). It holds that the external or internal frustration of intense oral-receptive and/or oral-aggressive drives and the regression of these frustrated drives to unconscious desires to eat or to be fed is the fundamental, unique psycho-logic process in peptic ulcer etiology. Overt attitudes and behavior might vary, but this process is reported to be invariably found upon analytic or detailed anamnestic study of peptic ulcer patients (1, 3). It is inferred that the unconscious desires to be fed or to eat, produced in the manner indicated, are accompanied by the gastric hyperfunction believed to be essential for peptic ulcer development. For convenience, this hypothesis will be referred to in this article as an oral-dependency hypothesis of peptic ulcer etiology.

There is also evidence from anamnestic study of personality processes of ulcer patients and studies of the incidence of peptic ulcer in certain life situations that chronic anxiety might play an important role in peptic ulcer etiology. Some of this evidence suggests that the source of the anxiety might not be critical. There is some evidence that chronic anxiety is accompanied by increased HCl secretion (see below). On the basis of these studies it is proposed as a present working hypothesis that: (a) the gastric hyperfunction essential for peptic ulcer etiology is positively associated with chronic anxiety; (b) if these two associated processes

From George F. Mahl."Anxiety, HC1 secretion, and peptic ulcer etiology." *Psychosomatic Medicine*, 1950, *12*, 158–169. Reprinted by permission.

persist peptic ulcer will develop; (c) it is not essential what the source of the anxiety is, whether it is produced and maintained by environmental stimulus conditions or by internal ideational or affective stimuli, whether these internal stimuli are conscious or unconscious, nor whether the anxiety is conscious or unconscious; (d) while the preceding factors might vary it is essential that the chronic anxiety be unrelieved by the development of adequate defense mechanisms or by changes in the stimulus conditions. The assumptions in (c) are the ones in the proposal with a minimum of empirical support. In the absence of critical positive or negative evidence they are adopted now only for theoretical reasons. They are specific assumptions to be tested empirically. For convenience, this working hypothesis will be called an anxiety hypothesis of peptic ulcer etiology.

The terms "acute anxiety" and "chronic anxiety" as presently used refer to a time continuum. They are temporal designations of the relative duration and/or frequency of anxiety responses. There are undoubtedly several important psychologic continua that are some function of this time continuum, but exactly what these are and whether or not they could be readily measured is at present an open question.

In this hypothesis and this paper, the writer does not distinguish between "fear" and "anxiety." •

* * *

PRESENT EXPERIMENT

I. THE PROBLEM

The study with dogs (5) showed that after chronic anxiety had been developed, increased HCl secretion was associated with *acquired anxiety* (conditioned anxiety). If an anxiety hypothesis of peptic ulcer etiology has any validity for humans it must be demonstrated that *acquired chronic anxiety* in humans is accompanied by increased HCl secretion.

The theoretical hypothesis of the study then is: Acquired chronic anxiety in humans is accompanied by increased HCl secretion.

The experimental hypothesis of the study is: The gastric acidity of young human males is greater when they are undergoing the stress of the undergraduate examination period, if they react to this with anxiety *over a period of days*, than before or after the period.

It is assumed that such acquired anxieties as fear of failure, fear of loss of prestige and status, fear of loss of parental approval, etc., are aroused during the examination period. In the study a judgment of the degree of the arousal of such acquired anxieties as manifested in overt behavior and overt statements is made independently of the measurement of the gastric samples. It is assumed that under the conditions of this study changes in the acidity of fasting gastric contents is an index of changes in the rate of HCl secretion.

Contradictory conclusions were reached by Floyer and Jennings (4) and Miller, Bergheim, and Hawk (6) concerning the effect of similar anxiety-producing situations on HCl secretion. This contradiction is more imaginary than real, however, because of the inadequate procedure used by the former and the fact that the latter investigated only one subject. The present study will have the secondary effect of helping to resolve this contradiction.

II. EXPERIMENTAL PROCEDURE

Subjects. Eight undergraduate male university students volunteered as subjects for the experiment. At the time he volunteered, each subject knew of the nature of the study and that it involved intubation. The subjects ranged in age from 21 to 25 years.

Method of Measurement. Control and experimental fasting gastric samples were obtained by aspirating the stomach contents through a Levin tube. The tube was passed nasally for some subjects, orally for others, depending upon the wish of the subject. In either case, it was passed by the same means for both the experimental and control measures for each subject. Five minutes after the tube was passed, the stomach contents were aspirated as completely as possible. The criterion for stomach emptiness was that point at which each of three successive aspirations yielded 2 cc. or less of fluid. This was done to clear the stomach of any fluids that may have been secreted on a conditioned response basis before the experimental and control sessions, when the subjects would normally have eaten breakfast or a mid-morning snack or would be anticipating lunch, or fluids that may have been secreted as a result of the trauma of intubation. The stomach was again aspirated at the end of a twenty-minute period. The fasting fluid obtained at this time constituted the test sample of the control and experimental conditions. It was titrated against .1 N NaOH for free HCl and total acid, using Topfer's reagent and phenopthalein respectively as indicators for the end-points.

Conditions of Measurement.

(a) Control measures. The control fasting gastric samples were measured from two to four weeks before the examination period for 5 subjects and from three to five weeks after the examination period for 3 subjects. They were split in this way to control for any adaptation to successive intubations. The dates for the control measures were arranged so that no subject had any pressing academic tasks at the time. During the twenty-minute control test period, the subject and E carried on a conversation. E directed it to the extent that he kept it centered about the subject's hobby interests and activities, otherwise he remained as passive as possible. Allowing for the varying degrees of discomfort due to the presence of the tube, all of the subjects appeared relaxed and undisturbed during this period. The control test sample thus contained those gastric fluids secreted during an innocuous twenty-minute conversation which occurred during a relatively stress-free period of the school year.

(b) Experimental measures. These were obtained during the final examination period. They were made on the morning of a day on which each subject had to take what he regarded as a difficult examination. The examination itself was to be taken in the afternoon. The hour of the experimental session was matched to that of the control session to control for any hourly variations in HCl secretion that might occur. During the twenty-minute experimental test period E and the subject again carried on a conversation. This now took the form of a stress interview in contrast to the relatively nonemotionally toned discussion of the control condition. E centered it about the following questions for each subject:

1. Had the subject ever failed any kind of an academic examination before and what were the consequences?

2. Did the subject realize the importance of doing well on today's examination in terms of being admitted to a graduate or professional school or obtaining a job? (Seven of the 8 subjects were pre-professional students.)

3. How did the subject's parents usually react to his not doing well on examinations and in courses?

4. How would his standing on today's examination affect his course grade and how would this affect his competitive status with his student friends?

5. How hard had the subject worked in preparing for today's examination? Did he feel sufficiently well prepared?

At the end of this experimental period, E dichotomized the subjects into two groups on the basis of the degree of anxiety motivation shown by them. These are recorded as "High Anxiety" and "Low Anxiety." This is a judgment of observable, overt anxiety behavior and verbalizations made during the interview on the experimental day. It was recorded immediately at the end of this period, prior to titration of the gastric sample obtained at that time.

The experimental test sample thus contains those gastric fluids secreted during an interview touching upon aspects of the current stress stimulation of the final examination period.

For both the control and experimental measures, no food was eaten by the subjects after midnight of the previous night and no water was taken for two hours prior to the aspiration of the gastric samples.

III. Results

Table 4.1 contains the results. Considering the group of subjects as a whole, the mean of the experimental free HCl and total acid measures is considerably higher than the mean of the same control measures. Both of these differences are in the predicted direction and the probability that such predicted increases would occur by chance selection of this sample of subjects is only three in a hundred for the free HCl mea-

TABLE 4.1

FREE HCL AND TOTAL ACID MEASURES, EXPRESSED IN CLINICAL UNITS, DURING CONTROL AND
EXPERIMENTAL CONDITIONS

Subject	Free HCl			Total acid			Anxiety Category
	Con.	Exp.	Con.-Exp.	Con.	Exp.	Con.-Exp.	
1	0	17	+17	16	27	+11	High
2	0	53	+53	5	61	+56	High
3	0	0	0	11	11	0	High
4	9	34	+25	20	43	+23	High
5	0	7	+ 7	5	16	+11	High
6	0	46	+46	4	53	+49	High
7	0	0	0	17	9	− 8	Low
8	0	0	0	6	7	+ 1	Low
X	1.1	19.6	+18.5	10.5	28.4	+17.9	
s	3	20.4	19.8	6	20	23.2	
t			2.467			2.168	
p			<.03			<.04	

t is based on t-test for related measures.
p is the probability that the predicted increase in acidity occurred by chance selection of this sample.
Subjects 1, 2, 3, 4, 7: Control preceded experimental measures.
Subjects 5, 6, 8: Experimental preceded control measures.

sures and four in a hundred for the total acid measures.

Two of the 8 subjects were judged by E to fall in the "Low Anxiety" category. These judgments were made for the following reasons. Subject 6 was a premedical student who had already been accepted for the following year's entering class at one of the most sought-after medical schools in the country even though he had not yet completed the first semester of the fourth year of his undergraduate course. In the midst of the stress interview he laughed and asked, "What are you trying to do, get me worried?" He stated that since he was already accepted for medical school all he had to do was pass his courses and that he could fail his examinations and still do this. Subject 2 was not a preprofessional student, was a member of the varsity hockey squad, and spent more time discussing the progress of the hockey team than his pending examination and his concern over it; he was planning to go on a skiing party in the midst of the final examination period. He was a typical "gentleman student" who said he was satisfied to get only passing grades. The remaining 6 subjects expressed sufficient concern in the stress interview to be placed in the

"High Anxiety" category. They all expressed frank concern about the outcome of their final examination and their final standing in the course involved. In no case was their concern over actual failure; all wanted to obtain an academic record considered acceptable by a medical or graduate school. While such interview judgments lack precision and are of unknown reliability the difference in anxiety level between the two groups was pronounced.

Since the group as a whole showed significantly higher gastric acidity values during the stress period than in the control period, one would predict that this increase would be greater for the "High Anxiety" group than for the "Low Anxiety" group. The following breakdown of the data yields results that are in agreement with this prediction.

MEAN CONTROL-EXPERIMENTAL DIFFERENCES IN
ACIDITY EXPRESSED IN CLINICAL UNITS

	"Low Anxiety" Group	"High Anxiety" Group	p
Free HCl	0	+24.7	<.09
Total acid	−3.5	+25	<.08
n	2	6	

Of the 6 subjects in the "High Anxiety" group, 5 showed the predicted increase in gastric acidity. Both of the subjects in the "Low Anxiety" group failed to show an increase in gastric acidity.

The differences between the 2 subgroups have fair reliability and are in agreement with the results for the group as a whole, but the number of cases making up the subgroups is small. This comparison of the subgroups is cited to show the consistency of the results.

Because intubation is traumatic in varying degrees for different subjects, especially on the first occasion, adaptation effects were controlled as described above. The following summary shows that the sequence of the control and experimental measures did not influence the increase in acidity during the experimental condition. Increases of the same magnitude are found when the control precedes the experimental period as when the experimental precedes the control condition.

MEAN CONTROL-EXPERIMENTAL DIFFERENCES IN ACIDITY EXPRESSED IN CLINICAL UNITS

	Exp. Measure Precedes Con.	Con. Measure Precedes Exp.	p
Free HCl	+17.7	+19	>.90
Total acid	+20.3	+16.4	>.80
n	3	5	

DISCUSSION

The present results agree with the findings of the previous study (5) with dogs and with the increase in HCl secretion predicted by an anxiety hypothesis of peptic ulcer etiology. To the extent that conscious chronic anxiety and concomitant increase HCl secretion are important in this etiology, these results support an anxiety hypothesis. They do not directly confirm the hypothesis, however, since one must still infer that peptic ulcers would develop if the anxiety and the associated increased HCl secretion were protracted. The study is also limited by its lack of study of mechanical and vascular factors.

Szasz (8) raised theoretical objections to an anxiety hypothesis of peptic ulcer etiology. He says that because anxiety is omnipresent it is inadequate and meaningless simply to correlate somatic processes with anxiety per se; he says that the only adequate correlation for psychosomatic theory is that between somatic processes and the way in which the ego defends itself against anxiety arising from specified stimulus conditions.

There are two important questions involved here. First, are anxiety and HCl secretion positively associated regardless of the stimulus conditions? The aspect of this question that is most important for peptic ulcer etiology is whether or not anxiety arising from varying concomitant affective processes (e.g., hostile wishes, incestuous wishes, fear of not being loved) as well as from external stimuli (e.g., reality danger situations, threatening parental figures) is positively associated with HCl secretion. What evidence there is available on this point refers almost completely to anxiety produced by external stimulus conditions and it suggests that regardless of the manner in which the anxiety is produced it is associated with increased HCl secretion. Whether or not this is true for all sources of anxiety, internal or external, is a problem for future investigation and not one simply to be dismissed a priori. It is assumed for the present for theoretical purposes that the source of anxiety is not critical, but the autonomic patterns may become very complex when additional affects are involved. This assumption will be modified in accordance with experimental findings.

The second principal question is what the relative role of anxiety and the defense reactions against it might be in peptic ulcer etiology. Here Szasz has confused the differential role of anxiety in conversion and the other defense mechanisms, on the one hand, and its role in psychosomatic disorders, on the other. In the former, anxiety is of primary importance as a motive for defense and its autonomic concomitants are not of major importance because conversion symptoms or other defense mechanisms can maintain the anxiety at a reduced level. In the case of peptic ulcer, however, it is proposed that anxiety is not successfully reduced by the defense mechanisms and that the resulting chronic anxiety and its autonomic concomitants then become of major importance.

physiologic aspects of these repressed emotions process in peptic ulcer development, Alexander (2) clearly pointed out that in the vegetative neuroses the essential factors are the physiologic aspects of chronic emotions per se. His point in the section on vegetative neuroses is that in these disorders the chronic autonomic excitation is not the result of conversion of repressed emotions (warded-off impulses) but are the physiologic aspects of these repressed emotions themselves.

The writer is proposing, in addition, that in the vegetative neuroses, the motive for the defense mechanisms ("the warding-off impulses") also becomes chronic and that its physiologic concomitants then become important. (Of course, in some instances anxiety might also be the unsuccessfully "warded-off impulse.")

Reluctance to consider the autonomic concomitants of anxiety per se in peptic ulcer etiology appears to the writer to be a joint result of the historical development of psychodynamic theory and the fact that psychosomatic theory early adopted Cannon's hypothesis of the emergency function of emotions and unqualifiedly extended it to chronic emotional processes without considering the fact that his hypothesis was based on studies of acute emotions. In the development of psychodynamic theory, emphasis was placed on anxiety as a motive for defense mechanisms and the elucidation of these defense mechanisms was the primary task undertaken. But anxiety has physiologic concomitants and when it becomes chronic these physiologic concomitants can contribute to the psychosomatic disorders. Cannon's hypothesis predicts inhibited HCl secretion during anxiety. But Cannon only considered one clear-cut observation of HCl secretion during anxiety (LeConte's observation) and that was an instance of acute anxiety. In the psychosomatic disorders, however, one deals with chronic emotional processes and there is strong evidence that increased HCl secretion is positively associated with chronic anxiety. As far as HCl secretion is concerned, one cannot simply extend Cannon's hypothesis to chronic anxiety. It has previously been suggested (5), on the basis of evidence cited in the introduction, that this disagreement between Cannon's hypothesis and an anxiety hypothesis of peptic ulcer etiology might be resolved by consideration of the acute-chronic variable. Reports of specific studies of this variable in monkeys and humans are now being prepared in which this point will be discussed in more detail.

The present proposal of an anxiety hypothesis of peptic ulcer etiology is similar in its formal aspects to the hostility theory of hypertension (7). Here one does not hesitate to speak of "hostilities" (i.e., hostility arising from varying sources) and of the physiologic concomitants of hostility per se. (It is even suggested (7) that "anxieties" per se might be important in this disorder.) In this case confusion of the role of hostility in the defense mechanisms and its role in the vegetative neuroses has not been troublesome. It appears to the writer that the lack of confusion in this instance might also be a joint result of the history of psychodynamic theory and the ease of extension of Cannon's hypothesis to the particular chronic emotional process emphasized. It was not the tradition in psychodynamic theory to place emphasis on hostility as a motive for defense mechanisms and there was no conflict between the changes in blood pressure predicted by Cannon's hypothesis and those predicted by the hostility theory of hypertension.

The increasing evidence that one of the autonomic concomitants of chronic anxiety is increased HCl secretion—considered together with the reports of chronic anxiety in ulcer patients and the belief that protracted increased HCl secretion is essential for peptic ulcer etiology —should make the role of chronic anxiety in this disorder a matter for intensive, disinterested research.

* * *

SUMMARY

1. It is impossible to make a critical evaluation of an oral-dependency and an anxiety hypothesis of peptic ulcer etiology solely on the basis of available anamnestic or psychoanalytic studies of personality processes in peptic ulcer patients.

A method which would enable one to do so is briefly described.

2. Both the oral-dependency and the anxiety hypothesis assume that increased HCl secretion is associated with the emotional processes emphasized. There are no published experimental data, positive or negative, concerning HCl secretion during the arousal of unconscious wishes to be loved, to eat, or to be fed. There is evidence that chronic overt anxiety behavior in dogs and conscious chronic anxiety in humans are positively associated with increased HCl secretion. Some of the results are contradictory, however, and further studies, especially at the human level, are needed. Such studies also aid in resolving the contradictory predictions of HCl secretion made by Cannon's emergency theory of emotions and by an anxiety hypothesis of peptic ulcer etiology.

3. A study of the gastric acidity of male students during the undergraduate examination period and during control periods is reported. The gastric acidity of these students was significantly higher during the examination period than during the control periods. The rise in gastric acidity was very closely related to the degree of conscious anxiety manifested by these subjects. These results agree with an anxiety hypothesis of peptic ulcer etiology; they do not bear directly upon an oral-dependency hypothesis.

4. A recent critique of an anxiety hypothesis of peptic ulcer etiology and of a previous experiment of the writer is considered. It is shown that this critique did not adequately describe the experimental procedure or the results of the study it discounted. The theoretical objections raised in this critique are shown to be a function of confusion of the differential role of anxiety in the conversion neuroses and in the vegetative neuroses. The reluctance to consider the autonomic concomitants of anxiety is regarded as a joint result of the history of psychodynamic theory and the unqualified extensions of Cannon's emergency theory of emotions to chronic emotional processes.

5. Possible fruitful lines of research for a comparative evaluation of the oral-dependency and anxiety hypotheses of peptic ulcer etiology are discussed.

REFERENCES

1. ALEXANDER, F. Treatment of a case of peptic ulcer and personality disorder. *Psychosomatic Medicine*, 1947, 9, 320–330.
2. ALEXANDER, F. Fundamental concepts of psychosomatic research. *Psychosomatic Medicine*, 1943, 5, 205–210 (as corrected p. 400).
3. ALEXANDER, F. *et al*. The influence of psychologic factors upon G-I disturbances: A symposium. *Psychoanalytical Quarterly*. 1934, 3, 501–588.
4. FLOYER, M., & JENNINGS, D. Fractional test meals on students awaiting examination results. *Lancet*, 1946, 251 (1), 356–357.
5. MAHL, G. F. Effect of chronic fear on the gastric secretion of HCl in dogs. *Psychosomatic Medicine*, 1949, 11, 30–44.
6. MILLER, R. J., BERGHEIM, O., & HAWK, P. B. Gastric response to foods, IX. The influence of worry on gastric digestion. *Science*, 1920, 52, 253–254.
7. SAUL, L. J. Hostility in cases of essential hypertension. *Psychosomatic Medicine*, 1939, 1, 153–161.
8. SZASZ, T. S. Factors in the pathogenesis of peptic ulcer: Some critical comments on a recent article by George F. Mahl. *Psychosomatic Medicine*, 1949, 11, 300–304.
9. WOLF, S., & WOLFF, H. G. *Human Gastric Function*. New York: Oxford University Press, 1943.

27.

FLANDERS DUNBAR

PERSONALITY TYPE HYPOTHESIS

One of the leading conclusions emerging from the study . . . is of particular interest in relating anxiety states to organic disease. It is that each recognized syndrome could be correlated with a well-defined personality type. In this statement there is no implication of cause and effect. The personality types in question were classified principally in terms of (a) the spheres of life adjustment in which their major conflict and anxiety occurred and (b) the characteristic reaction to the conflict in the form of patterns of behavior and of symptoms, both somatic and psychoneurotic. Of course it will remain for further studies of other serial admission groups to correct and define these personality types, but in this field we are still, so to speak, in the pre-Osler period. We lack even a descriptive psychosomatic nosology.

ACCIDENT

In the study of serial admissions to a general hospital (1) which I wish to discuss in some detail, accident enters in in a dual way. The aim in this project was to study the role of anxiety as well as of personality in general, in patients suffering from cardiovascular disease and diabetes. It was thought desirable to have what might be called a control group taken from the same geographic and population area. It was suggested that patients on the fracture ward in the same hospital might fulfill this requirement. Then it was discovered, first, that 80% of these patients suffered from an accident syndrome and, second, that the accident syndrome was closely related to a specific manner of handling anxiety.

From Flanders Dunbar,"The relationship between anxiety states and organic disease." *Clinics,* 1942, *1,* 879–908. The present excerpt begins with p. 886. Reprinted by permission.

A brief view of the personality types encountered may be obtained from a series of tables, each comparing in parallel columns two of the disease groups studied. It will be possible here only to comment briefly on certain outstanding points in these tables or personality profiles.

Table 4.2 is headed Personality Profile, Fracture—Coronary Occlusion, Group Statistics. This was actually the last table to be completed and was added because the authors became curious as to whether material from case records such as could be assembled by any statistician would tend to confirm or contradict the personality pictures derived on the basis of the psychosomatic history. The data for this table were obtained from statistical tabulations of the records, and are purely objective, containing no element of interpretation or judgment on the part of those who conducted the research. The statements in this table do not apply uniformly to every individual in the respective disease groups and therefore cannot be employed as an infallible guide either to diagnosis or to prognosis. The correlation, however, is sufficiently high to indicate a large element of statistical probability that in any group suffering from the syndrome in question a large majority will correspond with the picture presented, in a majority of the details, and in this respect stand in contradistinction with those in other disease groups.

It will be noted under Family History that there is little difference between the two groups in what might be called evidence of a hereditary tendency or predisposition to cardiovascular disease, which occurred in about 38% of the fracture patients and about 42% of those suffering from coronary occlusion. There is, however, a striking difference in the occurrence of accidents among family and siblings, the percentage being 40% for the fracture patients and

TABLE 4.2

PERSONALITY PROFILE FOR

FRACTURE   CORONARY OCCLUSION

GROUP STATISTICS

1. FAMILY HISTORY: Relative frequency of *accidents* in the family and siblings (about 40%), history of *cardiovascular disease*, however, not strikingly low (about 38%). Little *exposure* to disease (about 46% to accidents).
2. PERSONAL DATA: Typically orphaned or left home early. Both parents strict, and little, if any, actual emotional contact with them ever existed. *Average marriage rate. Few children, many divorces.*
3. HEALTH RECORD: *Excellent previous health* record, few operations except appendectomy. Women good pelvic histories. Interest in health and vigor, with tendency to be over-concerned about any symptom they have.
4. INJURIES: Eighty per cent two or more accidents, majority three or more. Accident habit especially frequent in decade 15–25. Mainly the result of falls and traffic accidents. Many childhood accidents.

1. FAMILY HISTORY: *Cardiovascular disease* in parents and siblings about average for the groups studied (42%). *Accident* history for parents and siblings about 9%. *Exposure* to cardiovascular disease or to sudden death in about 90% of the cases.
2. PERSONAL DATA: Both parents usually lived beyond the patient's majority; the father usually died first. Both parents typically strict. *High marriage rate. Many children, few divorces.*
3. HEALTH RECORD: *Bad previous illness* history with predominance of vegetative symptoms and many operations. Anginal symptoms frequent. Tendency to self-neglect. Women poor pelvic histories.
4. INJURIES: Rarely more than one injury. Rate for one accident above average, but these accidents were of a specific type; result of action by another person, typical cutting, shooting, or stabbing. Few childhood accidents.

9% for those with coronary occlusion. Of course it is absurd to think of fractures as being inherited in a literal sense. In view of the above facts it seemed much more to the point to consider the factor of exposure to disease or accident among not only family and siblings but also friends and acquaintances who had no blood relationship. Exposure to cardiovascular disease among the fracture patients was low, whereas exposure to such disease or to sudden death in the cases of coronary occlusion was about 90%.

Under the second item the important point to note is the bearing which the facts may have on the conflict with authority and its working out in both fracture and coronary cases. Both groups had strict parents but the fracture patients typically had contact with the parents only in early youth, while those with coronary occlusion were subjected to parental influence well beyond their majority.

Under item three (Cf. also Figure 4.4) there is a vivid contrast between the good health record of the fracture patients and the bad health record of those with coronary occlusion. When this table is corrected for sex distribution in each disease group there is no important modification of the pattern. The women in all cases have a worse previous disease history than the men, although the difference between the sexes is less in patients suffering from coronary occlusion than in any other disease group studied. When this table is corrected for age one important point comes into prominence. Patients suffering from the accident syndrome taken as a group maintain their good previous health record from decade to decade, that is, at the age of 50, their previous illness history is not importantly worse than it was at the age of 20. In all other disease groups studied, the record for previous illness increases from decade to decade, although when compared with patients suffering from the same illness in the same decade the differences remain approximately as shown on Figure 4.4, Health Record.

But the most obvious contrast of all occurs in item four (Cf. Figure 4.5). The fracture patients were for the most part accident-prone, as is indicated by the fact that 80% of them had two or more serious accidents, and the majority three or more, while those suffering from coronary occlusion rarely had more than one injury from accident and when they did suffer injury it was usually the result of action of another person rather than of an accident which

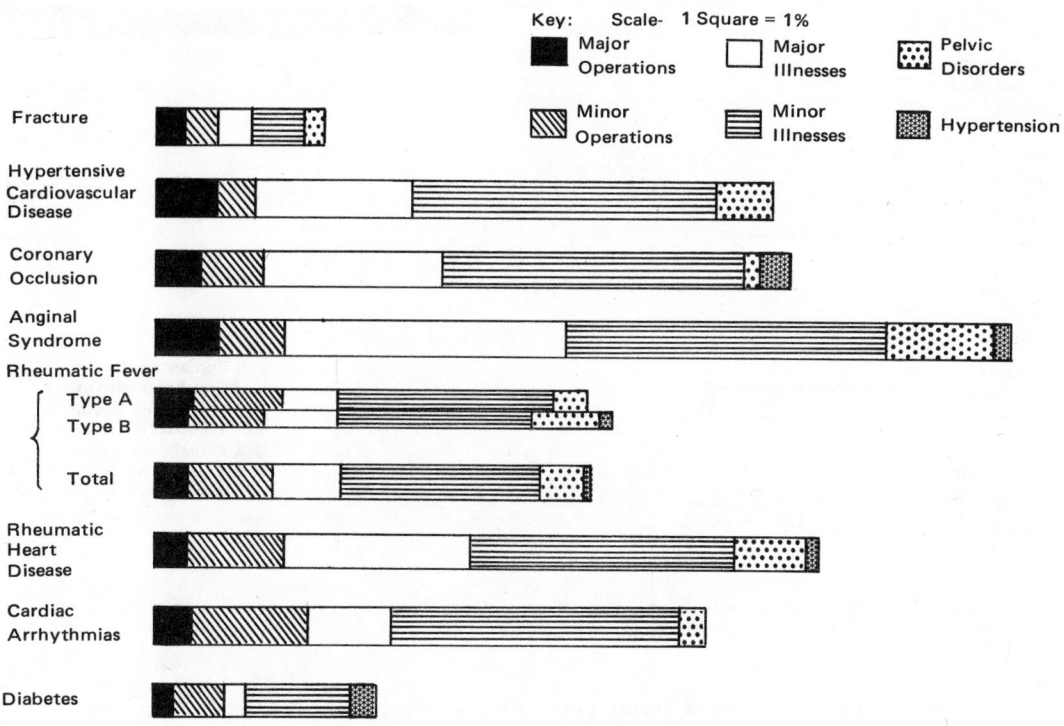

FIGURE 4.4. Previous illness incidence.

could have been due to their own carelessness, such as falls or motor vehicle accidents.

Reference to Figure 4.6, entitled Accidents showing Cardiac Pattern, will clarify this point. It shows the percentage of patients in each disease group whose accidents were the result of injury by someone else, whether because the patient had picked a fight with the other person and so gotten himself injured, or whether he was a passenger in a motor vehicle and had or had not unduly irritated the driver. Because such accidents accounted for almost the total accident history of patients with coronary occlusion and were prominent in the accident history of all other patients suffering from cardiovascular disease, this type of accident was labeled "cardiac pattern." The almost complete absence of accidents of this type among the accident-prone is striking. It is noteworthy

also that the small percentage recorded for fracture patients occurred in patients seen on the fracture ward who did not have a well established accident habit.

Figure 4.7, Accidents in Childhood, clarifies another point mentioned under item four of Table 4.2. Although accidents are particularly frequent in childhood, accident-prone patients have more accidents in childhood than patients in any other disease group (left-hand section of Figure 4.7). Nevertheless, childhood accidents account for a smaller percentage of total accidents in the fracture group than in any other group studied except patients suffering from coronary occlusion.

We now come to Table 4.3, Personality Profile, Fracture—Coronary Occlusion, Individual Picture. It contains material partly statistical in nature and partly the result of clinical observa-

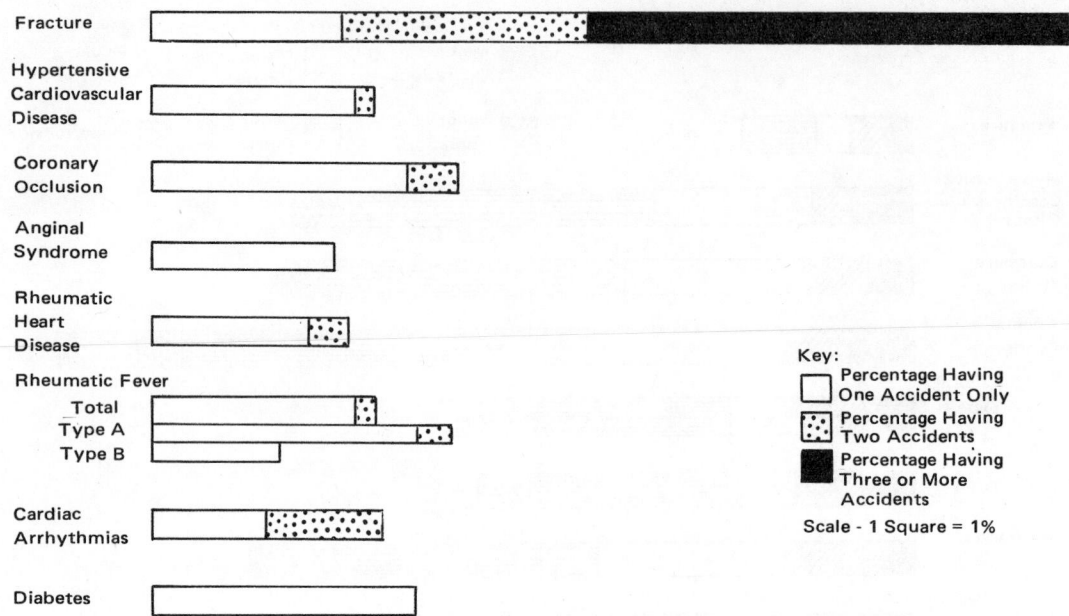

Key:
- ☐ Percentage Having One Accident Only
- ▦ Percentage Having Two Accidents
- ■ Percentage Having Three or More Accidents

Scale - 1 Square = 1%

FIGURE 4.5. Accident incidence. Omitting all patients suffering from more than one syndrome.

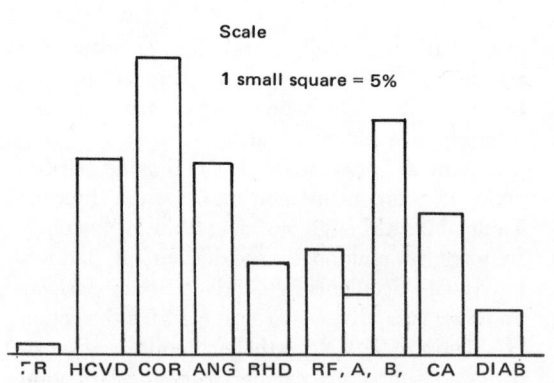

Scale

1 small square = 5%

FR HCVD COR ANG RHD RF, A, B, CA DIAB

FIGURE 4.6. Percentage of total accidents showing cardiac pattern.

tion. In general the material in this section applies to each individual in the respective groups, and has greater value for diagnosis and prognosis than that in the first section of the profile, Table 4.2. While any given individual in the coronary group, for instance, may not show all the details of the personality picture listed under "general adjustment," he will show enough of them so that his personality type may be easily recognized. Each of the characteristics set down in this section was found in 85-90% of the patients in the group in question, and was found only rarely (i.e., less than 10%) in patients in the other groups.

The fracture patients typically did not finish educational courses which they undertook (Cf. Figure 4.8, Educational Records of Patients with Anginal Syndrome, Coronary Occlusion, and Fracture), had an unstable work record, experienced many changes in their jobs coupled with ups and downs in their incomes, were spontaneous and casual in their social relationships, had superficially good sexual adjustment but were irresponsible toward their sexual partners and family.

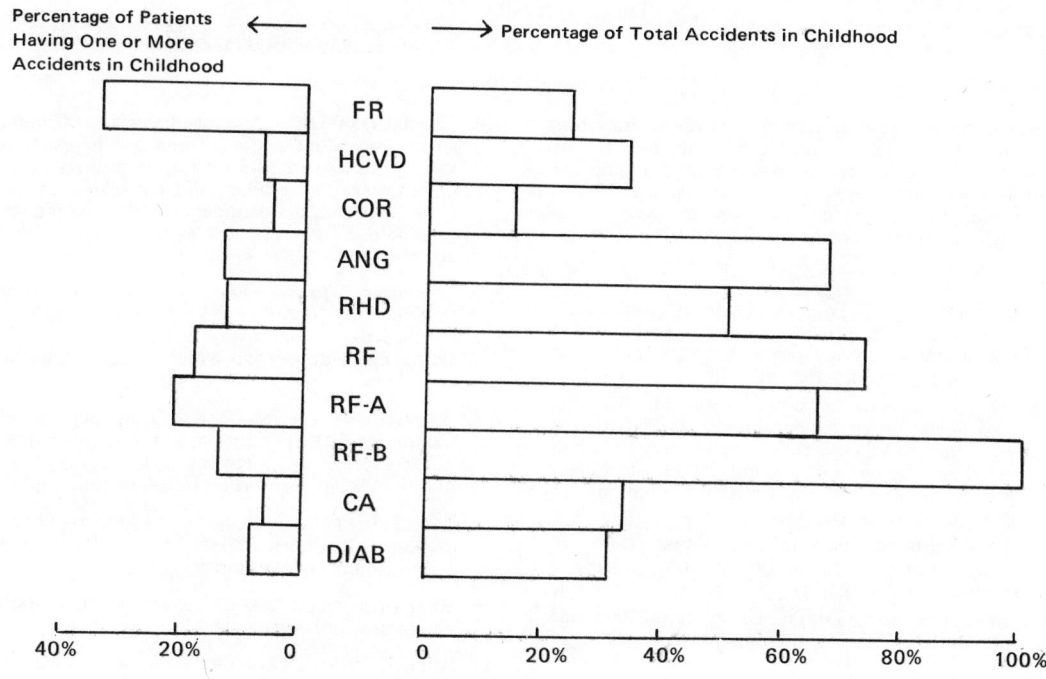

FIGURE 4.7. Accidents in childhood.

TABLE 4.3

PERSONALITY PROFILE FOR

FRACTURE   CORONARY OCCLUSION

INDIVIDUAL PICTURE

5. GENERAL ADJUSTMENT:

   A. *Education* interrupted in the middle, lack of planning.
   B. *Work Record* unstable. Many and diverse jobs.
   C. *Income and Vocational Level:* High but marked by sudden changes and many periods of being out of work.
   D. *Social Relationships:* Generally liked. Tendency to entertain. Casual with both sexes.
   E. *Sexual Adjustment* superficially good, but irresponsible except careful to avoid infection in promiscuous relationships, but without exaggerated fear.
   F. *Attitude Toward Family:* Irresponsible and little emotional contact.

5. GENERAL ADJUSTMENT:

   A. *Education:* Tendency to complete educational unit undertaken. Planned career.
   B. *Work Record:* Sticking to one job, working to the top.
   C. *Income and Vocational Levels:* Highest of all groups studied. Characteristically Class II (Executives and Officials).
   D. *Social Relationships:* Generally respected. Tendency to dominate. Argumentative with men, attentive to women.
   E. *Sexual Adjustment:* Role of exemplary husband and father combined with secret promiscuity; high venereal disease rate.
   F. *Attitude Toward Family:* Hostile toward father, better toward mother in early life, with marked tendency to cut off both later. Dominating, proud, and responsible toward wife and children.

TABLE 4.3 (Continued)

PERSONALITY PROFILE FOR

FRACTURE   CORONARY OCCLUSION

INDIVIDUAL PICTURE

6. CHARACTERISTIC BEHAVIOR PATTERN: Impulsive action. Tendency to avoid conflict with authority. Tendency to leave things unfinished. Conversation largely about action and things. *Tendency to attach emotion to people and action. Inarticulate about feelings.*

7. NEUROTIC TRAITS: *High percentage of early neurotic traits,* especially lying, stealing, and truancy, sleepwalking and sleeptalking. Later life almost no obvious neurotic traits except for a small group, particularly women, with phobias, especially fear of falling.

8. ADDICTIONS AND INTEREST: Addiction to coffee and cigarettes *to let off steam.* Marked interest in competitive sports or gambling (football, baseball, racing, auto-racing), and machinery. Practicing orthodox authoritative religion (institutionalized super-ego).

9. LIFE SITUATION IMMEDIATELY PRIOR TO ONSET: Some conflict with authority, job, parent, or spouse from which escape seemed impossible.

10. REACTION TO ILLNESS: Exaggerated tendency to exploit illness for compensations, financial or other.

11. AREA OF FOCAL CONFLICT AND CHARACTERISTIC REACTION: Authority—avoidance.

6. CHARACTERISTIC BEHAVIOR PATTERN: Compulsively consistent action. Tendency to seize authority, dislike of sharing responsibilities. Tendency to work long hours and not take vacations. Conversation an instrument of domination and aggression. *Tendency to attach emotion to ideas. Articulate about feelings.*

7. NEUROTIC TRAITS: *Few early neurotic traits,* tendency to brood and keep their troubles to themselves. In later life inner tension and a tendency to depression which is rarely admitted to others.

8. ADDICTIONS AND INTERESTS: Tendency to take stimulants to help *keep on working* (overwork). Little interest in sports, few hobbies. Skepticism about religion. Marked interest in philosophy.

9. LIFE SITUATION IMMEDIATELY PRIOR TO ONSET: Exposure to shock—especially in job or in relinquishment of authority.

10. REACTION TO ILLNESS: Tendency to minimize symptoms and self-neglect.

11. AREA OF FOCAL CONFLICT AND CHARACTERISTIC REACTION: Authority—attempt to subdue authority instead of avoiding it.

Those suffering from coronary occlusion had a tendency to complete their educational units, stick to one job and work to the top, achieve a high position, and be both dominating and responsible in their social relationships and toward their family. These traits in both groups fit the characteristic behavior pattern summarized under item six, Table 4.3. The fracture patients were impulsive in their action and solved their conflict with authority by a tendency to avoid or run away from it. Those suffering from coronary occlusion were compulsively consistent rather than impulsive, and instead of running away from authority tried to solve their conflict with it by working up to a position where they could themselves be the supreme authority and not share power with anyone else. This pattern of behavior had a bearing on the onset of illness.

This is interesting in view of Sherrington's statement (2) that the most satisfactory release of instinctual tension is action, the least

satisfactory is thought, and speech and fantasy stand half way between. He pointed out that those inclined to impulsive action might be expected to show fewer signs of internal tension—less vegetative symptomatology—than those inhibited in this sphere and more inclined to brooding. Our observations would tend to confirm this suggestion.

It is well known that vegetative symptomatology is the most characteristic accompaniment of anxiety in the organism and it is clear also that impulsive action under stress tends to eliminate such symptomatology as well as consciousness of anxiety. This helps to make more intelligible the behavior pattern found to be characteristic of each group. It may be useful to call attention to one particular point here: that accident-prone people are relatively inarticulate about their feelings, whereas patients suffering from coronary occlusion are extremely articulate about their feelings and are self-critical.

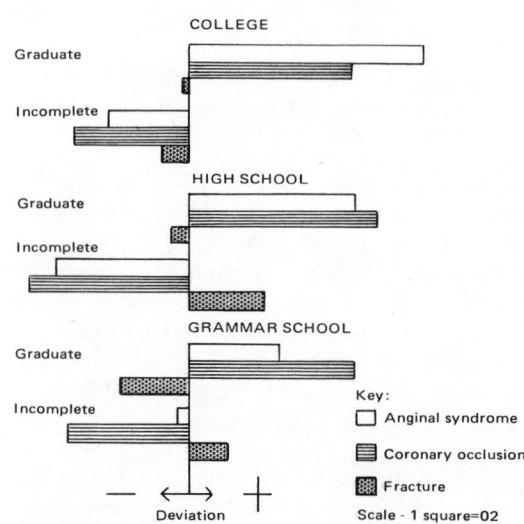

FIGURE 4.8. Educational records of patients with anginal syndrome, coronary occlusion, and fracture. Percentage of deviation of disease groups studied from educational norm for upper 60% of the population.

Among the remaining items in Table 4.3, nine is particularly interesting because it offers a clue to the precipitating factor of the illness in each group of cases. Among the fracture patients injuries usually occurred immediately after some conflict with job-authority, parent, or spouse from which escape seemed impossible. Ordinarily under such circumstances an anxiety state might be expected to arise. In these patients there is evidence that it does arise, but is quickly blotted out by recourse to

an impulsive act such as might and often does lead to an accident. This is a relationship between anxiety state and organic damage which has been largely overlooked. We are more familiar with the pattern followed by the patient with coronary occlusion or some other internal pathology. In the patients reported in this study, coronary occlusion usually occurred during a state of anxiety, and specifically immediately after a shock in the realm in which authority was being exercised, such as losing status, a job, money, or having to take a partner in business.

As a result of these and other observations it was concluded that while the area of life adjustment in which both groups of patients were most likely to come to grief was in relationships to authority, the characteristic reaction in the case of the fracture patients was avoidance of the conflict—perhaps specifically of anxiety—and the characteristic reaction among those suffering from coronary occlusion was the attempt to cope with or repress their anxiety and to subdue authority. These observations were supplemented and confirmed by intensive studies of selected patients. But, of course, there is much more to be said on the subject.

❋   ❋   ❋

REFERENCES

1. DUNBAR, H. F. *Problems in diagnosis and treatment of chronic illness.* A psychosomatic study of hospital admissions, with special reference to cardiovascular disease, fracture, diabetes, and allergy. (in press)
2. SHERRINGTON, C. *The brain and its mechanism.* The Rede lecture delivered before the University of Cambridge, December 5, 1933. Cambridge: Macmillan, 1933.

28.

Franz Alexander

SPECIFIC EMOTION HYPOTHESIS

The psychosomatic point of view meant a new approach to the study of the causation of disease. As mentioned before, the fact that acute emotions have an influence on body functions belongs to everyday experience. Corresponding to every emotional situation there is a specific syndrome of physical changes, psychosomatic responses, such as laughter, weeping, blushing, changes in the heart rate, respiration, etc. However, since these psychomotor processes belong to our everyday life and have no ill effects, medicine has, until recently, paid little attention to a detailed investigation of them. These changes in the body as reactions to acute emotions are of a passing nature. When the emotion disappears, the corresponding physiological process, weeping or laughter, heart palpitation or elevation of blood pressure, also disappears and the body returns to its equilibrium.

The psychoanalytic study of neurotic patients revealed, however, that under the influence of prolonged emotional disturbances, chronic disturbances of the body may develop. Such chronic bodily changes under the influence of emotion were first observed in hysterical patients. Freud introduced the concept of "conversion hysteria," in which bodily symptoms develop in response to chronic emotional conflicts. These changes were noted in the muscles controlled by the will and in sense perceptions. One of the most important discoveries of Freud was that when emotion cannot be expressed and relieved through normal channels by voluntary activity it may become the source of chronic psychic and physical disorders. Whenever emotions are repressed because of psychic conflicts—that is to say, excluded from consciousness and thus cut

off from adequate discharge—they provide the source of chronic tension which is the cause of the hysterical symptoms.

From the physiological point of view, a hysterical conversion symptom is similar in nature to any usual voluntary innervation, expressive movement, or sensory perception. In hysteria, however, the motivating psychological impulse is unconscious. In attacking someone, or in going to a certain place, our arms and legs are put into motion under the influence of conscious motivations and goals. The so-called expressive movements such as laughter, weeping, grimacing, gesticulating, are based on similar physiological processes. In the latter, however, the innervations take place not under the influence of conscious goals but under the stimulus of an emotional tension which is discharged in a complex physiological pattern. In a conversion symptom like hysterical paralysis or contracture "the leap from the psychic to the somatic" is not different from the leap which takes place in any common motor innervation such as voluntary movements or laughter or weeping. Apart from the fact that the motivating psychological content is unconscious, the only difference is that hysterical conversion symptoms are to a high degree individual, sometimes unique creations of the patient, invented by him for the expression of his particular repressed psychological content. Expressive movements like laughter are in contrast standardized and universal (Darwin).

A fundamentally different group of psychogenic bodily disturbances is that involving the internal vegetative organs. Earlier psychoanalytic authors have repeatedly attempted to extend the original concept of hysterical conversion to all forms of psychogenic disturbances of the body, including those which occur in the visceral organs. According to such views an elevation of the blood pressure or a gastric hemorrhage has a symbolic meaning like any conversion symptom. No attention was paid to the fact that the vegetative organs are controlled by the autonomic nervous system, which is not in direct connection with ideational processes. Symbolic expression of psychological content is known only in the field of voluntary innervations such as speech, or expressive movements, such as facial grimacing, gesticulation, laughter, weeping, etc. Possibly blushing could be included in this group. It is most improbable, however, that internal organs such as the liver or the small arterioles of the kidney can symbolically express ideas. This does not mean that they cannot be influenced by emotional tensions, which can be conducted to any part of the body via cortico-thalamic and autonomic pathways. It is well established that emotional influences can stimulate or inhibit the function of any organ. After the emotional tension relaxes, the body functions return to their normal equilibrium. Whenever such emotional stimulation or inhibition of a vegetative function becomes chronic and excessive, we refer to it as an "organ neurosis." This term embraces the so-called "functional" disturbances of the vegetative organs, which are caused at least partially by nervous impulses the ultimate origins of which are emotional processes which take place somewhere in the cortical and subcortical areas of the brain.

The concept of functional disturbances came originally not from psychiatrists but from specialists in the field of internal diseases. At first the neurotic (or functional) disturbances of the stomach, the bowels, and the cardio-vascular system became known under the name of gastric, intestinal, or cardiac neuroses. The term "functional disturbance" refers to the fact that in such cases even the finest study of the tissues does not reveal any discernible morphological changes. The anatomical structure of the organ is not changed; only the coordination and the intensity of its functions are disturbed. Such disturbances are more readily reversible, and are considered less serious, than diseases in which the tissues show definite morphological alteration, which frequently designates irreversible damage.

We can now define the difference between conversion symptom and vegetative neurosis. A conversion symptom is a *symbolic* expression of an emotionally charged psychological content: it is an attempt to discharge the emotional tension. It takes place in the voluntary neuromuscular or sensory-perceptive systems whose original function is to express and relieve emotional tensions. A vegetative neurosis is not an attempt to express an emotion but is the physiological response of the vegetative organs to constant or to periodically returning emotional states. Elevation of blood pressure, for example, under the influence of rage does not relieve the rage but is a physiological component of the total phenomenon of rage. As will be shown later, it is an adaptation of the body to the state of the organism when it prepares to meet an emergency. Similarly, increased gastric secretion under the influence of emotional longing for food is not an expression or relief of these emotions; it is the adaptive preparation of the stomach for the incorporation of food.

The only similarity between hysterical conversion symptoms and vegetative responses to emotions lies in the fact that both are responses to psychological stimuli. They are basically different, however, in their psychodynamics and physiology.

With the recognition that in functional disturbances emotional factors are of causal significance, psychotherapy gained a legitimate entrance into medicine proper and could no longer be restricted exclusively to the field of psychiatry. The chronic emotional conflicts of the patient, the ultimate cause of the disturbance, had to be resolved by psychological treatment. Since these emotional conflicts arose in the patient's relationships with other human beings, the personality of the patient became the object of the therapy. With this new emphasis, the emotional influence of the doctor upon the patient—medical art—found its place in scientific medicine. It could no longer be considered an appendage of therapy, a last artistic touch in therapeutic skill. In cases of organ neuroses the emotional influence of the physician upon the patient proved to be the main therapeutic factor.

The role of psychotherapy remained restricted, however, at this phase of development, to the functional cases generally considered as milder disturbances in contrast to the genuine organic disorders based on demonstrable tissue changes. In such organic disorders too, the emotional state of the patient had long been recognized as an important issue; yet a real causal connection between psychic factors and genuine organic disturbances had not been generally assumed.

Gradually, however, it became increasingly evident that nature does not know such strict distinctions as "functional" versus "organic." Clinicians began to suspect that functional disorders of long duration may gradually lead to serious organic disorders associated with morphological changes. A few instances of this kind have been known for a long time—for example, the fact that hyperactivity of the heart may lead to hypertrophy of the heart muscles or that hysterical paralysis of a limb may lead to certain degenerative changes in the muscles and joints because of inactivity. One had to reckon, therefore, with the possibility that a functional disturbance of long duration in any organ may

lead finally to definite anatomical changes and to the clinical picture of severe organic illness. Intensive psychological and physiological studies of cases of peptic ulcer brought convincing evidence for the view that emotional conflicts of long duration may lead as a first step to a stomach neurosis which in time may result in an ulcer. There are also indications that emotional conflicts may cause continued fluctuations of blood pressure which in time overtax the vascular system. This functional phase of fluctuating blood pressure may in time cause organic vascular changes, and finally an irreversible malignant form of hypertension may ensue.

These observations have been crystallized in the concept of "psychogenic organic disorder." These disorders, according to this view, develop in two phases: first, the functional disturbance of a vegetative organ is caused by a chronic emotional disturbance; and second, the chronic functional disturbance gradually leads to tissue changes, and to an irreversible organic disease.

29.

WILLIAM J. GRACE AND DAVID T. GRAHAM

SPECIFIC ATTITUDE HYPOTHESIS OF PSYCHOSOMATIC DISORDERS

The greater the extent to which the patient's way of looking at the situation is introduced into this formulation, the more closely it approaches the thesis of the present paper. No one, however, has given clear-cut statements of the patient's attitudes.

In the course of attempting to resolve these difficulties it became apparent that there was associated with each symptom a definite attitude which was peculiar to it, and without

From William J. Grace and David T. Graham. "Relationship of specific attitudes and emotions to certain bodily diseases," *Psychosomatic Medicine*, 1952, *14*, 243–251. This selection begins with p. 244. Reprinted by permission.

which it did not occur. In order to explore this approach further, a systematic method of questioning patients was employed.

METHOD

One hundred and twenty-eight patients, who had one or more of the twelve symptoms or diseases studied, were followed in treatment in the outpatient department. Interviews with the patients by one or the other of the authors were the only method of obtaining the information used in this paper. Interviews usually lasted about one hour, and took place as often as twice a week and as infrequently as once in three months. Most of the patients made a total of ten or more visits to the clinic.

In the interviews, emphasis was first placed on defining the situations temporally associated with attacks of the patient's symptoms. After such a situation had been identified, the next step was to obtain from him a description of his *attitude, by which is meant a clear and unambiguous statement of what he felt was happening to him, and what he wanted to do about it, at the time of the occurrence of the symptom.* This last point is of major importance, as it was found that often an individual felt in one way about the precipitating event during an interview, but in another way at the time symptoms were developing. Conventional names of "emotions," such as "anger," "resentment," "sadness," etc., were not accepted without further definition.

It was noted, in the first place, that many of the patients with the same symptom-complex spontaneously referred to their life-situations and their own reactions in the same way. Those who did not were asked to describe the situation in the terms outlined above. Patients who were still unable to grasp the task were given a set of possibilities from among which they were told to select those most applicable to themselves.

No attempt was made to utilize dream or associative material in collecting the data used in this study. All of the conclusions are based entirely on direct statements by the patients.

Surprisingly little difficulty was encountered with most patients in obtaining unequivocal answers to the questions asked. Obstacles arose chiefly with reticent or bland individuals in trying to discover exactly what the stressful situation was. Without this information the method described of eliciting the patient's attitude cannot be employed. There was an occasional patient who, although willing to say that he was "upset" by some event, refused to go any further without strong urging.

RESULTS

All patients with the same symptom-complex described their attitudes toward the situation which precipitated it in essentially the same way.

The following attitudes and physiological disturbances were found to be associated:

1. Urticaria (31 patients) occurred when an individual saw himself as being mistreated. This mistreatment might take the form of something said to him or something done to him. He was preoccupied entirely with what was happening to him, and was not thinking of retaliation or of any solution of his problem. Typical statements were: "They did a lot of things to me and I couldn't do anything about it." "I was taking a beating." "My mother was hammering on me." "The boss cracked a whip on me." "My fiancée knocked me down and walked all over me but what could I do?"

2. Eczema (27 patients) occurred when an individual felt that he was being interfered with or prevented from doing something, and could think of no way to deal with the frustration. His preoccupation was with the interference and the persons or things thwarting him, rather than with the goals or aims which concerned migraine patients. Typical statements were: "I want to make my mother understand, but I can't." "I couldn't do what I wanted but there wasn't anything I could do about it." "It upsets me because its interfered with what I wanted to do." "I felt terribly frustrated."

In addition, however, minor attacks of urticaria or exacerbations of eczema occurred when the individual felt that he was being looked at and had no response to make—the feeling commonly called "embarrassment." An additional feature in many instances of eczema was the aggression directed toward the self, expressed in the statement, "I take it out on myself."

3. Cold and moist hands (10 patients) occurred when an individual felt that he should undertake some kind of activity, even though he might not know precisely what to do. Typical statements were: "I wanted to hit him." "I just had to be doing something." "Something ought to be done." "I wanted to do something." In Raynaud's disease (4 patients) the coldness of the hands is carried to the extreme. The action contemplated by those with Raynaud's disease was characteristically a hostile one. Typical statements were

"I wanted to hit him." "I wanted to put a knife through him." "I wanted to strangle him."

4. Vasomotor rhinitis (12 patients) occurred when an individual was facing a situation with the wish that he didn't have to do anything about it, or that it would go away, or that somebody else would take over the responsibility. The essential feature was the desire to have nothing to do with the situation at all, to deal with it by excluding it. Typical statements were: "I wanted them to go away." "I didn't want to have anything to do with it." "I wanted to blot it all out, I wanted to build a wall between me and him." "I wanted to hole up for the winter." "I wanted to go to bed and pull the sheets over my head."

5. Asthma (7 patients) occurred in association with attitudes exactly like those associated with vasomotor rhinitis. Presumably in asthma the feelings are more intense, but since no measure of strength of attitude was employed, this cannot be categorically stated. It is consistent with this formulation that attacks of asthma are almost invariably accompanied by vasomotor rhinitis, although the reverse is not true. In short, the two seem to be essentially the same disease, the difference between them being one of severity. Typical statements were: "I wanted them to go away." "I didn't want to have anything to do with it." "I just couldn't face it."

6. Diarrhea (27 patients) occurred when an individual wanted to be done with a situation or to have it over with, or to get rid of something or somebody. One man who developed severe diarrhea after he had puchased a defective automobile said: "If I could only get rid of it!" "I want to dispose of it." Typical statements of others were: "If the war was only over with." "I wanted to get done with it." "I wanted to get it finished with."

7. Constipation (17 patients) occurred when an individual was grimly determined to carry on even though faced with a problem he could not solve. Typical statements were: "I have to keep on with this, but I know I'm not going to like it." "It's a lousy job but it's the best I can do." "This marriage is never going to be any better but I won't quit." "I have to keep on with this but I don't like it."

"I'll stick with it even though nothing good will come of it."

9. Nausea and vomiting (11 patients) occurred when an individual was thinking of something which he wished had never happened. He was preoccupied with the mistake he had made, rather than with what he should have done instead. Usually he felt responsible for what had happened. Typical statements: "I wish it hadn't happened." "I was sorry I did it." "I wish things were the way they were before." "I made a mistake." "I shouldn't have listened to him."

9. Duodenal ulcer (9 patients) occurred when an individual was seeking revenge. He wished to injure the person or thing that had injured him. Typical statements were: "I wanted to get even." "I wanted to get back at him." "I wanted revenge." "He hurt me so I wanted to hurt him." "I did it for spite."

10. Migraine headache (14 patients) occurred when an individual had been making an intense effort to carry out a definite planned program, or to achieve some definite objective. The headache occurred when the effort had ceased, no matter whether the activity had been associated with success or failure. The essential features were striving and subsequent relaxation. Typical statements were: "I had to get it done." "I had to meet a deadline." "I had a million things to do before lunch." "I was trying to get all these things accomplished."

11. Arterial hypertension (7 patients) occurred when an individual felt that he must be constantly prepared to meet all possible threats. Typical statements were: "I had to be ready for anything." "It was up to me to take care of all the worries." "Nobody is ever going to beat me, I'm ready for everything."

12. Low back pain (11 patients) occurred when an individual wanted to carry out some action involving movement of the entire body. The activity which such patients were most commonly thinking about was walking or running away. One 16-year-old girl spent most of her waking hours contemplating various schemes for running away from home. Typical statements were: "I just wanted to walk out of the house." "I wanted to run away." "I

wanted to get out of there." "I felt like taking a flying leap off that island."

COMMENT

It is interesting to inquire whether a generalization concerning these observed relations can be found. It appears that in many cases the attitude can be considered as a description of the function of the physiological process with which it is associated. This is an extension of the formulation previously made particularly by Cannon (4) and Wolff (14).

1. Vasodilatation is the reaction of the skin to trauma. Whealing occurs when vasodilatation is intense. The patient with urticaria feels that he is receiving a blow, and that there is nothing he can do about it (6).

3. Cold skin is the result of cutaneous vasoconstriction (2). Its occurrence in the individual who is contemplating some kind of action probably represents the functioning of a mechanism to raise body temperature by reducing heat loss. That an elevated body temperature is desirable for the active organism is suggested by the fact that the elevation occurs to the same extent with a standard amount of exercise whether heat loss is experimentally facilitated or interfered with (10).

4. and 5. The reaction of the respiratory mucous membrane to a noxious agent is to exclude it by swelling of the membrane with consequent narrowing of the passageway, and to dilute it and wash it out by hypersecretion (7). When these changes are limited to the nose, the reaction is called vasomotor rhinitis; when they are sufficiently intense to include the bronchi, so that wheezing occurs, the name "asthma" is applied.

6. Defecation is a way of ridding the body of substances which have been taken in but are no longer useful. Diarrhea, or frequent defecation, occurs in the setting of an intense desire to get something over with or to dispose of something.

7. Constipation is a phenomenon of holding on without change. This corresponds to the patients' attitudes of trying to continue with things as they are, without hope of immediate improvement, or definite desire to do anything different (1. 5).

8. Vomiting is a way of undoing something which has been done. It thus corresponds to the patient's wishes to restore things to their original situation, as if nothing had ever happened.

9. Duodenal ulcer is probably the end-result of protracted gastric hyperfunction. It has been suggested that such hyperfunction is part of the preparation for eating (13). Directing aggression into the particular channel of eating seems to make sense biologically, for the only way an injured animal can use the animal which injured him as a source of materials for tissue repair is to devour him. An individual with duodenal ulcer desires revenge—that is, he wishes to hurt the person who hurt him.

12. The backache which accompanies the desire of the individual to walk out of his situation is probably consequent to the tension of the lumbar muscles. The latter fix the spinal column in preparation for locomotion (12). It has been shown that thinking about lifting a weight is associated with increased electrical activity in the appropriate muscles (8). It has also been demonstrated that sustained contraction of skeletal muscles can be painful (11).

The biological function of the bodily changes underlying others of the symptoms is obscure. The value of elevation of the diastolic blood pressure is not clear at present, although it seems probable that there are circumstances under which it is a useful response. The vasodilatation of frustration, seen in eczema, may possibly represent a method of heat loss by an organism which has abandoned its readiness for action. The occurrence in the head of vasoconstriction followed by vasodilatation, which underlies migraine, has no useful function which is obvious at present.

DISCUSSION

The present approach differs from those discussed in its emphasis on the nature of the patient's reaction to the situations which precipitate attacks of his illness. The reaction of an adult human being consists of an *attitude*, which can be expressed verbally, and accompanying *bodily changes.* By "attitude" is meant the way in which he perceives his own position in the situation, and the action, if any, which he wishes to take to deal with it. The bodily changes, if sufficiently intense and prolonged, give rise to experiences which have names and are called "symptoms," such as palpitations or diarrhea. If the phenomena recur or persist, and especially if they lead to structural changes, they are said to represent a "disease." Most of the common diseases can be viewed as the outcome of physiological adjustments which, although perfectly appropriate in some circumstances, may eventually entail discomfort, disability and danger to the organism.

It will be noted that, although the above definition of attitude has two aspects, in many of the specific attitudes discussed—for example that accompanying diarrhea—there is no mention of the first component. The reason for this is that no consistencies were discovered in the statements of patients in question about what they felt was happening to them, although they all wished to deal with the traumatic situation in the same way. It is possible that further investigation in certain of the syndromes will reveal common denominators in the first component of the attitude as well as the second, and to this extent the attitude statements given may be incomplete. It may be, for instance, that persons with duodenal ulcer always regard the situations responsible for their symptoms as injuries of a particular kind.

The results of this study suggest that each attitude is associated with its own unique set of bodily changes. The possibility of the existence of such a relationship has been suggested by Bull (3). Nothing is implied in this connection about a cause-and-effect relation between "mental" and "physical" events, and, indeed, it seems unprofitable to look at the matter in this light.

This conclusion is in opposition to the widely-held view (9) that there is no predictable relation between the "emotion" felt and the physiological changes which accompany it. There seem to have been at least three reasons for the adoption of this position. The first was the attempt to work with an inadequate vocabulary, so that the range of possible attitudes was not sufficiently explored. Second, questioning was not conducted in such a way that precise attitudes were ascertained, the experimenter or therapist remaining content with the "name" of the emotion supplied by the subject or patient, or suggested by his own appraisal of the situation. This introduces the difficulty that not all individuals attach the same meanings to the common words denoting feeling-states. Third, only a very few of the large number of possible physiological variables were measured, for example cardiovascular changes and the galvanic skin responses.

These considerations suggest the advisability of defining the word emotion, so that it means *an attitude and the associated bodily changes.* This implies that there are a very large number of possible emotions, probably many more than are conventionally considered, since there are a large number of possible attitudes toward situations. It also implies that there is no such thing as "non-emotional" behavior, since it is presumably impossible to do anything or think about anything without adopting some attitude. In ordinary speech, however, emotions are not recognized until they reach a certain intensity.

* * *

It is important to know what it is in the life history of a patient which predisposed him to adopt the response (attitude and bodily change) which eventually culminated in disease. Are there common factors in the lives of persons with asthma, for instance, which have made them especially prone to wish to shut unpleasant things away from them? It seems probable that there are certain experiences, particularly exposure to attitudes and behavior of parents, which result in the development of predictable attitudes in any individual exposed to them, and that all patients with the same disease have had lives with these experiences in common. Their reactions to their present situations are, of course, in large part determined by their previous learning. There is, however, reason to think that certain situations encountered for the first time in adult life may have intrinsically a high potentiality for evoking particular attitudes and bodily changes, just as they would in a child.

It is probably also true that some persons

have been exposed to environments producing more than one kind of traumatic situation, repeated often enough to be significant. These individuals are presumably those who react as adults with many different symptoms, the nature of which is determined by the situation.

With a few of the common syndromes it has been possible to identify experiences of early life which seem highly relevant to adult attitudes and diseases, and which are found in the background of many of the patients with the syndrome. One girl whose chief complaint was backache, for instance, had a mother who constantly threatened to pack her bags and walk out of the home. Another woman, who developed severe vomiting as a reaction to her life situation, had been thoroughly indoctrinated with the idea of the impossibility of atonement for sin, so that having once done something which she felt was wrong she was completely preoccupied with wishing it hadn't happened.

This is a first report, and greater objectivity in the evaluation of attitudes is desirable in order to obviate the criticism that patients' statements are so loose as to be open to any number of interpretations, or that suggestion by the therapist may have played a part. The method of questioning was designed to avoid these difficulties, but, in addition, a questionnaire has been made up to be presented to patients after the event responsible for an attack of their symptoms has been clearly defined. It consists of about fifty questions representing a variety of possible attitudes toward life situations, the patient answering "yes" to those he thinks best represent his attitudes at the time the symptoms developed. For example, questions pertinent to diarrhea are, "Did you feel that you wanted to get rid of someone or something?," and "Did you feel that there was something you wanted to get over with or done with?"

SUMMARY AND CONCLUSIONS

1. One hundred and twenty-eight patients, who had one or more of the following symptoms or diseases as responses to life situations, were studied: urticaria, eczema, cold hands,

vasomotor rhinitis and asthma, diarrhea, constipation, nausea and vomiting, duodenal ulcer, migraine, arterial hypertension, low back pain.

2. It was found that each of these conditions was associated with a particular, completely conscious, attitude toward the precipitating situation. There were, in other words, physiological changes specific to each attitude.

3. These changes are biologically appropriate to the attitudes they accompany.

4. It is proposed that "emotion" be defined to mean "an attitude with its associated physiological changes."

REFERENCES

1. ALMY, T. P., KERN, F., & ABBOT, F. Constipation and diarrhea. *Association for Research in Nervous and Mental Disease*, 1950, 29, 724.
2. BROBECK, J. R. Regulation of energy exchange. In J. F. Fulton, *A textbook of physiology* (16th ed.) Philadelphia: Saunders, 1949.
3. BULL, N. Toward a clarification of the concept of emotion. *Psychosomatic Medicine*, 1945, 7, 210.
4. CANNON, W. B. *Bodily changes in pain, hunger, fear and rage.* New York: D. Appleton, 1929.
5. GRACE, W. J., WOLF, S., & WOLFF, H. G. *The human colon.* New York: Hoeber, 1951.
6. GRAHAM, D. T. The pathogenesis of hives. *Association for Research in Nervous and Mental Disease*, 1950, 29, 987.
7. HOLMES, T. H., GOODELL, H., WOLF, S., & WOLFF, H. G. *The nose.* Springfield, Ill.: Charles C Thomas, 1950.
8. JACOBSON, E. Electrophysiology of mental activities. *American Journal of Psychology*, 1932, 44, 677.
9. MUNN, N. L. *Psychology: The fundamentals of human adjustment.* Boston: Houghton Mifflin, 1946.
10. NIELSEN, M. Die Regulation der Körpertemperatur bei Muskelarbeit. *Skandinavisches Archiv für Psysiologic*, 1948, 79, 193.
11. SIMONS, D. J., DAY, E., GOODELL, H., & WOLFF, H. G. Experimental studies on headache; Muscles of the scalp and neck as sources of pain. *Association for Research in Nervous and Mental Disease*, 1943, 23, 228.
12. STEINDLER, A. *Mechanics of normal and pathological locomotion.* Springfield, Ill.: Charles C Thomas, 1935.
13. WOLF, S., & WOLFF, H. G. *Human gastric function*, (2d. ed.). New York: Oxford University Press, 1947.
14. WOLFF, H. G. Protective reaction patterns and disease. *Annals of Internal Medicine*, 1947, 27, 944.

30.

JAMES L. HALLIDAY

CULTURAL HYPOTHESIS OF PSYCHOSOMATIC DISORDERS

In an Editors' Footnote to my paper on *The Incidence of Psychosomatic Affections in Great Britain* published in the May issue of this JOURNAL objection was taken to the use of the expression "psychosomatic affection," a term under which I had subsumed such disease labels as peptic ulcer, gastritis, diabetes, the hypertensive cardiovascular disorders, exophthalmic goiter, "fibrositis," etc. The ground of the criticism was that, as the method of approach called psychosomatic medicine could be applied to the whole field of medicine, the employment of the expression *psychosomatic affection* seemed to be "arbitrary." I told the editors that I agreed with the first part of the statement but disagreed with the inference. As a result I was invited to discuss the reasons why I regarded the expression *psychosomatic affection* as a legitimate one. My present task, therefore, is to indicate the way in which this term symbolizes a scientifically constructed reference for certain designated disorders and diseases.

(A) THE NAIVE NEED FOR A GENERAL TERM OF REFERENCE FOR THOSE DISORDERS AND DISEASES IN WHICH THE APPLICATION OF A PSYCHOLOGICAL APPROACH PROVIDES INFORMATION OF HIGH ETIOLOGICAL RELEVANCE

This simple necessity may be illustrated by my own experience which has, however, been duplicated by many others.

After graduation I became a surgical intern and in this capacity I saw many patients with bruises, wounds and fractures. Instinctively I asked most primitive questions. One was: *When* did this happen? Another was: What happened? (*i.e.*, what did the individual meet, or to what

physical mass was this bruise, wound or fracture a reaction?) The answers provided data relevant to the etiology of medical events subsumed under the term of Injuries or Accidents. On becoming a resident physician in a large fever hospital I found myself asking similar elementary questions: When did the individual fall ill? and, What did he meet? (*i.e.*, what microorganism had he encountered and what person or "carrier" had been the vehicle of its transmission to the patient?) But I added a further question, viz., What kind of person is this? (*i.e.*, what characteristic, or characteristics, rendered him unduly susceptible to the "environmental factor"?) Answers to such questions again provide fundamental etiological information. Next, I served as a member of the staff of a Public Health Department in a large city and there I came to learn still more about environmental factors which brought about the reactions called disease. Thus I learned how the Infectious Diseases, although primarily a reaction to micro-organic life, were also etiologically associated with other environmental factors such as housing, poverty, feeding habits, deficient sanitation, etc. I learned too how many common diseases of infancy were associated not only with micro-organisms or with improper feeding but also with poverty and "feckless" mothers. Even the toxic reactive diseases of industry were not merely a function of a noxious chemical substance but were related to the "sensitiveness" as well as to the carefulness or carelessness of workers. These experiences in preventive medicine enabled me to appreciate not only the complexity of etiology, but they also demonstrated the practical usefulness, as a necessary preliminary to understanding, of the division of diseases into broad causal categories based largely on the nature of the dominating external etiological factor, as, for example, Infectious Diseases, Disorders of Nutrition, Injuries, Intoxications, etc.

From James L. Halliday."The significance of the concept of a psychosomatic affection." *Psychosomatic Medicine*, 1945, 7, 240–245. Reprinted by permission.

After several years in a Public Health Department I was appointed to act, under the National Health Insurance Act, as a medical referee, of insured persons who were sent by their insurance societies for an independent medical opinion on capacity for work. Thus, after many years of clinical experience mainly confined to the infectious diseases and the illnesses of children, I encountered again the disorders of general medicine—but I saw them with fresh eyes so to speak, my outlook on diseases having undergone a change as a result of my training in preventive medicine with its dominant emphasis on etiology. Instinctively I applied myself to find answers to the three fundamental "questions of the etiology of onset" (2) which I had so often asked when investigating a case of infectious disease: (i) Why of all the days in his life did he fall ill when he did? (*i.e.*, to what environmental factor was the illness a response?) (ii) What kind of person was he? (*i.e.*, what characteristic rendered him susceptible to the "causal" environmental factor?) (iii) Why did he fall ill in this way and not another?

This line of enquiry at first yielded little result because it took cognizance only of physical factors of environment. When, however, I began to investigate in addition the patient's emotional upsets and the external events which precipitated them, I began to obtain insight as to why many patients fell ill when they did. Viewed in this way the illness appeared often to be of the nature of a reaction of the individual to upsetting or frustrating factors, *i.e.*, to environment in its psychological aspects (*e.g.*, unemployment, domestic unsettlement, financial stringencies, loss of aim in life, and circumstances inhibiting the expression of particular creative activities). I concluded that *many of these patients would not have taken ill when they did had it not been for the social circumstances of the times* (1930-38) and that by altering social environment in its psychological aspects much incapacitating illness was preventable. Here was a new field for preventive medicine!

The group of disorders in which a psychological approach provided information of high etiological relevance covered a great variety of illness: hysteria; the anxiety states with visceral disturbances (*e.g.*, gastritis, "debility," disordered action of the heart, "rheumatism," "bronchitis," etc.); as well as disorders with definite structural changes (duodenal ulcer, coronary thrombosis, "fibrositis," asthma, etc.). To all these disorders I mentally applied the term *The Affections*, a word which has not only a medical connotation of malady or disease but also a deeper and older significance indicating the mental state, disposition, emotions, feelings, impulses, etc. (Indeed I have sometimes thought that the expression *The Affections* would be more suitable than the one which I finally adopted, namely, *The Psychosomatic Affections*.) Later as I came to realize in addition the etiological importance of the "kind of person" who "takes" these disorders I prefixed the term "psychosomatic" to the word "affection" as it emphasized that these illnesses could be regarded not only as reactions to psychological aspects of environment but also as "disorders of the personality." The insight that the organism could be viewed and considered not only by physical approaches, methods and techniques, but also by psychological ones was therefore supplemented by the insight that the environment of the individual as he grew in time could be viewed and considered not only in its physical but also in its psychological aspects. Seen in this light a "psychosomatic affection" appeared as a reaction of an individual (with his particular inherited endowment) to the flux of his total psychosocial situation—past, present and future—viz. his social conditioning in infancy and childhood, the painful upsetting or frustrating experiences of adult life, as well as his feelings and attitudes toward events yet to be.

A more adequate account of these matters is set forth in my paper, "The Principles of Etiology" (2).

(B) THE DEVELOPMENT OF THE MENTAL CONSTRUCT CALLED PSYCHOSOMATIC AFFECTION

A crude and preliminary definition of a psychosomatic affection would be:

"a bodily disorder in which the application of the psychological approach provides information of high etiological relevance";

or alternatively:

"a bodily disorder whose nature can be appreciated only when emotional disturbances, *i.e.* psychological happenings, are investigated in addition to physical disturbances, *i.e.* somatic happenings."

When we adopt one or the other of these tentative definitions we find that a great variety of illnesses and diseases could be assigned to this category and that these involve most of the systems of the body. On reviewing a list of these designated disorders (4) we note that superficially they seem to be unrelated but further consideration reveals that many, perhaps the majority, show peculiarities that distinguish them from illnesses in other categories such as the Infectious Diseases, Injuries, Disorders of Nutrition, etc. and in virtue of which they may be said to possess a common "form." These peculiarities relate both to the behaviour of the illness in time and to the nature of certain etiological factors and may conveniently be summarized by setting them down as a 6-point formula by means of which the construct of a psychosomatic affection becomes developed.

The Formulation of a Psychosomatic Affection

1. *Emotion as a Precipitating Factor.* Examination of patients in series shows that in a significantly high proportion of cases the bodily disturbance emerged, or recurred, on meeting an emotionally upsetting event.

2. *Personality Type.* A particular type of personality tends to be associated with each particular affection.

3. *Sex Ratio.* A marked disproportion in sex incidence, frequently of a "several times" order, is found in many, perhaps most of these disorders. (For the interesting phenomenon of sex-shift, see (5).) This is in marked contrast to what is found in the Infectious Diseases in which the incidence is practically even between the sexes.

4. *Association with Other Psychosomatic Affections.* Different affections may appear in the same individual simultaneously but the more usual phenomenon, as revealed in their natural history, is that of the alternation or the sequence of different affections. (These "associated, alternating, sequent, or displacing affections" were referred to by Flanders Dunbar in her book

Psychosomatic Diagnosis as "combined or overlapping syndromes.")

5. *Family History.* A significantly high proportion of cases give a history of the same disorder or of an "associated disorder" in parents, relatives and siblings.

6. *Phasic Manifestation.* The course of the illness tends to be phasic with periods of crudescence, intermission and recurrence.

The various items comprising the formula were fully discussed in the paper in which it was introduced (4). All that need be emphasized here is that by adopting a tentative definition of a psychosomatic affection and then "seeing how it works" we find that—*diseases assignable to the psychosomatic category have peculiarities quite distinct from those of diseases primarily assignable to other broad etiological categories.*

(C) THE PRAGMATIC VALUE OF THE CONCEPT OF A PSYCHOSOMATIC AFFECTION

A realization that certain common designated diseases are assignable to the psychosomatic category enables the physician to appreciate as a matter of routine the need for supplementing an academic medical examination by a psychological one if adequate guidance for action (*i.e.*, treatment) is to be attained.

The chief practical value of the concept however is probably in relation to preventive rather than curative medicine in that by its means the occurrence of certain common organic and disabling diseases can be etiologically linked with environment in its psychological aspects. As an example a few illustrations of the usefulness of the Incidence Rate of psychosomatic affections may be given.

The Incidence Rate of Psychosomatic Affections as an Index

1. *As an Index of Communal Frustration.* The official annual report on the morbidity statistics of Scottish insured persons for 1937 provided for the first time special data relating to the "chronic sick," *i.e.*, persons on the sick list for a year or more. These statistics show that during the years 1930-35 the rate of chronic sickness

in Scotland had increased by one-third. Analysis of the data showed that this increase was made up almost entirely of those disease labels which were indicative of illnesses in the psychosomatic category (1). The rising trends in the incidence of these affections was a striking social phenomenon which was clearly related to the increasing social frustration during the early 1930s following the financial crisis, when unemployment was at a high level: when, because of the existing scales of relief, it was almost as profitable not to work as to work; and when the way of life among all classes was becoming increasingly dark and uncertain.

2. *As an Index of Group or Occupational Morale.* In a study of the incapacitating disorders in underground coal miners in Scotland (3) in which it was shown that the incidence of psychosomatic affections (including hysterical manifestations) was definitely higher among underground coal miners than among males belonging to other occupations, I suggested that these incidence rates might be regarded as an index of group morale. (This statement is really oversimplified and the interested reader is advised to consult the original paper.)

3. *As an Index of Changes in "Personality Type."* My survey of "The Incidence of the Psychosomatic Affections in Great Britain"—the one that occasioned the Editors' Footnote which acted as stimulus to this article—showed, among many other interesting things, that certain diseases which had predominated in males during the nineteenth century became during the twentieth century relatively more frequent in females; and conversely that certain diseases which had predominated in females became relatively more frequent in males. I suggested that this finding was remarkable in that it seemed to provide a measurable index of the changes in psychological characteristics or "personality type" of male and female that had been progressively taking place as a result of altering social circumstances.

4. *As an Index of the Psychological (or Social) Health of a Community.* There seems to be some relationship between the rising incidence of the psychosomatic affections and the decline in the birth rate. Indeed these, together with the suicide rate, may be regarded as indices of the psychological or social health of the community. I quote a paragraph from the communication (6) in which these matters were discussed:

Until recently it was customary to regard the public health in terms of physical health alone. Thus before the war it was generally stated, and accepted, that the public health of Britain was "improving" in response to the improvement of various physical social factors, *e.g.*, improper feeding, impure water and food, poor housing, inadequate exercise, improper clothing, etc. The indices used to support this proposition were the declining rates referring to medical events known to have a primary etiological relationship to the communal environment considered physically. Measurements adopted as a yardstick of the public health included, accordingly, death rates, infant mortality rates, the expectation of life, tuberculosis and infectious disease rates, the height and weight of school children, etc. But the public health is Janus-faced, and at a time when its physical side was brightening, its psychological side was seen to be darkening by those who cared to look at it. The decline in psychological health was revealed by a different series of indices whose trend took a direction not towards improvement but towards deterioration. These referred to medical happenings demonstrated to have a primary etiological relationship to psychological factors of the environment. They comprised not only the increasing national sterility (as revealed in the declining birth rate) but also the rising rates for suicide, for psychoneurotic illness and for the numerous organic diseases now subsumed under the head of the "psychosomatic affections," *e.g.*, "gastritis," peptic ulcer, "fibrositis," exophthalmic goiter, diabetes, hypertensive cardiovascular disorders (including certain cases of coronary thrombosis and cerebral haemorrhage) etc. The increase in frequency of these morbid happenings could be interpreted broadly as a response to a progressive increase in noxious pressure of the communal environment considered psychologically, *e.g.*, mass unemployment, financial crises, increasing competition, decline of active religious faith, the loss of an end in view, and a general tendency to drift and safety first.

The notion of the *physical and psychological health* of a community may be represented diagramatically. The enclosed figure is an attempt to illustrate the trends of physical and psychological health in Great Britain (1900-1939). It will be seen how the trends took opposing directions. As the figure does not indicate the differential rates of increase and decrease it should not be taken over-literally. Its sole aim is to picture an idea in outline.

(D) FURTHER REFINEMENT OF THE CONCEPT OF A PSYCHOSOMATIC AFFECTION

Consideration of the incidence of the psychosomatic affections (5) enables the concept to be further refined as follows:

A psychosomatic affection is a disorder that complies with the 6-point formulation, and whose incidence rises or falls in accordance with the rise and fall of communal "upsetting events," *i.e.*, in accordance with the pressure of environment (or environmental flux) in its psychological, as distinguished from its physical aspects.

DISCUSSION

At the beginning of this paper I stated that I agreed with the Editors' statement that "the method of approach called psychosomatic medicine could be applied to the whole field of medicine." At this point I wish to suggest that a definition of the scope of the psychosomatic approach is clearly an irrelevancy as a ground of objection to the usage of a verbal term. An appropriate basis for an objection of this nature requires the "semantic approach" which takes cognizance of Things (referents), Thoughts (references), and Words (symbols for referents and references).

Viewed semantically, "psychosomatic affection" is a symbol. The facts from which it was derived (*i.e.*, its referents) are well enough established, and the inferences made from these referents (*i.e.*, its references) are legitimate and logical. I therefore see no reason to alter the conclusion to the contribution (4) in which I originally introduced the expression:

SCHEMATIC REPRESENTATION OF THE IDEA OF PHYSICAL AND PSYCHOLOGICAL HEALTH
(Based on the Trend of Health in Britain [1900–1939])

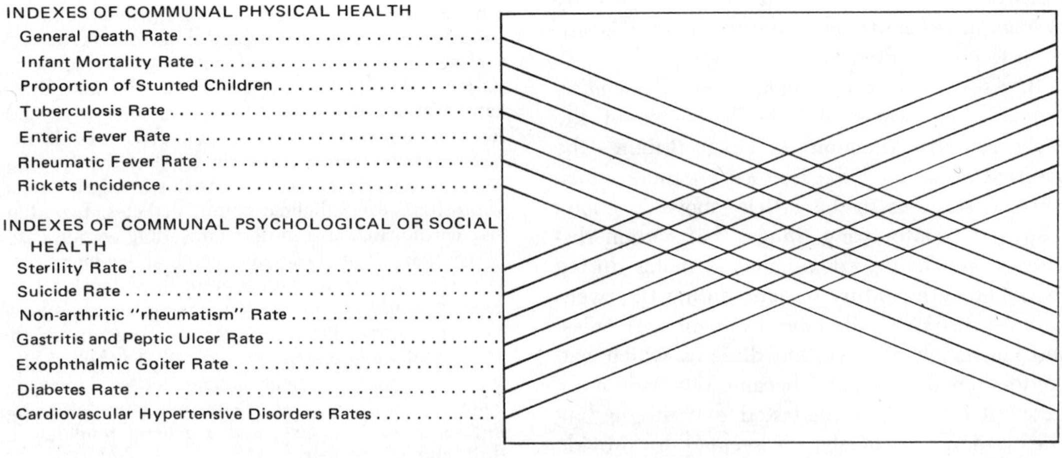

INDEXES OF COMMUNAL PHYSICAL HEALTH
General Death Rate . . . .
Infant Mortality Rate . . . .
Proportion of Stunted Children . . . .
Tuberculosis Rate . . . .
Enteric Fever Rate . . . .
Rheumatic Fever Rate . . . .
Rickets Incidence . . . .

INDEXES OF COMMUNAL PSYCHOLOGICAL OR SOCIAL HEALTH
Sterility Rate . . . .
Suicide Rate . . . .
Non-arthritic "rheumatism" Rate . . . .
Gastritis and Peptic Ulcer Rate . . . .
Exophthalmic Goiter Rate . . . .
Diabetes Rate . . . .
Cardiovascular Hypertensive Disorders Rates . . . .

NOTE: The items regarded as indexes of "Physical Health" refer to diseases and morbid happenings which are primarily etiologically related to environment in its physical, chemical and micro-organic aspects. The items regarded as indexes of "Psychological or Social Health" refer to diseases and morbid happenings which are primarily etiologically related to environment in its psychological aspects. For the purpose of this diagram the declining birth-rate has been regarded as an increasing sterility rate. The differential rates of increase or decrease are not shown as the aim of the diagram is to illustrate, in a broad way, the notions of physical and social health. In this respect the statistician may regard the figure as "misleading," but the student is more likely to regard it as illuminating.

COMMENT: The diagram shows how, during the present century, the trend of Physical Health steadily improved whereas the trend of Social Health took an opposite direction. In other words the "good life" in the sense of insurance companies was becoming less frustrated, whereas the "good life" in the sense of the philosophers was becoming increasingly frustrated. The rates of the frequency of sterility, of suicide, and of the psychosomatic affections represent the medical indices only of a morbid process which has been variously designated as "Western Civilization," "The socio-economic capitalist set-up," "The break-up of a culture," etc. From the medical point of view the best name for the communal *morbus* is "Social Disintegration." There are other indices of Social Disintegration in terms of other interests, *e.g.*, Industrial, Religious, Cultural, etc.

The concept of a psychosomatic affection in its developed form brings into relationship a large number of seemingly unrelated facts. The outlook gained shows that many "localized diseases," the names of which have hitherto been found scattered throughout textbooks of medicine under the headings of the various anatomical systems, may now be grouped under a unifying etiological category. The term psychosomatic affection is therefore a valid symbol which provides a new instrument for thinking, for investigation and for the direction of action.

But these conclusions in no sense imply that with further investigation further referents may not be discovered which will require us to alter the present reference and also perhaps to modify its symbolization. Indeed it is after such a manner that scientific knowledge advances.

SUMMARY

1. The mental construct (or concept) symbolized by the term *psychosomatic affection* is in no way imposed upon facts but is derived from the arrangement of the facts themselves.

2. It has proved itself pragmatically justified —it fits and it works—and it has important practical applications, especially in vital statistics, epidemiology and applied social medicine.

3. Far from being "arbitrary" it has a genuine creative value.

REFERENCES

1. HALLIDAY, J. L. The rising incidence of psychosomatic illness. *British Medical Journal,* 1938, 2, 11.
2. HALLIDAY, J. L. Principles of etiology. *British Journal of Medical Psychology,* 1943, 19, 367.
3. HALLIDAY, J. L. Dangerous occupation; psychosomatic illness and morale. *Psychosomatic Medicine,* 1943, 6, 71.
4. HALLIDAY, J. L. The concept of a psychosomatic affection. *Lancet,* 1943, 2,, 692.
5. HALLIDAY, J. L. The incidence of psychosomatic affections in Britain. *Psychosomatic Medicine,* 1945, 7, 135.
6. HALLIDAY, J. L. Psychosomatic medicine and the declining birth-rate. *Lancet,* 1945.

31.

J. GROEN

SUBSTITUTION THEORY OF PSYCHOSOMATIC DISORDER

PSYCHOSOMATIC PATTERNS OF ABNORMAL BEHAVIOUR (I.E. PSYCHOGENIC BODILY DISEASE)

At first sight it may seem unusual to classify bodily disease under behaviour. We are so accustomed to apply the term behaviour to the visible neuromuscular activity and movements of the individual, that we find it hard to apply the term, for example, to movements inside the body caused by smooth muscle, such as peri-

From J. Groen,"Psychosomatic disturbances as a form of substituted behaviour."*Journal of Psychosomatic Research,* 1957, 2, 85–96. The present selection begins with p. 90. This paper is the chairman's address before the Second European Conference on Psychosomatic Research, Amsterdam, April 17, 1956. Reprinted by permission.

staltic activity, or to changes in heart-rate. We are accustomed to classify weeping under behaviour, but find it difficult to apply this term to the secretion of tears. Yet if one studies the behaviour of the intact animal organism as a whole, it becomes obvious that reactions hardly ever take place in the neuromuscular system only, separated from simultaneous activity in the visceral organs or in the endocrine glands such as the adrenal medulla and cortex. If one is willing to accept the view that nature does not make a distinction into behaviour between the more or less voluntary movements and bodily changes, and the more or less involuntary movements inside the or-

ganism, but that every change in the homeostasis of the individual can be regarded and
studied as behaviour, whether it be visible
from the outside or inside, then the classification of psychosomatic disturbances becomes
much more easily understandable as natural
phenomena.

We then propose to regard as psychosomatic
abnormal behaviour (or, in other terms, psychogenic bodily disease), certain reaction patterns to frustration that occur when the individual conforms to the cultural norms of the
society to which he belongs, but, like the neurotic, is unable to find gratification along these
required and permitted pathways, and when
such an individual also rejects psychoneurotic
behaviour patterns (manifest hypersensitivity,
anxiety, phobias, egocentricity), controls weeping or complaining, does not openly demand
special care, and consciously or (and) subconsciously tries to avoid or control the outlet
of his emotions along neuromuscular pathways.
Such an individual does not behave by psychopathic discharges of behaviour, or only in special situations, such as, for example, during a
psychiatric interview. Neither does he act out
his emotional disharmony by psychoneurotic
behaviour, or only by outbursts in special situations. Only on careful observation does he appear *tense*, by which we understand a situation
of inhibited (usually neurotic) activity. We
hypothesize that when psychopathic or psychoneurotic reaction patterns to frustration
are thus inhibited from discharge, *somatic* reaction patterns are substituted in an increased
intensity and duration, so that they are called
diseased, and thus bring the individual to the
family doctor or the specialist.

Although psychosomatic disorders are in this
concept of a similar origin as psychopathic or
psychoneurotic behaviour patterns, it is often
difficult to recognize them as substituted reactions to frustration. Moreover, they affect
human relations in an entirely different way,
and this explains why the environment, at least
in our culture, reacts to the different forms of
behaviour patterns so differently. The public
reacts to psychopathic behaviour with moral
indignation, to psychoneurotic patterns with
irritation, amusement, or disdainful pity, to a
somatic symptomatology with sincere sympathy
and care. This is exemplified by the changing
behaviour which some doctors display towards
their patients, e.g., those with ulcerative colitis
or asthma, when they become aware of the
neurotic background of these diseases and from
then on are unable to give them the same un-
mixed attention; I need not tell you with what
disastrous results.

Although our knowledge of the psychosomatic reaction patterns is still grossly insufficient, enough material has now been brought
together to regard diseases like ulcerative
colitis, peptic ulcer, bronchial asthma, and essential hypertension as particularly belonging
to this aetiological category, together with
"functional" disorders like migraine, extrasy-
stoles, habitual constipation, dysmenorrhoea, or
sexual impotence. In other words, this aetiological hypothesis cuts right across those distinctions that make the "either organic or
functional" the basis of their classification.
Whatever the merits of such a classification
may be for practical purposes (which we certainly will not deny), from an etiological point
of view such a distinction seems untenable; indeed, it is by this identification of "functional"
with psychogenic and "organic" with somatogenic that the development of a comprehensive
system of medical thinking has been retarded.

BEHAVIOUR CHOICE

After having given psychosomatic reaction patterns a place as a form of human behaviour in
health and disease, the next question that arises
concerns the mechanism of "pattern choice."
Why do some individuals react by normal
patterns and remain bodily and mentally more
or less healthy, whereas others in comparable
situations "choose" a form of abnormal behaviour and as a result react by, or suffer from,
one of various forms of psychopathic, psychoneurotic, or psychosomatic disturbances?

As far as present knowledge goes, it seems
as if an interaction of several factors, partly in
the individual (innate, developmental, and acquired), partly in his environment (parental,
marital, occupational) are involved. Our own
researches into the life histories of healthy indi-

viduals certainly did not reveal that these people had not met with frustrating situations, either in their youth or later in life. But their behaviour in similar frustrating situations differed from that of our patients. These normal individuals seemed less sensitive, less predisposed to react with standardized patterns to which they were once conditioned. They seemed to find it easier to act by a form of substituted behaviour, which appeared to be the best adapted to the frustrating situation. We are beginning to suspect that certain inborn properties of their central nervous system make "normal" individuals less sensitive and less compulsively conditioned, so that the emotional impact of what to others is a severe frustration is less intense; it also seems as if they have more possibilities to find along the forms of gratification substitutive behaviour which the environment requires and permits in a given situation. In other words, they seem to adapt themselves more easily. The present knowledge of neurobiochemistry does not allow a concept of the chemical basis of the hypersensitivity and tendency to rigid conditioning, which seems to predispose some individuals to psychoneurotic, psychopathic, or psychosomatic behaviour. But the fact that one can change the sensitivity and reactivity of an individual by drugs, of which we are beginning to understand and localize the mechanism of action in the central nervous system, may clear up this lack in our knowledge in the near future. It has been found that some individuals are more easily conditioned to certain reaction patterns than others. Once conditioned, it must be more difficult for such an individual to avoid unrewarding behaviour and substitute it by better adapted patterns. An investigation into the rate of conditioning in psychoneurotic, psychopathic, and psychosomatic patients, compared to normal individuals, might reveal whether we are right in assuming a connection between this neurophysiological phenomenon and a predisposition towards the above-named forms of disturbed behaviour.

The *environment* is also important in determining behaviour choice. If an individual by his inborn tendencies, imprinting, and early conditioning is more inclined, for instance, towards aggressive or dominant behaviour, it is obvious that within a culture or during a cultural period where aggressive, dominating behaviour is acquired and appreciated, as in an army at war or in an aggressive business world or political situation, such an individual might be successful and his behaviour "healthy," whereas in a different, less competitive, more complacent environment a similar behaviour is considered abnormal and might bring the individual into conflict either with others or with himself, which would label him now as a psychopath or a psychoneurotic, or which could make him bodily ill.

The "choice" of behaviour in a given situation is made by the individual partly consciously, partly subconsciously (to deal with the distinction between these two from the biological point of view would lead us too far), partly involuntarily (which, from the biological point of view, is a preferable way of expressing, if not the same, then a very closely related mechanism). In any case, the "choice" is sometimes almost like a reflex, when the individual by heredity and earlier experiences is highly conditioned and disposes of only a limited number of freedoms in his possible responses, whereas in other individuals or in other situations, the number of the freedoms of choice is much greater. This depends, *inter alia,* on the stability with which certain experiences in early youth (like imprinting) have established themselves in the organization of the individual, on the regularity and rigidity with which the cultural behaviour patterns ("norms") of the parents and the group have been rewarded and other patterns have been punished during the individual's development, or if he has been submitted to controversial behaviour and influences or to neglect, so that these patterns have become only loosely incorporated in his personal behaviour structure. In later stages of development, identification, aspiration for reward, fear of punishment, conscious insight, or foresight of consequences, together with the incorporated norms (described by some psychiatrists as Super Ego or Ego Ideal) are all operative factors in determining which substituted form of behaviour appears in a given situation. In general, however, the result can still be understood as an interaction of the biological and social forces and experiences, incorporated in the individual as inherited, or acquired behaviour patterns, with the possibilities offered by his environmental situations.

A NEUROPHYSIOLOGICAL CONCEPT OF PSYCHOSOMATIC REACTION PATTERNS

Physiologically speaking, we can understand substitution by starting out from the concept that in principle the organism always reacts as a whole. Information from the environment reaching the central nervous system through the sense organs will provoke certain reactions there, depending on previous information and "disposition." As all parts of the central nervous system are interconnected, we may assume that, generally speaking, the output from the central nervous system can irradiate diffusely to all innervated organs, as is the case in primitive central nervous organizations. In more highly organized species this diffuse output, although in principle still possible, is soon directed, however, by a certain preference of the discharges for certain effector areas. Learning and conditioning, like other forms of facilitation, are the processes which, during the ontogeny and development of the individual, make a highly variable degree of specialized output possible, whereby some originally concomitant discharges are inhibited and others facilitated. In principle, however, every output from the central nervous system still takes place in the form of multiple discharges into the whole of the organism, of which some, however, predominate as the situation requires. These complex reaction patterns are therefore fundamentally inseparable. They can be classified for the purpose of understanding the problem of pattern choice as follows:

(a) Neuromuscular activity like food-seeking, hunting, running, fighting, fleeing, working, or sexual activities. These movements aim directly towards achieving certain goals either nutritive, aggressive, defensive, or in other ways consummatory; simultaneously they furnish the drives and outlet in bodily activity.

(b) Mimical expressions, as already studied and described by Darwin.

(c) Vocal expressions, which in animals already allow of certain specific discharges, to which the other members of the group also react specifically. In the human, vocalization has developed into verbalization and, as a result, can take place in immensely varied forms.

Both mimic and vocalization are of great biological usefulness, e.g., for finding, calling for help or warning the other members of the group, or for the frightening away of an opponent. In addition, they also serve the purpose that the central nervous activity is discharged into bodily actions of the individual. Vocalization and mimic therefore play an important part in giving substituted gratification where a consummatory act is impossible.

These neuromuscular patterns (a), (b), and (c) take place through feedback circuits from the central nervous system via myelinated nerve fibres to the striated voluntary muscles, and back. In addition, every activity of the organism is accompanied by:

(d) Changes in the visceral organs, innervated by the feedback system of the autonomic nervous system, consisting in contraction of smooth muscle, secretion of glands, and changes in the function of the heart and vessels.

(e) Changes, also originating from the central nervous system, which either directly or indirectly affect the production or secretion of hormones.

Normally these five reaction patterns irradiate from the central nervous system as one harmonious complex, a functional unity. But during his development and adaptation to his environment, man learns to regulate especially his mimic, vocal, and neuromuscular discharge patterns. He learns to direct, to postpone, and above all to inhibit them. The tremendous development of the cerebral connections has greatly enhanced the possibility of isolating, damping, and inhibiting discharges. These mechanisms come into action under the influence of imprinting, early conditioning to and learning of incorporated norms, and conscious insight, as described above.

A constant result of our studies of patients with psychosomatic disorders has been the finding that these individuals, although inclined towards discharge of a psychopathic or psychoneurotic pattern, *inhibit* this activity along mimical, vocal, or neuromuscular pathways to a high degree. Either because the emotion produced by frustration does not even penetrate into consciousness or because the incorporated norms or the actual environmental situation do not allow a psychopathic discharge, they do not act out; neither did they react by frank psychoneurotic patterns.

Upon these findings we formulated the hypothesis that when the discharges sub (a), (b), and (c) are inhibited, only the pathways via (d), the autonomic nervous system, or (e), the endocrine system, are left; apparently this partial inhibition disturbs the natural harmonious complex discharge and reinforces substitution along pathways which otherwise would carry only a minor output. What normally would have been a "concomitant" effect in the visceral system of limited duration and intensity, within the limits of the physiological range, now becomes an abnormally intense and (or) prolonged reaction which is thus productive of disease. This state of affairs is, for instance, most evident in patients with essential hypertension, who have been found to be at the same time hypersensitive and aggressive and yet inhibited in their aggressive discharges. A normal individual shows, when in an aggressive disposition, "normally" a slight and passing rise in arterial tension; in these patients, however, the inhibition of normal or excessive mimic, vocal, and neuromuscular activity produces an abnormally strong and prolonged substitution of the reaction into the cardiovascular system. Once conditioned to this type of response (and our hypertensive patients are all of the compulsive, rigidly conditioned type), new frustrations reinforce this reaction pattern by the mechanism of facilitation.

Similar substitution patterns have been described especially by Harold Wolff and his co-workers, and by ourselves, to be operative in the production of peptic ulcer, asthma, ulcerative colitis, rheumatoid arthritis, and hyperthyroidism. These diseases were found to occur in individuals who showed in different forms and varieties a combination of hypersensitivity to frustration on one hand, and a strong tendency to react by psychopathic or

psychoneurotic behaviour with inhibition of these forms of instinctive or substituted neuromuscular discharges on the other hand. This inhibition therefore seems to be an essential factor in the neurophysiological mechanism underlying the "choice" of psychosomatic behaviour.

THE ESSENCE OF THE BIOSOCIAL CONCEPT

The cause of this inhibition of neuromuscular activity in our patients appeared to be a partly conscious, partly subconscious rejection of certain substituted behaviour patterns like outbursts of temper, shouting or fighting, alcoholic excesses, staying away from work, or promiscuity, by their incorporated norms forbidding these forms of "psychopathic" behaviour. They also rejected weeping, hysterical manifestations, or the verbal expression of anxiety and insecurity which would have brought them along psychoneurotic patterns some form of substituted gratification. In many cases our western education, which is more and more directed towards self-control, restrained "gentlemanly" or "ladylike" behaviour, and in which outbursts of temper or grief are suppressed as uncivilized, which in other words forbids both psychopathic and psychoneurotic behaviour, had "overconditioned" these individuals so much that in a situation of frustration they could not act out either by healthy, psychopath, or psychoneurotic patterns. Thus, our modern culture, which is getting more and more complicated and in itself contradictory, so that more and more individuals are frustrated in acting out their innate behaviour patterns, by embracing in its rigid education and domestication an ever-widening number of individuals, limits these individuals at the same time in their possibilities of acting out along patterns that are forbidden as psychopathic or psychoneurotic. Thus the "shift" into psychosomatic patterns becomes understandable not only as an individual solution and a biological necessity, but also as a social phenomenon. The occurrence of these diseases is a manifestation of a general law: civilized man in his tendencies towards self-development and gratification is frustrated, more than by his dead environment, by his fellow men. But his fellow men create at the same time the limitations of the patterns within which he is required and allowed to act out his reactions to these interhuman frustrations. The control of neuromuscular discharges which western man must master to live adequately in this culture is, at least for individuals, both an educative and a potentially pathogenic factor, leading to the appearance of psychosomatic disease. This insight into the social root of disease, for long recognized in the aetiology of the various forms of mental illness, now appears to be also responsible for the psychosomatic disturbances. It is for this reason that psychosomatic research has united, among its workers, medical investigators with biologists, psychologists, and sociologists. It should give us all, so it seems, enough impulses for a combined form of *healthy* substituted behaviour.

SUMMARY

Psychosomatic research is hampered by dualistic thinking. This difficulty can be overcome by the realization that the understanding of man is possible *either* by studying him as a biosocial unit by exact scientific methods *or* as a unique totality, to be approached by introspection and phenomenological communication. For the medical investigator the first method appears the most fruitful. Once the choice beween these two ways of approach is made, there should be no deviation from the methods, concepts, and terminologies, which have proved themselves fruitful within a scientific frame of reference.

The author proposes to regard and study psychosomatic disorders as patterns of human behaviour, acted out via the cerebrospinal or autonomic nervous or endocrine systems, as a reaction to interhuman frustration. As such, psychosomatic diseases have a similar aetiology as sociopathic or neuropathic (neurotic or psychotic) behaviour patterns from which they differ, however, in symptomatology and biological and social consequences. Inhibitions enforced on the social behaviour of the individuals by cultural patterns may block sociopathic or neuropathic discharges and thereby favour the occurrence of psychosomatic syndromes.

It is suggested that psychosomatic syndromes represent a substitution of other activities and thus belong in the same category of phenomena as for example displacement in animal behaviour.

32.

Harold G. Wolff

SOMATIC WEAKNESS HYPOTHESIS

Interference with or threat to his life or love, or blocking the proper fulfillment of an individual's potential, causes him to react as though to assault. He responds defensively or offensively, or both, depending on his nature, his past experience, and the situation. Under these circumstances he struggles to regain what has been lost and to rid himself of interference, in order to fulfill his drives. Such struggles evoke what may be called emergency or crisis protective patterns.

A considerable part of the human equipment has to do with meeting emergencies and dealing with crises. Protective reactions are set off by threats usually in the form of symbols, which have been connected with danger in the past.

From Harold G. Wolff,"Protective reaction patterns and disease."*Annals of Internal Medicine,* 1947, 27, 944–969. Excerpt from pp. 967–968. Reprinted by permission.

Some of these reactions represent widespread mobilizations to provide extra fuel and energy for vital parts of the organism. Others appear to be focused on regional defenses, notably at portals of entry and exit. Offensive and defensive, general and local protective devices may operate together and separately.

Along with these conspicuous bodily preparations go certain feelings and attitudes which, stemming from the same needs, have the same goals.

The organism sacrifices at such times some functions or capacities for the sake of promoting others that are most important to meet the adverse situation. Although there is a degree of specialization in the sense that one or another protective arrangement is dominant, discrimination is not exact. In a threatened man it is common to find a variety of protective reactions, some of which are extremely pertinent, others less so, and still others minimally effective.

Because his drives are primitive and even violent, they may be out of keeping with a man's conception of himself and therefore unacceptable. Thus, the drive denied or not fully recognized by the subject, the subsequently evoked protective reaction patterns may unwittingly become sustained. A few of these reaction patterns have been intensively studied.

During assaults or threats arousing conflict with anger and a pattern of offense, the stomach prepares itself for eating with increased blood flow, acid secretion and motility. The gastric mucosa may become turgescent and the blood vessels friable. With forceful gastric contractions, bleeding readily ensues and erosions of the mucous membrane may follow.

Conspicuous among defensive protective reactions are those involving the nose and airways. It has been observed that in reaction to assault, certain individuals occlude their air passages and limit the ventilatory exchange by vasodilatation, turgescence, hypersecretion and smooth and skeletal muscle contractions. The changes, especially in the upper respiratory airways, give rise to a variety of symptoms, notably pain and obstruction, the latter often leading to secondary infection, and the prolongation of morbid processes. Also, a non-participation behavior pattern and attitude is exhibited in interpersonal relations.

Offensive protective reactions involving chiefly the cardiovascular and renal systems were exhibited in certain aggressive individuals. These persons, in reaction to assault, mobilized their equipment, causing the work of the heart to be greatly increased through increased rate, output and peripheral resistance. Especially notable in those with pressor reactions and essential hypertension was a significant reduction in renal blood flow during periods of experimentally induced assault, an effect with potentially ominous implications.

It is suggested that when the individual maintains such emergency measures, symptoms and tissue damage may follow.

In brief, man, feeling threatened, may use for long-term purposes, devices designed for short-term needs. Costly protective activities are essential and life saving. They are devised for fleeting emergencies so that he may destroy those forces that threaten his survival. But, they are not designed to be used as life long patterns, and when so utilized, may damage structures they were devised to protect.

These considerations constitute the basis of a good deal of human suffering and sickness. To prevent these disorders, more knowledge concerning the origin of these patterns in childhood is necessary. To interrupt them once they have become well established requires a vigorous and fresh approach to methods and means. To deal with these disturbances, it is necessary to study the functions of organs widely separated in the body, and because the methods require cutting across the lines which usually separate the various medical skills, the horizon of the physician must be broadened. It follows that interest in these illnesses cannot be limited by delineations of a new specialty. The pursuit of these matters is a prime medical responsibility of our day.

CHAPTER V

Psychoses: Schizophrenia (Including Paranoia)

DEFINITION OF SCHIZOPHRENIA

ALTHOUGH SCHIZOPHRENIA is probably the most baffling problem in psychopathology, yet the most remarkable scientific progress has been made in this area in recent decades. Today, there is a growing tendency to view schizophrenia, not as a single disease, but as a group of disorders sharing similar patterns (Noyes & Kolb, 1963). As early as 1911, Bleuler, who coined the term schizophrenia, recognized this variety among schizophrenics and incorporated the fact in the title of his classic treatise on the subject (1950).

The problem surrounding schizophrenia has encircled even the concept itself as to whether it is a genuine disease. While Menninger, Ellenberger, Pruyser and Mayman (1958, 1959) repudiate schizophrenia as indefinable and unidentifiable, Szasz (1957) regards the term as misleading and harmful. Weiner (1966) takes issue with these views, contending that the term has pragmatic value as an indicator, and to treat the term as of diagnostic unreliability is principally a myth.

Ullmann and Krasner have settled on a definition of schizophrenia as *"the crucial behavior, from which other indications of schizophrenia may be deduced, lies in the extinction of attention to social stimuli to which 'normal' people respond"* (1969, p. 383). A fair consensus exists that schizophrenics may be united on the basis of thought disorder, autism, and withdrawal (London, 1968).

Although psychoses are often dichotemized into organic and functional, there are numerous divisions not only under these two heads, but under any of their subheads. For example, schizophrenics may be divided according to their traditional clinical subtypes of simple, hebephrenic, catatonic paranoid, schizo-affective, pseudoneurotic (Hoch & Polatin, 1949), pseudopsychopathic schizophrenia (Dunaif & Hock, 1955), good premorbid and poor premorbid types (L. Phillips, 1953), process and reactive schizophrenia (Kantor, Wallner, & Winder, 1953); nuclear and peripheral schizophrenia (Benedict & Jacks, 1954), or according to Lorr and his associates (1962, 1963) 10 syndrome-based psychotic types (Mc-Nair *et al.*, 1964). Wolman (1966) views schizophrenia according to the following five levels: neurotic, schizoid character, latent schizophrenia, manifest schizophrenia or vectoriasis praecox, and the terminal phase of schizophrenia which he terms dementive schizophrenia. But Bowman and Rose (1959) contend that there is no answer to the question, "What is schizophrenia?" except a description of its signs and symptoms.

Payne and Sloane (1968) recommend the utilization of four independent syndromes for the classification of psychoses, thereby obviating any necessity of employing the term schizophrenia. The syndromes are (1) moderate retardation (on motor and intellectual tasks); (2) severe retardation (typical of chronic schizophrenic patients); (3) overinclusive thinking (affecting less than 50 percent of schizophrenics); and (4) over-inclusive perception (possibly a phase of overinclusive thinking), a syndrome suggested by Craig (1965).

Lorr (1962, 1968a, 1968b; Lorr, Klett & McNair, 1963), utilizing factor analysis, has successfully isolated and measured 10 psychotic syndromes: (1) excitement; (2) hostile belligerence; (3) paranoid projection; (4) grandiose expansiveness; (5) perceptual distortions; (6) anxious intropunitiveness; (7) retardation and apathy; (8)disorientation; (9) motor disturbances; and (10) conceptual disorganization. "The syndrome scores are related to ward assignment, to prominent features of psychopathology, and to conventional diagnostic class membership. The syndromes have also been found to be sensitive to change with tranquilizer treatment and to psychopathology as measured by other measuring devices" (1968b, p. 263). Lorr (with his associates) carried out a more extensive series of investigations and reported them in his *Explorations in Typing Psychotics* (1966).

Closely related to the notion of schizophrenia is *oneirophrenia* (Meduna, 1950), a dreamlike state submerging the personality yet without dissociating it. In simple oneirophrenia, the patient is aware of internal changes, but in deliroid oneirophrenia, the inner complications are projected to the external world as a dream, one usually complicated with hallucinations.

CHILDHOOD SCHIZOPHRENIA

Another unique type of autistic disorder, one occurring in children, is childhood schizophrenia which is currently under debate as to whether it should properly be identified with adult schizophrenia. As early as 1944, Kanner coined the term "early infantile autism" to characterize a syndrome in certain children of 2 to 3 years of age exhibiting extreme withdrawal, unresponsiveness, and obsessiveness. One such schizophrenic child, as described in Bettelheim (1959), concerns a nine-year-old existing mechanically in an imaginary world.

Bender's (1947, 1953a, 1953b, 1955) studies in childhood schizophrenia cite the importance of constitutional or biological factors interacting with psychological ones. Schizophrenia is produced from a "developmental lag of the biological processes from which subsequent behavior evolves by maturation at an embryological level, leading to anxiety and secondarily to neurotic mechanisms."

Goldfarb's (1961) findings revealed two clusters among schizophrenic children, organic and nonorganic, that is, those with and those without neurological disability. The organic came from adequate families, but were troubled by ego incompetence, while the nonorganic came from inadequate or disturbed families and were troubled by psychosocial or interpersonal factors.

In a monograph published in 1962, DesLauriers, offering an account of childhood schizophrenia from the psychoanalytic standpoint, regards schizophrenia as a "structural deficiency involving, in the schizophrenic individual, the incapacity to cathect his own bodily boundaries, so that the experience of reality was impossible, on a stable and consistent basis" (p. 193). For DesLauriers, schizophrenia is the loss of reality experience.

UNCOMMON PSYCHIATRIC SYNDROMES

Enoch and his associates (1967) have made a study of some uncommon psychiatric syndromes. Among them they discuss: (1) the *capgras syndrome,* that of believing a person (ordinarily one related to the patient) has been replaced by a double; (2) De Clérambault's syndrome or *psychose passionnelle* or *pure erotamania,* the patient, usually a woman, entertains the delusion that a man (generally of higher status, a celebrity and older man) is deeply in love with her; (3) the *Othello syndrome,* a morbid, sexual, psychotic jealousy in which the patient suffers from delusions of infidelity on the part of the spouse; (4) the *Ganser syndrome,* "that of giving of approximate answers to simple and familiar questions, in a setting of disturbed or clouded consciousness" (p. 41); (5) the *Couvade syndrome,* husbands, who during their wives' pregnancies, suffer that which pregnant women ordinarily suffer; (6) the *Munchausen or hospital addiction syndrome,* a hypochondriacoid disposition of a patient who deceives physicians with apparent illnesses and discharges himself from the hospital prematurely (usually following surgery); (7) *Gilles de la Tourette's syndrome,* i.e., generalized or multiple tics with coprolalia.

To these syndromes, Arieti and Meth (1959) have added other rare, unclassifiable, and exotic syndromes, including the *autoscopic syndrome* or the delusional experience of a double (capgras syndrome); *Cotard's syndrome* or the chronic delusional state of nihilism or negation of the existence of surrounding reality; *latah syndrome* with symptoms of echolalia, echopraxia, coprolalia, and sometimes fugues; *amok* (comparable to *beserk* of the ancient Vikings), a brooding followed by violence; *koro,* a phobic feeling that the penis will recede into the abdomen, causing death; *whitico psychosis,* fear of craving human flesh followed by melancholy, withdrawal, and insomnia; and *voodoo death* or *thanatomania,* death following awareness of transgressing a taboo or fear of being bewitched.

Grinker (1968) and his associates (in a lengthy research) report on the "borderline syndrome," with characteristics of: (1) anger affect; (2) "defect in his affectional relationships"; and "absence of indications of consistent self-identity" (1968, p. 90).

THEORIES OF SCHIZOPHRENIA

Theoretical formulations of schizophrenia are in abundant supply, and may be ordered according to genetic, constitutional, biochemical, sociocultural, and psychodynamic classifications. Rosenthal (1963), however, reduces theories treating schizophrenia to essentially three types: (1) monogenic-biochemical theories, those which treat schizophrenia as an inherited disease; (2) diathesis-stress theories, those that view schizophrenia as stemming from an inherited constitutional predisposition; and (3) life-experience theories, or those hypotheses attributing schizophrenia to life experiences, especially to the early experiences of life, without implicating inherited diathesis or genes.

GENETIC HYPOTHESES OF SCHIZOPHRENIA

Despite the scarcity of finding a psychopathologist who would regard schizophrenia as merely a genetic disorder, the majority of researchers tend to combine genetic predisposition with other important factors, such as, stress, strained familial relationships, or biochemical factors.

It still remains a question as to whether schizophrenia results from a genetic predisposition or not, or that the predisposition is necessary before a psychic trauma later in life can effectually result in schizophrenia. Fish expresses no doubt as to the genetic basis of schizophrenia, and concludes that it "is due to genetic predisposition which may or may not be expressed, depending on the overall genetic constitution, the modifications of the constitution during childhood, and the severity of the stress to which the patient is subjected in adolescence and adult life" (1962, p. 17).

⟍ According to Kallmann's (1938, 1946, 1952a, 1952b, 1953, 1959, 1961) *recessive theory of transmission,* schizophrenia is due to a major mutant recessive gene, the probable effect of which is an enzyme deficiency. Instead of specific symptoms being affected by this metabolic deficiency, general behavioral adjustment is. "Some gene-specific metabolic deficiency is at the root of the disorganizing personality disorder which often leads to adaptive incompetence" (1959, p. 100). Various forms of the recessivity hypothesis have been offered, especially by members of the Munich school.

⟍ A contending *dominance theory* has been presented by a number of authorities, including Böök (1953a, 1953b), who argues that major gene differences are "very likely the basic prerequisites for the ignition of a chain of events which may result in a psychosis" (1960, p. 208). In the absence of specific genetical prerequisites, schizophrenia will not occur. A dominant gene, but one that is weak and variable in its manifestations, produces schizophrenia. Of the two hypotheses, recessive and dominant theories, Fuller and Thompson (1960) contend that evidence at the present time favors the former. Gregory (1960) pessimistically concludes that the possible genetic factors in schizophrenia remain uncertain, but later (Rosen & Gregory, 1965) concedes that evidence strongly favors a genetic predisposition to schizophrenia, even though its mode of transmission is not as yet known with certainty. His latest comment is that owing to intrafamilial concentration of schizophrenia, it could be due to any combination of three mechanisms: (1) inheritance of disposition or vulnerability; (2) direct nongenetic transmission of pathogenic agents; and (3) exposure of schizophrenic persons to pathogenic agents or experiences (1968, p. 447).

⟍ Gottesman and Shields (1966), who believe that the schizophrenic mystery will be resolved during our lifetime, conclude that a "genetic specific aetiology for schizophrenia means only that the gene or genes are necessary, not that they are sufficient, for the disorder to occur" (p. 817).

BIOCHEMICAL THEORIES OF SCHIZOPHRENIA

Recently, there has been growing belief that schizophrenics (because one develops from apparently normal personalities and another from pre-existing schizoid personalities) are of two types, and that at least one of these is of a physical etiology (Smythies, 1968).

The Adrenocrome Metabolite Theory.   The adrenochrome-adrenolutin hypothesis, initially presented by Osmond and Smythies (1952; Smythies, 1963) and later cultivated by Osmond and Hoffer (1959, 1966; Hoffer & Osmond, 1960), reasons that a proportion of adrenaline found in tissues undergoes a conversion process becoming adrenochrome. It is readily transformed into 5:6 dihydroxy-N-methylinodole inasmuch as it is intensely reactive. Peculiarly, in the case of schizophrenics, the conversion is principally one of adrenolutin. Adrenochrome and adrenolutin, being mitotic poisons, account for schizophrenic mothers' abnormal fetuses; being antihistaminic, account for heightened histamine tolerance, but protection against allergies; being psychoses-mimicking when given to animals, account for psychotic phenomena in man. Hoffer and Osmond (1966; Hoffer, Osmond, Callbeck, & Kahan, 1957; Hoffer, 1962) used niacin and nicotinamide (vitamin B_3) in massive doses to treat schizophrenic patients. Of the 16 vitamin-treated patients, 12 (75 percent) needed no further hospital treatment, while 17 (63 percent) of 27 non-niacin patients did poorly.

Melatonin-harmine Hypothesis.   Greiner and Nicolson (1965) developed a theory based on McIsaac's (1961) observation of there being a chemical relationship existing between the hallucinogenic drug harmine and a congenital defect in the pineal gland's production of the hormone melatonin, an important pathogenic factor in schizophrenia. Their reasoning is:

The synthesis of melantonin in the pineal gland is congenitally defective, because of which a hallucinogenic agent is produced instead of melantonin; as a result, there is an occurrence of hallucinations and an increased melanin production; the defective enzyme is probably an o-methyltransferase (Greiner & Nicolson, 1965, p. 1167).

The Taraxein Hypothesis.   Heath (1960, 1966, 1967), who views schizophrenia as a "genetically determined inborn error of metabolism," theorizes that taraxein produces psychotic behavior by its affect on the limbic system of the brain. "The serum of schizophrenic patients contains antibody that can attach to antigenic sites of neural cell nuclei in the septal region and basal caudate nucleus of the brain. . . ." (1967, p. 1499). Schizophrenic symptoms are the result of an immune process brought on by a serum which contains antibody against the brain. A number of researchers are currently pursuing evidence substantiating the taraxein hypothesis and eliminating its weaknesses (Heath, 1963).

The Serotonin Hypothesis of Schizophrenia.   Woolley and Shaw (1954,

1956; Woolley, 1958a, 1958b) postulate that schizophrenia issues from a cerebral sorotonin hormone deficiency stemming from metabolic failure. Serotonin deficiency in the brain (responsible for mental disorder) is produced by those agents capable of antagonizing the action of serotonin, that is, the ergot, alkaloids, the harmala alkaloids, yohimbine, and their derivatives which operate as antimetabolites or serotonin in smooth muscle.

Kety (1959, 1960, 1965, 1969) cites five important areas of biochemical research in schizophrenia: (1) oxygen, carbohydrate, and energetics; (2) amino acids and amines; (3) the epinephrine hypothesis which traces schizophrenia to faulty metabolism of epinephrine, adrenochrome or adrenolutin, a hallucinogenic derivative of epinephrine, believed to cause symptoms of schizophrenia (the theory of Hoffer, Osmond, & Smythies, 1954; Osmond & Hoffer, 1959); (4) ceruloplasmin and taraxein, the work of Heath and others of the Tulane group; and (5) serotonin, especially the efforts of Woolley and Shaw (1954). In 1969, Kety embellished this list with additional hypotheses, including dimethoxyphenylethylamine and indoleamine theories.

A classic study of the biology of schizophrenia entailing its endocrinological ramifications was published by Hoskins (1946), to which he added research in hormone therapy (1954), but his efforts serve only as pioneer studies in this area.

The role of morphological characteristics in schizophrenia has been scored by Doust (1952a, 1952b), who noted morphological immaturity coupled to dysplastic factors in schizophrenia, such as, "a scanty upper lip without discrete lobulation; a high interpupillary index, double jointedness, and persistent remnants of the epicanthic fold." Chronic anoxemia is also common to schizophrenics.

Utilizing conditional reflex studies, Astrup (1962) traces schizophrenic deterioration to an impairment of the higher nervous activity, reasoning that the more pronounced the schizophrenic deterioration, the severer the impairment. He explains schizophrenia in the light of Gantt's autokinesis and schizokinesis, while rejecting brain lesions and psychodynamic mechanisms (Astrup & Noreik, 1966). Though Astrup follows in the tradition of Pavlov, Russians (such as Malis, 1961), explain schizophrenia as an infectious disease, owing to the toxic properties in the blood and other physical factors.

FAMILIAL AND SOCIOCULTURAL THEORIES
OF SCHIZOPHRENIA

No one has gone further than Harry Stack Sullivan (1953) in emphasizing the social factors involved in psychiatry. Defining psychiatry as the study of interpersonal relations, he asserted that "this made psychiatry the probable locus of another evolving discipline, one of the social sciences, namely, *social psychology*" (1947a, p. xi). Sullivan, who believes that the schizophrenic is alienated from social influences (1962, p. 220), claims the disorder ensues "when a person is driven by the insoluble character of his life situation" (1954, p. 206). Our sleep and a considerable portion of our childhood years are schizophrenic experiences. The essential nature of schizophrenia is the "failure of the self-system . . . to restrict the contents of consciousness to the higher referential processes that can be consensually validated" (1956, p. 182).

Psychiatry, the study of interpersonal phenomena according to Sullivan, examines phenomena occurring in interpersonal situations, configurations entailing two or more persons (1938). "Scientific psychiatry has to be defined as the study of interpersonal relations" (1948, p. 105). The therapeutic process itself must also be one of "participant observation," an interpersonal relationship of interpersonal influence affecting both patient and psychotherapist (1947a).

There are those psychiatrists who are so thoroughly convinced of the sociocultural factors of mental disorders that they are committed to social forms of therapy, that is, milieu therapy or a therapeutic community. Jones (1952, 1962) was an early pioneer in this field, but today a number of others have researched and are experimenting in this area of schizophrenia (Sanders, Smith, & Weinman, 1967; Artiss, 1962). Brown and his associates (1966) report a significant degree of severe distress on the part of relatives some time during the half year prior to hospitalization of the patient. "The number of problems, and the distress felt by relatives, were highly related to the degree of disturbed behaviour shown by the patient" (1966, p. 208).

The Double-Bind Hypothesis. Bateson and his colleagues Jackson, Haley, and Weakland (1956) and later Weakland (1960) developed a theory of schizophrenia based on communications analysis and Bertrand Russell's (1937) theory of logical types according to which a discontinuity exists between a class and its members, namely, a class can neither be a member of itself nor can any of its members constitute a class because the concept used for class is a different logical type, a different level of abstraction. This discontinuity is carried over into interpersonal relations or communications between mother and child, and breached with a resulting psychopathological outcome, schizophrenia.

Weakland (1960, p. 374–375) cites the general characteristics of the double-bind predicament:

1. When the individual is involved in an intense relationship; that is, a relationship in which he feels it is vitally important that he discriminate accurately

what sort of message is being communicated so that he may respond appropriately.

2. And, the individual is caught in a situation in which the other person in the relationship is expressing two orders of message and one of these denies the other.

3. And, the individual is unable to comment on the messages being expressed to correct his discrimination of what order of message to respond to, *i.e.*, he cannot make a metacommunicative statement.

A child in a double-bind situation cannot win, for whatever he does will be censored; furthermore, the breakdown in communications between mother and child is recurrent.

Sampson and his group (1964) studied women and mothers who were schizophrenic and concluded that schizophrenic wives underwent severe difficulty in the transition of leaving home, marrying, and assuming parenthood. A number of them, symbiotically tied to the maternal figure, encountered conflict in marital separation, while others confronted conflict in "synthesizing childhood identifications, especially those revived by becoming like the mother" (1964, p. 119).

The Quadruple-Bind Hypothesis. From a study comparing schizophrenic patients with nonschizophrenic siblings, Lu (1961, 1962) uncovered a couple of sets of binds. One, the dependence-independence conflict, relates to the American culture which demands of our youth that they enter adulthood with independence and autonomy. But in the case of the preschizophrenic who has played a dependent role patterned on an authoritarian mother, independence and autonomy present a problem—a bind. Being dependent and subordinate, yet expected to seek achievement, responsibility, and independence, is the cause of the bind. The bind ensues when the preschizophrenic vainly strives to fulfill the authoritarian mother's expectations that do not coincide with his own. The schizophrenic is engulfed in a "role pattern which is characterized by contradictory parental expectations coupled with the preschizophrenic's persistent efforts to fulfill them" (1962, p. 233).

Severe mental conflict is experienced when the desires of the preschizophrenic conflict—the desire to be independent of his mother clashes with that of desiring to remain dependent upon her. Nonschizophrenic siblings were involved in activities that took them away from home; they attended school or worked at distances from home; they married earlier; and they ignored their mother's domination. Hence, thereby they avoided both maternal control and serious mental conflicts. Kimble and Garmezy (1968; Garmezy, 1968) report that mothers of schizophrenic "patients are more deviant in their attitudes to their sons than are the mothers of good premorbid patients" (Kimble & Garmezy, 1968, p. 628). The poor premorbid group of schizophrenics (those prior to hospitalization exhibiting a poor social and sexual adjustment [Garmezy & Rodnick, 1959]) responded with sharply poorer discriminations to the critical mother, while the reactive group (good premorbids—those with successful adjustment prior to hospitalization) and sibling group were able to make adequate discriminations.

Marital Schism and Marital Skew Hypothesis. A number of studies conducted by Lidz and his associates (1957, 1958, 1965) linked the cause of schizophrenia to intrafamilial relationships. The schizophrenic is the product of a seriously disturbed family (Lidz & Lidz, 1949), involving psychopathological elements in the father as well as the mother. Such families were "either schismatic—that is, divided into two antagonistic and competing factions—or were 'skewed' in that the serious personality disturbance of one parent set the pattern of family interaction" (Lidz, Fleck, Alanen, & Cornelison, 1963, p. 3). The parents of such families, impervious and engaged in homosexual and incestuous struggles, proved detrimental to the child's ego development. The child, with only confused models for identification, relates poorly or inaccurately, and is victimized by irrational or paralogical modes of thought and communication. In schizophrenic families, there are "failures of the family to provide adequate nurturance to permit the child to develop autonomy, to achieve the essential structure required to direct the structuring of the personality, and to convey the basic adaptive techniques of the culture" (Lidz *et al.*, 1965, p. 375), all stemming from parental personality deficiencies. Accordingly, schizophrenia, essentially a deficiency disease, is the product of the family's inability to provide what is necessary for a suitable integrated personality development, including the schizophrenic's failure to attain autonomy, a faulty family structure impeding the structuring of personality, and unsound enculturation. Beck's (1965) studies also disclosed family behaviors associated with schizophrenia.

MEDNICK'S LEARNING THEORY OF SCHIZOPHRENIA

Mednick's (1958, 1959) hypothesis, grounded on learning theory, asserts that high levels of anxiety (acting as a drive) spiral in intensity, leading to excessive stimulus generalization. Unlike the normal, schizophrenics: (1) more readily acquire conditioned responses, (2) exhibit greater stimulus generalization responsiveness, and (3) perform with difficulty in complex situations. The spiralling process of anxiety proceeds from an acute to a chronic phase of schizophrenia.

The thinking of abstracted, irrelevant thoughts may be rewarded by anxiety reduction by removing disturbing ideation from consciousness. This would increase the probability of the recurrence of these irrelevant thoughts and would be an admirable vehicle for continual anxiety reduction and transition to a chronic phase (1958, p. 316).

Tactics, such as alcohol consumption, which once were effective in alleviating anxiety-provoking situations that were once bearable are now beyond control. Schizophrenic symptoms function as anxiety reducers, as a defense against anxiety. Schizophrenic irrelevant thoughts are effective anxiety reducers so much so that they reduce anxiety even below that of the normal individual. A similar relationship holds true in the case of depressives as well, according to Davies, who asserts that his "observations confirm the widely held view that depression protects the organism from excessive stimulation" (1964, p. 101).

INTERFERENCE OR SEGMENTAL SET THEORY IN SCHIZOPHRENIA

Interference theory, that view which regards the individual as a processing information system, is championed by Shakow (1962, 1963). The well-adapted organism, while choosing and responding to relevant environmental data, ignores its irrelevant or extraneous elements. In proper adaptation, irrelevant aspects are filtered out by a filter mechanism (Broadbent, 1958), but the schizophrenic has "difficulty in focusing on the relevant aspects of the defined situation," and is "susceptible to the influence of the peripheral. He does not habituate readily" (Shakow, 1962, p. 10). Instead of habituating, the schizophrenic perseverates by responding to stimuli that are weak while underresponding when they are intense. His two problems are that

he reacts to old situations as if they were new ones (he fails to habituate), and to new situations as if they were recently past ones (he perseverates); and second, he overresponds when the stimulus is relatively small, and he does not respond enough when the stimulus is great. . . . There is little doubt that the schizophrenic's is an inefficient unmodulated system, full of 'noise,' and of indeterminate figure-ground relationships. What a confusing world must be the schizophrenic's when such basic modes of relating to the world are so seriously disturbed!" (Shakow, 1963, p. 303).

When the time interval between stimulus and response is great, intervening stimuli distract the schizophrenic, and if it is brief, then he is unable to select among alternatives. Otherwise his performance may be comparable to normal individuals. In order to establish a set, the schizophrenic requires greater time and maintains it with greater difficulty. Operating under conditions of responsibility causes the schizophrenic to do poorly.

MULTIPLE-FACTOR PSYCHOSOMATIC THEORY
OF SCHIZOPHRENIA

Working toward a unified concept of schizophrenia, Bellak (1949, 1955) hypothesized in his multiple-factor psychosomatic theory that schizophrenia is a severe ego disturbance syndrome, rather than a disease entity. Ego impairment, however, may be the consequent of numerous somatogenic and psychogenic antecedents in diverse arrangements of combinations. Good and ill health, viewed as a continuum of ego strength, has normality at one end and schizophrenia occupying a range at the other, with neurosis and manic-depressive psychosis in an intermediary position. Childhood schizophrenia, a defect of or injury to the ego, may be grounded in genetics, brain damage, or a disruption of mother-child relationships occurring in the first half year of the infant's life. "The hypothesis is advanced that organic disorders and defects so often observed in childhood psychosis and in severe adult schizophrenias are also the result of severe disturbances of the mother-child relationship, which serves the underdeveloped sensorium of the infant as a necessary polarizing factor; when absent, the somatic substratum is affected" (Bellak, 1955, p. 65).

EXISTENTIAL HYPOTHESIS OF SCHIZOPHRENIA

Kantor and Herron (1966) have developed an existentialist approach to reactive schizophrenia. According to this view, reactive schizophrenics are individuals who once having possessed freedom are devoid of it. Vulnerability to schizophrenia is contingent upon the loss of freedom, since freedom is essential to mental health. Having once been in possession of freedom and life's meaningfulness, the reactive schizophrenic has lost his will-to-meaning (Frankl, 1969), purpose in life, choice, and self-image. Psychosis, instead of being the resultant of a shattered ego, passive repressions, or obstructions in living, is the inability to find meaning for one's existence. The loss of life's meaningfulness alienates one from his own sense of humanity. The schizophrenic's symptoms must be interpreted as attempts to impute meaningful values to his existence. It is in an encounter with his present self that he finds meaningful living.

The goal of therapy, one of empathy and participation on the part of the therapist, is to note what is happening to the patient instead of the cause of its occurrence. Therapeutic communication is transverbal, one stemming from the patient's "presence" (May, 1958); and his existence is structured as a being-in-the-world (Binswanger, 1963). Man, being a "socius," must have his psychotherapy keynoted with social interaction, dialogue with others, and freedom of choice, for schizophrenia is the antithesis of human freedom.

For the schizophrenic time lacks a future, hence life is devoid of purpose. He exists in the past; "it is this pervasive underlying preoccupation with what is behind one that is so striking in the schizophrenic" (Shakow, 1962, p. 15). His repetition of past actions is significant of his loss of futurity.

PROGRESSIVE TELEOLOGICAL REGRESSION HYPOTHESIS OF SCHIZOPHRENIA

A theory, developed by Arieti (1955, 1959, 1967) and termed progressive teleological regression, purports that "schizophrenia results not from reduction of the psyche to a concrete level, but from a *process of active concretization*, which follows psychodynamic (or teleologic, or restitutional) trends" (1967, p. 272). In active concretization, the psyche is yet able to conceive the abstract thought not sustaining it, owing to the abstract's being too anxiety-provoking or disintegrating. Schizophrenic regression, a returning to lower levels of adaptation, is purposeful in that it seeks to diminish intense anxiety and maintain equilibrium. Regression, though purposeful, is retrogressive. Failing in its purpose, regression tends toward repetition. While regressing to lower levels, the schizophrenic fails to maintain integration or organization at the regressed level, and deteriorates into still lower levels in a vain attempt to defend himself from disorganization.

If, in a situation of severe anxiety, behavior at a certain level of intellectual integration cannot take place or does not bring about the desired results, a strong tendency exists toward behavior of lower levels of integration in order to effect those results (1955, p. 191).

The prepsychotic undergoes four stages: (1) a family situation devoid of security and trust; (2) secondary process mechanisms replace the primary; (3) defenses tend to fail at puberty when undergoing contacts with the outside world; and (4) the psychotic stage commences with a regressive descent. By definition, a person is schizophrenic when his conflicts undergo progressive teleologic regression (Arieti, 1960). In a study over a period of five years, Brattemo (1968) sees as the more genuine schizophrenics those chronic patients with a poor clinical outcome despite treatment.

PSYCHOANALYTIC THEORIES OF SCHIZOPHRENIA

Though Freud sought to discourage the psychoanalytic treatment of schizophrenia, attempts to do so persisted. According to psychoanalysts (Freeman, 1965), two contributions have been made to research in schizophrenia: a technique of revealing the patient's subjective experiences; and the interpretation of the patient's denials or reluctance to communicate as manifestations of his anxiety.

Freud's formulation of a psychoanalytic theory of psychosis comes from his analysis of the Schreber case of paranoid schizophrenia, which he reported in 1911. He viewed the illness as a type of repression wherein libidinal cathexes are withdrawn from the external world of objects as well as from their intrapsychic representations, leaving the patient with only an incomplete capacity for retaining object cathexes. Hallucinations, topographic regressions, are interpreted as revived memory-traces experienced as genuine perceptions, but in 1916 he rejected the idea that topographic regression occurs in schizophrenia. Delusion-formation is an attempt at recovery. Freud (1915) attributed it to cathexes withdrawal from endopsychic object representation. "Paranoiacs are endowed with a *fixation at the stage of narcissism,* and . . . the amount of *regression* characteristic of paranoia is indicated by the length of *the step back from sublimated homosexuality to narcissism*" (1911). Psychosis is a regression to a state of narcissism, and its conflict centers on homosexual wish-phantasy. While neurosis is produced by a conflict between the ego and the id, psychosis results from a disturbance between ego and the outer world (environment) (Freud, 1924).

Contemporary psychoanalytic theories of schizophrenia utilize Freud's structure of the personality (id, ego, superego) originally presented by Freud in 1932, but stress only the role of ego and superego. Departing from Freud, Federn (1943, 1948, 1952) contended that ego defect was not the cause but the consequence of withdrawal from the object world. Ego insufficiency or dysfunction (ego cathexes deficiency), accounting for psychotic symptomatology, was initiated by Federn and accepted by the majority of psychoanalysts. Schizophrenic depersonalization ensues from loss of ego-boundary cathexes (1949).

Current psychoanalytic hypotheses regard schizophrenia as a regressive process and as a defense against guilt and anxiety vitalized by instinctual urges, though their mental phenomena may vary. The regressive process reverts to early childhood points of fixation. The fixation points are viewed as arrested forms of development, a failure in normal psychic development. Accordingly, a schizophrenic is mentally or emotionally a child, rather than an adult. The primitive regressive state is an escape from the unpleasant content of adult consciousness. The disdain for distasteful reality causes fragmentation (Bion, 1957). The schizophrenic does not think of his cognition as part of himself, but as part of the world of persecutors (Searles, 1959). Schizophrenic processes cause "varying degrees of splitting and projection of the ego. These processes are related to the working within the ego of destructive impulses, which are felt to be alien (split off) and therefore persecutors" (Rosenfeld, 1965). In earliest infancy the personality's psychotic elements are split off, claims Rosenfeld, and schizophrenia results when the split-off psychotic parts erupt through to the surface.

According to Melanie Klein (1948), should persecutory fear and schizoid mechanisms become too potent, then the ego becomes incapable of working through the depressive position. As a result the ego regresses to a paranoid schizoid state, thereby reinforcing earlier persecutory fears and schizoid elements.

Ladee, investigating hypochondriac psychosis from a psychoanalytic standpoint, claims that the disorder results from "an increase in the libidinous cathexis of a mentally resisted organ (function) and loss of an (ambivalently) loved object, let loose aggression which introjected in a somatized form" (1966, p. 262).

33.

SILVANO ARIETI

PROGRESSIVE TELEOLOGIC REGRESSION HYPOTHESIS AND PALEOLOGIC THOUGHT

We have already mentioned that the schizophrenic adopts different intellectual mechanisms. By that it was meant that he does not think with ordinary logic. His thought is not illogical or senseless, but follows a different system of logic which leads to deductions different from those usually reached by the healthy person. The schizophrenic is seen in a position similar to that of a man who would solve mathematical problems not with our decimal system, but with another hypothetical system, and would consequently reach different solutions. In other words, the schizophrenic seems to have a faculty of conception which is constituted differently from that of the normal man.

As we shall see in the following chapter, this different faculty of conception or different logic is the same as that which is followed in dreams, in other forms of autistic thinking, and in many manifestations of men living in prehistorical and certain other cultures. It was consequently called *paleologic* to distinguish it from our usual logic, which is generally called Aristotelian, since Aristotle was the first to enunciate its laws. The laws of paleologic, especially as they are deduced from the study of schizophrenic thought and dreams, will be examined in detail in the following chapter. Here it is sufficient to emphasize again why the patient abandons the Aristotelian way of thinking and adopts a primitive type. He does so in order to escape anxiety; as long as he interprets reality with Aristotelian logic, he is aware of the unbearable truth, and a state of panic may ensue. Once he sees things in a different way, with a new logic, his anxiety will decrease. This new logic will permit him to

see reality as he wants to, and will offer him a pseudo-fulfillment of his wishes. Once the patient sees things in a different way, with a new logic, no Aristotelian persuasion will convince him that he is wrong. He is right, according to his own logic.

The adoption of this paleologic way of thinking is predominant in that type of schizophrenia which has been termed hebephrenic. However, not all thinking in hebephrenics follows paleologic modes. Islands of logical thoughts remain, but they are more and more overwhelmed by the paleological way of thinking. In the paranoid type of schizophrenia a peculiar situation occurs: Aristotelian thought is preserved to a considerable extent, but, as we shall see later in detail, it is often strangely used to support the conclusions reached by paleologic thought. This situation is, to a certain degree, reminiscent of those defenses of the ego which in many neuroses protect or reinforce unconscious complexes.

Another mechanism by which the schizophrenic breaks with reality is the withdrawal from action. This mechanism is particularly pronounced in the catatonic type, following complicated processes which are connected, as we shall see later, with "psychological causality."

In the simple type of schizophrenia the mechanisms mentioned above are not present, or present only to a minimal degree. Rather than change reality, the simple schizophrenic limits reality. He narrows his horizon to a large extent, so that he will be able to make some kind of compromise with what is left of reality, without having to resort very much to paleologic or to withdrawal mechanisms. What he leaves out of his life is generally what pertains to the abstract. Since life in our present cultural environment, however, cannot be deprived of this increasingly important aspect of thought, the simple schizophrenic cannot successfully compromise. He will appear bizarre, odd and inappropriate.

Each of the mechanisms which have been mentioned, though predominantly found in one particular type of schizophrenia, may occur to a greater or lesser degree in every type of this illness. Transitional stages and different combinations of the various mechanisms are commonly found. In addition, there are two other mechanisms which are common to all types, the impairment of affect and desocialization. All of these mechanisms are, of course, interconnected, and possibly only different expressions of one process. In this part of the book, they will be considered separately for didactical reasons, but their interrelation will always be considered. This approach should not be interpreted as a return to psychological atomism. We are fully aware that the human psyche functions as a whole, but the problem under consideration is so involved that no other study of it is feasible except the examination of its parts separately. . . .

I. THE PRINCIPLE OF TELEOLOGIC REGRESSION

In this chapter the various intellectual alterations which occur in schizophrenia will be examined.

In this first section, however, it will be shown that intellectual distortions do not occur exclusively in schizophrenics, but occur in a much larger group of individuals than is generally assumed. These distortions never reach the intensity of the schizophrenic distortion, except in dreams. If we take mathematical thinking at one extreme, as the most typical example of pure logical Aristotelian thought, and schizophrenic thinking at the other extreme, we can also find all possible gradations between the two. Generally, the greater the intensity of the emotion involved, the greater may become the necessity for resorting to some kind of intellectual distortion. The amount of the distortion, however, is not proportional to the emotional need.

The most common of these distortions is what is generally called *rationalization*. Rationalizations are found in normal people and neurotics as well as psychotics, and consist of attempts to justify logically actions or ideas which in reality are directed, not by reason, but by an emotional need. These rationalizations are often not unrealistic at all from an intellectual point of view; as a matter of fact, they are supported by pure Aristotelian logic. For example, a patient was suffering from feelings of rivalry for his brother, who was a singer. The patient used to warn his brother in a paternal and affectionate tone of voice, "Don't sing so often at clubs and private parties. You will ruin your voice!" This was a correct recommendation. The singer had also been told by many experts that he should not strain his voice with too much work. Actually the motivation of the patient in repeating this recommendation was a different one: He was jealous of the consideration and honor that the brother was receiving when he sang, and wanted to prevent them.

Often the rational foundation which sustains the idea or action is less plausible. Some element of plausibility, however, must remain. . . . The patient, Peter, justified his father's saying that he had been a hero during the first World War, although actually he had been a deserter. According to Peter, his father had to say this in order to remove all doubts about his participation in the war, and by so doing, he was saving the honor of the family. Peter's need to consider his father a venerable authority compelled him to resort to such a fantastic rationalization. His brother, Gabriel, when he was already psychotic, sold a gold watch and some other valuable objects for a few cents. When he was questioned about it, he justified himself with the following rationalization: "These things were mine. Can't I do what I want with my things?" He switched the problem from the advisability of the act to the permissibility of the act, in an attempt to justify it. Actually, the motivation was different. In a latent way he was saying to his parents: "I had to become crazy in order to assert myself. You never let me do what I wanted. Now I can."

From these examples, and from many others which could be cited, it is evident that an attempt is always made to maintain an element of plausibility or logic, even when the wish to have one's way is very strong. As was mentioned before, human beings cannot accept anything which to them seems irrational. The need for rationality is as powerful as the need to gratify the irrational emotions. If rationality is never completely abandoned, a certain *level* of rationality, however, is often lost, especially in situations of emergency, and a regression to a lower level is often resorted to, even by normal human beings. Similar regressions have occurred innumerable times in human history. For instance, if diplomatic discussions do not bring about certain results, much more primitive methods, such as wars or persecution of minorities, may be resorted to.

This regression occurs so often that this process can be defined in the form of a principle. *If, in a situation of severe anxiety, behavior at a certain level of intellectual integration cannot take place or does not bring about the desired results, a strong tendency exists toward behavior of lower levels of integration in order to effect those results.*

The reader should note that the word "tendency" is used. In other words, this principle is not like a physical law, which must operate without exceptions. There is just a propensity toward its occurrence, but it may not occur, as for instance, in cases where something unexpected intervenes. It should also be noted that a situation of severe anxiety *must* be present.

By resorting to lower levels of integration, the human mind turns again to methods which were used in the past, but which were discarded when new methods had been adopted. It is a repetition of history in reversed chronology. This happens not only to human beings, but to animals as well. Mowrer has demonstrated this principle in rats with a very ingenious experiment. . . . The animals learned to protect themselves from an electric current by sitting on their hind legs. Later, the rats learned a much better way; they discovered how to turn off the current by pressing a pedal. When this habit was well ingrained, it replaced the previous one. Later the pedal too was charged with electricity, and the rats had to face another shock, if they continued to press it. At this point they went back to the method of sitting on their hind legs. Thus, they reverted to the earlier and inferior method.

When experimental animals have learned to solve a problem with the mechanism of insight and, for some reason, can no longer solve the problem with this method, they revert to the method of trial and error. In other words, there is a tendency toward a reversed hierarchy of responses,[1] from the highest to the lowest. I propose to call this principle *the principle of teleologic regression: regression* because less advanced levels of mental integration are used; *teleologic* because this regression seems to have a purpose, namely, to avoid anxiety by bringing about the wanted results. As a matter of fact, studies in abnormal psychology have revealed innumerable instances in which the mind in distress does not necessarily follow scientific thinking (events are the effects of previous causes), but rather teleologic thinking (events have a purpose). Thus, dreams, hallucinations, symptoms, delusions, etc., seem to have a purpose, even though they themselves are the results of previous causes.

More often than not, of course, thinking which follows the principle of teleologic regression does not effect the desired results, but will decrease the anxiety, at least temporarily. Legends and myths frequently reveal the adoption of this principle. For instance, the Jews, as described in the Bible, had reached that high cultural level which permitted them to worship an abstract God. When, however, they were under the stress of anxiety caused by the sudden disappearance of their leader, Moses, they reverted to the worship of the Golden Calf. When Moses reappeared and the anxiety was relieved, they went back to the cult of the abstract God.

At this point, a question of terminology must be clarified. The reader may be confused by the use of the words "logical," "rational," "intellectual," to indicate thoughts or actions which appear irrational and illogical. These terms are used because these thoughts or actions are intellectually organized . . . ; in other words, on

---

[1]The emphasis here, however, is given not to the response in a behavioristic way, but to the central process which is responsible for the response.

careful examination they reveal an intellectual process or effort, even if this process does not correspond to the one used in our common logic. In a rationalization, for instance, there is an intellectual or logical effort to justify something, even though this actual intellectual process may be at fault from our common point of view.

The difficulty that some people may experience in calling these processes intellectual or logical is in a certain way similar to the difficulty that some philosophically-minded people experienced in calling the unconscious mechanisms discovered by Freud "psychological." They thought that a necessary characteristic for a psychological phenomenon was that it be conscious; without consciousness a phenomenon could not be psychological. In a similar way, we call a process intellectual if it has some kind of intellectual organization, although it may not necessarily follow the Aristotelian logic (the only one known to us, usually) and may therefore appear to us very illogical. *What may seem to us as forms of irrationality are instead archaic forms of rationality.* As a matter of fact, we shall find more and more that intellectual organization is always present. As I have mentioned above, it is as difficult to escape from some type of intellectual organization as it is to escape from emotions. Even the most nonsensical, bizarre, and irrational thoughts have some kind of intellectual organization. When we understand the type of intellectual organization and its content, we understand the meaning of the process. In other words, it is possible to translate the archaic thought into an Aristotelian thought. Even the so-called "word salad" of the schizophrenic is not just a bizarre, whimsical *sequence* of words. When we understand it, we discover that it is a *consequence*.

II. VON DOMARUS' PRINCIPLE

Paleologic to a great extent is based on a principle enunciated by Von Domarus. This author, as a result of his studies on schizophrenia, formulated a principle which, in slightly modified form, is as follows: *Whereas the normal person accepts identity only upon the basis of identical subjects, the paleologician accepts identity based upon identical predicates.* For instance, the normal person is able to conclude, "John Doe is an American citizen," if he is given the following information: "Those who are born in the United States are American citizens; John Doe was born in the United States." This normal person is able to reach this conclusion because the subject of the minor premise, "John Doe," is contained in the subject of the major premise, "those who are born in the United States."

On the other hand, suppose that the following information is given to a schizophrenic: "The President of the United States is a person who was born in the United States. John Doe is a person who was born in the United States. In certain circumstances, the schizophrenic may conclude: "John Doe is the President of the United States." This conclusion, which to a normal person appears delusional, is reached because the identity of the predicate of the two premises, "a person who was born in the United States" makes the schizophrenic accept the identity of the two subjects, "The President of the United States" and "John Doe." Of course, this schizophrenic has an emotional need to believe that John Doe is the President of the United States, a need which will arouse anxiety if it is not satisfied. He cannot think that John Doe is the President of the United States if he follows Aristotelian logic; thus, following the principle of teleologic regression, he abandons Aristotelian logic and follows Von Domarus' principle.

A patient thought that she was the Virgin Mary. Her thought process was the following: "The Virgin Mary was a virgin; I am a virgin; therefore, I am the Virgin Mary." The delusional conclusion was reached because the identity of the predicate of the two premises (the state of being virgin) made the patient accept the identity of the two subjects (the Virgin Mary and the patient). She needed to identify herself with the Virgin Mary because of the extreme closeness and spiritual kinship she felt for the Virgin Mary.

34.

Wesley C. Becker

PROCESS-REACTIVE DISTINCTION

In the search for a place to get a foothold on the problem of schizophrenia, one glaring consistency is manifested in the research of the past twenty years. Schizophrenic patients with certain kinds of backgrounds and symptom pictures tend to improve, while those with other backgrounds and symptom pictures tend not to improve. The prognostic studies of Hunt and Appel (8), Langfeldt (12), Kant (9), Kantor, Wallner, and Winder (10), Becker and McFarland (4), Stotsky (16), Benjamin (5), and Wittman (17–19), all have pointed to systematic differences in the personalities and case histories of remitting and nonremitting schizophrenics. These studies have led to a number of terms, all describing the same distinction: malignant-benign, chronic-acute, process-reactive. The significance of these studies lies in their highlighting of an important criterion variable, prognosis, and in their implications for gaining estimates of prognosis in a given case without having to wait five years to obtain follow-up data. The above mentioned work provides one with a means for scaling schizophrenic patients along a dimension from good to poor prognosis, and then permits one to use this dimension as one means for organizing heterogeneous schizophrenic populations for systematic research. Gerald King's recent paper (11) provides an example of this. Many previous studies on autonomic reactivity in schizophrenia have revealed inconsistent findings, but when autonomic reactivity is studied in relation to a prognostic dimension, clear-cut relationships do appear.

Before developing further the implications of a prognosis dimension or a dimension of sever-

ity of disorder, a brief discussion of an alternative interpretation of these same findings is needed. Some have suggested that the poor prognosis syndrome represents one kind of schizophrenia, organically based, while the good prognosis syndrome represents another kind of schizophrenia, psychologically based. The notion of two types is very appealing, because such an outcome would make everybody happy —both the physiogenic and psychogenic theorists. However, individual cases do not fall into two groups, but spread out in such a way that the process syndrome moves imperceptibly into the reactive syndrome.

Accepting for the moment the notion of a process-reactive continuum, the syndromes serving to identify the end-points of a dimension of severity, is there a further research lead to be found in the analysis of the descriptive elements defining this continuum? In a previous paper (3), the writer has suggested that it might be profitable to consider this continuum as reflecting the level of organization reached by a given personality in its growth toward maturity. "Level of organization" is a difficult term to define precisely. It is concerned with changes in the content and structure of mental organization as the human organism develops toward maturity. A complete definition would encompass such factors as objectivity in perception, differentiation of needs, interests, and other aspects of personal motivation, and the degree of emotional control or adaptive functioning under stress. Lewin (13), Baldwin (1), and especially Werner (20) have all attempted to deal with this construct. Common to most attempts to conceptualize levels of personality is the general idea that "the development of biological forms is expressed in an increasing differentiation of parts and *increasing subordination*, or *hierarchization*" of the parts with respect to the whole (20). This principle ap-

Reprinted by permission. Wesley C. Becker, "The Process-Reactive Distinction: A Key to the Problem of Schizophrenia?" *Journal of Nervous and Mental Disease, 129,* 442–449. Copyright © 1959, The Williams & Wilkins Company, Baltimore, Maryland.

plies to phylogenesis as well as ontogenesis. It is appropriately applied to mental development. Werner uses such terms as syncretic-discrete, diffuse-articulated, rigid-flexible, and labile-stable in describing the progression from primitive functioning to higher levels of mental functioning.

While space does not permit an elaboration of details, there seems to be a marked parallel between the process-reactive distinction and Werner's description of levels of personality organization. At the process end of the continuum, the whole development is fixated, *for whatever reason*, at a primitive level; or it might also be that development has been very uneven and then regression has taken place easily and relatively completely. The process syndrome characterizes a person with a relative lack of personality differentiation. Interests are narrow and lacking intensity. There is a rigidity of structure and a lack of internal direction. There is an inability to establish normal heterosexual relations and independence. The need for hospitalization arises when such a person is faced with the normal problems of adult living in our complex culture.

On the other hand, a person falling closer to the reactive end of the continuum seems to have reached a higher level of personality differentiation. The prepsychotic personality is relatively more normal. Interests are more varied and intense. Heterosexual relations are more likely to have been established, and personal motivation and direction is more apparent. More and greater environmental stresses are tolerated before a regressive break occurs. In addition, the vestiges of a higher level of development are still pronounced even in regression and provide the compensating strength to allow recovery when the stresses are removed. The struggle which is indicative of continued ego-function is apparent in the strong affective reactions characteristic of this end of the continuum.

This hypothesis relating the process-reactive continuum to levels of personality organization does not prejudge the etiological basis of schizophrenia, but it does provide a rational guide for further study of this severity dimension.

A brief discussion of a study (3) carried out by the writer a few years ago will illustrate this last point. The problem was focused on the *measurement* of severity of thinking disorder in schizophrenia and on demonstrating the possible yield in regarding the process-reactive distinction as reflecting levels of personality organization.

In the past, many studies have shown significant differences between schizophrenics and normals, or between process and reactive groups in their response to the Rorschach, proverbs tests, and other mental tests. However, the quantification of degree of thinking disorder still remained a poorly defined process of clinical intuition and crude sign analysis. Looking at the severity problem in schizophrenia in terms of genetic levels immediately suggested both theoretical and empirical rationales for quantifying severity of thinking disorder. The theoretical rationale followed directly from Werner's thinking in that greater disorder should be reflected in more diffuseness of response, more rigidity, and so forth. An empirical rationale for scoring could be devised by comparing the responses of children at different levels of development. In the study under discussion, scoring systems were devised for the Rorschach and proverbs test based on such reasoning. The Rorschach scoring, which leads to a mean-genetic-level score (GL), was based on both empirical studies with children by Werner's students (6, 7, 15) and on Werner's theory; whereas the proverbs scoring was based solely on theory. A summary of the Rorschach scoring system is presented in Table 5.1. The reader is referred to Becker (2, 3) for more detailed rationale and for a description of the proverbs scoring system.

The basic question raised by the study was whether one could predict level of thinking disorder, scored in terms of a developmental rationale, from case history ratings on a process-reaction dimension. Wittman's Elgin Prognosis Scale was used to define the process-reactive dimension, or, in other terms, level of personality organization. The Elgin Scale consists of 20 subscales, weighted according to prognostic significance (the basic criterion). Included in the subscales are evaluations of prepsychotic personality, nature of onset, typicality of psychosis, heterosexual interests, etc., in other words,

TABLE 5.1

DEFINITIONS AND EXAMPLES FOR THE RORSCHACH GENETIC-LEVEL SCORING SYSTEM

Level	Classification	Definition	Examples
1	Amorphous Whole (*Wa*)	Shape plays no determinable role.	I. "Black paint" II. "Fire and smoke"
	Minus Whole (*W−*)	Content requires specific form not provided by blot.*	I. "A fly" IV. "Starfish"
	Confabulatory Response (*DW*)	A single detail is basis for interpretation of the whole.	VI. "Cat," because of "whiskers"
	Contaminated Response (*Con R*)	Fusing of two interpretations of the same blot area.	VI. "Turtle-skin rug"
	Fabulized Combination (*Fab C*)	Absurd combination on basis of spatial contiguity.	X. "Rabbit with worms coming out of eyes"
	Perseveration (*Per*)	Same content to 3 or more cards with little regard to form requirements.	I, IV, V. "Spider" VIII, IX, X. "Internal organs"
2	Amorphous Detail (*Da*)	Analogous to *Wa*.	II. (*D* 2) "Fire" VIII. (*D*) 6) "Flesh"
	Confabulatory Detail (*DdD*)	Analogous to *DW*.	VI. (*D* 3) "Cat's head," solely on "whiskers"
	Minus Detail (*D−*)	Analogous to *W−*.*	II. (*D* 2) "Kittens"
	Vague Detail (*Dv*)	Form element is so unspecific that almost any blot area could encompass content.	X. (*D* 9) "Island"
	Minus Unusual Detail (*Dd−*)	Analogous to *W−*.*	VI. (*Dd* 25) "Pig's foot"
3	Vague Whole (*Wv*)	Analogous to *Dv*.	I. "Piece of a puzzle" X. "Design," "Map"
	Oligophrenic Detail (*Adx-Hdx*)	Response to part of an *A* or *H* percept usually seen as a completed figure.	III. (*D* 6) "Head of a person" V. (*D* 4) "Wing"
	Plus Unusual Detail (*Dd+*)	Content is a reasonable match to blot area isolated.*	X. (*D* 26) "Funny face"
4	Mediocre Detail (*Dm*)	Form implied in outline and articulation matches blot area. At level of "populars."	III. (*D* 3) "Bow tie" X. (*D* 15) "Little Bird"
	Mediocre Whole (*Wm*)	Analogous to *Dm*, but applies only to unbroken blots.†	I. "Bat," "fox's head" VI. "Mud turtle"
5	Plus Detail (*D+*)	Two or more *D* areas are combined into one "good form" percept.*	II. (*D* 1's) "Bears fighting"
	Plus Whole (*W+*)	All *D* portions of a broken plot are combined into one "good form" percept.*†	II. "Two fellows at a bar toasting each other"
6	Plus-Plus Whole (*W++*)	An unbroken blot is perceptually articulated and reintegrated into a "good form" percept.†	IV. "A giant sitting on a stump"
	Plus-Plus Detail (*D++*)	A *D* area is articulated and reintegrated into a "good form" percept.	X. (*D* 8, left) "Guy riding a horse"

*Beck's tables are used as a guide in scoring.
†Unbroken blots are I, IV, V, VI, and IX; broken blots are II, III, VII, VIII, and X.

variables relevant to the process-reactive distinction. A brief identification of each scale can be found in Table 5.3.

The subjects for this study were 51 hospitalized schizophrenics. All but seven were first admission patients. The subjects were tested within the first week of hospitalization as a part of normal intake procedures. The details of the rating procedures and analysis can be found elsewhere (3). However, the reader should be assured that numerous safeguards were taken to avoid contamination of the test data with the case history ratings.

The major findings of this study were as follows. The Rorschach *GL* score correlated with the Elgin Scale $-.599$ (p $< .01$) for 24 males, and $-.679$ (p $< .001$) for 27 females. The average correlation for the total sample was $-.641$ (p $< .001$). A more process-like picture on the Elgin Scale was significantly related to a lower *GL* score on the Rorschach. The correlation of the proverbs test, corrected for vocabulary IQ, with the Elgin Scale was $-.682$ (p $< .001$) for males, and .048 for females. The failure of the proverbs test with females has not been explained.

Table 5.2 presents a breakdown of the Rorschach responses for good and poor prognostic scale groups. This allows one to examine the adequacy of the scaling assumption made earlier. There are only three exceptions out of a possible 19 to the assumptions made in placing scales from low to high genetic levels. *Dv* appears to belong at level 4 rather than level 2,

DW failed to show discrimination at level 1 (*cf.* the paper by Fine and Zimet), and *D + +* failed at level 6 (this response occurred only twice). These failures may be due to sampling and measurement errors or to actual misplacement. The findings presented in Table 5.2 give considerable support to the theoretical net discussed earlier and are consistent with thinking in terms of a dimension of severity.

In preparation for this symposium, some of the data from the above study were factor analyzed to see what light this might shed. The matrix which was factored included a number of background variables, the 20 Elgin Scale subscores, and a Rorschach *GL* score based on only the *first response to each card*. The Rorschach measures were entered into the score matrix as two half-scores, based on five cards each, and a total score. An answer was being sought to the question of whether a shorter form of the Rorschach could be used with adequate reliability. The corrected split-half reliability using only one response per card was .68. While this reliability is not exceptional, it is adequate for some research purposes.[1]

Seven centroid factors were extracted from the correlation matrix and rotated by an electronic computer to orthogonal simple structure.[2] The results of this analysis are presented in Table 5.3 together with the results of a previous factor analysis of the Elgin Scales made by Lorr, Wittman, and Schanberger (14). Factors 4, 6, and 7 represent intelligence, cooperativeness, and marital status of parents, respectively. Factor 5 is difficult to identify. The highest loadings on factor 5 are on history of mental illness in family,[3] excellent health history, lack of precipi-

TABLE 5.2

ITEM ANALYSIS OF THE RORSCHACH SCORING SYSTEM*

Level	Rorschach Category	Percentage of Responses		Within Category Percentage	
		Poor Prognosis Group	Good Prognosis Group	Poor Prognosis Group	Good Prognosis Group
1.	Per	1.29	0.00	100	00
	Wa	4.09	0.93	81	19
	W–	7.53	4.27	64	36
	DW	2.15	2.04	51	49†
	Con R	0.65	0.37	64	36
	Fab C	4.95	3.16	61	39
2.	Da	2.80	1.30	68	32
	DdD	1.29	1.12	54	46
	D–	11.40	10.97	51	49
	Dv	3.87	5.20	43	57†
	Dd–	4.30	2.79	61	39
3.	Wv	9.68	7.43	57	43
	Dd+	6.45	4.83	57	43
4.	Dm	23.66	31.41	43	57
	Wm	9.89	11.15	47	53
5.	D+	4.52	9.67	32	68
	W+	0.86	2.23	28	72
6.	W++	0.43	0.93	32	68
	D++	0.21	0.19	52	48†
		100.02	99.99		

*Based on an N of 49
†Deviations from predicted direction

[1] The correlation of this shorter form of the Rorschach with the Elgin Scale was $-.58$, which compares favorably with the $-.64$ found using all Rorschach responses, but does suggest some loss in reliability and therefore validity.

[2] The Quartimax method of Neuhaus and Wrigley was used. The correlation matrix and the arbitrary centroid factor matrix have been deposited as Document number 6045 with the ADI Auxiliary Publications Project, Photoduplication Service, Library of Congress, Washington 25, D.C. A copy may be secured by citing the Document number and by remitting $1.25 for photoprints, or $1.25 for 35 mm. microfilm. Advance payment is required. Make checks or money orders payable to: Chief, Photoduplication Service, Library of Congress.

[3] History of mental illness was scaled as follows: 0—no parent, aunt, uncle, or grandparent hospital-

TABLE 5.3

ROTATED FACTOR LOADINGS

Variables	B1*	L1†	B2	L2	B3	L3	B4	B5	B6	B7
1. Sex: male	48		—15		—34		—16	12	—20	—12
2. Age	—09		—13		05		—58	—07	—16	14
3. Marital status: married	—67		—20		—22		19	09	09	32
4. Cooperativeness	—39		—09		—21		09	27	—41	—28
5. Mental illness in family: present	—20		03		41		—17	47	19	—36
6. Marital status parents: divorced	07		—06		05		18	08	23	—80
7. Vocabulary IQ	—04		—26		11		—72	14	17	10
8. Rorschach R	—32		14		—19		11	30	—51	—15
9. Age of separation from parents	18		04		—01		—12	—09	—14	78
10. Rorschach GL I‡	—42		—55		13		—20	—29	17	—26
11. Rorschach GL II§	—33		—71		25		—06	03	—03	04
12. Rorschach GL Total	—46		—64		25		—07	—12	01	—19
13. Education	—24		06		19		—68	01	09	07
14. Defect of interest‖	92	93	04	19	00	—08	07	—09	07	04
15. Insidious onset	79	87	—08	35	—25	21	—12	12	—13	—04
16. Shut-in personality	84	86	06	17	30	—04	08	05	—10	—01
17. Schizothymic personality	85	85	—08	32	07	—02	05	08	07	10
18. Narrow range interests	85	81	02	36	—07	26	22	—01	20	05
19. Constitutional bias	67	73	04	—05	—12	04	30	—03	—17	—10
20. Low energy tone	84	70	—09	23	—06	—04	15	—17	03	17
21. Asthenic build	—09	68	14	38	08	01	—26	—26	—20	—42
22. Lack of heterosexual contact	79	65	13	03	18	24	—24	—04	—15	—08
23. Marked academic interests	49		—04		64		—07	00	29	—10
24. Careless indifference	12	12	25	23	—71	84	19	—06	16	14
25. Exclusiveness, stubbornness	11	—01	26	08	—71	84	07	02	16	07
26. Good health history	30		27		04		—24	56	13	—09
27. Lack of precipitating conditions	62		03		13		01	43	—08	25
28. Long duration psychosis	61	41	23	56	—46	27	02	16	—13	—03
29. Inadequate affect	64	47	30	43	—15	40	—31	16	22	18
30. Hebephrenic symptoms	54	41	48	59	—13	19	—06	—28	24	11
31. Ideas of influence	11	01	16	29	11	17	—21	—24	—29	—48
32. Physical interpretation delusions	45	00	48	65	00	01	26	01	—21	—04
33. Lack of typical symptoms	59	57	07	60	—37	03	—28	20	27	04
34. Clouded sensorium	25		00		—17		—04	60	17	—09
35. High life stress	27		19		—13		03	01	—23	72

*Quartimax orthogonal solution, Becker (B).
†Oblique solution, Lorr (L).
‡Based on the first response to cards I, III, IV, VII, and IX.
§Based on the first response to cards II, V, VI, VIII, and X.
‖Variables 14 to 33 are from the Elgin Prognosis Scale.

tating factors, and clouded sensorium.[4] The Rorschach GL score and the Elgin Scales did not load to any degree on factors 4 to 7.

The remaining three factors, as can be seen from Table 5.3, parallel very closely the three

ized for MI; 1—one aunt, uncle, or grandparent hospitalized for MI; 2—more than one aunt, uncle or grandparent hospitalized for MI; 3—one parent hospitalized for MI; 4—both parents hospitalized for MI.
[4]Sensorium was rated as follows: 0—clear, well oriented to time, place, person; 1—some clouding, moderate disorientation to time; 2—moderate clouding, vagueness about time and place; 3—severe clouding, shows marked disorientation to time, place, or person, or all of these.

factors Lorr et al. found with 17 of the 20 Elgin Scales, using an oblique solution. Factor 1 was called *schizophrenic withdrawal* by Lorr and loads on such things as defect of interest, insidious onset, shut-in personality, long duration of psychosis, and lack of precipitating conditions. This factor by itself might aptly be called the process-reactive dimension. At one end it defines the typical process syndrome and at the other the typical reactive syndrome. At the same time it is the major factor in a set of scales devised on the basis of a prognosis criterion. The Rorschach GL score loaded —.46 on this factor.

Factor 2 was called *reality distortion* by Lorr, loading on hebephrenic symptoms, bizarre delusions, and inadequate affect in the present analysis, and also on ideas of influence in the Lorr analysis. The Rorschach *GL* score loads −.64 on this factor. Factor 3 loaded mainly on careless indifference and exclusiveness-stubbornness in both analyses. The opposite pole of this factor is characterized by such traits as insecurity, inferiority, self-consciousness, and anxiety. This seems to be a factor of *emotional rigidity* versus *manifest anxiety*. The Rorschach *GL* score loaded .25 on this factor.

Before one can make any further inferences about the implications of these results, it is necessary to look more closely at the factor plots to find out if the orthogonal solution did justice to the data in terms of a simple structure criterion. When factors 1 and 2 are plotted against each other, it becomes immediately apparent that an oblique rotation is required which would introduce a correlation of from .60 to .70 between the schizophrenic withdrawal and reality distortion factors. Similar obliqueness is found between factors 2 and 3, suggesting the presence of a second-order factor. The writer did in fact carry out an oblique solution and second-order factorization using the Oblimax program on an electronic computer and did indeed find a major second-order factor loading schizophrenic withdrawal and reality distortion variables. However, there are several reasons for not giving too much attention to the actual results of this solution. First, the sampling of behaviors in the Elgin scale overweights the withdrawal factor since such variables as defect of interest, shut-in personality, schizothymic personality, narrow range of interests, lack of heterosexual contact and low energy tone are essentially repeat evaluations of the same behaviors. This behavior sampling bias (and the possible resulting correlated errors) gives factor 1 undue weight and biases the direction of a general factor (or second-order) toward the withdrawal component. Secondly, it is not possible accurately to locate second-order factors with only seven reference points (*i.e.* seven first-order factors). Finally, the sample size and the related sampling errors in the present study greatly limit inferences about any second-order factor derived

from the data. The present findings do *suggest,* however, a good probability that a general severity factor, loading primarily schizophrenic withdrawal and reality distortion variables, does exist. It is interesting to note in this respect that most definitions of schizophrenia describe as the essence of schizophrenia "withdrawal from and distortion of reality."

Theoretically the demonstration of a second-order severity factor, meeting simple structure criteria, would be of some interest and would support some of the assumptions made in this paper. From a practical point of view or from the point of view of research strategy, however, it makes little difference, for one can try both a general severity factor approach and a multiple factor approach. At this time sufficient evidence is available to justify a diagnostic procedure in which factor estimates are obtained for: (a) schizophrenic withdrawal, based on Elgin scale ratings for defect of interest, shut-in personality, insidious onset, lack of heterosexual contact, lack of precipitating conditions, and long duration of psychosis; (b) reality distortion, based on the Rorschach *GL* score; and (c) emotional rigidity, based on Elgin scale ratings for careless indifference, and exclusiveness-stubbornness traits. For various research purposes, these factor score estimates could be used separately or summed (with a double weighting for factors 1 and 2) to obtain a severity index.

Having good measures of severity of psychosis would of course be very useful in making diagnoses with truly prognostic significance. However, the research implications are even more important. With valid and reliable severity indices it becomes possible to test the relevance of suspected causal factors by relating them to these criteria. For example, if an enzyme deficiency or overproduction is suspected as playing a role in the schizophrenic process, one should expect variation in the amount of such a deficiency or overproduction to be related to variation in one or more of the severity measures. One would certainly wish to examine more closely a physiological variable which showed such covariance than a variable which did not, *but which might incidentally differentiate schizophrenics from normals.* In a similar way environmental variables could be evaluated.

Needless to say, this more stringent covariance criterion would lead to fewer false hopes than the currently used criterion of testing the ability of a suspected agent to differentiate schizophrenics from normals.

A reminder to the readers that schizophrenia has a temporal dimension is in order. With severity measures available, it becomes possible to study changes in severity of disorder over time, as well as changes under various therapies. Or again, it is possible to study the intraindividual covariance of biochemical measures with behavioral severity measures in seeking leads to causal relationships. When one moves from a general measure of severity at one time to a measure of change, however, it becomes more and more important that one have reliable criterion measures. At this point the Rorschach *GL* measure is probably not sensitive or reliable enough (particularly at the higher levels) for use in studies of change, although it certainly is adequate for basal state type studies. It is to be hoped that the current efforts by both Eysenck and Cattell to find objective test measures of psychoticism will provide the field with better measures in the near future.

SUMMARY

It has been proposed that looking at the process and reactive syndromes in schizophrenia as endpoints of a continuum of severity of illness, and at the same time as reflecting levels of personality organization, opens up a number of research strategies which offer promise of increasing our knowledge about schizophrenia. Several findings which support the value of the above mentioned proposals have been discussed. The implications of these findings for better measurement of severity of illness in schizophrenia have been pointed out. Finally, it has been suggested that systematic use of severity measures in research on the etiology of schizophrenia may provide the key to lock this mysterious door.

REFERENCES

1. BALDWIN, A. L. *Behavior and development in childhood.* New York: Dryden, 1955.
2. BECKER, W. C. The relation of severity of thinking disorder to the process-reactive concept of schizophrenia. Unpublished doctoral dissertation. Stanford University, 1955.
3. BECKER, W. C. A genetic approach to the interpretation and evaluation of the process-reactive distinction in schizophrenia. *Journal of Abnormal and Social Psychology,* 47, 1956, 489–496.
4. BECKER, W. C. & McFARLAND, R. L. A lobotomy prognosis scale. *Journal of Consulting Psychology,* 1955, *19,* 157–162.
5. BENJAMIN, J. D. A method for distinguishing and evaluating formal thinking disorders in schizophrenia. In Kasanin, J. S., (ed.), *Language and Thought in Schizophrenia.* Berkeley, University of California Press, 1946, pp. 66–71.
6. FRIEDMAN, H. Perceptual regression in schizophrenia. An hypothesis suggested by use of the Rorschach test. *Journal of Projective Techniques & Personality Assessment,* 1953, 17, 171–185.
7. HEMMENDINGER, L. Perceptual organization and development as reflected in the structure of Rorschach test responses. *Journal of Projective Techniques & Personality Assessment,* 1953, 17, 162–170.
8. HUNT, R. C. & APPEL, K. E. Prognosis in psychoses lying midway between schizophrenia and manic-depressive psychoses. *American Journal of Psychiatry,* 1936, 93, 313–339.
9. KANT, O. Differential diagnosis of schizophrenia in the light of concepts of personality stratification. *American Journal of Psychiatry,* 1940, 97, 342–357.
10. KANTOR, R. E., WALLNER, J. M., & WINDER, C. L. Process and reactive schizophrenia. *Journal of Consulting Psychology,* 1953, 17, 157–162.
11. KING, G. F. Differential autonomic responsiveness in the process-reactive classifications of schizophrenia. *Journal of Abnormal and Social Psychology,* 1958, 56, 160–164.
12. LANGFELDT, G. Prognosis in schizophrenia and factors influencing course of disease: Catamnestic study, including individual reexaminations in 1936 with some considerations regarding diagnosis, pathogenesis and therapy. *Acta Psychiatrica et Neurologica,* 1937, Supplement 13, 1–228.
13. LEWIN K. *A dynamic theory of personality.* New York: McGraw-Hill, 1935.
14. LORR, M., WITTMAN, P., & SCHANBERGER, W. An analysis of the Elgin prognostic scale. *Journal of Clinical Psychology,* 1951, 7, 260–263.
15. SIEGEL, E. L. Genetic parallels of perceptual structuralization in paranoid schizophrenia: an analysis by means of the Rorschach technique. *Journal of Projective Techniques & Personality Assessment,* 1953, 17, 151–161.
16. STOTSKY, B. A. A comparison of remitting and nonremitting schizophrenics on psychological tests. *Journal of Abnormal and Social Psychology,* 1952, 47, 489–496.

17. WITTMAN, P. Scale for measuring prognosis in schizophrenic patients. *Elgin State Hospital Papers,* 1941, *4,* 20–33.
18. WITTMAN, P. Follow-up on Elgin prognosis scale results. *Illinois Psychiatric Journal,* 1944, *4,* 56–59.
19. WITTMAN, P. & STEINBERG, D. L. Follow-up of objective evaluation. *Elgin State Hospital Papers,* 1944, 5, 216–227.
20. WERNER, H. *The comparative psychology of mental development.* (Rev. ed.) Chicago: Follet, 1948.

35.

R. W. PAYNE, W. K. CAIRD, AND S. G. LAVERTY

OVERINCLUSIVE THINKING IN SCHIZOPHRENIA

15 schizophrenics with paranoid delusions, 15 schizophrenics with no delusions, and a control group of 15 nonschizophrenic hospitalized patients were given the Benjamin Proverbs test, the Mill Hill Vocabulary Scale, and 3 of Babcock's psychomotor speed tests. As predicted, there was a significant relationship between the presence or absence of delusions, and overinclusive thinking, as assessed by the average number of words needed to explain the proverbs and 2 time scores. Overinclusive patients tend to have paranoid delusions. Also as expected, there was no significant relationship between retardation, as assessed by the Babcock tests, and the presence of delusions. This finding complements an earlier finding of Harris and Metcalfe (1956) that slowness in schizophrenic patients is specifically associated with inappropriate affect and a poor prognosis, and Payne's (1962) finding that a group of chronic schizophrenics was not overinclusive.

The cause of delusional thinking has always been of interest to psychiatrists, who have elaborated a number of explanations. This work has been well reviewed by Cameron (1959). All these theories have in common the assumption that delusions are not basically due to a cognitive defect, but rather are symptomatic of an emotional disturbance. Most psychiatric explanations follow Freud's initial hypothesis that, at basis, a delusion is the result of the mechanism of "denial," and is associated with a strong but repressed emotional drive. Thus, for example, a

From R. W. Payne, W. K. Caird, and S. G. Laverty, "Overinclusive thinking and delusions in schizophrenia patients," *Journal of Abnormal and Social Psychology,* 68, 1964, 562–566. © 1964 by the American Psychological Association, and reproduced by permission.

paranoid delusion (by far the most frequently occurring type of delusion) occurs in a patient who has a strong, but mainly unconscious and unwanted homosexual love for a member of his own sex. This love is denied, successfully, by feeling the opposite emotion, *hate,* towards the individual concerned. However, this emotion is also unwanted, and is thus "projected" onto the other person. In this way, the patient is able to hate back, and successfully denies his homosexuality. This explanation leads to the prediction that deluded patients should show other signs of repressed homosexuality. However, it is not entirely successful in explaining how it is that paranoid delusions become so general, and usually involve a large and more or less organized group of people, all of whom hate and persecute the patient.

It is curious that, although paranoid delusions are frequently found in association with thought disorder in schizophrenic patients, no causal link is usually postulated. Thus, although Norman Cameron was one of the first to describe "overinclusive thinking," one of the cardinal features of thought disorder in schizophrenics, he did not directly relate this to delusion formation, and appears to accept (Cameron, 1959) that delusions are essentially affectively determined.

Norman Cameron (1938a, 1938b, 1939a, 1939b) defined overinclusive thinking as the inability to preserve conceptual boundaries, so that irrelevant or distantly associated elements become incorporated into concepts, making thought less accurate, more vague, and more abstract. More recently, Payne, Mattussek, and George (1959) have suggested that overinclusive thinking might be one aspect of a more general disability, consisting essentially of an attention defect. They have suggested that over-inclusive patients suffer from some defect of a hypothetical central "screening" mechanism whereby irrelevant stimuli, both internal (for example, irrelevant thoughts) and external (for example, irrelevant perceptions) are excluded, in order to allow the most efficient processing of incoming information.

Since Cameron's early work, a number of ex-periments have been performed, and a number of measures of overinclusive thinking have been developed. This work has been summarized re-cently by Payne (1961). It suggests that: (a) Overinclusive thinking is confined to patients diagnosed as schizophrenic. It has not been found in normals, depressed patients, or in neurotics. (b) Different measures of overinclu-sive thinking correlate significantly, yielding a common factor when the correlations are ana-lyzed. (c) Overinclusive thinking is relatively independent of the general retardation which characterizes many psychotic patients. (d) Only about half those patients who are diagnosed as schizophrenics suffer from overinclusive think-ing. The remainder, unlike those who are over-inclusive, tend to be abnormally retarded in a wide range of psychological tests of speed of mental and motor functioning.

In addition to these findings, it has since been reported (Payne, 1962) that chronic schizo-phrenics as contrasted to acute schizophrenics are not especially overinclusive.

Payne (1961) has speculated that overinclu-sive thinking should be specifically related to the presence of delusions in schizophrenic pa-tients. It is reasonable to suppose that delusions have a number of causes, not necessarily mu-tually exclusive. A small minority of patients seem to have hallucinations which are so de-tailed and compelling, that the only reasonable way for them to account for their perceptions is by developing an explanation which normal people, not sharing these perceptions, must

inevitably regard as a delusion. No doubt emo-tional factors also play a role in the formation of delusions in many patients. In addition, how-ever, overinclusive thinking could easily help to lead to the induction of unwarranted generaliza-tions. The overinclusive patient, in addition to perceiving the essential features of any problem, or situation, is also apparently unable to screen out irrelevant perceptions, and these become incorporated into the data of the problem. This is likely to delay solution, but it may also lead to an overgeneral conclusion which is unwar-ranted. Thus, for example, a patient may gen-uinely (and normally) believe that a certain individual dislikes him. However, his overin-clusive "concept" (cerebral representation) of this individual may extend to other similar people (for example, all foreigners, all dark men) so that he may develop the same negative emotional reactions to this entire category of people, being incapable of the necessary dis-crimination which normally circumscribes fairly precisely the stimuli which will evoke the par-ticular response. This could partly explain how it is that delusions so frequently come to include a broad category of people as they develop.

This theory is consistent with one other clin-ical observation, to which attention is seldom drawn. Many paranoid patients appear to per-ceive an unusually wide range of stimuli. Thus, for example, a patient may note that one of the two men across the street in shabby raincoats has a folded copy of The Times in his pocket, and that he periodically touches this in an un-usual way. This the patient may interpret as a signal with some special significance. The delu-sion is of course abnormal, but what may also be abnormal is the amount of detailed perception on which the delusion is based. In normal people the range of perceptions around whatever en-gages the attention is very limited, such details go unnoticed, and could thus not form the basis of delusional ideas. The sort of perceptual over-inclusion which Payne (1961) believes forms the basis of overinclusive sorting behavior may thus help to develop delusional thinking.

So far no studies appear to have been carried out to test this hypothesis. The present investi-gation was designed to do so.

METHOD

TESTS USED

The measure of overinclusive thinking used in the present study is derived from Benjamin's (1944) Proverbs test. Subjects were asked to interpret this list of 14 proverbs, using the standardized instructions developed by Payne and Hewlett (1960). The main departure from the usual procedure is that the subjects are asked to give a positive indication that they have completed their explanation. (The next proverb is not read until this has been done, although subjects may be reminded to say when they have finished.) The answers were recorded on tape and later transcribed. This was shown to be necessary in earlier studies, where it was found nearly impossible to avoid paraphrasing and condensing answers when they were copied down by hand.

The overinclusion score used is merely the average number of words required to explain each proverb. (Proverbs which the subject says he does not know are excluded.) The rationale is that an overinclusive individual should be unable to exclude from his answer associations to the proverb which are irrelevant to its explanation. These associations may include concrete examples. In addition, the proverb itself should illustrate a more complex and extensive concept for such subjects, and thus require a more extensive explanation. Both factors should increase the number of words needed. Payne and Hewlett found that this score was among the best of a number of measures of overinclusive thinking used in a recent study, as judged by its efficiency in discriminating schizophrenic patients from all others. It also had a relatively high factor saturation on their overinclusion factor (.58), suggesting that it was reasonably representative of a group of overinclusion measures. It has the additional advantage of being independent of intelligence. Payne and Hewlett found a saturation of 0.00 on their factor of general intelligence, and report similarly insignificant correlations with specific intelligence tests.

Two other scores were derived from this test: the average reaction time, and the total time.

The average reaction time is the number of seconds elapsing between the time the examiner finishes reading the proverb, and the time the subject begins his answer. Overinclusive subjects should have slower reaction times, since they have more complicated answers to consider before they begin to speak. The total time is the number of seconds required to complete the answer from the time the examiner finishes reading the proverb. Again overinclusive subjects should be slower. Unfortunately, neither time score is a pure measure of overinclusive thinking, as subjects who are merely retarded will also be slow. Note that these times were taken later from the recorded tapes, and were not measured during the interview.

In addition to the test of overinclusion, three simple psychomotor speed tests were included. All are from the Babcock-Levy (1940) test battery, and are the speed of writing the "United States of America," the speed of writing one's own full name, and the speed of writing the sentence "I hope to leave here very soon."

Payne and Hewlett (1960) found that a combined score derived from these three tests had a loading of .48 on their factor of general retardation, suggesting that they are reasonably representative of a large group of speed tests. In the present study, the normal procedure was modified in order to allow for individual differences in spelling ability found to be very large in this partly rural sample. Subjects were required merely to copy the sentence and the "United States of America" from a printed card.

In addition, the subjects were given the Mill Hill Vocabulary Scale (Raven, 1958), to provide a measure of their pre-illness general intellectual level.

PATIENTS TESTED

In order to determine whether there is, within a schizophrenic group, a tendency for delusions to be associated with overinclusive thinking, a group of 15 schizophrenic patients without delusions was selected and compared with another group of 15 schizophrenic patients without delusions. In addition, a third group of 15 nonschizophrenic patients was tested as a control. All the subjects were recent admissions to the Ontario

Hospital, Kingston, and an attempt was made to test each one before treatment was started. This was not always possible, but in all cases (with the exception of 3 disturbed schizophrenics) the patients were tested not later than 48 hours after treatment had started. In addition to the psychological tests, the subjects were given, at the same time, a prolonged interview to appraise their symptoms at the time of testing. The interviewer (SGL) had no knowledge of the test results, nor had the staff psychiatrists who made the initial diagnoses.

The 15 nondeluded schizophrenics consisted of 10 males and 5 females. All were regarded as typical schizophrenics, excepting that none was judged to have either ideas of reference or delusions of any sort at the time of testing.

The 15 deluded schizophrenics included 6 males and 9 females. All were judged to have paranoid delusions at the time of testing. Some had other delusions in addition (for example, somatic), and most had ideas of reference.

The 15 nonschizophrenic patients were intended to be a random sample of the nonschizophrenic intake of the Ontario Hospital. It consisted of 8 males and 7 females. Seven were diagnosed as depressive, 4 were regarded as personality disorders, 3 were alcoholics, and 1 was diagnosed as an obsessional neurotic with marked depressive features. None of the patients in this group had received any treatment prior to testing. None of these patients was deluded.

It had initially been hoped to match the groups for sex. This did not prove feasible. Indeed it required 5 months to secure the samples obtained, due to the relatively slow rate of admission of suitable schizophrenic patients. The age and vocabulary of the groups are shown in Table 5.4. It can be seen that the groups are reasonably well matched in both respects.

RESULTS

OVERINCLUSIVE MEASURES

The results from the Proverbs test are shown in Table 5.5. As can be seen, all three scores yielded significant differences, and all are in the expected direction, the largest differences being produced by the purest overinclusion measure. On each score, the nondeluded schizophrenic

TABLE 5.4

AGE AND INTELLECTUAL STATUS OF THE THREE GROUPS

	Deluded Schizophrenics	Nondeluded Schizophrenics	Controls
Age			
M	30.87	33.13	36.60
SD	13.10	9.72	6.22
Range ..	16–56	21–56	25–47
F		1.23	
Mill Hill Vocabulary IQ equivalents[*]			
M	93.87	89.53	90.80
SD	5.72	4.61	5.39
Range ..	86–105	81–97	84–102
F		2.67	

Note.—For each group N = 15.
[*]Computed from Raven's (1958) percentile tables, and based on an M of 100 and an SD of 15 for Raven's normal standardization group.

TABLE 5.5

OVERINCLUSION SCORES DERIVED FROM THE PROVERBS TEST

	Deluded Schizophrenics	Nondeluded Schizophrenics	Controls
Average number of words per proverb			
M	33.42	23.44	14.48
SD	15.42	22.82	9.49
Range ..	10.4–67.2	6.1–101.3	2.5–43.6
F		4.76[*]	
Average reaction time (seconds)			
M	12.43	11.02	7.70
SD	4.89	6.34	3.83
Range ..	4.9–22.1	3.6–24.3	3.5–16.8
F		3.37[*]	
Average total time (seconds)			
M	30.89	24.91	14.43
SD	11.04	18.34	6.59
Range ..	10.3–51.0	7.2–81.9	6.7–27.7
F		3.28[*]	

Note.—For each group N = 15.
[*]$p < .05$.

group has an intermediary position, being more overinclusive than the controls, but not as overinclusive as the deluded schizophrenic group. This is not surprising, as it is very difficult in an interview to be certain that a schizophrenic patient is *not* deluded, since many are defensive about their beliefs. Some of the nondeluded schizophrenics may in fact have been deluded at the time of testing. It is worth commenting that the most verbose of the nonschizophrenic subjects was the single obsessional neurotic.

As a further test of the predicted relationship, all the patients, regardless of diagnosis, were divided into two groups on the basis of the average number of words per proverb. Those who used over 25 words were labeled "overinclusive," the remainder "nonoverinclusive." This score was chosen because previous results suggest (Payne & Hewlett, 1960) that this is for all practical purposes the limit of the normal range. Table 5.6 shows the relationship between this dichotomy, and the presence or absence of delusions. As can be seen, the relationship is very marked, achieving significance at beyond the .01 level. This table yields a contingency coefficient of .380, where the maximum upper limit is .707.

TABLE 5.6
RELATIONSHIP BETWEEN OVERINCLUSION
AND DELUSIONS
(Number of Cases)

	Overinclusive	Nonoverinclusive	Total
Deluded	10	5	15
Nondeluded ..	6	24	30
Total	16	29	45

Note.—After Yates' correction, $x^2 = 7.56$, $p < .01$.

RETARDATION MEASURES

The results from the three psychomotor speed tests are presented in Table 5.7. Previous research (Payne & Hewlett, 1960) suggested that overinclusion and retardation are virtually independent in a mixed normal, neurotic, and psychotic population. In the present study a combined retardation score was computed from the three Babcock tests following Payne and Hewlett's (1960) procedure. The correlation between this speed score and overinclusion, as assessed by the average number of words per proverb, is .138 (slowness and overinclusion being slightly associated), a value not significantly greater than zero. These results are nearly

TABLE 5.7
BABCOCK SPEED TEST SCORES (IN SECONDS)
FOR THE THREE GROUPS

	Deluded Schizophrenics	Nondeluded Schizophrenics	Controls
Speed of writing "United States of America"			
M	17.20	18.60	15.20
SD	4.15	9.46	5.13
Range ..	10–40	11–47	8–26
F		.77	
Speed of writing own name			
M	11.60	11.60	9.27
SD	3.41	4.99	3.30
Range ..	7–33	7–28	6–17
F		1.07	
Speed of writing sentence			
M	18.13	20.40	16.27
SD	4.25	8.70	5.85
Range ..	12–41	9–45	8–32
F		1.18	

Note.—For each group $N = 15$.

identical with those found by Payne and Hewlett. Therefore, the lack of any significant relationship between slowness and the presence or absence of paranoid delusions in the present study is not surprising. The fact that the nonschizophrenic patients are slightly but not significantly faster is again exactly as expected. Most patients in this group were depressed, and depressives on average have been found to be just as slow as schizophrenics in previous work (Payne, 1961). It is interesting to note that, just as the present study suggests a specific relationship between overinclusive thinking and delusions in a schizophrenic population, an earlier study by Harris and Metcalfe (1956) suggests a specific relationship between slowness and inappropriate affect in a schizophrenic population. The same study reported a significant correlation between slowness and a bad prognosis. Payne (1962) found a group of chronic schizophrenics were not overinclusive. It is interesting to speculate that overinclusive thinking in contrast to slowness might prove to be a relatively good prognostic index in acute schizophrenic patients.

REFERENCES

BABCOCK, H., & LEVY, L. *Manual of directions for the revised examination of the measurement of efficiency of mental functioning.* Chicago: Stoelting, 1940.

BENJAMIN, J. D. A method for distinguishing and evaluating formal thinking disorders in schizophrenia. In J. S. Kasanin (Ed.), *Language and thought in schizophrenia.* Berkeley: University of California Press, 1944, pp. 65–90.

CAMERON, N. Reasoning, regression and communication in schizophrenics. *Psychological Monograph,* 1938, *50* (1, Whole No. 221). (a)

CAMERON, N. A study of thinking in senile deterioration and schizophrenic disorganization. *American Journal of Psychology,* 1938, *51,* 650–664. (b)

CAMERON, N. Deterioration and regression in schizophrenic thinking. *Journal of Abnormal and Social Psychology,* 1939, *34,* 265–270. (a)

CAMERON, N. Schizophrenic thinking in a problem-solving situation. *Journal of Mental Science,* 1939, *85,* 1012–1035. (b)

CAMERON, N. Paranoid conditions and paranoia. In S. Arieti (Ed.), *American handbook of psychiatry.* Vol. 1. New York: Basic Books, 1959, pp. 508–539.

HARRIS, A., & METCALFE, M. Inappropriate affect. *Journal of Neurology, Neurosurgery and Psychiatry,* 1956, *19,* 308–313.

PAYNE, R. W. Cognitive abnormalities. In H. J. Eysenck, (Ed.), *Handbook of abnormal psychology.* New York: Basic Books, 1961, pp. 193–261.

PAYNE, R. W. An Object classification test as a measure of overinclusive thinking in schizophrenic patients. *British Journal of Social and Clinical Psychology,* 1962, *1,* 213–221.

PAYNE, R. W., & HEWLETT, J. H. G. Thought disorder in psychotic patients. In H. J. Eysenck (Ed.), *Experiments in personality.* Vol. 2. London: Routledge & Kegan Paul, 1960, pp. 3–104.

PAYNE, R. W., MATTUSSEK, P., & GEORGE, E. I. An experimental study of schizophrenic thought disorder. *Journal of Mental Science,* 1959, *105,* 627–652.

RAVEN, J. C. *Guide to using the Mill Hill vocabulary scale with the progressive matrices scale.* London: Lewis, 1958.

36.

ARNOLD H. BUSS AND PETER J. LANG

I. PSYCHOLOGICAL DEFICIT IN SCHIZOPHRENIA

This, the first of two papers reviewing laboratory studies of psychological deficit in schizophrenia, considers the effects of social censure, affective stimuli, cooperation, urging, and verbal and nonverbal reinforcers on performance on a variety of tasks. Thus, disturbance in concept formation is evaluated in terms of: loss of abstract attitude, communication disturbance, regression, and the consequence of erratic attention. Finally, various theories of schizophrenic deficit are evaluated. Although motivational constructs cannot be wholly dismissed, interference theory is generally more comprehensive and

parsimonious. Many specific hypotheses of interference theory still need to be substantiated by experiment, however.

The term *psychological deficit* was coined by Hunt and Cofer (1944) who wanted a neutral phrase to describe the decrement shown by psychiatric patients in comparison to normals on various laboratory and intellectual tasks. They reviewed the substantial body of research accumulated prior to World War II.

Since that time there has been a prolific output of research on deficit, too much to encompass within a single review. Therefore we shall consider only laboratory studies of psychological deficit in schizophrenia, omitting reports of tests and clinical observations.

Organizing the voluminous literature proved to be a difficult task. One possibility was to group studies on the basis of the major theoretical

From Arnold H. Buss and Peter J. Lang, "Psychological deficit in schizophrenia: I. Affect, reinforcement, and concept attainment," *Journal of Abnormal Psychology,* 1965, *70,* 2–24. (Excerpts from pp. 2–3, 13–14, 17–21); and from Peter J. Lang and Arnold H. Buss, "Psychological deficit in schizophrenia: II. Interference and activation," *Journal of Abnormal Psychology* 1965, *70,* 77–106. (Excerpts from pp. 77–78, 95–100). © 1965 by the American Psychological Association, and reproduced by permission.

approaches to deficit, since theories of deficit are essentially theories of schizophrenia; but this would have led to excessive repetition. Therefore the literature has been organized around seven areas defined in part by theory but more broadly in terms of issues and methods of investigation: (a) affect and reinforcement, (b) concept attainment, (c) attention, (d) set, (e) associative interference, (f) drive, and (g) somatic arousal.

The dominant orientation in the affect and reinforcement area might be called a social-motivational view, which has two main variants. One suggests that schizophrenics are oversensitive to punishing and/or affective stimuli, which cause them to withdraw and which produce performance deficit. The other assumes that schizophrenics are already so withdrawn from interpersonal situations that the usual incentives, rewards, and punishments employed in experimental situations do not motivate them, and their performance suffers.

In the concept attainment area, research relevant to four explanatory concepts is reviewed. The first approach holds that both schizophrenics and brain-damaged patients suffer from a loss of the "abstract attitude." A second view argues that deficit is attributable to a communication disturbance, and a third emphasizes regression: later, more mature modes of functioning are ostensibly given up for earlier, more concrete, and less efficient modes. Finally, more recent research suggests that differences in the concepts of normals and schizophrenics occur because the latter are distractible and respond to irrelevant cues.

Research on attention, set, and association further emphasizes the importance of interference effects in deficit. The schizophrenic is regarded as being excessively distracted by both incidental, external stimuli and intrusive associations, as failing to maintain a proper set or orientation, and as failing to alter the set when such a change is appropriate.

Two drive theories are evaluated. The better known theory assumes that the schizophrenic is extremely anxious, this anxiety being a high drive state that worsens performance, especially on complex tasks. The lesser known theory suggests that in schizophrenia there is a protective (cortical) inhibition that slows down learn-

ing and increases reminiscence. Interpretations of deficit in terms of the neurophysiological concept of arousal are also considered, and the relevant research on the somatic responses of schizophrenics is evaluated.

The exposition is divided into two papers. In this first paper we review the affect-reinforcement and concept-regression areas. A subsequent paper considers research on interference effects (attention, set, and associative interference) and activation (drive and arousal) as well as general problems of method in deficit research.

. . . . .

SUMMARY

The research on affect and reinforcement will be summarized under four headings: affective stimuli, information, punishment, and diagnosis.

Affective stimuli. Certain "affective" stimuli disturb schizophrenics enough to produce psychological deficit, but the stimuli are so varied that this term has no precise referent. Concerning affective stimuli, the social censure hypothesis appears to be incorrect. Schizophrenic deficit occurs not only with stimuli connoting censure but also with human, symbolic, and taboo stimuli. A promising hypothesis is that affective stimuli elicit more associations from schizophrenics and that these associations interfere with performance.

Information. It is clear that schizophrenic subjects improve when they are given information about their responses, and they can profit from cues that may be superfluous to normals. Lang (1959) and Losen (1961) have pointed out that schizophrenics, unlike normals, fail to make statements during tasks which suggest self-guidance (e.g., "I got that one wrong"; "I'll have to watch it next time."). It seems likely that external reinforcing cues serve a directive purpose in schizophrenics that normal subjects accomplish for themselves.

The task usually determines whether positive or negative information is more valuable in improving performance. Most tasks have been complex (initiate many alternate responses), and change (improvement), rather than the maintenance of an initially offered response, has been the desired result. If the task also has sufficient ceiling, both normals and schizophrenics profit more from information about errors than they do from knowledge of successes.

Punishment. In some tasks psychotics make more use of punishment than reward, relative to normal subjects, but there is little evidence to suggest this is due to schizophrenics' personal reaction to social censure. Punishment seems to assist the schizophrenic by breaking up perseverative tendencies, whereas reward maintains a previous correct response that is wrong on subsequent trials. This could happen in paired-associate learning, in which a correct response to one stimulus word is wrong for every other stimulus. The process is probably dependent on instructions the subject gives to himself, and it is here that schizophrenics appear to be deficient.

Physical punishment facilitates the performance of schizophrenics, and in fact it is the only contingency that has led to a complete elimination of deficit on some tasks (concept formation). However, it is conceivable that "noise" and shock serve a focusing or arousal function, rather than the traditional role of incentive or reinforcer.

Diagnosis. Response to motivating instructions, social stimuli, and information about performance all seem to vary with diagnosis. These variables are sensitive to personality differences in normal subjects, and perhaps at least an equal effect should be anticipated in schizophrenics. Because of the variety of populations and experimental situations employed, generalizations about the consequences of motivational factors are difficult. However, paranoid-nonparanoid, good premorbid versus poor premorbid, and the acute-chronic typologies have all proved to be experimentally distinct and cannot be ignored in research with schizophrenics.

. . . . .

SUMMARY

This section has considered four interpretations of schizophrenic deficit in concept attainment. The loss of abstractness theory appears to be incorrect: schizophrenics' concepts are not especially concrete although they tend to be eccentric and deviant. Schizophrenics' concepts are not necessarily childlike, and the evidence for such regression may be attributed to both the limited responses available on the tasks used and

to the scoring of idiosyncratic responses as concrete.

Concerning lack of communication, there is no doubt that schizophrenics have difficulty in making their concepts comprehensible to others. However, this appears to be due to the bizarre nature of the concepts rather than an inability to communicate them. Thus the disorder appears to involve thought processes rather than communication skills.

Interference theory appears to be the most promising approach. The overinclusion hypothesis has been sustained by a number of studies: schizophrenics' concepts are excessively broad, and they suffer from the intrusion of extraneous and irrelevant elements. Whether this is true of all schizophrenics or mainly of paranoids is an interesting question. One possibility is that paranoids are more inclusive and less deteriorated than nonparanoids (catatonics and hebephrenics).

DISCUSSION

This section will focus on five theories that attempt to explain schizophrenic deficit in the two research areas covered in this paper. Three theories emphasize interpersonal and social aspects: social censure, sensitivity to affective stimuli, and insufficient motivation. The other two, while not ignoring interpersonal aspects completely, emphasize more impersonal aspects of psychological functioning: regression and interference.

SOCIAL CENSURE

This theory exists in two basic forms, one general and the other a specific corollary. The general theory holds that schizophrenics are abnormally sensitive to, and disrupted by, social censure and stimuli connoting censure. In its support is the fact that in some experiments deficit has been found to increase when censure stimuli are introduced. However, other research has found no difference in the censure response of schizophrenics and normals, or effects for one type of schizophrenic and not for another. Furthermore, data interpreted in support of censure theory are often more parsimoniously explained in other terms (differential information or the saliency of cues). The strongest negative evidence is that on a great variety of tasks social censure *reduces* deficit in schizophrenia rather than increases it, i.e., facilitates performance relative to praise or no reinforcement.

The specific censure theory argues that schizophrenics with good and poor premorbid histories are differentially responsive to parental chastisement: the former are disturbed by paternal and the latter by maternal censure. While there are data consistent with this view, replication has infrequently supported original studies, and methodological problems abound. Both schizophrenic groups have shown disturbance with parental stimuli, regardless of whether the stimuli were positive or negative; both types of schizophrenics have, in specific experiments, been similar to normals in their response to censure.

Furthermore, while distinctions are made within the schizophrenic group, control subjects are treated as a homogeneous population. We cannot help but speculate that the subdivision of a hospital attendant or neurotic group —following similar criteria of general social or sexual adequacy—might yield similar differences in response to parental stimuli. In other words, we do not know that the findings are in any way unique to schizophrenia. In fact, while good and poor premorbid patients are treated as subtypes of schizophrenia, group assignment is actually determined by a scale defining a continuous dimension of social maturity (Phillips, 1953). The scales' author has already provided strong evidence:

that the relationship of achieved level of maturity (defined in terms of premorbid social competence) to certain dimensions of psychopathology is not unique to schizophrenia, but instead cuts across all forms of functional mental disorder, Zigler and Phillips, (1962), p. 216.

As a general theory of deficit the social censure approach is not sufficiently comprehensive and involves a major inconsistency: stimulus conditions other than censure have been found to yield deficit in schizophrenia, and censure may reduce rather than increase deficit. The specific theory involves a questionable typology. It also needs the support of less equivocal experiments. Dividing schizophrenics into good

and poor premorbid groups does not account for the variable effects of censure, a full explanation of which must include *task variables*.

This evaluation does not necessarily negate the clinical theory from which the social censure hypothesis originated. Parental censure may still be an important variable in the histories of schizophrenics and may shape some symptoms. However, social censure does not provide a general explanation for schizophrenic deficit in the laboratory.

SENSITIVITY TO AFFECTIVE STIMULI

This theory resembles social censure theory, but it is broader in that it assumes that schizophrenics are especially sensitive to, and disrupted by, *all* affective stimuli. This assumption has been verified in many experiments which have demonstrated poorer performance by schizophrenics with affective stimuli than with neutral stimuli. The difficulty with this evidence is that so many stimuli have been labeled *affective* that the term no longer has precise referents. The underlying assumption in this theory is that past events in schizophrenics' lives have rendered them abnormally sensitive to stimuli that connote traumatic situations or anxiety-laden interpersonal relationships. While some of the affective stimuli that lead to deficit pertain to special areas of maladjustment such as sexuality, censure, or competition, others have only a vague connection with personal adjustment or emotion, e.g., human-nonhuman, symbolic-nonsymbolic, and patient-attendant stimulus dimensions have all been shown to influence the performance of schizophrenics. Furthermore, as we have seen with censure stimuli, the effect of specific affective contents varies considerably from experiment to experiment, and perhaps from subject to subject.

The dilemma is as follows. If the term affective is loosely defined, the theory can account for all the data, but it lacks precision. If the term affective is restricted to a narrow, precise meaning, then the reliability of the phenomenon must be questioned; furthermore, non-affective stimuli have been found to produce deficit. Shakow (1962) has suggested that the associations of schizophrenics constitute a kind of apperceptive mass:

full of elements—both affective and nonaffective—of past experience. For the schizophrenic, many of these elements are floating around on top of the barrel, ready to be attached to almost any new situation [p. 9].

This conception accommodates the data and provides the basis for an interference explanation. Evidence for this view will be assessed in the next paper. However, the psychodynamic concept of affective stimuli is clearly not a sufficient theory of schizophrenic deficit.

INSUFFICIENT MOTIVATION

Another group of theorists argue that schizophrenic deficit is attributable not to an oversensitivity to social stimuli but to a reduced sensitivity to such inputs. Schizophrenics are held to be unmotivated, uninterested in pleasing the experimenter, or uninterested in meeting task requirements; Hunt and Cofer (1944) suggested that responses to social stimuli have been extinguished in schizophrenic patients. In general, the evidence is against this formulation. Testable schizophrenics are as responsive to persuasion as normals or brain-damaged patients whether the social pressure is based on encouragement or on critical admonishment. Many studies stimulated by this theory have confounded the effects of praise and criticism or reward and punishment with the effects of giving subjects different information about their task performance. Evaluating their separate effects is difficult. Nevertheless, schizophrenics and normals generally show a similar pattern of responding: on most tasks information about errors leads to better performance than the signaling of correct responses. However, the importance of this additional information seems to be greater for schizophrenics than for normal subjects. Schizophrenics show relatively greater improvement with clear supplementary cues than do normals, and there is some evidence that information about errors is particularly useful to schizophrenics. The effect of these cues does not appear to be social motivational but rather to help maintain attention and guide responding. It has been suggested that the schizophrenic fails to instruct himself as normals do, and the additional information provided after each response fulfills this guidance function.

Physical punishment tends to facilitate the performance of schizophrenics, and it has occasionally eliminated schizophrenic deficit. This fact has been used to support the lowered motivation hypothesis: if schizophrenics are able to approach normal functioning when reinforced with pain termination but not when social reinforcers are administered, a deficit in social motivation is implied. An alternate view is that physical punishment may be a better source of information about errors, breaking up incorrect sets, and guiding responding. The importance of cue emphasis as opposed to motivational instigation has been demonstrated in studies of normal subjects, in which improvement was occasioned by delivering electric shock for correct responses. Furthermore, when intense stimuli are coincident with important discriminative stimuli, the latter are lent emphasis and more clearly separated from the irrelevant cues in the situation. Evidence for these alternate motivation and interference interpretations of studies employing aversive stimuli will be evaluated in the subsequent paper.

REGRESSION

The loss of abstractness theory received support mainly from early studies, but later work revealed that the excessive concreteness of schizophrenics may be attributed to methods of scoring responses rather than to a loss of the abstract attitude. Schizophrenics are capable of attaining abstract concepts, although their concepts may be bizarre, eccentric, and deviant from those given by normals.

The loss of abstractness theory is but one variant of regression theory, which includes not only Goldstein's formulation but those of Freud, Arieti (1955), and Werner (1948). Regression theory makes two fundamental assumptions: (*a*) there is a fixed sequence of developmental stages that ends in maturity or adult normality, and (*b*) psychopathology represents a retracing of these developmental steps. Concerning deficit, the theory should demonstrate: (*a*) a fixed sequence or hierarchy of psychomotor learning and thinking behavior in childhood, and (*b*) a retracing of the sequence in psychopathology. The only one to attempt such a specific formulation with respect to schizophrenic deficit has been Goldman (1962), using Werner's developmental approach. Whether or not one accepts Goldman's developmental sequence of learning and thinking, there is considerable doubt that the learning and thinking of schizophrenics resemble those of children of any given age. There are occasional similarities between schizophrenics' concepts and those of children: tendencies toward more primitive concepts and deviance from adult concepts. However, there are also marked differences between children's and schizophrenics' concepts: those of schizophrenics are usually more abstract, bizarre, and eccentric than those of children.

Furthermore, it is not sufficient to demonstrate vague similarities between schizophrenics and children. It must be shown that as an individual becomes schizophrenic, he retraces the developmental sequence (if there is one) of learning and thinking; as he recovers, he again moves forward toward demonstrably more mature modes of learning and thinking. These corollaries of regression theory have yet to be established empirically, and therefore we conclude that the regression theory of schizophrenic deficit is unproved.

INTERFERENCE

This theory assumes that when a schizophrenic is faced with a task, he cannot attend properly or in a sustained fashion, maintain a set, or change the set quickly when necessary. His ongoing response tendencies suffer interference from irrelevant, external cues and from "internal" stimuli which consist of deviant thoughts and associations. These irrelevant, distracting, mediated stimuli prevent him from maintaining a clear focus on the task at hand, and the result is psychological deficit.

If the schizophrenic has difficulty in shifting to a new set, he should benefit from stimuli that break the old set. This is precisely what has been established. Schizophrenics benefit from punishment, which eliminates previously correct response tendencies that are no longer appropriate. Physical punishment, in some instances, has been found to eliminate schizophrenic deficit entirely.

If the presence of distracting, internal stimuli prevents the schizophrenic from giving self-instructions (as normals do), he should benefit from external cues. It has been established that schizophrenics are helped more than normals by external reinforcing cues which help direct responses, although normals are also helped. Thus interference theory has an explanation for the effects of punishment and of the rewarding and punishing stimuli that follow responses.

Interference theory can account for schizophrenic deficit with affective stimuli. The theory assumes that the schizophrenic's associations distract him, thereby producing disturbance of performance. The more associations, the greater the deficit. Since affective stimuli elicit more associations than neutral stimuli (Deering, 1963), it follows that they should produce more schizophrenic deficit.

Conceptual deficit is explained by assuming excessive variability in attention. The schizophrenic is either overinclusive because he allows irrelevant stimuli to intrude or overexclusive because he attempts to defend against the distracting, internal stimuli. It follows that some schizophrenics should be overinclusive, some overexclusive, and some alternating between the two; all three possibilities have been found to exist in schizophrenics when they are confronted with conceptual tasks.

Interference theory may be viewed as a devil's advocate in that in each research area it offers an alternative to the theories of social censure, sensitivity to affective stimuli, insufficient motivation, and regression. Obviously, the theory is sufficiently comprehensive, but a theory must do more than merely offer alternatives. Also needed is evidence that tests specific hypotheses, in this instance about the particular interfering effects of environmental, associational, and also somatic stimuli. Such evidence is reviewed in the subsequent paper.

II. INTERFERENCE AND ACTIVATION

This is the second of two papers reviewing laboratory studies of psychological deficit in schizophrenia. The present report first considers experiments on attention, set, and association. Research based on drive interpretation of deficit is then evaluated, followed by an assessment of psychophysiological studies of schizophrenia. Four theories of deficit are discussed: social motivation, drive, arousal, and interference. It is suggested that a fundamental sensori-motor defect underlies psychological deficit in schizophrenia. A final section describes methodological problems raised by research reviewed in both papers.

During the last 20 years a voluminous research literature has appeared on the subject of psychological deficit in schizophrenia, and the relative incapacity of this patient group has been demonstrated with a host of different laboratory tasks. In a previous paper Buss and Lang (1965), the authors reviewed deficit experiments concerned with concept formation, the possible disrupting character of social censure and affective stimuli, and the enhancing effect on performance of various reinforcers and motivational devices.

These findings revealed that testable schizophrenics are about as responsive to social pressure (reward or punishment) as other patients and normal controls. The hypothesis that in schizophrenia social censure invariably leads to deficit is not tenable. Regression theory interpretations of psychotic behavior receive little specific empirical corroboration.

A large body of literature indicates that affective stimuli in general disrupt the functioning of schizophrenics, but this may be due to a broader inability to inhibit any interfering stimulus. Similarly, while schizophrenics do not appear to have lost the capacity to form concepts, the concepts achieved are deviant—overinclusive or overexclusive—a flaw often traceable

to the intrusion of task-irrelevant events. On the positive side, deficit can be significantly reduced by extra instructions, feedback about responses, and intense, physical reinforcers.

Guided by these considerations, the present paper is oriented around the two broad conceptions: interference and activation. The first of these directly concerns schizophrenics' ability to attend to specific stimuli and to inhibit inappropriate responses. The relevant literature on attention, set, and association is explored. In general, schizophrenics show interference effects in all three of these areas. They are distracted by external stimuli. Responses are more likely to be determined by incidental physical properties of the perceptual field than by meaningful relationships. There is difficulty in initiating and maintaining a set over time and in changing a set that is no longer suitable to the experimental task. Finally, schizophrenics' associations are uncommon, intrusive, and interfere with performance.

While the first paper suggested that social motivational constructs have limited value, the fact of greatly reduced responsivity in schizophrenia argues for a thorough exploration of formal theories of motivation or activation. Experimental studies relevant to two classical drive theories are reviewed. One holds that the associational disturbance of schizophrenics is a consequence of high-anxiety drive; the other stresses reactive inhibition, which slows down learning and increases reminiscence. The drive approach is completed by the neurophysiological concept of arousal. From this perspective, schizophrenics have been viewed both as underaroused and as so hyperactivated that effective responding is impossible. Evidence for these conceptions is evaluated in a review of research on the somatic response system in schizophrenia.

Thus, the present paper considers five specific topics: attention, set, associative interference, drive, and somatic arousal. A final discussion of deficit theory and a consideration of methodological problems follow the research review.

The following abbreviations will be used: reaction time (RT), preparatory interval (PI), critical flicker frequency (CFF), galvanic skin response (GSR), electroencephalograph (EEG), electromyograph (EMG), autonomic nervous system (ANS), and stimulus generalization (SG).

SUMMARY

The picture of schizophrenic deficit that emerges from these findings is remarkably consistent across a number of very different response systems. Latency and/or amplitude of psychomotor, vestibular, cardiovascular, sweat gland, and cortical EEG responses are reduced, relative to normal subjects. In at least three of the above systems and in verbal association, excessive intraindividual variability of response has also proved to be pathognomic of schizophrenic disorder. In addition, the levels of cardiovascular activity and muscular tension are unusually high among these patients. All these behaviors—reduced responsivity, deterioration of associational or psychomotor control, and high somatic tension—are positively related to increased withdrawal or clinically judged exacerbation of the illness. They are more marked for chronic and process schizophrenics than for acute and reactive patients. These relationships do not appear to hold for relatively intact paranoids, and perhaps not for early schizophrenics (recent, first admissions).

The experimental manipulation of stimulus intensity has yielded consistent data in studies of RT, ocular nystagmus, and cortical potentials. Deficit in chronic schizophrenia is greatest for low-intensity inputs and least when stimulus amplitude is high. Related to these findings are results of distractibility experiments, which reveal both the schizophrenic's susceptibility to irrelevant cues and his improved performance when background noise is reduced.

A host of studies indicate set disturbances in schizophrenia. On the one hand, schizophrenics are unable to maintain response readiness, and response latency increases if stimuli are presented in more than one modality. On the other hand, these patients seem unduly influenced by a previous set, and responses persist long after they are demonstrably ineffective.

In general, the hypothesis that schizophrenic deficit is attributable to the interference of competing stimuli, internal or external, receives considerable support. The theory that schizophrenics are underaroused may be maintained only if studies of activity level are ignored. This latter research argues that even long-term chronic patients may be physiologically hyperaroused relative to normal subjects, although the frequency and amplitude of overt behavior is greatly reduced.

DISCUSSION

THEORY

In the previous review (Buss and Lang, 1965) three general theories of schizophrenic deficit were considered. The first of these can be roughly described as social or interpersonal in emphasis: deficit is variously attributed to social censure, oversensitivity to affective stimuli, or lowered social motivation. The second approach holds that schizophrenic deficit is a consequence of regression. A third view argues that associative interference underlies many instances of the schizophrenic's behavior disturbance.

Regression theory received little support from data summarized in the first paper, and the current review adds nothing that alters conclusions drawn there. In this discussion, three motivational constructs (social motivation, drive, and arousal) and a more broadly conceived interference theory will be considered as explanations of schizophrenic deficit.

Social motivation. The hypothesis that schizophrenics suffer from lowered social motivation was examined in the previous review. It was seen that schizophrenics and normals respond similarly to general encouragement or chastisement on laboratory tasks. Furthermore, when specific responses are reinforced, differences between groups may be attributed to the greater value of information about performance for the schizophrenic subject. A guidance function is served for patients, which normals apparently provide for themselves. For example, punishment breaks up the perseverative behavior of psychotics, resulting in a closer approximation of normal performance.

The fact that schizophrenics improve more than normals when aversive, physical reinforcers are used has been interpreted to mean that schizophrenics' response to social reward is reduced. However, the research reviewed in the present paper suggests that the intense stimuli employed in these experiments serve to emphasize relevant cues and focus attention, rather than function as special motivators for an indifferent patient.

Some theorists argue that the schizophrenics' problem is not *undersensitivity* to social motivators; it is held that their *oversensitivity* to the affective meaning of stimuli disrupts performance. While affective stimuli may increase deficit, this property is not restricted to one type, such as social censure. In fact, the considerable variety of stimuli (symbolic, human versus nonhuman, etc.) capable of producing these effects calls into question the value of a category so loosely defined. In the previous paper, the authors suggested that the deficit produced by so-called affective or emotionally arousing stimuli is due to an inability to inhibit irrelevant associations. Most of these stimuli instigate more associations than do the neutral comparison stimuli. Evidence presented here indicates that the capacity to suppress *any* intruding cognition is greatly reduced in schizophrenia.

In summary, the hypotheses that schizophrenics are indifferent to social stimuli or particularly sensitive to the affective meaning of stimuli, have very limited value. Experiments relevant to both views are more parsimoniously interpreted in the context of interference theory, which will be reconsidered after a discussion of drive and arousal.

Drive. Negative drive theory applies Pavlov's notion of protective inhibition in schizophrenia to the learning process. Specifically, schizophrenics are held to develop reactive inhibition faster than normals and should therefore show greater reminiscence. Concerning reactive inhibition, there is no consistent evidence that schizophrenics classically condition slower than normals. Concerning reminiscence, the results are similar: no established difference between schizophrenics and normals. It seems safe to conclude that negative drive theory is incorrect.

Mednick, labeling the potential schizophrenic as high-anxious, used the Spence-Taylor approach in making predictions: faster conditioning in simple situations, slower conditioning in complex situations, and flattened generalization gradients. As we showed earlier, these predictions have received only weak support, and there is strong opposing evidence. Thus Mednick's theory has, in general, not been sustained by research findings.

What appears to be wrong with the theory is its specification of anxiety as the crucial drive that leads to schizophrenia. While it is true that many schizophrenics appear anxious, this could as readily be a reaction to incapacity as a cause of it. The theory is embarrassed not only because the predictions from anxiety theory are not supported but also because more chronic and severe schizophrenics show less clinical anxiety. The fact that chronic, withdrawn patients frequently have high-somatic activity levels appears partially to save the theory. However, Mednick has already explained that the chronic schizophrenic's associational defense successfully eliminates anxiety!

These weaknesses of Mednick's theory do not necessarily apply to all drive theories. In fact, drive theory can be shown to be consistent with much research evidence if it is assumed that: (*a*) it is a generalized drive state rather than a specific one such as anxiety, and (*b*) generalized drive can be measured by, or is the same as, physiological arousal. Two sets of facts seem to fit a generalized drive theory. First, schizophrenics tend to be over-aroused, the physiological hyperactivity varying directly with chronicity and/or severity. Second, schizophrenic deficit also varies directly with chronicity and/or severity. These facts can be combined in a causal sequence: schizophrenic deficit is due to the disruptive effects of an excessively high arousal or generalized drive state. Stated this way drive theory can be seen to be one variant of interference theory.

Arousal. Complementary to drive theory is what may be called arousal theory. This view was originally based on the neurological speculations of Hebb (1955) and Lindsley (1951), the EEG work of the latter, and studies of the ANS and muscle tension system by Freeman (1948), Duffy (1962) and Malmo (1958). This conception orders behavior on a continuum from deep sleep to intense excitement. These behavioral states are held to be a function of the degree of diffuse activity in the lower brain, particularly in the reticular formation. From this site collateral impulses ascend to the cortex and descend to the ANS. Alertness, attention, and reactivity are thus determined by the organism's level of "arousal." As with the social motivational point of view, schizophrenics have been held to be both overaroused and underaroused.

The hypothesis that schizophrenics suffer from an underactive arousal mechanism would seem to receive support from studies demonstrating psychomotor and physiological hyporeactivity in chronic patients. However, Malmo (1958) argues cogently that activation is measured more directly in studies of basal physiological level than in research on responsivity. Thus, studies showing high resting somatic activity in schizophrenia would indicate that schizophrenics are generally hyperaroused rather than the opposite. Furthermore, their reduced responsivity is not inconsistent with this view. Malmo (1958), Lacey (1956), and Wilder (1950) have all presented evidence that responsivity progressively decreases when plotted on an abscissa of increasing activation (defined by base activity level). A similar function is obtained in normal subjects when "adequacy of performance" in a complex psychological task replaces responsivity on the ordinate. These facts not only argue that testable chronic schizophrenics are habitually in a hyperaroused state, but in this context the performance deterioration of schizophrenics appears to be analogous to the psychological stress response of a normal subject. However, the symmetry of this analogy is only apparent. Whereas it is complex functioning of normal subjects that mainly suffers under stress (while perhaps more primitive and less adequate but well organized responses emerge), the schizophrenic patient shows deterioration of the simplest and most fundamental behaviors. For example, the schizophrenic performs poorly on a RT task, not because he is anxious, an overready impulsive responder, but because the stimulus seems to arrive unexpectedly. He is not prepared or set, and the response is slow and reduced in amplitude. The psychomotor performance of chronic schizophrenics is more similar to that of aged normals or young adults with general cerebral damage than to that of psychologically stressed normals or anxiety neurotics.

In summary, the underarousal theory of schizophrenia, in terms of the nonspecific projection system, is directly contradicted by most of the psychophysiological research reviewed here, and it may be considered incorrect. The hypothesis that schizophrenics are overaroused receives some support. However, the exact mechanism by which overarousal can produce hyporesponsivity, high-response variability, inattention, disturbances of set and association, and the other symptoms of chronic schizophrenia is yet to be explained.

Interference theory. Interference theory has focused mainly on association and attention-set. The associations of schizophrenics are idiosyncratic and deviant, and they deteriorate performance because they serve as distractors. Schizophrenics have difficulty in focusing on relevant stimuli and excluding irrelevant stimuli, in maintaining a set over time, in shifting a set when it is necessary, in instructing themselves and in pacing themselves, and generally in performing efficiently, in Wishner's sense (1955). These difficulties are pervasive, occurring over a wide range of perceptual, motor, and cognitive tasks. In brief, interference theory, as a broad explanation of schizophrenic deficit, has clearly been supported by research findings and appears to be the only theory comprehensive enough to account for what is known.

The generality of interfering effects suggests a fundamental sensori-motor defect. However, the reactions of patients vary somewhat according to subtype. The defect is seen most clearly in the behavior of chronic, withdrawn patients; acute schizophrenics and particularly early paranoids seem to be compensating for their disability. In many tasks they are overprecise or overresponsive. The fact that in some experiments, among paranoid schizophrenics only the most chronic cases show deficit, suggests that their bizarre attempts at organizing the world may have functional value. Support is gained for Bleuler's contention that many of these behaviors are secondary symptoms—responses to the fundamental disturbance, rather than intrinsic expressions of it.

The locus of the sensori-motor defect is a matter for speculation. It seems clear that the defect is not at the level of the peripheral sensors[1] or effectors, although feedback from the musculature and the ANS may contribute to the disturbance. Lacey and Lacey (1958a) suggest that attention, set, and psychomotor control are directly influenced by autonomic feedback. They propose the carotid sinus as one such steering mechanism: blood pressure changes stimulate the carotid, which has "a profound tonic and inhibitory effect" on cortical electrical activity, and thus alters the organism's orientation to the environment. Furthermore, these researchers have demonstrated a relationship between cardiac variability and failure to inhibit psychomotor responses. Recently, they have also shown that heart rate changes correlate with RT fore-period effects. This raises the interesting possibility that the motor and perceptual symptoms of schizophrenia are related to defects in this carotidcortical mechanism.

The disturbance that appears in all studies of deficit concerns the initiation of responses to selected stimuli and the inhibition of inappropriate responses. All intelligent behavior represents a compromise between the demands of the immediate environment and a previously established set of the organism, but the schizophrenic makes a uniquely poor bargain. External stimuli, associational and biological "noise," routinely suppressed by normal subjects, intrude, and responses to the appropriate stimuli are not made.

These facts suggest that researchers in schizophrenia should concentrate on the processes by which stimuli adapt out or habituate and response competition is resolved. The ascending reticular activating system is the neurological site of greatest relevance. In addition to general arousal, this system appears to have a specific alerting or focusing function. Hernandes-Péon and his associates (1956) demonstrated that cortical potentials in the cochlear nucleus of the cat, normally elicited by a tone, were suppressed when a competing odor of fish or a jar

of mice was simultaneously presented. These authors write:

> Attention involves the selective awareness of certain sensory messages with the simultaneous suppression of others. . . . During the attentive state, it seems as though the brain integrates for consciousness only a limited amount of sensory information, specifically, those impulses concerned with the object of attention [p. 332].

The data on schizophrenic deficit are consistent with the hypothesis that such sensory inhibition centers are defective. These centers and the related behavior should be given extensive study in schizophrenic patients.

METHODOLOGICAL CONSIDERATIONS

It is appropriate that a research review should conclude on a methodological note. The issues raised are many, and their listing amounts to a set of guidelines and admonishments to future investigators.

1. A number of studies have shown that schizophrenics as a group are more variable than normals, and no one regards the nonpsychiatric population as being especially homogeneous. Furthermore, schizophrenics are known to vary in the extent of deficit in relation to several variables which are usually dichotomized: mild-severe, acute-chronic, reactive-process, good premorbid-poor premorbid, and paranoid-nonparanoid. It seems likely that these variables overlap, but empirical data are limited. We need studies relating these dimensions of schizophrenia to each other, as well as more precise data on their relation to deficit.

The paranoid-nonparanoid dichotomy is of special interest. For over a century there has been doubt about including paranoids under the heading of schizophrenia or keeping them separate as "paranoid conditions." Paranoids have been found to show less deficit, e.g., Payne and Hewlitt (1960), and clinically they have been observed to show less thought disorder and less deterioration over time than have schizophrenics of other subgroups. However, these statements are not true of all paranoids; some patients with delusions do manifest considerable deficit and deterioration of thought processes. Perhaps the presence of delusions is less important than the relative absence of defi-

---

[1]Schizophrenics are no different from normals in pure tone threshold and speech reception but are disrupted more quickly and easily by auditory feedback and noise. Ludwig, Wood, & Downs (1962).

cit. Stated another way, perhaps the important dimension is intactness of sensori-motor and intellectual processes, and the paranoid-nonparanoid distinction partially reflects or is partially correlated with this dimension.

Recently Johannsen and his associates (1963) examined correlations between different measures used to describe schizophrenics. High correlations were found between placement on process-reactive, acute-chronic, and good-poor premorbid scales. Only the paranoid-nonparanoid dimension appeared to be an independent dimension. Furthermore, this latter dichotomy was the only one that yielded a significant difference on a double alternation learning task. Whether delusional behavior is an epiphenomenon in low-deficit schizophrenics or a positive effort to reduce deficit as was suggested earlier, future investigators must consider paranoid symptoms in selecting experimental samples.

A less known source of variability among schizophrenics may be found in sex differences. The subjects in most research have been men, with a minority of experiments including both sexes or using women only. It is possible that results found with men cannot be generalized to women, and sex differences might account for some of the discrepancies in results that occur among studies otherwise comparable.

The importance of this issue is pointed up by Schooler's (1963) study of affiliation. He found that the relationships that held for men did not hold for women, and vice versa, which led him to conclude:

A major implication of the study is that theories based on experimental findings with one sex cannot be generalized to explain the behavior of chronic schizophrenics of the other sex [p. 445].

2. In many instances the range of tasks used to study deficit is not sufficient to sustain the broad conclusions of the investigators. For example, on the basis of demonstrated deficiency on conceptual tasks, some researchers have concluded that the basic problem of schizophrenic deficit is an inability to handle concepts. Taken at face value, this conclusion is an overgeneralization because of the absence of evidence that schizophrenics show no deficit on nonconceptual tasks. In the light of the evidence with nonconceptual tasks, the conclusion is patently false.

Generalizations about schizophrenic deficit require a sampling of tasks that tap a variety of psychological functions.

It would be of considerable help if we knew more about what various tasks are measuring and their relations to each other. The appropriate tool is factor analysis, which has been employed mainly by English researchers such as Payne and his collaborators Payne, Mattussek, and George (1959); Payne and Hewlett (1960).

3. When the investigator is interested in particular characteristics of his stimuli, a special problem may arise. He may assume, for example, that some of his stimuli are "affect-laden" without having any evidence for this assertion. A priori statements that stimuli differ along a dimension such as "emotionally arousing" cannot be accepted. It behooves the investigator to present evidence on this point, and the evidence must be independent of the effects obtained with his dependent variable. A similar problem appeared in studies of positive and negative incentives. These experiments were generally interpreted in a socialmotivational context, while the more important differences in the degree of information conveyed by these stimuli were largely ignored.

4. General methodological problems in psychophysiological research have been adequately described elsewhere, Lacey (1956); Lacey and Lacey (1958b). However, these difficulties are accentuated when schizophrenics are the experimental subjects. For example, the low-positive correlations between physiological measures noted in studies of normal subjects may be lower or even negative in schizophrenics. Single measures of arousal or drive are necessarily misleading. Thus, hypoactivity in schizophrenia is frequently found for skin resistance, while muscle tension is generally reported to be high. Such results are provocative, and further study of relationships between sweat gland, cardiovascular, and muscle tension systems may prove valuable.

The pervasive use of drugs in the treatment of psychosis creates problems for both the behavioral and psychophysiological investigator. For example, Reynolds (1962) found a significant interaction between diagnostic subtype (process-reactive) and tranquilizer-nontranquilizer conditions in a study of somatic responses in schizophrenia. No research should be undertaken unless the drug variable is properly controlled.

Researchers have begun to emphasize individual variability in behavioral studies of schizophrenia. Investigations of somatic inter- and intrasession variability are also needed. Furthermore, there may be profit in studying somatic responses recorded concurrently with tasks that elicit deficit. Lacey and Lacey (1958a) have reported important relationships between autonomic activity and psychomotor functioning in normals, and studies cited here encourage this experimental strategy.

Better estimates of resting somatic activity levels are needed . Despite the elaborate care of some investigators, what purport to be differences in basal levels between psychotics and normals may actually be differences in reaction to the laboratory situation. Long-term studies are needed in which information is telemetered from patients while they proceed with the usual hospital routine.

5. While only psychological deficit in schizophrenia has been considered in this review, it is important to reaffirm that these patients share many of the characteristics of deficit with other psychiatric disorders and cases of cerebral damage. The psychomotor retardation, inattention, increased response variability, muscle tension and ANS hyperactivity, and even to some extent the associative disturbance, may be found in many aged, paretic, severe epileptic, or arterial sclerotic patients. Deficit behavior can be produced in normal subjects through the administration of drugs or surgical intervention, and there is some evidence that it may be manipulated by brain stimulation, Heath (1954).

There is ample evidence that severity of psychopathology and psychological deficit are positively related. Some theorists hold that this is the only meaningful relationship between deficit and diagnosis, and they argue that specific consideration of schizophrenia is superfluous. They emphasize the unity of deficit in psychiatric illness and suggest a common neurological defect underlies all its manifestations.

Certainly, further demonstrations that schizophrenics differ from normals are not needed. If the schizophrenic label has experimental validity,

the deficit specific to this diagnosis must be more clearly defined. Are variables such as maternal censure or pictures of hospital aids uniquely important to the behavior of schizophrenics, or might they similarly influence the responses of other patient groups? An answer to this question can only come from studies employing control subjects other than normals, i.e., anxiety neurotics, aged, epileptic, brain-damaged or other chronically ill patients. While some experiments have compared schizophrenics to these groups, the evidence is fragmentary and the interpretations usually emphasize the safer, more reliable distinction between normality and psychosis.

The theoretical point of studies in this area often needs sharpening. Deficit is simply performance decrement. In trying to explain it we must distinguish between what is basic to the disorder and what is epiphenomenal. For example: Is the schizophrenic's anxiety the instigator of deficit, or is it an individual reaction to an insidious and pervasive sensorimotor defect? Issues of this type will tax the ingenuity of the behavioral researcher.

In summary, the problem of psychological deficit remains as broad and as challenging now as in 1944. However, the last 20 years have done much to clarify fundamental symptoms and define conditions which increase or decrease deficit. Many theories have failed to receive empirical support and may now be discarded. Fruitful lines of investigation have also been revealed, and the researcher today, guided by this work, is better equipped to discover the basic nature of schizophrenia.

REFERENCES

Buss, A. H., & Lang, P. J. Psychological deficit in schizophrenia: I. Affect, reinforcement, and concept attainment. *Journal of Abnormal Psychology,* 1965, 70, 2–24.

Deering, G. Affective stimuli and disturbance of thought processes. *Journal of Consulting Psychology,* 1963, 27, 338–343.

Duffy, E. *Activation and behavior.* New York: Wiley, 1962.

Freeman, G. L. *The energetics of human behavior.* Ithaca: Cornell University Press, 1948.

Goldman, A. E. A comparative-developmental approach to schizophrenia. *Psychological Bulletin,* 1962, 59, 57–69.

HEATH, R. (Ed.), *Studies in schizophrenia.* Cambridge: Harvard University Press, 1954.

HEBB, D. O. Drives and the CNS (conceptual nervous system). *Psychological Review,* 1955, *62,* 243–254.

HUNT, J. McV., & COFER, C. Psychological deficit in schizophrenia. In J. McV. Hunt (Ed.), *Personality and the behavior disorders.* Vol. 2. New York: Ronald Press, 1944. Pp. 971–1032.

LACEY, J. I. The evaluation of autonomic responses: Toward a general solution. *Annals of the New York Academy of Sciences,* 1956, *67,* 123–164.

LACEY, J. I., & LACEY, B. C. The relationship of resting autonomic activity to motor impulsivity. *Research Publications of the Association for the Study of Nervous and Mental Diseases,* 1958, *36,* 144–209. (a)

LACEY, J. I., & LACEY, B. C. Verification and extension of the principle of autonomic response stereotypy. *American Journal of Psychology,* 1958, *71,* 50–73. (b)

LANG, P. J. The effect of aversive stimuli on reaction time in schizophrenia. *Journal of Abnormal and Social Psychology,* 1959, *59,* 263–268.

LINDSLEY, D. B. Emotion. In S. S. Stevens (Ed.), *Handbook of experimental psychology.* New York: Wiley, 1951. Pp. 473–516.

LOSEN, S. M. The differential effect of censure on the problem solving behavior of schizophrenics and normal subjects. *Journal of Personality,* 1961, *29,* 258–272.

LUDWIG, A. M., WOOD, B. S., & DOWNS, M. P.
Auditory studies in schizophrenia. *American Journal of Psychiatry,* 1962, *119,* 122–127.

MALMO, R. B. Measurement of drive: An unsolved problem in psychology. In M. R. Jones (Ed.), *Nebraska symposium on motivation.* Lincoln: University of Nebraska Press, 1958. Pp. 44–105.

PAYNE, R. W., & HEWLETT, J. H. G. Thought disorder in psychotic patients. In H. J. Eysenck (Ed.), *Experiments in personality.* London: Routledge & Kegan Paul, 1960, Vol. II. Pp. 3–104.

PAYNE, R. W., MATTUSSEK, P., & GEORGE, E. I. An experimental study of schizophrenic thought.

PHILLIPS, L. Case history data and prognosis in schizophrenia. *Journal of Nervous and Mental Disease,* 1953, *117,* 515–525.

REYNOLDS, D. J. An investigation of the somatic response system in chronic schizophrenia. Unpublished doctoral dissertation, University of Pittsburgh, 1962.

SCHOOLER, C. Affiliation among schizophrenics: Preferred characteristics of the other. *Journal of Nervous and Mental Disease* 1963, *137,* 438–446.

SHAKOW, D. Segmental set: A theory of the formal psychological deficit in schizophrenia. *Archives of General Psychiatry,* 1962, *6,* 17–33.

WILDER, J. The law of initial values. *Psychosomatic Medicine,* 1950, *12,* 392–401.

WISHNER, J. The concept of efficiency in psychological health and in psychopathology. *Psychological Review,* 1955, *62,* 69–80.

37.

THEODORE LIDZ, ALICE R. CORNELISON, STEPHEN FLECK, AND DOROTHY TERRY

MARITAL SCHISM AND MARITAL SKEW

We are engaged in a long-term intensive study of the intrafamilial environment in which the schizophrenic patient grows up. Space does not permit an adequate exposition of the theoretic framework behind these investigations, and we

From Theodore Lidz, Alice R. Cornelison, Stephen Fleck, and Dorothy Terry,"The intrafamilial environment of schizophrenic patients: II. Marital schism and marital skew." *American Journal of Psychiatry,* 1957, *114,* 241–248. Reprinted by permission of International Universities Press, Inc.

shall seek to impart only an indication of our orientation. Previous studies have indicated that serious pathology of the family environment is the most consistent finding pertaining to the etiology of schizophrenia. We are considering schizophrenia as an extreme form of a social withdrawal, specifically characterized by efforts to modify reality into a tenable form by distorting the symbolization of reality, or through extreme limitation of the interpersonal environment. A theory of schizophrenia must explain both the patient's need to withdraw regressively and symbolically from the realm of shared living and meanings, and also his ability to do so. As the family is the primary teacher of social interaction and emotional reactivity, it appears essential to scrutinize it exhaustively. There is now considerable evidence that the schizophrenic's family can foster paralogic ideation, untenable emotional needs, and frequently offers contradictory models for identification which cannot be integrated. The importance of the very early mother-child relationship seems clear, but we are tentatively considering that deficiencies in this relationship may only establish a necessary *anlage* for the development of schizophrenia—or for certain other psychiatric and psychosomatic disorders. An *anlage* is not a cause. It remains possible that specific determinants may be found in the later difficulties in interpersonal relationships. We hypothesize that the ego weakness of the schizophrenic may be related to the introjection of parental weakness noted in the mother's dependency upon the child for fulfillment; to the introjection of parental rejection of the child in the process of early identification with a parent; and to the depreciated images for identification presented by the devaluation of one parent by the other.

The careful collection of data from 16 families has now continued for several years, through weekly interviews with family members; observation of their interaction with each other and the staff; visits to the home, by projective testing, and other techniques. The methodologic problems in collecting and assessing data are many, but technical difficulties cannot continue to bar exploration of an area which appears vital to the study of schizophrenics.

It is important to point out that the families studied are middle and upper class, able and willing to maintain a patient in a private psychiatric hospital for a long period. The only criteria for inclusion in the study are relative youth of the patient, hospitalization in the Yale Psychiatric Institute, and that the mother and at least one sibling are available as informants. By comparison with other groups, it has become quite certain that there is a bias toward the selection of better organized families of schizophrenics rather than toward the more disorganized.

The material which is being collected is complex and its analysis is difficult and time consuming. A year ago we reported briefly our initial survey of the fathers in 12 of these families (7) calling attention to the serious psychopathology found in the fathers of schizophrenic patients, which had previously been generally neglected because of the focussing of attention upon the early mother-child relationship and the pathology of the mothers. Today we report briefly on another fragment of the work in progress, namely on the defects in the marital relations of parents of schizophrenic patients. The topic is selected because, like the psychopathology of the fathers and mothers, the marital difficulties stand out in bold relief; and also because these marital problems are basic to the study of the intrafamilial milieu. The potential relationship of these parental difficulties to the maldevelopment of the children will have to remain largely implicit in this paper.

From past experience, we know that we must emphasize as strongly as possible that we do not seek to establish a direct etiologic relationship between marital discord between parents and the appearance of schizophrenia in an offspring. It is obvious that bad marriages do not, in themselves, produce schizophrenic children. The presentation is simply one of a series of efforts to convey various facets of the family environment as they become apparent in our study. It is not a matter of conjecture but observation, amply documented, and it is unlikely that it does not have some relevance to the problem of schizophrenia.

The deficiencies in the relationships between parents of schizophrenic patients have been noted and studied by relatively few investigators. Lidz and Lidz (6), in 1949, called attention to the frequency of broken homes, markedly unstable parents, and unusual patterns of child rearing, and found that at least 61% of 33 patients had come from homes marked by strife. Tietze (12), in 1949, reported that 13 of 25 mothers of schizophrenic patients reported that their marriages were very unhappy but that the statements by 9 that their marriages were "perfect" did not stand up under investigation, for the marriages were strained and far from happy. Helen Frazee (3), in 1953, found that 14 of 23 parental couples were in severe conflict and none was "normal" or had "only moderate conflict," whereas 13 of the control parental couples were near normal or showed only moderate conflict. None of the parents of schizophrenic patients revealed any degree of marital stability, whereas well over one-half of the control group manifested only moderate conflict or had made a good marital adjustment. Gerard and Siegel (4) (1950) found open discord between 87% of the parents of 71 male schizophrenics as against 13% in the controls. Reichard and Tillman (10) cite the unhappy marriages of the parents of schizophrenics and analyze the sources of discord in terms of parental personalities. Of interest, too, is Murphy's report (8) (1952) of the family environment of 2 adopted children who became schizophrenic, in which the marital relationship was filled with hostility and mutual recrimination between two seriously disturbed parents. Many individual case reports emphasize or mention the bad marital relationship between the parents.

In our efforts to study and describe marital relationships, it has become apparent—as it has to others—that one cannot adequately describe a family or even a marriage in terms of the personalities of each member alone. A family is a group and requires description in terms of group dynamics and the interaction among its members. We are indebted to Parsons and Bales and their co-workers (9); to J. Spiegel and F. Kluckhohn (11); Nathan Ackerman (1); Reuben Hill and his co-workers (5): Bradley Buell and the Community Research Associates (2), and others for their efforts to analyze marital and family interrelationships. We are still searching for suitable frames of reference, but the deficiencies of descriptive method should not blur the basic consideration —that the parental relations are highly disturbed in all of the 14 cases whose study is nearly finished, as well as those which are still incomplete.

The requisites for successful marriages are unfortunately far from clear, but some essentials are emerging. A couple must find reciprocal interrelating roles with each other and in their respective roles with their children. Absence of such role reciprocity means making constant decisions, self-consciousness and tension. As Spiegel (11) has pointed out, role reciprocity requires common understanding and acceptance of each other's roles, goals and motivations, and a reasonable sharing of cultural value orientation. Mutual trust and effective communication between partners are important requisites given effect by support of the spouse's role and self-esteem during periods of loss of confidence. We have been particularly impressed by the need to maintain lines between generations: that is, not to confuse or blur distinctions between parents and children. Spouses cannot remain primarily in a dependent position to their parents to the exclusion of an interdependent marital relationship; nor can one behave primarily as the other's child; nor as a rival with one's own children for the spouse's attention, nor reject a parental role completely (9). The need for both parents to form sources of primary love relationships for children and objects for stable identification will not be entered upon here, as we are concerned primarily with marital interaction.

It seems helpful to follow the lead of Parsons and Bales (9) and consider the father's role in the family as primarily "adaptive-instrumental" and the mother's as "integrative-expressive." In broad terms, which may differ somewhat from Parsons', the father supports the family, establishes its position with respect to other families, determines prestige, and the social patterns of interaction with other groups. The mother's basic functions pertain to intrafamilial interactions; tensions and their regulation; supplying the oral needs, both tangible and affectional. Each parent, in addition to filling his own role, must support the role of the other through his or her prestige, power, and emotional value to other family members.

The marriages of these parents of schizophrenics are beset by a wide variety of problems and ways of adjusting to them. However, the 14 marriages can be placed in 2 general groupings, which, of course, tend to overlap in places. Eight of the 14 couples have lived in a state of severe chronic disequilibrium and discord, which we are calling marital schism. This paper will focus primarily upon these 8 couples. The other 6 couples have achieved some state of relative equilibrium, in which the continuation of the marriage was not constantly threatened; and the marital relationship could yield some gratification of needs to one or both partners. However, the achievement of parental satisfaction or the sacrifices of one parent to maintain marital harmony resulted in a distorted family environment for the children.

Marital Schism

In the 8 families in which the state of disequilibrium designated as marital schism existed, both spouses were caught up in their own personality difficulties, which were aggravated to the point of desperation by the marital relationship. There was chronic failure to achieve complementarity of purpose or role reciprocity. Neither gained support of emotional needs from the other; one sought to coerce the other to conform to his or her expectations or standards, but was met by open or covert defiance. These marriages are replete with recurrent threats of separation, which are not overcome by efforts at re-equilibration, but through postponement of coming to grips with the conflict or through emotional withdrawal from one another—but without hope or prospect of improvement or ever finding any gratification in the marriage. Communication consists primarily of coercive efforts and defiance, or of efforts to mask the defiance to avoid fighting. There is little or no sharing of problems or satisfactions. Each spouse pursues his needs or objectives, largely ignoring the needs of the other, infuriating the partner and increasing ill-will and suspiciousness. A particularly malignant feature in these marriages is the chronic "undercutting" of the worth of one partner to the children by the other. The tendency to compete for the children's loyalty and affection is prominent; at times to gain a substitute to replace the affection missing from the spouse, but at times perhaps simply to hurt and spite the marital partner. Absence of any positive satisfaction from the marital relationship (excluding the children) is striking, though strong dependency needs may be gratified in a masochistic fashion in a few instances. Mutual distrust of motivations is the rule and varies only in the degree with which realistic causes for mistrust extend into the paranoid.

In 7 of these 8 families, the husband retains little prestige in the home and with the children, either because of his own behavior or his wife's attitudes toward him. He becomes an outsider or a secondary figure who cannot assert his instrumental leadership, and when he strives to dominate in tyrannical fashion, he eventually forces the family to conspire to circumvent him. His instrumental role is basically limited to financial support, which he may have originally considered as a husband's basic function, or he is relegated to this position. The ineffectual role of the father applies equally to 5 of the 6 marriages in the other group in which marked schism is not present.

The wives will be considered only in respect to their wifely functions, excluding the complex maternal relationships which also cause marital discord because eccentric, cold, rigid, or over-indulgent attitudes toward the children antagonized the husband. All distrusted their husbands and had no confidence in them. They were openly defiant in major areas of interaction and rather habitually disregarded or circumvented their husbands' demands. They were emotionally cold and distant and, with one or two exceptions, sexually aloof. They competed for the attention and affection of the children and tried to instill their value systems, which differed from those of their husbands.

Communication in these marriages is greatly impeded by mutual withdrawal and by masking of motives from one another, but is further hindered because 4 wives show seriously scattered thinking and 4 husbands show paranoid thinking and rigidity. The imperviousness to the feelings of others, characteristic of many parents of schizophrenics, also creates communicative difficulties.

It seems of interest that in 5 of the 8 marriages, the focus of the partners' loyalties remained in their parental homes, preventing the formation of a nuclear family in which the center of gravity rests in the home. The grandparents or the parental siblings often carried out much of the expressive and instrumental roles rather than the marital partners. The cardinal emotional attachment and dependency of one or both partners remained fixed to a parental figure and could not be transferred to the spouse.

The 8 families can be grouped into 3 categories, according to the groupings of the Community Research Associates in their "Classification of Disorganized Families," which describes 10 combinations of masculine and feminine personalities which are potentially hazardous to successful marital and family relationships (2).

Four marriages seem best described as "Man Dominated Competitive Axes." The husband strives to assert his male dominance to a pathologic degree, rather clearly in reaction to his feminine dependent strivings. He needs an admiring wife who supports insatiable narcissistic needs and complies with his rigid expectations, and is angered when she reacts with defiance and disregard. Indeed, her inadequacies as a wife or mother may well produce exasperated frustration. He distrusts her increasingly and undercuts her prestige with the children. The wives are disappointed and disillusioned in the father figure they married who cannot grasp their needs, and, if they are overwhelmed by force, they manage to gain their ends through circumvention. The husbands are rigid paranoids or obsessives, and the wives are poorly organized obsessives or schizophrenics. The marriages are marked by chronic severe mistrust without (except in the least serious instance) any semblance of affection. The family is split into 2 factions by the conflict and mutual undercutting. Although both members are fighting, it is the husband's moral brutality, his disregard and contempt for the wife whom he tries to force into compliance that dominates the picture.

Mr. Reading, a forceful and successful but paranoidally suspicious man, sought to control his wife's behavior from the start of the marriage. He was infuriated and disillusioned when she joined a church group against his orders to remain aloof from any organizations. He was dependent upon his mother, who lived in the home for many years, following her advice in household matters in opposition to his wife's, whom he considered incompetent to furnish the house. Marked strife began with the birth of the elder of 2 daughters, for he was clearly jealous of the attention the wife paid the child. He disapproved of everything she did in raising the child, often with good reason, but he competed rather than supported. Mrs. Reading was obviously overprotective of the children, whereas her husband wished to inure them to the hard knocks of life. Violent scenes, filled with Mr. Reading's dire threats and marred by occasional violence, were commonplace. The marriage further disintegrated into a hostile battleground after Mrs. Reading discovered that her husband was having an affair, which she reported to her mother-in-law to gain an ally her husband feared. Mr. Reading never forgave his wife for this betrayal and, apparently to spite her, sold their home in the best section of the city to move into a 2-family house in an undesirable neighborhood. Thus, he struck a foul blow at Mrs. Reading's major preoccupations—her social aspirations and her insistence that her daughters associate with only "proper" companions. The family, previously split into 2 groups, now united against Mr. Reading and refused to eat meals with him. The difficulties engendered by the wife's indecisive obsessiveness and the husband's paranoid trends cannot be depicted here. Both partners used interviews primarily to incriminate the other and persuade the interviewer to judge in their favor against the spouse.

The second group of 2 families may be categorized as "Women Dominated Competitive Axes," according to the "Classification of Disorganized Families (2)." The outstanding common feature is the wife's exclusion of the passive and masochistic husband from leadership and decision making. She derogates him in word and deed and is emotionally cold and distant to him. Her attention is focused on her narcissistic needs for completion and admiration. These wives are extremely castrating and their husbands are vulnerable. The husband withdraws from the relationship in an effort to preserve some integrity when defeated in the struggle, and may find solace in alcohol. The husband's function in the family is restricted to providing a living or, if willing, to supporting the wife in her domination of the family. The wife does not fill an expressive, supportive role to her husband and her expressive functions with the children are seriously distorted.

Both Mr. and Mrs. Farell were closely tied to the parental families. Mrs. Farell, the youngest of 3 sisters, was very dependent upon her eldest sister, a masculine aggressive woman with open contempt for men, who tended to dominate the Farell household. Mrs. Farell refused to live at any distance from her family and spent 2 months each year with them away from her husband. She was an extremely cold, narcissistic woman and a "tease," who flirted constantly but denied her husband sexual relations. Mr. Farell was a passive man who sought to assert a pseudo-domination of his family when his men friends were about. He formed fawning attachments to men, which increased his wife's contempt for him. He was excluded increasingly from the family circle, his opinions disregarded; and felt like an outsider who was barely tolerated. He was closely attached to his mother, whom he helped to support. Mr. Farell finally took steps to separate unless his wife would detach herself from her sisters. She capitulated but became pregnant in the process of reconciliation. She was ashamed and concealed the pregnancy, and then took it out on her husband. Separated from her sisters, she began to drink heavily and carried on open flirtations, or perhaps affairs, neglecting her baby. The discord heightened. After Mrs. Farell was seriously disfigured in an accident for which her husband was responsible, she became depressed and withdrew into seclusion until plastic surgery restored her appearance. Mr. Farell then tried to make amends through becoming a weak and spineless husband who mothered the youngest neglected child. However, he soon developed cancer and his wife displayed a physical abhorrence for him, fearing that she might catch the disease. She refused to nurse him during his terminal illness.

The remaining 2 marriages may be classified as "Dual Immature Dependency Axes." Mutual withdrawal of the spouses and dependency on members of the parental families was outstanding. It is difficult to say which spouse dominated the marriage, though both tried and at the same time resented not having a strong figure who would provide leadership. Resentment of the mates' attachments to their families was prominent. The inability to gain mutual gratification of needs and support led to mounting disregard of the other and increasing emptiness of both lives. These marriages were replete with threats of separation by both members, but each tended to go his or her own way, undermining the other to the children by deeds and attitudes more than by words. Despite the long duration of both marriages, they remained tentative, as if both partners were awaiting and contemplating release.

The Nussbaums' dissension had started shortly after their marriage 25 years ago. Mr. Nussbaum had been largely supported by his elder brother, whom he regarded as a father. Mrs. Nussbaum's father had been fatally injured following business reverses, which her family blamed upon his affiliation with Mr. Nussbaum's brother. Mrs. Nussbaum appeared to side with her family in their accusation of her husband's brother. Mr. Nussbaum considered her attitude to show utter disloyalty as it furnished the finishing blow to his feelings of being excluded by her close-knit family. There was little or no discussion of the matter, but they drew apart. Mrs. Nussbaum was very sensitive lest her husband dominate her, and stood her ground with the help of a violent temper. She refused to accompany him on social engagements essential to his career and antagonized his friends. Mr. Nussbaum felt unloved and unwanted and constantly deprecated. He stayed away from home much of the time, and fostered the impression that he was having affairs, either to spite his wife or to mask his impotence, or both. Weeks would pass when the couple would not speak to one another. The wife found solace in her relationship to her son, and the husband in his seductive attachment to his daughter, our patient.

Although the Newbergs had been in violent disagreement and there had been repeated threats of separation, some elements of good-will toward each other could be uncovered. Mr. Newberg is a very disturbed man, pushing numerous impractical schemes that are often grandiose; talking incessantly in a loud voice; seeking to dominate but with faulty judgment and, although a steady and hardworking provider, he had frightened his wife for years lest he leave his job and launch upon one of his impracticable schemes. He spent little time with his family, partly because of his attachment to his mother and partly because of his wife's attachment to her sisters, which forced the family to live in a home 2 hours from his job. Mr. Newberg resented his wife's attachment to her 3 sisters and mother, and her domination by one sister who constantly disparaged him to his wife and children. Mrs. Newberg claimed that she remained dependent upon her sisters because her husband provided her neither emotional support nor help in raising the children. She considered him impossible to live with because of his demands, his thoughtlessness, and the constant confusion he produced in the home. She remained with him only because she felt the children needed a father but found she had to treat him as a child, humoring him to avoid strife. They blame each other's families for interfering and discourage and disparage each other's interests. The situation reached a crisis when Mr. Newberg wished to move to the west coast because his mother and brother were moving there. He threatened to leave his wife if she would not move and she threatened to leave him if he tried to force the move. Both had intense needs which the other could not begin to satisfy. Although Mr. Newberg had strong paranoid trends and Mrs. Newberg had difficulties in being close, and the hostility was marked, this family offered the best chance of any for some reconciliatory movement, because both showed potential ability to recognize the other's needs as well as his own difficulties.

The portrayals of these marriages are little more than symbolic fragments of the wealth of material collected. Still, they indicate the virtual absence of complementarity in each marriage. Husband and wife do not support each other's needs and the marital interaction increases the emotional problems of both, deprives the spouses of any sense of fulfillment in life, and deteriorates into a hostile encounter in which both are losers. Instead of any reciprocal give and take, there is demand and defiance leading to schism between partners that divides the entire family, leaving the children torn between conflicting attachments and loyalties.

MARITAL SKEW

In 6 of the 14 marriages, this type of schism did not exist, although the family life was distorted by a skew in the marital relationship. In all, the rather serious psychopathology of one marital partner dominated the home. In some, the dissatisfaction and unhappiness of one spouse is apparent to the other and to the children, but husband and wife manage to complement or support each other sufficiently to permit a degree of harmony. In the others, the distorted ideation of one partner was accepted or shared by the other, creating an atmosphere of *folie à deux*, or even of *folie à famille* when the entire family shared the aberrant conceptualizations.

In all of these families, one partner who was extremely dependent or masochistic had married a spouse who had appeared to be a strong and protecting parental figure. The dependent partner would go along with or even support the weaknesses or psychopathological distortions of the parental partner because dependency or masochistic needs were met. In

contrast to the marriages with overt schism, one partner could gratify rather than combat a spouse's narcissistic needs. It may be significant that no member of these 6 marriages had intense emotional bonds to the parental family, and it is possible that the absence of such alternative sources of gratification tended to hold these spouses together. A striking feature in all cases was the psychopathology of the partner who appeared to be dominant, creating an abnormal environment which, being accepted by the "healthier" spouse, may have seemed to be a normal environment to the children. Considerable "masking" of potential sources of conflict occurred, creating an unreal atmosphere in which what was said and admitted differed from what was actually felt and done. Two and perhaps 3 of the marriages may be classified as "Woman Oriented Self-depreciatory Axes," according to the "Classification of Disorganized Families"(2), in which the wife's masochistic self-sacrifice to support a narcissistic and disappointing husband was striking. One, and perhaps 2 of the marriages could be designated as "Man Oriented, Self-depreciatory Axes" in which a husband with a meek and self-effacing disposition supported a wife who was an ambulatory schizophrenic.

We shall cite examples in cursory fashion, primarily to illustrate that even though these marriages provided some gratification to the marital partners, the family milieu was as distorted and disturbed as in the case of the schismatic marriages.

The Schwartz family was completely dominated by a paranoid mother who supported the family. Her husband had left her on one occasion, unable to tolerate her demands, but had returned long before the patient, the youngest son, had been born. Soon thereafter the father suffered a nervous breakdown, after which he lived as a sort of handyman around the house and worked as a menial helper in the wife's business. The wife was extremely ambitious for her 4 sons, pushing them and dominating their lives, as well as making it clear that they must not become like their father. She was paranoidally fearful of outsiders, believing that their telephone was tapped and that the family was physically endangered because they were Jewish. A severe schism actually existed despite the peace between the marital couple. The mother was intensely protective of her oldest son, a gambler and embezzler, who consumed all of her attention as well as much of the family income. A chronic ambivalent conflict existed between them that tended to exclude the husband and the other sons. The husband did not intervene, but merely told his sons that the trouble in the family existed because they did not obey their mother as he did.

Here the father had abdicated and the mother was a paranoid instrumental leader, while the father supplied no masculine image with whom the younger sons could identify.

Illustrative of the *folie à deux* and the *folie à famille* group, the Dollfuss family lived as European landed gentry in a New England suburb, isolated from their neighbors. The family life was centered in the needs and opinions of Mr. Dollfuss, a successful but paranoidally grandiose inventor. The children were raised by a seductive nursemaid of whom the cold and distant mother was intensely jealous. However, Mrs. Dollfuss devoted her life to her husband, catering to his whims, and keeping the children out of his way. Mr. Dollfuss' major interest was an oriental religious sect. He believed that he and a friend were among the few select souls who would achieve a particular type of salvation. Both Mrs. Dollfuss and the nursemaid virtually deified him. They and the children shared his beliefs as well as his grandiose notions of himself, living in what we termed a *folie à famille*. Here, the children were largely excluded from the lives of the parents, the model of the father was an unrealistic one for the son, and the intellectual and emotional environment was estranged from that of the larger culture into which they had to emerge.

In all of these 6 families, the fathers were particularly ineffectual, assuming little responsibility for family leadership other than earning a livelihood. They were either weak, ineffectual men who went along with wives who were schizophrenic or at least questionably so, or they were disturbed men who could maintain an outward form of capability and strength because of the support of a masochistic wife. In all instances, the psychopathology that pervaded the home was masked or treated as normal.

The analysis of the pathologic environment in these last 6 cases, and of the effects upon the children, cannot be gone into here, but I trust we have shown that we have not simply discarded less disturbed family environments in choosing to focus this paper upon the 8 marriages in which overt schism between the partners existed. In considering the 8 schismatic

marriages we do not seek, as emphasized previously, to relate directly the appearance of schizophrenia in an offspring to the marital disorganization. There are many other factors in the family environment which we are studying that affect the children, but they all bear some relationship to the personalities of the parents and the atmosphere created by their interaction. We are only seeking to describe bit by bit what this family environment is like, until we can assemble the fragments into a meaningful description of the whole. We are still occupied with the grossest factors, for unless we start with what appears fairly obvious, these factors may be overlooked during our preoccupation with subtleties. In this presentation, we have paid minimal attention to the individual personalities of the parents in order to concentrate upon problems created by their interaction.

DISCUSSION

We find a number of features in these marriages that are theoretically adverse to the "normal" development process of a child. In these families each parent constantly denigrates and undercuts the other, making it clear to the children that each does not respect or value, but rather dislikes or hates the other. Each parent more or less openly expresses fears that a child will resemble the other, and a child's resemblance to one parent is a source of concern or rejection by the other parent. One or both parents seek to win the child away from the other. The boundary between the generations is violated. A child may feel the burden of being expected or required to complete the life of one or both parents; and this creates a block to growth into an independent individual. A child may be used and needed as a replacement for the spouse. There is excellent opportunity for intensification of the Oedipal rivalry rather than for its resolution. The child can insert himself in the wedge between the parents, becoming inordinately adept at widening the breach and becoming caught in the incestuous concern that the parent can be seduced or might seduce, as well as in the guilt over hostile-destructive impulses toward the other parent. A parent of the same sex with whom the child should identify during latency and adolescence who is not an acceptable love object to the other parent but is hated and despised, cannot provide a model through which a child can achieve mature identity. Potential homosexual trends, which play a large role in schizophrenia, are opened. Many other serious impediments are placed in the way of the child's achievements of a stable identification with a parental figure, a requisite to the formation of a stable ego-identity by the end of adolescence. In addition, children of a rejected marriage are likely to feel rejected themselves. Caught in the anxiety that a needed parental love-object can be lost through separation of the parents, the children may devote much energy toward balancing the precarious marriage. The stronger the incestuous tendencies, the greater the need for protection by the presence of both parents. When one or both parents have paralogic and scattered ways of thinking and behaving, the difficulties are further heightened.

SUMMARY

The careful scrutiny of the 14 families containing schizophrenic offspring reveals that the marital relationships of all parents were seriously disturbed. Eight of the families were split into 2 factions by the overt schism between the parents. In these schismatic families the parents repeatedly threatened to separate; one spouse sought to coerce the other to conform to rigid expectations and aroused defiance; difficulties of almost any type engendered recriminations between parents rather than mutual support. The parents derogated and undercut one another, and thus the child could not use one parent as a model for identification or as a love object without antagonizing the other parent. The other 6 couples lived together in reasonable harmony, but the family environments provided by their marriages were badly distorted or "skewed" because in each marriage the serious psychopathology of the dominant parent was accepted or shared by the other. Studies now in progress will seek to clarify further the difficulties in these marriages, the personalities involved, and the effects upon the children.

REFERENCES

1. ACKERMAN, N. *Social Casework*, 35, April, 1954.
2. BUELL, B., *et al. Classification of disorganized families for use in family oriented diagnosis and treatment.* New York: Community Research Associates, 1953.
3. FRAZEE, H. E. *Smith College Studies in Social Work*, 23, 125, 1953.
4. GERARD, D. L., & SIEGEL, J. *Psychiatric Quarterly*, 24, 47, 1950.
5. HILL, R. *et al. Eddyville's Families. Institute for Research in Social Science*, Chapel Hill, N. C., 1953.
6. LIDZ, R. W., & LIDZ, T. *American Journal of Psychiatry*, 106:332, 1949.
7. LIDZ, T., PARKER, B., & CORNELISON, A. R. *American Journal of Psychiatry*, 113: No. 1, July, 1956.
8. MURPHY, B. *Psychiatric Quarterly*, 26, 450, 1952.
9. PARSONS, T., & BALES, R. *The Family*. Glencoe, Ill.: Free Press, 1955.
10. REICHARD, S., & TILLMAN, C. *Psychiatry*, 13: 247, 1950.
11. SPIEGEL, J. P. *Psychiatry*, 20, 1, 1957.
12. TIETZE, T. *Psychiatry*, 12, 55, 1949.

38.

GREGORY BATESON, DON D. JACKSON, JAY HALEY,
AND JOHN WEAKLAND

DOUBLE-BIND HYPOTHESIS OF SCHIZOPHRENIA

Schizophrenia—its nature, etiology, and the kind of therapy to use for it—remains one of the most puzzling of the mental illnesses. The theory of schizophrenia presented here is based on communications analysis, and specifically on the Theory of Logical Types. From this theory and from observations of schizophrenic patients is derived a description, and the necessary conditions for, a situation called the "double bind"—a situation in which no matter what a person does, he "can't win." It is hypothesized that a person caught in the double bind may develop schizophrenic symptoms. How and why the double bind may arise in a family situation is discussed, together with illustrations from clinical and experimenal data.

This is a report[1] on a research project which has been formulating and testing a broad, systematic view of the nature, etiology, and therapy of schizophrenia. Our research in this field has proceeded by discussion of a varied body of data and ideas, with all of us contributing according to our varied experience in anthropology, communications analysis, psychotherapy, psychiatry, and psychoanalysis. We have now reached common agreement on the broad outlines of a communicational theory of the origin and nature of schizophrenia; this paper is a preliminary report on our continuing research.

From Gregory Bateson, Don D. Jackson, Jay Haley, and John Weakland,"Toward a theory of schizophrenia."*Behavioral Science*, 1956, *1*, 251–264. Reprinted by permission.
[1]To Jay Haley is due credit for recognizing that the symptoms of schizophrenia are suggestive of an inability to discriminate the Logical Types, and this was amplified by Bateson who added the notion that the symptoms and etiology could be formally described in terms of a double bind hypothesis. The hypothesis was communicated to D. D. Jackson and found to fit closely with his ideas of family homeostasis. Since then Dr. Jackson has worked closely with the project. The study of the formal analogies between hypnosis and schizophrenia has been the work of John H. Weakland and Jay Haley.

THE BASE IN COMMUNICATIONS THEORY

Our approach is based on that part of communications theory which Russell has called the Theory of Logical Types (17). The central thesis of this theory is that there is a discontinuity between a class and its members. The class cannot be a member of itself nor can one of the members *be* the class, since the term used for the class is of a *different level of abstraction*—a different Logical type—from terms used for members. Although in formal logic there is an attempt to maintain this discontinuity between a class and its members, we argue that the psychology of real communications this discontinuity is continually and inevitably breached (2), and that a priori we must expect a pathology to occur in the human organism when certain formal patterns of the breaching occur in the communication between mother and child. We shall argue that this pathology at its extreme will have symptoms whose formal characteristics would lead the pathology to be classified as a schizophrenia.

Illustrations of how human beings handle communication involving multiple Logical Types can be derived from the following fields:

1. *The Use of Various Communicational Modes in Human Communication.* Examples are play, non-play, fantasy, sacrament, metaphor, etc. Even among the lower mammals there appears to be an exchange of signals which identify certain meaningful behavior as "play," etc. These signals are evidently of higher Logical Type than the messages they classify. Among human beings this framing and labeling of messages and meaningful actions reaches considerable complexity, with the peculiarity that our vocabulary for such discrimination is still very poorly developed, and we rely preponderantly

upon nonverbal media of posture, gesture, facial expression, intonation, and the context for the communication of these highly abstract, but vitally important, labels.

2. *Humor.* This seems to be a method of exploring the implicit themes in thought or in a relationship. The method of exploration involves the use of messages which are characterized by a condensation of Logical Types or communicational modes. A discovery, for example, occurs when it suddenly becomes plain that a message was not only metaphoric but also more literal, or vice versa. That is to say, the explosive moment in humor is the moment when the labeling of the mode undergoes a dissolution and resynthesis. Commonly, the punch line compels a reevaluation of earlier signals which ascribed to certain messages a particular mode (e.g., literalness or fantasy). This has the peculiar effect of attributing *mode* to those signals which had previously the status of that higher Logical Type which classifies the modes.

3. *The Falsification of Mode-Identifying Signals.* Among human beings mode identifiers can be falsified, and we have the artificial laugh, the manipulative simulation of friendliness, the confidence trick, kidding, and the like. Similar falsifications have been recorded among mammals (3, 13). Among human beings we meet with a strange phenomenon—the unconscious falsification of these signals. This may occur within the self—the subject may conceal from himself his own real hostility under the guise of metaphoric play—or it may occur as an unconscious falsification of the subject's understanding of the other person's mode-identifying signals. He may mistake shyness for contempt, etc. Indeed most of the errors of self-reference fall under this head.

4. *Learning.* The simplest level of this phenomenon is exemplified by a situation in which a subject receives a message and acts appropriately on it: "I heard the clock strike and knew it was time for lunch. So I went to the table." In learning experiments the analogue of this sequence of events is observed by the experimenter and commonly treated as a single message of a higher type. When the dog salivates between buzzer and meat powder, this sequence

is accepted by the experimenter as a message indicating that "the dog has *learned* that buzzer means meat powder." But this is not the end of the hierarchy of types involved. The experimental subject may become more skilled in learning. He may *learn to learn* (1, 7, 9), and it is not inconceivable that still higher orders of learning may occur in human beings.

5. *Multiple Levels of Learning and the Logical Typing of Signals.* These are two inseparable sets of phenomena—inseparable because the ability to handle the multiple types of signals is itself a *learned* skill and therefore a function of the multiple levels of learning.

According to our hypothesis, the term "ego function" (as this term is used when a schizophrenic is described as having "weak ego function") is precisely *the process of discriminating communicational modes either within the self or between the self and others.* The schizophrenic exhibits weakness in three areas of such function: (*a*) He has difficulty in assigning the correct communicational mode to the messages he receives from other persons. (*b*) He has difficulty in assigning the correct communicational mode to those messages which he himself utters or emits nonverbally. (*c*) He has difficulty in assigning the correct communicational mode to his own thoughts, sensations, and percepts.

At this point it is appropriate to compare what was said in the previous paragraph with von Domarus' (16) approach to the systematic description of schizophrenic utterance. He suggests that the messages (and thought) of the schizophrenic are deviant in syllogistic structure. In place of structures which derive from the syllogism, Barbara, the schizophrenic, according to this theory, uses structures which identify predicates. An example of such a distorted syllogism is:

> Men die.
> Grass dies.
> Men are grass.

But as we see it, von Domarus' formulation is only a more precise—and therefore valuable—way of saying that schizophrenic utterance is rich in metaphor. With that generalization we agree. But metaphor is an indispensable tool of thought and expression—a characteristic of all human communication, even of that of the scientist. The conceptual models of cybernetics and the energy theories of psychoanalysis are, after all, only labeled metaphors. The peculiarity of the schizophrenic is not that he uses metaphors, but that he uses *unlabeled* metaphors. He has special difficulty in handling signals of that class whose members assign Logical Types to other signals.

If our formal summary of the symptomatology is correct and if the schizophrenia of our hypothesis is essentially a result of family interaction, it should be possible to arrive a priori at a formal description of these sequences of experience which would induce such a symptomatology. What is known of learning theory combines with the evident fact that human beings use *context* as a guide for mode discrimination. Therefore, we must look not for some specific traumatic experience in the infantile etiology but rather for characteristic sequential patterns. The specificity for which we search is to be at an abstract or formal level. The sequences must have this characteristic: that from them the patient will acquire the mental habits which are exemplified in schizophrenic communication. That is to say, *he must live in a universe where the sequences of events are such that his unconventional communicational habits will be in some sense appropriate*. The hypothesis which we offer is that sequences of this kind in the external experience of the patient are responsible for the inner conflicts of Logical Typing. For such unresolvable sequences of experiences, we use the term "double bind."

The Double Bind

The necessary ingredients for a double bind situation, as we see it, are:

1. *Two or More Persons.* Of these, we designate one, for purposes of our definition, as the "victim." We do not assume that the double bind is inflicted by the mother alone, but that it may be done either by mother alone or by some combination of mother, father, and/or siblings.

2. *Repeated Experience.* We assume that the double bind is a recurrent theme in the experience of the victim. Our hypothesis does not invoke a single traumatic experience, but such repeated experience that the double bind structure comes to be an habitual expectation.

3. *A Primary Negative Injunction.* This may have either of two forms: (*a*) "Do not do so and so, or I will punish you," or (*b*) "If you do not do so and so, I will punish you." Here we select a context of learning based on avoidance of punishment rather than a context of reward seeking. There is perhaps no formal reason for this selection. We assume that the punishment may be either the withdrawal of love or the expression of hate or anger—or most devastating—the kind of abandonment that results from the parent's expression of extreme helplessness.[2]

4. *A Secondary Injunction Conflicting with the First at a More Abstract Level, and Like the First Enforced by Punishments or Signals Which Threaten Survival.* This secondary injunction is more difficult to describe than the primary for two reasons. First, the secondary injunction is commonly communicated to the child by nonverbal means. Posture, gesture, tone of voice, meaningful action, and the implications concealed in verbal comment may all be used to convey this more abstract message. Second, the secondary injunction may impinge upon any element of the primary prohibition. Verbalization of the secondary injunction may, therefore, include a wide variety of forms; for example: "Do not see this as punishment"; "Do not see me as the punishing agent"; "Do not submit to my prohibitions"; "Do not think of what you must not do"; "Do not question my love of which the primary prohibition is (or is not) an example"; and so on. Other examples become possible when the double bind is inflicted not by one individual but by two. For example, one parent may negate at a more abstract level the injunctions of the other.

5. *A Tertiary Negative Injunction Prohibiting the Victim from Escaping from the Field.* In a formal sense it is perhaps unnecessary to list this injunction as a separate item since the reinforcement at the other two levels involves a threat to survival, and if the double binds are

---

[2]Our concept of punishment is being refined at present. It appears to us to involve perceptual experience in a way that cannot be encompassed by the notion of "trauma."

imposed during infancy, escape is naturally impossible. However, it seems that in some cases the escape from the field is made impossible by certain devices which are not purely negative, e.g., capricious promises of love, and the like.

6. Finally, the complete set of ingredients is no longer necessary when the victim has learned to perceive his universe in double bind patterns. Almost any part of a double bind sequence may then be sufficient to precipitate panic or rage. The pattern of conflicting injunctions may even be taken over by hallucinatory voices (14).

THE EFFECT OF THE DOUBLE BIND

In the Eastern religion, Zen Buddhism, the goal is to achieve Enlightenment. The Zen Master attempts to bring about enlightenment in his pupil in various ways. One of the things he does is to hold a stick over the pupil's head and say fiercely, "If you say this stick is real, I will strike you with it. If you say this stick is not real, I will strike you with it. If you don't say anything, I will strike you with it." We feel that the schizophrenic finds himself continually in the same situation as the pupil, but he achieves something like disorientation rather than enlightenment. The Zen pupil might reach up and take the stick away from the Master—who might accept this response, but the schizophrenic has no such choice since with him there is no not caring about the relationship, and his mother's aims and awareness are not like the Master's.

We hypothesize that there will be a breakdown in any individual's ability to discriminate between Logical Types whenever a double bind situation occurs. The general characteristics of this situation are the following:

1. When the individual is involved in an intense relationship; that is, a relationship in which he feels it is vitally important that he discriminate accurately what sort of message is being communicated so that he may respond appropriately.

2. And, the individual is caught in a situation in which the other person in the relationship is expressing two orders of message and one of these denies the other.

3. And, the individual is unable to comment on the messages being expressed to correct his discrimination of what order of message to respond to, i.e., he cannot make a metacommunicative statement.

We have suggested that this is the sort of situation which occurs between the preschizophrenic and his mother, but it also occurs in normal relationships. When a person is caught in a double bind situation, he will respond defensively in a manner similar to the schizophrenic. An individual will take a metaphorical statement literally when he is in a situation where he must respond, where he is faced with contradictory messages, and when he is unable to comment on the contradictions. For example, one day an employee went home during office hours. A fellow employee called him at his home, and said lightly, "Well, how did you get *there?*" The employee replied, "By automobile." He responded literally because he was faced with a message which asked him what he was doing at home when he should have been at the office, but which denied that this question was being asked by the way it was phrased. (Since the speaker felt it wasn't really his business, he spoke metaphorically.) The relationship was intense enough so that the victim was in doubt how the information would be used, and he therefore responded literally. This is characteristic of anyone who feels "on the spot," as demonstrated by the careful literal replies of a witness on the stand in a court trial. The schizophrenic feels so terribly on the spot at all times that he habitually responds with a defensive insistence on the literal level when it is quite inappropriate, e.g., when someone is joking.

Schizophrenics also confuse the literal and metaphoric in their own utterance when they feel themselves caught in a double bind. For example, a patient may wish to criticize his therapist for being late for an appointment, but he may be unsure what sort of a message that act of being late was—particularly if the therapist has anticipated the patient's reaction and apologized for the event. The patient cannot say, "Why were you late? Is it because you don't want to see me today?" This would be an accusation, and so he shifts to a metaphorical statement. He may then say, "I knew a fellow once who missed a boat, his name was Sam and the boat almost sunk, . . . etc.," Thus he develops a metaphorical story and the therapist may or may not discover in it a comment on his being late. The convenient thing about a metaphor is that it leaves it up to the therapist (or mother) to see an accusation in the statement if he chooses, or to ignore it if he chooses. Should the therapist accept the accusation in the metaphor, then the patient can accept the statement he has made about Sam as metaphorical. If the therapist points out that this doesn't sound like a true statement about Sam, as a way of avoiding the accusation in the story, the patient can argue that there really was a man named Sam. As an answer to the double bind situation, a shift to a metaphorical statement brings safety. However, it also prevents the patient from making the accusation he wants to make. But instead of getting over his accusation by indicating that this is a metaphor, the schizophrenic patient seems to try to get over the fact that it is a metaphor by making it more fantastic. If the therapist should ignore the accusation in the story about Sam, the schizophrenic may then tell a story about going to Mars in a rocket ship as a way of putting over his accusation. The indication that it is a metaphorical statement lies in the fantastic aspect of the metaphor, not in the signals which usually accompany metaphors to tell the listener that a metaphor is being used.

It is not only safer for the victim of a double bind to shift to a metaphorical order of message, but in an impossible situation it is better to shift and become somebody else, or shift and insist that he is somewhere else. Then the double bind cannot work on the victim, because it isn't he and besides he is in a different place. In other words, the statements which show that a patient is disoriented can be interpreted as ways of defending himself against the situation he is in. The pathology enters when the victim himself either does not know that his responses are metaphorical or cannot say so. To recognize that he was speaking metaphorically he would need to be aware that he was defending himself and therefore was afraid of the other person. To him such an awareness would be an indictment of the other person and therefore provoke disaster.

If an individual has spent his life in the kind of double bind relationship described here, his way of relating to people after a psychotic break would have a systematic pattern. First, he would not share with normal people those signals which accompany messages to indicate what a person means. His metacommunicative system—the communications about communication—would have broken down, and he would not know what kind of message a message was. If a person said to him, "what would you like to do today?" he would be unable to judge accurately by the context or by the tone of voice or gesture whether he was being condemned for what he did yesterday, or being offered a sexual invitation, or just what was meant. Given this inability to judge accurately what a person really means and an excessive concern with what is really meant, an individual might defend himself by choosing one or more of several alternatives. He might, for example, assume that behind every statement there is a concealed meaning which is detrimental to his welfare. He would then be excessively concerned with hidden meanings and determined to demonstrate that he could not be deceived—as he had been all his life. If he chooses this alternative, he will be continually searching for meanings behind what people say and behind chance occurrences in the environment, and he will be characteristically suspicious and defiant.

He might choose another alternative, and tend to accept literally everything people say to him; when their tone or gesture or context contradicted what they said, he might establish a pattern of laughing off these metacommunicative signals. He would give up trying to discriminate between levels of message and treat all messages as unimportant or to be laughed at.

If he didn't become suspicious of metacommunicative messages or attempt to laugh them off, he might choose to try to ignore them. Then he would find it necessary to see and hear less and less of what went on around him, and do his utmost to avoid provoking a response in his environment. He would try to detach his interest from the external world and concentrate on his own internal processes and, therefore, give the appearance of being a withdrawn, perhaps mute, individual.

This is another way of saying that if an individual doesn't know what sort of message a message is, he may defend himself in ways which have been described as paranoid, hebephrenic, or catatonic. These three alternatives are not the only ones. The point is that he cannot choose the one alternative which would help him to discover what people mean; he cannot without considerable help, discuss the messages of others. Without being able to do that, the human being is like any self-correcting system which has lost its governor; it spirals into never-ending, but always systematic, distortions.

A DESCRIPTION OF THE FAMILY SITUATION

The theoretical possibility of double bind situations stimulated us to look for such communicative sequences in the schizophrenic patient and in his family situation. Toward this end we have studied the written and verbal reports of psychotherapists who have treated such patients intensively; we have studied tape recordings of psychotherapeutic interviews, both of our own patients and others; we have interviewed and taped parents of schizophrenics; we have had two mothers and one father participate in intensive psychotherapy; and we have interviewed and taped parents and patients seen conjointly.

On the basis of these data we have developed a hypothesis about the family situation which ultimately leads to an individual suffering from schizophrenia. This hypothesis has not been statistically tested; it selects and emphasizes a rather simple set of interactional phenomena and does not attempt to describe comprehensively the extraordinary complexity of a family relationship.

We hypothesize that the family situation of the schizophrenic has the following general characteristics:

1. A child whose mother becomes anxious and withdraws if the child responds to her as a loving mother. That is, the child's very existence has a special meaning to the mother which arouses her anxiety and hostility when she is in danger of intimate contact with the child.

2. A mother to whom feelings of anxiety and hostility toward the child are not acceptable, and whose way of denying them is to express overt loving behavior to persuade the child to respond to her as a loving mother and to withdraw from him if he does not. "Loving behavior" does not necessarily imply "affection"; it can, for example, be set in a framework of doing the proper thing, instilling "goodness," and the like.

3. The absence of anyone in the family, such as a strong and insightful father, who can intervene in the relationship between the mother and child and support the child in the face of the contradictions involved.

Since this is a formal description we are not specifically concerned with why the mother feels this way about the child, but we suggest that she could feel this way for various reasons. It may be that merely having a child arouses anxiety about herself and her relationships to her own family; or it may be important to her that the child is a boy or a girl, or that the child was born on the anniversary of one of her own siblings (8), or the child may be in the same sibling position in the family that she was, or the child may be special to her for other reasons related to her own emotional problems.

Given a situation with these characteristics, we hypothesize that the mother of a schizophrenic will be simultaneously expressing at least two orders of message. (For simplicity in this presentation we shall confine ourselves to two orders.) These orders of message can be roughly characterized as (a) hostile or withdrawing behavior which is aroused whenever the child approaches her, and (b) simulated loving or approaching behavior which is aroused when the child responds to her hostile and withdrawing behavior, as a way of denying that she is withdrawing. Her problem is to control her anxiety by controlling the closeness and distance between herself and her child. To put this another way, if the mother begins to feel affectionate and close to her child, she begins to feel endangered and must withdraw from him; but she cannot accept this hostile act and to deny it must simulate affection and closeness with her child. The important point is that her loving behavior is then a comment on (since it is compensatory for) her hostile behavior and consequently it is of a different *order* of message than the hostile behavior—it is a message about a sequence of messages. Yet by its nature it denies the existence of those messages which it is about, i.e., the hostile withdrawal.

The mother uses the child's responses to affirm that her behavior is loving, and since the loving behavior is simulated, the child is placed in a position where he must not accurately interpret her communication if he is to maintain his relationship with her. In other words, he must not discriminate accurately between orders of message, in this case the difference between the expression of simulated feelings (one Logical Type) and real feelings (another Logical Type). As a result the child must systematically distort his perception of metacommunicative signals. For example, if mother begins to feel hostile (or affectionate) toward her child and also feels compelled to withdraw from him, she might say, "Go to bed, you're very tired and I want you to get your sleep." This overtly loving statement is intended to deny a feeling which could be verbalized as "Get out of my sight because I'm sick of you." If the child correctly discriminates her metacommunicative signals, he would have to face the fact that she both doesn't want him and is deceiving him by her loving behavior. He would be "punished" for learning to discriminate orders of messages accurately. He therefore would tend to accept the idea that he is tired rather than recognize his mother's deception. This means that he must deceive himself about his own internal state in order to support mother in her deception. To survive with her he must falsely discriminate his own internal messages as well as falsely discriminate the messages of others.

The problem is compounded for the child because the mother is "benevolently" defining for him how he feels; she is expressing overt maternal concern over the fact that he is tired. To put it another way, the mother is controlling the child's definitions of his own messages, as well as the definition of his responses to her (e.g., by saying, "You don't really mean to say that," if he should criticize her) by insisting that she is not concerned about herself but only about him. Consequently, the easiest path for the child is to accept mother's simulated loving behavior as real, and his desires to interpret what is going on are undermined. Yet the result

is that the mother is withdrawing from him and defining this withdrawal as the way a loving relationship should be.

However, accepting mother's simulated loving behavior as real also is no solution for the child. Should he make this false discrimination, he would approach her; this move toward closeness would provoke in her feelings of fear and helplessness, and she would be compelled to withdraw. But if he then withdrew from her, she would take his withdrawal as a statement that she was not a loving mother and would either punish him for withdrawing or approach him to bring him closer. If he then approached, she would respond by putting him at a distance. *The child is punished for discriminating accurately what she is expressing, and he is punished for discriminating inaccurately—he is caught in a double bind.*

The child might try various means of escaping from this situation. He might, for example, try to lean on his father or some other member of the family. However, from our preliminary observations we think it is likely that the fathers of schizophrenics are not substantial enough to lean on. They are also in the awkward position where if they agreed with the child about the nature of mother's deceptions, they would need to recognize the nature of their own relationships to the mother, which they could not do and remain attached to her in the *modus operandi* they have worked out.

The need of the mother to be wanted and loved also prevents the child from gaining support from some other person in the environment, a teacher, for example. A mother with these characteristics would feel threatened by any other attachment of the child and would break it up and bring the child back closer to her with consequent anxiety when the child became dependent on her.

The only way the child can really escape from the situation is to comment on the contradictory position his mother has put him in. However, if he did so, the mother would take this as an accusation that she is unloving and both punish him and insist that his perception of the situation is distorted. By preventing the child from talking about the situation, the mother forbids him using the metacommunicative level—the level we use to correct our perception of communicative behavior. The ability to communicate about communication, to comment upon the meaningful actions of oneself and others, is essential for successful social intercourse. In any normal relationship there is a constant interchange of metacommunicative messages such as "What do you mean?" or "Why did you do that?" or "Are you kidding me?" and so on. To discriminate accurately what people are really expressing we must be able to comment directly or indirectly on that expression. This metacommunicative level the schizophrenic seems unable to use successfully (2). Given these characteristics of the mother, it is apparent why. If she is denying one order of message, then any statement about her statements endangers her and she must forbid it. Therefore, the child grows up unskilled in his ability to communicate about communication and, as a result, unskilled in determining what people really mean and unskilled in expressing what he really means, which is essential for normal relations.

In summary, then, we suggest that the double bind nature of the family situation of a schizophrenic results in placing the child in a position where if he responds to his mother's simulated affection her anxiety will be aroused and she will punish him (or insist, to protect herself, that *his* overtures are simulated, thus confusing him about the nature of his own messages) to defend herself from closeness with him. Thus the child is blocked off from intimate and secure associations with his mother. However, if he does not make overtures of affection, she will feel that this means she is not a loving mother and her anxiety will be aroused. Therefore, she will either punish him for withdrawing or make overtures toward the child to insist that he demonstrate that he loves her. If he then responds and shows her affection, she will not only feel endangered again, but she may resent the fact that she had to force him to respond. In either case in a relationship, the most important in his life and the model for all others, he is punished if he indicates love and affection and punished if he does not; and his escape routes from the situation, such as gaining support from others, are cut off. This is the basic nature of the

double bind relationship between mother and child. This description has not depicted, of course, the more complicated interlocking gestalt that is the "family" of which the "mother" is one important part (11, 12).

ILLUSTRATIONS FROM CLINICAL DATA

An analysis of an incident occurring between a schizophrenic patient and his mother illustrates the "double bind" situation. A young man who had fairly well recovered from an acute schizophrenic episode was visited in the hospital by his mother. He was glad to see her and impulsively put his arm around her shoulders, whereupon she stiffened. He withdrew his arm and she asked, "Don't you love me any more?" He then blushed, and she said, "Dear, you must not be so easily embarrassed and afraid of your feelings." The patient was able to stay with her only a few minutes more and following her departure he assaulted an aide and was put in the tubs.

Obviously, this result could have been avoided if the young man had been able to say, "Mother, it is obvious that you become uncomfortable when I put my arm around you, and that you have difficulty accepting a gesture of affection from me." However, the schizophrenic patient doesn't have this possibility open to him. His intense dependency and training prevents him from commenting upon his mother's communicative behavior, though she comments on his and forces him to accept and to attempt to deal with the complicated sequence. The complications for the patient include the following:

1. The mother's reaction of not accepting her son's affectionate gesture is masterfully covered up by her condemnation of him for withdrawing, and the patient denies his perception of the situation by accepting her condemnation.

2. The statement "don't you love me any more" in this context seems to imply:

(*a*) "I am lovable."

(*b*) "You should love me and if you don't you are bad or at fault."

(*c*) "Whereas you did love me previously you don't any longer," and thus focus is shifted from his expressing affection to his inability to be affectionate. Since the patient has also hated her, she is on good ground here, and he responds appropriately with guilt, which she then attacks.

(d) "What you just expressed *was not* affection," and in order to accept this statement the patient must deny what she and the culture have taught him about how one expresses affection. He must also question the times with her, and with others, when he thought he was experiencing affection and when they *seemed* to treat the situation as if he had. He experiences here loss-of-support phenomena and is put in doubt about the reliability of past experience.

3. The statement, "You must not be so easily embarrassed and afraid of your feelings," seems to imply;

(a) "You are not like me and are different from other nice or normal people because we express our feelings."

(b) "The feelings you express are all right, it's only that *you* can't accept them." However, if the stiffening on her part had indicated "these are unacceptable feelings," then the boy is told that he should not be embarrassed by unacceptable feelings. Since he has had a long training in what is and is not acceptable to both her and society, he again comes into conflict with the past. If he is unafraid of his own feelings (which mother implies is good), he should be unafraid of his affection and would then notice it was she who was afraid, but he must not notice that because her whole approach is aimed at covering up this shortcoming in herself.

The impossible dilemma thus becomes: "If I am to keep my tie to mother I must not show her that I love her, but if I do not show her that I love her, then I will lose her."

The importance to the mother of her special method of control is strikingly illustrated by the interfamily situation of a young woman schizophrenic who greeted the therapist on their first meeting with the remark, "Mother had to get married and now I'm here." This statement meant to the therapist that:

1. The patient was the result of an illegitimate pregnancy.

2. This fact was related to her present psychosis (in her opinion).

3. "Here" referred to the psychiatrist's office and to the patient's presence on earth for which

she had to be eternally indebted to her mother, especially since her mother had sinned and suffered in order to bring her into the world.

4. "Had to get married" referred to the shotgun nature of mother's wedding and to the mother's response to pressure that she must marry, and the reciprocal, that she resented the forced nature of the situation and blamed the patient for it.

Actually, all these suppositions subsequently proved to be factually correct and were corroborated by the mother during an abortive attempt at psychotherapy. The flavor of the mother's communications to the patient seemed essentially this: "I am lovable, loving, and satisfied with myself. You are lovable when you are like me and when you do what I say." At the same time the mother indicated to the daughter both by words and behavior: "You are physically delicate, unintelligent, and different from me ('not normal'). You need me and me alone because of these handicaps, and I will take care of you and love you." Thus the patient's life was a series of beginnings, of attempts at experience, which would result in failure and withdrawal back to the maternal hearth and bosom because of the collusion between her and her mother.

It was noted in collaborative therapy that certain areas important to the mother's self-esteem were especially conflictual situations for the patient. For example, the mother needed the fiction that she was close to her family and that a deep love existed between her and her own mother. By analogy the relationship to the grandmother served as the prototype for the mother's relationship to her own daughter. On one occasion when the daughter was seven or eight years old the grandmother in a rage threw a knife which barely missed the little girl. The mother said nothing to the grandmother but hurried the little girl from the room with the words, "Grandmommy really loves you." It is significant that the grandmother took the attitude toward the patient that she was not well enough controlled, and she used to chide her daughter for being too easy on the child. The grandmother was living in the house during one of the patient's psychotic episodes, and the girl took great delight in throwing various objects at the mother and grandmother while they cowered in fear.

Mother felt herself very attractive as a girl, and she felt that her daughter resembled her rather closely, although by damning with faint praise it was obvious that she felt the daughter definitely ran second. One of the daughter's first acts during a psychotic period was to announce to her mother that she was going to cut off all her hair. She proceeded to do this while the mother pleaded with her to stop. Subsequently the mother would show a picture of *herself* as a girl and explain to people how the patient would look if she only had her beautiful hair.

The mother, apparently without awareness of the significance of what she was doing, would equate the daughter's illness with not being very bright and with some sort of organic brain difficulty. She would invariably contrast this with her own intelligence as demonstrated by her *own* scholastic record. She treated her daughter with a completely patronizing and placating manner which was insincere. For example, in the psychiatrist's presence she promised her daughter that she would not allow her to have further shock treatments, and as soon as the girl was out of the room she asked the doctor if he didn't feel she should be hospitalized and given electric shock treatments. One clue to this deceptive behavior arose during the mother's therapy. Although the daughter had had three previous hospitalizations the mother had never mentioned to the doctors that she herself had had a psychotic episode when she discovered that she was pregnant. The family whisked her away to a small sanitarium in a nearby town, and she was, according to her own statement, strapped to a bed for six weeks. Her family did not visit her during this time, and no one except her parents and her sister knew that she was hospitalized.

There were two times during therapy when the mother showed intense emotion. One was in relating her own psychotic experience; the other was on the occasion of her last visit when she accused the therapist of trying to drive her crazy by forcing her to choose between her daughter and her husband. Against medical advice, she took her daughter out of therapy.

The father was as involved in the homeostatic aspects of the intrafamily situation as the mother. For example, he stated that he had to quit his position as an important attorney in order to bring his daughter to an area where competent psychiatric help was available. Subsequently, acting on cues from the patient (e.g., she frequently referred to a character named "Nervous Ned") the therapist was able to elicit from him that he had hated his job and for years had been trying to "get out from under." However, the daughter was made to feel that the move was initiated for her.

On the basis of our examination of the clinical data, we have been impressed by a number of observations including:

1. The helplessness, fear, exasperation, and rage which a double bind situation provokes in the patient, but which the mother may serenely and un-understandingly pass over. We have noted reactions in the father that both create double bind situations, or extend and amplify those created by the mother, and we have seen the father passive and outraged, but helpless, become ensnared in a similar manner to the patient.

2. The psychosis seems, in part, a way of dealing with double bind situations to overcome their inhibiting and controlling effect. The psychotic patient may make astute, pithy, often metaphorical remarks that reveal an insight into the forces binding him. Contrariwise, he may become rather expert in setting double bind situations himself.

3. According to our theory, the communication situation described is essential to the mother's security, and by inference to the family homeostasis. If this be so, then when psychotherapy of the patient helps him become less vulnerable to mother's attempts at control, anxiety will be produced in the mother. Similarly, if the therapist interprets to the mother the dynamics of the situation she is setting up with the patient, this should produce an anxiety response in her. Our impression is that when there is a perduring contact between patient and family (especially when the patient lives at home during psychotherapy), this leads to a disturbance (often severe) in the mother and some-

times in both mother and father and other siblings (10, 11).

CURRENT POSITION AND FUTURE PROSPECTS

Many writers have treated schizophrenia in terms of the most extreme contrast with any other form of human thinking and behavior. While it is an isolable phenomenon, so much emphasis on the differences from the normal— rather like the fearful physical segregation of psychotics—does not help in understanding the problems. In our approach we assume that schizophrenia involves general principles which are important in all communication and therefore many informative similarities can be found in "normal" communication situations.

We have been particularly interested in various sorts of communication which involve both emotional significance and the necessity of discriminating between orders of message. Such situations include play, humor, ritual, poetry, and fiction. Play, especially among animals, we have studied at some length (3). It is a situation which strikingly illustrates the occurrence of metamessages whose correct discrimination is vital to the cooperation of the individuals involved; for example, false discrimination could easily lead to combat. Rather closely related to play is humor, a continuing subject of our research. It involves sudden shifts in Logical Types as well as discrimination of those shifts. Ritual is a field in which unusually real or literal ascriptions of Logical Type are made and defended as vigorously as the schizophrenic defends the "reality" of his delusions. Poetry exemplifies the communicative power of metaphor —even very unusual metaphor—when labeled as such by various signs, as contrasted to the obscurity of unlabeled schizophrenic metaphor. The entire field of fictional communication, defined as the narration or depiction of a series of events with more or less of a label of actuality, is most relevant to the investigation of schizophrenia. We are not so much concerned with the content interpretation of fiction—although analysis of oral and destructive themes is illuminating to the student of schizophrenia—as with the formal problems involved in simultaneous existence of multiple levels of message in the fictional presentation of "reality." The drama is especially interesting in this respect, with both performers and spectators responding to messages about both the actual and the theatrical reality.

We are giving extensive attention to hypnosis. A great array of phenomena that occur as schizophrenic symptoms—hallucinations, delusions, alterations of personality, amnesias, and so on—can be produced temporarily in normal subjects with hypnosis. These need not be directly suggested as specific phenomena, but can be the "spontaneous" result of an arranged communication sequence. For example, Erickson (4) will produce a hallucination by first inducing catalepsy in a subject's hand and then saying, "There is no conceivable way in which your hand can move, yet when I give the signal, it must move." That is, he tells the subject his hand will remain in place, yet it will move, and in no way the subject can consciously conceive. When Erickson gives the signal, the subject hallucinates the hand moved, or hallucinates himself in a different place and therefore the hand was moved. This use of hallucination to resolve a problem posed by contradictory commands which cannot be discussed seems to us to illustrate the solution of a double bind situation via a shift in Logical Types. Hypnotic responses to direct suggestions or statements also commonly involve shifts in type, as in accepting the words "Here's a glass of water" or "You feel tired" as external or internal reality, or in literal response to metaphorical statements, much like schizophrenics. We hope that further study of hypnotic induction, phenomena, and waking will, in this controllable situation, help sharpen our view of the essential communicational sequences which produce phenomena like those of schizophrenia.

Another Erickson experiment (12) seems to isolate a double bind communicational sequence without the specific use of hypnosis. Erickson arranged a seminar so as to have a young chain smoker sit next to him and to be without cigarettes; other participants were briefed on what to do. All was ordered so that Erickson repeatedly turned to offer the young man a cigarette, but was always interrupted by a question from someone so that he turned away, "inadvertently" withdrawing the cigarettes from the young man's reach. Later another participant asked this young man if he had received the cigarette from Dr. Erickson. He replied, "What cigarette?", showed clearly that he had forgotten the whole sequence, and even refused a cigarette offered by another member, saying that he was too interested in the seminar discussion to smoke. This young man seems to us to be in an experimental situation paralleling the schizophrenic's double bind situation with mother: An important relationship, contradictory messages (here of giving and taking away), and comment blocked—because there was a seminar going on, and anyway it was all "inadvertent." And note the similar outcome: Amnesia for the double bind sequence and reversal from "He doesn't give" to "I don't want."

Although we have been led into these collateral areas, our main field of observation has been schizophrenia itself. All of us have worked directly with schizophrenic patients and much of this case material has been recorded on tape for detailed study. In addition, we are recording interviews held jointly with patients and their families, and we are taking sound motion pictures of mothers and disturbed, presumably preschizophrenic, children. Our hope is that these operations will provide a clearly evident record of the continuing, repetitive double binding which we hypothesize goes on steadily from infantile beginnings in the family situation of individuals who become schizophrenic. This basic family situation, and the overtly communicational characteristics of schizophrenia, have been the major focus of this paper. However, we expect our concepts and some of these data will also be useful in future work on other problems of schizophrenia, such as the variety of other symptoms, the character of the "adjusted state" before schizophrenia becomes manifest, and the nature and circumstances of the psychotic break.

THERAPEUTIC IMPLICATIONS OF THIS HYPOTHESIS

Psychotherapy itself is a context of multilevel communication, with exploration of the am-

biguous lines between the literal and metaphoric, or reality and fantasy, and indeed, various forms of play, drama, and hypnosis have been used extensively in therapy. We have been interested in therapy, and in addition to our own data we have been collecting and examining recordings, verbatim transcripts, and personal accounts of therapy from other therapists. In this we prefer exact records since we believe that how a schizophrenic talks depends greatly, though often subtly, on how another person talks to him; it is most difficult to estimate what was really occurring in a therapeutic interview if one has only a description of it, especially if the description is already in theoretical terms.

Except for a few general remarks and some speculation, however, we are not yet prepared to comment on the relation of the double bind to psychotherapy. At present we can only note:

1. Double bind situations are created by and within the psychotherapeutic setting and the hospital milieu. From the point of view of this hypothesis we wonder about the effect of medical "benevolence" on the schizophrenic patient. Since hospitals exist for the benefit of personnel as well as—as much as—more than—for the patient's benefit, there will be contradictions at times in sequences where actions are taken "benevolently" for the patient when actually they are intended to keep the staff more comfortable. We would assume that whenever the system is organized for hospital purposes and it is announced to the patient that the actions are for *his* benefit, then the schizophrenogenic situation is being perpetuated. This kind of deception will provoke the patient to respond to it as a double bind situation, and his response will be "schizophrenic" in the sense that it will be indirect and the patient will be unable to comment on the fact that he feels that he is being deceived. One vignette, fortunately amusing, illustrates such a response. On a ward with a dedicated and "benevolent" physician in charge there was a sign on the physician's door which said "Doctor's Office. Please Knock." The doctor was driven to distraction and finally capitulation by the obedient patient who carefully knocked every time he passed the door.

2. The understanding of the double bind and its communicative aspects may lead to innova-

tions in therapeutic technique. Just what these innovations may be is difficult to say, but on the basis of our investigation we are assuming that double bind situations occur consistently in psychotherapy. At times these are inadvertent in the sense that the therapist is imposing a double bind situation similar to that in the patient's history, or the patient is imposing a double bind situation on the therapist. At other times therapists seem to impose double binds, either deliberately or intuitively, which force the patient to respond differently than he has in the past.

An incident from the experience of a gifted psychotherapist illustrates the intuitive understanding of a double bind communicational sequence. Dr. Frieda Fromm-Reichmann (5) was treating a young woman who from the age of seven had built a highly complex religion of her own replete with powerful gods. She was very schizophrenic and quite hesitant about entering into a therapeutic situation. At the beginning of the treatment she said, "God R says I shouldn't talk with you." Dr. Fromm-Reichmann replied, "Look, let's get something into the record. To me God R doesn't exist, and that whole world of yours doesn't exist. To you it does, and far be it from me to think that I can take that away from you, I have no idea what it means. So I'm willing to talk with you in terms of that world, if only you know I do it so that we have an understanding that it doesn't exist for me. Now go to God R and tell him that we have to talk and he should give you permission. Also you must tell him that I am a doctor and that you have lived with him in his kingdom now from seven to sixteen—that's nine years—and he hasn't helped you. So now he must permit me to try and see whether you and I can do that job. Tell him that I am a doctor and this is what I want to try."

The therapist has her patient in a "therapeutic double bind." If the patient is rendered doubtful about her belief in her god then she is agreeing with Dr. Fromm-Reichmann, and is admitting her attachment to therapy. If she insists that God R is real, then she must tell him that Dr. Fromm-Reichmann is "more powerful" than he—again admitting her involvement with the therapist.

The difference between the therapeutic bind and the original double bind situation is in part the fact that the therapist is not involved in a life and death struggle himself. He can therefore set up relatively benevolent binds and gradually aid the patient in his emancipation from them. Many of the uniquely appropriate therapeutic gambits arranged by therapists seem to be intuitive. We share the goal of most psychotherapists who strive toward the day when such strokes of genius will be well enough understood to be systematic and commonplace.

REFERENCES

1. BATESON, G. Social planning and the concept of "deutero-learning." *Conference on Science, Philosophy, and Religion, Second Symposium.* New York: Harper, 1942.
2. BATESON, G. A theory of play and fantasy. *Psychiatric Research Reports,* 1955, 2, 39–51.
3. CARPENTER, C. R. A field study of the behavior and social relations of howling monkeys. *Comparative Psychological Monographs,* 1934, 10, 1–168.
4. ERICKSON, M. H. *Personal communication,* 1955.
5. FROMM-REICHMANN, F. *Personal communication,* 1956.
6. HALEY, J. Paradoxes in play, fantasy, and psychotherapy. *Psychiatric Research Reports,* 1955, 2, 52–58.
7. HARLOW, H. F. The formation of learning sets. *Psychological Review,* 1949, 56, 51–65.
8. HILGARD, J. R. Anniversary reactions in parents precipitated by children. *Psychiatry,* 1953, 16, 73–80.
9. HULL, C. L., *et al. Mathematico-deductive theory of rote learning.* New Haven: Yale University Press, 1940.
10. JACKSON, D. D. An episode of sleepwalking. *Journal of the American Psychoanalytic Association,* 1954, 2, 503–508.
11. JACKSON, D. D. Some factors influencing the Oedipus complex. *Psychoanalytic Quarterly,* 1954, 23, 566–581.
12. JACKSON, D. D. The question of family homeostasis. Presented at the American Psychiatric Association Meeting, St. Louis, May 7, 1954.
13. LORENZ, K. Z. *King Solomon's ring.* New York: Crowell, 1952.
14. PERCEVAL, J. *A narrative of the treatment experienced by a gentleman during a state of mental derangement, designed to explain the causes and nature of insanity, etc.* London: Effingham Wilson, 1836 and 1840.

15. RUESCH, J., & BATESON, G. *Communication: the social matrix of psychiatry.* New York: Norton, 1951.

16. VON DOMARUS, E. The specific laws of logic in schizophrenia. In J. S. Kasanin (Ed.), *Language and thought in schizophrenia.* Berkeley: University of California Press, 1944.

17. WHITEHEAD, A. N., & RUSSELL, B. *Principia mathematica.* Cambridge: Cambridge University Press, 1910.

39.

NORMAN GARMEZY AND ELIOT H. RODNICK

PREMORBID ADJUSTMENT AND PERFORMANCE IN SCHIZOPHRENIA

INTRODUCTION

The observation that schizophrenic patients are a heterogeneous lot is not an uncommon one. A symposium directed solely toward reiterating such an obvious fact would be prosaic and commonplace at best, since a substantial body of evidence drawn from fields such as physiology, biochemistry, psychology, genetics and psychiatry support a concept of schizophrenia as one encompassing a heterogeneous group of disorders. Thus the concept of reaction-types has evolved to denote differences in various symptom pictures subsumed under the disorder. Hoskins aptly stated the problem posed by using the single term "schizophrenia" for a wide range of symptoms when he noted that "the possibility must still be faced that 'schizophrenia' may be an entity by fiat only, as are disorders in general that are delimited merely on a basis of symptoms. For all that we know explicitly to the contrary the psychosis may be strictly comparable to such diagnostic entities as 'head ache' or 'hypertension,' each of which has a common core manifestation but each of which may represent very dissimilar disorders. The

first and most fundamental question of all then, explicitly what *is* schizophrenia must continue disconcertingly to face us. . . ." (19, p. 72).

Attesting to the complex and diverse nature of the disorder as wide variations in such relevant factors as these: premorbid personality patterns of patients; the time interval preceding the onset of the disorder; the types of precipitants which presumably actuate the disease; the symptom picture during the course of the illness and subsequent prognosis. A variety of terms—dementia praecox-schizophrenia, process-reactive, chronic episodic, typical-atypical, evolutionary-reactive, true-schizophreniform—have appeared in the literature to describe these differing patterns of the disorder. Of these, the concept of a "process" type of schizophrenic patient in contrast to a "reactive" one has received wide acceptance in some quarters. The former is used to describe a patient who has exhibited a poorly integrated prepsychotic personality, characterized by marked sexual, social and occupational inadequacy, a lack of emotional responsiveness and social isolation. The slide into psychosis, for this patient, is usually insidious and without pertinent stress and most frequently occurs in late adolescence. The disorder is made manifest by the gradual onset of emotional blunting, withdrawal from daily activities, apathy and indifference, somatic delusions and marked disturbances in thinking—a pattern which may be maintained through long years of hospitalization.

Wiener has recently provided a description of the modal "reactive" type as follows:

From birth to the fifth year, the maturational and developmental history showed no defects, physical health was good. Generally school and home adjustment was good. Parents were accepting. Heterosexual relationships were established. The patient had friends and domestic troubles did not disrupt his behavior.

The onset of the illness was often sudden with a clear-cut, understandable precipitating event. Aggression was expressed verbally. Decency was retained. The course was fulminating, with massive hallucinatory experiences, ideas of reference, and mild paranoid trends, as well as sensorial impairment. A thought disorder was present according to some authors, but not others. Response to treatment was good" (34, pp. 156–7).

In the light of these descriptions it is quite obvious that from a clinical standpoint some differentiated typology of schizophrenia would seem to be warranted. But the somewhat arbitrary separation of patients into "process" and "reactive" types sets forth a dichotomous conception of the disorder. This dichotomy has been accentuated by the application of a dualistic conception of etiology. Thus, fundamental to the separation have been the twin etiologic notions of an organic substrate for one (process) and a psychogenic base for the other (reactive).

"The most enlightened psychiatric thought," wrote Hoskins, "is gradually coming to an acceptance of the assumption that the psychosis is a genuine entity that consists of true 'process' or 'constitutional' schizophrenia and should be set aside from the various schizophreniform reactions that are frequently grouped with the true psychosis" (19, p. 71).

SCHIZOPHRENIA AS A DICHOTOMOUS TYPOLOGY

Despite recurrent failures to find support for a fundamental biological deviation associated with the disorder (24) the view of schizophrenia as a dichotomous typology influenced either by somatic *or* by psychic factors has been maintained for many years. One can identify some of the reasons underlying such a persistent and tenaciously-held formulation:

1. The fact that some types of schizophrenia seem to have a readily identifiable psychogenic precipitant whereas no obvious stressors are seen in other cases all too frequently has led to the conclusion that somatic considerations alone influence the latter group.

2. Discomfort with the current state of psychological research—its complexity, diffuseness, imprecision and (at times) superficiality—has led some investigators to look longingly toward the greater exactitude and lesser complexity promised by the biological sciences. Recent advances in studying the biology of schizophrenia (7, 24) undoubtedly have reinforced the belief that the complex problems of the genesis of this disease are more researchable in fields such as biochemistry and physiology. Coupled with these advances has been an awareness by investigators of the great methodological difficulties inherent in any effort to reconstruct retrospectively, through the verbal reports of patients or parents, the early family milieu of an individual (4, 16).

3. The biases of individual investigators have also played a role in accentuating a simplified dichotomous conception of the disorder. Benjamin (7) has pointed out how the reductionistic biases of some investigators deny the possibility of attributing causality to psychological variables. Graduate training in all disciplines all too frequently produces the type of tunnel vision in research to which Benjamin has assigned the very appropriate terms of "biophobia" and "psychophobia."

4. The comfort of the "*either-or*" solution creates ready adherents to a mind-body dualism. The lack of an adequate theoretical conceptualization of schizophrenia which can effectively incorporate both psychological and biological variables tends to foster such simple choices. On the other hand, a tolerance for ambiguity above and beyond the call of duty is required of investigators who are called upon to accept a "psychosomatic view of schizophrenia which conceives of any given case as actually occurring on some point of a continuum from a hypothetical point of complete psychogenicity to a hypothetical point of complete organicity" (5, p. 444). Such a vague begging of the question fails to create islands of comfort for either the biophile, the psychophile or their phobic counterparts.

DEVELOPMENT OF PROCESS-REACTIVE CONCEPT

Certainly, on the basis of empirical evidence, there is little substantial support for a process-organic versus reactive-psychogenic formulation of the etiology of schizophrenia (24). Nevertheless, this view has been maintained for many years and has been reinforced by the historical development of the concept of schizophrenia. A brief examination of several highlights of that development may indicate how the process-reactive formulation came to be associated with the concept of differentiated etiologies and prognoses.

Kraepelin, as the great taxonomer of the psychoses, brought order and system to the chaotic mass of symptoms he studied. His criteria for classification was essentially a prognostic one—some disorders (*e.g.*, manic-depressive) were reversible or self-limiting with recovery and remission predetermined for such patients; others were not only incurable but actually were deteriorative in nature. Dementia praecox occupied the latter niche and therapeutic efforts were "based on the complacent expectant attitude that if (the disease) is a dementia praecox the patient will deteriorate" (38, p. 456). The Kraepelinian influence was modified by the genius of Bleuler whose perceptive systematizing of observations of patients led him to conclude that dementia praecox could not be considered a disease entity but rather a group of reactions for which there existed correlated dimensions based upon premorbid, mental status and prognostic factors. By indicating that not all cases of schizophrenia showed the deteriorative consequences postulated by Kraepelin, the study of remission and the factors potentially responsible for it came into more central focus. Although Bleuler, like his great predecessor, believed in a basic organic substrate for the disorder, his conceptualization of "the group of schizophrenias" allowed for the gradual introduction of a more psychologically oriented position in which mechanisms of autism, delusions and the like were seen as secondary adaptive symptoms (often dependent upon "psychic influences and interests") in contrast to a primary thought (association) disturbance. Thus, the way was opened for subsequent psychodynamic formulations of schizophrenia and a development of interest in its psychological antecedents and correlates. Concern with a process-reactive concept could only occur as greater attention came to be focused on both the behavioral antecedents for schizophrenia and the variations and qualitative dissimilarities of behavior exhibited during the period of psychosis. Bleuler's observation that the disease "may take a course which is both qualitatively and temporally rather irregular (with) constant advances, halts, recrudescences or remissions possible at any time" (9, p. 245) paved the way for many prognostic studies which were carried out in the late 30's and early 40's in America (10, 21, 22, 27, 30). To this development must be added the contribution of Adolf Meyer who conceived of schizophrenia as an abnormal type of habit pattern which evolved out of biological, cultural, sociological and psychological influences and experiences. To understand the patient and the disorder, Meyer made extensive use of life history methods which provided a framework for correlating case history antecedents with subsequent prognosis.

The irregularities in the clinical course of the disorder which had been observed by Bleuler and others is simply another manifestation of the variability so characteristic of the schizophrenic patient. With such clearly disparate clinical patterns present in the disorder an obvious research strategy for investigators (irrespective of discipline) would be to search out the sources of the heterogeneity in one's observations. By paying greater attention to subject variables one could reasonably expect that greater patient homogeneity would result in a reduction in response variability—whether such responses reflected biological or psychological variables.

It is all the more surprising, then, to find a marked neglect of the problem of differentiating among schizophrenic patients in experimental research—this despite the recognition of an almost ubiquitous variability which characterizes data obtained from samples of schizophrenic patients in both physiological (19) and psychological (20) investigations.[1]

---

[1] There have, of course, been many attempts to categorize patients on the basis of the more traditional diagnostic sub-types. The ambiguous results obtained by such methods are not surprising since

However, the *need* for a more adequate separation of patients in research has been recognized. In an earlier review of the literature, Bellak wrote:

> We believe that it may be helpful to make a diagnostic division by differentiating definitely between schizophrenia and dementia praecox. . . . We believe that such a differentiation is justified in view of the results of prognostic studies. . . . The most significant result of all (studies) was that almost any data observed showed a greater variability than in normals. . . . We believe, in general, that differentiation of the group may lead to more clear-cut results in all fields of research and its problems. . . .
> It is believed that with the help of such diagnostic criteria the results on studies of any nature will become more uniform, will be interpreted more easily, and, therefore, lead to a final clarification of many still obscure problems (5, pp. 445–447).

DIAGNOSTIC CRITERIA: METHODOLOGICAL PROBLEMS

Although the conclusions drawn by Bellak may be overly optimistic, his suggestion of differentiating among schizophrenic patients seems eminently sensible. However, more than a decade later this dictum has been largely ignored by many investigators interested in schizophrenia. What are the criteria to be used for the selection of schizophrenic subjects for research which would reduce some of the response variability? Even the researcher with a pervasive belief in more adequately differentiating within a schizophrenic group would be greatly handicapped when confronted with subjective descriptions of unscaled dimensions, however valid these would be as prognostic criteria.

The Elgin Prognostic Scale (35) does provide

a quantitative ordering of 20 relevant dimensions which are weighted for prognostic significance. Its disadvantages, however, include an unwieldiness rooted in an overly-elaborate, multivariate structure, a partial adherence to a constitutional and somatotypic bias, a descriptive vagueness in several dimensions and a dependence upon extensive life history and mental status data which often are not available in the typical case history file. Despite these shortcomings the scale has been used effectively by a number of investigators (3, 23, 28, 36).

Several of these objections have been overcome in the simpler, empirically-derived Scale of Premorbid Adjustment developed by Phillips (32). Both the Phillips and Elgin Prognostic Scales stress such factors as interest and participation in social activities, heterosexual activity and the maintenance of object relations, the type of precipitant presumed to actuate the disorder, and manifestations of the disease process including such mental status contents as adequacy of affect and mood, thought disturbances, etc. On the other hand, the Phillips Scale does not include ratings of such elusive concepts as constitution (*e.g.* "a healthy, strong, energetic, physical and mental makeup that makes the interplay between heredity and environmental influence during childhood a satisfactory one,") low energy tone, asthenic build, toxicity or exhaustion, etc. The Phillips Scale provides for a quantitative rating of three types of case history data—social and sexual history in the premorbid period, the precipitating event and the signs of the disease process. Recent research (1, 8, 12, 14, 15, 17, 18, 26, 33, 37) suggests that separating patients on the basis of adequacy or inadequacy of social-sexual premorbid adjustment (*i.e.* into so-called "good" and "poor" premorbid subjects) results in a marked reduction in the variability in schizophrenic performance.[2]

a distribution by sub-types varies markedly along a prognostic dimension. Although the simple and hebephrenic groups tend to become the more chronic cases with catatonics showing a more favorable prognosis, the greater bulk of experimental cases are frequently drawn from the paranoid subgroup (largely because of their relative intactness). Such patients, however, are distributed quite widely along a continuum of social adequacy in the premorbid period; samples of these groups, then, are invariably heterogeneous and contain an admixture of prognostically favorable and unfavorable subjects. A recent survey we have completed of 120 schizophrenic patients varying in sub-type and divided into "good" and "poor" premorbid sub-groups lends support to these generalizations.

[2] To the reader the separation of patients into "good" and "poor" premorbid categories may suggest that we too have a dichotomous conception of the disorder which is coterminous with the process-reactive differentiation. This is not so. The separation of patients into "goods" and "poors" is not founded on a theoretic belief involving differentiated etiologies but is simply a first entry into the problem of reducing variance through the use of a scaling instrument with marked limitations. Al-

Other reasons for using the premorbid subscale alone are these: (1) The types of case history data needed to secure a valid scale rating is minimal; (2) Phillips' original study (32) indicates that the premorbid scale is the best predictor of remission;[3] (3) Case history information available for rating the precipitating event and descriptions of the mental status report are frequently skimpy or indeterminate; (4) Several reliability studies indicate a high correlation. ($r = +.80$ and higher) for the premorbid scale ratings of experienced clinical faculty members and less sophisticated graduate students who have been trained in the use of the scale. Of even greater importance are recent findings that ratings secured from patient informants result in assignments to premorbid categories which are virtually identical with those based upon case history data. In one study in which information obtained from patients was compared with data available from the case record, it was found that the assignment to the same premorbid category occurred

though "goods" and "poors" do share some attributes which have been assigned to "reactive" and "process" cases, our own position is theoretically neutral and makes no assumptions involving an exogenous-endogenous position. Indeed the research of our group strongly suggests that premorbid adjustment can be thought of as a continuous rather than a dichotomous distribution. In several recent studies the use of the scale in a trichotomous fashion provides further differentiations within the groups (15). For experimental conveniences, however, we have taken to using the extremes of the distribution —an arbitrary but useful procedure. Therefore, our own view of "goods" and "poors" is based upon utilitarian considerations. The critical empirical problem which remains unanswered is that of determining the nature of the range of differences in performance between the groups in various tasks and the exploration of personality variables and life history factors which are correlated with such differences. Such research is now in progress at Duke University.

[3]Originally we believed that this finding held primarily for male patients. A larger proportion of non-remitted female patients score in the "good" premorbid range because marriage and maintaining a stable home appear to be less differentiating items for such patients. However, a recent comparison of 24 remitted and 19 non-remitted female schizophrenic patients indicates significant differences between the groups in level of premorbid social and sexual adequacy. Marital status, too, has proved to be highly differentiating. These data are now being cross-validated on another sample of female patients.

in 43 of the 46 cases. Thus in the absence of an adequate case history, the patient can be used as a respondent to secure data necessary for assignment to an appropriate premorbid category.

RESEARCH REPORTS

The predictive and construct validity of the Phillips Scale has been described in considerable detail elsewhere (33). A brief description of three experiments will indicate the effectiveness of the scale in reducing the characteristic variability in performance of groups of schizophrenic patients and in "teasing out" significant differences between such groups and control patients —differences which although present may be obscured by the heterogeneity of the schizophrenic sample.

VISUAL DISCRIMINATION

In a study of visual discrimination, Dunn (13) presented schizophrenic and normal control Ss with the stimulus scenes which appear in Figure 5.1. These scenes (which were selected for their presumed cue relevance for the patients) consisted of a series of silhouetted mother-boy figures depicting *Scolding*, *Whipping*, and *Feedings* interactions with a more neutral *Objects* (*house-tree*) picture. A series of five variations of each scene was prepared in which an incidental component of the standard picture was systematically modified. The standard and five variations of the Scolding scene are illustrated in Figure 5.2. In this sequence the mother's arm gradually descended in a 45° arc toward the boy. In similar fashion the angle of the tree limb was varied in the Object scene; the variant for Whipping and Feeding was the spatial separation of the figures. The procedure of the experiment involved a brief (1 sec.) exposure of the standard scene followed, after a 2 sec. pause, by a ⅕ sec. exposure of either the standard or one of its variations. The subject's task was to determine, after each paired exposure, whether the two pictures were the same or different. This judgment was indicated to the experimenter when the subject made an appropriate movement of a switch lever: A plot of the frequency of "same" judgments as a function

FIGURE 5.1. The four scenes used in Dunn's experiment (From [13]).

of the magnitude of the figural variation afforded a measure of the relative discriminative skills of the normal and schizophrenic groups. These gradients of discrimination for all four stimulus scenes are presented in Figure 5.3. The results indicated that there were no differences between the groups for the *Whipping, Feeding,* and *Object* scenes. For *Scolding,* however, the schizophrenic patients exhibited a markedly flatter gradient and presumably poorer discrimination relative to the control group. When the Phillips Scale was later used to subdivide further the patient sample into so-called "good" and "poor" subgroups on the basis of social and sexual adequacy prior to the illness, the results indicated quite clearly that the variance in the *Scolding* scene was produced primarily by the poor pre-

morbid schizophrenics. These results, which are presented graphically in Figure 5.4, lend support to a hypothesis of a differential sensitivity to pictorial representations of censure by poor relative to either normal or good premorbid schizophrenic subjects. Of relevance here are the additional findings that patients with poor premorbid histories report more intensely disturbed relationships with their mothers (13, 17, 18, 33).

VERBAL LEARNING: REMINISCENCE

In another study, performed by Bleke, (8) a verbal learning task was used to compare reminiscence in schizophrenic and normal (control) patients. Reminiscence has been defined as an increase in retention which occurs over time

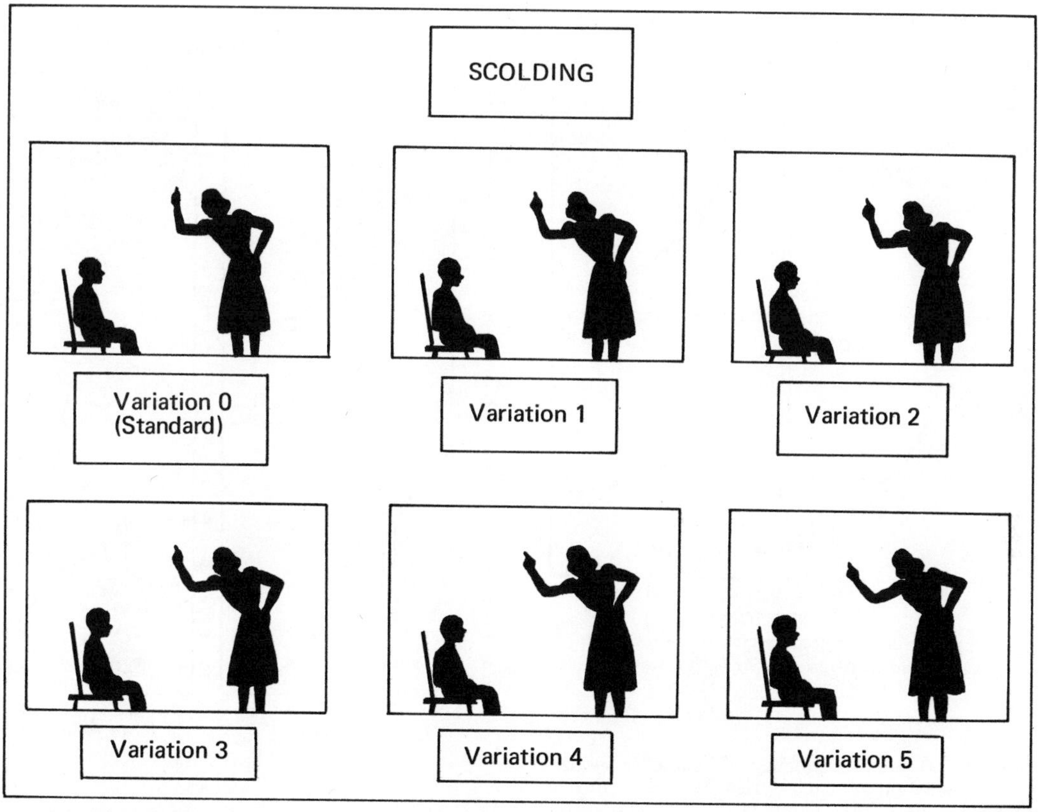

FIGURE 5.2. Variations in the Scolding scene used in Dunn's experiment (From [13]).

(and in the absence of practice) and follows the cessation of learning once a partial criterion has been reached. The theoretical relevance of the concept has been detailed elsewhere (29) but central to many theories of reminiscence is the notion that interferences which are generated during learning, dissipate in the course of a rest interval, leading to improved retention in the post-rest period. Bleke hypothesized that a verbal task learned under "punishment" (the lighting of a "Wrong" signal to provide information about errors) would generate marked interferences and subsequent reminiscence effects following a rest period for schizophrenic but *not* for normal control patients. On the other hand, no improvement in retention was posited for either group under a "reward" condition in which a "Right" signal operated to signal correct responses.

When the two groups were compared for reminiscence under the reward and punishment conditions the results indicated a trend in support of the hypothesis, although the heightened variability of the schizophrenic group did not permit a rejection of the null hypothesis.

In Table 5.8 these results, together with data derived by again separating the total schizophrenic group into subgroups of "*Goods*" and "*Poors*" are presented. It can be seen that the premorbid separation helps to clarify the findings. It is the poor premorbid group, confronted with a learning problem under threat of punishment, which shows the greatest amount of reminiscence. If threat of censure does generate in-

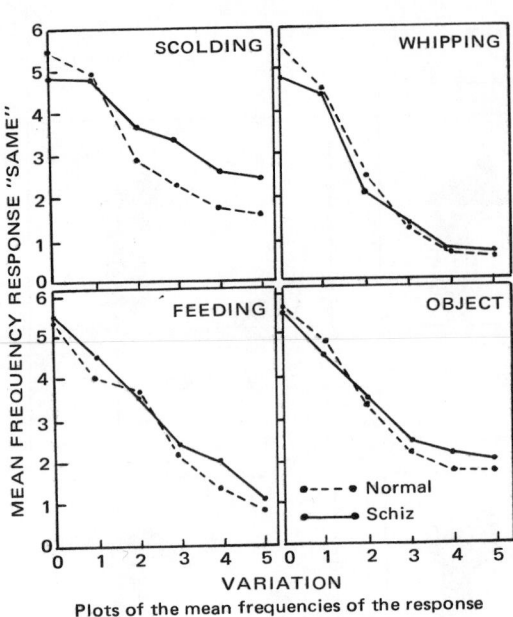

FIGURE 5.3. Mean frequency of "Same" responses to each variation of each series for schizophrenic and normal Ss (From Dunn [13]).

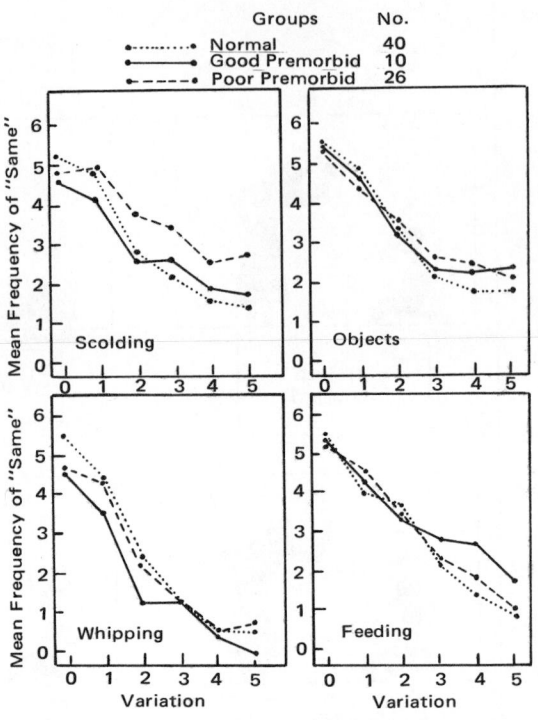

FIGURE 5.4. Mean frequency of "Same" responses to each variation of each series for good and poor premorbid schizophrenic and normal Ss.

terferences, these are rather specific to patients whose prepsychotic behavioral patterns were tenuous and inadequate.[4] In addition, as can be seen from an examination of the measure of variability (standard deviation) in Table 5.8, these patients also show greater homogeneity under punishment than either the good premorbid or normal control subjects. Certainly, these results run counter to the more usual observations of heightened variability in the performance of schizophrenic patients. Is it possible that such variability does not reflect an attribute of the disorder *per se* as much as it does the procedures

used in selecting samples of schizophrenics for research purposes?

SIZE ESTIMATION AND SYMBOLIC VALUE

In a third study, Harris (18) related distortions in size estimation to the symbolic value of stimuli which were being judged by schizophrenic and control Ss. Patients were asked to judge from memory the sizes of pictures which had been previously shown to them. These pictures, seen in Figure 5.5, were accompanied by appropriate verbal descriptions so as to eliminate any ambiguity regarding their contents. These included mother-son scenes of over-protecting, rejecting (ignoring), dominating and feeding (acceptance) relationships together with a more neutral tree-brush scene and that of a geometric figure (square).

---

[4]An analysis of Bleke's data suggests that such interferences may be a function of competing responses produced by the demands of the task itself and the growth of avoidance-type behaviors which are generated by poor premorbid patients only during the course of learning under punishment (33).

TABLE 5.8

REMINISCENCE SCORES FOR GOOD AND POOR
PREMORBID SCHIZOPHRENIC SS AND NORMAL SS
UNDER CONDITIONS OF REWARD AND PUNISHMENT*

Experimental Conditions and Groups	N	Mean Reminis- cence Score	SD
Total Normal Group— Reward	20	+0.75	2.14
Total Normal Group— Punishment	20	0.00	2.28
Total Schiz. Group—Reward	20	+0.20	1.77
Total Schiz. Group— Punishment	20	+1.10	2.42

SCHIZOPHRENIC GROUP SUBDIVIDED ON BASIS OF
PREMORBID LEVEL OF ADJUSTMENT

Poor Premorbid Schiz. Ss— Reward	10	0.00	1.94
Poor Premorbid Schiz. Ss— Punishment	10	+2.50	1.68
Good Premorbid Schiz. Ss— Reward	10	+0.40	1.56
Good Premorbid Schiz. Ss— Punishment	10	−0.30	2.23

+ = Reminiscence......

*From Bleke (8).

When the schizophrenic group was once again separated along the dimension of social adequacy as measured by the Phillips Scale, striking trends emerged. Figure 5.6 offers a comparison of the size estimates made by groups of good and poor premorbid patients and normal control subjects. It can be seen that Poors showed a marked tendency to overestimate the sizes of mother-son pictures, whereas Goods leaned toward underestimation with the normal subjects most clearly approximating objective equality.

What if Harris had failed to separate his patient group? In that event, his results would have proved disappointingly ambiguous. In Figure 5.7 the data for the two subgroups of schizophrenic patients have been combined. It can be seen that schizophrenic and normal groups do not differ significantly in accuracy in judging the sizes of contentually relevant pictures. Combining the data of good and poor premorbid Ss results in mean values which approximate the objective reality achieved by normals in estimating the size of a standard stimulus; but this is clearly an artifact produced by summing the widely disparate and bidirectional behaviors of the two subgroups of pa-

FIGURE 5.5. The scenes used in the size-estimation task. The actual pictures were negatives of the above scenes (From Harris [18]).

tients. Had Harris, then, viewed the schizophrenic group as a totality he would have committed a Type I error (the rejection of a hypothesis which is true). To return once more to the problem of variability, it is of importance to note that the combined schizophrenic group showed such marked variability in performance that a comparison of the variances of the experimental and control groups by F tests for each scene necessitated, in most instances, rejecting an assumption of homogeneity of variance—a condition which did not obtain when the good and poor premorbid separation was employed.

RECENT STUDIES: SIGNIFICANCE
OF CENSURE

A study recently completed by Engelhart (14)

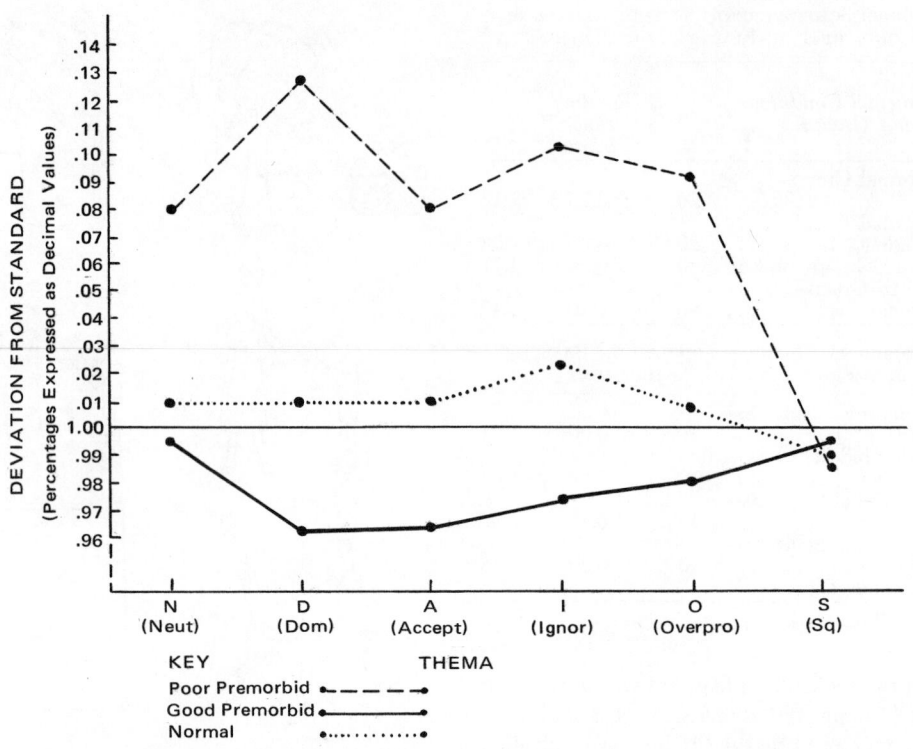

FIGURE 5.6. Mean size estimates of each of the six scenes for good and poor premorbid schizophrenic and normal groups (From Harris [18]).

affords some insight into the sensitivity of poor premorbid patients to criticism or censure and its consequent influence on their performances as manifested in the Dunn and Bleke studies. Using Osgood's Semantic Differential (31) (an objective method for studying the multivariate differentiation of the meanings of individual words or concepts) Engelhart had good and poor premorbid schizophrenic and normal control patients rate concepts of affection (*Sympathetic, Affectionate, Loving*), rejection (*Indifferent, Neglecting,* and *Ignoring*), domination (*Dominating*), punitiveness (*Scolding, Fault Finding, Punishing*), overprotection (*Protecting, Sheltering, Babying*), and severity or strictness (*Severe, Harsh, Strict*). These traits were paired with scales from the Semantic Differential

reflecting maximum loadings on the three major dimensions of meaning defined by the instrument. The dimensions and the polarities representative of each were these: *evaluative* (nice –awful, kind–cruel, fair–unfair); *potency* (heavy–light, large–small, strong–weak) and *activity* (sharp–dull, fast–slow, hot–cold). Figures 5.8, 5.9 and 5.10 respectively present graphically the results of the ratings of all groups for 14 of the above concepts on the evaluative, potency, and activity dimensions. Engelhart will detail these results in a forthcoming publication. Briefly, however, he found that although the groups did not differ in the semantic attributes assigned to the concepts on the evaluative dimension, the poor premorbid patients tended to rate concepts of rejection,

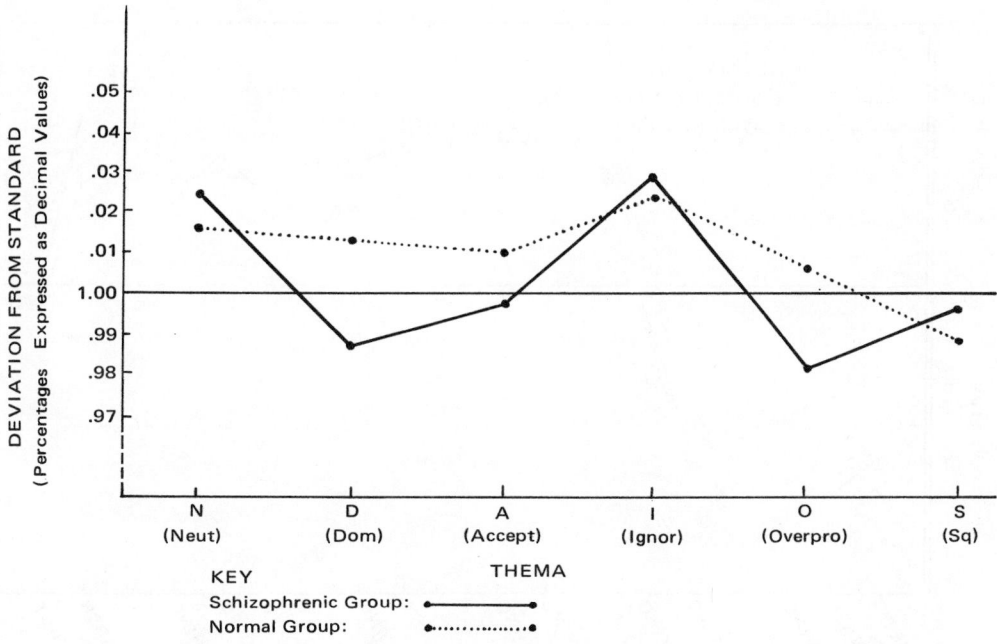

FIGURE 5.7. Mean size estimates of each of the six scenes for total schizophrenic and normal groups (From Harris [18]).

domination and punishment as significantly more potent and active relative to the good premorbid and normal control subjects.

These results may clarify the earlier findings of performance deficits exhibited by Poors when confronted with tasks involving experimenter-induced censure or the pictorial representation of censorious parent-child relationships (33). Engelhart's demonstration that Poors perceive censuring concepts as distinctly more powerful and vigorous would suggest that such schizophrenic patients bring to situations in which censorious stimuli are operative marked differences in the meanings they are prepared to assign to such cues. Such differential meanings would be congruent with the patient's omnipresent perception of threat in his external environment (2, 11) and could serve to mobilize habitual patterns of avoidance or withdrawal in response to such threat which would conflict

with effective task performance (33). Bleke (8) and Zahn (37) have both shown that poor premorbid schizophrenic patients who are engaged in learning and discrimination tasks which require them to manipulate a switch lever to indicate an appropriate response, tend to avoid (more frequently than do normal or good premorbid subjects) those lever movements which are immediately followed by the illumination of a box reading "Wrong". Subsequently, Alvarez (1) demonstrated that merely pairing a photograph of a person (rated previously by patients as affectively neutral) with a "Wrong" signal in an incidental learning task, results in a greater decline in preference for such pictures by poor premorbid schizophrenic patients.

A final point is quite relevant to the earlier discussion of the attributes of a process-reactive dichotomy. As has been noted, the term "process" schizophrenia has been equated in the

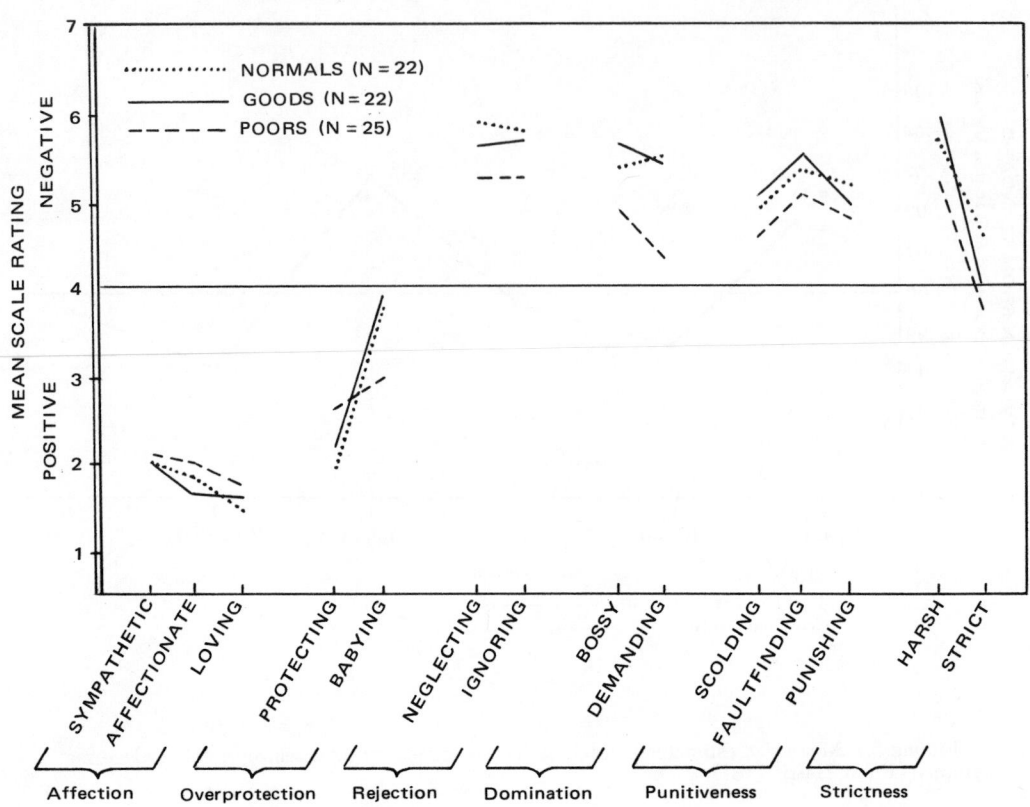

FIGURE 5.8. Mean ratings on the evaluative scale of the semantic differential for good and poor premorbid schizophrenic and normal groups (From Engelhart [14]).

literature with origins that are essentially endogenous and organic in contrast to the presumed exogenous-psychogenic antecedents of a "reactive" schizophrenia. Indeed, such assertions have been made so repetitively that the process-organic, reactive-psychogenic pairing has been treated as if it were a truism by some investigators. Thus an oversimplified dichotomy of types of schizophrenia has been made isomorphic with an equally oversimplified picture of causation. It seems necessary to observe that a premature declaration of support for such a simple distinction can conceivably do a major disservice to research in the psychology of schizophrenia.

RECENT STUDIES: PATIENT-PARENT RELATIONSHIPS

Several recent studies conducted at Duke suggest that variations in premorbid adequacy may be related to differences in familial organization —a finding which could conceivably have implications for understanding the schizophrenic disorder. Garmezy, Stockner and Clarke (17) had patients give answers to child rearing attitude scales as they believed their mothers and fathers would have answered these when they were "growing up." Poor premorbid patients relative to Goods and Normals assigned more deviant attitudes to both parents. However, intrafamily comparisons based upon the same items indi-

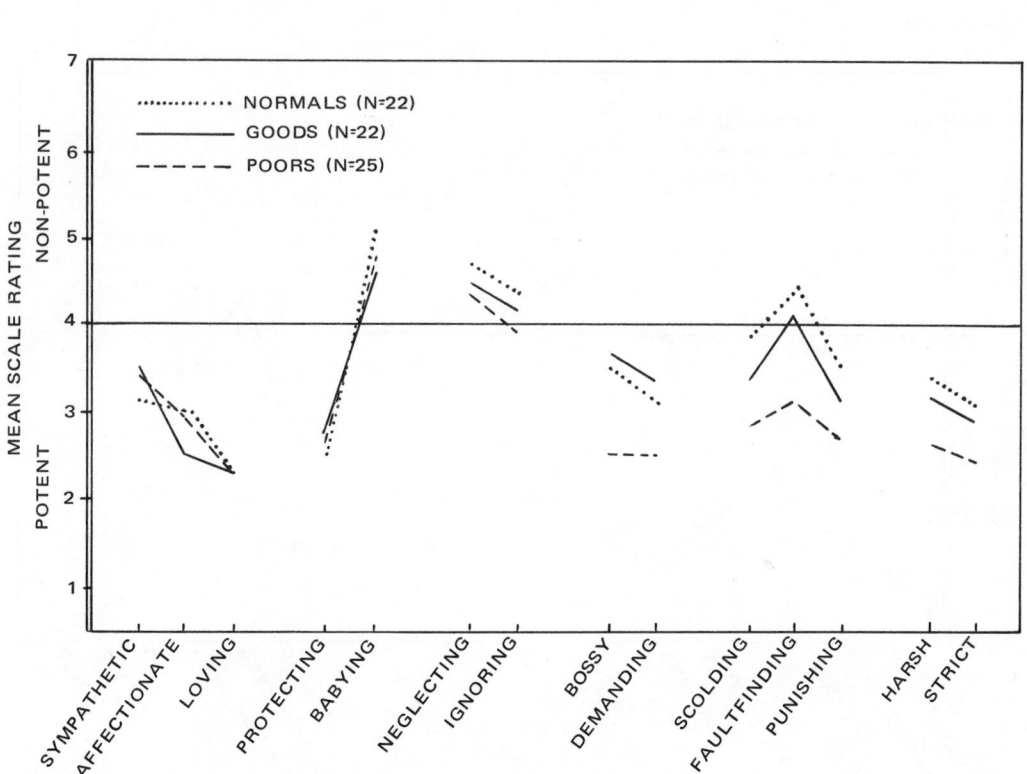

FIGURE 5.9. Mean ratings on the potency scale of the semantic differential for good and poor premorbid schizophrenic and normal groups (From Engelhart [14]).

cated that, unlike the maternal dominance asserted by Poors, striking patterns of paternal dominance were characteristic of the Goods. The typical clinical pattern of a dominant mother and an ineffectual father so frequently described as characteristic of the families of schizophrenic patients (25) may hold (from the standpoint of the patient's perception) for the poor premorbid group, but such role patterns tend to be reversed in the good premorbid group.

Recently, Farina completed a study (15) in which he used a structured situational test to examine patterns of dominance and conflict in parents of schizophrenic patients. Using 36 sets

of parents (equated for education and social class status), divided into three groups based upon the hospital status of their biological sons (poor and good premorbid schizophrenics and a control group of parents of tubercular patients who had never exhibited psychiatric symptoms), Farina presented his subjects with a series of hypothetical situations depicting either the misbehavior of a son or a problem situation involving parent and son. Typical of the situations he used were these:

While shopping for a windbreaker for your twelve year old son you see a coat his size which you like very much. You know your son wants a windbreaker and this coat is very different from what he wants

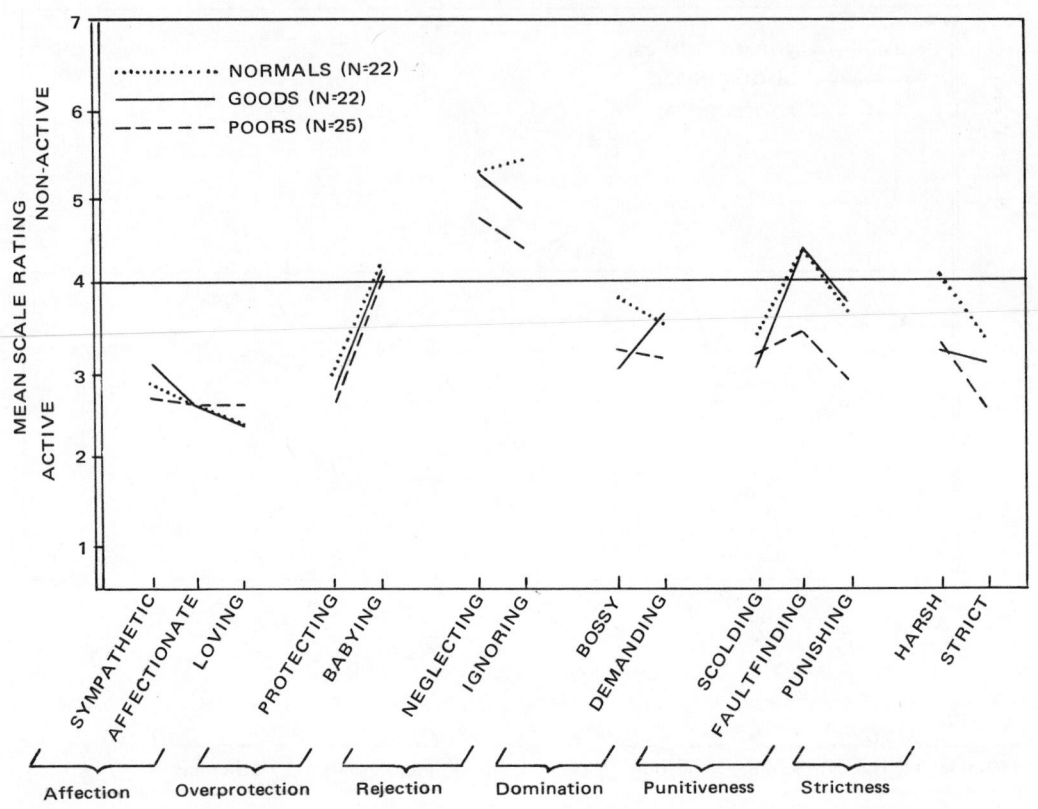

FIGURE 5.10. Mean ratings on the activity scale of the semantic differential for good and poor premorbid schizophrenic and normal groups (From Engelhart [14]).

but you think the coat would be much better for him. Which do you buy?

A gang of boys calls to your eight year old son to come out and play. You don't think it is good for your son to play with these boys but now he starts to leave the house to go with them.

These and comparable structured situations were presented to each parent for solution singly and then to the two parents in concert. Farina used objective indices suggestive of dominance, such as the frequency of times each parent spoke first and last, the extent to which one parent yielded his or her own solution to one provided by the partner, the frequency of occasions in which one spouse passively accepted the solutions suggested by the other, etc.

For indications of conflict, indices such as these were used: frequency and duration of simultaneous (overlapping) speech, frequency of interruptions by mother and father, the number of failures by the parents to come to a mutually acceptable solution, the frequency of disagreements and aggressions exhibited by each parent, etc.

Figures 5.11 (Speaks First and Last) and 5.12 (Yielding)[5] present graphic evidence in support

---

[5]"Speaks First," "Speaks Last" and "Total First and Last" refers to the frequency of times (summed for all 12 stories) a parent initiated and concluded an interaction. For the "Yielding" measure Farina ordered the parental solutions along a dimension of amount of pressure placed upon the

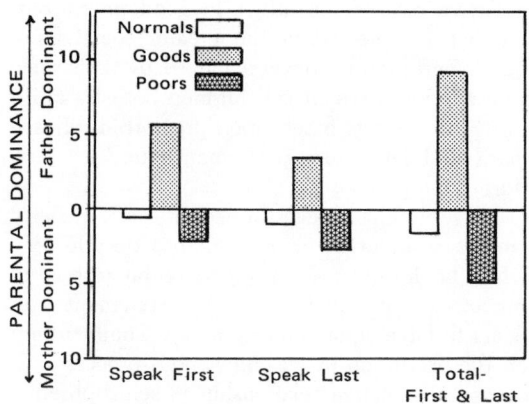

FIGURE 5.11. Dominance behavior (Speaks First, Speaks Last and Total-First and Last) of parents of good and poor premorbid schizophrenic and normal patients (From Farina [15]).

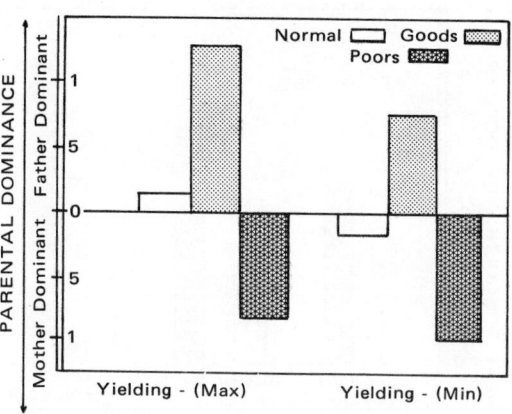

FIGURE 5.12. Dominance behavior (Yielding) of parents of good and poor premorbid schizophrenic and normal patients (From Farina [15]).

of greater mother dominance in the poor premorbid parent group and greater father dominance among the Goods. Conflict measures are represented in Figures 5.13 (Disagreements and Aggressions) and 5.14 (Interruptions). These graphs reveal the marked conflict which characterized the behavior of the poor premorbid families. The results of Farina's experiment may be summarized in this fashion:

Good Premorbid Parent Group. The father is strongly ascendant—far more so than is true for the normal control group; the mother is weak and submissive. Although there are some signs of overt discord these are not as striking as those evidenced by the poor group.

Poor Premorbid Parent Group. The mother is markedly dominant with father tending toward the submissive. Striking patterns of conflict and discord are present.

---

child to conform. The "Yielding" score indicated the extent to which a parent during the interaction session relinquished his or her individual solution to the problem in the direction asserted by the spouse. The terms "maximum" and "minimum" refer to alternate solutions to a problem which were occasionally given by a parent. Since these alternatives often varied along the pressure-for-conformity dimension, maximum and minimum yielding scores were computed based upon these variations.

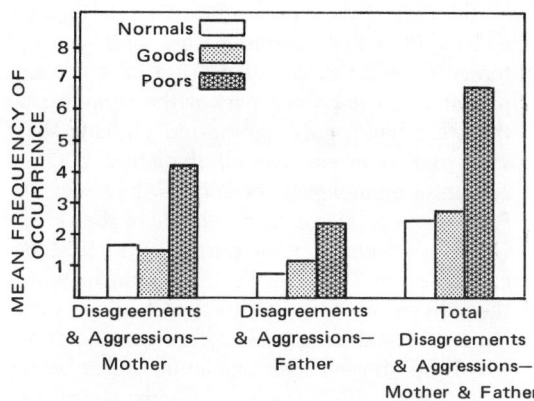

FIGURE 5.13. Conflict behavior (Disagreements and Aggressions) of parents of good and poor premorbid schizophrenic and normal patients (From Farina [15]).

Normal Control Parent Group. There tends to be a shared pattern of authority with a minimal tendency toward maternal dominance and very little indication (if any) of conflict between parents.

These findings appear to be supported by

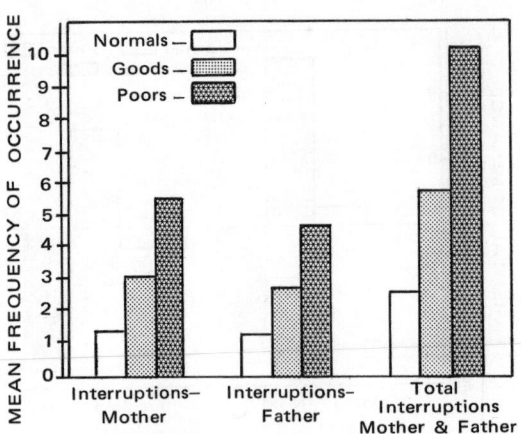

FIGURE 5.14. Conflict behavior (Interruptions) of parents of good and poor premorbid schizophrenic and normal patients (From Farina [15]).

more recent data obtained by Dunham (12) and Kreinik (26). These studies indicate tendencies on the part of poor premorbid patients to show deficits in visual discrimination and concept formation when maternal censure cues are employed as a component part of the stimulus; on the other hand, good premorbid patients show some deficit if cue stimuli depicting paternal censure are employed. In general, however, the Poors show greater deficits relative to the Goods. Dunham's research is of particular interest because he repeated Dunn's technique, in which the subject was required to detect minor variations in tachistoscopically presented materials. The Poors showed their maximum deficit on the mother-son scolding scene; Goods were most adversely affected by the father-son scolding picture. In a somewhat related fashion, Alvarez (1) had found a maximum decline in preferences by Poors for female-censured photographs. On the other hand, Goods showed their greatest decline with male-censured pictures.

These studies tentatively suggest that two groups of schizophrenic patients differing in prognostic potential also differ in sensitivity to experimental cues. These differential reaction sensitivities, in turn, may be related to variations in early child-rearing experiences. It would cer-

tainly be congruent with current knowledge of the identification process to find that the more assertive role of the father in good premorbid families is reflected in the greater social adequacy and maturity level achieved by their sons —an adequacy which is confirmed both by Phillips Scale ratings based upon premorbid adjustment and laboratory performance under stress during the psychosis.

These findings suggest a need to reassert Benjamin's admonition of more than a decade ago when he introduced an experimental test of a process-reactive dichotomy. His statement appears to have equal validity today. Commenting on the ascription of an endogenous-process and exogenous-reactive relationship in schizophrenia Benjamin wrote, "That this assumption is premature in the present state of our knowledge of schizophrenia is clear. Perhaps it is true; perhaps not. But the demonstration of qualitative differences between the two types of illness and a reliable method for distinguishing between them, would surely obligate the investigators in this field to consider the possibility of differences in etiology and pathogenesis and to conduct his researches accordingly, whether these be along psychological or neurophysiological lines" (6, pp. 70–71).

We do not urge the acceptance of a given position regarding psychological or biological antecedents in schizophrenia. Quite the contrary. The findings of our research group of an interrelationship among the variables of premorbid adequacy, differential sensitivity to censure, prognosis and types of familial organization suggest that varying patterns of early experience *may be* related to the schizophrenic disorder. Continued research and a growing understanding of dimensions such as these may help one day to understand the nature of antecedent-consequent relationships in schizophrenia. One can only agree with Kety that "it is not necessary that one be convinced of the truth of a particular hypothesis to justify devoting one's energies to testing it. It is enough that one regard it as worth testing and that the tools be adequate" (24, p. 1596). Perhaps it is time that a general moratorium be declared on idle speculations about the genesis of schizophrenia and that investigators turn their energies instead toward creating those conceptual and methodological "tools" which will ultimately help to provide the data necessary for long sought solutions to the problem of schizophrenia.

REFERENCES

1. ALVAREZ, R. R. A comparison of the preferences of schizophrenic and normal subjects for rewarded and punished stimuli. Unpublished Ph.D. thesis. Duke University, 1957.
2. ARIETI, S. *Interpretation of schizophrenia.* New York: Brunner, 1955.
3. BECKER, W. C. A genetic approach to the interpretation and evaluation of the process-reactive distinction in schizophrenia. *Journal of Abnormal and Social Psychology,* 1952, *47,* 489–496.
4. BELL, R. Q. Retrospective attitude studies of parent-child relations. *Child Development,* 1958, *29,* 323–338.
5. BELLAK, L. *Dementia praecox.* New York: Grune and Stratton, 1948.
6. BENJAMIN, J. D. A method for distinguishing and evaluating formal thinking disorders in schizophrenia. In Kasanin, J. S. (Ed.), *Language and thought in schizophrenia.* Berkeley: University of California Press, 1946. Pp. 67–74.
7. BENJAMIN, J. D. Some considerations in biological research in schizophrenia. *Psychosomatic Medicine,* 1958, *20,* 427–445.
8. BLEKE, R. C. Reward and punishment as determiners of reminiscence effects in schizophrenic and normal subjects. *Journal of Personality,* 1955, *28,* 479–498.
9. BLEULER, E. *Dementia praecox; or The group of schizophrenias.* New York: International Universities Press, 1950.
10. CHASE, L. S., & SILVERMAN, S. Prognosis in schizophrenia: An analysis of prognostic criteria in 150 schizophrenics treated with metrozol or insulin. *Journal of Nervous and Mental Disease,* 1943, *98,* 464–473.
11. CHOLDEN, L. Observations on psychotherapy of schizophrenia. *Progress in Psychotherapy,* 1956, *1,* 239–247.
12. DUNHAM, R. M. Sensitivity of schizophrenics to parental censure. Unpublished Ph.D. thesis. Duke University, 1959.
13. DUNN, W. L., JR. Visual discrimination of schizophrenic subjects as a function of stimulus meaning. *Journal of Personality,* 1954, *23,* 48–64.
14. ENGELHART, R. S. Semantic correlates of interpersonal concepts and parental attributes in schizophrenia. Unpublished Ph.D. thesis. Duke University, 1959.
15. FARINA, A. Patterns of role dominance and conflict in the interaction of parents of schizophrenic patients. Unpublished Ph.D. thesis.

Duke University, 1958. *Journal of Abnormal and Social Psychology,*
16. GARMEZY, N., FARINA, A., & RODNICK, E. H. The structured situation test: A method for studying family interaction in schizophrenia. Mimeographed, 1959. Presented at 1959 annual meeting of American Orthopsychiatric Association.
17. GARMEZY, N., STOCKNER, C., & CLARKE, A. R. Child-rearing attitudes of mothers and fathers as reported by schizophrenic and normal control patients. *American Psychologist,* 1959, *14,* 333.
18. HARRIS, J. G. Size estimation of pictures as a function of thematic content for schizophrenic and normal subjects. *Journal of Personality,* 1957, *25,* 651–671.
19. HOSKINS, R. G. *The Biology of schizophrenia.* New York: W. W. Norton, 1946.
20. HUNT, J. M., & COFER, C. N. Psychological deficit. In J. M. Hunt (Ed.), *Personality and the behavior disorders.* New York: Ronald, 1944. Pp. 971–1032.
21. KANT, O. A comparative study of recovered and deteriorated schizophrenic patients. *Journal of Nervous and Mental Disease,* 1941, *93,* 616–624.
22. KANT, O. Differential diagnosis of schizophrenia in light of concepts of personality stratification. *American Journal of Psychiatry,* 1940, *97,* 342–357.
23. KANTOR, R. E., WALLNER, J. M., & WINDER, C. L. Process and reactive schizophrenia. *Journal of Consulting Psychology,* 1953, *17,* 157–162.
24. KETY, S. S. Biochemical theories of schizophrenia. *Science,* 1959, *129,* 1528–1532, 1590–1596, 3362–3363.
25. KOHN, M. L. & CLAUSEN, J. A. Parental authority behavior and schizophrenia. *American Journal of Orthopsychiatry,* 1956, *26,* 297–313.
26. KREINIK, P. S. Parent-child themas and concept attainment in schizophrenia. Unpublished Ph.D. thesis. Duke University, 1959.
27. LEWIS, N. D. C. The prognostic significance of certain factors in schizophrenia. *Journal of Nervous and Mental Disease,* 1944, *100,* 414–419.
28. LORR, M., WITTMAN, P., & SCHANBERGER, W. An analysis of the Elgin Prognostic Scale. *Journal of Clinical Psychology,* 1951, *7,* 260–263.
29. MCGEOCH, J. A. & IRION, A. L. *The psychology of human learning.* New York: Longmans, Green, 1952.
30. MALAMUD, W., & RENDER, N. Course and prognosis in schizophrenia. *American Journal of Psychiatry,* 1939, *95,* 1039–1057.
31. OSGOOD, C. E., SUCI, G. J., & TANNENBAUM, P. H. *The measurement of meaning.* Urbana, Ill.: University of Illinois Press, 1957.
32. PHILLIPS, L. Case history data and prognosis in schizophrenia. *Journal of Nervous and Mental Disease,* 1953, *117,* 515–525.

33. RODNICK, E. H. & GARMEZY, N. An experimental approach to the study of motivation in schizophrenia. In M. R. Jones (Ed.), *Nebraska symposium on motivation*. Lincoln, Neb.: University of Nebraska Press, 1957. Pp. 109–184.

34. WIENER, H. Diagnosis and symptomatology. In L. Bellak (Ed.), *Schizophrenia: A review of the syndrome*. New York: Logos Press, 1958. Pp. 107–173.

35. WITTMAN, P. A scale for measuring prognosis in schizophrenic patients. *Elgin State Hospital Papers*, 1944, 4, 20–33.

36. WITTMAN, P. & STERNBERG, L. Follow-up of an objective evaluation of prognosis in dementia praecox and manic-depressive psychoses. *Elgin State Hospital Papers*, 1944, 5, 216–227.

37. ZAHN, T. P. Acquired and symbolic affective value as determinants of size estimation in schizophrenic and normal subjects. *Journal of Abnormal and Social Psychology*, 1959, 58, 39–47.

38. ZILBOORG, G. & HENRY, G. W. *A History of medical psychology*. New York: W. W. Norton, 1941.

40.

MAURICE LORR

SYMPTOMS OF PSYCHOSIS

BACKGROUND

The aim of this paper is to present a digest of four studies, each designed to identify mutually exclusive and homogeneous subgroups among psychotic patients. Emphasis will be on substantive findings rather than methods used.

Before launching into a description of these investigations and their findings, some of the methodological problems involved will be sketched. The view of the author is that the general problem is one of sorting people into subgroups or types when these are not known a priori. Similar problems are encountered by the zoologist, the political scientist, the dress manufacturer, and the occupational specialist. First it is necessary to choose and measure a set of characteristics on the basis of which individuals can be compared. Next some index of similarity between individuals must be selected. Then a procedure must be found for identifying the subgroups in the nonrandom population studied. Once the K subgroups have

been distinguished, the next problem is to draw boundaries between them so as to separate them optimally. Finally decision functions must be specified for assigning new individuals to the subgroups identified.

There are certain conditions that must be met by the set of defining characteristics selected in a domain of interest. It is essential that all major sources of behavior variation be represented. Should some important sources of trait variation be excluded then the profiles delineated will be incomplete. The addition of new dimensions could alter these profiles in significant ways. A related requirement is that the defining variables be descriptive of independent dimensions. A major reason is that most indices of similarity assume that the profile elements are independent. One approach to the satisfaction of this condition is to conduct a series of factor analyses in order to isolate the major dimensions of a given universe.

Once the defining characteristics have been selected it is necessary to choose some index of resemblance between individuals. A wide variety of indices of similarity have been proposed. As early as 1898 Heincke suggested the use of a distance measure (D^2). Pearson (1926) proposed the coefficient of racial likeness and Ma-

From Maurice Lorr, A typology for functional psychotics. In M. M. Katz, J. O. Cole & W. E. Barton (Eds.), *The role and methodology of classification in psychiatry and psychopathology*. Chevy Chase, Md.: National Institute of Mental Health, 1968. Pp. 261–275. Reprinted by permission.

halanobis described a generalized distance function. Cronbach and Gleser (1963) have reviewed most of these methods for assessing similarity. They have shown that most coefficients may be subsumed under a general measure of distance between two individuals.

The third step in the development of a classification scheme is to identify subgroups or hierarchies of subgroups in nonrandom populations. The grouping process begins with a basic data matrix consisting of K scores on N persons (entities). The data matrix is then converted into a symmetric derived matrix of similarity indices among the N persons. The problem is to recover information about the grouping of persons given such a matrix.

Two formal algebraic models have been suggested for use in identifying homogeneous subgroups. Stephenson (1952) and Nunnally (1962) have recommended factor analysis as a solution. Others have suggested the use of Lazarfeld's latent class model. A variety of numerical techniques for defining groups called cluster analysis has an equally long history beginning with Zubin (1938). One of the earliest reviews of cluster search methods was by Cattell (1944). Since then McQuitty (1954, 1964) has proposed a considerable array of specific procedures such as linkage and typal analysis. Thorndike (1953) developed a clustering procedure later modified by Sawrey, Keller, and Conger (1960). Zubin, Fleiss, and Burdock (1963) have described a process resembling Thorndike's. Saunders and Schuchman (1962) developed a procedure called syndrome analysis based on sets of profiles that are mutually closest. A detailed review of these and other procedures may be found elsewhere (Lorr, 1965).

THE MEASURING INSTRUMENT

The studies to be reported all utilized the Inpatient Multidimensional Psychiatric Scale (IMPS).The rating schedule is designed to measure 10 psychotic syndromes confirmed in repeated factor analyses (Lorr, Klett, and McNair, 1963). IMPS consists of 75 brief rating scales and dichotomous items. Ratings are made following interviews of 30 to 45 minutes in length.

Each syndrome is defined by a set of scales, from 5 to 11 in number, that measure a unitary pattern of behavior. The labels given the syndromes are intended to describe the underlying response tendency. For convenience in referral each syndrome is also identified by three letters. The 10 syndromes are briefly characterized below:

1. Excitement (EXC): The patient's speech is hurried, loud, and difficult to stop. His mood level and self-esteem are elevated and his emotional expression tends to be unrestrained or histrionic. He is also likely to exhibit controlling or dominant behavior.

2. Hostile belligerence (HOS): The patient's attitude toward others is one of disdain and moroseness. He is likely to manifest much hostility, resentment and a complaining bitterness. His difficulties and failures tend to be blamed on others.

3. Paranoid projection (PAR): The patient gives evidence of fixed beliefs that attribute a hostile, persecuting, and controlling intent to others around him.

4. Grandiose expansiveness (GRN): The patient's attitude toward others is one of superiority. He exhibits fixed beliefs that he possesses unusual powers. He reports divine missions and may identify himself with well-known or historical personalities.

5. Perceptual distortions (PCP): The patient reports hallucinations (voices and visions) that threaten, accuse, or demand.

6. Anxious intropunitiveness (INP): The patient reports vague apprehension as well as specific anxieties. His attitudes toward himself are disparaging. He is also prone to report feelings of guilt and remorse for real and imagined faults. The underlying mood is typically dysphoric.

7. Retardation and apathy (RTD): The patient's speech, ideation, and motor activity are delayed, slowed, or blocked. In addition he is likely to manifest apathy and disinterest in the future.

8. Disorientation (DIS): The patient's orientation with respect to time, place, and season is defective. He may show failure to recognize others around him.

9. Motor disturbances (MTR): The patient

assumes and maintains bizarre postures and he makes repetitive facial and body movements.

10. Conceptual disorganization (CNP): Disturbances in the patient's stream of thought are manifested in irrelevant, incoherent, and rambling speech. Repetition of stereotyped phrases and coining of new words are also common.

The syndromes have been shown to be sufficiently reliable in a variety of settings (Lorr, Klett, McNair, and Lasky, 1962). Some of the evidence for the validity of the syndromes has been reported (Lorr *et al.*, 1963). In brief, it has been shown that the syndrome scores are related to ward assignment, to prominent features of psychopathology, and to conventional diagnostic class membership. The syndromes have also been found to be sensitive to change with tranquilizer treatment and to psychopathology as measured by other measuring devices.

METHOD OF ANALYSIS

The findings from four studies will be summarized here. The first investigation sought to find the psychotic subgroups among a random sample of acutely disturbed psychotics newly admitted to 16 State and university hospitals. The second and third analyses dealt with: (*a*) relatively chronic but newly admitted male psychotics, and (*b*) a sample of long-term patients examined in connection with two drug discontinuation studies. The fourth analysis was based on a nine-hospital NIMH study of a sample of newly admitted schizophrenics.

The methods of analysis were essentially the same in the first three studies described. Since the computer program developed for clustering profiles into homogeneous subgroups is capable of handling not more than 150 profiles simultaneously, it was necessary to subdivide each study sample. Thus each study sample was partitioned into three subsamples. Next the clustering program was applied separately to the correlations (*Q*) and the congruency coefficients (*C*) among the 150 cases represented in each of the three subsamples. The clusters were first matched within each subsample across the two indices of similarity. Next the clusters were matched across the three subsamples. Finally a stratified sample was selected as a further check on the cross-sample and cross-index matching.

Each clearly defined type found in at least two subsamples was represented in the stratified sample in proportion to its relative frequency. Analysis of the stratified sample provided not only a check on the accuracy of the matching but provided a test of cluster invariance. Any type or class evolved should be replicable under changes in the sample of persons examined providing it is represented in sufficient numbers.

Matching within a subsample across similarity indices involved several steps. Two clusters defined by a high proportion of identical cases were judged identical. In addition the 10 standard scores of cluster members were averaged. Then congruency coefficients between the mean syndrome profiles of the two sets of clusters being compared were computed. Clusters were considered identical if the congruency coefficient between their profiles was at least 0.75.

Type matching across subsamples was also achieved by comparing the congruency coefficients between the mean syndrome profiles of the various clusters. Two clusters were judged identical if the congruency coefficient between their profiles was 0.75 or greater and all other indices of similarity were negative or close to zero. Such matching was checked by resort to the clusters identified in the stratified sample. When subsample clusters had been correctly matched their representatives in the stratified sample were nearly all found in the same cluster evolved. Thus the matching by congruency coefficient could readily be confirmed or rejected.

METHOD OF LABELING TYPES

The profile of a type can be characterized in terms of those mean syndrome scores that lie at some point above or below the general mean on the standard score scale. Since the syndromes are descriptive of behavior deviation, the higher the score the greater the deviation from the norm. Thus the most critical syndromes are those in which all members score above the mean. Syndromes on which all members of a type score below the mean are also important; they indicate the relative absence of pathology. On the other hand, syndromes on which members of a type score as frequently above as below the mean are simply undifferentiating and can be ignored.

For convenience and brevity let each syndrome be identified by a number as follows:

1. Excitement
2. Hostile belligerence
3. Paranoid projection
4. Grandiose expansiveness
5. Perceptual distortion
6. Anxious intropunitiveness
7. Retardation and apathy
8. Disorientation
9. Motor disturbances
10. Conceptual disorganization

Each type profile can be designated by a numerical label to indicate which mean syndrome scores are elevated 0.15 or more above the general mean. Thus a 1–10 profile means elevated "Excitement" (1) and "Conceptual disorganization" (10) scores. Similarly a 2–3 type profile implies that "Hostile belligerence" (2) and "Paranoid projection" (3) are elevated above the mean. This notation will be used hereafter as a shorthand but objective way to identify each type. Each subgroup has been labeled additionally by its most characteristic syndromes. For example the 2–3 subgroup members are called hostile-paranoids.

THE ACUTE PSYCHOTIC TYPES

The patient sample, drawn from 16 state and university hospitals and clinics, consisted of 374 men and 448 women. All patients manifested a functional psychosis, were hospitalized either for the first (54 percent) or second (41 percent) time, and were between 18 and 55 years of age. Cases with central nervous system or other neurological disorders, as well as alcoholics, were excluded. Interviews were conducted within 10 days of admission while patients were either not on tranquilizers or on a minimum drug dosage schedule. Approximately 75 percent were diagnosed schizophrenics, 23 percent as depressives, and 5 percent as manics. Of the total, 82 percent were white and the remainder of other ethnic origins.

A. Types among Men

The mean syndrome score profiles for each of the types are given in Tables 5.9 and 5.10. The labels applied are tentative and designed to be descriptive mainly of the salient syndromes. The male patient classes are as follows:

Excited (1–10) Type. The members of this group are characterized mainly by elevated excitement scores. While high scores on conceptual disorganization are frequent not all are above the mean. Occasionally patients in the group also manifest above-average scores on motor disturbances and grandiosity. All other syndromes average well below the general mean. Twenty-two percent of the excited type are diagnosed as manic.

Excited-Hostile (1–2–3–10) Type. The scores of all members are above the scale mean with respect to excitement and hostility. Elevated scores on paranoid projection are also common. Conceptual disorganization, although slightly elevated, is only slightly discriminating. Roughly two-thirds of the type were diagnosed as paranoid. It is thus likely that the class represents one variety of paranoid disturbance.

Hostile-Paranoid (2–3) Type. Most patients in this class have scores elevated on both hostile belligerence and paranoid projection. However, some members exhibit elevated scores mainly on hostile belligerence or mainly on paranoid projection. Excitement scores tend to be conspicuously low. Approximately 64 percent of the type are diagnosed paranoid type.

Hallucinated Paranoid (3–5–8) Type. The third paranoid class has as members patients scoring well up on paranoid projection and perceptual distortion. In addition some members score high on disorientation. This means that in addition to delusional misinterpretation of the action of others as persecutory or conspiratory, the type members also hear voices that accuse, threaten, or order. Diagnostically 71 percent of the group are categorized as paranoid type.

Grandiose-Paranoid (3–4–5) Type. All type members have extremely high scores on grandiose expansiveness. Most members, but not all, have in addition elevated scores on paranoid projection and perceptual distortion. In brief, members exhibit attitudes of self-importance and superiority, and report the possession of unusual gifts and powers. At times they identify with well-known personalities or claim special divine missions. Approximately 78 percent are diagnosed paranoid type.

Anxious-Depressed (6) Type. The members of this class all manifest above-average anxious intropunitiveness. A few patients also receive

TABLE 5.9

MEAN SYNDROME SCORES OF 9 ACUTE PSYCHOTIC TYPES AMONG MALE PATIENTS

Type	Syndromes									
	EXC	HOS	PAR	GRN	PCP	INP	RTD	DIS	MTR	CNP
Excited	1.29	—0.65	—0.80	—0.32	—0.53	—0.68	—0.48	—0.28	—0.03	0.47
Excited-hostile	1.42	1.39	0.33	0.05	—0.51	—0.75	—0.74	—0.46	—0.29	0.34
Hostile paranoid	—0.52	0.80	0.17	—0.42	—0.55	—0.43	—0.55	—0.24	—0.40	—0.61
Hallucinated paranoid	—0.53	0.04	1.24	—0.23	1.32	—0.05	—0.24	0.22	—0.52	—0.12
Grandiose paranoid ..	0.12	—0.41	0.20	2.02	0.51	—0.46	—0.45	—0.14	—0.61	—0.13
Anxious-depressed ..	—0.46	—0.63	—0.80	—0.54	—0.43	1.15	—0.45	—0.45	—0.44	—0.62
Retarded-motor disturbed	—0.70	—0.83	—0.68	—0.56	—0.55	—0.30	1.43	0.06	0.52	—0.26
Disoriented	—0.43	—0.84	—0.93	—0.60	—0.38	—0.88	0.87	3.29	0.39	0.18
Anxious-disorganized	—0.50	0.10	1.28	—0.44	2.20	1.19	1.61	0.62	1.18	0.48

TABLE 5.10

MEAN SYNDROME SCORES OF 9 ACUTE PSYCHOTIC TYPES AMONG FEMALE PATIENTS

Type	Syndromes									
	EXC	HOS	PAR	GRN	PCP	INP	RTD	DIS	MTR	CNP
Excited	1.49	—0.62	—0.89	—0.25	—0.55	—0.58	—0.70	—0.39	0.21	0.17
Excited-hostile	1.32	1.39	0.49	—0.04	—0.57	—0.49	—0.65	—0.39	—0.28	0.48
Excited-disorganized	2.13	0.54	1.40	2.28	1.16	—0.04	0.13	—0.20	1.51	1.81
Hostile paranoid	—0.63	0.70	0.41	—0.42	—0.53	—0.58	—0.59	—0.27	—0.43	—0.55
Hallucinated paranoid	—0.51	0.59	1.56	0.04	1.73	⸱—0.44	—0.42	—0.24	—0.52	—0.56
Grandiose paranoid ..	—0.15	—0.07	0.33	2.56	0.36	—0.79	—0.47	—0.05	—0.46	0.00
Anxious-depressed ..	—0.46	—0.51	—0.67	—0.52	—0.45	1.13	—0.33	—0.35	—0.47	—0.63
Anxious-disorganized	—0.62	0.13	0.73	—0.38	1.74	1.20	1.23	—0.30	0.38	—0.33
Retarded-disorganized	—0.73	—0.92	—0.83	—0.51	—0.41	—0.25	1.50	1.13	0.38	—0.19

mildly elevated scores on retardation, perceptual distortion, or hostile belligerence. However, the intropunitive score is always highest. Fifty-five percent of the group is diagnosed as depressed (psychotic or involutional) while the remainder are classed as schizo-affective, acute undifferentiated, or paranoid. The intropunitives are the most frequent of the types identified.

Retarded with Motor Disturbances (7–9) Type. Members of this class all have scores elevated on retardation and apathy. In brief, they are seen as slowed in speech and movement; they may also whisper, block, or fail to answer at all. Many of the class members also manifest high motor disturbances scores. This means they may posture, manifest bizarre or manneristic move-

ments, talk to themselves, and show muscular tension. The diagnoses for this group varied widely, the most common being acute undifferentiated (37 percent).

Disoriented (7–8–9–10) Type. This patient type is relatively small. Its members all have extreme disorientation scores. In addition some members have high scores on retardation, motor disturbances, and conceptual disorganization. The most frequent psychiatric diagnosis is schizophrenia, simple type (36 percent).

Anxious-Disorganized (3–5–6–7–8–9–10) Type. The most striking feature of this class is the presence of anxiety in conjunction with behaviors indicative of behavior disorganization or disintegration. All members of the type show elevated scores on anxious intropunitiveness, perceptual distortion, and retardation. Some members also receive high scores on paranoid projection, disorientation, motor disturbances, and conceptual disorganization. Patient members are typically diagnosed as paranoid or as acute undifferentiated.

Thus the acute male psychotic sample can be viewed as including four kinds of patient classes. There is one excited type and four paranoid types (excited-hostile, hostile, grandiose, and hallucinated). The intropunitiveness represents the anxious-depressive disorders. The behaviorally disorganized types are the anxious-disorganized who may represent transitional states, the disoriented, and the retarded-motor disturbed.

B. Types among Women

Seven of the nine types isolated in the sample of women are essentially the same as those found among men. The excited (1–9–10) type closely resembles the male patient type except for a more elevated score on motor disturbances. As can be seen in Table 5.10, the four female paranoid classes differ little from the corresponding groups identified in the male sample. There is an excited-hostile (1–2–3–10), a hostile-paranoid (2–3), an hallucinated paranoid (2–3–5), and a grandiose paranoid (3–4–5). The hostile paranoid among women is somewhat more paranoid than the male variety. The hallucinated paranoid more frequently manifests hostile behavior, while the grandiose type is less prone to exhibit excitement than corresponding male type members. Most of the paranoid types are diagnosed as paranoid.

The anxious-depressives (6) manifest a syndrome profile that is almost a duplicate of the corresponding male variety. The anxious-disorganized (3–5–6–7–9) resembles the correlative male class very closely with regard to paranoid projection, perceptual distortion, intropunitiveness, and retardation: The female type, on the other hand, is distinctly less disoriented and less motor disturbed.

The female types that appear to be different from those found among men may now be described.

Excited-Disorganized (1–2–3–4–5–9–10) Type.

All members of this class have elevated scores on excitement, paranoid projection, grandiosity, and conceptual disorganization. In addition, many score high on hostile belligerence, perceptual distortion (hallucinations), and motor disturbances. However, none of the group is disoriented. Evidently the excited-disorganized represented an acutely disturbed group. Members are most likely to be diagnosed as manic or as schizophrenic, acute undifferentiated type. Further research is needed to determine whether the class is a transitional one.

Retarded-Disorganized (7–8–9) Type. Among men the disoriented (7-8-9-10) patient type was differentiated from the retarded-motor disturbed (7–9). Such a separation was not possible among women although both profiles appear among them. All members of the retarded-disorganized type have strongly elevated scores on retardation and apathy. In addition about two-thirds of the group also manifest high scores on disorientation and motor disturbances. Members tend to be diagnosed either as depressed or as catatonic.

THE CHRONIC PSYCHOTIC TYPES

The second study was based on two groups of relatively chronic male psychotics with several previous hospital admissions. One sample of 207 was specially selected to assure representation of all likely sources of symptom variation. Another sample consisted of 359 schizophrenics newly admitted or readmitted to 32 Veterans Administration hospitals. In all, 44 state and federal institutions contributed to the sample. The modal patient was 36 years old, hospitalized three or four times previously for durations of 18 to 24 months. The age range was from 18 to 55. At the time of interview and rating patients were receiving at most either light sedatives or mild dosages of tranquilizer drugs.

Seven male patient types emerged from the analyses of the 3 chronic patient subsamples of 150. Their mean syndrome profiles are presented in Table 5.11. Six of the chronic patient subgroups are substantially the same as corresponding acute patient subgroups. The retarded type represents the only new subgroup evolved. On the other hand, the excited type and the

TABLE 5.11

MEAN SYNDROME SCORES OF 7 CHRONIC PSYCHOTIC TYPES

Type	Syndromes									
	EXC	HOS	PAR	GRN	PCP	INP	RTD	DIS	MTR	CNP
Excited-hostile	1.88	1.08	0.02	0.19	—0.60	—0.46	—0.68	—0.39	—0.03	0.37
Grandiose paranoid ..	0.77	0.35	0.70	2.51	0.79	—0.41	—0.46	—0.33	—0.02	0.66
Hostile paranoid	—0.32	1.28	0.94	—0.24	0.00	0.06	—0.33	—0.29	—0.45	—0.55
Anxious-depressed ..	—0.51	—0.53	—0.74	—0.55	—0.34	1.54	—0.03	—0.34	—0.49	—0.66
Retarded	—0.74	—0.69	—0.84	—0.58	—0.46	—0.50	1.15	—0.38	—0.38	—0.45
Anxious-disorganized	—0.57	—0.04	1.03	0.06	2.02	1.70	1.03	—0.38	0.31	0.72
Retarded disorganized	—0.41	—0.52	—0.60	—0.45	—0.15	—0.55	1.59	1.89	1.25	0.79

hallucinated paranoid type failed to appear within the chronic subsamples. The extent of similarity between corresponding acute and chronic types as measured by the congruency coefficient is shown in Table 5.13.

What differences are there in corresponding type profiles? The chronic excited-hostile subgroup is more often grandiose but less often paranoid than the acute subgroup. The chronic grandiose paranoid manifests slightly higher scores on excitement and hostile belligerence than the corresponding acute type. The corresponding intropunitive subgroups are quite similar in profile. The chronic anxious-disorganized type is less often disoriented than its correlative among acute patients. The chronic retarded-disorganized subgroup profile resembles the acute disoriented type (C = 0.86). However, there are differences that preclude a match. Retardation scores are always elevated above the mean, while disorientation and motor disturbances may or may not be elevated in the retarded-disorganized subgroup. Among the acute disoriented type members, it is disorientation that is always elevated while retardation and motor disturbances are not. The closest match for the chronic retarded-disorganized type is the acute female type of the same name.

The retarded subgroup members exhibit high scores on retardation only. All other syndrome scores are typically below the mean.

THE LONG-TERM PSYCHOTIC TYPES

While the so-called chronic sample included a high proportion of patients who had been hospitalized three and four times, emphasis was not on long-term hospitalization. In view of the high proportion of chronic long-term patients in psychiatric hospitals, further investigation of existing subgroups seemed to be of value. Accordingly a sample of 450 cases was drawn from data collected in connection with 2 nationwide Veterans Administration studies of tranquilizer effects.

One-third of the 450 cases came from a drug discontinuation study (project 9). The average patient was 40 years old with 10 years of hospitalization. The most common diagnosis was schizophrenic reaction, paranoid type. Patients were interviewed either after 16 weeks on placebo or at the time of their clinical relapse following withdrawal of medication.

The remaining 300 cases were drawn from another VA drug study (project 14) of schizophrenics. The average patient was 41 years old with approximately 9.5 years of hospitalization. The most common diagnoses were chronic undifferentiated, paranoid, and hebephrenic. Each patient was interviewed and rated after 1 month on placebo capsules.

Seven subgroups were isolated among the long-term patients' subsamples. Their mean profiles are presented in Table 5.12. Five of the types had been found in the acute and/or chronic samples, but the excited-disorganized and the hostile-motor disturbed were new. All members of the excited-disorganized subgroup have highly elevated scores on motor disturbances and conceptual disorganization. Nearly

TABLE 5.12

MEAN SYNDROME SCORES OF 7 CHRONIC LONG-TERM PSYCHOTIC TYPES

Type	Syndromes									
	EXC	HOS	PAR	GRN	PCP	INP	RTD	DIS	MTR	CNP
Excited-motor disturbed	1.27	—0.38	—0.36	—0.10	—0.34	—0.71	0.28	0.03	2.03	1.12
Hostile-motor disturbed	—0.26	0.66	—0.49	—0.46	—0.49	—0.36	—0.27	—0.46	0.33	—0.65
Hallucinated paranoid	—0.36	—0.44	0.71	—0.25	1.93	0.13	—0.46	—0.33	0.53	—0.59
Anxious-depressed ..	—0.37	—0.87	—0.91	—0.35	—0.27	0.95	—0.47	—0.46	—0.44	—0.73
Retarded	—0.75	—0.98	—1.15	—0.52	—0.62	—0.68	0.21	—0.46	—0.94	—0.70
Retarded-motor disturbed	—0.53	—0.93	—1.01	—0.58	—0.61	—0.64	1.08	—0.37	0.86	—0.17
Disoriented	—0.48	—0.94	—0.99	—0.55	—0.59	—0.88	1.12	4.38	1.07	—0.11

all have above average scores additionally on excitement. At the same time roughly two-thirds of the group score above average on retardation and apathy. The pattern is analogous to a catatonic excitement.

The hostile-motor disturbed subgroup is relatively small and defined mainly by elevated scores on hostile belligerence. Scores on motor disturbances are frequently, but not always, above the sample mean. Further data are needed to evaluate the stability of this type.

The similarity between five of the long-term subgroups and the acute and chronic subgroups can be assessed by examining Table 5.13. The size of the congruency coefficient indicates rather strong agreement in the mean syndrome profiles.

AN ACUTE SCHIZOPHRENIC SAMPLE

A study of the newly admitted acutely disturbed schizophrenics was reported by McNair, Lorr, and Hemingway (1964). The data came from a phenothiazine study conducted by the Psychopharmacology Service Center of NIMH. A subsample of 150 men and 2 subsamples of 108 women were randomly selected for analysis. The age range was from 16 to 40 and the average age was 28. A clustering process was applied by hand to the two female subsamples. First a multiple cutting-score procedure was used to classify the male profiles. The procedure was followed by a search for new patient types.

The mean syndrome profiles for the types established are shown in Table 5.14. The degree

TABLE 5.13

RELATIONS BETWEEN PROFILES OF CORRESPONDING PSYCHOTIC TYPES IN 3 SAMPLES

Type	Patient samples		
	Acute versus chronic	Acute versus long term	Chronic versus long term
Excited-hostile	0.95		
Hostile paranoid	.75		
Grandiose paranoid	0.85		
Hallucinated paranoid		0.74	
Anxious-depressed	0.96	0.98	0.91
Anxious-disorganized	0.89		
Retarded-motor disturbed		0.93	
Disoriented		0.99	
Excited			
Retarded			0.89

TABLE 5.14

MEAN STANDARD SCORES OF 9 NIMH PATIENT TYPES

Type	Syndromes									
	EXC	HOS	PAR	GRN	PCP	INP	RTD	DIS	MTR	CNP
Excited-grandiose ...	1.4	0.0	0.0	2.0	0.0	—0.7	—0.7	—0.2	0.0	0.2
Excited-hostile	1.8	0.7	—0.3	—0.3	—0.7	—0.7	—0.9	—0.4	—0.1	—0.2
EXC-HOS-GRN-PAR	1.4	1.4	1.1	2.0	0.0	—0.9	—0.9	—0.3	—0.1	0.6
Hostile paranoid	0.0	1.2	0.9	—0.4	—0.4	—0.5	—0.7	—0.3	—0.4	—0.2
Hallucinated paranoid	—0.6	—0.2	1.2	—0.4	1.2	0.3	—0.6	0.0	—0.4	—0.6
Anxious-depressed ..	—0.2	—0.1	—0.7	—0.4	—0.6	1.2	—0.5	—0.3	—0.4	—0.4
Retarded-intropunitive	—0.8	—0.8	—0.4	—0.6	—0.5	0.7	0.4	—0.3	—0.7	—0.4
Retarded	—0.6	—0.2	—0.8	—0.5	—0.4	—0.5	1.2	—0.1	0.0	—0.2
Retarded-disorganized	0.0	—0.4	—0.8	—0.4	—0.4	—0.6	0.7	3.6	1.3	0.1

TABLE 5.15

RELATIONS BETWEEN PROFILES OF NIMH SCHIZOPHRENICS AND ACUTE PSYCHOTIC TYPES

Acute psychotic sample	C	NIMH schizophrenic sample
Excited-hostile	0.89	Excited-hostile.
Hostile paranoid	0.82	Hostile paranoid.
Hallucinated paranoid	0.92	Hallucinated paranoid.
Anxious-depressed	0.94	Anxious-depressed.
Disoriented	0.95	Retarded-disorganized.
Excited	0.40	Excited grandiose.
Grandiose paranoid	0.60	EXC-HOS-GRN-PAR.

of similarity between the schizophrenic types and comparable acute psychotic types was evaluated by means of the congruency coefficient. (See Table 5.15.) As may be seen five of the types agree very closely. There were several conditions that could account for the lack of agreement in the remaining types identified. First, the scoring key applied to the NIMH schizophrenics differed slightly from that applied to all other rating data. In all subsequent studies item No. 15 (attitude of superiority) was dropped from the excitement syndrome. Item No. 30 (slovenly appearance) was eliminated from motor disturbances and added to retardation. Thus three of the syndrome scores have slightly different bases. Another reason for the differences is that the cluster method applied was not as rigorous as in other analyses. The cross-cluster correlations of type (1–2–3–4) and of retarded-intropunitive are too high; these subgroups should have been eliminated. If these differences are considered, then the extent of agreement between the types in the two studies compared is high. Further, none of the types isolated is new or different from those found in the acute psychotic sample or the chronic psychotic sample.

It is of considerable interest to note that a sample of carefully diagnosed schizophrenics includes nearly all psychotic types found among a random sample of acute psychotics. This finding supports the need for a reappraisal of currently accepted diagnostic classes.

SUMMARY OF PSYCHOTIC TYPES ISOLATED

A summary of the findings is given in Table

5.16. The table shows that 12 subgroups have been indentified at least twice in the 4 studies described. Four paranoid groups emerged: Excited, hostile, grandiose, and hallucinated. These results suggest that the category schizophrenic reaction, paranoid type, is divisible in several subcategories. The excited type, to be found only in acute nonchronic samples, resembles the classical manic. Five subgroups can perhaps be categorized as disorganized in behavior in contrast to the paranoid groups. These are the retarded-motor disturbed, the disoriented, the retarded disorganized, the anxious disorganized, and the excited disorganized. The first two types may represent a further differentiation of the type called retarded-disorganized. Finally the classical depressive disorders appear to be represented by the intropunitives and the retarded. However, reports by Grinker *et al.* (1961) suggest that a more detailed study of the intropunitive subgroup with use of inner state reports could reveal additional depressed subgroups.

RELIABILITY OF THE TYPES

Nine acute psychotic male types were established through application of the clustering procedure to the combined rater syndrome scores. The subgroups were then enlarged by adding members to each type if they satisfied the bounds set by multiple cutting scores. Klett and McNair (1965) then tested type reliability by determining the extent to which interviewer and observer separately classified the same patients into each type. First the syndrome scores of the 374 males were standardized separately for the interviewer and the observer. Next the profiles for the interviewer were machine sorted into nine types using the multiple cutting score boundaries. The process was repeated for the set of observer scores, and the resulting classifications compared.

The findings were that altogether the interviewer and observer agreed in their rating of 73 percent of the 374 males. They jointly assigned 38 percent of the males to the same type category. The two judges also agreed that another 34 percent of the males were unclassifiable. Most of the disagreement between judges consisted in one rater classifying the patient when he could not be classified by the other rater's scores. Rarely did the two raters assign the same patient to different types.

Another problem was to determine how closely the combined rater classification could be approximated by the scores of only one rater. The analyses indicated that roughly 85 percent of the typing decisions would have been the same whether based on one or two raters.

VALIDITY OF THE PSYCHOTIC TYPES

The evidence presented thus far has been supportive of the replicability of the types in a

TABLE 5.16

SUMMARY OF PSYCHOTIC TYPES ISOLATED IN 4 STUDIES

Type	Samples			
	Acute random	Chronic random	Long-term schizophrenics	Acute schizophrenics
Excited	(*)			(?)
Excited-hostile	(*)			(*)
Hostile paranoid	(*)	(*)		(*)
Grandiose paranoid	(*)	(*)		
Hallucinated paranoid	(*)		(*)	(*)
Anxious-depressed	(*)	(*)	(*)	(*)
Retarded-motor disturbed	(*)		(*)	
Disoriented	(*)		(*)	(*)
Retarded-disorganized	(1)	(*)		
Anxious disorganized	(*)	(*)		
Retarded		(*)	(*)	(*)
Excited-disorganized	(1)			(?)
Excited-motor disturbed			(*)	

[1]NOTE—Found only among women.

variety of patient samples. Data concerning reliability of the acute psychotic types have also been encouraging since disagreement between raters was found to be minimal. However, the types will be of little interest unless and until some evidence can be presented of their validity. What are the antecedents of the psychotic types? Can the types be differentiated with respect to social history, genetic background, or premorbid personality structure? Do the types respond differentially to available psychiatric treatment modalities? Are they useful for predicting length of hospitalization, duration of illness, or treatment response? Can concurrent validity be established through correlations with other measures of behavior disturbance?

The only validity evidence now available is given in a report by Klett and Lorr (1965) on the acute psychotic types. Identification of the psychotic types has been too recent to permit accumulation of much validity data. In the study of the acute psychotics, data were collected relative to age, ethnic origin, religion, highest grade completed, marital status, residence (rural versus urban), occupation, diagnosis, duration of hospitalization, type of treatment received, and outcome status. Because of the relatively small number of cases within each of the nine types no statistical tests were attempted. The types were compared with the base rates for the variable and with each other. Thus any findings reported provide only exploratory and suggestive evidence of differences in background, clinical condition and outcome.

Table 5.17 presents a summary of the characteristics that appeared to differentiate the acute male types. Since a detailed report is available only two types will be described to illustrate the findings. For example, the anxious-depressed type members are 92 percent white. They are likely to be married currently and more likely than most to come from urban areas. Their fathers tend to have upper class jobs. Intropunitives are very likely to be diagnosed as depressive reaction, and to be placed on open wards. They receive psychotherapy more often than any other subgroup and tend more than most to get an approved discharge 6 months after admission. The disoriented subgroup, in contrast, are made up primarily of the less

educated, lower class, unmarried, rural patients. Frequently mute during the interview, type members are usually diagnosed schizophrenic reaction, simple type, catatonic type, or chronic undifferentiated type. They had been ill a long time before they were committed involuntarily to a hospital and tended to stay hospitalized at 6 months far more than any other type.

A sizable number of IMPS ratings of newly admitted and chronic schizophrenic men were available from a series of drug evaluations included in the VA Cooperative Studies in Psychiatry. Two projects were concerned with newly admitted, acutely ill psychotics while three projects sampled chronic long-term patients. The IMPS syndrome scores of 1,610 patients from these 5 studies were standardized on the same metric as the acute psychotic males described earlier. A multiple cutting score program was then applied to all cases. Of the total, 41 percent were classifiable, including 36 percent of the newly admitted and 46 percent of the chronic patients. Table 5.18 shows that the retarded-motor disturbed and the disoriented subgroups are likely to be chronic. The anxious subgroups and the paranoid subgroups are more likely to be newly admitted. The excited type is about equally chronic or acute. It is also noteworthy that of the classified chronic sample 76 percent are disoriented and retarded-motor disturbed.

What proportion of cases are classified within the limits set for members of a type? To answer this question a system of scoring was developed based on multiple cutting scores (MCS) for each type. From the distributions of the 10 syndromes, a cutting score or limit was set for each and every differentiating syndrome (nondiscriminating syndromes were ignored). The classification rules established for each type were applied sequentially by computers to all cases in the sample. The results on the acute psychotic sample indicated that approximately 60 percent of men and women could be classified. Cases unassigned by MCS were then correlated with the mean syndrome profile of each type. This procedure resulted in the addition of another 20 percent. Thus these nonoptimal procedures show that 80 percent of cases can be classified. Use of multiple discriminant functions

TABLE 5.17

Summary of Characteristics of the Male Types

Type	Excited	Excited-hostile	Hostile-paranoid	Hallucinated paranoid	Grandiose paranoid	Anxious-depressed	Retarded-motor	Disoriented	Anxious disorganized
Ethnic origin	...	White	...	1/3 Negro	1/3 Negro	White	...	...	...
Religion	Protestant	Protestant	...	...	Protestant	...	...	...	...
Education	High school	...	...	8th grade	College or 8th grade	...	...	Few college	...
Marital status	Most remarried	...	...	Most married	...	...	Never married	Never married	...
Residence	...	...	City	Rural	...	City	Rural	Rural	City
Patient occupation	...	Middle class	...	Lower and middle class	...	Upper class	Lower class	Lower class	...
Father occupation	...	...	...	Lower class	Lower and middle class	Middle and upper class	...	Lower class	...
Diagnosis	Manic and paranoid	Paranoid	Paranoid	Paranoid	Paranoid	Depressed	Acute undifferentiated	Simple	Paranoid and acute undifferentiated
Commitment	...	...	...	Involuntary	...	Voluntary	...	Involuntary	Voluntary
Ward type	...	...	Open or Partial	Closed	Closed	Open	...	...	...
Duration of episode	>10 months	...	...	...	...	...	...	< 9 months	...
Primary treatment	...	ECT	...	...	Drugs	Psycho-therapy	...	...	Psycho-therapy
Adjunct treatment	Drugs	...	Antidepressant drugs	...	...	...	...	...	Drugs
Outcome status	...	...	...	Approved release	AWOL/AMA	Approved release	Still Hospitalized	Still hospitalized	...
Length of stay	...	...	...	<119 days	> 61 days	...	Longest	Longest	...
Age	(older)	...	(older)	...	...	...	(younger)	...	(younger)

TABLE 5.18

TYPE MEMBERSHIP OF OTHER SAMPLES

Types (males)	Newly admitted		Chronic	
	N	Percent	N	Percent
Excited	32	52	29	48
Excited-hostile	28	76	9	24
Hostile paranoid	40	68	19	32
Hallucinated paranoid	16	70	7	30
Grandiose paranoid	27	79	7	21
Anxious-depressed	48	80	12	20
Retarded-motor disturbed	66	38	109	62
Disoriented	18	10	171	90
Anxious disorganized	15	83	3	17
Total	290	44	366	56

would, of course, classify an even greater proportion of cases.

REFERENCES

CATTELL, R. B. A note on correlation clusters and cluster search methods. *Psychometrika*, 1944, 9, 169–184.

CRONBACH, L. J., & GLESER, G. C. Assessing similarity between profiles. *Psychological Bulletin*, 1953, 50, 456–473.

HEINCKE, F. Naturgeschichte des Hering. Die Lokalformen und die Wanderungen des Hering in den Europaeischen Meeren. *Abhandlungen des Deutschen Seefischerei-Vereins*, 1898, 2, 1–223.

KLETT, C. J., & LORR, M. Validity of the acute psychotic types. In M. Lorr (Ed.). *Explorations in typing psychotics.* Oxford: Pergamon Press 1965. Chapter 6.

KLETT, C. J., & McNAIR, D. Reliability of the acute psychotic types. In M. Lorr (Ed.). *Explorations in typing psychotics.* Oxford: Pergamon Press. 1965. Chapter 6.

LORR, M. (Ed.). *Explorations in typing psychotics.* Oxford: Pergamon Press, 1965.

LORR, M., KLETT, C. J., & McNAIR, D. M. *Syndromes of psychosis.* New York: the Macmillan Co., 1963.

LORR, M., KLETT, C., McNAIR, D. M., & LASKY, J. J. Inpatient Multidimensional Scale. *Manual.* Palto Alto: Consulting Psychologists Press, 1962.

NUNNALLY, J. The analysis of profile data. *Psychological Bulletin*, 1962, 59, 311–319.

McQUITTY, L. L. Pattern analysis illustrated in classifying patients and normals. *Educational and Psychological Measurement*, 1954, 14, 598–604.

McQUITTY, L. L. Capabilities and improvements of linkage analysis as a clustering method. *Educational and Psychological Measurement*, 1964, 24, 441–456.

SAUNDERS, D. S., & SCHUCHMAN, H. Syndrome analysis: An efficient procedure for isolating meaningful subgroups in a nonrandom sample of a population. Paper read at annual Psychonomic Society meeting. St. Louis, Mo., September 1962.

SAWREY, W. L., KELLER, L., & CONGER, J. J. An objective method of grouping profiles by distance functions and its relation to factor analysis. *Educational and Psychological Measurement*, 1960, 20, 651–673.

STEPHENSON, W. Some observations on Q technique. *Psychological Bulletin*, 1952, 49, 483–498.

THORNDIKE, R. L. Who belongs in the family? *Psychometrika*, 1953, 18, 267–271.

ZUBIN, J. Socio-biological types and methods for their isolation. *Psychiatry*, 1938, 237–247.

ZUBIN, J., FLEISS, J., & BURDOCK, E. L. A method for fractionating a population into homogeneous subgroups. Unpublished paper, 1963.

41.

LUDWIG BINSWANGER

EXISTENTIAL ANALYSIS OF SCHIZOPHRENIA

To achieve some clarity concerning existential analysis—*Daseinsanalyse*—what it is, what its aims and its achievements are, and what they are not, we must first of all try to define its characteristic method, or, better, its mode of apprehension, its *Erfahrungsweise*. Existential analysis does not proceed by means of the discursive scientific method of clinical psychiatry and psychotherapy, nor does it fall back upon the inferential constructs of psychoanalysis. Rather, it follows the phenomenological procedure of apprehending essences. Its procedure is phenomenological in that it seeks to reveal each thing in its own terms, without dissimulation or distortion by extrinsic theoretical constructs. Its statements about things derive solely from these things, and they are free of what Flaubert called the "rage de conclure." So much for the first characteristic of existential analysis.

The second, specifically characteristic feature of our procedure, is that the "thing" described in existential analysis, is not a "thing" at all but a process (*Geschehen*). More precisely, it is the event *where existence is essentially concerned with his own being (in dem es dem Dasein in seinem Sein wesenhaft um sich selbst geht)*. What the being in general and the being of man is as such, that is a problem for ontology (*fundamental ontologie*). The psychiatric problem consists in clearly grasping the alterations to which the fundamental structure of existence is subject, to apprehend the idiosyncratic structure of individual existences regardless of distinctions between health and disease, normal and abnormal. In this task we avail ourselves of the basic concepts developed in the ontological analysis of human existence by Martin Heidegger in his book *Sein und Zeit*.

From Ludwig Binswanger, "Existential analysis, psychiatry, schizophrenia." *Journal of Existential Psychiatry*, 1960, *1*, 157–165. Reprinted by permission.

To grasp the articulated structure of a *particular* individual's existence and its development, in the first place requires the art of discovering those moments which are responsible for the given structure. But it is equally decisive, although frequently overlooked, that these determining moments are significantly related to one another.

We therefore do not simply ask: "Who is this man, and how does *he* speak about the world and about himself," but we go further, and ask, "how does existence here speak about existence?" We thus also interpret how this man interprets himself.

From all this you will see that, unlike psychoanalysis, existential analysis did not develop in response to inadequacies in psychotherapy, but in response to scientific inadequacies. Specifically, it developed in response to the dissatisfaction with the absence of a solid scientific foundation of all psychopathology, psychoanalysis included. All psychopathology *arbitrarily* borrowed its concepts now from this discipline, now from that, relying especially upon biology and a rather confused psychology. But a science is based on solid scientific foundation only once its *proper* sphere has been delimited on a-priori grounds. This is equally true of psychopathology and psychotherapy, whose specific scientific foundation is to be sought especially in the nature of human existence.

All this must have made it clear that since existential analysis and psychiatry seek for different kinds of understanding, they also speak entirely different languages. Obviously their two languages are not without affinities. But one cannot simply translate from the one to the other. Clinical psychiatry speaks of a psychosomatic organism, subject to certain natural processes, which can be subsumed under various functional biological concepts and judgments, and which admit of such conclusions as are implied in the notions of illness, diagnosis, aetiology, prognosis, and so on. You will seek in vain for these, or cognate expressions in the language of existential analysis. Indeed, existential analysis seeks to penetrate to a level which *underlies* what outwardly manifests itself to the psychopathologist, to discover the very structure of existence and its transformations, which the symptoms dissimulate.

Turning now to specific disorders, to understand *schizophrenia* in existential analytic terms is considerably more difficult than to understand the manic or the depressive states. It proved relatively easy to discover the moments that determine the existential structure of manics or of depressives, and the ceremonious joy with its attendant confidence in the one, the painful dejection with its corresponding anxiety in the other. And it proved equally easy to lay bare the relationship between these moments and the decisive dimensions of human existence. I remind you of my *Studien Ueber Ideenflucht*.

An entirely different situation confronts us when we turn to the schizophrenias. They assume a great many more forms than the manias and the depressions, or even than the compulsive forms of existence and their worlds, so splendidly described by Erwin Straus and by von Gebsattel. We therefore could not undertake our schizophrenia studies by taking as our point of departure either schizophrenia *as such,* or *the* schizophrenias. Instead we had to start by limiting ourselves to the analysis of the existential development of individual schizophrenics. We were guided in this procedure by a remark Freud once made to me about his own, much more encompassing, work. "Men always want a completed whole. But, after all, one has to start somewhere, and progress is slow." Despite many years' strenuous effort, I am not yet in a position today to present you with a total picture of the aberrations in the existential structure of those whom clinically we designate as schizophrenics. In the light of this, existential analysis can, of course, not present you with a theory, an aetiology, or a technique of psychotherapy for schizophrenia.

The aim, first of all, of our research, here as everywhere else, is to reclaim the schizophrenic human being from the language, the conceptual apparatus, the theories and the habits of thought prevalent in clinical psychiatry. Our aim is to reinstate this human being in his full humanity, his existence, and his being-in-the-world (*in-der-Welt-sein*). This is achieved by discovering the cruxes responsible for the schizophrenic development of the existential structure, and by noting how these cruxes articulate into the total structure.

We now take a further step. With Szilasi, to whom we owe more than to anyone else for the clarification of our method, we recognize that these critical moments are moments of *failure* in the process of existence. They are moments at which *the sequential character of experience becomes problematic.* On these occasions experience cannot follow an orderly course, nor can it be appeased and come to rest. This is why schizophrenics experience contradictions and irreconcilable alternatives in a world torn asunder. The world of living experience is no longer open, it is no longer an acceptance of being as Heidegger puts it, but instead it is closed to being, without exits, in other words, it is a world where it has become impossible to conduct one's life. Now, patients suffer from this condition, so that we feel called upon to help them. Existential analysis must never lose sight of this requirement.

What we call experience *does have* consequence, *it is* sequential. Whenever this sequence is interrupted, a vacuum is, so to say, inserted into experience. It is therefore all important to discover where these vacuums occur, and how schizophrenics fill them up. In other words, what exits do they find in a world without exits, how do they conduct a life impossible to conduct. In so far as my own schizophrenia studies provide any indications, the specific schizophrenic solution consists in substituting for the uninterrupted, objective sequence of experience, a set of rigid alternatives, a hard and fast either-or. These alternatives are totally inadequate to serve as the presumed escapes from an inescapable situation. As a consequence, the schizophrenic, at least this is what I have observed in my own cases, no longer knows either inside or out, he can no longer move either forward or back. Yet he tries to move on within the confines of his alternatives, of his either-or. But precisely in this way he shuts himself off from the world of others and himself, and most especially, of course, he shuts himself off from any possibility of a loving relatedness with men and the world about him (*das liebende Miteinandersein*). He thus becomes more and more entangled in his alternatives, and since they do not admit of a sequential continuity in experience, he becomes forced into still further contradictions.

In view of the limited time at my disposal, I cannot go into details, but must refer you to my schizophrenia studies in the *Swiss Archives for Neurology and Psychiatry*. I only point out that everyone of my cases manifested with striking clarity this nonsequential character of experience, this being caught between rigid alternatives, and the consequent impossibility of conducting one's own life, in what I have called a *verstiegene Idealbildung*. (The term is untranslatable in its precise ambiguity, because it combines the root *steigen*, to rise, to climb, with the qualification *ver*, *versteigen*, which indicates that one has lost one's way while ascending to a height. In addition the word is also used idiomatically to mean "missing the mark" in any aim one takes, or "losing one's way." By extension it also means "being off," and hence maladjusted. I beg you to keep these nuances in mind when I clumsily translate *verstiegen* by misguided. A *verstiegene Idealbildung* is, then, a misguided formation and pursuit of misguided ideals.)

In the case of Ilse the misguided ideal consisted in showing to the father what love is capable of, by burning her hand in the stove; in the case of Ellen West the misguided ideal of slenderness with all its variations was exemplified; Jürg Zünd's misguided ideal was aristocratic; Lola Voss' of being guided by a spoken oracle; and Suzanne Urban's was the most painstaking care for the welfare of the family. These ideals were contradicted by Ilse's experience of her father's lack of love and of his imperturbability; by Ellen West's experience of gluttony and of gaining weight; by Jürg Zünd's experience of his proletarian manner; by Lola Voss' experience of the untoward and harrowing; by Suzanne Urban's experience of the constant

threat to the welfare of the family which erupted into her existence with the diagnosis of her husband's cancer. It is readily apparent from even these few indications how varied can be the life situations in which the sequential character of experience can be shattered for schizophrenics. This shattering has its roots in the deepest depths of existence, which is of course why we must be careful not to conceive of this shattering in merely logical, or psychological, or biological terms. It is important to remain mindful of this throughout the abbreviated verbal formulations we shall now give of the alternatives confronting each of the cases mentioned. The break in Ilse's fulfillment of existence—*Daseinsvollzug*—can be succinctly formulated as a break into the either-or alternatives of the power and the impotence of her love for her father; Ellen West's into the mutually exclusive alternatives of slenderness or obesity, with its manifold ramifications of significance; Jürg Zünd's into the alternatives of aristocrat and proletarian; Lola Voss' into the alternatives of being sheltered by the world and simultaneously exposed to the untoward and the harrowing; Suzanne Urban's into the "either" of the family's being unharmed, and the "or" of the family's being threatened by illness, suffering and death. It is readily evident that in none of these alternatives could experience *follow an orderly sequential* course, or *come to a rest*. Existence is here constantly rubbed raw in the truly desperate effort to maintain its one solid hold, the misguided ideal. This is an unviable situation, and we therefore regularly observe the formation of what I have described as an *attempted masking—Deckungsversuch—*of the constantly threatening experience of contradiction. Jürg Zünd masks the proletarian by an arbitrary and artificial imitation of aristocratic mannerisms; Ellen West by eccentric devices to avoid gaining weight; Lola Voss by highly mannered and eccentric oracular statements; Suzanne Urban by the disproportionate concern for her husband and family. We thus see how closely related are the forms by which mishappened existences become expressed: misguidedness, eccentricity, and mannerism. All these forms of existence are to be understood as consequences of the breakdown in the sequential order of experience and the resulting experience of existence with no exits. They are so many attempts, inappropriate or inadequate as they may be, of somehow coping with life nevertheless. Behind all this hovers an *existential anxiety—Daseinsangst* —the anxiety of not being able to cope with life after all. The misguided ideal already proved to be a supposed escape from this anxiety. That is also why we see this anxiety erupt when the attempted masking fails, and the patient is exposed to his anxiety without refuge or protection. The escapes from this triad, the misguided ideal, the attempted masking, and the eruption of anxiety, once again differ widely in their results. (Ilse found her way out of the shattered continuity of experience in its various manifestations—including even delusions of persecution—back into integrated and sequential experience, that is to say, clinically speaking, back into *sanity*. Ellen West returned to orderly experience and to a calm and tolerable existence by means of a carefully considered decision to commit *suicide*, as providing the only escape from "the stage of life" all of whose exits, to use her own simile, were guarded by men armed with drawn swords, so that she collapsed in despair. Jürg Zünd finally achieved some peace by a constriction of existence, manifesting itself in considerably reduced mental activity. In the cases of Lola Voss and Suzanne Urban there was no way back to sequential and orderly experience, and the tension was only resolved by a total swing to one of the alternatives, the threatening alternative, thus resulting in chronic delusions of multiple persecution.)

Allow me to say a few, and hence necessarily inadequate, words about how existential analysis understands delusions of persecution. I shall restrict my remarks to the case of Suzanne Urban. Special caution is required here in order to resist the temptation of conceptually isolating structural components of existence from its totality, without showing their articulation with one another into a whole, and thus to resort to intellectual constructions instead of recognizing the need of existence as it is. The danger, as to the method, consists here as everywhere else, in "deducing" from, or "explaining" delusions of persecution in terms of some isolated elements of the total existential structure. Even phenomenological descriptions proper, the doctrine of a conviction in experiential space, the "rétrécissement de l'espace vécu et de l'ampleur de la vie," so splendidly outlined by Eugene Minkowski, and developed by Merleau-Ponty, fail to go far enough. It is true that we owe by far the greatest and the most valuable contributions to our understanding of schizophrenia —and not of schizophrenia *alone*—to our friend Eugene Minkowski. But Minkowski stops with describing phenomena and their relationships, without being interested in the fundamental ontological structure of existence. A true disciple of Bergson, he is satisfied with going back to living experience (*Erlebnis, le vécu*), and to life (*la vie*). Although his monograph on schizophrenia, and especially his study of "la distance vécue et l'ampleur de la vie," contains the most remarkable insights into the phenomenological essence of schizophrenia, it is to be remembered that le vécu and la vie are not structural articulations of a process in the same way as is what we call existence, *Dasein*. They do not reveal to us either the *structure* or the *articulation* of the crucial moments in the existential process. To point out the constriction of experienced space does not suffice for an existential-analytic understanding of delusions of persecution. Rather, this constriction must first of all be seen in the total context of the existential process. After many preparatory studies we undertook such an analysis in the case of Suzanne Urban. It proved possible to show there how the entire existential structure became increasingly overpowered by the existential power of the dreadful, that is to say, how it is driven to the abyss of anxiety. And it is precisely this anxiety which she desperately attempted to mask by her wholly disproportionate concern for husband and family. In delusions of persecution the endless and bootless efforts at following through the consequences of experience are simply given up. Existence may be said to abdicate fulfillment, it no longer confronts the alternatives that are present in its life-situation, and it simply yields itself up entirely to *one* of the alternatives before it: namely, the alternative which it had fought and feared up to then. Experience henceforth follows but *one single* direction, and it now does so in the most rigorously sequential manner, wholly oriented as it is toward the furtive and the foreign, dread and the dreadful, intent upon the dreadful threat, the suffering and the torture of the family. Once this occurs, all attempted masking of the situation has proved illusory, and anxiety freely erupts everywhere. Once the experience of the dreadful becomes all absorbing and, so to speak, methodical, and *then only,* "the physiognomy of the world," as Erwin Straus calls it, quite naturally changes into the untoward, and, to use another expression of Straus's, the "sympathetic relationships" become constricted into relationships of malice and persecution.

In conclusion let me add a word regarding the lively interest with which existential analysis watches modern developments in the treatment of schizophrenia. This is primarily due to the fact that the modern treatment of schizophrenia also does not restrict itself to a description and treatment of *symptoms,* but that it looks behind them for the specific *modes of existence* which alone can render symptoms intelligible and indicate appropriate therapeutic measures. All this is clear enough in the case of Renée, where Mme. Séchehaye points out a certain mode of existence and its structure. True, she describes this only negatively, as "antérieur à la formation du langage parlé," as preceding the development of spoken language. But it can easily be described in positive terms as a magical mode of thought. Nowhere is a better illustration to be found of the meaning of psychotherapy in general, and in particular of the psychotherapy of schizophrenics, than in this case. Here it becomes evident that psychotherapy consists in guiding the patient back from an unchartered existence to new roads, where the possibility of experiencing in an orderly sequential manner once again obtains, and where the patient is able freely to dispose of his innermost existential resources.

42.

R. D. LAING

PHENOMENOLOGICAL APPROACH TO SCHIZOPHRENIA

JONES: (*Laughs loudly, then pauses.*) I'm McDougal, myself. [This actually is not his name.]

SMITH: What do you do for a living, little fellow? Work on a ranch or something?

JONES: No, I'm a civilian seaman. Supposed to be high mucka-muck society.

SMITH: A singing recording machine, huh? I guess a recording machine sings sometimes. If they're adjusted right. Mm-hm. I thought that was it. My towel, mm-hm. We'll be going back to sea in about—eight or nine months though. Soon as we get our—destroyed parts repaired. (*Pause.*)

From R. D. Laing, "Is schizophrenia a disease?" *International Journal of Social Psychiatry,* 1964, *10,* 184–193. A version of this paper is found in R. D. Laing, *The politics of experience,* Chap. 5, The schizophrenic experience. New York: Ballantine Books; and Pantheon Books, 1967. Reprinted by permission of The Avenue Publishing Co., London.

JONES: I've got lovesickness, secret love.

SMITH: Secret love, huh? (*Laughs.*)

JONES: Yeah.

SMITH: I ain't got any secret love.

JONES: I fell in love, but I don't feed any woo— that sits over—looks something like me— walking around over there.

SMITH: My, oh, my only one, my only love is the shark. Keep out of the way of him.

JONES: Don't they know I have a life to live? (*Long pause.*)

SMITH: Do you work at the air base? Hm?

JONES: You know what I think of work, I'm 33 in June, do you mind?

SMITH: June?

JONES: Thirty-three years old in June. This stuff goes out the window after I live this, uh— leave this hospital. So I lay off cigarettes. I'm a spatial condition, from outer space myself, no shit.

SMITH: (*Laughs.*) I'm a real space ship from across.

JONES: A lot of people talk, uh—that way, like crazy, but Believe It or Not by Ripley, take it or leave it—alone—it's in the *Examiner*, it's in the comic section. Believe It or Not by Ripley, Robert E. Ripley. Believe It or Not, but we don't have to believe anything, unless I feel like it. (*Pause.*) Every little rosette—too much alone. (*Pause.*)

SMITH: Yeah, it could be possible. (*Phrase inaudible because of airplane noise.*)

JONES: I'm a civilian seaman.

SMITH: Could be possible. (*Sighs.*) I take my bath in the ocean.

JONES: Bathing stinks. You know why? 'Cause you can't quit when you feel like it. You're in the service.

SMITH: I can quit whenever I feel like quitting. I can get out when I feel like getting out.

JONES: (*Talking at the same time.*) Take me, I'm a civilian, I can quit.

SMITH: Civilian?

JONES: Go my—my way.

SMITH: I guess we have, in port, civilian. (*Long pause.*)

JONES: What do they want with us?

SMITH: Hm?

JONES: What do they want with you and me?

SMITH: What do they want with you and me? How do I know what they want with you? I know what they want with me. I broke the law, so I have to pay for it. (*Silence.*) (Haley, J.: *Strategies of Psychotherapy.* New York: Grune & Stratton, 1963, pp. 99–100).

This is not a conversation from a Pinter play, it is a conversation between two persons diagnosed as schizophrenic. What does this diagnosis mean?

In this article I wish to call in question the prevailing attitude in respect to schizophrenia, and to suggest an alternative point of view. Before I shall be able to put forward the alternative point of view, however, I shall have to examine some of our prevailing attitudes about normality and sanity, since the concept of schizophrenia as a form of madness implies a concept of sanity as the norm against which madness is judged.

PRESENT POSITION

Some people come to behave and to experience themselves and others in ways that are strange and incomprehensible to most people, including themselves.

If this behaviour and experience fall into certain broad categories, they will be likely to be diagnosed as subject to a condition called schizophrenia. By present calculations almost one in every hundred children born will fall into this category at some time or other before the age of forty-five, and in this country at the moment there are roughly 60,000 men and women in mental hospitals, and many more outside hospital, who are termed schizophrenic.

The most commonly held view among psychiatrists is that these persons suffer from some inherited predisposition to experience and to act in a predominantly meaningless way, and that an unknown genetic defect acts in some as yet undetermined biochemical-endocrinological-organic manner to produce a change. What we, the others, observe are the signs of this underlying process.

Psychiatrists have struggled for years to discover what those people who are diagnosed as schizophrenic have or have not in common with each other. The results are so far inconclusive.

No generally agreed objective clinical criteria for the diagnosis of "schizophrenia" have been discovered.

No consistency in pre-psychotic personality, course, duration, outcome, has been discovered.

Every conceivable view is held by authoritative people as to whether "schizophrenia" is a disease or a group of diseases; whether an identifiable organic pathology has been, or can be expected to be, found.

There are no pathological anatomical findings *post mortem*. There are no organic structural changes noted in course of the "illness." There are no physiological-pathological changes that can be correlated with these illnesses. There is no general acceptance that any form of treatment is of proven value, except perhaps sustained careful interpersonal relations and tranquillization. "Schizophrenia" runs in families, but observes no genetically clear law. It appears usually to have no adverse effect on physical health, and, given proper care by others, it does not cause death or foreshorten life. It occurs in every constitutional type. It is not associated with any known other physical malfunctions.

It is most important to recognize that the diagnosed patient is not suffering from a disease whose aetiology is unknown, unless he can prove otherwise. The American psychiatrist Thomas Szasz develops this argument to considerable effect in his book *The Myth of Mental Illness.* The schizophrenic is someone who has queer experiences and/or is acting in a queer way, from the point of view usually of his relatives and of ourselves. Whether these queer experiences and actions are constantly associated with changes in his body is still uncertain, although it is highly likely that relatively enduring biochemical changes may be the consequence of relatively enduring interpersonal situations of particular kinds.

That the diagnosed patient is suffering from a pathological process is either a fact, an hypothesis, an assumption or a judgment.

To regard it as fact is unequivocally false. To regard it as an hypothesis is legitimate. It is unnecessary either to make the assumption or to pass the judgment.

Now, the psychiatrist adopting his clinical stance in the presence of the pre-diagnosed person, whom he is already looking at and listening to as a patient, has too often come to believe that he is in the presence of the "fact" of "schizophrenia." He acts "as if" its existence were an established fact. He then has to discover its "cause" or multiple "aetiological factors," to assess its "prognosis" and to treat its course. The heart of the "illness," all that is the outcome of process, then resides outside the agency of the person. That is, the illness, or process, is taken to be a "fact" that the person is subject to or undergoes, whether it is supposed to be genetic, constitutional, endogenous, exogenous, organic or psychological, or some mixture of them all. This, we submit, is a mistaken starting-point.

The judgment that the diagnosed patient is behaving in a biologically dysfunctional (hence pathological) way is, I believe, premature, and one that I shall hold in parenthesis.

There have been many studies of social factors in relation to schizophrenia. These include attempts to discover whether schizophrenia occurs more or less frequently in one or other ethnic group, social class, sex, ordinal position in the family, and so on. The general conclusion from all such studies has been that social factors do not play a significant role in the genesis of schizophrenia.

However, such studies do not get close enough to the relevant situation, besides posing the problem as though "schizophrenia" existed as some condition like pneumonia. If the police wish to determine whether a man has died of natural causes or has committed suicide or been murdered, they do not look up prevalence or incidence figures. They investigate the circumstances attendant upon each single case in turn. Each investigation is an original and unrepeatable research project, and it comes to an end when enough evidence has been gathered to answer the relevant questions.

My colleagues and I have been engaged in studying the actual circumstances around the social event when one person comes to become regarded as schizophrenic. We have studied over fifty cases, and without exception it seems to us that the experience and behaviour that gets labelled schizophrenic is a special sort of strategy that a person invents in order to live in an unlivable situation. In his life situation the person has come to be placed in an untenable position. He cannot make a move or make no move, without being beset by contradictory pressures both internally, from himself, and externally, from those around him. He is, as it were, in a position of checkmate. I must make it clear that this state of affairs may not be perceived as such by any of the people in it. The man at the bottom of the heap may be crushed and suffocated to death without anyone noticing, much less intending it. The situation in and around the schizophrenic is often impossible to see by studying the different people in it singly, as has always been done. Recently, however, different research groups in America have found ways of overcoming the great methodological difficulties in work of this kind, and their conclusions and our own are in substantial agreement.

Now, the diagnosis as such of schizophrenia is simply a social event. But among the heterogeneous motley of persons diagnosed, there are many who have found themselves, or rather have lost themselves, in regions of the inner world, into which they have been precipitated for reasons they do not know, and in realms of frightening or strange experience are temporarily unable to function competently at the same time in the shared so-called external world.

When a person finds himself in a total impasse, if he does not commit suicide, Nature sometimes calls upon a healing process that has been available to mankind at all times and in all places. No age, however, has so lost touch with this process as has our own. I refer to the ceremonies of initiation practised all over the world until very recently, when a person was conducted through an experience of (i) death; of (ii) journeying in the Other World; of (iii) rebirth from that Place and that Time back into this world with its here and now.

Schizophrenia is a confused attempt to conduct such a sequence. It is hardly surprising that the person in his terror may stand in curious postures to control the spirits that occupy him (counterparts to which are the Yoga positions), that he projects the inner onto the outer, and the outer onto the inner, that he tries in short to protect himself from destruction by every means that he has, by projection, splitting, denial and so on.

The anthropologist Gregory Bateson, in a brilliant introduction to a nineteenth-century autobiographical account of schizophrenia, has said this:

It would appear that once precipitated into psychosis the patient has a course to run. He is, as it were, embarked upon a voyage of discovery which is only completed by his return to the normal world, to which he comes back with insights different from those of the inhabitants who never embarked on such a voyage. Once begun, a schizophrenic episode would appear to have as definite a course as an initiation ceremony—a death and rebirth—into which the novice may have been precipitated by his family life or by adventitious circumstances, but which in its course is largely steered by endogenous process.

In terms of this picture, spontaneous remission is no problem. This is only the final and natural outcome of the total process. What needs to be explained is the failure of many who embark upon this voyage to return from it. *Do these encounter circumstances either in family life or in institutional care so grossly maladaptive that even the richest and best organized hallucinatory experience cannot save them?* (Bateson, G. (ed.). *Perceval's Narrative. A Patient's Account of His Psychosis.* Stanford, Calif.: Stanford University Press, 1961, pp. xiii-xiv; italics mine.)

I am in substantial agreement with this view.

THE CASE FOR A SHIFT OF POINT OF VIEW

To regard the conversational gambits of Smith and Jones (at the beginning of this article) as indicative of some incapacity or defect in thinking, is like saying that a man doing a hand-stand on a bicycle on a tight-rope a hundred feet up with no safety net is suffering from an inability to stand on his own two feet. We may well ask why these people have to be so brilliantly devious, elusive and incongruous, such adepts at making themselves so slickly and unremittingly incomprehensible.

Actually, records of such conversations between schizophrenics do not exist in psychiatric textbooks. The diagnosis of schizophrenia has always been made, and still is, on the basis of the person's behaviour during what is called a clinical examination.

It is only recently that the relationships between patients themselves have been studied without presuppositions. The best such study has been made by an American sociologist, Erving Goffman.

Goffman spent a year as an assistant physical therapist in a large mental hospital of some 7,000 beds, near Washington. His lowly staff status enabled him to fraternize with the patients in a way that upper echelons of the staff, notably psychiatrists, were unable to do. One of his conclusions is:

There is an old saw that no clear-cut line can be drawn between normal people and mental patients; rather there is a continuum with the well-adjusted citizen at one end and the full-fledged psychotic at the other. I must argue that after a period of acclimatization in a mental hospital the notion of a continuum seems very presumptuous. A community is a community. Just as it is bizarre to those not in it, so it is natural, even if unwanted, to those who live it from within. The system of dealings that patients have with one another does not fall at one end of anything, but rather provides one example of human association, to be avoided, no doubt, but also to be filed by the student in a circular cabinet along with all the other examples of association that he can collect. (Goffman, E.: *Asylums. Essays on the Social Situation of Mental Patients and Other Inmates.* New York: Doubleday-Anchor Books, 1961, p. 303.)

A large part of his study is devoted to a detailed documentation of how it comes about that persons can become defined as non-agents, non-responsible, non-blameable essences, be treated accordingly, and even come to regard themselves in this light.

The psychiatrist and patient is one of those fascinating couples that history throws up from time to time: guru-disciple, inquisitor-heretic, priest-confessor. The one person in the set of reciprocals that characterize their relationship is meaningless extrapolated from the context. They fit together like lock and key. Each indeed is the key to understanding the other.

A feature of the psychiatrist-patient reciprocals is that if the patient's reciprocals are extrapolated, as is the tactic in the clinical description, they can be plausibly represented as very odd, whereas the psychiatrist's responses are seen as congruent with our common-sense view of normality. In other words, the psychiatrist seems to us in varying degrees sane, and the patient in varying degrees mad. This is because the psychiatrist's behaviour is assumed axiomatically to be the yardstick against which the abnormality of the patient is scaled.

But if one puts the clinical stance and perspective in brackets, and looks at the psychiatrist-patient couple as far as possible without presuppositions, then one may find it difficult to sustain this naïve polarization of the situation.

Consider, for instance, the following interaction between Kraepelin, regarded by many as one of the great psychiatrists, and a patient (given in his words):

Gentlemen, the cases that I have to place before you today are peculiar. First of all, you see a servant-girl, aged twenty-four, upon whose features and frame traces of great emaciation can be plainly seen. In spite of this, the patient is in continual movement, going a few steps forward, and then back again; she plaits her hair, only to unloose it the next minute. *On attempting to stop her movement,* we meet with unexpectedly strong resistance; *if I place myself in front of her with my arms spread out* in order to stop her, if she cannot

push me on one side, she suddenly turns and slips through under my arms, so as to continue her way. If *one takes firm hold of her,* she distorts her usually rigid, expressionless features with deplorable weeping, that only ceases so soon as one lets her have her own way. We notice besides that she holds a crushed piece of bread spasmodically clasped in the fingers of the left hand, which she absolutely *will not allow to be forced from her.* The patient does not trouble in the least about her surroundings so long as you leave her alone. If *you prick her in the forehead with a needle,* she scarcely winces or turns away, and leaves the needle quietly sticking there without letting it disturb her restless, beast-of-prey-like wandering backwards and forwards. *To questions* she answers almost nothing, at the most shaking her head. But from time to time she wails: 'O dear God! O dear God! O dear mother! O dear mother!' always repeating uniformly the same phrases. If *you try to grasp her hand* she draws it away very suddenly, and at last, if she can no longer avoid you, begins to roll it up in her apron. *Orders are of no use:* on the contrary, she resists in everything you try to do with her. But when she quickly hides her hand directly *one speaks of taking away the bread,* it becomes evident that she understands what is happening around her. (Kraepelin, E.: *Lectures on Clinical Psychiatry* (Johnstone, T., ed.). London: Baillière, Tindall & Cox, 1906, pp. 30–31; italics mine.)

Here is a man and a young girl. Because we have the fixed idea that this is a doctor examining a patient, it all immediately falls into place. He is sane, she is insane: he is rational, she is irrational. But if we take Kraepelin's actions (I have italicized them: he tries to stop her movements, stands in front of her with arms outspread, tries to force a piece of bread out of her hand, sticks a needle in her forehead, and so on) out of the context of the situation *as experienced and defined by him,* how extraordinary they are!

In studying the issues raised by "schizophrenia," we have to include experience as well as behaviour in our domain of relevance. The behaviour of the person diagnosed as schizophrenic is different because his experience is different. But we absolutely must not suppose that there is something sacrosanct about modern sane experience. Here there are certain matters of principle that we must bear in mind.

In the first place, we all experience far fewer things than the total possible spectrum of experience. There are certain types of experience that many people are not aware of at all, and there are some that are regarded with fear and mistrust. The ordinary person is almost totally amnesic for the first five years of life, and many people remember very few dreams, and then only scrappily. Compared to the Yogi, the ordinary man has only a vestigial experience of his body. Many people are unaware of experiences in the modality of what psychoanalysts call fantasy (to be distinguished sharply from imagination), and even more, experiences that have been common among Western men and women until very recently (demons). Experiences of telepathy, clairvoyance, the impression of a life of some kind between death and birth, reincarnation, are perhaps more common than is often supposed.

If this is the case, it means that while evidence must be drawn from the realm of one's own and the other person's experience, not only from observation of behaviour, unfortunately, we cannot use our own adult experience of ourselves as an instrument of unqualified validity for such an inquiry. On the contrary, in becoming aware of ourselves and others as persons, we come to realize that we have to begin from a position wherein we are largely alienated from experience.

If we naïvely regard our norm of sanity as the measure of insanity, then we are led to precisely the point of view that is currently held about schizophrenia. But if we see our sanity as already a state of extreme alienation, then we will be less ready to suppose that the schizophrenic is more alienated than we are from the totality of reality.

Putting one of the essential realizations from the practice of psychotherapy in a non-technical idiom, we can say that by the time each of us is fifteen we are all likely to be to a large extent strangers to ourselves (to our childhoods, our minds, our bodies), and strangers to one another.

While not rejecting any human form of experience in so far as it is a phenomenon, that is, in so far as it makes its appearance to someone, whether this is a dream, a perception, an image, a vision, one must also place in parenthesis any judgment as to the validity of this experience.

Psychiatrists have paid very little attention to the *experience* of the patient from the patient's point of view, tending to regard this as not the hard stuff of science. One might have hoped that psychoanalysis would step in here. But there is an abiding tendency in psychoanalysis to suppose that the schizophrenic's experiences are somehow unreal or invalid; one can make sense out of them only by interpreting them; without truth-giving interpretations the patient is enmeshed in a world of delusion and self-deception. Kaplan, an American psychologist, in an introduction to an excellent collection of self-reports on the experience of being psychotic, says very justly:

With all virtue on his side, he [the psychiatrist or psychoanalyst] reaches through the subterfuges and distortions of the patient and exposes them to the light of reason and insight. In this encounter between the psychiatrist and patient, the efforts of the former are linked with science and medicine, with understanding and care. What the patient experiences is tied to illness and irreality, to perverseness and distortion. The process of psychotherapy consists in large part of the patient's abandoning his false subjective perspectives for the therapist's objective ones. But the essence of this conception is that the psychiatrist understands what is going on, and the patient does not. (*The Inner World of Mental Illness.* New York: Harper & Row, 1964.)

H. S. Sullivan used to say to young psychiatrists when they came to work with him, "I want you to remember that in the present state of our society, the patient is right, and you are wrong." This is an outrageous over-simplification. I mention it to loosen any fixed ideas that are no less outrageous, that we are right, and *they* are wrong. I think it is a sober estimate, however, that schizophrenics have had more to teach psychiatrists about the inner world than psychiatrists their patients.

It is necessary to admit all domains of experience into our context of relevance if we are going to understand schizophrenia. Since natural science studies only the relation between things, we are thus in a context of relevance half outside and half inside the range of natural scientific investigation, but always within the legitimate domain of social science. We have to realize the phenomenal existence of an "inner" world, that goes beyond the realm of imagination, reveries, dreams and personal unconscious fantasy (which is already beyond what most people are aware of, and which itself frequently requires several years of psychoanalysis before a person becomes familiar with this domain). I still can think of no better word for this experiential domain that lies "beyond" the usual level of perception, thinking, imagination, dreams, fantasy, than the spiritual world—or the domain of spirits, Powers, Thrones, Principalities, Seraphim, Cherubim, the Light.

It is necessary to admit such experiences to our context of relevance because it frequently is into these reaches of experience that the schizophrenic may enter, without guide or guideline.

THERAPY

It is important to note that an increasing number of psychiatrists are becoming aware of the contradiction in fitting what is essentially a human drama intrinsically implicating a number of protagonists, into clinical terms designed to fit what goes on inside the skin of one body. It must be emphasized, moreover, that a number of very serious organic conditions, e.g. forms of epilepsy, brain tumour, may easily be mistaken for schizophrenia. Before anyone is regarded as a schizophrenic, that is, suffering from no known organic process in the present state of our knowledge, he should have been competently examined to exclude any discernible organic illness. Once this has been excluded, therapy is another matter.

The following are a few necessarily telegrammatic remarks on therapy.

(1) A bare minimum is care and respect for the whole person. In the acute breakdown "he" or "she" is only partially in this world. Although his body is all here, "he" may be all "there." While the patient is *in absentia,* he should be treated with full human dignity.

(2) Occasionally another patient, or member of the staff, may have some understanding of the internal drama that is going on.

The psychiatrist should realize that nothing in his training as a doctor or psychiatrist gives him any special claim to understand this process. He may, however, be humble and gifted enough to sense when someone else does; and very rarely he may have an understanding of what is involved himself. The patient badly needs guidance, but he is much better not given any advice or "interpretations" made with no genuine authority.

The priest traditionally ought to know this realm, but he has almost totally lost direct experiential contact with that domain from which his own beliefs and liturgy emanate, and in which the schizophrenic is travelling, in a realm in which no one speaks his language.

(3) If the person is wearing out himself or his nurses beyond the limits of his or their stamina, then for his sake or theirs, tranquillization is indicated.

If he is subject to enthusiastic attempts to "cure" him by means of electricity, and by cutting off bits of his brain, it is quite likely that he will be cut off from his connection with heaven or hell and function once more comparatively well in this world.

(4) Preparation for the person's return to his family and community requires work with his family and other social networks before he leaves hospital, as well as thereafter. Continuity of care is required, without the existing tendency to separate, economically and organizationally, the "cure" of the "illness" from the "care of the person."

Today, most people sent to hospital as "schizophrenics" for the first time are out again in six months, but most of these are back again in another year. The discharge rate is encouraging and the relapse rate is unnecessary.

Admirable Half-way Homes, ex-patients' clubs and flexible day or night hospitals are beginning to be set up.

An increasing number of doctors, nurses and patients now feel that what is required for the treatment of the acute breakdown is a small Centre (with not more than twenty-four patients) that will be neither a mental hospital nor a psychiatric unit in a general hospital; where treatment will consist of the experience of community in a tranquil human setting, and where there will be people who have themselves been in and out of the world that the schizophrenic enters in terror, lost and confused. More people than are at present given a chance to be social therapists, possess patience, understanding, responsibility, stamina, and sometimes the capacity to act as guides.

Easy is the descent to Avernus; everyone agrees that it is the way back that is difficult.

When patients become integrated they would be able to work from the Centre. There would be no pressure on people to leave. One would keep in close touch with those patients who had left, and they would be free to return if they felt the need. Just as there would be no upper limit to the length of time a patient might stay, there would be no lower limit. Patients would be able to come and go, staying only a night or a few days at a time, as their situation dictated. One would also wish to provide an Emergency Home Visiting Service, to deal with family crises, and family treatment sessions would be held for those patients who were not resident. Such a Centre could pioneer new approaches to schizophrenia and to psychiatric theory and practice generally.

Schizophrenia used to be a new name for dementia praecox—a slow, insidious illness that was supposed to overtake young people in particular, and to be liable to go on to a terminable dementia.

Perhaps we can still retain the now old name, and read into it its original meaning: *Schiz—*broken; *Phrenos—*soul or heart.

The schizophrenic is one who is brokenhearted. But even broken hearts can mend, if we have the heart to let them.

43.

Seymour S. Kety

BIOCHEMICAL HYPOTHESES OF SCHIZOPHRENIA

Biochemistry, which has had notable success in elucidating etiologic factors in many areas of medicine, has also been brought to bear on the problem of schizophrenia. Although these efforts have not to date been successful in demonstrating a biochemical "lesion," a number of arguments can be made to support the viewpoint that chemical factors operate significantly and specifically in schizophrenia.

Perhaps the strongest of these arguments is the good evidence for the operation of genetic factors in the transmission of schizophrenia,[92] consisting of a higher concordance rate for the disorder in the monozygotic twins of afflicted individuals[43,57,59,67,99] and in the biologic families of schizophrenics where early adoption or removal from their natural parents has served to disentangle the operation of genetic and environmental factors in its transmission.[50,64,93]

Another argument which has been used is the ability of a number of exogenous chemical substances (iodides, mescaline, LSD, amphetamine, iproniazid, psilocybin) or some endogenous biochemical disturbances (porphyria, thyroid disorders) to produce psychoses resembling schizophrenia in some or many of its features.

Biochemical hypotheses and findings related to schizophrenia have been the subject of several exhaustive and critical reviews of which only a few are cited for further reference.[22,61,63,109] In spite of the large number of abnormal chemical findings which have been reported in schizophrenia, few have been independently confirmed and on none is there general agreement with regard to its significance. This may be attributed to the operation of an inordinate number of variables, difficult to control, which are associated with the clinical studies of schizophrenia.

From Seymour S. Kety, Biochemical hypotheses and studies. In Leopold Bellak and Laurence Loeb (Eds.), *The schizophrenic syndrome.* New York: Grune & Stratton, 1969. Pp. 155–171. Reprinted by permission.

Despite the phenomenologic similarities which permitted the concept of schizophrenia to emerge, there is little evidence that all of its forms have a common etiology or pathogenesis. Errors involved in the study of relatively small samples from heterogeneous populations may help to explain the frequency with which findings of one group fail to be confirmed by another.

Most biochemical research in schizophrenia has been carried out in patients with a long history of hospitalization in institutions where overcrowding is difficult to avoid and hygienic standards cannot always be maintained. It is easy to imagine the spread of chronic infections such as infectious hepatitis among such patients, and one wonders how often this may account for findings attributable to disturbed hepatic function or elevated plasma titres of antibody globulins. Even in the absence of previous or current infection, the development of a characteristic pattern of intestinal flora in a group of patients living together for long periods of time may occasionally contribute to the finding of what appear to be deviant metabolic pathways.

The variety and quality of the diet of the institutionalized schizophrenic is rarely comparable to that of the nonhospitalized normal control. In the case of the acute schizophrenic, the weeks of continual turmoil which precede recognition of the disorder are hardly conducive to a normal dietary intake. It is not surprising that a dietary vitamin deficiency has been found to account for at least one biochemical abnormality which had been attributed to schizophrenia.[77] Horwitt[55] found signs of liver dysfunction during long periods of borderline protein ingestion.

Emotional stress is known to cause profound changes in man, in adrenocortical and thyroid function, in excretion of water, electrolytes, creatinine, epinephrine and norepinephrine, to mention only a few recently reported findings. On the other hand, physical inactivity would be expected to produce changes in a number of body functions. Schizophrenic illness is often characterized by indolence and lack of exercise or by marked emotional disturbance in the basal state and frequently exaggerated anxiety in response to routine and research procedures. The disturbances in behavior and activity which mark the schizophrenic process would also be expected to cause deviations from the normal in many biochemical and metabolic measures: in urinary volume and concentration, in energy and nitrogen metabolism, in the state and activity of numerous organ systems and metabolic pathways. The biochemical changes which are secondary to the psychologic and behavioral state of the patient are often of interest in themselves; it is important, however, not to attribute to them etiologic roles.

Another incidental feature of the schizophrenic patient which differentiates him from the normal control and from many other types of patient is the long list of therapies to which he may have been exposed. The ataractic drugs which are often used over extended periods of time are particularly prone to produce metabolites which appear in the urine and interfere with a number of chemical determinations long after the drug has been withdrawn.

With this combination of many variables and the subjective judgments necessary for diagnosis and the evaluation of clinical course, it is not unexpected that subjective bias would from time to time affect the results of research in schizophrenia and make even more necessary in that field than in many others the employment of rigorous research design.

ENERGY METABOLISM

A decrease in basal metabolism was found in schizophrenia by earlier workers, although more recent work has not confirmed this,[89] and hypotheses attributing the disease to disturbances in the fundamental mechanisms of energy supply or conversion in the brain have been formulated but on the basis of rather inadequate evidence. Kelsey and co-workers[60] found a decreased B.M.R. in their series of schizophrenics to be associated with an increased uptake of ^{131}I by the thyroid, correctible by the addition of iodine to the diet, and attributed it to a lack of that element in the institutional diet. Periodic catatonia and some other schizophreniform psychoses seem to be associated with disturbances in thyroxine or thyrotropic hormone regulation,[21,41] but little evidence exists to suggest that such disturbances are characteristic of schizophrenia generally.

The oxygen consumption and blood flow of the brain as a whole have been found to lie within the normal range in a variety of forms of schizophrenia,[65] and although localized changes in these functions have sometimes been postulated, there is no evidence to support this supposition. The clear consciousness usually present in schizophrenia does not suggest the manifestation of cerebral anoxia.

Richter[89] has pointed out the uncontrolled factors in earlier work which implicated a defect in carbohydrate metabolism as a characteristic of the schizophrenic process. The finding in schizophrenia of an abnormal glucose tolerance in conjunction with other evidence of hepatic dysfunction, or evidence of a retarded metabolism of lactate by the schizophrenic,[2] does not completely exclude incidental hepatic disease, nutritional deficiencies or the psychophysiologic influences on carbohydrate metabolism as possible sources of error. Horwitt and associates[56] were able to demonstrate and correct similar abnormalities by altering the dietary intake of the B group of vitamins.

A deficiency of glucose-6-phosphate dehydrogenase, known to occur in 10-20 per cent of American Negroes, has been found to show an incidence significantly different from normal in Negro catatonic and paranoid schizophrenics,[19] an observation which has received partial confirmation by an independent group.[29] Findings that schizophrenia is associated with cellular changes in oxidative phosphorylation or in the uptake[44] or metabolism of glucose[35] require further confirmation.[17]

It is difficult to believe that a generalized defect in energy metabolism, a process fundamental to every cell in the body, could be responsible for the highly specialized features of schizophrenia. For this reason, perhaps, interest has developed in other aspects of metabolism, the substrates or products of which appear to have some special role in the brain.

PROTEIN

Although Gjessing[41] found definite alterations in bodily nitrogen balance correlated with and sometimes preceding the changes in mental state of periodic catatonics, there has been no evidence to indicate a major change in protein metabolism for schizophrenia generally. On the other hand, some interest has been focused recently on more specific protein constituents or the metabolism of particular amino acids or their amines.

Interest in the possible presence of an abnormal protein constituent of blood of schizophrenics was stimulated by a report, in 1958, that a serum fraction obtained from schizophrenic patients was capable of causing some of the symptoms of that disorder when injected into nonschizophrenic volunteers.[49] This material, which was given the name "taraxein," appeared to have some relationship to ceruloplasmin, the copper-containing globulin of normal plasma which the same group had found to be elevated in schizophrenia[71] and, upon its intravenous injection, to produce rapid clinical improvement.[48] Very recently, Martens, in a thorough examination of the relationships between ceruloplasmin and schizophrenia,[76] has reported an equivalent elevation of serum copper in that disorder and in delirium tremens. In a controlled, double blind series he was unable to confirm the earlier report of clinical improvement following intravenous injections of ceruloplasmin. One attempt to replicate the production of psychotic symptoms in volunteers by means of taraxein was not successful,[91] and to date the original findings have not been confirmed in a significant and well controlled series.

A number of groups, however, have reported evidence compatible with the thesis that an abnormal protein is present to a greater extent in the blood of some schizophrenics than in normals and that this substance is capable of producing certain behavioral, metabolic, or cellular changes in lower animals. Haddad and Rabe,[45] replicating and extending an earlier report by Malis,[73] found some evidence for an antigenic abnormality in the pooled serum of chronically ill schizophrenic patients. More recent studies by this group using different immunologic methods have yielded negative results which they do not regard as conclusive. Faurbye, Lundberg and Jensen[23] were unable to confirm Malis' results. Using another approach, Vartanyan[108] has found evidence for an immunologic abnormality in schizophrenia.

Heath and co-workers[47] have advanced an auto-immune concept as the biologic basis of schizophrenia. The studies with fluorescent antibodies, electrophysiologic, immunologic and behavioral observations, on which the concept is based, await independent confirmation. Precipitin reactions have yielded positive[79] and negative[58,84,90] results with respect to the occurrence of specific proteins in the serum of schizophrenics.

Fessel and co-workers[26,28] have reported increases in 4S and 19S macroglobulins in a considerable proportion of schizophrenic patients and the ability to differentiate schizophrenic from manic depressive patients on this basis. Mental stress in nonpsychotic individuals was found to elevate the same macroglobulins.[27] Certain of these findings have been confirmed by two independent groups.[66,97] Gammack and Hector,[37] while failing to confirm Fessel's findings, observed a highly significant increase in the α-globulin fraction and the haptoglobin component in the serum of schizophrenics. They also questioned the specificity of such findings which occur frequently in many types of chronic disease. Others have not confirmed this increase in haptoglobins.[72] It seems fair to conclude that to the present time no abnormal protein characteristic of schizophrenia has been characterized by physicochemical technics.

Some special properties of the plasma of schizophrenics have been reported by workers using various biologic assays. Bishop[11] has reported evidence for the effect of plasma from schizophrenic patients upon learning and retention of learning in the rat. Other investigators[8,112] found a slowing of rope climbing activity in rats injected with whole serum or certain fractions from schizophrenic patients as compared with normal fractions. The specificity of this response for schizophrenia has not been demonstrated and later findings were not confirmatory.[96] German[38] reported an effect of serum of schizophrenics on cortical evoked responses in rats which in later more rigorously controlled studies he and his associates were unable to confirm.[39] In well controlled studies of the effects of plasma from psychotic patients on behavior, Ferguson and Fisher[25] have reported observations using a precision timing task in cebus monkeys in which a highly significant delay in responsiveness was produced by the injection of plasma from some newly admitted catatonic patients. It is of interest that in their studies plasma from normal individuals under preoperative stress produced a similar but not as marked slowing of response.

Frohman and his associates[34] have reported increases in the ratio of lactate-to-pyruvate in the medium after chicken erythrocytes are incubated with plasma or plasma fractions of some schizophrenic patients as compared to normal controls. Mangoni and associates[74] have been unable to confirm this. In a subsequent paper, Frohman and associates[36] were able to demonstrate this difference in the lactate:pyruvate ratio only when the subjects had engaged in moderate exercise before the blood samples were drawn; no appreciable difference was found when the subjects were at complete rest, in normal activity, or exercising vigorously. This, plus the fact that exercise affected the lactate:pyruvate ratio in the incubation mixture more than did the presence or absence of schizophrenia, suggests the need for better definition of what may be a large number of variables involved in this reaction.

Recently, Ryan, Brown and Durell[94] have succeeded in clarifying some of the fundamental processes involved in the ability of human plasma to affect the lactate production of chicken erythrocytes, which appears to be the determining variable of the lactate:pyruvate ratio. In their test system, lactate production by aerobic glycolysis did not occur in completely intact erythrocytes but was contingent upon and correlated with hemolysis. This, in turn, was caused by a complement-requiring antibody present in variable titre in all human plasma tested. The plasma of schizophrenics could not be reliably distinguished from that of nonschizophrenic patients from the same hospital.[95] Turner and Chipps[107] found a higher heterophile hemolysin titre in the blood of schizophrenics than of nonschizophrenics. Chronic alcoholics, however, also showed a higher titre of the hemolysin. Although Frohman and his associates have consistently found this phenomenon with higher frequency among schizophrenics, a possibility which remains to be ruled out is that the titre of this antibody is more closely related to a history of chronic hospitalization and greater exposure to a variety of antigens than to the presence of schizophrenia. An interesting further possibility is the significantly greater antibody responsiveness of schizophrenic patients than normal or depressed individuals to a standard antigen challenge.[33a]

The evidence with regard to the biologic or behavioral effects of the plasma of schizophrenics is far from conclusive at the present time. Most of the effects reported have failed of confirmation and none have been shown to be properties of plasma which are characteristic of schizophrenia.

Further work is necessary to determine to what extent the abnormalities in plasma found by physico-chemical analysis, when they are confirmed, are characteristic of schizophrenia or a reflection of the stress, exposure to chronic endemic infections, dietary or other adventitious factors which accompany the disorder and are associated with chronic institutionalization.[61]

AMINO ACIDS AND AMINES

Although an earlier report indicated abnormalities in amino acid excretion in schizophrenia,[114] this has not been confirmed. Much interest, on the other hand, has been attached to the possibility that abnormal metabolism of one or another amine could be of etiologic importance in schizophrenia.[51] The great sensitivity and relative nonspecificity of chromatographic methods and the ease with which findings may be affected by exogenous factors such as diet or drugs increase the likelihood of false positives in this area, and great caution must be exercised in identifying the particular metabolite which appears to be involved or interpreting the significance which should be attached to it.[42,75]

The significance of an unidentified Ehrlich positive substance ("the mauve spot") attributed to a new form of schizophrenia by Hoffer and Osmond[52] has been brought into question by O'Reilly and his associates[80,81] who found it with high frequency in the urines of patients with affective psychosis, alcoholism, psychoneurosis, personality disorders and cancer.

TRANSMETHYLATION

In 1952, Osmond and Smythies[82] pointed out some similarities between mescaline psychosis and schizophrenia and between that drug and epinephrine. They included a biochemical note by Harley-Mason which stated, in part:

It is extremely probable that the final stage in the biogenesis of adrenaline is a transmethylation of noradrenaline, the methyl group arising from methionine or choline. It is just possible that a pathological disordering of its transmethylation mechanism might lead to methylation of one or both of its phenolic hydroxyl groups instead of its amino group. . . . Methylation of phenolic hydroxyl groups in the animal body is of rare occurrence but a significant case has been reported recently. . . . It is particularly interesting to note that out of a series of phenylethylamine derivations tested by Noteboom, 3,4-dimethoxyphenylethylamine was the most potent in producing catatonia in animals.

Since that time the transmethylation of norepinephrine to epinephrine has been established,[12] while Axelrod, Senoh and Witkop[5] have demonstrated the O-methylation of both catecholamines as an important step in their normal metabolism.

The suggestion that pathologic transmethylation may occur in schizophrenia was further strengthened by the recognition that a number of psychotomimetic agents, in addition to mescaline, were methylated congeners of normal body metabolites. On this basis, Hoffer and associates[53] used niacin and niacinamide, methyl accepters, in an effort to inhibit competitively the possible abnormal process. They reported beneficial results which have not been independently confirmed. In 1961, Pollin, Cardon and Kety[86] tested this hypothesis by administering large doses of L-methionine to chronic schizophrenic patients in conjunction with a monoamine oxidase inhibitor to permit the accumulation of any monoamines formed. This substance is an essential precursor of S-adenosylmethionine, the active substance which was shown by Cantoni[18] to transfer its methyl group to accepter compounds in the process of transmethylation. In some of the patients during the administration of the L-methionine there was a brief intensification of psychosis which involved an exacerbation of some of the schizophrenic symptoms. No other amino acids tested (glycine, tyrosine, phenylalanine, tryptophan, histidine, glutamine) were associated with this phenomenon. The intensification of psychosis in schizophrenics with methionine has since, in essence, been confirmed by four other groups[1,15,46,83] and in addition, Brune and Himwich[16] found that betaine, another methyl donor, was equally effective in accentuating psychotic symptoms in schizophrenics. Baldessarini and Kopin[6] found that feeding L-methionine to rats produced a significant increase in S-adenosylmethionine concentration in the liver and brain. Axelrod[4] demonstrated the presence in normal mammalian tissue of an enzyme capable of methylating normal metabolites, i.e., tryptamine and serotonin to their dimethyl derivatives for which psychotomimetic properties have been reported.

DIMETHOXYPHENYLETHYLAMINE

In 1962, Friedhoff and Van Winkle[32] examined the urine of patients with early schizophrenia and reported the occurrence of 3,4-dimethoxyphenylethylamine (DMPEA), to which Harley-Mason had alluded as a possible abnormally methylated metabolite. This compound is a dimethylated derivative of dopamine and closely related to mescaline, which represents a trimethylated congener of this biogenic amine.

Since 1962 a number of groups have attempted to confirm the excretion of DMPEA in schizophrenia and further to define the variables which affect it. Friedhoff and Van Winkle[32] had found it in the urine of 15 of 19 schizophrenics and in none of 14 normal urines. Kuehl and associates[68] confirmed its presence in 7 of 22 schizophrenics and in none of 10 normals. Takesada and associates[105] found it in 70 of 78 (90 per cent) schizophrenics but also in 35 of 67, or 52 per cent, of normals. Faurbye and Pind,[24] who modified the method to increase its sensitivity and to avoid interference by phenothiazine metabolites, were unable to detect DMPEA in the urine of 15 schizophrenics and 10 normals. Perry, Hansen and Macintyre[85] were unable to find the compound in 10 schizophrenics on a diet free of fruits and vegetables. After finding DMPEA in the urine of 4 out of 6

schizophrenics and 2 of 3 controls, Studnitz and Nyman[104] demonstrated its disappearance when the same individuals were placed on a pure carbohydrate regimen.

In an extensive series in which biochemical determinations and psychiatric diagnoses were made independently, Bourdillon and his associates[14] reported the presence of a "pink spot" having some of the characteristics of DMPEA in the urines of 46 of 84 (55 per cent) schizophrenics, while it was absent in all of 17 nonschizophrenic patients and 149 normal controls. A second experiment with less striking results showed a low incidence (3 per cent) of the spot in the urine of paranoid patients and a 29 per cent incidence in nonparanoid schizophrenics. Drug administration which was not controlled could have been different in type of drug or dosage for different diagnostic categories. Drugs or their metabolites are known to interfere with DMPEA determinations, and at least one group[24] has observed a phenothiazine metabolite with Rf value and color reactions similar to DMPEA which persisted in the urine for as long as 25 days after withdrawal of the drug. Williams[110] has examined the technic used by Bourdillon and found it relatively insensitive to DMPEA. Further studies by his group[111] and by others using more specific technics[7,13] have indicated that Bourdillon's "pink spot" was not, in fact, DMPEA and that DMPEA is not excreted in abnormal amounts by schizophrenics. Friedhoff,[33] on the other hand, on the basis of its behavior in six solvent systems, a number of color reactions, thin layer and gas chromatography and melting point determinations, has concluded that the material he has found in the urine of schizophrenics is identical to DMPEA. Although this substance, when administered to schizophrenics is rapidly converted to 3,4-dimethoxyphenyl-acetic acid,[31] Kuehl and associates[69] could not detect a significant difference in the excretion of that acid between normal subjects and schizophrenics.

These findings—the intensification of psychosis in schizophrenics by methionine or betaine, the increase in S-adenosylmethionine in the brain and liver of rats by methionine feeding, the existence of at least one enzyme capable of transmethylating normal metabolites to psycho-to-mimetic compounds, the evidence obtained by some workers for the excretion of DMPEA in a substantial number of schizophrenics—are compatible with the hypothesis that the process of biologic transmethylation is somehow disturbed in schizophrenia with the production or persistence of excessive amounts of methylated derivatives of normal metabolites capable of inducing some of the symptoms of schizophrenia. That hypothesis, however, is far from having been validated. Although methionine and betaine are the only ones of a large number of amino acids which have been shown capable of briefly exacerbating psychosis in some schizophrenics, it has not been established that the clinical changes resulted from any specific methylated derivatives, and the possibility that this was a nonspecific toxic psychosis or a peculiarly schizophrenic response to nonspecific toxic changes has not been ruled out. Haydu, et al.,[46] who confirm the ability of methionine to exacerbate schizophrenic symptomatology, found an ameliorating effect from hydroxychloroquine and suggest that the clinical effects of these agents result from their activation or suppression of thiol groups. A special sensitivity of schizophrenics to methionine has not been established although a similar regimen of methionine without iproniazid in a small number of normal volunteers produced no hint of a psychotic reaction.[62] The accumulated evidence for the excretion of dimethoxyphenylethylamine in association with some forms of schizophrenia is as yet inconclusive. Several groups have been unable to confirm it and the possibility that it is an artifact of drug therapy has not been completely ruled out. There is evidence that some dietary factors are necessary for its appearance although the same is true for phenylketonuria and does not argue against its significance or relevance to schizophrenia. On parenteral administration to man, DMPEA has not been shown to produce perceptible mental effects,[31] but this does not preclude an effect from higher concentrations locally within the brain. The transmethylation hypothesis appears to require and merit further examination and development.

INDOLEAMINES

Although Woolley[113] was impressed with indirect evidence for the possibility of a disorder in serotonin metabolism in schizophrenia, significant differences between schizophrenic and normal populations with respect to this amine or its metabolites have not been established.[61] Earlier findings of indolic compounds (indole acetamide and 6-hydroxyskatole) with abnormal frequency in the urine of schizophrenics[78,101] have more recently been found to a similar extent in the urine of other types of mental patient and are probably to be attributed to exogenous or nondisease-related factors.[20,100,115]

Tryptamine excretion may have some significance in schizophrenia since an increase has been found to occur in such patients before a period of exacerbation.[9] An increase in urinary tryptophan metabolites has also been observed following the administration of methionine,[10,102,103] and it has been suggested that the conversion of tryptamine to its hallucinogenic methylated derivative may occur. Aside from one positive report,[30] the search for dimethyltryptamine or dimethylserotonin in the urine of schizophrenics has yielded negative results.[98,102,106]

EPINEPHRINE

The hypothesis that adrenochrome or other abnormal metabolites of circulating epinephrine were formed in schizophrenia and accounted for many of the symptoms[54] has received careful scrutiny made possible by the recently acquired knowledge of the normal metabolism of this hormone.[3] No evidence was found for the abnormal metabolism of labeled epinephrine infused into schizophrenic patients,[88] and in one study which accounted almost entirely for the excreted label in terms of unchanged epinephrine and four metabolites (3-methoxy-4-hydroxymandelic acid, metanephrine, 3,4-dihydroxymandelic acid, and 3-methoxy-4-dihydroxyphenylglycol), no qualitative or quantitative differences were found in this pattern between chronic schizophrenics and normal volunteers.[70] The infusion of epinephrine into schizophrenics was not found to intensify the psychosis[87] which would have been expected if the psychosis were associated with abnormal metabolites of circulating epinephrine.

SUMMARY AND CONCLUSIONS

Although it would be difficult to demonstrate that a definitive increase in our knowledge of biochemical mechanisms in the schizophrenic psychoses has occurred in the past decade, substantial progress has nonetheless been made. There is an increasing awareness of the complexity of the problem and of the sophistication of research design necessary to cope with it. Most important, there has been a burgeoning of fundamental knowledge in biochemistry and neurochemistry and their interaction with behavior on which depend meaningful hypotheses relating to schizophrenia and from which may eventually come an understanding of whatever biochemical mechanisms operate significantly in its etiology, pathogenesis, or therapy.

Before the etiology of any syndrome has been established, it is idle to regard it as a single disease, and, in the case of schizophrenia, the striking resemblance which certain temporal lobe epilepsies or chronic intoxications (bromidism, iodism, amphetamine psychosis, porphyria) bear to it makes tenable the possibility that the syndrome may emerge from different etiologic pathways. Recognition of such a possibility aids in the interpretation of genetic and biologic findings and would facilitate the characterization of more specific subgroups.

Those interested in exploring the biologic aspects of schizophrenic disorders cannot with impunity ignore the psychologic, social, and other environmental factors which operate significantly at various stages of their development. Leaving aside etiologic considerations, it is clear that exogenous factors may precipitate, intensify, or ameliorate the symptoms and confound the biologic picture. To what extent the classical psychologic features of chronic schizophrenia are created by prolonged isolation and hospitalization will become apparent with the increasing adoption of community-oriented treatment. Examples are readily found in which uncontrolled

nutritional, infectious, or pharmacologic variables may have accounted for specific biochemical abnormalities in populations of chronic schizophrenics. These secondary variables are so manifold that it is hard to imagine a design which could anticipate and control them all, and successive studies concentrating on particularly relevant controls will probably continue to be called for. There is, in addition, much to be said for broadening the scope of the typical sample from chronic hospitalized schizophrenia to the early, more acute, remitting, episodic, or periodic forms[21, 40] in which it may not only be possible to obviate some of the difficulties imposed by chronic hospitalization and drug administration but, by study of the same patient in psychotic and nonpsychotic states, to avoid the effects of interindividual variance.

An unavoidable difficulty at the present time is the fact that the crucial processes of diagnosis and evaluation of change are based almost entirely on subjective estimates. It is not insensitivity which diminishes the reliability of such measures as much as their vulnerability to bias; failure to recognize and guard against this source of error probably accounts for much of the inconsistency in the study of schizophrenia not only from biologic but also from sociologic and psychologic points of view.

The single-gene-single-enzyme concept of the biologic disorder in schizophrenia was encouraged by the very high concordance rate found in monozygotic twins in earlier studies. More recent twin studies in which selective bias in sampling has been more effectively controlled have yielded a concordance rate of 40 per cent or less. Studies with adopted schizophrenics[64,93] where environmental factors can be more successfully controlled have still reinforced the importance of genetic factors but have emphasized the genetic transmission of a vulnerability to schizophrenia or to a variety of personality or character disorders. This suggests that personality or intelligence may be more appropriate models for schizophrenia than phenylketonuria. A polygenic inadequacy interacting with particular life situations seems more compatible with all of the evidence.[92] The biologic component of the schizophreniform illnesses may lie in the mechanisms which underlie arousal, inhibition, perception, cognition, affect, or the complex relationships among them, all of which appear to be involved at one time or another. Although a single chemical substance such as mescaline or lysergic acid diethylamide may produce disturbances in all of these areas, it would be well to keep in mind the possibility that more complex neurochemical, neurophysiologic and psychologic interactions may form the biologic substrate of schizophrenia.

REFERENCES

1. ALEXANDER, F., CURTIS, G. C., SPRINCE, H., & CROSLEY, A. P. L-Methionine and L-tryptophan feedings in nonpsychotic and schizophrenic patients with and without tranylcypromine. *Journal of Nervous and Mental Disease*, 1963, *137*, 135–142.
2. ALTSCHULE, M. D., HENNEMAN, D. H., HOLLIDAY, P., & GONCZ, R,-M. Carbohydrate metabolism in brain disease. VI. Lactate metabolism after infusion of sodium d-lactate in manic-depressive and schizophrenic psychoses. *AMA Archives of Internal Medicine*, 1956, *98*, 35–38.
3. AXELROD, J. Metabolism of epinephrine and other sympathomimetic amines. *Physiological Review*, 1959, *39*, 751–776.
4. AXELROD, J. Enzymatic formation of psychotomimetic metabolites from normally occurring compounds. *Science*, 1961, *134*, 343.
5. AXELROD, J., SENOH, S., & WITKOP, B. O-Methylation of catecholamines *in vivo*, *Journal of Biological Chemistry*, 1958, *233*, 697–701.
6. BALDESSARINI, R. J., & KOPIN, I. J. Assay of tissue levels of S-adenosylmethionine. *Anal. Biochem*, 1963, *6*, 289–292.
7. BELL, C. E., & SOMERVILLE, A. R. Identity of the "pink spot." *Nature*, 1966, *211*, 1405–1406.
8. BERGEN, J. F., PENNELL, R. B., SARAVIS, C. A., & HOAGLAND, H. Further experiments with plasma proteins from schizophrenics. *In* R. G. Heath, (Ed.). *Serological fractions in Schizophrenia*. New York: Harper & Row, 1963. Pp. 67–76.
9. BERLET, H. H., BULL, C., HIMWICH, H. E., KOHL, H., MATSUMOTO, K., PSCHEIDT, G. R., SPAIDE, J., TOURLENTES, T. T., & VALVERDE, J. M. Endogenous metabolic factor in schizophrenic behavior. *Science*, 1964, *144*, 311–313.
10. BERLET, H. H., MATSUMOTO, K., PSCHEIDT, G. R., SPAIDE, J., BULL, C., & HIMWICH, H. E. Biochemical correlates of behavior in schizophrenic patients. *Archives of General Psychiatry*, 1965, *13*, 521–531.
11. BISHOP, M. P. Effects of plasma from schizo-

phrenia subjects upon learning and retention in the rat. *In* R. G. Heath, (Ed.). *Serological fractions in schizophrenia*. New York: Harper & Row, 1963. Pp. 77–91.
12. BLASCHKO, H. The development of current concepts of catecholamine formation. *Pharmacological Review*, 1959, *11*, 307–316.
13. BOULTON, A. A., & FELTON, C. A. The "pink spot" and schizophrenia. *Nature*, 1966, *211*, 1404–1405.
14. BOURDILLON, R. E., CLARKE, C. A., RIDGES, A. P., SHEPPARD, P. M., HARPER, P., & LESLIE, S. A. "Pink spot" in the urine of schizophrenics. *Nature*, 1965, *208*, 453–455.
15. BRUNE, G. G., & HIMWICH, H. E. Effects of methionine loading on the behavior of schizophrenic patients. *Journal of Nervous and Mental Disease*, 1962, *134*, 447–450.
16. BRUNE, G. G., & HIMWICH, H. E. Biogenic amines and behavior in schizophrenic patients. In *Recent advances in biological psychiatry*, Vol. 5. New York: Plenum Press, 1963. Pp. 144–160.
17. BUHLER, D. R., & IHLER, G. S. Effect of plasma from normal and schizophrenic subjects on the oxidation of labeled glucose by chicken erythrocytes. *Journal of Laboratory and Clinical Medicine*, 1963, *62*, 306–318.
18. CANTONI G. L. S-Adenosylmethinine: a new intermediate formed enzymatically from L-methionine and adenosine-triphosphate. *Journal of Biological Chemistry*, 1953, *204*, 403–416.
19. DERN, R. J., GLYNN, M. F., & BREWER, G. J. Studies on the influence of hereditary G-6-PD deficiency in the expression of schizophrenic patterns. *Clinical Research*, 1962, *10*, 80.
20. DOHAN, F. C., EWING, J., GRAFF, H., & SPRINCE, H. Schizophrenia: 6-hydroxyskatole and environment. *Archives of General Psychiatry*, 1964, *10*, 420–422.
21. DURELL, J., LIDOW, L. S., KELLAM, S. F., & SHADER, R. I. Interrelationships between regulation of thyroid gland function and psychosis. *Research Publications: Association for Research in Nervous and Mental Disease*, 1966, *43*, 387–399.
22. DURELL, J., & SCHILDKRAUT, J. J. Biochemical studies of the schizophrenic and affective disorders. *In* S. Arieti, (Ed.). *American handbook of psychiatry*, Vol. III. New York: Basic Books, 1966. Pp. 423–457.
23. FAURBYE, A., LUNDBERG, L., & JENSEN, K. A. Studies on the antigen demonstrated by Malis in serum from schizophrenic patients. *Acta Pathalogica et Microbiologica Scandinavica*, 1964, *61*, 633–651.
24. FAURBYE, A., & PIND, K. Investigation on the occurrence of the dopamine metabolite 3,4-dimethoxyphenylethylamine in the urine of schizophrenics. *Acta Psychiatrica Scandinavica*, 1964, *40*, 240–243.

25. FERGUSON, D. C., & FISHER, A. E. Behavior disruption in cebus monkeys as a function of injected substances. *Science,* 1963, *139* 1281–1282.

26. FESSEL, W. J. Macroglobulin elevations in functional mental illness. *Nature,* 1962, *193,* 1005.

27. FESSEL, W. J. Mental stress, blood proteins and the hypothalamus: experimental results showing effect of mental stress upon 4S and 19S proteins. *Archives of General Psychiatry,* 1962, *7,* 427–435.

28. FESSEL, W. J., & GRUNBAUM, B. W. Electrophoretic and analytical ultracentrifuge studies in sera of psychotic patients: elevation of gamma globulins and macroglobulins, and splitting of alpha₂ globulins. *Annals of Internal Medicine,* 1961, *54,* 1134–1145.

29. FIEVE, R. R., BRAUNINGER, G., FLEISS, J., & COHEN, G. Glucose-6-phosphate dehydrogenase deficiency and schizophrenic behavior. *Journal of Psychiatric Research,* 1965, *3,* 255–262.

30. FISCHER, E., FERNANDEZ-LAGRAVERE, T. A., VAZQUEZ, A. J., & DI STEFANO, A. O. A bufotenin-like substance in the urine of schizophrenics. *Journal of Nervous and Mental Disease,* 1961, *133,* 441–444.

31. FRIEDHOFF, A. J., & HOLLISTER, L. E. Comparison of the metabolism of 3,4-dimethoxyphenylethylamine and mescaline in humans. *Biochemical Pharmacology,* 1966, *15,* 269–273.

32. FRIEDHOFF, A. J., & VAN WINKLE, E. The characteristics of an amine found in the urine of schizophrenic patients. *Journal of Nervous and Mental Disease,* 1962, *135,* 550–555.

33. FRIEDHOFF, A. J., & VAN WINKLE, E. New developments in the investigation of the relationship of 3,4-dimethoxyphenylethylamine to schizophrenia. *In* H. E. Himwich, S. S. Kety, and J. R. Smythies, (Eds.). *Amines and Schizophrenia.* Oxford: Pergamon Press, 1967. Pp. 19–21.

33a. FRIEDMAN, S. B., COHEN, J., & IKER, H. Antibody response to cholera vaccine. Differences between depressed, schizophrenic, and normal subjects. *Archives of General Psychiatry,* 1967, *16,* 312–315.

34. FROHMAN, C. E., CZAJKOWSKI, N. P., LUBY, E. D., GOTTLIEB, J. S., & SENF, R. Further evidence of a plasma factor in schizophrenia. *Archives of General Psychiatry,* 1960, *2,* 263–267.

35. FROHMAN, C. E., LATHAM, L. K., BECKETT, P. G. S., & GOTTLIEB, J. S. Evidence of a plasma factor in schizophrenia. *Archives of General Psychiatry,* 1960, *2,* 255–262.

36. FROHMAN, C. E., LATHAM, L. K., WARNER, K. A., BROSIUS, C. O., BECKETT, P. G. S., & GOTTLIEB, J. S. Motor activity in schizophrenia; effect on plasma factor. *Archives of General Psychiatry,* 1963, *9,* 83–88.

37. GAMMACK, D. B., & HECTOR, R. I. A study of serum proteins in acute schizophrenia. *Clinical Science,* 1965, *28,* 469–475.

38. GERMAN, G. A. Effects of serum from schizophrenics on evoked cortical potentials in the rat. *British Journal of Psychiatry,* 1963, *109,* 616–623.

39. GERMAN, G. A., ANTEBI, R. N., DEAR, E. M. A., & MCCANCE, C. A further study of the effects of serum from schizophrenics on evoked cortical potentials in the rat. *British Journal of Psychiatry,* 1965, *111,* 345–347.

40. GJESSING, L. R. Studies of periodic catatonia. II. The urinary excretion of phenolic amines and acids with and without loads of different drugs. *Journal of Psychiatry Research,* 1964, *2,* 149–162.

41. GJESSING, R. Disturbances of somatic functions in catatonia with a periodic course, and their compensation. *Journal of Mental Science,* 1938, *84,* 608–621.

42. GOLDENBERG, H., FISHMAN, V., WHITTIER, J., & BRINITZER, W. Urinary aromatic excretion patterns in schizophrenia. *Archives of General Psychiatry,* 1960, *2,* 221–230.

43. GOTTESMAN, I. I., & SHIELDS, J. Schizophrenia in twins: sixteen years' consecutive admissions to a psychiatric clinic. *Diseases of the Nervous System,* 1966, *27,* (Suppl.), 11–19.

44. HAAVALDSEN, R., LINGJAERDE, O., & WALAAS, O. Disturbances of carbohydrate metabolism in schizophrenics: effect of serum fractions from schizophrenics on glucose uptake of rat diaphragm *in vitro. Confinia Neurologica/Borderland of Neurology,* 1958, *18,* 270.

45. HADDAD, R. K., & RABE, A. An antigenic abnormality in the serum of chronically ill schizophrenic patients. *In* R. G. Heath, (Ed.). *Serological fractions in schizophrenia.* New York: Harper & Row, 1963. Pp. 151–157.

46. HAYDU, G. G., DHRYMIOTIS, A., KORENYI, C., & GOLDSCHMIDT, L. Effects of methionine and hydroxychloroquine in schizophrenia. *American Journal of Psychiatry,* 1965, *122,* 560–564.

47. HEATH, R. G., & KRUPP, I. M. The biologic basis of schizophrenia: an autoimmune concept. *In* O. Walaas, (Ed.). *Molecular basis of some aspects of mental activity,* Vol. 2. London: Academic Press, 1967. Pp. 313–344.

48. HEATH, R. G., LEACH, B. E., BYERS, L. W., MARTENS, S., & FEIGLEY, C. A. Pharmacological and biological psychotherapy. *American Journal of Psychiatry,* 1958, *114,* 683–689.

49. HEATH, R. G., MARTENS, S., LEACH, B. E., COHEN, M., & FEIGLEY, C. A. Behavioral changes in nonpsychotic volunteers following the administration of taraxein, the substance obtained from serum of schizophrenic patients. *American Journal of Psychiatry,* 1958, *114,* 917–920.

50. HESTON, L. L. Psychiatric disorders in foster

home reared children of schizophrenic mothers. *British Journal of Psychiatry*, 1966, *112*, 819–825.

51. HIMWICH, H. E., KETY, S. S., & SMYTHIES, J. R. (Eds.). *Amines and schizophrenia*. Oxford: Pergamon Press, 1967.

52. HOFFER, A., & OSMOND, H. Malvaria: A new psychiatric disease. *Acta Psychiatrica Scandinavica*, 1963, *39*, 335–366.

53. HOFFER A., OSMOND, H., CALLBECK, M. J., & KAHAN, I. Treatment of schizophrenia with nicotinic acid and nicotinamide. *Journal of Clinical and Experimental Psychopathology*, 1957, *18*, 131–158.

54. HOFFER, A., OSMOND, H., & SMYTHIES, J. Schizophrenia: A new approach. II. Result of a year's research. *Journal of Mental Science*, 1954, *100* 29–45.

55. HORWITT, M. K. Report of Elgin Project No. 3 with emphasis on liver dysfunction. In *Nutrition symposium*, Series No. 7. New York: National Vitamin Foundation, 1953. Pp. 67–83.

56. HORWITT, M. K., LIEBERT, E., KREISLER, O., & WITTMAN, P. Investigations of human requirements for B-complex vitamins. In *National Research Council Bulletin No. 116*. Washington, D.C.: National Academy of Sciences, 1948.

57. INOUYE, E. Similarity and dissimilarity of schizophrenia in twins. In *Proceedings of the Third World Congress of Psychiatry*, Vol. I, Montreal: 1961. Pp. 524–530.

58. JENSEN, K., CLAUSEN, J., & OSTERMAN, E. Serum and cerebrospinal fluid proteins in schizophrenia. *Acta Psychiatrica Scandinavica*, 1964, *40*, 280–286.

59. KALLMANN, F. J. The genetic theory of schizophrenia. An analysis of 691 schizophrenic twin index families. *American Journal of Psychiatry*, 1946, *103*, 309–322.

60. KELSEY, F. O., GULLOCK, A. H., & KELSEY, F. E. Thyroid activity in hospitalized psychiatric patients. *AMA Archives of Neurological Psychiatry*, 1957, *77*, 543–548.

61. KETY, S. S. Biochemical theories of schizophrenia. *Science*, 1959, *129*, 1528–1532, 1590–1596.

62. KETY, S. S. Possible relation of central amines to behavior in schizophrenic patients. *Federal Proceedings*, 1961, *20*, 894–896.

63. KETY, S. S. Current biochemical approaches to schizophrenia. *New England Journal of Medicine*, 1967, *276*, 325–331.

64. KETY, S. S., ROSENTHAL, D., WENDER, P. H., & SCHULSINGER, F. The types and prevalence of mental illness in the biological and adoptive families of adopted schizophrenics. *Journal of Psychiatric Research*, 6, (Suppl.), 1968

65. KETY, S. S., WOODFORD, R. B., HARMEL, M. H., FREYHAN, F. A., APPEL, K. E., & SCHMIDT, C. F. Cerebral blood flow and metabolism in schizophrenia. The effects of barbiturate seminarcosis, insulin coma and electroshock. *American Journal of Psychiatry*, 1948, *104*, 765–770.

66. KOPELOFF, L. M., & FISCHEL, E. Serum levels of bactericidin and globulin in schizophrenia. *Archives of General Psychiatry*, 1968, 9, 524–528.

67. KRINGLEN, E. Schizophrenia in twins: An epidemiological-clinical study. *Psychiatry*, 1966, *29*, 172–184.

68. KUEHL, F. A., JR., HICHENS, M., ORMOND, R. E., MEISINGER, M. A. P., GALE, P. H., CIRILLO, V. J., & BRINK, N. G. Para-O-methylation of dopamine in schizophrenic and normal individuals, *Nature*, 1964, *203*, 154–155.

69. KUEHL, F. A., JR., ORMOND, R. E., & VANDENHEUVEL, W. J. A. Occurrence of 3,4-dimethoxyphenylacetic acid in urines of normal and schizophrenic individuals. *Nature*, 1966, *211*, 606–608.

70. LABROSSE, E. H., MANN, J. D., & KETY, S. S. The physiological and psychological effects of intravenously administered epinephrine and its metabolism in normal and schizophrenic men. III. Metabolism of $7\text{-}H^3$-epinephrine as determined in studies on blood and urine. *Journal of Psychiatric Research*, 1961, *1*, 68–75.

71. LEACH, B. E., COHEN, M., HEATH, R. G., & MARTENS, S. Studies of the role of ceruloplasmin and albumin in adrenaline metabolism. *AMA Archives of Neurological Psychiatry*, 1956, *76*, 635–642.

72. LOVEGROVE, T. D., & NICHOLLS, D. M. Haptoglobin subtypes in a schizophrenic and control population. *Journal of Nervous and Mental Disease*, 1965, *141*, 195–196.

73. MALIS, C. Y. *K Etiologii Schizofrenii*. Moscow: Medgiz, 1959.

74. MANGONI, A., BALAZS, R., & COPPEN, A. J. The effect of plasma from schizophrenic patients on the chicken erythrocyte system. *British Journal of Psychiatry*, 1963, *109*, 231–234.

75. MANN, J. D., & LABROSSE, E. H. Urinary excretion of phenolic acids by normal and schizophrenic male patients. *Archives of General Psychiatry*, 1959, *1*, 547–551.

76. MARTENS, S. *Effects of exogenous human ceruloplasmin in the schizophrenia syndrome*. Stockholm: Tryckeri Balder AB, 1966.

77. MCDONALD, R. K., WEISE, V. K., EVANS, F. T., & PATRICK, R. W. Studies on plasma ascorbic acid and ceruloplasmin levels in schizophrenia. In J. Folch-Pi (Ed.). *Chemical pathology of the nervous system*. Oxford: Pergamon Press, 1961. Pp. 404–412.

78. NAKAO, A., & BALL, M. The appearance of a skatole derivative in the urine of schizophrenics. *Journal of Nervous and Mental Disease*, 1960, *130*, 417–419.

79. NOVAL, J. J., & MAO, T. S. S. Abnormal immunological reaction of schizophrenic serum. *Federal Proceedings*, 1966, *25*, 560.

80. O'REILLY, P. O., ERNEST, M., & HUGHES, G. The incidence of malvaria. *British Journal of Psychiatry*, 1965, *111*, 741–744.

81. O'REILLY, P. O., HUGHES, G., RUSSELL, S., & ERNEST, M. The mauve factor: An evaluation. *Diseases of the Nervous System*, 1965, *26*, 562–568.

82. OSMOND, H., & SMYTHIES, J. Schizophrenia: A new approach. *Journal of Mental Science*, 1952, *98*, 309–315.

83. PARK, L., BALDESSARINI, R. J., & KETY, S. S. Methionine effects on chronic schizophrenics. *Archives of General Psychiatry*, 1965, *12*, 346–351.

84. PENNELL, R. B., PAWLUS, C., SARAVIS, C. A., & SCRIMSHAW, G. Further characterization of a human plasma component which influences animal behavior. *Transactions of the New York Academy of Science*, 1965, *28*, 47–58.

85. PERRY, T. L., HANSEN, S., & MACINTYRE, L. Failure to detect 3,4-dimethoxyphenylamine in the urine of schizophrenics. *Nature*, 1964, *202*, 519–520.

86. POLLIN, W., CARDON, P. V., & KETY, S. S. Effects of amino acid feedings in schizophrenic patients treated with iproniazid. *Science*, 1961, *133*, 104–105.

87. POLLIN, W., & GOLDIN, S. The physiological and psychological effects of intravenously administered epinephrine and its metabolism in normal and schizophrenic men. II. Psychiatric observations. *Journal of Psychiatric Research*, 1961, *1*, 50–67.

88. RESNICK, O., & ELMADJIAN, F. Excretion and metabolism of dl-epinephrine-7-C^{14}-d-bitartrate infused into schizophrenic patients. *American Journal of Physiology*, 1956, *187*, 626.

89. RICHTER, D. Biochemical aspects of schizophrenia. *In* D. Richter (Ed.). *Schizophrenia: Somatic aspects*. London: Pergamon Press, 1957, pp. 53–75.

90. RIEDER, H. P., RITZEL, G., SPIEGELBERG, H., & GNIRSS, F. Serologische Versuche zum Nachweis von "Taraxein," *Experientia*, 1960, *16*, 561–562.

91. ROBINS, E., SMITH, K., & LOWE, I. P. Discussion of clinical studies with taraxein. *In* H. A. Abramson (Ed.). *Neuropharmacology: Transactions of the Fourth Conference*. New York: Josiah Macy Jr. Foundation, 1957. Pp. 123–135.

92. ROSENTHAL, D., & KETY, S. S. (Eds.). The transmission of schizophrenia. *Journal of Psychiatric Research*, 1968, 6 (Suppl.).

93. ROSENTHAL, D., WENDER, P. H., KETY, S. S., SCHULSINGER, F., WELNER, J., & OSTERGAARD, L. Schizophrenics' offspring reared in adoptive homes, *Journal of Psychiatric Research*, 1968, (Suppl.).

94. RYAN, J. W., BROWN, J. D., & DURELL, J. Antibodies affecting metabolism of chicken erythrocytes: Examination of schizophrenic and other subjects. *Science*, 1966, *151*, 1408–1410.

95. RYAN, J. W., STEINBERG, H. R., GREEN, R., BROWN, J. D., & DURELL, J. Controlled study of effects of plasma of schizophrenic and nonschizophrenic psychiatric patients on chicken erythocytes. *Journal of Psychiatric Research*, 1968, *6*, 33–44.

96. SANDERS, B. E., SMALL, S. M., AYERS, W. J., OH, Y. H., & AXELROD, S. Additional studies on plasma proteins obtained from schizophrenics and controls. *Transactions of the New York Academy of Science*, 1965, *28*, 22–39.

97. SAPIRA, J. D. Immunoelectrophoresis of the serum of psychotic patients. *Archieves of General Psychiatry*, 1964, *10*, 196–198.

98. SIEGEL, M. A sensitive method for the detection of N,N-dimethylserotonin (bufotenin) in urine; failure to demonstrate its presence in the urine of schizophrenic and normal subjects. *Journal of Psychiatric Research*, 1965, *3*, 205–211.

99. SLATER, E. *Psychotic and neurotic illnesses in twins*. London: H. M. Stationery Office, 1953.

100. SOHLER, A., NOVAL, J. J., & RENZ, R. H. 6-Hydroxyskatole sulfate excretion in schizophrenia. *Journal of Nervous and Mental Disease*, 1963, *137*, 591–596.

101. SPRINCE, H., HOUSER, E., JAMESON, D., & DOHAN, F. C. Differential extraction of indoles from the urine of schizophrenic and normal subjects. *Archives of General Psychiatry*, 1960, *2*, 268–270.

102. SPRINCE, H., PARKER, C. M., JAMESON, D., & ALEXANDER, F. Urinary indoles in schizophrenic and psychoneurotic patients after administration of tranylcypromine (parnate) and methionine or tryptophan. *Journal of Nervous and Mental Disease*, 1963, *137*, 246–251.

103. SPRINCE, H., PARKER, C. M., JAMESON, D., & JOSEPHS, J. A. Effect of methionine on nicotinic acid and indoleacetic acid pathways of tryptophan metabolism *in vivo*. *Proceedings of the Society for Experimental Biology and Medicine*, 1965, *119*, 942–946.

104. STUDNITZ, W. V., & NYMAN, G. E. Excretion of 3,4-dimethoxyphenylethylamine in schizophrenia. *Acta Psychiatrica Scandinavica*, 1965, *41*, 117–121.

105. TAKESADA, M., KAKIMOTO, Y., SANO, I., & KANEKO, Z. 3,4-Dimethylphenylethylamine and other amines in the urine of schizophrenic patients. *Nature*, 1963, *199*, 203–204.

106. TAKESADA, M., MIYAMOTO, E., KAKIMOTO, Y., SANO, I., & KANEKO, Z. Phenolic and indole amines in the urine of schizophrenics. *Nature*, 1965, *207*, 1199–1200.

107. TURNER, W. J., & CHIPPS, H. I. A heterophil

hemolysin in human blood. I. Distribution in schizophrenics and non-schizophrenics. *Archives of General Psychiatry*, 1966, *15*, 373–377.

108. VARTANYAN, M. E. Immunological investigation of schizophrenia. Zh. Nevropat. Psikhiat. Korsakov, 1963, *63*, 3–12.

109. WEIL-MALHERBE, H. The biochemistry of the functional psychoses. In *Advances in enzymology*, Vol. XXIX. New York: Interscience Publishers, 1967. Pp. 479–553.

110. WILLIAMS, C. H. The pink spot. *Lancet*, 1966, *1*, 599–600.

111. WILLIAMS, C. H., GIBSON, J. G., & McCORMICK, W. O. 3,4-Dimethoxphenylethylamine in schizophrenia. *Nature*, 1966, *211*, 1195.

112. WINTER, C. A., FLATAKER, L., BOGER, W. P., SMITH, E. V. C., & SANDERS, B. E. The effects

of blood serum and of serum fractions from schizophrenic donors upon the performance of trained rats. *In* J. Folch-Pi, (Ed.). *Chemical pathology of the nervous system*. Oxford: Pergamon Press, 1961. Pp. 641–646.

113. WOOLLEY, D. W. *The biochemical bases of psychoses*. New York: Wiley, 1962.

114. YOUNG, H. K., BERRY, H. K., BEERSTECHER, E., & BERRY, J. S. Metabolic patterns in schizophrenic and control groups. *In Biochemical Institute Studies IV*, University of Texas Publication No. 5109. Austin: University of Texas, 1951. Pp. 189–197.

115. YUWILER, A., & GOOD, M. H. Chromatographic study of "Reigelhaupt" chromogens in urine. *Journal of Psychiatric Research*, 1962, *1*, 215–227.

44.

JOHN L. FULLER AND WILLIAM R. THOMPSON

BEHAVIOR GENETICS IN SCHIZOPHRENIA

We shall now examine evidence on the inheritance of schizophrenia as a general syndrome, presenting both proband and twin studies. In all instances, comparisons must be made with frequency of schizophrenia in the general population which has been estimated to be between 0.5 and 1.0% (Kallmann, 1938; Pollock and Malzberg, 1940; Fremming, 1947; Slater, 1953b). Expectancy rates vary slightly when corrections are made for inbreeding, mortality rates, and age. Although a few estimates have been higher, 3% by Böök (1953a), for example, the range mentioned appears to be typical of a wide variety of different populations in America, Germany, and Scandinavia and may consequently be regarded as reasonably accurate (Kallmann, 1953). In mental hospitals schizophrenia has a high frequency among first admissions. Its somewhat lower frequency among readmissions, however, indicates its tendency to

be a chronic disease (Noyes and Kolb, 1958). Among relatives of proband cases in both lineal and collateral lines, expectancy rates are very much higher. Some of the evidence, as summarized by Kallmann in several publications, is set out in Table 5.19. It is obvious that these figures are a great deal higher than the general expectancy rate and generally correlate with degree of kinship. Such a correlation is a strong indication of hereditary factors. Kallmann's data have been generally confirmed by a number of other investigators. Elsässer (1939) has calculated the expectancy for children of two schizophrenic probands at 50%, whereas Schulz (1939) obtained 31% (41% if both had the typical form) and Luxenburger (1928) 68% for the same relationship.

It should be noted that Kallmann's figures represent the risk for persons of both sexes who survive the manifestation period of the disease, a period estimated to extend from 15 to 44 years of age. Within this age range there are no differences between the sexes in expectancy rates.

From John L. Fuller and William R. Thompson, *Behavior genetics*. New York: Wiley, 1960. Pp. 273–283. Reprinted by permission.

TABLE 5.19

EXPECTANCY OF SCHIZOPHRENIA IN RELATIVES
OF PROBAND CASES
(Kallmann, 1946; Kallmann and Barrera, 1942)

Relationship to Proband	% Expectancy[*]
Step-sibs	1.8
Half-sibs	7.0–7.6
Full sibs	11.5–14.3
Children,	
one parent affected	16.4
both parents affected	68.1
Parents	9.3–10.3
Grandparents	3.9
Grandchildren	4.3
Nephews and nieces	3.9

[*]Ranges are shown where different figures were obtained.

TABLE 5.20

MARRIAGE AND BIRTH RATES IN NORMAL AND
SCHIZOPHRENIC POPULATIONS
(Kallmann, 1946)

	% Marriage rate	% Birth rate
General population	71	3.3
Schizophrenics		
Nuclear Group	39.1	1.4
Peripheral Group	70.1	3.1
All	50.3	1.9

Although Kallmann's data have been criticized on a number of technical grounds (Pastore, 1949, 1952), the general conclusion to which they point is probably sound, as Hurst (1951, 1952) has indicated. At the same time, some work done in the field is in notable disagreement. Pollock and Malzberg (1940) studied the families of 175 proband cases. Among their relatives, only a few cases of schizophrenia were diagnosed, giving hardly more than chance expectancy. It is difficult to know why there is such a discrepancy between these results and those obtained by other workers. Possibly one reason for it is the rather small sample used by Pollock and Malzberg. Since those studied by Kallmann are considerably larger, perhaps it is fair to place more confidence in his conclusions. His conclusions are also supported by a greater number of studies.

Kallmann (1946) considers that the expectancy rates obtained in his proband families are probably underestimates, owing mainly to the fact that celibacy is considerably higher and fertility lower in schizophrenics than in normal individuals. Table 5.20 shows this quite clearly. In view of these facts, we might expect that proband data, particularly in the direct lines, will be obtained from the less deteriorated cases of schizophrenia, since only the more mildly afflicted individuals mate and have children. Hence expectancy rates will probably be lower than predicted from simple genetic hypotheses. The same factors that permit a schizophrenic to marry and propagate probably also provide his children with a certain resistance to the psychotic process.

Twin studies lend direct support to the conclusions drawn from proband data. Almost without exception, investigators in psychiatric genetics have shown high concordance rates for schizophrenia in twins. Some sample studies are presented in Table 5.21. Although some of the concordance rates that have been found for MZ twins are low, notably those of Luxenburger (1930) and Rosanoff *et al.* (1934c), the general picture presented strongly supports the hereditary point of view. It is important to note that the degree of concordance found depends a great deal on the method and care of the diagnosis. Very often diagnoses differ from hospital to hospital or even in the same hospital from time to time. It is difficult to tell whether such differences relate only to superficial aspects of the disease entity or whether they are basic. The best way of meeting this difficulty is to use only cases that have been personally interviewed by the investigator himself, using reliable diagnostic procedures. This procedure was followed by Slater (1953a, 1953c) in a careful study of 67 MZ and over 200 DZ twins. Since the concordance rates found by him (see Table 5.21) were not very different from those found by other investigators, we can assume that most of the data have not been seriously biased by inconsistent diagnostic procedures. Rosanoff *et al.* (1934c) dealt with the problem of consistent diagnosis in a similar way but also attempted to get gradations of similarity between members of the twin pairs. Where both individuals in MZ pairs were affected, they found that 43.9% showed similar affections, 17.1% showed a quan-

TABLE 5.21
EXPECTANCY RATES IN MZ AND DZ COTWINS
OF SCHIZOPHRENICS, AS FOUND
IN SEVERAL STUDIES
(Kallmann, 1953)

Author	DZ		MZ	
	No.	% Expectancy	No.	% Expectancy
Luxenburger (1928, 1930)	60[*]	3.3	21	66.6
Rosanoff *et al.* (1934b)	101	14.9	41	68.3
Essen-Möller (1941)	24	16.7	7	71.4
Slater (1951)	115	14.0	41	76.0
Kallmann (1938–1953)	685	14.5	268	86.2

[*]These include 23 cases of twins whose zygosity was not definitely ascertained.

titative dissimilarity, and 7.3% showed qualitative dissimilarity. Corresponding figures for DZ twins are 5% for each of the three categories. It has been claimed by Rosenberg (1944) that the figure of 43.9% represents the most accurate assessment of concordance and, as such, is too low to support a genetic hypothesis. Rosenberg apparently feels that when concordance is not perfect in monozygotic twins, we must hold to an environmentalist viewpoint on the causation of schizophrenia. In the light of modern genetic theory which does not postulate a one-to-one relation between genotype and phenotypic expression, this criticism does not have much cogency.

Recently in psychiatric literature a great amount of work has been devoted to so-called childhood or preadolescent schizophrenia (Hoch and Zubin, 1954, 1955). Unlike the classical syndrome which usually has its onset during or after puberty, the childhood variety may begin very early, often in the first few years of life. According to Kallmann and Roth (1956), about 1.9% of all schizophrenias have the onset before age fifteen, and these represent 0.6% of all first admissions in mental hospitals. While there is no question that this disease entity, like its adult counterpart, is strongly influenced by a variety of environmental factors, there is also strong evidence that genetic causation plays a part. Kallmann and Roth (1956) studied 35 DZ and 17 MZ pairs of twins reared apart. Cotwin expectancy rates were 17.1% and 70.0%, respectively. These figures do not deviate much from those for the total schizophrenic population of

22.9% and 88.2%, respectively (with age corrections). Sometimes schizophrenia in cotwins of child schizophrenics occurs before, sometimes after, adolescence. Consequently, the authors conclude that preadolescent schizophrenia is determined genetically to the same extent and apparently by the same genotype as the adult form. They suggest that the difference between the two forms lies in the number of secondary factors which lower constitutional resistance or interfere with the containability of early cases. Expectancy rates calculated on relatives of singleton cases of childhood schizophrenia were as follows: for parents, 8.8%; for sibs, 9.0%; or 9.2% and 12.2%, respectively, with corrections for age. These figures approximate those obtained for adult schizophrenia and therefore support the main conclusions based on the proband and twin data that we have just presented above.

A second set of experimental data bearing on childhood schizophrenia has been obtained by Bender and Gruggett (1956). Their genetic findings are set out in Table 5.22. Although the sample size is small, the figures shown do generally support those of Kallmann and Roth, both as to the genetic basis of the syndrome in question and as to its close relation to the adult form. Kanner (1954), on the other hand, has had reservations both in respect to its genetic determination and its relation to adult schizophrenia.

Before leaving this general section on the inheritance of schizophrenia, we should discuss one more question. This concerns the general transmission of schizoid personality or what

TABLE 5.22
EXPECTANCY OF SCHIZOPHRENIA IN RELATIVES
OF CHILDHOOD SCHIZOPHRENIC PROBAND CASES
(Bender and Gruggett, 1956)

	% Affected				
	Mother	Father	Sibs	Paternal Collaterals	Maternal Collaterals
Schizophrenic child	14	12	3	11	11
Normal child	3	1	1	0	0

Kallmann has called *schizoidia*. As the name suggests, the personality syndrome involves the main characteristics of schizophrenia but in lesser degree. Because the disturbance is less acute, it is considerably harder to diagnose accurately. Nevertheless, some investigators have attempted genetic studies. Hoffman (1926) suggested that so-called schizoid personality which might manifest itself in acute psychosis was not a unitary clinical entity, but rather a collection of traits that should be investigated separately. Kallmann (1946), however, presented empirical data on the subject along with his expectancy rates for schizophrenia. These are reproduced for a number of degrees of kinship in Table 5.23. The data do not appear to be consistent. The twin cases suggest that schizoidia depends rather less on hereditary factors than the psychosis it presumably underlies. The proband cases, however, support a hereditary hypothesis. Kallmann (1953) considered it to represent either heterozygous expression of the schizophrenic genotype coupled with weak resistance or homozygous expression with strong resistance. However, the evidence for this idea is by no means decisive as yet. It is a rather interesting hypothesis that certainly justifies further study.

TABLE 5.23
EXPECTANCY OF SCHIZOID PERSONALITY IN RELATIVES
OF SCHIZOPHRENIC PROBAND CASES
(Kallmann, 1946)

	% Expectancy*
Step-sibs	2.7
Half-sibs	12.5
Sibs	31.5
DZ cotwins	23.0
MZ cotwins	20.7
Parents	34.8

*Only definite cases included.

THE SPECIFICITY OF SCHIZOPHRENIA

The specificity of the schizophrenic genotype is a problem that has been widely discussed and one on which complete agreement has not yet been reached. Concretely, the question has at least two parts: First, is the schizophrenic genotype inherited as a simple unit underlying the diverse phenotypic forms the syndrome may take? Second, does the genotype underlying schizophrenia also underlie other forms of mental illness such as manic-depression, mental deficiency, and others? Since the second of these questions can be examined better after the presentation of material on other mental diseases, we shall consider only the first at this point.

We must recognize that schizophrenia as a syndrome covers not only the four classical subtypes, namely, simple, paranoid, catatonic, and hebephrenic, but also a great variety of unclassifiable symptoms that make even the most elementary subdivision difficult. The relevant question here concerns the genetic dependence or independence of these different aspects of the schizophrenic phenotype. Is there evidence for a nuclear schizophrenic genotype underlying all varieties and phases of the syndrome, or are the facts better explained in terms of a number of distinct genotypes which may or may not relate to each other? This question has been widely debated and presently opinions are held on both sides of the issue. Kallmann (1946, 1953, 1954a), for example, with many others (Luxenburger, 1937; Zehnder, 1941; Elsässer, 1952; Slater, 1953a), supports the view that there is a unitary genotype for schizophrenia which may express itself in different ways depending mainly on the environmental pressures. It is quite characteristic for the disease to take many clinical forms in the same families, as many workers have pointed out. Kallmann (1938) has further shown that the subtypes of schizophrenia differ somewhat in the expectancy rates they show. In children of probands these rates are as follows: for hebephrenic, 20.7%; for catatonic, 21.6%; for simple schizophrenia 10.4%; and for paranoid schizophrenia, 11.6%. Kallmann argues from these figures that the first two were more closely related to the nuclear genotype than the last two. He suggests that the different symptomatology in each of these subdivisions is due to the action of genetic modifiers superimposed on the major genotype.

In contrast to Kallmann's point of view, Rosanoff *et al.* (1934a), Weinberg and Lobstein (1943), and Essen-Möller (1941, 1952) have stressed the variations in the symptoms and suggested that different genetic mechanisms may be necessary to account for such differences as are found. Obviously, the conflict between these points of view is not serious and represents simply a difference in emphasis. It is quite likely that there is a nuclear genotype for basic schizophrenic psychosis, and it is equally possible that the variations in the symptoms which are manifested by individuals in this broad category are also dependent on particular genetic mechanisms. Any decision regarding these possibilities, however, must be delayed until a firmer liaison has been established between diagnosis of phenotype and genetic analysis. Still different views have been offered by other writers. Leonhard (1936) has distinguished between so-called typical and atypical schizophrenics. The former have strongly distinct subtypes and are deteriorative; the latter are characterized by a cyclical course with generally favorable prognosis. According to Leonhard, the typical cases show less hereditary causation than those in the atypical group. Bleuler (1930) has similarly attempted to distinguish between two groups of schizophrenias, one with and the other without hereditary causation. He concludes that although schizoid traits are probably caused by a specific genotype, a trend to actual dementia is not. This appears to be rather similar to the suggestion of Essen-Möller (1952) that the manifestation of the schizophrenic genotype depends on the presence of a basic schizoid personality

which is more common in relatives of probands than actual schizophrenia. Witterman (1926) and Wildermuth (1927) found evidence that the psychotic syndrome is composed of a number of inherited symptom complexes which are transmitted separately and may be traced in family lines.

Obviously a considerable degree of confusion still surrounds the problem of the schizophrenic genotype. There are evidently a number of possibilities, different ones having support from different investigators. A carefully planned program of research done on a large scale could perhaps settle the matter and make a basic contribution to our understanding of the genetics of schizophrenia.

The final question that will concern us in this section relates to the genetic mechanisms by which schizophrenia is transmitted. In discussing these we shall also examine briefly the part played by constitution in determination of the schizophrenic syndrome.

GENETIC TRANSMISSION OF SCHIZOPHRENIA

Perhaps more studies have been done on the genetics of schizophrenia than on any other behavioral trait. In spite of the value of this work, however, the picture is still by no means clear. Two main possibilities are open. In the first place, one or a few Mendelian unit factors may be involved. These may be either dominants, recessives, or both in some combination. On the other hand, polygenic systems may be operating on an essentially continuously distributed trait.

It is fair to say that most of the work done in the area has favored the first of these two alternatives. This is probably due partly to historical factors in the development of psychiatric genetics in Munich and elsewhere and in part to the fact that schizophrenia is usually defined in an all-or-none way. Unlike personality characteristics or intelligence, schizophrenia is present or not, operationally speaking, and hence can be treated in much the same way as traits such as "taste blindness" or phenylketonuria. At the same time it must be stressed that the categorical definition of schizophrenia is somewhat arbitrary and is mostly a matter of convenience. Individuals who have deteriorated beyond a certain point can no longer function properly in society and must then be hospitalized for treatment. This does not mean, however, that there is no gradation of symptoms from normal to acutely deteriorated. Some workers, Eysenck (1958), for example, have gathered evidence favoring this view, though it has been criticized by others (Pearson and Kley, 1958). Consequently, we must be very cautious about jumping to any conclusions regarding the mode of transmission of schizophrenia. From what we know about the nature of the behavioral trait alone, there are no strong grounds for favoring either the simple Mendelian model or the polygenic model.

As already stated, however, most workers in the field have tried to explain their data in terms of a few unit dominants or recessives. Planansky (1955) has pointed out, in fact, that no investigator has directly argued for a multiple-gene model. Consequently we shall turn directly to models along the more classical Mendelian lines.

In this category a division may be made between workers favoring primarily recessivity theories and those favoring dominance theories. One of the foremost proponents of the former view has been Kallmann (1953). He has suggested that schizophrenia is carried by a major mutant recessive gene whose effect is probably to produce some enzyme deficiency. The metabolic deficiency in turn affects general behavioral adjustment rather than specific symptoms, since different types of symptoms may be observed not only in monozygotic twin pairs and in different members of the same family, but even in the same affected individuals at different times.

The recessivity hypothesis has been presented in various forms by a number of other workers, including many from the Munich School (Rüdin, 1916; Luxenburger, 1935; Weinberg and Lobstein, 1943). It has been clearly recognized by workers holding this position, however, that the data are not fully in agreement with such a hypothesis in any simple form. Usually the disease does not reach the 25% expectancy rate in siblings of schizophrenic probands. Furthermore, theoretically, all children of two schizophrenic probands should turn out to be schizophrenic, but, empirically, the figures obtained are usually between 40% and 66%. One solution to this problem, suggested by Rüdin (1916), is to postulate that more than one pair of genes are operating. Initially he favored the idea of a double recessive. Later (1923) he hypothesized a trifactorial mode for the inheritance of psychoses in general, involving two recessives and a dominant.

Neither of these models fully explains the low incidence of the disease in children of twin probands nor have such complex hypotheses proved useful in physiological analyses. Perhaps the more common and, in our opinion, the more cogent point of view involves the assumption of varying degrees of penetrance of the schizophrenic genotype. Kallmann (1948, 1953, 1954) suggested that expressivity is determined by a genetically non-specific constitutional defense mechanism which he regards as "unquestionably polygenic." This mechanism relates to the effect of certain mesodermal tissue elements which inhibit expression of the disease. It will be recognized that this suggestion is almost identical with the early theories of Kretschmer (1951) and others of the Munich school (Luxenburger, 1939) who related aesthenic physique to schizophrenia. The relationship is expressed in Table 5.24.

As things stand now, Kallmann's view of this relationship is probably more accurate than the rather simple theory originally proposed. A study by Kline and Tenney (1951), for example, appears to indicate that whereas the aesthenic or in Sheldon's terms the ectomorphic physique shows little correlation with schizophrenia, strong presence of athletic or mesomorphic components is usually an indication of good prognosis for surgical therapy among those affected. This finding clearly supports Kallmann's thesis. Kallmann further suggests (1953) that under certain circumstances, a heterozygote with low

TABLE 5.24

RELATIONSHIP BETWEEN PHYSIQUE AND DEGREE OF DETERIORATION IN SCHIZOPHRENICS
(Kallmann and Barrera, 1942)

Degree of Deterioration	Body Type (Mean Rating)		
	Pyknic	Athletic	Aesthenic
Extreme	3.01	2.82	4.41
Moderate	3.01	3.17	4.20
Slight	3.16	3.76	3.72

resistance may break down under stress such as mescalin or lysergic acid (Kallmann, 1954b), for example, as easily as a homozygote with strong resistance. Evidently a theory such as this has enough flexibility to give it wide explanatory value. But for the same reason, it is a rather difficult theory to test. The data at present certainly do not contradict it, but, on the other hand, they do not definitely support it in preference to other theories.

A contrary dominance theory of schizophrenia has been supported by such workers as Patzig (1938), Böök (1953b), Koller (1939), and Schulz (1940a, 1940b). This hypothesis, also, must assume lowered penetrance to account for the empirical expectancy rates in relatives of probands. Slater (1958) has shown that a number of surveys give results in accordance with monogenic inheritance with a manifestation rate of 26% in heterozygotes and 100% in homozygotes.

At the present time, the empirical data are too scanty to allow definitive choice between the various views presented. On the whole, a recessivity hypothesis appears to have a slight edge, mainly in view of the low frequency of schizophrenia in the population. To interpret this according to the dominance model would perhaps put undue strain on the concept of penetrance, a construct that is a little too elastic to be very useful empirically. On the other hand, a dominance theory is able to explain much of the data, especially the relatively low expectancy rates in offspring of two schizophrenic parents (Slater, 1958). Each theory has its strong points and its weak points.Until a model can be specified so precisely that it, and it alone, predicts the occurrence of schizophrenia in relatives of index cases, judgment between the present alternatives must be withheld.

Success in relating schizophrenia to one or several metabolic defects would be of great value in clarifying the genetics of this condition (see Kety, 1959). Research in this area is active, and the eventual outcome may well provide the kind of decisive evidence which is needed. In the meantime the case for heritability of schizophrenia must stand on the genetic evidence alone. Experience with the so-called psychomimetic drugs has indicated that extremely minute amounts of certain chemical configurations can seriously disturb brain function. The organic basis for schizophrenia may likewise be a minor disturbance in terms of overall metabolism, though of critical importance for behavior.

REFERENCES

BENDER, L., & GRUGGETT, A. E. A study of certain epidemiological factors in a group of children with childhood schizophrenia. *American Journal of Orthopsychiatry*, 1956, 26, 131–143.

BLEULER, M. Vererbungsprobleme bei Schizophrenen. *Zeitschrift für die gesamte Neurologie und Psychiatrie*, 1930, 127, 321–388.

BÖÖK, J. A. Schizophrenia as a gene mutation. *Acta Genetica et Statistica Medica*, 1953, 4, 133–139.

BÖÖK, J. A., SCHUT, J. W., & REED, S. C. A clinical and genetic study of micricephaly. *American Journal of Mental Deficiency*, 1953, 57, 637–660. (a)

ELSÄSSER, G. Endogen geisteskranken Elternpaare und ihre Nachkommen. *Zeitschrift für die gesamte Neurologie und Psychiatrie*, 1939, 165, 108–112.

ELSÄSSER, G. *Die Nachkommen geisteskranken Elternpaare.* New York: Stechert-Haffner, 1952.

ESSEN-MÖLLER, E. Psychiatrische untersuchungen an einer Serie von Swillingen. *Acta Psychiatrica et Neurologica*, 1941, 23.

ESSEN-MÖLLER, E. *Psychiatrische Geisteskranken Elternpaare.* Stuttgart: Thieme, 1952.

EYSENCK, H. J. The continuity of abnormal and normal behavior. *Psychological Bulletin*, 1959, 55, 429–465.

FREMMING, K. H. *Morbid risk of mental diseases and other mental abnormalities in an average Danish population.* Copenhagen: Munksgaard, 1947.

HOCH, P. H., & ZUBIN, J. (Eds.). *Depression.* New York: Grune & Stratton, 1954.

HOCH, P. H., & ZUBIN, J. (Eds.). *Psychopathology of childhood.* New York: Grune & Stratton, 1955.

HOFFMAN, H. *Familienpsychosen in schiziphrenen Ebkreis.* Berlin: Karger, 1926.

HURST, L. A. Genetics of schizophrenia: Reply to Pastore. *Psychological Bulletin*, 1951, 48, 402–412.

HURST, L. A. The genetics of schizophrenia: Further rejoinder to Pastore. *Psychological Bulletin*, 1952, 49, 544–546.

KALLMANN, F. J. *The genetics of schizophrenia.* New York: J. J. Augustin, 1938.

KALLMANN, F. J. The genetic theory of schizophrenia. *American Journal of Psychiatry*, 1946, 103, 309–322.

KALLMANN, F. J. Heredity and constitution in relation to the treatment of mental disorders. In P. H. Hoch (Ed.). *Failures in psychiatric treatment.* New York: Grune & Stratton, 1948.

KALLMANN, F. J. *Heredity in health and mental disorder.* New York: Norton, 1953.

KALLMANN, F. J. The genetics of psychotic behavior patterns. *Association for Research in Nervous and Mental Disease*, 1954, *33*, 357–366.

KALLMANN, F. J. Genetic principles in manic-depressive psychosis. In P. H. Hoch and J. Zubin (Eds.), *Depression*. New York: Grune & Stratton, 1954.

KALLMANN, F. J., & ROTH, B. Genetic aspects of preadolescent schizophrenia. *American Journal of Psychiatry*, 1956, *112*, 599–606.

KANNER, L. To what extent is early infantile autism determined by constitutional inadequacies? *Association for Research in Nervous and Mental Disease*, 1954, *33*, 378–385.

KETY, S. S. Biochemical theories of schizophrenia. *Science*, 1959, *129*, 1528–1532, 1590–1596.

KLINE, N., & TENNEY, A. M. Prognosis in topectomies and lobectomies relative to body type. *A.M.A. Archives of Neurological Psychiatry*, 1951, *63*, 323–325.

KOLLER, S. Über den Erbgang der Schizophrenie. *Zeitschrift für die gesamte Neurologie und Psychiatrie*, 1939, *164*, 199–228.

KRETSCHMER, E. *Korperbau und Character* (20th ed.) Berlin: Springer, 1951.

LEONHARD, K. *Die Defeckt-schizophrenen Krankheitsbilder*. Leipzig: Thieme, 1936.

LUXENBURGER, H. Vorläufigen Bericht über psychiatrische Serienunterschungen an Zwillingen. *Zeitschrift für die gesamte Neurologie und Psychiatrie*, 1928, *116*, 297–326.

LUXENBURGER, H. Psychiatrische-neurologische Zwillingspathologie. *Zentralblatt für die gesamte Neurologie und Psychiatrie*, 1930, *14*, 56–57, 145–180.

LUXENBURGER, H. Untersuchungen an schizophrenen Zwillingen und ihren Gewchwistern zur Prufung der Realität von Manifestationsschwankungen. *Zeitschrift für die gesamte Neurologie und Psychiatrie*, 1935, *154*, 351–394.

LUXENBURGER, H. Bemerkungen sum Vortag von F. Lenz: Medeln die Geisteskrankheiten. *Zeitschrift für indukive Abstammungs und Vererbungslehre*, 1937, *73*, 505–558.

LUXENBURGER, H. Die Schizophrenie und ihr Erbkreis. In G. Just (Ed.). *Handbuch die Erbbiologie. 5.* Berlin: Springer, 1939.

NOYES, A. P., & KOLB, L. *Modern clinical psychiatry* (5th ed.) Philadelphia: Saunders, 1958.

PASTORE, N. The genetics of schizophrenia. *Psychological Bulletin*, 1949, *46*, 285–302.

PASTORE, N. Genetics of schizophrenia: a rejoinder. *Psychological Bulletin*, 1952, *49*, 542–544.

PATZIG, B. Untersuchungen zur Frage des Erbanges und der Manifestierung schizophrener Erkrankungen. *Zeitschrift für Neurologie*, 1938, *161*, 521–532.

PEARSON, J. S., & KLEY, I. B. Discontinuity and correlation. A reply to Eysenck. *Psychological Bulletin*, 1958, *55*, 433–435.

PLANANSKY, K. Heredity in schizophrenia. *Journal of Mental and Nervous Disease*, 1955, *122*, 121–142.

POLLOCK, H. M., & MALZBERG, B. Hereditary and environmental factors in the causation of dementia praecox and manic-depressive psychoses. *American Journal of Psychiatry*, 1940, *96*, 1227–1247.

ROSANOFF, A. J., HANDY, L. M., & ROSANOFF, I. A. Criminality and delinquency in twins. *Journal of Criminal Law and Criminology*, 1934, *24*, 923–934. (a)

ROSANOFF, A. J., HANDY, L. M., & ROSANOFF, I. A. Etiology of epilepsy with special reference to its occurrence in twins. *A.M.A. Archives of Neurology and Psychiatry*, 1934, *31*, 1165–1193.

ROSANOFF, A. J., HANDY, L. M., PLESSET, I. R., & BRUSH, S. The Etiology of so-called schizophrenic psychoses. *American Journal of Psychiatry*, 1934, *91*, 247–286. (c)

ROSENBERG, R. Heredity in the functional psychoses. *American Journal of Psychiatry*, 1944, *101*, 157–165.

RÜDIN, E. *Zur Verebung und Neuenstehung der Dementia Praecox*. Berlin: Springer, 1916.

RÜDIN, E. Ueber Verebung geistigen Störungen. *Zeitschrift fur die gesamte Neurologie und Psychiatrie*, 1923, *81*, 459 ff.

SCHULZ, B. Empirische untersuchungen uber die Bedeutung beidseitigen Belastung mit endogenen Psychosen. *Zeitschrift für die gesamte Neurologie und Psychiatrie*, 1939, *165*, 97–108.

SCHULŻ, B. Kinder schizophrenen Elternpaare. *Zeitschrift für die gesamte Neurologie und Psychiatrie*, 1940a, *168*, 332–381.

SCHULZ, B. Erkrankungshalter schizophrenen Eltern und Kinder. *Zeitschrift für die gesamte Neurologie und Psychiatrie*, 1940b, *168*, 709–721.

SLATER, E. Genetic investigations in twins. *Journal of Mental Science*, 1953a, *99*, 44–52.

SLATER, E. Psychiatry. In A. Sorsby (Ed.). *Clinical genetics*. London: Butterworth, 1953b. Pp. 332–349.

SLATER, E. Psychotic and neurotic illnesses in twins. *Medical Research Council, Special Report No. 278*. London: H. M. Stationery Office, 1953 (c).

SLATER, E. The monogenic theory of schizophrenia *Acta Genetica et Statistica Medica*, 1958, *8*, 50–56.

WEINBERG, I., & LOBSTEIN, J. Inheritance in schizophrenia. *Acta Psychiatrica et Neurologica*, 1943, *18*, 93–140.

WILDERMUTH, H. Geschwisterpsychosen. *Zeitschrift für die gesamte Neurologie und Psychiatrie*, 1927, *110*, 60–80.

WITTERMAN, E. Klinische Psychiatrie und Familienforschung. *Zeitschrift fur die gesamte Neurologie und Psychiatrie*, 1926, *105*, 459–493.

ZEHNDER, M. Ueber Krankheitsbild und Krankheitsverlauf bei schizophrenen Ceschwistern. *Monatsschrift fur Psychiatrie und Neurologie*, 1941, *103*, 231–277.

45.

Norman Cameron

THE PARANOID PSEUDO-COMMUNITY

ABSTRACT

The pseudo-community is reformulated as a cognitive structure which attempts to solve the problem of reconciling social reality with the products of paranoid projection. Delusional development follows regression and the loss of social reality. It begins with the estrangement experienced by a partially regressed person when he attempts to regain object relations and proceeds through successive provisional reconstructions of reality until a cognitive solution is reached which seems to justify paranoid action. Aggressive action is likely to make social reality confirm the expectations of the pseudo-community.

A decade of experience with intensive clinical studies of paranoid thinking, in the course of psychoanalyzing psychoneurotics and in the long-term therapy of ambulatory psychotics, has led me to a reworking of the concept of the pseudo-community as formulated in this *Journal*[1] and further developed elsewhere.[2] The social aspects of the concept require little change. It is in its individual aspects—in a greater concern with the evidence of internal changes and with the signs that forces are operative which are not open to direct observation—that the pseudo-community acquires deeper roots and greater usefulness.

From Norman Cameron,"The paranoid pseudo-community revisited."*American Journal of Sociology*, 1959, 65, 52–58. The University of Chicago Press. Copyright © 1959 by The University of Chicago.

[1]Norman Cameron, "The Paranoid Pseudo-Community," *American Journal of Sociology*, XLIX (1943), 32–38. Reprinted in A. M. Rose (ed.), *Mental Health and Mental Disorder: A Sociological Approach* (New York: W. W. Norton & Co., 1955).

[2]Norman Cameron, *The Psychology of Behavior Disorders: A Biosocial Interpretation* (Boston: Houghton Mifflin Co., 1947), and "Perceptual Organization and Behavior Pathology," in R. Blake and G. Ramsey (eds.), *Perception: An Approach to Personality* (New York: Ronald Press Co., 1951); and Norman Cameron and A. Magaret, *Behavior Pathology* (Boston: Houghton Mifflin Co., 1951), chap. xiii, "Pseudo-Community and Delusion."

ORIGINAL PRESENTATION

In the normal evolution and preservation of socially organized behavior the most important factor is the developing and maintaining of genuine communication. In each individual, language behavior grows out of preverbal interchange between infant and older person. It evolves in accordance with whatever traditional patterns prevail in the immediate environment, since communication is always at first, between a child who operates at preverbal levels and older individuals whose language is already a highly organized interactive system. Through sharing continuously in such language and prelanguage interchange, each child develops shared social perspectives and skill in shifting from one perspective to another in time of need.

A highly significant result of this gradual process is that, as time goes on, the child normally acquires an increasingly realistic grasp of how other people feel, what their attitudes, plans, hopes, fears, and intentions are, and in what ways these all relate to his own. Eventually, he is able to take the roles of other people around him in imagination and to view things more or less realistically from their perspectives as well as from his own. In this way he also develops a workable degree of objectivity toward himself, learning to respond to his body, his personality, and his behavior more or less as others do. In the final product, there is considerable difference between the socialization achieved in behavior publicly shared and genuinely communicated and behavior that has remained private and little formulated or expressed in language.

The adult who is especially vulnerable to paranoid developments is one in whom this process of socialization has been seriously defective. His deficient social learning and poorly developed social skills leave him unable to understand adequately the motivations, attitudes, and intentions of others. When he becomes disturbed or confused under stress, he must operate under several grave handicaps imposed by a lifelong inability to communicate freely and effectively, to suspend judgment long enough to share his tentative interpretations with someone else, to imagine realistically the attitudes that others might have toward his situation and himself, and to imagine their roles and thus share their perspectives.

Left to his own unaided devices in a crisis, the paranoid person is able only to seek and find "evidence" that carries him farther in the direction he is already going—toward a more and more delusional interpretation of what seems to be going on around him.[3] This process may culminate in a conviction that he himself is the focus of a community of persons who are united in a conspiracy of some kind against him. It is this supposed functional community of real persons whom the patient can see and hear, and of other persons whom he imagines, that we call the *paranoid pseudo-community*. It has no existence as a social organization and as soon as he attempts to combat it, or to flee, he is likely to come into conflict with his actual social community.

INCOMPLETENESS OF THE DESCRIPTIVE PSEUDO-COMMUNITY

This, in brief, is the background and structure of the paranoid pseudo-community, as originally described. As it stands, it still seems valid; but it is unnecessarily restricted. In the first place, the account of the delusional development pays scant attention to internal dynamics because of the limits imposed by a behavioristic orientation. Patients, of course, recognize no such limitations. In the course of long-term intensive therapy they can sometimes furnish important information about what is going on within them to a therapist who is ready to receive it. Some of this they describe as it happens, in their own terms, and often in their own idiom. Some of it one can infer from what is said and done, with the help of material communicated in parallel

cases. Some of it one must postulate in an effort to make one's observations and direct inferences more intelligible, just as is done in other empirical sciences.

In the original account not enough emphasis was given to the positive achievements of delusion formation. As we shall see, the pseudo-community is the best means a paranoid patient has at the time for bridging the chasm between his inner reality and social reality. Its use for this purpose may lead to a progressive reduction in desocialization and the reappearance of more normal communicative channels.

And, finally, the concept of the pseudo-community needs a background of structural postulates. In order to make sense out of the experiences which people actually have in fantasies, daydreams, dreams, and psychoses, one is obliged to go beyond such impermanent concepts as perception, response, and behavior—upon which the writer earlier relied—and to assume probable forces and mechanisms operating within personality systems and interacting subsystems. Here, again, the patient often comes to the rescue with empirical data. And, every now and then, one comes across a patient who describes with naïve simplicity and directness —but consistently over a long period of time— phenomena which seem purely theoretical and highly abstruse, as reported in the literature. Exposed to such material the therapist may still be left with a sense of strangeness; but his previous feeling of their abstruseness and incredulity sooner or later vanishes.[4]

PARANOID LOSS OF SOCIAL REALITY

Paranoid delusional development begins with an impairment of social communication. It is preceded by experiences of frustration to which, like many normal persons, the paranoid individual reacts by turning away from his surroundings, and taking refuge in fantasy and daydream. This is the phase of withdrawal and preoccupation which is sometimes obvious even to an untrained observer.

When a paranoid person withdraws like this,

---

[3]For a detailed discussion of this process of *desocialization* see "Desocialization and Disorganization," in Cameron and Magaret, *op. cit.*, pp. 448–517.

[4]See, e.g., the clinical material in Norman Cameron, "Reprojection and Introjection in the Interaction between Schizophrenic Patient and Therapist" (submitted for publication).

he is far more likely than a normal person to lose effective contact with his social environment (i.e., with social reality) and to undergo regression. If this happens, he may abandon social reality for a time completely and become absorbed in primitive regressive thinking and feeling. Occasionally, a patient openly expresses some of his regressive experiences at the time; more often they can be inferred only from what emerges later on.

PRECURSORS OF THE PSEUDO-COMMUNITY
I. BEGINNING RESTITUTION

It is a fact, of both clinical observation and subjective report, that paranoid patients, while still withdrawn, preoccupied, and regressed, begin to make attempts to regain their lost relationships with social reality. We may conceptualize these as marking the tapering-off of regression and the beginning of the integration of personality. The attempts fail to recover the lost social reality, however, because the patient's internal situation is not what it was before his regression. It is no longer possible for him to regain social reality as, for example, a normal person does when he wakes up in the morning. Instead, as we shall see, paranoid reintegration involves a restitutive process, the construction of a pseudo-reality which culminates in the paranoid pseudo-community.

Paranoid personalities suffer all their lives from defective repressive defenses and a heavy reliance upon the more primitive defenses of denial and projection. If they undergo a psychotic regression, which involves partial ego disintegration, their repressive defenses become still more defective. Primitive fantasies and conflicts now begin to emerge and to threaten ego disruption. The patient is forced to deal with them somehow, if he is to preserve what personality integration he still has and avoid further regression. Since he cannot successfully repress them, he vigorously denies them and projects them. An immediate result of the intense projective defense is that the products of the patient's emerging fantasies and conflicts now appear to him to be coming from outside him. Thus he seems to escape disintegration from within only to be threatened with destruction from without.

PRECURSORS OF THE PSEUDO-COMMUNITY
II. ESTRANGEMENT AND DIFFUSE VIGILANCE

In the process of denying and projecting, the paranoid patient makes a start toward regaining contact with his surroundings. But this process neither simplifies nor clarifies the situation for him; and it does not bring about a return to social reality. On the contrary, the surroundings now seem somehow strange and different. Something has unquestionably happened. The patient misidentifies this "something" as basically a change in the makeup of his environment instead of what it actually is, a fundamental change within himself. If he expresses his feelings at this point, he is likely to say that things are going on which he does not understand; and this, of course, is literally true.

It is hardly surprising that the patient, finding himself in a world grown suddenly strange, should become diffusely vigilant. He watches everything uneasily; he listens alertly for clues; he looks everywhere for hidden meanings. Here his lifelong social incompetence makes matters still worse. He lacks even ordinary skill in the common techniques for testing social reality. He is unable to view his threatening situation even temporarily from the perspective of a neutral person. The more anxious and vigilant he grows, the less he can trust anybody, the less he dares to share with anyone his uneasiness and suspicion. He is condemned to pursue a solitary path, beset by primal fears, hates, and temptations which he cannot cope with nor escape.

PRECURSORS OF THE PSEUDO-COMMUNITY
III. INCREASED SELF-REFERENCE

Strong tendencies toward self-reference are characteristic of paranoid personalities. When a paranoid adult becomes deeply and regressively preoccupied, his habitually egocentric orientation is greatly increased. And when he next resorts to wholesale projection, he in effect converts his environment into an arena for his projected fantasies and conflicts. This destroys whatever neutrality and objectivity the environment may have previously possessed for him. He is now engrossed in scrutinizing his surroundings for signs of the return of what he is denying and projecting. To these he has become selectively sensitive. He is watching out for something that will explain away the strangeness and enable him to escape his frightening sense of isolation.

It is an unfortunate fact that a badly frightened person—even a normal one—is likely to notice things and make interpretations that increase rather than diminish his fear. And this is especially the case if he feels alone, in strange surroundings, and threatened by an unknown danger. Many non-paranoid adults, for example, walking alone through a large cemetery at night, or lost at night in a forest, become extremely alert and feel personally threatened by harmless things wholly unrelated to them. The paranoid adult, who is peopling his surroundings with projected phantoms from his own past, likewise creates a situation in which everything seems somehow dangerously related to him. Since he cannot escape, he tries to understand the situation he has unconsciously created, in the vain hope that he may then be able to cope with it.

PRECURSORS OF THE PSEUDO-COMMUNITY
IV. PRELIMINARY HYPOTHESES

Being human, the paranoid patient is driven irresistibly to make hypotheses; but, having partially regressed, and being paranoid as well, he cannot test them. He tends, therefore, to pass from one guess or one suspicion to another like it. Using the materials provided by his environment and by his projected fantasies and conflicts, he constructs a succession of provisional hypotheses, discarding each as it fails to meet the contradictory demands of his internal needs and the environment. This is characteristic also of complex normal problem-solving. It is an expression of what is called the synthetic function of the ego.

Everyone who works with paranoid patients discovers that some kind of delusional reconstruction of reality is essential to their continued existence as persons. Even a temporary and unsatisfactory delusional hypothesis may be at the time a patient's sole means of bridging the gap between himself and his social environment. It gives a distorted picture of the world; but a distorted world is better than no world at all. And this is often a regressed person's only choice. To abandon his projected fears, hates, and temptations might mean to abandon all

that he has gained in the reconstruction of reality, to have his world fall apart and fall apart himself. Patients sense this danger, even expressing it in these words, and they rightly refuse to give up their delusional reality. Their fear is not unrealistic, for clinically such catastrophes actually occur, ending in personality disintegration.

A great many paranoid persons never go beyond the phase of making and giving up a succession of preliminary delusional hypotheses. Some of them regain a good working relationship with social reality, something approaching or equaling their premorbid status. Some are less successful and remain chronically suspicious, averse, and partially withdrawn but manage even so to go on living otherwise much as they had lived before. They may appear morose, irascible, and bitter; but they do not fix upon definite enemies or take definite hostile action. At most they suffer brief outbursts of protest and complaint without losing their ability to retreat from an angry delusional position. In this paper, however, we are concerned primarily with paranoid patients—by no means incurable —who go on to crystallize a more stable delusional organization.

FINAL CRYSTALLIZATION:
THE PSEUDO-COMMUNITY

A great many paranoid persons succeed in crystallizing a stable conceptual organization, the pseudo-community, which gives them a satisfactory cognitive explanation of their strange altered world and a basis for doing something about the situation as they now see it. Their problem is exceedingly complex. It is impossible for them to get rid of the unconscious elements, which they have denied and projected, but which now return apparently from the outside. They cannot abandon or even ignore their environment without facing a frightening regression into an objectless world. Their task is somehow to integrate these internal and external phenomena which appear before them on a single plane into a unified world picture.

The human environment which others share (*social reality*) provides the patient with real persons having social roles and characteristics which he can utilize in making his delusional reconstruction. It also provides real interaction among them, including interaction with the patient himself. Many things actually happen in it, some of them in direct relation to the patient, most of them actually not.

Internal reality provides two sets of functions. One is made up of the previously unconscious impulses, conflicts, and fantasies—now erupted, denied, and projected. This, as noted, introduces imagined motivation, interaction, and intentions into the observed activities of other persons. It gives apparent meaning to happenings which do not have such meaning for the consensus. The other set of functions is included in the concept of ego adaptation. It is the ego synthesis mentioned above, by means of which the demands of internal reality and the structure of social reality are integrated into a meaningful, though delusional, unity.

What the paranoid patient does is as follows: Into the organization of social reality, as he perceives it, he unconsciously projects his own previously unconscious motivation, which he has denied but cannot escape. This process now requires a perceptual and conceptual reorganization of object relations in his surroundings into an apparent community, which he represents to himself as organized wholly with respect to him (delusion of self-reference). And since the patient's erupted, denied, and projected elements are overwhelmingly hostile and destructive, the motivation he ascribes to the real persons he has now organized into his conceptual pseudo-community is bound to be extremely hostile and destructive.

To complete his conceptual organization of a paranoid conspiracy, the patient also introduces imaginary persons. He ascribes to them, as to real persons, imagined functions, roles, and motivations in keeping with his need to unify his restitutional conception and make it stable. He pictures helpers, dupes, stooges, go-betweens, and masterminds, of whose actual existence he becomes certain.

It is characteristic of the pseudo-community that it is made up of both real and imaginary persons, all of whom may have both real and imaginary functions and interrelations.[5] In form it usually corresponds to one or another of the common, dangerous, hostile groups in contemporary society, real or fictional—gangs, dope and spy rings, secret police, and groups of political, racial, and religious fanatics. Many paranoid patients succeed in creating a restitutional organization which has well-formulated plans. The chief persecutor is sometimes a relative or acquaintance, or a well-known public figure, while the rest of the imaginary personnel forms a vague, sinister background. Sometimes one finds the reverse—the chief persecutor is unknown, a malevolent "brain" behind everything, while the known dangerous persons play supporting roles in the delusional cast.

The final delusional reconstruction of reality may fall into an integrated conceptual pattern that brings an experience of closure: "I suddenly realized what it was all about!" the patient may exclaim with obvious relief at sudden clarification. The intolerable suspense has ended; the strangeness of what has been "going on" seems to disappear and confusion is replaced by "understanding," and wavering doubt by certainty. A known danger may be frightening; but at least it is tangible, and one can do something about it. In short, the pseudo-community reduces the hopeless complexity and confusion to a clear formula. This formula—"the plot"—the patient can now apply to future events as he experiences them and fit them into the general framework of his reconstruction.

The organization of a conceptual pseudo-community is a final cognitive step in paranoid problem-solving. It re-establishes stable object relations, though on a delusional basis, and thus makes integrated action possible. To summarize what this reconstruction of reality has achieved for its creator:

a) Reduction in Estrangement. As a direct result of paranoid problem-solving, experienced external reality is distorted so as to bring it into line with the inescapable projected elements. This lessens confusion and detachment and allows the patient to recover some of his lost sense of ego integrity. The world seems dangerous but familiar.

---

[5]This is in contrast to the autistic community which is composed of wholly imaginary persons

(see "Autistic Community and Hallucination," in Cameron and Magaret, *op. cit.*, pp. 414–47).

b) *Internal Absorption of Aggression.* Construction and maintenance of a conceptual pseudo-community absorb aggression internally, in the same sense that organizing a baseball team, a political ward, or a scientific society absorbs aggression. This reduces the threat of ego disintegration which the id eruptions pose.

c) *Basis for Action.* Any new cognitive construct can serve as a basis for new action; in this respect the paranoid pseudo-community is no exception. It organizes the drive-directed cognitive processes, leads to meaningful interpretations in a well-defined pseudo-reality structure, and paves the way for overt action with a definite focus. The patient is enabled to go ahead as anyone else might who had powerful urges and felt sure that he was right.

d) *Justification of Aggressive Action.* Finally, a persecutory pseudo-community justifies attack or flight, either of which involves a direct aggressive discharge in overt action. Fighting or running away is less disintegrative psychologically than prolonged frightened inaction. And under the circumstances, as the patient now conceptualizes them, he need feel neither guilt for attacking nor shame for fleeing.

Paranoid Cognition and Paranoid Action

When a patient succeeds in conceptualizing a pseudo-community, he has taken the final cognitive step in paranoid problem-solving. He now "knows" what his situation is. But he is still faced with his need to do something about it. As a matter of fact, the crystallization of a hostile delusional structure usually increases the urge to take action. A circular process may quickly develop. The imagined threats of the now structured imaginary conspiracy seem to the patient concrete and imminent. They stimulate more and more his anxiety and defensive hostility—and the latter, being as usual projected, further increases the apparent external threat. Often this kind of self-stimulation spirals upward, while more and more "incidents" and people may be drawn into the gathering psychotic storm.

Paranoid action, however inappropriate it may be, still represents the completion of restitutional relationships and the fullest contact with his human environment of which the patient is capable at the time. He switches from his previous passive role of observer and interpreter, with all its indecision and anxiety, to that of an aggressive participant in what he conceives as social reality. For him this is genuine interaction, and he experiences the gratification that comes with certainty and with a massive discharge of pent-up aggressiveness. He may give a preliminary warning to the supposed culprits or make an appeal for intervention to someone in authority before taking direct action himself, which, when it comes, may be in the form of an attack or sudden flight, either of which may be planned and executed with considerable skill.

Making Social Reality Conform to the Pseudo-Community

Paranoid patients who take aggressive action often achieve a pyrrhic victory. They succeed finally in making social reality act in conformity with the delusional reality which they have created. As long as a patient confines himself to watching, listening, and interpreting, he need not come into open conflict with the social community. But, when he takes overt action appropriate only in his private pseudo-community, a serious social conflict will arise.

Social reality is the living product of genuine sharing, communication, and interaction. Valid social attitudes, interpretations, and action derive continuously from these operations. The restitutional reality in which the patient believes himself to be participating has no counterpart outside of himself: it is illusory. Other persons cannot possibly share his attitudes and interpretations because they do not share his paranoid projections and distortions. Therefore they do not understand action taken in terms of his delusional reconstruction. The patient, for his part, cannot share their attitudes and interpretations because he is driven by regressive needs which find no place in adult social reality.

When an intelligent adult expresses beliefs and makes accusations which seem unintelligible to others, as well as threatening, he may make the people around him exceedingly anxious. This is particularly the case when his words tend to activate their unconscious fantasies and conflicts. And when such a person begins to take aggressive action, which seems unprovoked as well as unintelligible, he inevitably arouses defensive and retaliatory hostility in others. The moment the social community takes action against him, it provides him with the confirmation he has been expecting—that there is a plot against him.

Thus, in the end, the patient manages to provoke action in the social community that conforms to the expectation expressed in his pseudo-community organization. His own internal need to experience hostility from without—as a defense against being overwhelmed by internal aggression—is satisfied when actual persons behave in accordance with his projections. His need for a target against which to discharge hostility is also met. This is his victory and his defeat.

The defeat need not be final. Much will depend, of course, upon the patient's basic personality organization, particularly his emotional flexibility, his potentiality for internal change, and his residual capacity for establishing new ego and superego identifications. The depth and extent of his regression are also important, as are the fixity and the inclusiveness of his delusional structure. Much will also depend upon his potential freedom to communicate, to develop reciprocal role-taking skills with another person, and to include another's alternative perspectives in his own therapeutic orientation.

THERAPY

The primary therapeutic consideration, of course, is not the character of the delusional structure but what makes it necessary. A reduction in anxiety is among the first objectives. The source of anxiety lies in the regressive changes and in the threat these have brought of an unconscious breakthrough. But it is also aggravated by anything in the environment which tends to increase the patient's hostility and fear. Once the setting has been made less anxiety-provoking, the most pressing need is for someone in whom the patient can ultimately put his trust—someone not made anxious by the patient's fear and hostility or driven to give reassurances and make demands.

For the paranoid patient who is ready to attempt social communication, an interested but neutral therapist can function as a living bridge between psychotic reality and social reality. Through interacting with such a person, who neither attacks the delusional structure nor beats the drums of logic, a patient may succeed in gaining new points of reference from which to build a new orientation. The therapeutic process now involves another reconstruction of reality, one which undoes the restitutional pseudo-community without destroying the patient's defenses and forcing him to regress further.

As anxiety and the threat of disintegration subside, paranoid certainty becomes less necessary to personality survival. The patient can begin to entertain doubts and consider alternative interpretations. Such changes, of course, must come from within if they are to come at all. If he is able to work through some of the origins and derivatives of his basic problems, the patient may succeed eventually in representing to himself more realistically than ever before how other people feel and think. In this way the conceptual structure of his pseudo-community may be gradually replaced by something approaching the conceptual structure of social reality.

CHAPTER VI

Psychoses:
Affective Reactions

ARIETI (1967) INFORMS US that manic-depressive psychosis is on the wane and is no longer a serious threat, accordingly research in this area has decreased considerably. In New York state first admissions for manic depressive psychosis diminished from 177 per 100,000 in 1920 to 71 in 1950 (Kolb, 1968). Lehmann (1966) contends that depression is singularly human, absent in the animal.

In a factor analytic approach studying the phenomena of depression; Grinker (1961; Grinker & Nunnally, 1968; Grinker, Miller, Sabskin, Nunn, & Nunnally, 1961) noted the following factors: 5 feelings and concerns, 10 current behaviors, and 4 factor patterns that combine the two sets. The characteristics of the five feelings and concerns are: (1) hopelessness, helplessness, failure, sadness, unworthiness, guilt, and internal suffering; (2) concern over material loss; (3) sense of guilt and a desire for atonement; (4) free anxiety; and (5) envy, loneliness, martyred affliction, secondary gain, gratification from illness, and instilling guilt so that the world is forced to make redress. The 10 factors acquired from the current behavior list are (1) isolation, withdrawal, and apathy; 2) retardation, deceleration of thought processes and speech, and a disregard for personal appearance; (3) retardation of behavior and gait; (4) behavior traits of anger, provocation, and complaint; (5) somatic complaints; (6) memory impairment, confusion, concentration difficulties, and repetitive or limited thought content; (7) agitation, restlessness, and tremulousness; (8) rigidity and psychomotor retardation; (9) somatic symptoms (dry skin and hair); (10) ingratiating behavior (assisting others and expressing appreciation). The four patterns, a combination of the 15 above-listed factors are:

Feelings	*Behavior*
1. Dismal, hopeless, loss of self-esteem, slight guilt feelings.	1. Isolated, withdrawn, apathetic, speech and thinking slowed with some cognitive disturbances.
2. Hopeless with low self-esteem, considerable guilt feelings, much anxiety.	2. Agitation and clinging demands for attention.
3. Abandonment and loss of love.	3. Agitated, demanding, hypochrondriacal.
4. Gloom, hopelessness, and anxiety.	4. Demanding, angry, provocative. (Grinker, 1961, p. 228–233)

Suicidal preoccupation was infrequent in this research. In Dublin's (1963) findings, however, it was reported that suicide rates for manic depressives and those with involutional melancholia were far above the next two categories (cerebral arteriosclerosis and dementia praecox).

Studying the characteristics of persons with depression, Silverman (1968) noted that all types of depression were invariably more common in women than in men, but with regard to suicide among depressives the practice is more common among the males. Women with hysterectomies prior to age 40 have lower rates of mental illness than their female counterparts, and a low incidence during pregnancy (suggesting pregnancy's protective effect); but in postpartum illness, depression was frequent (Paffenbarger & McCabe, 1966). Bragg (1965) records less incidence of depression in women having undergone hysterectomy than those with cholecystectomy. Reviewing children (3-14 years of age) attempting suicide, Lourie (1965) discovered the absence of depressions, but the presence of situational depressions, a view confirmed by Jennings (1965).

In a comparison of distinguished characteristics of endogenous and reactive depression, Watts (1966) cites those of endogenous depression as: lacking an apparent cause, futility of psychotherapy, accompaniment by mania, presence of insomnia, stages of mood swing, disappearance without treatment (but with rapidity with E.C.T.), unaffected by environmental changes, and common in the obsessional hard-working type. Those of reactive depression are: an external cause, usefulness of psychotherapy, absence of mania, insomnia minor (though falling off to sleep may be difficult), minor mood swings, disorder alleviated with the removal of its cause, E.C.T. ineffective or detrimental, patient easily diverted from his symptom (e.g., by viewing an amusing film), patient usually the worrying type, and reporting ill (with regard to work).

Kendell (1968), utilizing factor analysis and criterion analysis of

Eysenck (1950), found significant differences between psychotic and neurotic depression, and between neurotic depression and involutional melancholia. The only difference discernible between psychotic depression and involutional melancholia was merely one of a difference of age, hence the recommendation that involutional melancholia should not be retained as a diagnostic category. He further concluded that "depressive illnesses are best regarded as a single continuum extending between the traditional neurotic and psychotic stereotypes" (Kendell, 1968, p. 83). Others (Bosselman, 1964) draw dichotomous or sharp distinctions among depressions as a normal reaction, a neurosis, and a psychosis. Frazier and Carr (1964) define neurotic depression in terms of the patient's ability to test and evaluate reality as being intact, while in psychotic depression reality testing has undergone serious disruption.

Kiloh and Garside (1963), experimenting with imipramine (Tofranil), also draw a distinction between neurotic and endogenous depression. Comparing 35 clinical features entailing symptoms and personality traits of 143 patients, their factor analysis indicated the necessity of two factors in order to account adequately for the data observed. Their review cites clinical features identifiable with neurotic depression and others related to endogenous depression. Buss (1966, p. 182) listed a table of the features cited by Kiloh and Garside for neurotic and psychotic depression:

CLINICAL FEATURES OF NEUROTIC VERSUS PSYCHOTIC
DEPRESSION

Feature	Neurotic Depression	Psychotic Depression
1. Quality of depression	Normal despondency	Abnormal melancholy
2. Variability of depression	Much	Little or none
3. Delusions	Absent	Sometimes present
4. Depersonalization	Absent	Present
5. Anxiety component	Strong	Weak
6. Neurotic components (hysteria, obsessive compulsiveness, etc.)	Strong	Weak
7. Diurnal variation	None	Worse in morning or evening
8. Concentration	Intact	Poor
9. Guilt	None or insincere	Intense remorse
10. Reaction to self	Pity	Pitiless
11. Weight loss	Variable	Invariable
12. Constipation	Variable	Invariable
13. Health	Usually poor	Good except during episode
14. Precipitating event	Clear and strong	Absent or weak
15. Family history of depression	Absent	Present

"The clinical features suggesting a good response to imipramine are some of those commonly regarded as characteristic of endogenous depression, while those suggesting a poor response are characteristic of neurotic depression" (Kiloh, Ball & Garside, 1962, p. 1227). Hodern and his associates (1965) contend that amitriptyline (Elavil) is preferred to imipramine because the rate of relapse is very low and the response high. Some researchers have found the response to imipramine unfavorable with paranoids (Pollack, Klein, Willner, Blumberg, & Fink, 1965; Wittenborn, Dempster, Maurer, & Plante, 1964), and damaging to depressed schizophrenics (Gershon, Holmberg, Matson, & Marshall, 1962; Greenblatt, Grosser, & Wechsler, 1964).

According to the investigation of orphans by Beck and his associates (1963) there is a larger incidence of depression among patients who lost their parents by the age of 16, and the high-depressed group comprised those cases where orphanhood occurred before four years of age. Beck inferred that "the death of a parent in childhood may be a factor in the later development of a severe depression" (1967, p. 227) in a number of patients.

Beck claimed that depressives misconstrue reality due to an altered cognitive function that produces erroneous conceptualizations. "If the patient incorrectly perceives himself as inadequate, deserted or sinful, he will experience corresponding affects such as sadness, loneliness, or guilt" (1963, p. 332). The interaction between cognition and affect spirals downward engulfing low self-evaluation, self-criticism, deprivation, exaggeration of difficulties. Such led Beck to the theory that thought disorder is common to all psychopathic disorders, particularly since depressed patients experienced distorted ideas immediately prior to the intensification of their depressive affects. He also offered the thesis that

cognitive distortions in depression result from the progressive dominance of the thought processes by idiosyncratic schemas. By superseding more appropriate schemas, the idiosyncratic schemas force the conceptualization of experience into certain rigid patterns with the consequent sacrifice of realistic and logical qualities (1963, p. 333).

Attitudes, beliefs, and assumptions, termed schemas, influence persons. In depressed persons, negative conceptions of self-worth, called idiosyncratic schemas, produce an unwholesome thought content that evinces feelings of depression, i.e., guilt, sadness, loneliness, and pessimism. The severer the depression, the more dominant are the schemas upon the cognitive processes and the more distorted becomes the cognitive outlook on reality, and the more downward is the spiral of depression. Hence, the fundamental thesis regarding depression is that "*certain idiosyncratic cognitive structures (schemas) become prepotent during depression, dominate the thought processes, and lead to cognitive distortions*" (Beck, 1964, p. 561).

Therapy indicated is that of orienting the patient's mode of self-judgment from one of deduction to that of induction, or from biased subjectivity to factual objectivity.

THEORIES OF DEPRESSION

Catecholamine Hypothesis of Depression. Schildkraut (1965; Durell & Schildkraut, 1966) developed a biochemical theory of affective disorders in which he links depressions to a depletion of catecholamines (especially norepinephrine), while elation is attributed to the excess of amines. From animal experimentation it may be inferred that

both major classes of antidepressant drugs are mediated through the catecholamines. The monoamine oxidase inhibitors increase brain concentrates of norepinephrine while imipramine-like agents potentiate the physiological effects of norepinephrine. Reserpine, a drug which can cause clinical depression, depletes catecholamines (1965, p. 518).

Although the hypothesis has a quantity of supporting evidence, at the present time its value is essentially heuristic.

Neurological Theory of Depression. Kraines (1957a, 1957b, 1965) developed a neurological theory of depression in which he based depression on "hereditary susceptibility." Hormonal changes account for depression. The absence of precipitating stress in well-adjusted persons indicates a physiological cause, as does the spontaneous remission, successful shock therapy, and the failure of psychotherapy to prevent recurrences or to shorten the length of illness. Furthermore, the ailment is precipitated in susceptible individuals by the intake of massive·doses of phenothiazines. Hypothalamic pathology is at the root of manic-depressive psychosis. The hypothalamus, excited by a stimulus from the cerebral cortex, stimulates the somato-visceral system which, in turn, excites the reticular system and the impulses eventually reach the cerebral cortex. This circuit being an emotional one, results in moodiness.

Campbell (1953) also offered a theory based on autonomic or hypothalamic dysfunction.

Integrity Theory of Depression. Mowrer interprets *promotion depression* (depression resulting from the reception of distinction, honors, new responsibilities; Lidz, 1968, p. 462), as a threat to one's integrity rather than to his dependency. Interpreting depression as an expiation of guilt resulting from the accumulation of moral transgressions against one's moral nature (conscience), the depressive is overcome by any crisis of life causing a confrontation with his personal deficiencies.

His unresolved load of guilt comes to *exceed* his capacity for self-affirmation and approval, then . . . we must once again recognize radical openness with the "significant others" in one's life, not only as the most effective means of "treatment," but also as the best form of *prevention*, as a *way of life* (Mowrer, 1964, p. 90).

What is called for is an action therapy which Mowrer terms *integrity therapy* (Drakeford, 1967), a form of behavior therapy based on the assumption that the patient has "stupidly" or mistakenly used as his personal strategy deception, denial, and "phoniness." Such a strategy must be superseded by one of honesty and openness, that is, by "sharing" and "modeling" through encouragement, persuasion, and inspiration (Mowrer, 1966). Inasmuch as guilt is a violation of one's integrity, "therapy should be aimed at exposing the *behavioral* source of guilt and encouraging its expiation" (London, 1968, p. 404).

Psychoanalytic Theories of Depression. Among the psychodynamic interpreters of depression patterning their ideas according to the adaptational or motivational model are: those who construe symptoms as a defense against drives (Freud, 1917); those who explain symptoms as the fulfillment of needs or drives (Abraham, 1916; Rado, 1928); and those who view symptoms as modes of adaptation (Adler, 1961; Davies, 1964; Rado, 1928).

Distinguishing mourning from melancholia, Freud depicts melancholia as a "regression from object-cathexis to the still narcissistic oral phase of the libido" (1917). A narcissistic type of object-choice typifies the melancholic. Transforming the loss of object into a loss of ego, and a conflict of the ego and the loved person into a cleavage between superego ("criticizing aspect of the ego") and the ego is Freud's explanation of psychotic depression.

Abraham (1911, 1916, 1924) believed the root of depression to be in feelings of hatred and hostility that diminish the depressive's love ability, a state emanating from unfulfilled sex needs. Regressing to the analsadistic stage and even to the oral stage, the melancholic, disappointed in pre-oedipal experiences in love and associating sex with nutritive gratification, resorts to autoeroticism to counteract and diminish depression.

Viewing depression as a desperate cry for love, Rado (1928, 1961) saw depression as a need for oral gratification ("alimentary orgasm"). The melancholic rebels with hostility against love, the factor behind his guilt, remorse, and reproach. The depressed individual, torn in opposite directions by coercive rage and guilty fear (with guilty fear taking the upper hand), experiences rage "vented in remorseful bouts of self-reproach." Contemptuous of inability to measure up to his expectations, he resorts to self-punishment. "This deeply hidden meaning of self-punishment from retroflexed rage makes mockery of the patient's remorse and reveals the real root of his sense of unworthiness" (1954, p. 153). With the loss of self-confidence, his adaptive degradation is seen to lie at the root of his depressive spell. Interpreting his condition as a threat of starvation, the patient like a hungry infant with excessive guilty fear and retroflexed rage is driven to expiation, that is, of punishing himself in order to regain the mother's loving care and feeding breast. The disturbance in melancholia "finds clamourous expression in the patient's delusional self-accusations and self-aspersions, which we call 'the delusion of moral inferiority'" (1928, p. 421). Thus is summarized Rado's theory of intrapsychic propitiation or adaptational theory of depression.

As for other psychoanalysts, Melanie Klein (1934) interpreted depression rooted in children as insufficient love; adult depression is infantile depression reactivated. Bibring (1953) construed it as a conflict raging within the ego that originates as a loss of self-esteem rooted in childhood traumatic experiences, frustration, and lack of love. Jacobson (1953, 1954), sharing Bibring's loss of self-esteem theory, saw in the childhood of the psychotic depressive an inability to tolerate hurt, frustration, and disappointment, utilizing denial as a defense mechanism, even to the point of reality withdrawal. Zetzel (1966) attributes the predisposition to psychotic depression to the failure of achieving psychological maturity, that is, the inability to accept the facts of reality and strive for realistic goals. One must recognize, master, and have a tolerance for depression as he does for other stress situations of normal adult life as a developmental challenge. Bellak, *et al.* (1952), comparing manic-depressive psychosis to schizophrenia, relate both disorders to extreme ego weakness; as ego weakness continues to develop, schizophrenia is the outcome.

ROY R. GRINKER AND JUM C. NUNNALLY

THE PHENOMENA OF DEPRESSIONS

INTRODUCTION

Experiences during and after World War II intensified an interest in psychodynamics by American psychiatrists leading to the development of stereotypes and a lessened concern with observations and description of clinical entities. On the other hand, the inadequacy of current nosological classifications stimulated the military psychiatrists to modify our systems of diagnosis (1). These efforts are continuing because of psychiatrists' resurgent interest in behavior. Studies on the therapeutic effectiveness of a hospital milieu and the efficacy of a wide variety of new drugs require rating scales for behavioral changes which cut across diagnostic categories. Clusters of traits became the source of classifications of types within the formal diagnostic categories.

When we became interested in the depressive syndrome, it seemed to have become the forgotten disease although about half the population in private psychiatric hospitals were admitted and discharged with this diagnosis. It is a self-limited cyclical affliction although each attack may last a long time without or even with treatment. The frequency, painfulness, and family disruption caused by depression stimulated little work with the syndrome and little has been added to its understanding since Kraepelin's and Bleuler's descriptions which were only somewhat better than the accounts left by the ancients.

Applications of psychoanalytic theory and methods had defined stereotypes of intrapsychic dynamics during depressive attacks and within the premorbid personality. Precipitating factors

From Roy R. Grinker and Jum C. Nunnally, The phenomena of depressions. In M. M. Katz, J. O. Cole, & W. E. Barton (Eds.), *The role and methodology of classification in psychiatry and psychopathology.* Chevy Chase, Md.: National Institute of Mental Health, 1968. Pp. 249–258. Reprinted by permission.

were attributed to events corresponding to dynamic theory, and contents of communications were stressed. These advances in understanding did not help in adequately determining the indications and contraindications for the modern therapeutic approaches of psychotherapy, electric shock or antidepressive drugs. An unfortunate by-product of focusing on the dynamics of depression has been the underemphasis on sound clinical observations and adequate descriptions of these and other mental patients. Most of American psychiatry is dynamic psychiatry and the word descriptive has become an appellation of derogation. As a result, the details of clinical syndromes are little known and the natural history of psychiatric diseases has been neglected.

When in 1954 we decided to take a "new look" at the depressive syndrome, etiological considerations had for long crystallized the classification of endogenous and reactive depression (2). Behavioral criteria maintained the diagnoses of neurotic and psychotic depressions. From these divisions nor from psychodynamic features could correlations be made with demographic data, physiological or biochemical variables, longitudinal course, recurrences, or therapeutic outcome. A new system of diagnostic classification of types of depression seemed to be badly needed.

Such a diagnostic typology is the basis of science which has been so successful in furthering advances in medicine. Empirically derived clinical types should furnish the basis for valid correlations with other systems as well as facilitate etiological and prognostic probability statements.

PURPOSE OF THE RESEARCH

The purpose of the research was to gain an understanding of some of the prominent trait-dimensions along which depressive patients vary with respect to their illness. Secondary purposes were to correlate those traits with background characteristics of patients and to explore some of the judgmental processes of psychiatrists with respect to depressive patients. Thus at the outset we had a "how" and a "why" as well as methodological questions.

SUBJECTS

All subjects in the research were persons who had been diagnosed as depressed on admittance to the Psychiatric Institute of Michael Reese Hospital. With whatever fallabilities may have been entailed, the diagnosis was made on the basis of the conventional psychiatric interview. At this point, neither patients nor admitting physician had contact with our research activities, and none of our trait measures was employed in the diagnosis. The aim of our research was to investigate the characteristics of depressive parties after they had been so diagnosed by conventional psychiatric approaches, and for this purpose we were willing to take the full variety of whatever types of people are usually diagnosed as depressive. By this method we would probably include nondepressives who would serve as controls and exclude a few only. In all, 117 such patients participated in our research, 21 in a pilot study and 96 in the major studies.

RATERS

Our studies were intimately involved with the measurement of behavioral characteristics from which later we might be able to develop more objective measures. It was necessary then to rely instead on human judgments regarding the behavioral characteristics of depressive patients. Those judgments were objectively recorded through the use of various rating methods, and they were objectively analyzed by statistical and mathematical methods; but nonetheless, one (feelings and concerns category) stemmed from the silent intuitive processes of the raters. The other (current behaviors) was derived from observations.

Since the research results hinge entirely on the particular raters employed in the studies, one naturally wonders to what extent the results can be generalized to other psychiatrists in other medical settings. A score of psychiatrists served as raters in different phases of the research. They ranged in age and experience from new residents to psychiatrists with many years of experience. It would be hard to estimate the effects on the research of whatever particular esprit there was in the institutional setting or of the background and personal characteristics of the psychiatrists. Some investigations were made of differences in our psychiatrists in reliability of ratings and in stereotyped conceptions of depressive patients. To our satisfaction two subsequent investigations made elsewhere have essentially confirmed our results.

PROCEDURE

From start to finish, the intentions of the research were to (a) obtain a large sample of persons diagnosed as depressive, (b) have ratings made of those patients on a large number of particular traits thought to be related to depression, (c) statistically analyze the ratings in such a way as to arrive at more general traits or factors, and (d) correlate those factors with other characteristics of the patients.

TRAITS

As much time probably was spent in gathering traits for use in the studies as was spent in the subsequent investigation of those traits. For this purpose, the major works on depression were studied, and from those were gleaned a very large number of particular attributes that had been ascribed to depressive patients, e.g., "feels hopeless," "dryness of the mouth," "dresses carelessly," "has dreams of suicide." In addition, many particular traits were suggested by the experiences of psychiatrists participating in the research. The criterion for including a particular trait was that it had been mentioned, observed, or reported by someone as possibly differentiating depressive patients from other types of psychiatric patients, from normal persons, or depressive patients from one another. At this stage the investigators were quite liberal in their inclusion of particular traits, because the main purposes of subsequent studies were to determine if those traits could discriminate depressive patients from one another.

A study of the traits suggested that they could be meaningfully divided into groups as follows:

1. *Precipitating experiences.* Events of recent history that may have pushed the patient over the brink into a depressive state, e.g., loss of loved one, major illness, economic loss.

2. *Dreams,* e.g., has frightening dreams, dreams of suicide (manifest content).

3. *Physical symptoms,* e.g., loss of weight, high blood pressure, breathes rapidly.

4. *Feelings and concerns.* The inner dispositions of the patient, which were necessarily inferred by the rater, e.g., feels a failure, concerned with death or dying, feels envious of others.

5. *Current behavior.* Either visible actions of patient (e.g., asks many questions, speech is accelerated) or traits that require only a low level of inference on the part of the rater (e.g., tries to be witty and charming, denies need for help).

6. *Meanings of the precipitating events.* Interpreted by the investigators.

Because the research mainly was concerned with psychological and behavioral traits, relating to depression, the major emphasis in our studies was on traits concerning "feelings and concerns" and "current behavior" (4 and 5 above). This emphasis was further strengthened by pilot studies of the other three classes of traits.

RATING TASKS

Each trait in the first three classes above was rated as either present or absent in each patient. In pilot work with traits relating to "current behavior" and "feelings and concerns," the Q-sort was employed. Although results from the pilot study were quite suggestive, because of psychometric problems with employing Q-sorts on materials of these kinds, conventional rating scales were employed in the major studies. Each trait was rated on a seven-step scale, anchored by "not present" and "present to a marked extent."

In the pilot studies, raters were, in comparison to usual standards, well trained to perform the ratings. They worked closely together on formulating the lists of traits, on applying the trait lists to a small number of patients, and on deciding the future course of the research. Also, raters in the pilot study were, on the average, more experienced psychiatrists than those who participated in the later study. In the pilot study ratings were based mainly on unstructured and structured interviews with each patient observed through a one-way screen by another member of the team who made suggestions for questions to be asked in subsequent interviews.

In the major study, ratings were made by psychiatric residents on the ward of each patient. The residents had far less training in the use of the rating scales than was the case for psychiatrists participating in the pilot study, but the residents had much more direct contact with patients. For reasons which will be mentioned later, there was much circumstantial evidence that ratings by residents based on ward contact were superior to those of the better trained raters in the pilot study.

ANALYSIS AND RESULTS

Results from the pilot study made it apparent that there was little to be gained from continued study of dreams and precipitating experiences, at least not by the methods we were studying them. Psychiatrists reported almost no dreams, even though they realized that they would be required to make ratings of dreams. Results for precipitating experiences were highly scattered: few were noted for each patient, those did not appear to go together in any meaningful manner, and none was related to "current behavior" or "feelings and concerns" traits. From these findings, and our continued thinking, we concluded that one precipitating experience is not systematically related to the behavioral manifestations of depression. Whereas there may be definite precipitating experiences (plural and cumulative) in many cases, almost anything unfortunate will serve for that purpose, and, whatever it happens to be, it is not predictive of the behavioral characteristics of the depression itself.

Numerous physical symptoms were noted, and, in most cases those were ones that typically are identified with depressive states. A reduced list of physical symptoms then was carried over into the major study. Those were combined with current behavior traits to form 1 overall checklist of 139 items, each trait being rated as either present or absent. Since in the pilot work most of the current behavior traits occurred with moderate frequency, most of those traits were retained for the major studies.

Most of the remaining pilot work and the major studies concerned factor analysis in one form or another. Except for one analysis to be discussed later, the analyses were of product-moment correlations. In some cases multiple-groups methods were employed to test hypotheses about supposed groupings of traits. In other instances the centroid method and the principal axes methods were employed as agents of discovery, the results of these being subject to rotation either by hand or by computerized analytic methods.

The first factor analysis was that of composite Q-sorts with the "feelings and concerns" traits, the composite sort for each of 21 patients being obtained by averaging the "sorts" by 4 psychiatrists. The three factors obtained from this analysis were helpful in composing a shortened list of traits for the feelings and concerns (from 111 to 47) rating form used in the major studies. Results discussed in the following sections will be from the major studies, in which the feelings and concerns rating form and the current behavior checklist (including physical symptoms) were applied to 96 depressive patients.

RELIABILITY

Because ratings notoriously have only modest reliability, it was necessary for us to make extensive studies of that issue. In the pilot study it was found that psychiatrists did not agree very well with one another. Surprisingly there was more agreement on "feelings and concerns" than on "current behavior." In other words, psychiatrists agreed more when it was necessary to make an inference about inner states of the patient than when the behavior was available to the naked eye. This told us, we think, something about the habits of psychiatrists in interview situations.[1]

Because of differences in rating tasks in the pilot study and in the major study, it was hard to make a direct comparison of the reliability of ratings in the two, but there was much circumstantial evidence that reliability was considerably higher in the latter. This was so in spite of the fact that ratings in the pilot study were by more experienced psychiatrists, more experienced professionally and more experienced in the purposes of the study. This probably echoes what has been found before about the reliability (and perhaps the validity) of ratings: the professional standing of a rater is not nearly as important as the amount and kinds of information available about the person to be rated. The psychiatric residents who made ratings in the major studies had considerable daily contact with patients in lifelike situations.

FACTORS AMONG FEELINGS AND CONCERNS

Five (rather strong) factors were found in the "feelings and concerns" ratings. There were some surprises, in that in a number of cases items loaded highly on factors where one ordinarily would not have anticipated their presence. Loadings on the factors are higher than those typically found for rating scales. Internal consistency reliabilities for groups of items used to define the factors ranged from 0.61 to 0.90.

We have established the existence of five factors, which are patterns of traits descriptive of the feelings and concerns of these patients. These factors illustrate aspects of patients, and, although they indicate what may be predominant for some, any single patient may show evidence of more than one factor. They are not mutually exclusive; nor do they attempt to illustrate all aspects of any single patient. These factors may be roughly characterized as follows:

(I) A factor describing characteristics of

---

[1] This finding has had a profound effect on subsequent research still in progress by Grinker, Werble and Drye on the borderline states in that observations and descriptions of behavior are being made by the entire body of attendants in a nursing unit around the clock, dictated in detail, and the resultant protocol rated by trained, skilled professionals.

hopelessness, helplessness, failure, sadness, unworthiness, guilt, and internal suffering. There is self-concept of "badness."

(II) A factor describing characteristics of concern with material loss and an inner conviction that this feeling state (and the illness) could be changed if only the outside world would provide something.

(III) A factor describing characteristics of guilt over wrongdoing, wishes to make restitution, and a feeling that the illness was brought on by the patient himself and is deserved.

(IV) A factor describing characteristics of free anxiety.

(V) A factor describing characteristics of envy, loneliness, martyred affliction, secondary gain with gratification from the illness, and attempts by provoking guilt to force the world into making redress.

The clinical interpretation of these factors suggests that factor I is the essence of depression, and hence its strength indicates the depth of the affective disturbance. The anxiety factor, IV, seems to indicate activity in the process and perhaps also a signal of mobilizing or declining unconscious aggression. On the other hand, the remaining factors indicate varying attempts at defense and resolution of the depression. Hence factor II indicates the projective defense; III, the restitution resolution; and V, the attempt by enslavery of external objects to deny anger, and secondarily to regain love. The control groups seem to show that the diagnosis of the depressive syndrome is contingent not only on the depressed affect but also on the presence of anxiety. In fact, in the presence of minimum sadness, anxiety is enough to weigh heavily for the diagnosis of depression. Finally, the nondepressed patient whose admission diagnosis was accurate has in common with depressions the factor of dependency and demand for secondary gain.

FACTORS IN CURRENT BEHAVIOR

Ten factors were found in the "current behavior checklist." Because of their number, and because their meanings are not all obvious, no efforts will be made to give capsule interpretations of them. After the fact they make sense (as most factors do), but we could not guess their nature in advance, and on seeing them no one is likely to say, "Just as I suspected." Also, on inspecting those factors one gets the distinct impression that they would be useful in describing any psychiatric patients, depressive patients included, indicating that there are a limited number of behavioral "final common pathways," whereas the factors found in the feelings and concerns traits appear more specifically relevant to depressed patients. Internal consistency reliabilities for the groups of items used to define the factors ranged from 0.64 to 0.86.

These factors tend to be less sharp and distinct than the feelings and concerns factors, which reflect our finding that behavior is an area of less interest to psychiatrists and that our behavioral observations are not as accurate as our observations of content. Like the other factors, they are not mutually exclusive, and any single patient participates in a number of factors. These behavioral factors may be roughly characterized as follows:

(1) Characteristics of isolation, withdrawal, and apathy; (2) characteristics of retardation, slowing of thought processes and speech, with little regard for personal appearance; (3) characteristics of general retardation in behavior and gait, but less isolated and withdrawn than factor (1); (4) characteristics of angry, provocative, complaining behavior; (5) characterized by somatic complaints, including dizzy spells and constipation; (6) characteristics which sound like an "organic" syndrome: impairment of memory, confusion, inability to concentrate, and limited and repetitive thought content; (7) characteristics of agitation, tremulousness and restlessness; (8) characteristics of rigidity and psychomotor retardation; (9) characterized by somatic symptoms such as dry skin and hair, along with some abnormalities on physical examination; (10) characteristics of ingratiating behavior, attempts to help patients and staff, appreciative for the interest of the staff and the facilities of the hospital.

RELATIONS BETWEEN TWO SETS OF FACTORS

After factor scores were obtained for the 96 patients on the 15 factors, correlations were computed among the factors. We were surprised to find that feelings and concerns factors did not correlate at all with current behavior factors. For example, anxiety did not correlate with agitation. This suggests that, to the extent that one can consider such ratings of feelings and concerns as valid indicators of the "internal dynamics" of depression, such dynamics are not related in any known systematic way to the patient's outward behavior. It appeared as though the outward signs were not really symptomatic of the depression itself but, rather, that they were expressions in a characteristic personal behavioral pattern of an inner distress.

CORRELATIONS OF FACTORS WITH BACKGROUND VARIABLES

The factors should correlate with something in the history of the patient, and, more important, they should correlate with what happens to the patient in the course of treatment and beyond. We were able only to make a few exploratory investigations of this kind. We found interesting differences on our factors between males and females, e.g., the former tend to focus on external concerns and the latter are dominated by guilt. We found that older patients tended to be higher on all of the current behavior factors, showing that older people are more prone to show the aggravated outward signs of depression.

One of the most interesting findings with regard to the patient's stay in the hospital concerned changes in diagnosis. We found a regular relationship between changes in diagnosis and our factor of anxiety. Patients who originally were classified as depressive but later were classified otherwise were rated originally as being high on anxiety but not high on our factor of "dismal affect." The reverse was true of patients who were not diagnosed as depressed originally but were diagnosed as depressed after prolonged hospitalization. It has been confirmed elsewhere that anxiety is not only an indicator of activity but also of elevated adrenocorticoid steroids, all of which are related to intense suicidal drives.

STEREOTYPES

At times in our studies we felt that we were learning as much about psychiatrists as about patients. Studies mentioned previously about the amounts of agreement about psychiatrists working with different types of information about patients were instructive in that regard. Special studies of psychiatric stereotypes provided other suggestive evidence. Using our rating scales, psychiatrists were asked to describe the typical depressed patient. Those ratings were factor analyzed (correlating psychiatrists with one another), and the loadings of psychiatrists on the factors were correlated with various aspects of their previous ratings of patients. We found, for example, that more experienced psychiatrists had stronger stereotypes than less experienced psychiatrists. Also, we found that the relative similarity of stereotypes for two psychiatrists was somewhat predictive of the amount of their agreement in rating particular patients. In studying the major factor in the stereotype it was obvious that "it" was a woman, a separate factor (shared by only some of the psychiatrists) relating to characteristics of male depressives.

PROFILE CLUSTERS

One of the final analyses in our studies was to investigate clusters of patients in terms of our 15 factors. Each patient was scored on each of the factors, sums of cross-products of those factor scores were obtained for all possible pairs of patients, and the resulting 96 x 96 matrix of cross-products terms were submitted to a centroid analysis. Essentially what was different about this analysis from more customary approaches to factoring is that it was a "raw score" analysis rather than the more customary analysis of correlations or covariances (3). The analysis produced factors, each factor relating to a type of depressive patient. The major factor was interpreted as the "garden variety" depressive, and the other two factors were interpreted as less prevalent types. Factor patterns were developed from the combination of 15 factors of both trait lists. As a result four factor patterns were elicited from which clinical profiles can be described to serve as fairly sharp hypotheses for future testing. The factor patterns are as follows:

(A) Feelings: dismal, hopeless, loss of self-esteem, slight guilt feelings. Behavior: isolated, withdrawn, apathetic, speech and thinking slowed with some cognitive disturbances.

(B) Feelings: hopeless with low self-esteem, considerable guilt feelings, much anxiety. Behavior: agitation and clinging demands for attention.

(C) Feelings: abandonment and loss of love. Behavior: agitated, demanding, hypochondriacal.

(D) Feelings: gloom, hopelessness, and anxiety. Behavior: demanding, angry, provocative.

IMPLICATIONS FOR DIAGNOSIS

The major purpose of our studies was to provide some understanding of the traits of depressive patients. To achieve that understanding, however, we were mainly concerned with central tendencies—central tendencies of all our depressive patients and differences in central tendencies of subgroups of our patients. Of course, even if one finds marked differences in such central tendencies, that does not mean that differences could be used effectively for diagnosis. In diagnosis one must take account not only of differences in central tendency but also of variabilities within groups. For example, as a group our depressive patients were moderately high on a factor relating to anxiety, and this helps us understand the modal characteristics of depressive patients. But our depressive patients varied markedly with respect to anxiety, so much so that it would provide only a small amount of discriminative information with respect to normal people. Similarly for the various subgroups determined by our factors: Such subgroups differ markedly in central tendencies with respect to the factors, but the variabilities within groups also are large.

USE OF OUR FACTORS IN DIAGNOSIS

It is possible that our 15 factors will prove useful in diagnosis, but, if so, there is psychometric work yet to be done with them. The reliabilities of some of the factors are too low to permit efficient diagnosis with them. More items should be added to some of the factors, and new studies should be done to determine if the new items are placed where they should be. In addition, the factor measures could probably be improved by clarifying the instructions and experimenting with different types of rating scales.

THE MEANING OF DIAGNOSIS

The problem of diagnosis is not so much a mathematical problem as it is a psychological problem. It is proper to ask "Diagnosis for what?" If diagnosis is to be more than a legal obligation, or make-work activity, then it should be relevant to the prognosis of the illness or, even more to the point, predictive of the effects of different treatments. In other words, any set of diagnostic categories should have to prove itself in terms of its ability to add valid predictive variance to that which can be obtained from less formal ways of making decisions.

Presently, the major problem is that no one can say what class of decisions is most relevant to a scheme of diagnosis. Should these decisions relate to (a) reactions to different types of hospital environments, (b) effects of different types of drugs, or (c) improvement in different types of psychotherapy? The diagnostic categories that might be valid with respect to one of these might be nearly worthless with respect to another, and the traits that might be required for forming diagnostic categories for one of these purposes might be different for the others.

One gets the impression that much of current diagnostic practice is not so much related to decisions about future events but is used to justify decisions that already have been made about patients. Thus, in justifying why a patient should be hospitalized, the psychiatrist can argue that this is because he is schizophrenic. In justifying why shock treatment was given to a particular patient, the psychiatrist can argue that this is because he is depressive. In justifying why a patient is allowed to go home, the psychiatrist can say that this is because the patient has a reactive depression and thus it can be expected to be transitory. In these instances, the impression is that the diagnosis was not so much instrumental in making the decisions but, rather, that the diagnosis was as much influenced by the decision as vice versa.

Another, and perhaps the most important, use of diagnosis is simply to provide a description of the patient with respect to important traits. If nothing else, this gives one some cognitive closure in dealing with patients, and, in an informal way, it probably plays an important part in daily interactions between psychiatrists and patients. In these interactions numerous decisions are made, e.g., to permit a patient to spend a weekend at home, but these decisions are so numerous and sundry, and different for different patients, that it is hard to see how they could be made the basis for an efficient scheme of diagnosis.

TYPOLOGIES

In thinking of diagnostic schemes it is difficult to keep from thinking in terms of types. Methods for clustering profiles essentially search for types, and discriminatory analysis is concerned with differentiating among a priori types. Unfortunately, people are not sympathetic to the mathematical requirements for employing such types, because most people prove to be atypical. This is evidenced in the major studies with the multiple discriminant function to date, where it has uniformly been found that there is far more overlap than separation among groups. Is there any reason to believe that mental patients will neatly divide themselves into "types" where the between-groups variance is large relative to the total variance?

It is however, difficult to keep from thinking in terms of types. We found it difficult to discuss one of our factors without thinking of how it would combine with other factors in an actual person. For example, we wanted to talk about the melancholic-anxious-guilt ridden patient. But to take account of all of our factors would require 14 hyphens, and long before that point is reached, meaning would be gone from the system.

SALIENT ATTRIBUTES

What usually occurs in actual diagnosis, and what may have much to recommend itself, is that a patient is described only in terms of salient attributes, and such attributes may be salient in two ways. First, attributes may be salient in that they are extreme in a particular patient. For example, if a patient is extreme only with respect to two of our factors, e.g., melancholic and anxious, then those two terms would offer a capsule description of the outstanding features of the patient.

Saliency in the above sense probably has been the basis for the presently employed diagnostic categories. For example, even though there may be other things wrong with him, if a patient is severely melancholic, he probably would be classified as depressed. If the most outstanding feature of another patient is disrupted thought processes, he probably would be classified as schizophrenic. Of course, atypicality alone is not the only aspect of saliency that is involved in diagnosis: The severity of the symptoms also is considered. Thus, if a person were equally extreme in terms of melancholia and disrupted thought processes, he would be classified in terms of the most dangerous symptoms and declared schizophrenic.

Attributes may be salient in another way; some of them may be much more predictive than others of the outcomes of certain classes of decisions. Thus, for example, even if we obtained 15 factors, we suspect that one of them, anxiety, is more predictive than the other of the course of the illness and the response of the patient to treatment. Saliency in this sense relates to multiple-regression models for predicting criterion variables, and this approach to diagnosis has much to recommend it. It is not bogged down in the psychology of types and it can be employed quite flexibly with respect to any forms of treatments where the outcomes are measurable.

MATHEMATICAL MODELS FOR DIAGNOSIS

In this section we will admit the future possibility of a computerized diagnosis for action and speculate about the most effective mathematical models for that purpose. The word "diagnosis" is so frequently linked with the word "classification," and the latter is so frequently mentioned with respect to discriminatory analysis, that it is easy to assume that the problem of diagnosis can be handled by the multiple discriminant function. If that type of analysis is employed in the usual way, it may not be the most effective approach. By "usual way" is meant that each person is placed in one of a limited number of categories and some utility is placed on the person's correct classification. This would be the case, for example, if each person is to be assigned to one of three drug groups. In that instance, it probably would be the case that many of the patients would fare much the same on any of the drugs and some of the patients would do very badly on any one of the three. Then if one must assign each patient to one of the three drug groups, it might be necessary to make some very bad decisions. To take an extreme example, it may be that the probability is high that any of the three drugs will kill the patient, but, since the probability is only 0.8 that he will be killed by A rather than 0.9 for the other two drugs, he is administered drug A.

One way to get around the problems inherent in classifying patients in terms of discriminatory analysis is to include a no-treatment group. Then, unless the person has a high probability of fitting in one of the other groups, he would be assigned to the no-treatment group. But in doing this one is, in essence, shifting from the logic of discriminatory analysis to the logic of regression analysis. In discriminatory analysis, each person is assigned to the group where he will perform better (no matter how good that is in absolute sense); in regression analysis an individual need be assigned to a treatment only if the predicted outcome is good in an absolute sense.

Multiple regression analysis probably is a more effective paradigm for diagnosis than the usual forms of discriminatory analysis for another reason. Discriminatory analysis (and related methods of classification such as the use of centours) starts with a priori groupings of people, and the effectiveness of the analysis can be no better than the original methods for grouping people. Of course the present problem is that there are no effective ways of forming a priori groups of patients, and thus there is no way of effectively employing discriminatory analysis and the attendant methods of classification.

One possible way to obtain important groupings of patients is through methods for clustering profiles, such as that performed in one of our studies. However, by this method groups are defined in a circular sense in terms of behavioral characteristics, and, although this may aid in understanding the present characteristics of patients it is not obviously relevant for the outcomes of decisions about them.

One way to obtain groups for discriminatory analysis would be by experimenting with treatments. Persons who respond much better to one treatment than another would be placed in groups with respect to those treatments. Discriminatory analysis could be used to differentiate those groups in terms of psychological traits, and, subsequently the obtained discriminants could be used for classification of new persons. In order to perform the necessary experiments, however, it would be required either to assign each patient to all treatments or to randomly assign each patient to one treatment, neither of which is practicable. In a sense, multiple regression would be hobbled with the same problem, but, with that method, corrections for restrictions in ranges would lessen the problem considerably.

If, and when, diagnosis-for-action is computerized, it probably will be based on the logic of multiple regression. In addition to its other virtues, it is free from questions of typologies and not dependent on the assertion of a priori groups. Although such an approach might be effective in a statistical sense, it would provide little help in understanding individual patients, for which purpose psychiatrists are likely to continue thinking in terms of salient attributes.

REFERENCES

1. GRINKER, R. R., SR., & SPIEGEL, J. P. *Men under stress.* Philadelphia: Blakiston, 1945.
2. GRINKER, R. R., SR., MILLER, J., SABSHIN, M., NUNN, R., & NUNNALLY, J. C.: *The Phenomena of Depressions.* New York: Hoeber, 1961.
3. NUNNALLY, J. C. The analysis of profile data. *Psychological Bulletin,* 1962, 59, 311.

47.

L. G. KILOH AND R. F. GARSIDE

DISTINCTION BETWEEN NEUROTIC AND ENDOGENOUS DEPRESSION

INTRODUCTION

In 1926 Mapother stated that in manic depressive psychosis we are dealing with "a merely quantitative deviation" from the normal, morbid only in its undue prolongation or if disproportionate or disastrous in its degree. He included anxiety neuroses along with mania and all varieties of depression as members of the manic depressive group. Perhaps these beliefs reflected the inevitable pessimism of a period when therapy was largely expectant and custodial. Somewhat despondently Mapother goes on to say "sub-division serves little purpose unless the types discriminated are correlated with differences in the unknown—for example in causation, prognosis and treatment."

In the 1930's there was considerable conflict between those accepting the traditional diagnostic distinctions and those who adopted Mapother's views; the arguments and counter-arguments are well summarized by Partridge (1949). It is interesting that these long and sometimes acrimonious discussions centered entirely on the problems of depression and anxiety. No one seemed prepared to follow Mapother to the logical extreme that any argument valid in the field of depression must equally be applicable to cases of mania.

Mapother's views on depression were made the basis of an M.D. thesis (1929) and of two lengthy papers by Lewis (1934, 1936) which still exert considerable influence on psychiatric thought, in spite of the fact that Mapother's "unknown" has undergone considerable contraction and correlations between the depressive

From L. G. Kiloh and R. F. Garside,"The independence of neurotic depression and endogenous depression." *British Journal of Psychiatry*, 1963, *109*, 451–463. Reprinted by permission.

syndromes and both prognosis and treatment are now possible.

Not only did Mapother consider it pointless to differentiate between a host of widely differing clinical pictures, but he found the task difficult in practice. Certainly, differentiation may be very difficult indeed; but this is no justification for saying that distinctions do not exist. It may even be that the two broad categories of depressive illness themselves are heterogeneous and as Kraines (1957) has pointed out, endogenous depression may itself prove a source of stress and provoke further "reactive" symptoms. These symptoms in turn may vary widely in form according to the personality of the individual, so that it is indeed difficult and often impossible, to evaluate accurately the various constituents of the illness. It is not as easy in psychiatry as in other branches of medicine to differentiate an illness from its consequences. Such difficulties reflect the inadequacy of our clinical methods and the lack of objectivity in our approach and should not be construed as a criticism of the nosological aspects of these cases.

The fact that certain symptoms show a continuous distribution throughout the clinical material does not imply that the material is aetiologically homogeneous. In the cases under consideration depression is continuously distributed, for the cases were selected on this account. A material may in fact be aetiologically heterogeneous even though the clinical features are identical—class A and class B mongols, which have only recently been differentiated by elaborate cytological techniques, provide a case in point.

Many of the clinical features observed in cases suffering from depressive states must be secondary in nature, and some, as Sloane (1961) suggests, may even be of a tertiary order. In view of the relatively small range of phenomena that occurs in the affective disorders, it is hardly surprising that a considerable overlap in the clinical features should exist.

The need for an adequate system of classification in psychiatry is not accepted by everyone as pressing, yet it is difficult to see how we can progress far without one. There is a common feeling—implicit in the writings of some of the authors already quoted—that knowledge of aetiology must precede classification. This of course is simply not true and as Cattell (1943) has pointed out forcibly, the reverse is the case —"nosology necessarily precedes aetiology." Eysenck (1960) reiterates the same inescapable fact—"before we can reasonably be asked to look for the cause of a particular dysfunction or disorder we must have isolated, however crudely, the dysfunction or disorder in question and we must be able to recognize it and differentiate it from other syndromes."

Semantic problems as usual have contributed to the confusion. Arguments about the validity of the concepts of neurosis and psychosis, of the meanings of such words as "endogenous," "reactive" and "psychogenic" served to obscure the basic issue. Sometimes—a reflection of the unitary approach—the word psychotic is used as an index of the depth of depression which may be described as "of psychotic intensity." The word "reactive" in particular has been a source of much fruitless discussion. It is often correctly pointed out that many attacks of endogenous depression are precipitated by adverse circumstances and are therefore in this sense reactive, but this does not necessarily indicate that the precipitants play an important causal role. The word "reactive" may also be employed in the sense that the depression is reactive—or responsive—to day-to-day vicissitudes.

Few of the terms we use are beyond criticism, and until aetiological factors are fully elucidated and understood it is difficult to see how a rational and acceptable terminology can be achieved. In the meantime, it is as well to make do with what we have and to cease to indulge in profitless arguments on this score.

In this paper the terms "neurotic depression" and "endogenous depression" are employed, as

it is felt that these are the best of an imperfect range available. They have the advantage of being understood, even by those who profess not to accept them. There seems little point in introducing new terms to add to the confusion. An exception occurs when other authors are quoted, their terminology usually being retained.

METHOD AND RESULTS

In the course of a double-blind controlled clinical trial of the effects of imipramine upon patients suffering from depressive states, a great deal of clinical and social data was amassed upon the patients treated (Ball and Kiloh, 1959; Kiloh and Ball, 1961). It was clear from the results that those patients diagnosed as suffering from endogenous depression made a significantly better response to the drug than those regarded as showing neurotic depression. A discriminant function analysis was carried out on the data from 97 patients all treated with imipramine, which showed that one cluster of symptoms correlated positively and a second cluster of symptoms correlated negatively with a good response to imipramine. The first cluster included items which many regard as characteristic of endogenous depression whilst the second cluster included items often accepted as features of neurotic depression. It was felt that these results suggested that endogenous and neurotic depression were distinct nosological entities (Kiloh *et al.*, 1962).

In order to test this hypothesis further it was felt desirable to carry out a factor analysis and the opportunity was taken to extend the clinical material, 46 further cases being added. These were mostly patients that one felt could be diagnosed confidently as suffering either from endogenous or from neurotic depression, using the same criteria as in the original group.

The entire material consisted therefore of 143 cases, in 92 of which the diagnosis was made with reasonable confidence (see Table 6.1). Of a total of 60 items assessed in each patient, 35 (see Table 6.2) were selected for further study. It was necessary to reduce the number of items, owing to the limitations of the Ferranti Pegasus Computer which was used to process the data.

TABLE 6.1

DISTRIBUTION BY DIAGNOSIS

	Reasonably Certain	Doubtful	Total
Endogenous depression ..	31	22	53
Neurotic depression	61	29	90
Total	92	51	143

TABLE 6.2

CLINICAL FEATURES SELECTED FOR ANALYSIS

Personal details
1. Age (when first seen)
2. Sex
3. Married at any time

Personality traits
4. Anxiety
5. Obsessionality
6. Reactive depression
7. Hysterical features; immaturity
8. Inadequacy

Previous history
9. Previous attacks of depression

Present illness
10. Duration
11. Mode of onset (insidious or sudden)
12. Precipitants
13. Depth of depression
14. Quality of depression
15. Reactivity of depression
16. Depression worse in early morning
17. Depression worse in evening
18. Self-reproach or guilt
19. Retardation
20. Agitation (Motor restlessness)
21. Weight loss of 7 lbs. or more
22. Suicidal ideas
23. Suicidal attempt
24. Subjective anxiety
25. Phobias
26. Irritability
27. Failure of concentration
28. Hypochondriasis
29. Hysterical features
30. Self-pity
31. Paranoid features
32. Variability of illness
33. Initial insomnia
34. Restless sleep
35. Early awakening

Definitions

Most of the terms used are self explanatory. Those requiring further elucidation are dealt with below.

Duration. In the case of patients having had previous attacks, the duration of the present episode was recorded.

Mode of Onset. The onset of the illness is described as sudden when it reaches its maximal or near maximal intensity within seven days. In such cases precipitants are frequently recorded. The onset is described as insidious where the evolution of the illness is slower than this.

Precipitants. Psychological disturbances clearly related to the onset of the illness and which appeared to the observer to play an important role in its genesis.

Quality of Depression. Patients may describe their depression as similar to "normal" sadness or gloom, differing only in degree: others describe their experience as something beyond normal experience, having a quality distinct from "normal" depression.

Reactivity of Depression. The depression is described as "reactive" (or responsive) when it responds quickly to environmental changes.

Retardation. This term is used inclusively to describe the subjective experience of slowness of thought or action and objective psychomotor slowing.

Variability of Depression. The depression is described as "variable" when the mood fluctuates markedly on a day-to-day or week-to-week basis.

A score of 1 was assigned to each clinical feature when present and a score of 0 when absent, except that in the case of the following features 1 was assigned to moderate or severe and 0 assigned to absent or slight: depth of depression, reactivity of depression, agitation, subjective anxiety, failure of concentration and variability of illness. Moreover, age was scored 1 for 40 years and over and 0 for under 40 years; sex, 1 for female and 0 for male; married, 1 for married and 0 for single; duration, 1 for one year or less, 0 for over 1 year; onset, 1 for sudden, 0 for insidious; quality of depression, 1 for different from "normal" depression and 0 if the same; 1 for depression worse in morning, 0 if not; 1 for depression worse in evening, 0 if not; weight loss, 1 for 7 lbs. or more, 0 for less.

Product moment correlations were calculated between each of the 35 clinical features and a simple summation factor analysis was carried out (Burt, 1940). Two factors were extracted and the correlation was calculated between the second factor loadings and the correlation coefficients between diagnosis and each feature. These diagnosis correlations were based upon the 92 cases in which a definite diagnosis was made out of the total of 143 patients.

The intercorrelation coefficients between the features are given in Table 6.3. The number of patients scoring 1 for each feature, the factor loadings and the correlations with diagnosis are given in Table 6.4. The first factor is a general factor and thus the first factor loading indicates the extent to which each feature is related to all the features as a whole, that is to depressive illness as defined by the sum of the 35 features. To test the hypothesis that the first factor loadings alone were sufficient to produce the original correlations between features, the statistical

TABLE 6.3

INTERCORRELATIONS

(Decimal Points omitted)

Feature	1	2	3	4	5	6	7	8	9	10	11	12	13	14	15	16	17
2	023																
3	174	-015															
4	014	139	097														
5	021	103	171	185													
6	-025	033	-041	349	257												
7	-225	060	-086	201	066	379											
8	-148	-093	-138	077	-135	235	387										
9	167	-017	094	079	-059	-043	-016	-065									
10	-069	024	-035	-191	-131	-100	007	-097	069								
11	-079	-033	-030	062	022	108	-001	084	-190	-131							
12	-124	-070	-074	-023	050	087	070	214	-234	-215	368						
13	026	024	090	-116	-164	-152	-055	015	-029	290	-071	-169					
14	093	006	074	-064	046	-087	-294	-214	018	215	-145	-221	111				
15	-133	-047	-031	048	059	165	271	290	-100	-287	059	328	-298	-209			
16	178	060	009	027	-166	-096	-186	-189	079	100	-166	210	132	239	-197		
17	-125	-013	-019	-149	-031	-020	046	102	-015	175	003	072	110	-104	050	-528	
18	-048	-003	-112	-193	-106	-028	037	093	167	039	-007	-135	003	010	-031	166	005
19	179	029	-026	-167	-200	-045	-126	-069	183	143	-104	-202	244	142	221	311	-063
20	147	092	-130	027	-041	007	003	080	139	-013	052	-004	018	122	080	106	057
21	029	-002	030	036	017	074	-183	-194	090	162	-106	-114	118	172	-186	196	044
22	-096	-007	-047	-060	021	120	037	148	-119	009	052	034	186	-034	-095	047	-012
23	-059	053	004	-096	-177	-078	-113	-085	042	-045	064	-017	038	073	-013	049	-123
24	087	059	-150	112	-010	092	109	014	-018	-072	-177	058	-106	060	130	-058	168
25	-002	134	026	139	109	123	090	130	-013	-161	077	079	-092	-079	120	033	-041
26	-122	-029	010	-006	036	124	-050	137	-043	-106	-081	111	-059	-037	288	-104	089
27	130	093	-041	075	-049	109	097	133	073	058	014	007	137	052	-093	090	007
28	082	047	074	-028	-065	042	140	070	001	-158	-096	070	012	-099	116	-110	024
29	-123	101	-207	093	099	183	354	197	-016	-201	133	101	-133	-167	142	-183	-024
30	-045	-094	-015	-047	069	033	197	017	-083	-223	069	282	-068	-218	208	-128	-013
31	-061	-038	-004	-117	-086	-089	-001	023	030	-018	-047	-096	075	023	-016	-020	-023
32	-225	-097	-177	-087	021	042	223	148	-072	-099	-010	202	-295	-026	477	-125	149
33	-026	157	-041	133	108	144	128	031	043	-114	014	007	-093	-067	203	-201	131
34	-053	020	-031	-124	161	175	012	077	-148	-076	065	178	-003	-027	098	-120	041
35	282	-026	-021	-093	-113	-158	-294	-214	141	186	-018	310	198	340	-507	416	-229

Feature	18	19	20	21	22	23	24	25	26	27	28	29	30	31	32	33	34
19	302																
20	227	075															
21	061	130	196														
22	184	127	218	090													
23	—009	192	049	104	257												
24	—010	014	212	—086	123	045											
25	—021	—008	—026	—146	082	—040	099										
26	096	030	—031	064	120	078	081	222									
27	173	279	149	017	309	164	117	052	125								
28	067	—112	091	—053	—073	—096	007	—099	—091	—142							
29	036	—159	171	—076	—038	—103	091	128	048	093	199						
30	130	—132	—065	—188	117	—069	059	006	326	—002	172	171					
31	197	067	052	060	075	072	—120	—123	103	071	176	062	079	088			
32	136	—220	077	—032	047	—063	135	004	187	—026	062	268	123	—037	207		
33	—135	—227	119	—012	108	108	117	111	052	—057	148	191	030	074	088	—180	
34	124	—047	—031	087	—003	—090	—071	—027	098	—001	022	180	149	—050	088	—304	—180
35	135	323	092	201	140	130	021	—049	—185	260	—187	—101	—250		—349	—304	—178

TABLE 6.4

NUMBERS OF PATIENTS SHOWING EACH FEATURE, FACTOR LOADINGS AND
CORRELATIONS WITH DIAGNOSIS

Clinical Feature	No. of Patients Showing Feature, i.e., Scoring 1	Factor Loadings		Correlations with Diagnosis
		First	Second	
1. Age 40 or above	100	—.017	—.250	—.376
2. Sex—female	102	.139	—.007	—.088
3. Married	128	—.120	—.064	—.027
4. Anxiety	68	.073	.156	.192
5. Obsessionality	42	.027	.201	.229
6. Reactive depression	31	.443	.311	.319
7. Hysterical features (immaturity)	41	.311	.409	.376
8. Inadequacy	33	.247	.315	.332
9. Previous attacks	47	.039	—.231	—.228
10. Duration 1 year or less	69	—.181	—.342	—.423
11. Sudden onset	42	—.041	.179	.286
12. Precipitation	90	.067	.476	.654
13. Depth of depression	76	.013	—.369	—.301
14. Quality of depression	53	—.027	—.389	—.523
15. Reactivity of depression	89	.179	.605	.666
16. Depression worse in morning	59	—.053	—.531	—.570
17. Depression worse in evening	44	—.062	.170	.294
18. Self-reproach—guilt	45	.347	—.198	—.191
19. Retardation	52	.193	—.547	—.522
20. Agitation	59	.485	—.170	—.166
21. Weight loss 7 lbs. or more	73	.127	—.315	—.239
22. Suicidal ideas	76	.459	—.133	—.038
23. Suicidal attempt	10	.029	—.231	—.184
24. Subjective anxiety	120	.244	.075	.082
25. Phobias	53	.178	.166	.198
26. Irritability	116	.288	.172	.261
27. Failure of concentration	87	.572	—.258	—.242
28. Hypochondriasis	82	.046	.120	.243
29. Hysterical features	38	.353	.366	.412
30. Self-pity	102	.145	.322	.457
31. Paranoid features	28	.079	—.080	—.070
32. Variability of illness	59	.196	.386	.444
33. Initial insomnia	87	.178	.237	.332
34. Restless sleep	51	.095	.145	.195
35. Early awakening	53	—.065	—.692	—.831

significance of the first factor residuals was estimated by calculating χ^2. This is admittedly an approximate procedure when used in conjunction with a simple summation analysis, but it is probably the best method available and has empirical support (Burt, 1952). Moreover, the value of χ^2 obtained, 1415 with 560 degrees of freedom, corresponds to a unit variance normal deviate (Fisher, 1941) of 19·7. This is ten times the value usually adopted (1·96) as indicating statistical significance. Thus the hypothesis that the data are consistent with there being one factor only is definitely disproved. The data cannot be produced by a single depressive condition, but must be produced by two separate conditions. These conditions may, of course, have some clinical features in common, as indicated by the first factor loadings, but they also differ from each other, as indicated by the bipolar second factor loadings. The sum of the squares of the first factor loadings is 1·833 and that of the second factor loadings is 3·518, and thus the second factor is more important than the first in producing the original correlations between the 35 features.

The bipolar second factor loadings in Table 6.4 are very similar to the correlations with diagnosis. The correlation between these two sets of figures is in fact ·986. This is very high, particularly as no rotation was carried out. Thus the bipolar second factor differentiates between neurotic and endogenous depression. No further factor was extracted; such a factor, even if significant, would be superfluous to the present issue.

The clinical features which correlate significantly (P < ·05) with diagnosis are listed in Table 6.5. The features are given in order of the magnitude of their correlations with diagnosis and according to the diagnosis suggested by the presence of each feature.

TABLE 6.5

CLINICAL FEATURES CORRELATING SIGNIFICANTLY (*p < .05*) WITH DIAGNOSIS, IN ORDER OF MAGNITUDE OF CORRELATION AND ACCORDING TO DIAGNOSIS SUGGESTED BY PRESENCE OF FEATURE

Diagnosis	
Neurotic Depression	*Endogenous Depression*
Reactivity of depression	Early awakening
Precipitation	Depression worse in
Self-pity	morning
Variability of illness	Quality of depression
Hysterical features	Retardation
Hysterical features	Duration one year or less
(immaturity)	Age 40 or above
Inadequacy	Depth of depression
Initial insomnia	Failure of concentration
Reactive depression	Weight loss 7 lbs. or more
Depression worse in	Previous attacks
evening	
Sudden onset	
Irritability	
Hypochondriasis	
Obsessionality	

DISCUSSION

The results reported in this paper indicate clearly that the group of depressive states consists of two separate entities conforming with those conditions known so long as "endogenous" depression and "neurotic or reactive" depression. A great deal of evidence exists which supports this conclusion and some of it is summarized and discussed below.

GENETIC STUDIES

There is considerable agreement that a single dominant autosomal gene showing incomplete penetrance is an essential prerequisite to the development of endogenous depression (Kall-

mann, 1954; Shields and Slater, 1960; Stenstedt, 1952). It is possible that incomplete penetrance may play some part in determining the mildness of so many cases of endogenous depression, a fact which accounts for much of the difficulty in differentiating them from neurotic depressions.

In neurotic depression the evidence suggests strongly that, as with intelligence, stature and personality traits, we are dealing with a graded phenomenon. Slater (1950) regards neurosis as a dimension along which variation may occur—"neurotics do not show the marks of pathological determinance, they are heterogeneous"—and points out that the genetic basis for such states must be multifactorial. Much of the work of Eysenck (1960) has been directed to the same end and provides strong support for this hypothesis.

It seems then that genetic distinctions have been established between the two types of depression, the one being a pathological variant, the other differing only quantitatively from the normal experience of sadness or gloom. Merrell (1951) suggests that the fact that heredity plays differing aetiological roles in these states might be of value in tackling the problems of differential diagnosis insofar as these may be reflected in "physically measurable differences between the normal and the abnormal." Some of the evidence summarized later in this paper suggests that in fact this may be the case. If the genetic basis for the two conditions differs it might be anticipated that they would show differing associations with other genetically determined conditions. Parker *et al.* (1961) have made the as yet unsubstantiated claim that the incidence of the type O blood group is significantly greater in the manic depressives than in patients suffering from neurotic depression. They have also found the incidence of Rhesus factor E to be significantly greater in the neurotic depression group than in either manic depressives or in the general population.

STUDIES OF PREVIOUS PERSONALITY AND OF SYMPTOMATOLOGY

In his elaborate study of manic depressive psychoses and of "reactive psychoses" most of which were equivalent to the more severe examples of neurotic depression referred to in this paper, Astrup *et al.* (1959) confess that differential diagnosis may be difficult and sometimes impossible. Nevertheless, they found that such features as ideas of guilt and inferiority and a positive family history favour the former diagnosis, and noted that such patients usually show a syntonic and well integrated personality, being free from neurotic traits. In the reactive group the illness was often coloured by the patient's life experiences and personality traits, evidence of a neurotic or psychopathic personality being present in the majority. Kay (1959) reached similar conclusions after studying a group of depressed patients over the age of 60 years. When cases were selected that showed retardation, severe agitation, ideas of guilt or self depreciation, nihilistic or hypochondriacal delusions, positive correlations could be established with a history of stable personality, good physical health and relatively little stress at the onset. The morbidity risk for manic depressive illness in first degree relatives was 10 to 12·7 ± 2·1 per cent. It was found that in these patients E.C.T. was the likeliest form of treatment to be selected. In the patients whose depressive illnesses lacked these clinical features, the premorbid personality tended to be unstable, and there was often a history of social difficulties or physical disease related to the onset. The risk of manic depressive illness in the first degree relatives was only 3·5 to 5·7 ± 1·4 per cent and E.C.T. was not generally indicated. Kay concludes that the latter group may be regarded as the neurotic depressions of old age.

Stenstedt (1959) in his study of 307 cases of involutional melancholia also found that these fell into two sharply delimited groups, the one consisting of cases of manic depressive illness and the other of "exogenous depression" characterized by low genetic loading for manic depressive illness and an onset related to stress.

Using a symptom-sign inventory, Foulds (1960) found that 14 of the 86 items recorded, enabled him to distinguish between cases of neurotic and endogenous depression. In 20 patients under 60 years of age diagnosed as suffering from endogenous depression the mean score was 6·85 (SD = 2·56) and in a similar group of patients with neurotic depression the mean score was 2·35 (SD = 2·94) (t = 5·7 p < 0·01).

Agreement with the clinical diagnosis was obtained in 90 per cent of the psychotic depressions and 80 per cent of the neurotic depressions. The differentiating items included ideas of unworthiness and guilt, anxiety, agitation, suicidal ideas, hypochondriasis and retardation. Application of the scale to 20 cases over 60 years of age regarded initially as suffering from psychotic depression more because of their age than on phenomenological grounds, produced a bi-modal distribution, 65 per cent falling in the psychotic depressive range and 35 per cent in the neurotic depressive range. The findings of these observers, Astrup, Stenstedt, Kay and Foulds, show a striking similarity, each achieving a cleavage in a group of depressed patients which corresponds closely to the classical distinction between endogenous and neurotic depressions.

Hamilton and White (1959) carried out a factor analysis on data obtained from 64 severely depressed patients using Hamilton's rating scale (1960). The first of the four factors obtained covered such clinical features as depressed mood, guilt, retardation, loss of insight, suicidal attempts and loss of interest. It proved to be correlated with a clinical diagnosis of retarded depression. The patients were divided into four groups depending on the presence or absence of precipitating factors—endogenous, doubtful endogenous, doubtful reactive and reactive. Significantly different mean scores were obtained for this first factor between the endogenous and reactive groups, the intermediate groups obtaining intermediate scores. This finding suggests that the two conditions differ, but does not indicate if the difference is a qualitative or merely a quantitative one. When plotted in the form of a graph, the scores showed a normal distribution but with two humps. It was felt that it might have been more definitely bi-modal had the number of cases studied been larger.

PHYSIOLOGICAL RESPONSES AND TESTS

Sedation Threshold. Shagass and Jones (1958), using the well-known technique of measuring the sedation threshold, have shown that cases of endogenous depression have significantly lower sedation thresholds than those of neurotic depression even though agitation is marked. In a study of 141 cases of endogenous depression and 94 of neurotic depression, the distribution of the scores showed a very marked bi-modal distribution. Boudreau (1958) and Nymgaard (1959), using a modified technique, reached the same conclusion. Others, it must be confessed, notably Ackner and Pampiglione (1959) found the sedation threshold test impossible to validate. Roberts (1959b) too could find no significant difference between the groups, but he used slurring of speech as an index of the threshold, a method regarded by Shagass as unreliable. Even using the less precise "sleep threshold" which dispenses with the need for an electroencephalograph, Shagass and Kerenyi (1958) found the same significant bi-modal distribution of scores when 30 psychotic depressives and 28 neurotic depressives were studied, though Martin and Davies (1962) were unable to confirm this finding.

The cycle of cortical excitability following electrical stimulation of the ulnar nerve has been investigated by Shagass and Schwartz (1961, 1962). Neurotic patients, including those suffering from depression, showed no difference from normals, but in 21 patients with psychotic depression the mean recovery time was significantly increased. After successful treatment this returned to normal.

The Funkenstein Test has proved more difficult to apply and less reliable than the sedation threshold test, though Sloane et al. (1957) found some indication of dichotomous results within a group of depressed patients. Roberts (1959b) failed to confirm Funkenstein's claims concerning the prognostic value of the test in cases of depression treated with E.C.T., though in a similar study by Hamilton and White (1960) the test results showed a correlation of $+ 0.26$ with outcome, a finding they regarded as being "disappointing, but suggesting that the test was worthy of further investigation."

Strongin and Hinsie (1939) developed a method of measuring the parotid secretion and found that if a secretion rate of 0 01 ml. per 5 minutes was taken as the dividing line, 23 of 25 cases of endogenous depression showed rates below this figure. Of 25 patients with other varieties of depressive states—these included some schizophrenics and organic disorders as well as examples of neurotic depression—the rate of salivary secretion was above this level in 24. Busfield et al. (1961) although finding no difference between cases of mild and severe depression, confirmed that the sub-division into exogenous and endogenous cases was correlated with significantly different rates of secretion, that for the endogenous examples being the lower.

The effects of methylamphetamine upon cases of depression have been shown by Roberts (1959b) to have diagnostic value and his findings suggest strongly that there is a qualitative difference between the endogenous and neurotic cases. The intravenous administration of 15 mg. methylamphetamine produced effects on mood, behaviour and symptoms. In all but two patients, either of two responses occurred, a "normalization" or an "intensification" of the symptoms.

	Neurotic Depression	Endogenous Depression	Unclassified
N (normalization) response	25	3	3
I (intensification)	1	16	0
Atypical response.	2	0	0
Total	28	19	3

$X^2 = 26.8$, Df $= 1$, p $< .01$
(unclassified cases and those with a typical response omitted)

An earlier study by Monro and Conitzer (1950) though not so conclusive, showed rather similar results. Cases of depression were arranged in groups according to prognostic factors established as the result of giving E.C.T. The effect of methylamphetamine was found to be poor, except in the final group, the members of which showed the highest number of unfavourable features, including duration of illness over one year, age over 60 years, and a poor previous personality with marked neurotic or psychopathic traits.

The work of Dawson also shows a dichotomy in a depressive material. Dawson, Hullin and Crockett (1956) demonstrated that the blood level of acetymenthylcarbinol (AMC), a breakdown product of pyruvic acid, was raised before and during the onset of a depressive phase in patients with manic depressive psychosis. Dawson (1960) and Anderson and Dawson (1962) studied 98 cases of depression aged under 65 years. A high fasting level of blood AMC showed a significant positive correlation with high scores for verbal retardation and preoccupation with ideas of guilt and self-blame. Such patients (type A depressions) tended to have higher scores on such features as general anxiety, specific or phobic anxiety, hypochondriasis, depersonalization, obsessive compulsive manifestations, and paranoid ideas. The high AMC level in these cases appeared to be related to Na + retention. The remaining cases (type B depressions) in which biochemical changes were slight or absent, showed clinical features corresponding to neurotic depression. Dawson emphasized that though the dichotomy was evident, it tended in some respects to cut across the usual diagnostic categories. There was, however, a broad correspondence between type A and endogenous depression and between type B and neurotic depression.

DEPRESSIVE SYNDROMES AND BODY BUILD

Although it is commonly accepted that a pyknic or endomorphic body build is associated with a propensity to manic depressive psychosis, few attempts appear to have been made to establish links between indices of body build and discrete depressive syndromes. Rees (1944) demonstrated an association between anxiety, neurotic depression, obsessional symptoms and a leptomorphic physique, as compared with the eurymorphic association found in a group of manic depressives. The patients were all males. The mean age of the manic depressive group was significantly higher than that of the neurotic patients, but it was felt that this could account for only part of the difference in physique. In a later study limited to females, Rees (1950) reached the same conclusions but admitted that the differences though significant were not sufficiently marked to be of diagnostic value or to have prognostic import. Hamilton and White (1960) measured the Rees-Eysenck body index in a group of 20 endogenous and 29 reactive male depressives. There was a correlation of + 0.29 between an endomorphic body build and a

successful outcome with E.C.T. Roberts (1959a), using the same scale, also confirmed a tendency for an endomorphic physique to be associated with a better outcome after E.C.T., this trend being more evident at three months than at one month. The correlation coefficient between body index and symptom score was in fact 0·617 at one month and 0·767 at three months, both being significant at the .001 per cent level.

RELATIONSHIP OF PROGNOSIS TO THE DEPRESSIVE SYNDROMES

In discussing the prognosis of the affective disorders, Lewis (1950) suggests that this depends upon the balance between particular intrinsic and extrinsic causal factors. He goes on to suggest that a history of a definite affective psychosis in the parent or grandparent indicates a greater probability of recovery from the attack, the suggestion being, therefore, that when "intrinsic factors" are stronger, the prognosis is better. Milder forms of illness, a group heavily weighted with those cases regarded as neurotic depression in this paper, he admits tend to become more chronic. These would seem to be two paradoxes which, if true, are surely without parallel in medicine.

In his well-known prognostic study of melancholia, Lewis (1936) was unable to establish any consistent prognostic signs, and when the series of 61 patients was arranged in order of prognosis, no feature or combination of features clustered at either end. It is important to bear in mind that no statistical methods were used to examine the data, and more important perhaps that the study was made before convulsive therapy became available.

It is in regard to the effects of the physical treatments, that the dichotomous nature of depressive states is most apparent. There is general agreement, much of it perhaps impressionistic, that cases of endogenous depression respond better to E.C.T. than those of neurotic depression. Some go farther and stress that E.C.T. may make these latter patients worse (Sargant, 1961). Kalinowsky (1959) suggests that the different response in these two types of depression may have diagnostic significance. Even when the treatment is beneficial in cases of neurotic depression, all too often its effects prove to be ephemeral (Kalinowsky, 1954). The series of cases described by Roth (1959) demonstrates the discrepant response with convincing clarity.

	Total	Symptom Free	Marked Improve- ment	Slight Improve- ment
Endogenous depression ..	64	45	12	7
Reactive depression ..	21	3	9	9

$X_2 = 21.07$, Df $= 2$, p < 0.01

If neurotic depression is merely a mild variety of endogenous depression, here then is a third extraordinary paradox to set alongside the two already indicated—that a mild condition fails to respond and may even be made worse by a form of treatment that is effective in severe varieties of the same condition!

Several investigations have been carried out to determine whether any of the clinical features which occur in cases suffering from depressive states have prognostic relationship to the outcome with E.C.T. Hobson (1953) recorded the presence or absence of 121 clinical items in each of 127 in-patients at the Maudsley Hospital. Features which proved to be significantly correlated with good outcome were sudden onset, good insight, obsessional personality, self-reproach and short duration. Those indicating a poor outcome were hypochondriasis, depersonalization, emotional lability, neurotic traits, hysterical attitude to symptoms, above average intelligence and a fluctuating course. Prediction of outcome of the illness based on these correlates proved successful in 79 per cent of cases. It is interesting to note the similarity between Hobson's findings and those reported by Kiloh *et al.* (1962). At first sight a glaring exception would appear to be "sudden onset." In Hobson's material, however, onset was described as sudden if the condition developed over a period of eight weeks. The two groups of clinical features show a reasonable correspondence to endogenous and neurotic depression respectively. It is interesting that Hobson himself gave no consideration to this possibility and in fact made no attempt to classify his patients in any way.

It would doubtless be of interest to carry out a factor analysis on his data.

Roberts (1959a) investigated 50 women aged 40-60 years all suffering from depressive illnesses regarded as justifying treatment with E.C.T. Using Hamilton's rating scale for depression, symptom scores were obtained for each patient before, and one month and three months after, treatment. He confirmed that Hobson's clinical item score was of value in predicting outcome and also that patients with high initial symptom scores tended to respond better to treatment. The clinical item score (Hobson) of these patients showed a correlation of -0.495 (significant at .001 per cent level) with the initial symptom scores. In other words, a high clinical item score tended to be associated with a low initial symptom score and therefore with a poor outcome to E.C.T. To obtain a high score on the clinical items (Hobson) a fairly large number of neurotic features must be present. As Roberts points out, it seems improbable, if the difference were merely a quantitative one, that marked neurotic traits would be so much more common in the less severely depressed patients. When the question of diagnosis was considered, it was found that none of the 20 patients with psychotic depression had a clinical item score (Hobson) over 5, whilst of the 27 cases regarded as suffering from neurotic depression, 20 had scores of 6 or more. Roberts concludes that this evidence strongly supports that there are in fact two qualitatively different groups of depressed patients; firstly, those characterized by low initial symptom scores on Hamilton's rating scale, a high incidence of neurotic features—and therefore a high clinical item score (Hobson)—and a tendency to do less well with E.C.T.; and secondly, a group in which the converse features are found. These correspond to neurotic and endogenous depression.

A paper which concludes there is no distinction between neurotic and endogenous depression, and which has exerted considerable influence, is that of Garmany (1958). Garmany groups his cases into the orthodox categories and his material consists of 295 cases of endogenous depression, 36 cases of involutional depression, and 194 cases of reactive depression. In each case he recorded whether constitutional loading (inferred from such factors as pyknic habitus, positive family history, and history of previous unprovoked attacks) or stress factors (including not only environmental stresses but "personal stress factors," in other words "those facets of personality structure which make living less easy but do not of themselves predispose to depression") were present. The age distributions were noted, and he also recorded the treatment recommended, including E.C.T. In regard to constitutional loading, the importance of stress factors and age distribution, Garmany believed there was no significant difference between the three diagnostic categories. This statement was entirely impressionistic, and, in fact, when his figures are subjected to statistical tests—even accepting his very loose and wide-flung definitions—there are significant differences between the groups of patients classified as endogenous and reactive depression in relation to each item.

	Endogenous Depression	Reactive Depression
Number	295	194
Notable constitutional loading	98	40
Not stated	5	17

$X_2 = 6.616$; Df = 1, p < 0.02

	Endogenous Depression	Reactive Depression
Number	295	194
Stress factors absent	64	11

$X_2 = 23.14$; Df = 1, p < 0.01

When χ^2 is calculated on the age group frequencies given by Garmany for the two categories it again shows a significant difference ($\chi^2 = 10.65$; Df = 4; p < 0.05).

In 109 of 295 cases of endogenous depression E.C.T. was advised whilst this same advice was tendered in only 9 of 194 patients with reactive depression. It was not known whether or not the cases in fact received this treatment and no information was available concerning its outcome. Garmany concluded that the distinction between these three forms of depression and particularly that between endogenous and re-

active varieties is an unreal one. If there is a fundamental distinction between the groups he believes it is only in regard to "the reactivity or the readiness with which the patient responds to the mood of the examiner." This quality he thinks "is used to determine the need for E.C.T., the risk of suicide and . . . the diagnosis." Lesser reactivity he equates with depth of depression— "this is different from saying depression is more endogenous." And yet as Roth (1959) has pointed out, it is a remarkable thing that when one uses the traditional division into endogenous and neurotic depression one finds that it correlates so highly with the choice of E.C.T. or psychotherapy. Moreover, as has been pointed out, closer scrutiny of Garmany's figures demonstrates further correlates between diagnosis, the amount of constitutional loading, the presence of stress factors, and age.

It is of interest to compare Garmany's figures with those obtained from a survey of mental illness in the North-East of England requiring in-patient treatment between 1957 and 1960. This demonstrates that the frequency of choice of E.C.T. and the response of those given this form of treatment show highly significant differences in the two forms of depressive illness.

	Endogenous Depression	Neurotic Depression
Total	1330	774
Treated with E.C.T. ...	1062 (79.8%)	359 (46.4%)
Symptom free after E.C.T.	513 (48.3%)	91 (25.3%)

Similar discrepant results have been found in relation to treatment by prefrontal leucotomy. Sargant (1961) emphasizes that the results of leucotomy are better in cases of reactive depression—that is in the patient who is nervous and tense and is thrown into depression by "difficulties in his internal or external life." In endogenous depression, although the attacks are usually modified, their periodicity may remain unaffected. The figures given by Partridge (1949) clearly show a differential effect. Symptoms persisted after operation in 20 of 61 cases of endogenous depression, but in none of 21 cases of reactive depression. Pippard's cases

(1955) show the same trend, a good result being obtained in 10 of 15 cases of neurotic depression and in 10 of 30 patients suffering from endogenous depression. The difference however does not quite reach the level of statistical significance.

Elithorn (1959) found himself in agreement with Partridge and Pippard and concluded that his results support the view that "some endogenous depressions are prognostically and aetiologically distinct from most reactive depressions." The group of cases subjected to leucotomy is, of course, a very highly selected one, the great majority having been subjected to all other forms of treatment without avail.

The discrepant response of cases of endogenous depression and neurotic depression to imipramine have been referred to earlier. When cases were selected in which the diagnosis could be made with confidence, it was found that all but one of 15 cases of endogenous depression responded well to imipramine within four weeks and remained well after six months, whereas only 16 of 32 cases of neurotic depression were improved after four weeks and 5 of these had relapsed within six months. (At 4 weeks $\chi^2 = 6.54$; $p < 0.02$: at 6 months $\chi^2 = 11.99$; $p < 0.01$; Kiloh *et al.*, 1962). Ibor (1962) found that 51.2 per cent of 125 patients suffering from depressive states responded to imipramine, but when cases of "vital depression"—that is, typical endogenous depression—were selected, the response rate was found to be 84.5 per cent suggesting that the "vital" types of depression are much more responsive to pharmacological treatment. Similar findings have been achieved with other drugs. In an uncontrolled pilot study of the effects of a dibenzazepine compound (G.33 040) on a mixed group of depressions it was found that cases of endogenous depression did significantly better than cases of neurotic depression (Kiloh *et al.*, 1962).

	Endogenous Depression	Neurotic Depression
Total number of cases...	28	34
Good result at 3 weeks..	16 (57%)	8 (24%)
Good result at 3 months.	12 (43%)	4 (12%)

3 weeks = $\chi^2 = 5.71$; Df = 1; $p < 0.02$
3 mths. = $\chi^2 = 6.21$; Df = 1; $p < 0.02$

Harrington and Imlah (1960) reported comparable results following the use of phenelzine.

	Endogenous Depression	Neurotic Depression
Total number of cases ..	54	28
Recovered or much improved	38 (70%)	7 (25%)
Improved or no change.	16 (30%)	21 (75%)

$\chi^2 = 13.55$; Df = 1; $p < 0.01$

CONCLUSIONS

This survey of the literature shows that a considerable number of studies have been carried out, each pointing to the same conclusion. Not all those quoted are equally valid or important, but together they constitute a mass of evidence consistent with and supporting the traditional dichotomy of depressive cases into neurotic and endogenous varieties—a division strongly supported by the findings reported in this paper.

There may once have been some justification for refusing to distinguish one depressive patient from another—pessimistic and unrealistic though this may have been. Now on the contrary there is every reason to make the distinction for the choice of treatment and the accurate assessment of prognosis is dependent upon it. Unfortunately, although the importance of the distinction has become more apparent over the years it has scarcely become any easier, dependent as we are on our fallible clinical methods.

The emphasis should now be on the greater refinement of these methods and on the development of objective tests which would aid the differentiation of those cases which for one reason or another show mixed features and are a source of such diagnostic difficulties.

Acknowledgements

We are deeply indebted to Professor Martin Roth for his advice and encouragement. We are grateful to Dr. E. S. Page, Director of the Computing Laboratory, University of Durham, Miss E. D. Barraclough, computer operator, and Miss S. O. Allison for their help in processing the data.

REFERENCES

ACKNER, B., & PAMPIGLIONE, G. *Journal of Psychosomatic Research*, 1959, 3, 271.

ASTRUP, C., FOSSUM, A., & HOLMBOE, R. *Acta Psychiatrica et Neurologica Scandinavica*, 1959, *34*, Supp. 135.

ANDERSON, W. McC., & DAWSON, J. *Journal of Mental Science*, 1962, *108*, 80.

BALL, J. R. B., & KILOH, L. G. *British Medical Journal*, 1959, *2*, 1052.

BOUDREAU, D. *Archives of Neurology and Psychiatry*, 1958, *80*, 771.

BURT, C. *The factors of the mind*. London: University of London Press, 1940.

BURT, C. *British Journal of Psychology*, 1952, stat. Sect., *5*, 109.

BUSFIELD, B. L., WECHSLER, H., & BARNUM, W. J. *Archives of General Psychiatry*, 1961, *5*, 472.

CATTELL, R. B. *Psychological Review*, 1943, *50*, 559.

DAWSON, J. Biochemistry of depression. In *Final Report on the Symposium on Depression*, held at Royal College of Surgeons, 24 May 1960, p. 24.

DAWSON, J., HULLIN, R. P., & CROCKETT, B. M. *Journal of Mental Science*, 1956, *102*, 168.

ELITHORN, A. *Proceedings of the Royal Society of Medicine*, 1959, *52*, 203.

EYSENCK, H. J. Classification and the problem of diagnosis. In H. J. Eysenck (Ed.) *Handbook of abnormal psychology*. London: Pitman, 1960.

FISHER, R. A. *Statistical methods for research workers*. (8th Ed.) Edinburgh: Oliver & Boyd, 1941.

FOULDS, G. A. *Journal of Mental Science*, 1960, *106*, 1394.

GARMANY, G. *British Medical Journal*, 1958, *2*, 341.

HAMILTON, M. *Journal of Neurological and Neurosurgical Psychiatry*, 1960, *23*, 56.

HAMILTON, M., & WHITE, J. M. *Journal of Mental Science*, 1960, *106*, 1031.

HAMILTON, M., & WHITE, J. M. *Journal of Mental Science*, 1959, *105*, 985.

HARRINGTON, J., & IMLAH, N. W. A preliminary evaluation of phenelzine in a neurosis unit. In *Final Report of the Symposium on Depression*, held at Royal College of Surgeons, 24 May 1960, p. 55.

HOBSON, R. F. *Journal of Neurological and Neurosurgical Psychiatry*, 1953, *16*, 275.

IBOR, J. L. *Comprehensive Psychiatry*, 1962, *3*, 15.

KALINOWSKY, L. B. Some problems in electric convulsive therapy of depression. In P. H. Hoch and J. Zubin (Eds.) *Depression*. New York: Grune & Stratton, 1954, p. 190.

KALINOWSKY, L. B. *Canadian Psychiatry Association Journal* (Spec. Supplement) 1959, *4*, S, 138.

KALLMANN, F. J. Genetic principles in manic-depressive psychosis. In P. H. Hoch and J. Zubin (Eds.) *Depression*. New York: Grune & Stratton, 1954, p. 1.

KAY, D. *Proceedings of the Royal Society of Medicine*, 1959, *52*, 791.

KILOH, L. G., & BALL, J. R. B. *British Medical Journal*, 1961, *1*, 168.

KILOH, L. G., BALL, J. R. B., & GARSIDE, R. F. *British Medical Journal*, 1962, *1*, 1225.

KILOH, L. G., ROY, J. R., & CARNEY, M. W. P. *Journal of Neuropsychiatry*, 1963.

KRAINES, S. H. *Mental depressions and their treatment*. New York: Macmillan, 1957.

LEWIS, A. J. A clinical and historical survey of depressive states based on the study of 61 cases. M. D. Thesis. University of Adelaide, 1929.

LEWIS, A. J. *Journal of Mental Science*, 1934, *80*, 277.

LEWIS, A. J. *Journal of Mental Science*, 1936, *82*, 488.

LEWIS, A. J. Psychological medicine. In F. W. Price (Ed.) *A textbook of the practice of medicine*. Sec. XX (8th ed.). London: Oxford University Press, 1950, Pps. 1924 and 1933.

MAPOTHER, E. *British Medical Journal*, 1926, *2*, 872.

MARTIN, I., & DAVIES, B. M. *Journal of Mental Science*, 1962, *108*, 466.

MERRELL, D. J. *Archives of General Psychiatry*, 1951, *66*, 272.

MONRO, A. B., & CONITZER, H. *Journal of Mental Science*, 1950, *96*, 1037.

NYMGAARD, K. *Archives of Neurological Psychiatry*, 1959, *1*, 530.

PARKER, J. B., THEILIE, A., & SPIELBERGER, C. D. *Journal of Mental Science*, 1961, *107*, 936.

PARTRIDGE, M. *Journal of Mental Science*, 1949, *95*, 795.

PIPPARD, J. *Journal of Mental Science*, 1955, *101*, 756.

REES, W. L. *Proceedings of the Royal Society of Medicine*, 1944, *37*, 635.

REES, W. L. *Journal of Mental Science*, 1950, *96*, 426.

ROBERTS, J. M. *Journal of Mental Science*, 1959, *105*, 683. (a)

ROBERTS, J. M. *Journal of Mental Science*, 1959, *105*, 703. (b)

ROTH, M. *Canadian Psychiatric Journal* (Spec. Supplement), 1959, *4*, S. 32.

ROTH, M. *Comprehensive Neuropsychiatry*, 1960, *1*, 135.

SARGANT, W. *Journal of Neuropsychiatry*, 1961, *2*, Suppl. 1, S. 1.

SHAGASS, C., & JONES, A. L. *American Journal of Psychiatry*, 1958, *114*, 1002.

SHAGASS, C., & KERENYI, A. *Canadian Psychiatry Association Journal*, 1958, *3*, 101.

SHAGASS, C., & SCHWARTZ, M. *Abstracts*—3rd World

Congress of Psychiatry, Montreal, 1961, Part 1, p. 76.

SHAGASS, C., & SCHWARTZ, M. *Archives of General Psychiatry,* 1962, *6,* 235.

SLATER, E. The genetical aspects of personality and neurosis: In *Congrès International de Psychiatrie,* Paris. VI: *Psychiatrie sociale,* 1950. P. 119.

SHIELDS, J., & SLATER, E. Heredity and psychological abnormality. In H. J. Eysenck (Ed.) *Handbook of abnormal psychology.* London: Pitman, 1960.

SLOANE, R. B., *Journal of Neuropsychiatry,* 1961, *5,* (Suppl. No. 1), S. 11.

SLOANE, R. B., LEWIS, D. J., & SLATER, P. *Archives of Neurology and Psychiatry,* 1957, *77,* 540.

STENSTEDT, A. *Acta Psychiatrica et Neurologica Scandinavica,* 1952, *27* (Supp.), 79.

STENSTEDT, A. *Acta Psychiatrica et Neurologica Scandinavica,* 1959, *34,* Supp. 127.

STRONGIN, E. I., & HINSIE, L. E. *Psychiatry Quarterly,* 1939, *13,* 697.

48.

S. H. KRAINES

NEUROLOGICAL THEORY OF DEPRESSION

Psychopathology of the Manic Depressive Syndrome. The manic depressive syndrome (3) is a self-limiting disease manifested primarily by alterations in mood, rate of intellectual activity, somatic symptoms, and secondarily by psychopathology. Clinically, this syndrome appears to be physiologic in origin, neurophysiologic evidence suggesting that it may result from hypothalamic pathology. In archetypical form, the depressive illness begins insidiously and follows a gradually descending cycle until the nadir is reached; the cycle is then reversed, with gradual improvement until the patient's normal baseline is reached. The depressive cycle is divided into six phases, each phase having characteristic symptoms. (Figure 6.1) There are innumerable variations not only from patient to patient but from one episode to another in the same patient. The manic cycle is a mirror image of the depressive cycle.

From S. H. Kraines,"Manic depressive syndrome: a physiologic disease."*Diseases of the Nervous System,* 1966, *27,* 573–582, 670–676. Presented at American Psychiatric Association meeting May 6, 1965. The present selection begins with p. 576. Reprinted from *The American Journal of Psychiatry,* Vol. 114, pp. 206–211, 1957. Copyright 1957, The American Psychiatric Association.

THE PHYSIOLOGIC BASIS

Studies of the etiologic factors, course, and therapy indicate that the manic depressive illness is an endogenous physiologic disease.

The etiologic factors include:

1. A frequent history of hereditary susceptibility (4)—especially in identical twins (7).

2. Hormonal changes such as occur in:

a) The frequent onset of post-partum depressions (13) in hitherto well-adjusted women

b) Depressions-in-miniature in the premenstrual phase, disappearing with the onset of menses

c) The greater frequency of manic attacks in youth, (14) and depressive attacks later in life, reflecting existing levels of biologic energy

The *course* of the illness which suggests a physiologic basis includes:

3. Onset in well-adjusted personalities

4. Onset frequently without significant precipitating stress

5. Basically identical onset, symptoms, and course in the majority of patients despite their otherwise radical difference in culture, status, etc.

The *therapeutic results* which suggest a physiologic basis include:

6. Spontaneous termination of the illness in the absence of *any* therapy

7. Failure of psychotherapy or psychoanalysis to shorten the illness or to prevent recurrences

8. Beneficial results of such physical therapies as drugs and electric shock

Confirmatory evidence is offered by:

9. Seasonal influence, with peak periods of onset in the spring or the fall of the year, (3, 15) and

10. Precipitation of a depressive syndrome in susceptible persons by the use of large doses of phenothiazines (16, 17) and reserpine (3).

Even the psychologic manifestations of this diencephalic disease are determined by the fact that emotion itself is essentially a physiologic process.

HYPOTHALAMIC PHYSIO-PATHOLOGY

The thesis is advanced that *a persistent, intensifying inhibition of hypothalamic function* is the mechanism of a depressive syndrome and that a *gradually increasing excitation of this area* produces the manic state.

This hypothesis is based not only on clinical evidence suggesting a physiologic basis for the illness but also on neurophysiologic studies indicating the importance of the hypothalamus in emotional expression; on theoretical considerations of the emotional circuit; and on the therapeutic benefits from stimulation of the hypothalamus by such drugs as the amphetamines and the MAO inhibitors and also by shock therapy. The drugs which are of benefit in the manic phase (e.g., the phenothiazine group) decrease the sympathetic activity of the hypothalamus (2, 16).

Neurohormones, particularly the catecholomines, play a major role in activating the hypothalamus and the emotional circuit. Norepinephrine energizes the ergotropic system (energy expression, alertness, and "drive"); acetylcholine and serotonin, the trophotropic system (energy conservation, relaxation "passive" pleasure). The adrenal hormones (medullary epinephrine and cortical steroids) activate that portion of the sympathetic system associated with stress, fear, and flight.

Clinical experience supports the neurophysiologic studies:

1. Drugs which increase the availability of nor-epinephrine (6) increase ergotropic activity

2. Drugs which diminish nor-epinephrine secretion (phenothiazines) decrease ergotropic function

3. Drugs which increase the availability of serotonin (reserpine) produce relaxation (19)

4. Clinical signs of fear (tachycardia, dry mouth, dilated pupils, etc.) indicate excessive secretion of epinephrine.

It is therefore postulated that the depressive states result from decreasingly available nor-epinephrine and increasing epinephrine secretion. Moreover, the nor-epinephrine-epinephrine ratio is altered (17, 20); there is both a relative and an absolute decrease in nor-epinephrine and a relative and absolute increase in circulating epinephrine. The converse is true in the manic states.

Although the physiologic dysfunction of the hypothalamus explains the *mechanisms* of the manic depressive states, the etiology lies elsewhere. Psychic stress only occasionally precipitates the manic depressive illness.

PATHOLOGY OF THE EMOTIONAL CIRCUIT

At least five components influence the type of symptoms found in the manic depressive illness: (1) central sympathetic, (2) central parasympathetic, (3) adrenal, (4) hormonal and (5) symbolic (psychopathologic) activity. The impact of any one of these factors varies from person to person, and with different phases of the illness. Any one of these factors may synergize, negate, or reverse the activity of another factor.

Central Sympathetic Activity. The posterior hypothalamus is essentially sympathetic in action (2, 5); its chemical mediator is nor-epinephrine (4) which it secretes in large quantities (10). One of its functions is ergotropic activity. The clinical course of the depression suggests the following physiologic pattern.

TABLE 6.6
PHASES OF THE DEPRESSIVE CYCLE

Phase I

Clinical:

Boredom
Indecisiveness
Hypersomnia
Vague psychosomatic symptoms
Morning depression evening alertness

Physiologic:

"Troughs" of sympathetic inhibition
Overcompensatory parasympathetic activity

Phase II

Clinical:

Depression
Crying spells
Phobias
Intense psychosomatic symptoms
Insomnia
Anorexia
Unreality feelings
Weight loss

Physiologic:

Marked sympathetic inhibition
Parasympathetic peaks
Increased adrenal activity
Thalamic dysfunction

Phases III & IV

Clinical:

Deep melancholia
Inability to cry
Moaning with emotional pain
Intense anorexia
Intractable insomnia
Nihilistic delusions

Physiologic:

Marked inhibition of entire
diencephalon
Diminished adrenal activity

Phase V

Clinical:

Anxiety with depression
Irritability
Physical inertia alternating with
restlessness
Weight gain
Complaint: "I cannot love or hate"
Peaks of improvement (for days and deep
troughs of despair)
Unreality feelings
Transient peptic ulcer
Transient hypertension

Physiologic:

Wide "homeostatic" hypothalamic swings
Peak sympathetic and
Peak parasympathetics "bursts"
Increased adrenal activity

Phase VI

Clinical:.

Long periods (weeks) of improvement
alternating with long periods of anxiety-
depression with anorexia, weight loss,
fatigue
Hypersomnia
Transient and shifting psychosomatic
symptoms
Evening depression morning alertness

Physiologic:

Increasing stability of hypothalamic activity
Epinephrine-Nor-epinephrine stabilizing

Early in the depressive cycle, there is minimal decrease in nor-epinephrine secretion (18)—and the patient is subject to minimal fatigue, minimal depression (boredom, disinterest), minimal indecisiveness. (Table 6.6.) The active homeostatic mechanism in this phase results in compensatory peaks of nor-epinephrine with short peaks of "normalcy." When the existing depressive trough is followed by compensatory overproduction of this hormone, there occurs a brief period of increased activity and excitability.

As the hypothalamic inhibition intensifies, nor-epinephrine becomes less and less available until an "exhaustion" of this neurohormone occurs. The patient becomes completely anergic, without energy to move, "think," talk; he is completely depressed. At this level there is minimal homeostatic activity and hence minimal fluctuations in mood. Shock therapy (8, 21) and drugs (e.g. MAO inhibitors) (6) which increase nor-epinephrine activity elevate mood; drugs which depress sympathetic activity depress mood (16, 18).

The nadir of the depression, having passed

FIGURE 6.1
The Manic Depressive Cycle

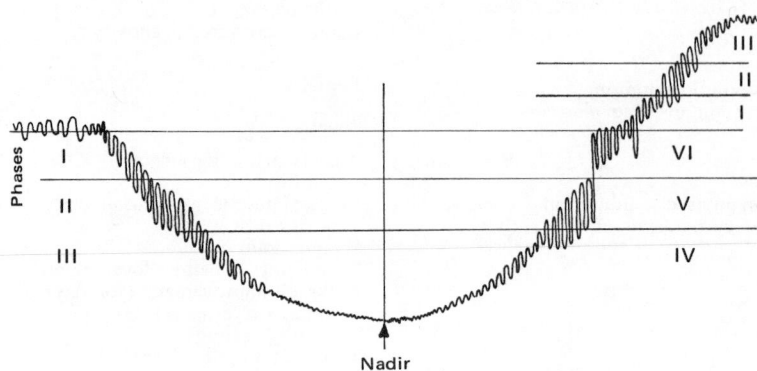

and recovery forces (hereditary and/or hormonal) having resumed operation, the hypothalamus becomes more active. Nor-epinephrine again becomes sporadically available so that recovery occurs in peaks with many intervening troughs. In the middle of the ascending curve (the 5th phase) the peaks of nor-epinephrine secretion are expressed clinically by bursts of energy. Increased nor-epinephrine in combination with increased adrenalin produces irritability. Occasionally, there is a transitory elevation of blood pressure. Each peak is followed by a trough, minimal production of this hormone resulting in decrease in energy.

These "depressive troughs" contrasted with preceding "peaks," are so disturbing that often suicide is attempted in this "recovery phase." Transitory peaks of these catecholamines (with bursts of energy and often with subsequent troughs of depression) may occur weeks or months after apparent recovery.

Parasympathetic Activity. The anterior hypothalamus is the nodal area for the parasympathetic system. In health, there is continuous and reciprocal relationship between sympathetic and parasympathetic activity. If one system is depressed, usually the opposite system is overactive —in anger, the sympathetic system is dominant— the parasympathetic system, quiescent, in sleep, the reverse is true. However, in the depths of

the depression, both systems become relatively inactive, or at the zenith of a manic swing, both operate at high levels.

Initially, inhibition of the sympathetic system is accompanied by overcompensatory parasympathetic activity. As a result, early in the illness, typical symptoms are hypersomnia, frequent crying spells, and many vagotonic (psychosomatic) symptoms.

In the depths of the depression, with complete hypothalamic "exhaustion," there is minimal parasympathetic activity, resulting in intractable insomnia and inability to cry. Psychosomatic symptoms are minimal; X-ray studies reveal complete visceral atony (22).

Parasympathetic activity increases in the recovery phase; peaks and troughs may or may not synchronize with those produced by nor-epinephrine.

In the 5th phase, vagal stimulation from excessive parasympathetic activity contributes to the formation of peptic ulcer (23); vago-insulin stimulation (4) produces a craving for sweets and later for meats with a consequent gain in weight. Hypersomnia also occurs. These symptoms are transitory; as parasympathetic activity becomes stabilized the peptic ulcer disappears, the desire for food decreases, and normal sleep returns.

Adrenal Activity. Clinical evidence suggests

increased adrenal activity. Increased circulating epinephrine is manifested by tachycardia, dilated pupils, dryness of the mouth, etc. Blood chemistry reveals an increase in circulating cortical steroids (1). This stimulated adrenal activity is probably the result of the stress reaction with consequent greater proportion of epinephrine in the normal nor-epinephrine-epinephrine ratio (2, 24, 25) (cf. Selye's alarm reaction).

The predominant psychologic sign of increased epinephrine is the feeling of fear. Intravenous adrenalin induces a feeling of fear (26, 27). In the depressive syndrome, the origin of this fear is physiologic without an initiating symbolic component; so the patient has "free-floating anxiety."

When adrenal activity is greatest, usually in the 2nd and 5th phases, phobias are most common, the physiologic alarm activating dormant symbolic conflicts. In the 2nd phase, with nor-epinephrine decreasing, the increasing epinephrine results in pure fear, which, secondarily, may become attached to a symbolic object; in the 5th phase, the combination of increasing nor-epinephrine (associated with energy output) and increased epinephrine evokes the feeling tone of anger. The patient in this phase is not only generally irritable with a torrent of complaining speech, but also is markedly hostile. In the 6th phase, the normalization of adrenalin output results in the spontaneous disappearance of irritability and hostility.

Endocrine Activity. Many depressive reactions occur in the post-partum period (37, 39) —often within a few days of childbirth. During the depressive illness, particularly in the later phases, there is often delayed menstruation. Libido decreases early in the depression, but in the 5th phase, there may be a transient—and excessive—increase in sex desire in women and potency in men.

The pituitary—the "master gland"—which anatomically and physiologically is intimately and reciprocally related to the hypothalamus (9) acts upon and is influenced by other endocrine structures. In pregnancy there is a gradual increase in blood levels of estrogen and pregnandial until childbirth, when they, and other related endocrine factors, precipitously return to their normal baseline (28). This sudden drop may act as a precipitating factor in the depressions. The comparable sudden drop of these hormones just before the onset of menses would explain pre-menstrual tension—a "depression-in-miniature."

The changes in sexual desire and activity may be associated with alteration of the pituitary hormones which mediate sexual response.

That electric shock therapy influences pituitary activity is evidenced by the delayed menstruation after a course of these treatments.

"ETIOLOGIC" PSYCHOPATHOLOGY

Rarely does psychic stress result in manic depressive symptoms. In most cases, the so-called precipitating psychic factor is coincidental rather than causal. Personalities, pre- and post- illness reveal similar "psychic stress" without the onset of a depressive syndrome. Countless other persons suffer severe and identical "psychic stress" without developing this syndrome.

When, however, a reactive depression does follow a severe psychic trauma (e.g., the sudden death of an only son) then not only do the classical symptoms of an endogenous depression develop, but also the focus of the patient's concern shifts from complaints about the "precipitating" cause to typical phobias.

In such cases there appears to be similar though less intense constitutional susceptibility. The "grief response" places such a severe stress upon the hypothalamus as to result in its rapid "exhaustion" (particularly of nor-epinephrine secretion), and then the typical depressive syndrome follows. Because in reactive depressions susceptibility is minimal, restoration of normal hypothalamic activity can be more quickly obtained than in the endogenous depression.

FLUCTUATIONS

In the initial phases of the depression, hypothalamic fluctuations are of short duration and quickly compensated, with the depressive mood lasting for several hours to several days then returning to normal. In the depths of the depression when the hypothalamus is so "exhausted" that minimal fluctuations occur, the patient suffers a continuous, non-fluctuating, unrelieved melancholia.

In the middle of the ascending curve (phase 5) hypothalamic fluctuations become extreme, with high peaks followed by sharp troughs; the clinical expression is alternating periods of marked improvement and intense depression. Anxiety and/or irritability co-exist with the depressive mood in this phase and fluctuate with it.

As the curve approaches the normal baseline, peaks become plateaus of several weeks' duration. Simultaneously, fluctuations occur within fluctuations (17), so that several hours of improved mood alternate with comparable episodes of depressive mood in an over-all period of improvement. Even weeks or months after apparent recovery, there may be occasional troughs of depression and peaks of excessive energy.

THE MANIC STATE

Clinical manifestations of the manic state are: physical over-activity, intellectual over-activity, and euphoria.

Hypothalamic Physiopathology. The "mirror image" of the depressive physiopathology occurs in the manic state. Nor-epinephrine production is increased above the patient's baseline (17), with consequent increased activity of the ergotropic system—essentially increased energy expenditure. The *responsiveness* of the emotional circuit is increased; the reticular system is activated both by the stimuli originating in the external world and by a greater volume of impulses from the hypothalamus. At the zenith of the manic phase, the responsiveness may be so excessive as to produce the clinical picture of a delirium (29).

Since the entire hypothalamus is hyperactive, the level of activity in the parasympathetic system is elevated with resultant intensification of pleasure tone. Usually the parasympathetic pleasure centers are associated with decreased physical activity and relaxation; the pleasure tone is "passive" (contentedness). When there is simultaneous stimulation of these centers and of sympathetic activity (nor-epinephrine in-

duced), there is evoked an "active" sense of pleasure, keen appreciation of stimuli, a sense of exhilaration.

Psychosomatic symptoms which usually accompany marked parasympathetic activity are infrequent in the manic state because of the over-compensatory role of the dominating sympathetic system.

Simultaneously, the nor-epinephrine-epinephrine ratio (17) is altered: increased nor-epinephrine, decreased epinephrine. Since epinephrine induces the feeling tone of fear, its decrease results in diminution of fear.

The unrestrained manic patient releases his nor-epinephrine induced energy freely and feels euphoric. When he is frustrated and cannot obtain his wish of the moment, a stress situation results. Stress increases the output of epinephrine; epinephrine combined with manic levels of nor-epinephrine induces the feeling tone of anger (25). (Table 6.7.) However, manic anger quickly subsides, primarily because manic desires are so transitory that the stress quickly disappears, and the level of epinephrine is reduced.

Personalities whose symbolic orientation continually stimulates high levels of both of these hormones may have "chronic anger" which in the manic state is manifested as paranoia. While nor-epinephrine levels are high, paranoid patients are acutely disturbed; when the hormonal levels are exhausted the paranoid becomes a "burned-out" (energyless) schizophrenic.

Manic patients respond therapeutically to sympathetic inhibitors (e.g., phenothiazines) and to frequent (several times a day for several days) electric shock treatments which "exhaust" the excessive hypothalamic activity.

The manic phase is shorter than the depressive (4 to 5 months versus 1½ to 5 years) because energy is more quickly expended than restored. Youth, characterized by high levels of biologic energy, is more prone to manic episodes; aging persons, with decreasing biologic energy, are more subject to depressive attacks. An aged person experiencing a manic attack has the appearance of youth—good skin tone, glistening eyes, marked alertness, quick purposeful movements, many ideas, etc.

Specific Symptoms: Their Origin and Nature

There are four categories of symptoms in the manic depressive illness (Figure 6.2). (1) Mood alterations, (2) Somatic responses, (3) Intellectual disturbances, (4) Psychopathologic reactions which are secondary and arise from the accompanying psychic stress.

Figure 6.2
Physiogenic Symptoms of an Endogenous Depression

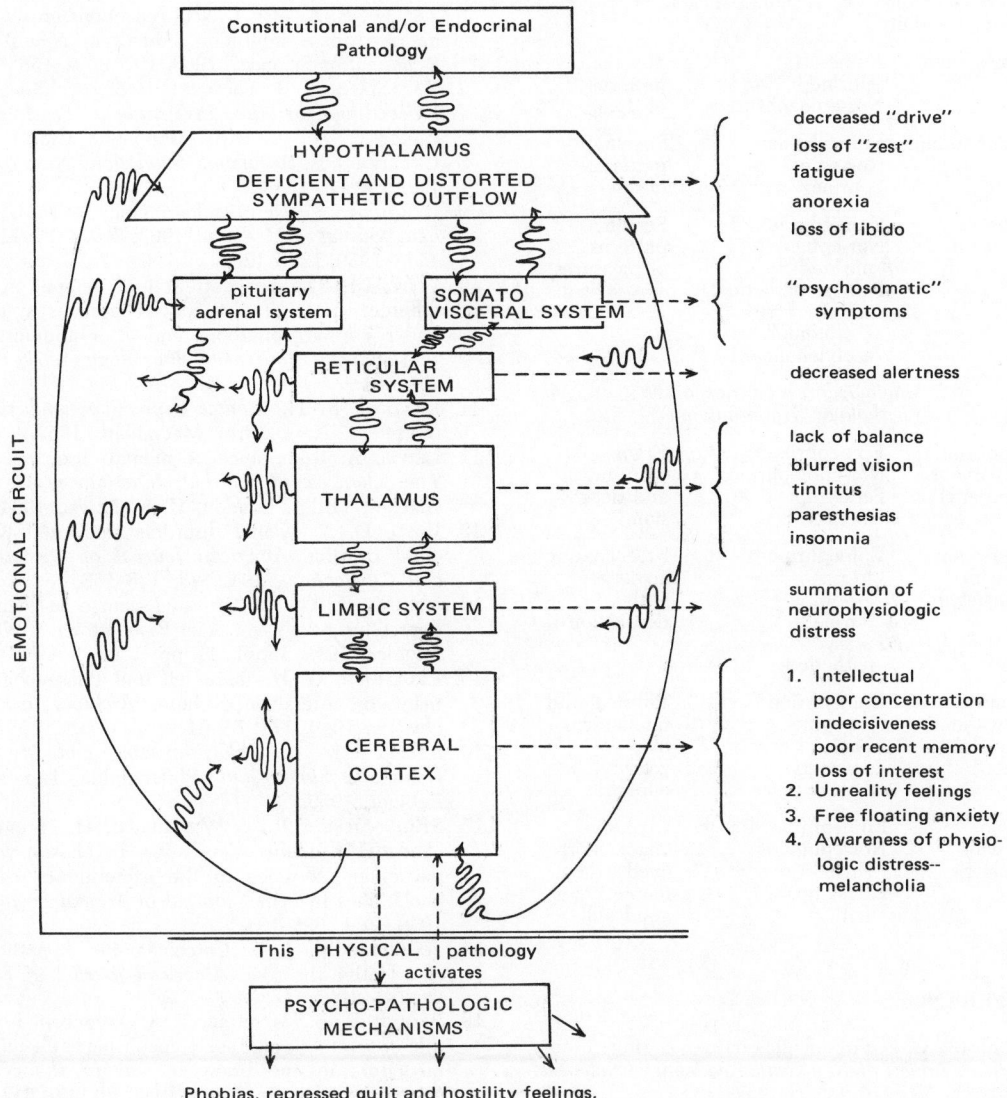

decreased "drive"
loss of "zest"
fatigue
anorexia
loss of libido

"psychosomatic" symptoms

decreased alertness

lack of balance
blurred vision
tinnitus
paresthesias
insomnia

summation of neurophysiologic distress

1. Intellectual
   poor concentration
   indecisiveness
   poor recent memory
   loss of interest
2. Unreality feelings
3. Free floating anxiety
4. Awareness of physiologic distress-- melancholia

TABLE 6.7

EMOTIONS VIA NEUROHORMONES

Principle: A stimulus in the cerebral cortex (newly presented or in memory) activates specific neurohormones in the hypothalamus. In turn, a specific pattern is activated in the emotional circuit. Each emotion depends upon a specific combination of neurohormones (activated above basic physiologic need).

"Normal" Responses (Normal Hypothalamus) Cortical stimuli activate neurohormones which in turn evoke emotions. + is minimal and + + + + is maximal activity.

Fear stimuli	Epine-phrine+ + + Nor-epinephrine+	Specific patterns of fear
Anger stimuli	Epinephrine+ + Nor-epine-phrine+ + +	Specific patterns of anger
Pleasure stimuli	Epinephrine —O— Nor-epine-phrine+ + Parasympathetic activity+ + + (serotonin? acetylcholine?)	Specific patterns of pleasures

Manic Depressive Responses
(Pathologic Hypothalamus)

Depression (without anxiety)	Epinephrine+ Nor-epinephrine+ Parasympa-thetic+	Ergotropic withdrawal and depression
Depression (with anxiety)	Epinephrine+ to+ + + + Nor-epine-phrine+ Parasym-pathetic+	Free floating anxiety with depression
Manic (without frustra-tion)	Epinephrine+ Nor-epine-phrine+ + + + Parasympa-thetic+ + +	Physical and intellectual over-activity, euphoria
Manic (with anger)	Epinephrine + + + Nor-epine-phrine+ + + + Parasympa-thetic+	Explosive anger, short-lived, then manic good will

REFERENCES

1. MAHL, G. F. Physiologic changes during chronic fear. *Annals of New York Academy of Sciences,* 1953, *56,* 240–252.
2. BRODIE, B. B., SPECTOR, S., & SHORE, P. A. Interaction on drugs with the norepinephrine in the brain. In *Symposium on Catecholamines.* Baltimore, Williams and Wilkins, 1959.
3. EVERETT, G. M., TOMAN, J. E. P., & SMITH, A. H. Central and peripheral effects of reserpine and desmethoxyreserpine on the nervous system. *Federal Proceedings,* 1957, *16,* 295.
4. GELLHORN, E., & LOOFBURROW, G. N. *Emotions and emotional disorders.* New York: Harper and Row, 1963.
5. BRODIE, B. B., SPECTOR, S., & SHORE, P. A. Interaction of monoamine oxidase inhibitors with physiological and biochemical mechanisms in brain. *Annals of New York Academy of Sciences,* 1959, *80,* 609–616.
6. ZELLER, E. A. (Ed.). New reflections on monoamine oxidase inhibition. *Annals of New York Academy of Sciences,* 1963, *107,* 809–1158.
7. KALLMANN, F. J. The genetics of psychoses. In *Proceedings of the International Psychiatric Congress,* Vol. 6. Paris, Herman & Cie, 1950.
8. GELLHORN, E. *Autonomic regulations.* New York: Interscience, 1943.
9. REICHLIN, S. Neuroendocrinology. *New England Journal of Medicine,* 1963, *269,* 1182–1191, 1246–1250, 1296–1303.
10. VOGT, M. The concentration of sympathin in different parts of the central nervous system under normal conditions and after administration of drugs. *Journal of Physiology,* 1954, *123,* 451–481.
11. KRAINES, S. H. *Mental depressions and their treatment.* New York: Macmillan, 1957.
12. LEWIS, A. Inheritance of mental disorders. In *The chances of morbid inheritance,* C. P. Blacker, (Ed.). London, H. K. Lewis, 1934.
13. BOYD, D. A. Mental disorders associated with child bearing. *American Journal of Obstetrics and Gynecology,* 1942, *43,* 148–163.
14. LUNDQUIST, G. Progress and course in manic-depressive psychoses. *Acta Psychiatrica et Neurologica,* 1945, suppl. 35, pp. 1–96.
15. LEUTHOLD, G. H. Jahreszeit und Phasenbeginn manisch-depressiver psychoses. *Archives für Psychiatria,* 1940, *111,* 55–61.
16. AYD, F. J. In *Chlorpromazine and Mental Health, a Symposium.* Philadelphia, Lea and Febiger, 1955.
17. STROM-OLSEN, R., & WEILHERBE, H. Humoral changes in manic depressive psychoses with particular reference to the excretion of catecholamines in urine. *Journal of Mental Science,* 1958, *104,* 696–704.
18. SCHILDKRAUT, J. J. Catecholamine hypothesis of affective disorder. *American Journal of Psychiatry,* 1965, *122,* 509–522.
19. BRODIE, B. B., & SHORE, P. A. A concept for a role of serotonin and nor-epinephrine as chemical mediators in the brain. *Annals of the New York Academy of Science,* 1957, *66,* 631–642.
20. ELDMADJEAN, F. In *Molecules and mental health.* F. A. Gibbs, (Ed.) Philadelphia, Lippincott, 1959.
21. WEIL-MALHERBE, H. The effect of convulsant therapy on plasma adrenalin and noradrenalin.

Journal of Mental Science, 1955, *101*, 156–162.

22. HENRY, G. W. Gastrointestinal motor functions in manic depressive psychoses. *Research of Nervous and Mental Disease*, 1931, *11*, 19–28.

23. FELDMAN, S., BEHAR, A. J., & BIRNBAUM, D. Gastric lesions following hypothalamic stimulation. *AMA Archives of Neurology*, 1961, *4*, 308–317.

24. REDGATE, E. S., & GELLHORN, E. Factors influencing the neural and hormonal (adrenomedullary) components of the sympathico-adrenal discharge. *Arch. International Physiol. Biochem.* 1958, *66*, 160–176.

25. REGAN, P. F., & REILLY, J. Circulating epinephrine and nor-epinephrine in changing emotional states. *Journal of Nervous and Mental Disease*, 1958, *127*, 12–16.

26. COHEN, S. I. & SILVERMAN, A. J. Physiological investigation of vascular response variability. *Journal of Psychosomatic Research*, 1959, *3*, 185–210.

27. KRAINES, S. H. & SHERMAN, I. C. Neurotic symptoms and changes in blood pressure and pulse following injection of epinephrine. *Journal of American Medical Association*, 1940, *114*, 843–845.

28. VENNING, E. Excretion of various hormone metabolites in normal pregnancy. Proc. Conf. of Common. on Human Reproduction, National Res. Council, *Obstetrical and Gynecological Survey*, 1948, *3*, 662–673.

29. KRAINES, S. H. Bell's Mania (Acute Delirium). *American Journal of Psychiatry*, 1934, *91*, 29–40.

49.

P. R. J. BURCH

MANIC DEPRESSIVE PSYCHOSIS AS OF AUTOIMMUNE AETIOLOGY

My purpose in this article is to draw attention to certain statistical features of manic depressive psychosis and to inquire into their possible aetiological significance.

I shall show that some of these statistical characteristics are very similar to comparable aspects of diseases that are widely considered to be autoimmune. Although it does not follow that manic depressive psychosis is an autoimmune disorder, the parallels and coincidences are perhaps sufficiently striking to warrant further investigation.

The remainder of the introduction will be devoted to a brief résumé of conclusions that have been drawn regarding the aetiology of some human autoimmune diseases.

It emerges that the age- and sex-specific incidence rates or prevalence of rheumatoid arthritis, chronic discoid and systemic lupus erythematosus, progressive systemic sclerosis and Hashimoto's thyroiditis, are consistent with the following propositions: (1) each disease is restricted to a subpopulation of individuals with a specific predisposing genotype; (2) the phenotypic expression of the disease—that is, its initiation—depends upon the accumulation of a rather small number (generally < 10) of specific random events (Burch, 1963a; Burch and Rowell, 1963); and (3) the detailed characteristics of the "age pattern" of several autoimmune disorders suggest that the average rate of the specific random pathogenic events is virtually constant throughout postnatal life (Burch and Rowell, 1963).

Burnet (1959a) has suggested that random somatic gene mutations in the stem cells of the lymphoid series could initiate the growth of "forbidden clones." The expression, "forbidden clone," is applied to immunologically competent cells, deriving from a single stem cell, that react with "self" antigenic determinants as though they were "not-self." In other words, the normal

From P. R. J. Burch, "Manic depressive psychosis: some new aetiological considerations." *British Journal of Psychiatry*, 1964, *110*, 808–817. Reprinted by permission.

condition of immunological tolerance to self-constitutents is abrogated with the growth of a forbidden clone. Burnet's (1959a) suggestion offers a very ingenious escape from an awkward dilemma—how can a small number of random events, such as gene mutations in somatic cells, give rise to a systemic disease? In some auto-immune disorders it is probable that the primary pathogenic agents are not humoral auto-antibodies but small lymphocytes carrying cell-bound autoantibody (Burnet, 1959b; Green and Sperber, 1962; Richardson, 1963; Burch, 1963a). Clonal growth, therefore, is a mechanism capable of amplifying one or a small number of gene mutations in somatic stem cells into a widespread systemic disorder. There is a close and obvious parallel here with neoplastic disease. The discovery of germinal centres in the thymus in association with myasthenia gravis (Burnet and Mackay, 1962), and more recently in association with an untreated case of systemic lupus erythematosus (Mackay and deGail, 1963), indicates that some autoimmune diseases are associated with intense proliferative changes in the thymus.

An unexpected finding in connection with rheumatoid arthritis was that the average rate of pathogenic (somatic) events in women is about twice that in males (Burch, 1963a, 1963c). The most obvious interpretation of this rate-difference is that the pathogenic events affect X-linked genes. This view conflicts with Lyon's (1961) hypothesis of Barr-body formation in normal XX females because it implies that both homologous genes on the X-chromosomes in the stem cells "at risk" engage in messenger-and/or repressor-RNA synthesis, either simultaneously or on some kind of alternating basis (Burch and Burwell, 1963). However, investigation of other autoimmune diseases (Burch and Rowell, 1963) shows that a prominent aetiological role (inherited and/or somatic) can often be attributed to the X-chromosome. It is probable therefore that Lyon's hypothesis does not apply to those X-linked genes in the stem cells that are at "mutational" risk with respect to the phenotypic expression of autoimmune disease.

Of special interest is the conclusion that in some autoimmune diseases at least there is an endogenous defence mechanism directed against forbidden clones; where the pathogens are small lymphocytes defence probably involves specific humoral antibody (Green and Sperber, 1962; Burch, 1963a, 1963c). Moreover the efficiency of defence appears generally to be markedly higher in women than in men. This sex difference manifests itself in two ways: (1) where the clinical severity of a disease is related to the number of genetically identical forbidden clones, more such clones are needed to produce a given grade of the disease in women than in men; (2) the interval or latent period between the completion of the last somatic mutation (and hence the initiation of the last forbidden clone) and symptoms or signs of the disease is longer in women than in men (Burch, 1963b; Burch and Rowell, 1963). Exacerbations and remissions in antoimmunity are attributed to fluctuations in the efficiency of the defence mechanism against forbidden clones; this mechanism is vulnerable to environmental and stress factors, especially infections.

AGE- AND SEX-SPECIFIC ONSET RATES FOR MANIC DEPRESSIVE PSYCHOSIS

The analysis is based very largely on the detailed statistics of admission-rates to hospitals in New York State published by Malzberg (1955). These span the period 1919 to 1951 and they show some interesting secular trends, the significance of which will be discussed later.

THEORETICAL

Age-, and sex-specific incidence rates for certain spontaneous disturbed tolerance autoimmune diseases conform to the following general equation (Burch and Rowell, 1963; Burch, 1963c):

$$dN/dt = k\, P_o\, t^{(r-1)} \exp(-kt^r/r) \quad (I)$$

Where dN/dt = sex-specific incidence-rate of the disease at age t. (Age from birth is a good approximation for diseases studied so far.)

k is a constant throughout postnatal life. Its precise value depends upon the details of the aetiology; but in a special situation, where r specific somatic mutations, at r available sites, must be accumulated in any one of the L cells at risk, in any sequence, $k = rL(m_s)r$. It is assumed here that m_s is an average rate of somatic mutation (Burch, 1962) applicable to the r sites.

P_o is the fraction of the male or female population at birth that is at risk, through inheritance, with respect to the disease in question.

Equation (I) is relevant when the r random initiating events are of the dependent kind. By "dependent" is meant that the occurrence of one event markedly affects the probability of another. If a disease is initiated by r somatic mutations, at a limited number of sites, in any one stem cell out of many, or, for example, in adjacent stem cells, such events would be "dependent." The equation (Burch, 1963c) for the age-specific initiation-rate of *independent* but genetically identical forbidden-clones will be discussed in connection with the aetiology of involutional psychosis.

The relation between the k values (equation I) for male and female data analysed separately gives the relative rates of somatic mutation in males and females, and it enables a distinction to be drawn between somatic mutation of genes on the X-chromosome and of autosomal genes. This depends upon the inference that somatic mutation of genes at risk on the X-chromosome occurs with twice the frequency in females as in males (Burch, 1963a, 1963c; Burch and Rowell, 1963).

By integrating equation (I) from $t = O$ to ∞, one obtains the value of P_o, that is, the proportion of the male or female population, at birth, that is at risk with respect to the disease in question.

In general terms, the significance of equation (I) is as follows: It describes (with the above restrictions) the age-, and sex-specific incidence-rate of a disease, the phenotypic expression of which depends upon the accumulation of r, specific, random, but dependent somatic mutations. The term: exp. $(-kt^r/r)$ becomes important when the penetrance of the disease approaches unity. When the penetrance is low (say less than about 20 per cent) and when the mortality in the subpopulation of interest is the same as that in the general population, the age-specific incidence rate, dN/dt, is effectively equal to $k P_o t^{(r-1)}$. In other words, at low penetrance, the age-specific incidence rate of the disease will be proportional to a constant power of age. However, with increasing age and increasing penetrance the proportion of people who have not already developed the disease will decline sharply. Consequently the incidence rate climbs to a maximum and then drops sharply. Examples of the family of curves described by equation (I) are given elsewhere (Burch and Rowell, 1963). The *shape* of a particular curve drawn on log-log graph paper depends only on r, although the *position* of the curve on the grid (up, down, left or right), depends on k and P_o. P_o affects the "up and down" aspects only, k affects both vertical and horizontal positions. For the diseases investigated so far, it appears that the k values for females are either equal to, or 2^x times, the corresponding k values for males, where x, a positive integer, is presumed to be the number of pathogenic somatic mutations affecting X-linked genes.

The chief interpretational complication is the problem of the latent period. Theory describes the relation between incidence rate—marked by the occurrence of the last somatic mutation—and age. However, the biological "endpoint" is usually the manifestation of symptoms or signs, or for example death; in the present instance it is the first admission to hospital. Obviously there must be some lag between the initiation of a forbidden-clone, its growth into many cells, and subsequent damage to target tissue of sufficient intensity to produce detectable pathological effects. In autoimmunity, this lag, or latent period, is further complicated by the action of the defence mechanism (involving humoral antibody) and it is probably susceptible to environmental factors such as severe infections. In rheumatoid arthritis the "average severity" of the disease depends upon the number of forbidden-clones; more of these are required in women to produce the same clinical grade of arthritis as in males (Burch, 1963a, 1963c). However, where a single clone is sufficient to produce a pathological condition, we may expect that the latent period will generally be longer in women than in men. Using very accurate statistics in conjunction with the theoretical premises, this latent period can be assessed mathematically. The present statistics (for 1949 to 1951) indicate that the average latent period for manic depressive psychosis in males is about 2.5 years, whereas the corresponding interval in females is about 5 years.

Making these rather minor corrections for the effect of the latent period, age- and sex-specific *incidence*-rates are derived from first-*admission*-rates to hospital in New York State for 1949 to 1951 (Malzberg, 1955) and are plotted on log-log scales in Figure 6.3. The continuous

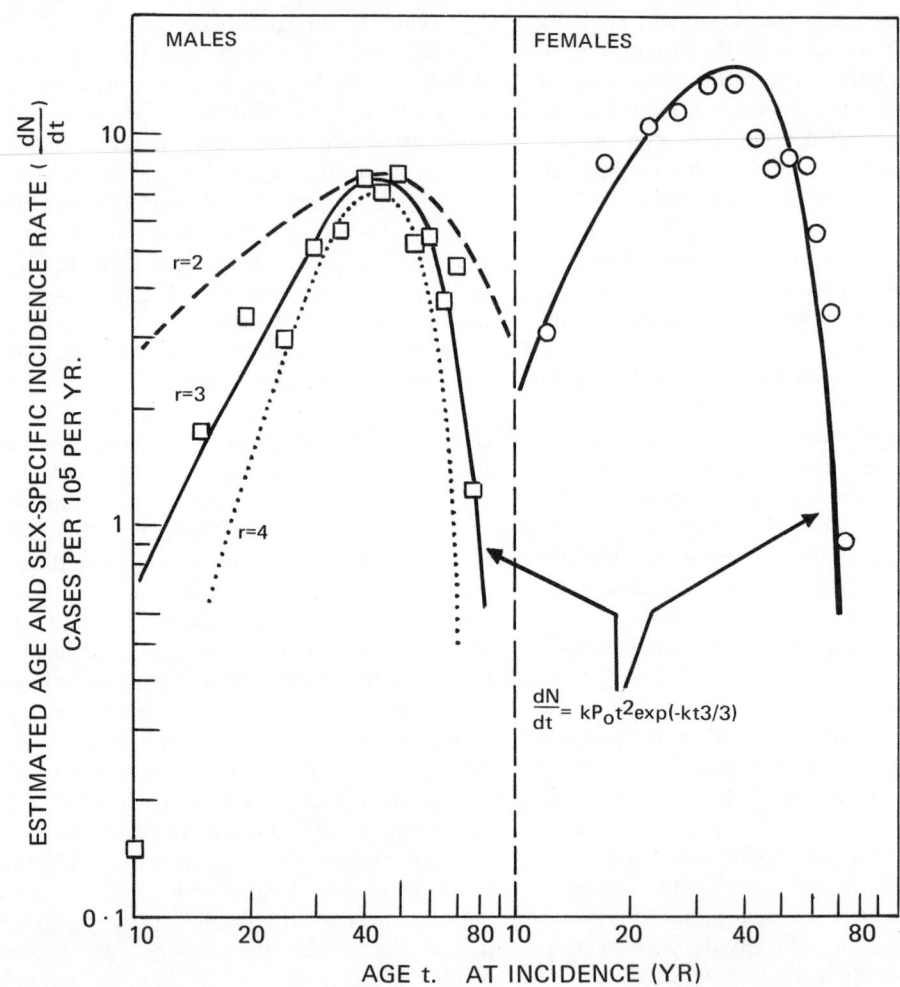

FIGURE 6.3. Incidence rates of manic depressive psychosis, specific for age and sex, plotted against age on log-log scales. Derived from Malzberg's (1955) statistics of first-admission-rates to hospital in New York State 1949 to 1951. It is assumed that the average interval, or latent period (see text) between the final "somatic mutation" and first admission to hospital is 2.5 years for males and 5 years for females. There is a suggestion of "humps" in the statistics for females at 15 to 25 years and at 45 to 60+ years. These discrepancies between the statistics and the smooth theoretical curve are attributed mainly to diagnostic error (see text and subsequent papers). Schizophrenics should be responsible for the first hump and involutional psychotics for the second.

lines in the figure are based on $dN/dt \propto t^2 \exp(-kt^3/3)$. There is a misfit for the admissions age-group 10–14 (presumed average age at "incidence" 5 to 11·5 years) but apart from this one group, it will be seen that the fit of the points to the theoretical expression is—in view of the diagnostic difficulties—surprisingly good. It indicates that three random events are responsible for the initiation of the disorder. The misfit for $r = 2$ and $r = 4$ (broken lines) is very marked and neither of these provides a realistic alternative. The age of peak incidence-rate is about 46 years in men, and 37 in women.

The relationship between the curves for males and females is particularly interesting.

$$t = \infty$$

The integral, $\int\limits_{t=0}^{} dN/dt$, $(=P_o)$ is about

$5·7 \times 10^{-3}$ for females and $3·4 \times 10^{-3}$ for males, giving a sex-ratio, (F/M) of 1·7. That is to say, at birth about 0·57 per cent of the female population and 0·34 per cent of the male population in New York State have an inherited predisposition to manic depressive psychosis. A sex-ratio (F/M) of approximately 1·7 could be readily accounted for if *one* of the inherited requirements is a rather common dominant allele (say XM_1) and the X-chromosome. For a dominant allele that is rare in the population, the sex-ratio would be 2, but for a very common (50 per cent) dominant allele (with equal selection pressures against homozygous females, X_1/X_I and X_2/X_2) the sex-ratio would be 1·5. An apparent ratio of 1·7 indicates that perhaps about 30 per cent of alleles in the population at the XM locus are XM_I.

The remaining important detail that can be extracted from these curves is the sex-ratio of the somatic mutation rates; this is given by the ratio of the k values, (k_F/k_M). It is equal to 2. Viewed in conjunction with earlier findings (Burch, 1963a; Burch and Rowell, 1963), this evidence is in accord with the view that one somatic mutation affects a gene on the X-chromosome and that the other two somatic mutations involve autosomal genes. Mathematically it is not possible to deduce whether one, two or three forbidden-clones are generated, but if more than one clone is involved they have a dependent relationship, such as proximity.

SECULAR TRENDS AND DIAGNOSTIC RELIABILITY

When the records (Malzberg, 1955) for earlier periods, 1919–1921, 1929–1931 and 1939–1941 are examined, we find (Figures 6.4, 6.5 and 6.6) that first-admission-rates to hospital have shown a more or less consistent decline with time. Furthermore, the age- and sex-specific incidence-rates for these earlier periods do not lie on the smooth (continuous) curves of Figure 6.3. It is considered that the secular decline reflects progressive improvement in diagnosis. Kallmann (1953) has noted that it was rather common for patients to be diagnosed as manic depressive on their first admission to hospital, but subsequently, to be re-diagnosed as schizophrenic. The discrepancy between the earlier statistics and those of 1949 to 1951 certainly bears out Kallmann's observation. It will be seen from the next article [not reprinted here] that the peak in first-admission-rates for schizophrenia occurs between 20 to 30 and it is clear that the earlier statistics plotted in Figures 6.4, 6.5 and 6.6 are "contaminated" by the schizophrenic peak. Indeed, there is a suggestion that in 1949 to 1951 the admission rate for the diagnosis of manic depressive psychosis in females was still slightly too high in the 15 to 25 years age range. (The curve has been adjusted to give a compromise fit to all the points, but the "true" curve may lie slightly below the one drawn in the figure.)

It will be noticed that the earlier statistics show an excess above 1949 to 1951 levels not only in the younger but also in the older age groups; this shows a peak in the 40 to 60 years are range. In a later article [not reprinted here] it will be shown that this peak corresponds to the diagnostic category involutional psychosis. Again, there is an indication in Figure 6.3 that traces of this diagnostic error persist in the 1949 to 1951 statistics, especially in females. Nevertheless, the fit of these later statistics to the theoretical curve is good enough to indicate that manic depressive psychosis is a definite, and

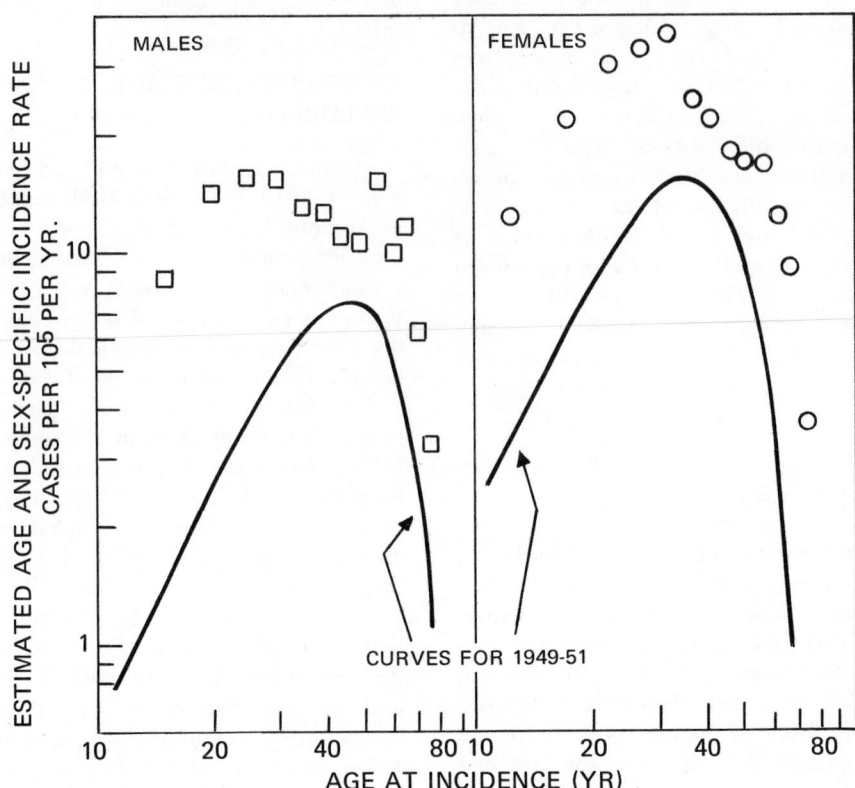

FIGURE 6.4. Comparison between statistics (Malzberg, 1955) of manic depressive psychosis for 1919 to 1921, and for 1949 to 1951. (The latent period correction has been applied to first-admission-rates to hospital.) Contribution from schizophrenia and involutional psychosis . . . are very prominent in the earlier statistics both for males and females.

largely definable, organic disease. Moreover, the generally good fit of incidence-rates from about 15 years of age to about 75 suggests that there has been no significant change in the proportion of genetic carriers at birth in New York State over at least a 60-year period. The apparent change is perhaps entirely attributable to the difficulties of diagnosis.

FAMILIAL STUDIES AND GENETIC ASPECTS

From the above analysis of pathogenic events affecting somatic cells, it has already been concluded that one of the inherited requirements is

a rather common (frequency about 30 per cent) dominant allele, XM_I at a locus on the X-chromosome. Because the penetrance approaches 100 per cent at 70 to 80 years of age, and because the disorder is a comparatively rare one, it follows that another specific inherited factor is implicated. Analysis of the familial evidence indicates that this is a simple autosomal dominant—say AM. Knowing the approximate proportion of carriers and the frequency of the XM_I allele, the frequency of AM in the population of New York State, at birth, can be calculated to be about $1 \cdot 1_3 \times 10^{-2}$. From this genetical scheme, it is easy to calculate (assuming all genotypes are viable) that the theoretical

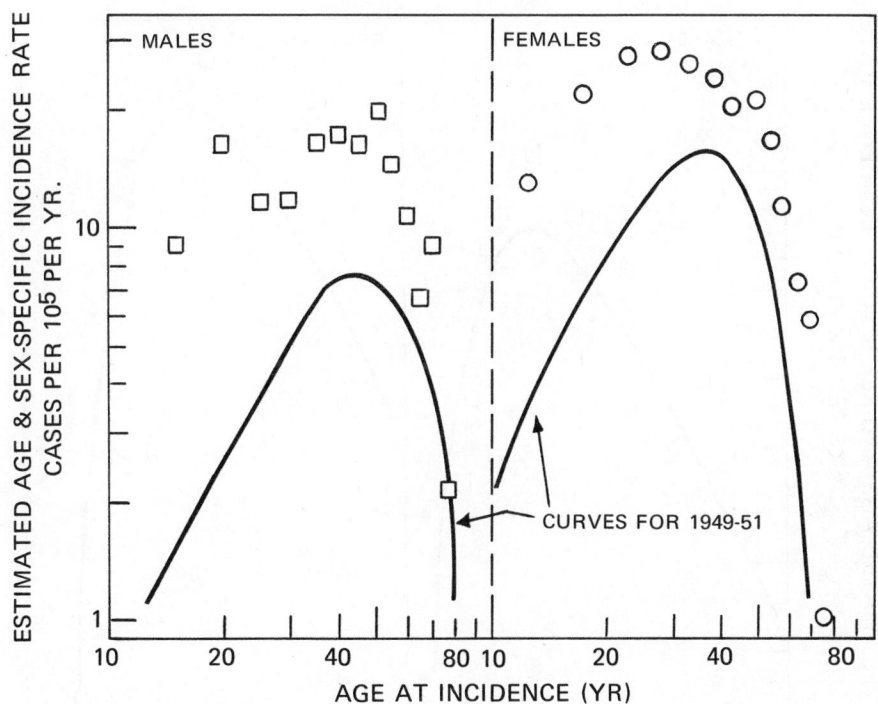

FIGURE 6.5. Comparison between statistics (Malzberg, 1955) of manic depressive psychosis for 1929 to 1931 and for 1949 to 1951. (The latent period correction has been applied to first-admission-rates to hospital.) Diagnostic errors in 1929 to 1931 were apparently similar to those in 1919 to 1921 (see Figure 6.4).

ratio: (concordance in monozygotic)/(concordance in dizygotic twins) should be about 3.2_5. The observed ratio is 3·6 (Kallmann, 1959). If a propositus is manic depressive, the calculated chance of a sibling being a carrier is 0.30_8. However, the average penetrance is less than 100 per cent for a typical life-span, and the observed risk of 0·227 (Kallmann, 1959) for full siblings is equivalent to an average penetrance of 73 per cent.

The chance of a parent of a propositus being a carrier of AM and XM_I is also 0.30_8. The observed risk of parents is 0·234 (Kallmann, 1959) indicating an average penetrance of 76 per cent.

The calculated chance of a half-sibling of a propositus being a carrier is 0.26_5 and the observed risk is 0·167 (Kallmann, 1953) indicating an average penetrance of 63 per cent.

In view of the relative scarcity of observations and the difficulties of diagnosis and follow-up, agreement between theory and familial observations is very satisfactory. The possibility of any simple alternative genetic scheme fitting all the observations better than the present one would appear to be remote. The statistical evidence does not of course reveal the role of the dominant autosomal and X-chromosomal alleles. However, a close connection may well exist between the inherited XM_I and AM alleles and the somatic mutations which also affect both X- and autosomal genes.

DISCUSSION

The good measure of agreement between equation (1) and estimated age-, and sex-specific incidence-rates suggests that manic depressive

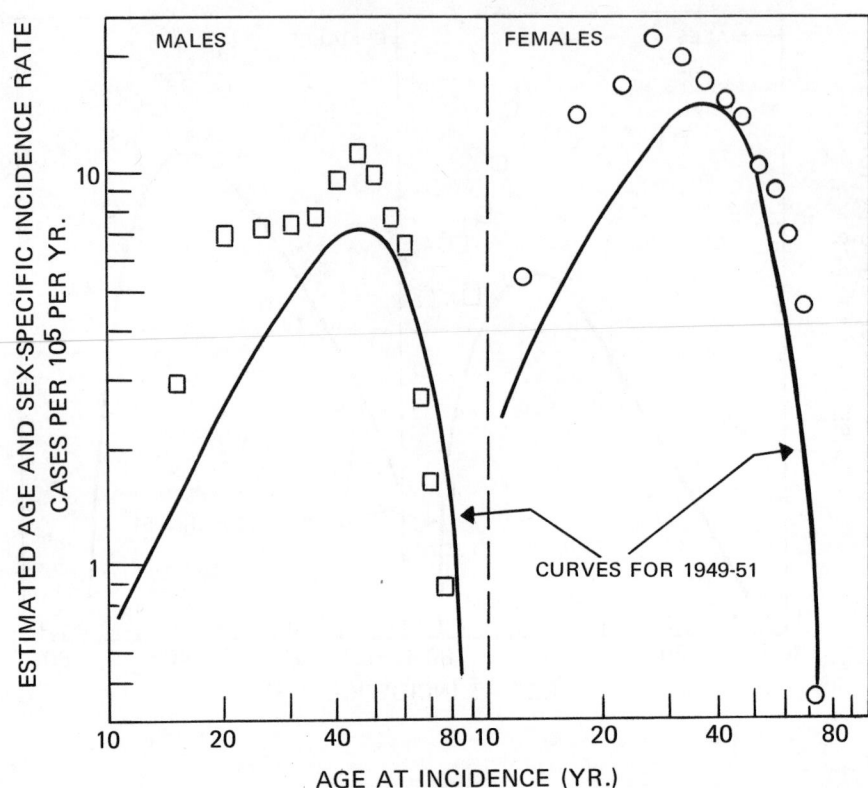

FIGURE 6.6. Comparison between statistics (Malzberg, 1955) of manic depressive psychosis for 1939 to 1941 and for 1949 to 1951. (The latent period correction has been applied to first-admission-rates to hospital.) There appears to have been a substantial improvement in diagnostic accuracy between 1930 and 1940.

psychosis, as diagnosed in New York State, 1949 to 1951, is a definite organic disease. There are some indications that this disorder was still being slightly over-diagnosed in 1949 to 1951—especially in women—but the statistics reveal a progressive improvement in the accuracy of diagnosis over the period 1919 to 1951.

The disease is restricted to a carrier subpopulation and the phenotypic expression appears to depend upon the accumulation of three specific random events. It is suggested, in the absence of any plausible alternative, that these random events are some form of somatic mutation. It appears that their average rate is constant—in a given individual and from one person to another of the same sex—from 10 years of age

(or earlier), to the end of the life span. One somatic mutation probably affects an X-linked gene because its rate in females is twice that in males; the remaining two somatic mutations should affect genes at one or two autosomal loci. The interval between the occurrence of the last somatic mutation and first admission to hospital is, on the average, about 2·5 years in males and about 5 years in females.

As in many autoimmune diseases, and in certain manifestations of ageing, (Burch, 1963a, 1963b; Burch and Rowell, 1963) it is necessary to explain how a disease can arise from a small number of random events which could well correspond to gene mutations. Burnet's (1959a, 1959b) forbidden-clone hypothesis of disturbed tolerance autoimmunity provides a plausible solution to this problem (see the Introduction) and it is suppported by observations which reveal germinal centres in the thymuses of untreated patients with autoimmune disease (Burnet and Mackay, 1962; Mackay and deGail, 1963). The pathogenesis of manic depressive psychosis must in fact include some mechanism for converting and amplifying three specific random events, accumulated during the lifetime of a carrier, into a mental disorder. Although the statistical features of the "system at risk" closely resemble those of the immune system, it does not, of course, follow that an immune mechanism must be implicated—nevertheless, the autoimmune hypothesis is perhaps among the first that should be disproved. It should be mentioned that the mood swings in manic depressive psychosis might conceivably depend upon an oscillation in the balance between the effective number of pathogenic cells in a forbidden clone and the efficiency of a humoral antibody defence mechanism.

To establish the autoimmune hypothesis it would be necessary: (1) to identify the autoantibodies (humoral or cell-bound); (2) to identify their target tissue; (3) to show that the autoimmune attack on the target tissue produced the mental disorder. The sex difference in the latent period favours the view that the primary pathogens are cell-bound (lymphocytic) autoantibodies. In view of the bloodbrain barrier and the absence of any gross pathological lesions in the central nervous system, it is to be expected that an indirect mechanism is involved. The blood-brain barrier inevitably raises the issue of the aetiology of multiple sclerosis. On another occasion I shall argue that this disease—associated with demyelinated axons in the central nervous system—arises from disturbances in a system that has characteristics similar to, but not quite the same as those of the system involved in manic depressive psychosis. Thus it appears that the average "latent period" is of approximately the same duration in males and in females, whereas in disturbed tolerance autoimmunity involving forbidden-clones of lymphocytes it is generally longer in females than in males. Multiple sclerosis (and kuru) may therefore result from disturbances in some other system, and the

pathogenic agent might be a "forbidden" humoral factor that diffuses through the bloodbrain barrier. However in the next two articles [not reprinted here] I shall argue that schizophrenia and "involutional psychosis"—in common with manic depressive psychosis—result from defects in a system similar or identical to that which generates forbidden clones of lymphocytes carrying cellbound autoantibody.

SUMMARY

Attention is directed to the age-specific and sex-specific incidence rates of manic depressive psychosis in relation to age. Using Malzberg's (1955) statistics for New York State, it is shown that certain statistical features of this mental disorder closely resemble comparable features of diseases that are widely believed to have an autoimmune aetiology. The age pattern of incidence rates, and the familial evidence, indicate that predisposition to manic depressive psychosis is confined to individuals of a sub-population that is characterized by a particular genotype. There are more females at risk than males. The specific genetic requirements appear to be: one dominant allele at an X-linked locus, and one dominant allele at an autosomal locus. Phenotypic initiation of the disease depends upon the accumulation in a carrier of three specific random events. The average rate of each type of event is constant from 10 years of age (or earlier), to the end of the life span, although the rate of one event is twice as high in females as in males. It is concluded that these random events are most probably some form of somatic gene mutation, and that one mutation affects an X-linked gene while the other two affect an autosomal gene or genes. Burnet's forbidden-clone hypothesis offers a possible explanation as to how a few somatic gene mutations can be "amplified" into a general systemic or mental disorder. The statistics indicate that the average interval, or latent period, between the occurrence of the final initiating somatic mutation and first admission to hospital is about 2·5 years in males and about 5 years in females.

The pathogenesis of manic depressive psychosis appears therefore to involve disturbances either in the immune system of a carrier or in some other system with similar genetical and statistical characteristics.

In the preceding article I stated that "The sex difference in the latent period favours the view that the primary pathogens are cell-bound (lymphocytic) autoantibodies." This suggestion depends on the interpretation of the sex- and age-statistics for first-admission-rates to hospital in New York State, 1949 to 1951 plotted in Figure 6.1. In the caption to that figure I pointed out: "There is a suggestion of 'humps' in the statistics for females at 15 to 25 years and at 45 to 60+ years. These discrepancies between the statistics and the smooth theoretical curves are attributed mainly to diagnostic error. . . ." I have since used the age-patterns for schizophrenia and involutional psychosis in an attempt to allow for diagnostic error. After correction, it seems likely that the latent period in accurately diagnosed manic depressive psychosis will show no sex-difference. If this is the case, the frequency of relapses should also show no sex-difference. This suspicion receives support from the study, "The course of manic-depressive psychosis" reported by O. Bratfos and J. O. Haug (*Acta Psychiatrica Scandinavica*, 1968, *44*, 89–112). These authors find no significant sex-difference in the stability of remission, or in the frequency of relapse.

If these conclusions are verified, then the primary pathogenic agent in manic depressive psychosis is expected to be humoral and not cellular. (In schizophrenia and involutional psychosis the primary pathogen should be cellular.) The predicted humoral factor is likely to belong to the α_2-globulin fraction of the serum proteins, and perhaps to be an α_2-macroglobulin. The target tissue in manic depressive psychosis probably lies behind a blood-tissue barrier, such as the blood-brain barrier. Hence, neurons or their supporting cells in the central nervous system could be the target cells attacked by the products of the forbidden clone.

My colleagues and I have argued that the "forbidden clones" responsible for many diseases and conditions of aging arise from spontaneous somatic gene mutations in stem cells of the central system of growth-control. We believe the *primary* pathogenic agents in the so-called idiopathic autoimmune diseases are never im-munoglobulins. Accordingly, we prefer the expression *autoaggressive* to *autoimmune*. (For details, see, for example, P. R. J. Burch, Oliver and Boyd, *An Inquiry Concerning Growth, Disease and Ageing* [Edinburgh; University of Toronto Press 1968]; P. R. J. Burch and A. Milunsky, "Early-onset diabetes mellitus in the general and Down's syndrome populations," *Lancet*, 1969, *i*, 554–558.)

REFERENCES

BURCH, P. R. J. A biological principle and its converse: Some implications for carinogenesis. *Nature, Lond.*, 1962, *195*, 241–243.

BURCH, P. R. J. Autoimmunity: some aetiological aspects. Inflammatory polyarthritis and rheumatoid arthritis. *Lancet*, 1963, *i*, 1253–1257. (a)

BURCH, P. R. J. Mutation, autoimmunity and ageing. *Lancet*, 1963, *ii*, 299–300. (b)

BUBCH, P. R. J. A genetic theory of inflammatory polyarthritis. *Lancet*, 1963, *ii*, 636–637. (c)

BURCH, P. R. J., & ROWELL, N. R. Autoimmunity. Aetiological aspects of chronic discoid and systemic lupus erythematosus, systemic sclerosis and Hashimoto's thyroiditis. Some immunological implications, *Lancet*, 1963, *ii*, 507–513.

BURCH, P. R. J., & BURWELL, R. G. Lyonisation of the N chromosome. *Lancet*, 1963, *ii*, 943–944.

BURNET, F. M. *The clonal selection theory of acquired immunity.* Cambridge: Cambridge University Press, 1959. (a)

BURNET, F. M. Autoimmune disease. I. Modern immunological concepts. *British Medical Journal*, 1959, *ii*, 645–650, *ii*, 720–725 (b).

BURNET, F. M., & MACKAY, I. R. Lymphoepithetical structures and autoimmune disease. *Lancet*, 1962, 1030–1033.

GREEN, I., & SPERBER, R. J. Hypogammaglobulinemia, arthritis, sprue and megaloblastic anemia. *New York State Journal of Medicine*, 1962, *62*, 1679–1686.

KALLMANN, F. J. *Heredity in health and mental disorder.* London: Chapman and Hall, Ltd., 1953.

KALLMANN, F. J. Genetics of mental illness. In S. Arieti (Ed.), *American handbook of psychiatry.* New York: Basic Books, 1959.

LYON, M. F. Gene action in the X-chromosome of the mouse (*Mus musculus L*). *Nature, Lond.*, 1961, *190*, 372–373.

MACKAY, I. R., & DEGAIL, P. Thymic "germinal centres" and plasma cells in systemic lupus erythematosus. *Lancet*, 1963, *ii*, 667–668.

MALZBERG, B. Age and sex in relation to mental diseases. *Mental Hygiene*, 1955, 39, 196–224.

RICHARDSON, J. *Connective tissue disorders.* Oxford. Philadelphia: Davis, 1963.

CHAPTER VII

Brain Disorders
and Mental Retardation

Oᴿɢᴀɴɪᴄ ʙʀᴀɪɴ ᴅɪsᴏʀᴅᴇʀs affecting thought, emotion, and behavior may be classified in several ways, one order (Gregory, 1968; Rosen & Gregory, 1965) being a dichotomous one as to whether the brain impairment is acute (temporary and reversible) or chronic (permanent and irreversible). Both forms exhibit at least five primary symptoms of intellectual dysfunction: (1) orientation (particularly for time, but also for place and person); (2) memory (especially for recent events, but also for remote ones); (3) intellectual dysfunction, including ideational; (4) impairment of judgment, including conscience and planning ability; (5) shallowness, lability, or affective responses (emotional responses).

The following tables (7.1; 7.2) by Gregory (1968, pp. 564, 566) cite the relationship of acute or reversible to chronic or irreversible brain disorders; and the main acute and chronic brain syndromes.

Brain disorders consist of a variety of types and subtypes. Kolb (1968) lists (1) *disorders that are caused by or are associated with impairment of brain tissue function:* meningococcal (epidemic) meningitis; tuberculous meningitis; acute (Sydenham's) chorea; epidemic encephalitis; deliria; (2) *brain syndromes stemming from drug or poison intoxication:* barbiturates and other tranquilizers; sympathomimetic amines (amphetamines); hallucinogenic agents (LSD-25 and mescaline); bromides; cortisone and ACTH; isoniazid; sulfonamides; thiocyanates; lead; mercury; manganese; carbon monoxide; carbon disulfide; (3) *acute brain*

TABLE 7.1
CHARACTERISTICS OF ACUTE (REVERSIBLE) AND
CHRONIC (IRREVERSIBLE) BRAIN DISORDERS[1]

ACUTE REVERSIBLE BRAIN DISORDERS	CHRONIC IRREVERSIBLE BRAIN DISORDERS
Usual clinical syndrome delirium (sometimes stupor or coma).	Usual clinical syndrome dementia.
Primary impairment of orientation, memory, all intellectual functions, judgment, and affective response.	Primary impairment of orientation, memory, all intellectual functions, judgment, and affective response.
Usually associated with disordered perception (especially visual illusions and hallucinations), consciousness (e.g., stupor), and psychomotor activity (excitement or retardation).	May be prominent secondary "functional" manifestations due to release or accentuation of latent personality characteristics—psychotic, neurotic, or behavioral (e.g., depressed, paranoid, anxious, or antisocial behavior).
Due to temporary, reversible changes in brain cell function, or "biochemical lesions."	Due to permanent, irreversible damage to brain structure, or "morphological lesions."
Frequently "symptomatic" of generalized toxic, infective or metabolic disorder, also affecting other parts of the body.	May result from all the same pathogenic agents as acute (reversible) disorders; but also from insidious, localized intracranial lesion or degenerative process (sometimes hereditary).
Commonly encountered on general medical and surgical, pediatric, or obstetric wards of general hospitals.	Commonly encountered on neurological services of general hospitals or in mental hospitals.
Course brief, and may terminate in (1) death, (2) complete remission, (3) chronic (irreversible) brain disorders.	Course may be (1) chronic, or (2) progressive (with fatal termination).

syndromes associated with metabolic disturbances: hyperthyroidism, hypocalcemia; Cushing's syndrome; adrenogenital syndrome; hypoglycemia; acute pancreatitis; acute vitamin deficiency syndrome; exhaustion delirium; postoperative neuroses and psychoses; (4) *chronic brain disorders:* syphilitic meningoencephalitis; syphilitic meningitis; (5) *brain syndromes associated with chronic arteriosclerosis;* (6) *senile psychoses;* (7) *brain syndromes associated with convulsive disorders (epilepsy):* grand mal; petit mal; cerebral dysrhythmias; narcolepsy; cataplexy; epileptic personality; epileptic deterioration; (8) *chronic brain syndrome associated with intracranial neoplasm;* (9) *chronic brain syndromes associated with disturbance of metabolism, growth, or nutrition:* Alzheimer's disease; vitamin deficiency syndromes; Wernicke syndrome; psychoses with pellagra; mental syndromes associated with pernicious anemia; porphyria; hepatolenticular degeneration; myxedema; acromegaloid personality; (10) *chronic brain syndromes associated with diseases of doubtful causes:* demyelinating diseases (multiple sclerosis; diffuse sclerosis); paralysis agitans; Huntington's chorea; Pick's disease; lupus erythematosus.

To this list may be added those that fall under *mental retardation,*

---

[1]From I. Gregory. *Fundamentals of psychiatry.* (2nd ed.) Philadelphia: W. B. Saunders. 1968. P. 564. Reprinted by permission of the publisher and the author.

TABLE 7.2
THE MAIN ACUTE AND CHRONIC BRAIN SYNDROMES[2]

I. *Chronic brain syndromes associated with congenital cranial anomaly, congenital spastic paraplegia, mongolism, prenatal maternal infectious disease, birth trauma*
Consists of all congenital brain disorders producing secondary or "pathological" mental deficiency

II. *Acute and chronic brain syndromes associated with infection*
   A. Intracranial infections such as encephalitis, meningitis, brain abscess, and central nervous system syphilis.
   B. Systemic infections such as pneumonia, typhoid fever, rheumatic fever, and malaria.

III. *Acute and chronic brain syndromes associated with intoxication*
   A. Drugs (and withdrawal of drugs) generally used in medical practice, such as hypnotics and narcotics, stimulants, antibiotics, and analgesics, antihistamines, and hormones.
   B. Poisons not ordinarily used in medical practice, such as lead and other metals, carbon monoxide and other gases, and methyl alcohol ("wood alcohol or rubbing alcohol").
   C. Alcohol (ethyl alcohol) and associated vitamin deficiencies.

IV. *Acute and chronic brain syndromes associated with trauma*
Any physical brain injury, including that caused by surgical operations.

V. *Acute and chronic brain syndromes associated with circulatory disturbances*
   A. High blood pressure, heart and kidney diseases.
   B. Cerebral arteriosclerosis.

VI. *Acute and chronic brain syndromes associated with conculsive disorder*
Due to uncontrolled seizures caused by primary or "idiopathic" epilepsy.

VII. *Acute and chronic brain syndromes associated with disorders of metabolism*
   A. With recognized metabolic disorders, such as anoxia, anemia, vitamin deficiencies, and disorders of the thyroid or other endocrine glands.
   B. With presumed disorders of metabolism, as in senile brain disease and Alzheimer's presenile dementia.

VIII. *Acute and chronic brain syndromes associated with intracranial neoplasm*
   A. Primary tumors, originating within the skull, may be invasive (malignant) or localized (benign).
   B. Secondary (metastatic) tumors from primary cancer elsewhere in the body.

IX. *Acute and chronic brain syndromes associated with diseases of unknown or uncertain cause*
These are usually chronic degenerative diseases of the brain and nervous system whose causation is only partly established, such as multiple sclerosis, Huntington's chorea, and Pick's presenile dementia.

such as *those due to infection:* cytomegalic inclusion body disease, congenital rubella, influenza, congenital syphilis, toxoplasmosis; *those due to intoxication:* bilirubin encephalopathy (kernicterus) and other encephalopathies; *those due to disorders of nutrition, growth or metabolism:* lipoidoses (sphingolipoidoses), including Tay-Sach disease, Niemann-Pick disease, Gaucher disease, metachromatic leukodystrophy; aminoacidurias, including phenylketonuria, maple syrup urine disease; *defects of carbohydrate metabolism,* including galactosemia, gargoylism, hypothyroidism; *those due to new growths:* tuberous sclerosis; *those due to chromosomal aberrations:* mongolism, Klinefelter's syndrome, Turner's syndrome; *those due to unknown prenatal influence:* craniostenosis, including hydrocephalus and hypertelorism.

[2]From I. Gregory. *Fundamentals of psychiatry.* (2nd ed.) Philadelphia: W. B. Saunders, 1968, p. 566. Reprinted by permission of the publisher and the author.

The term "mental retardation" is used interchangeably with "mental deficiency" (and sometimes with "feeblemindedness"), though some authors prefer to draw distinctions between them (Sarason, 1966), yet these diagnostic labels refer to a heterogeneous group of individuals (Sarason & Doris, 1969). Ellis (1963) also concurs with the view that mental deficiency is not a unitary state, but a collection of numerous and varying conditions. While the American Psychiatric Association prefers the term "mental deficiency," "mental retardation" is the choice of the American Association on Mental Deficiency. Mental retardation, as is true of other areas of psychopathology (e.g., psychopharmacology), should not be viewed as the exclusive province of any single discipline (Philips, 1966).

THEORIES OF BRAIN PATHOLOGY

Goldstein's Organismic and Holistic Theory of Brain Pathology

According to Goldstein (1939, 1940, 1952), the personality with but a single drive strives to actualize itself and to "come to terms" with its environment. But in certain cases of brain damage, a "catastrophic reaction" of anxiety prevails that inhibits the individual from coming to suitable terms with the world. Brain-damaged patients find their ability to think abstractly impaired, with other portions of the brain striving to undertake the function of the impaired area. Brain-damaged patients "have lost initiative and the capacity to look forward to something and to make plans and decisions; they lack phantasy and inspiration; their perceptions, thoughts, and ideas are reduced; they have lost the capacity for real contact with others, and they are therefore incapable of real friendship" (Goldstein, 1952, p. 255). The brain-damaged patient, being in a catastrophic condition characterized by anxiety, cannot achieve self-realization. Such persons seek to achieve self-realization by exhibiting fanatical orderliness and preferring familiar surroundings. Their inability to cope with change creates within them a state of anxious excitement.

Penfield's Theory of the Memory Mechanism

Penfield, in experiments with Rasmussen (1950) that entailed the frontal lobes of monkeys, found that these lobes are involved in memory information storage. In surgical operations on epileptics, Penfield (1952, 1959; Penfield & Milner, 1958; Penfield & Roberts, 1959) found that the electrical stimulation of the temporal cortex evoked memories of both a visual and auditory character. Occasionally, and while the patient is yet conscious, the stimulation of the same or an adjacent area on the cortex at a later date could reproduce the same recollection, the assumption being that the reactivation of the brain patterns in question was part of the original experience. At times, stimulation of the same area produces a quite different response; on these occasions, the patient "has somehow changed his own interpretation of what he is seeing at the moment, or hearing or thinking" (Penfield, 1959, p. 1720). Penfield concluded that the interpretive cortex contains a mechanism capable of reactivating instantly and in detail one's past record in memory. In addition it possesses mechanization capable of producing interpretive signals.

50.

KURT GOLDSTEIN

EFFECT OF BRAIN DAMAGE ON PERSONALITY

When I was asked to speak before the Psychoanalytic Association about the changes of the personality in brain damage, I was somewhat hesitant because I was not quite sure that I would be able to make myself understood by an audience which thinks mainly in such different categories and speaks in such a different terminology from my own. I finally accepted the invitation, because I thought that members of the Association apparently wanted to hear what I think and because it brought me the opportunity to express an old idea of mine—the idea that it is faulty in principle to try to make a distinction between so-called organic and functional diseases, as far as symptomatology and therapy are concerned.[1] In both conditions, one is dealing with abnormal functioning of the same psychophysical apparatus and with the attempts of the organism to come to terms with that. If the disturbances—whether they are due to damage to the brain or to psychological conflicts—do not disappear spontaneously or cannot be eliminated by therapy, the organism has to make a new adjustment to life in spite of them. Our task is to help the patients in this adjustment by physical and psychological means; the procedure and goal of the therapy in both conditions is, in principle, the same.

This was the basic idea which induced a group of neurologists, psychiatrists, and psychotherapists—including myself—many years ago, in 1927, to organize the Internationale Gesellschaft für Psychotherapie in Germany and to invite all physicians interested in psychotherapy to meet at the First Congress of the Society. Psychotherapists of all different schools responded to our invitation, and the result of the discussions was surprisingly fruitful. At the second meeting in 1927, I spoke about the relation between psychoanalysis and biology.[2] During the last twenty years, in which I have occupied myself intensively with psychotherapy, I have become more and more aware of the similarity of the phenomena of organic and psychogenic conditions.

It is not my intention to consider the similarities in this paper. I want to restrict myself to the description of the symptomatology and the interpretation of the behavior changes in patients with damage to the brain cortex, particularly in respect to their personality, and would like to leave it to you to make comparisons.

The symptomatology which these patients present is very complex.[3] It is the effect of various factors of which the change of personality is only one. Therefore, when we want to characterize the change of personality, we have to separate it from the symptoms due to other factors: (1) from those which are the effect of *disturbance of inborn or learned patterns* of performances in special performance fields—such as motor and sensory patterns; (2) from those which are the *expression of the so-called catastrophic conditions;* and (3) from those which are the *expression of the protective mechanisms* which originate from the attempt of the organism to avoid catastrophies.

From Kurt Goldstein," The effect of brain damage on the personality." *Psychiatry,* 1952, *15,* 245–260. This paper was presented, by invitation, at the annual meeting of the American Psychoanalytic Association, Atlantic City, May, 1952. Reprinted by special permission of The William Alanson White Psychiatric Foundation, Inc.; and the Estate of Kurt Goldstein. Copyright 1952 by The Foundation.
[1]See K. Goldstein, "Ueber die gleichartige functionelle Bedingtheit der Symptome in organischen und psychischen Krankheiten," *Monatsschrift für Psychiatrie und Neurologie,* 1924, 57, 191.

[2]K. Goldstein, "Die Beziehungen der Psychoanalyse zur Biologie"; in *Verhandlungen d. Congresses für Psychotherapie in Nauheim* (Leipzig: Hirzel, 1927).

[3]See K. Goldstein, *Aftereffects of Brain Injuries in War* (New York: Grune & Stratton, 1942).

In order to avoid terminological misunderstandings, I want to state what I mean by personality: Personality shows itself in behavior. Personality is the mode of behavior of a person in terms of the capacities of human beings in general and in the specific appearance of these capacities in a particular person. Behavior is always an entity and concerns the whole personality. Only abstractively can we separate behavior into parts—as for instance, bodily processes, conscious phenomena, states of feelings, attitudes, and so on.[4]

According to my observation, all the phenomena of behavior become understandable if one assumes that all the behavior of the organism is determined by one trend,[5] the *trend to actualize itself*—that is, its nature and all its capacities. This takes place normally in such harmony that the realization of all capacities in the best way possible in the particular environment is permitted. The capacities are experienced by a person as various *needs* which he is driven to fulfill with the cooperation of some parts of the environment and in spite of the hindrance by other parts of it.

Each stimulation brings about some disorder in the organism. But after a certain time—which is determined by the particular performance—the organism comes back, by a process of *equalization*, to its normal condition. This process guarantees the constancy of the organism. A person's specific personality corresponds to this constancy. Because realization has to take place in terms of different needs and different tasks, the behavior of the organism is soon directed more by one than by another need. This does not mean that organismic behavior is determined by separate needs or drives. All such concepts need the assumption of a controlling agency. I have tried to show in my book, *The Organism*, that the different agencies which have been assumed for this purpose have only made for new difficulties in the attempt to understand organismic behavior; they are not necessary if one gives up the concept of separate drives, as my theory of the organism does. All of a person's capacities are always in action in each of his activities. The capacity that is particularly important for the task is in the foreground; the others are in the background. All of these capacities are organized in a way which facilitates the self-realization of the total organism in the particular situation. For each performance there is a definite figure ground organization of capacities; the change in the behavior of a patient corresponds to the change in the total organism in the form of an alteration of the normal pattern of figure-ground organization.[6]

Among patients with brain damage we can distinguish between alterations which occur when an area belonging to a special performance field—such as a motor or sensory area—is damaged somewhat isolatedly, and alterations which occur when the personality organization itself is altered. In lesions of these areas—according to a dedifferentiation of the function of the brain cortex[7]—qualities and patterns of behavior (both those developing as a result of maturation and those acquired by learning) are disturbed. Indeed, these patterns never occur isolatedly. They are always embedded in that kind of behavior which we call personality. The personality structure is disturbed particularly by lesions of the frontal lobes, the parietal lobes, and the insula Reili; but it is also disturbed by diffuse damage to the cortex—for instance, in paralysis, alcoholism, and trauma, and in metabolic disturbances such as hypoglycemia. The effect of diffuse damage is understandable when we consider that what we call personality structure apparently is not related to a definite locality of the cortex[8] but to a particular complex function of the brain which is the same for all its parts. This function can be damaged especially by lesions in any of the areas I have mentioned. The damage of the patterns certainly modifies the personality too. Although for full understanding of the personality changes, we should discuss the organization of the patterns and their destruction in damaged patients, that would carry us too far and is not absolutely

[4]See K. Goldstein, *The Organism: A Holistic Approach to Biology* (New York: American Book Co., 1939), pp. 310 ff.

[5]See K. Goldstein, *Human Nature in the Light of Psychopathology* (Cambridge: Harvard University Press, 1940), p. 194.

[6]Goldstein, *The Organism, op. cit.*, p. 109.

[7]*Ibid.*, p. 131.

[8]*Ibid.*, pp. 249 ff.

necessary for our discussion. I shall therefore restrict my presentation to consideration of the symptoms due to damage of the personality structure itself.[9]

There would be no better way of getting to the heart of the problem than by demonstrating a patient. Unfortunately I have to substitute for this a description of the behavior of patients with severe damage of the brain cortex. Let us consider a man with an extensive lesion of the frontal lobes.[10] His customary way of living does not seem to be very much disturbed. He is a little slow; his face is rather immobile, rather rigid; his attention is directed very strictly to what he is doing at the moment—say, writing a letter, or speaking to someone. Confronted with tasks in various fields, he gives seemingly normal responses under certain conditions; but under other conditions he fails completely in tasks that seem to be very similar to those he has performed quite well.

This change of behavior becomes apparent particularly in the following simple test: We place before him a small wooden stick in a definite position, pointing, for example, diagonally from left to right. He is asked to note the position of the stick carefully. After a half minute's exposure, the stick is removed; then it is handed to the patient, and he is asked to put it back in the position in which it was before. He grasps the stick and tries to replace it, but he fumbles; he is all confusion; he looks at the examiner, shakes his head, tries this way and that, plainly uncertain. The upshot is that he cannot place the stick in the required position. He is likewise unable to imitate other simple figures built of sticks. Next we show the patient a little house made of many sticks—a house with a roof, a door, a window, and a chimney. After we remove it, we ask the patient to reproduce the model. He succeeds very well.

---

[9] See K. Goldstein, *Handbuch der normalen und pathologischen Physiologie* (Berlin: J. S. Springer, 1927), Vol. 10, pp. 600 ff. and 813.

[10] K. Goldstein, "The Significance of the Frontal Lobes for Mental Performances," *Journal of Neurology and Psychopathology*, 1936, 17, 27–40; and "The Modifications of Behavior Consequent to Cerebral Lesions," *Psychiatric Quarterly*, 1936, 10, 586.

IMPAIRMENT OF ABSTRACT CAPACITY

If we ask ourselves what is the cause of the difference in his behavior in the two tasks, we can at once exclude defects in the field of perception, action, and memory. For there is no doubt that copying the house with many details demands a much greater capacity in all these faculties, especially in memory, than putting a single stick into a position which the patient has been shown shortly before. A further experiment clarifies the situation. We put before the patient two sticks placed together so as to form an angle with the opening pointing upward (V). The patient is unable to reproduce this model. Then we confront him with the same angle, the opening downward this time (Λ), and now he reproduces the figure very well on the first trial. When we ask the patient how it is that he can reproduce the second figure but not the first one, he says, "This one has nothing to do with the other one." Pointing to the second one, he says, "That is a roof"; pointing to the first, "That is nothing."

These two replies lead us to an understanding of the patient's behavior. His first reply makes it clear that, to him, the two objects with which he has to deal are totally different from one another. The second answer shows that he apprehends the angle with the opening downward as a concrete object out of his own experience, and he constructs a concrete thing with the two sticks. The two sticks that formed an angle with the opening upward apparently did not arouse an impression of a concrete thing. He had to regard the sticks as representations indicating directions in abstract space. Furthermore, he had to keep these directions in mind and rearrange the sticks from memory as representatives of these abstract directions. To solve the problem he must give an account to himself of relations in space and must act on the basis of abstract ideas. Thus we may conclude that the failure of the patient in the first test lies in the fact that he is unable to perform a task which can be executed only by means of a grasp of the abstract. The test in which the opening of the angle is downwards does not demand this, since the patient is able to grasp it as a concrete object and therefore to execute it perfectly. It is for the same reason that he is able to copy the little house, which seems to us to be so much more complicated. From the result of his behavior in this and similar tasks we come to the assumption that these *patients are impaired in their abstract capacity.*

The term "abstract attitude," which I shall use in describing this capacity, will be more comprehensible in the light of the following explanation.[11] We can distinguish two different kinds of attitudes, the concrete and the abstract. In the concrete attitude we are given over passively and bound to the immediate experience of unique objects or situations. Our thinking and acting are determined by the immediate claims made by the particular aspect of the object or situation. For instance, we act concretely when we enter a room in darkness and push the button for light. If, however, we reflect that by pushing the button we might awaken someone asleep in the room, and desist from pushing the button, then we are acting abstractively. We transcend the immediately given specific aspect of sense impressions; we detach ourselves from these impressions, consider the situation from a conceptual point of view, and react accordingly. Our actions are determined not so much by the objects before us as by the way we think about them: the individual thing becomes a mere accidental representative of a category to which it belongs.

The impairment of the attitude toward the abstract shows in every performance of the brain-damaged patient who is impaired in this capacity. He always fails when the solution of a task presupposes this attitude; he performs well when the appropriate activity is determined directly by the stimuli and when the task can be fulfilled by concrete behavior. He may have no difficulty in using known objects in a situation that requires them; but he is totally at a loss if he is asked to demonstrate the use of such an object outside the concrete situation, and still more so if he is asked to do it without

the real object. A few examples will illustrate this.

The patient is asked to blow away a slip of paper. He does this very well. If the paper is taken away and he is asked to think that there is a slip of paper and to blow it away, he is unable to do so. Here the situation is not realistically complete. In order to perform the task the patient would have to imagine the piece of paper there. He is not capable of this.

The patient is asked to throw a ball into open boxes situated respectively at distances of three, nine, and fifteen feet. He does that correctly. When he is asked how far the several boxes are from him, he is not only unable to answer this question but unable even to say which box is nearest to him and which is farthest.

In the first action, the patient has only to deal with objects in a behavioral fashion. It is unnecessary for him to be conscious of this behavior and of objects in a world separated from himself. In the second, however, he must separate himself from objects in the outer world and give himself an account of his actions and of the space relations in the world facing him. Since he is unable to do this, he fails. We could describe this failure also by saying that the patient is unable to deal with a situation which is only possible.

A simple story is read to a patient. He may repeat some single words, but he does not understand their meaning and is unable to grasp the essential point. Now we read him another story, which would seem to a normal person to be more difficult to understand. This time he understands the meaning very well and recounts the chief points. The first story deals with a simple situation, but a situation which has no connection with the actual situation of the patient. The second story recounts a situation he is familiar with. Hence one could say the patient is able to grasp and handle only something which is related to himself.

Such a patient almost always recognizes pictures of single objects, even if the picture contains many details. In pictures which represent a composition of a number of things and persons, he may pick out some details; but

---

[11]See K. Goldstein and M. Scheerer, *Abstract and Concrete Behavior,* Psychological Monographs. No. 239, 1941.

he is unable to understand the picture as a whole and is unable to respond to the whole. The patient's real understanding does not depend on the greater or smaller number of components in a picture but on whether the components, whatever their number, hang together concretely and are familiar to him, or whether an understanding of their connection requires a more abstract synthesis on his part. He may lack understanding of a picture even if there are only a few details. If the picture does not reveal its essence directly, by bringing the patient into the situation which it represents, he is not able to understand it. Thus one may characterize the deficiency as an inability to discover the essence of a situation which is not related to his own personality.

MEMORY AND ATTENTION

This change in behavior finds its expression in characteristic changes in memory and attention. Under certain circumstances the faculty for reproduction of facts acquired previously may be about normal. For example, things learned in school may be recalled very well, but only in some situations. The situation must be suited to reawakening old impressions. If the required answer demands an abstract attitude on the part of a patient or if it demands that he give an account of the matter in question, the patient is unable to remember. Therefore he fails in many intelligence tests which may seem very simple for a normal person, and he is amazingly successful in others which appear complicated to us. He is able to learn new facts and to keep them in mind; but he can learn them only in a concrete situation and can reproduce them only in the same situation in which he has learned them. Because the intentional recollection of experiences acquired in infancy requires an abstract attitude toward the situation at that time, the patient is unable to recall infancy experiences in a voluntary way; but we can observe that the aftereffect of such experiences sometimes appears passively in his behavior. Such a patient has the greatest difficulty in associating freely; he cannot assume the attitude of mind to make that possible. He is incapable of recollection when he is asked to recall things which have nothing to do with the given situa-

tion. The patient must be able to regard the present situation in such a way that facts from the past belong to it. If this is not the case, he is completely unable to recall facts which he has recalled very well in another situation. Repeated observation in many different situations demonstrates clearly that such memory failures are not caused by an impairment of memory content. The patient has the material in his memory, but he is unable to use it freely; he can use it only in connection with a definite concrete situation.

We arrive at the same result in testing attention. At one time the patient appears inattentive and distracted; at another time, he is attentive, even abnormally so. The patient's attention is usually weak in special examinations, particularly at the beginning before he has become aware of the real approach to the whole situation. In such a situation he ordinarily seems much distracted. If he is able to enter into the situation, however, his attention may be satisfactory; sometimes his reactions are even abnormally keen. Under these circumstances he may be totally untouched by other stimuli from the environment to which normal persons will unfailingly react. In some tests he will always seem distracted; for example, in those situations which demand a change of approach (a choice), he always seems distracted because he is incapable of making a choice. Consequently, it is not correct to speak of a change of attention in these patients in terms of plus or minus. The state of the patient's attention is but part of his total behavior and is to be understood only in connection with it.

EMOTIONAL RESPONSES

The same holds true if we observe the emotions of the patients. Usually they are considered emotionally dull and often they appear so, but it would not be correct to say simply that they are suffering from a diminution of emotions. The same patients can be dull under some conditions and very excited under others. This can be explained when we consider the patient's emotional behavior in relation to his entire behavior in a given situation. When he does not react emotionally in an adequate way, investigation reveals that he has not grasped the situation in such a way that emotion could arise. In fact, we might experience a similar lack of emotion through failing to grasp a situation. The patient may have grasped only one part of the situation —the part which can be grasped concretely— and this part may not give any reason for an emotional reaction. The lack of emotion appears to us inappropriate because we grasp with the abstract attitude the whole situation to which the emotional character is attached. This connection between the emotions and the total behavior becomes understandable when we consider that emotions are not simply related to particular experiences but are, as I have shown on another occasion,[12] inherent aspects of behavior—part and parcel of behavior. No behavior is without emotion and what we call lack of emotion is a deviation from normal emotions corresponding to the deviation of behavior in general. From this point of view, one modification of reactions that is of particular interest in respect to the problem of emotions in general, becomes understandable. Often we see that a patient reacts either not at all or in an *abnormally quick manner*. The latter occurs particularly when the patient believes he has the correct answer to a problem. Although this behavior might seem to be the effect of a change in the time factor of his reactivity, it is rather the *effect of an emotional factor*—that is, it is the modification of his emotional feelings because of the impairment of his ability for abstraction— which in turn modifies the time reaction.

PLEASURE AND JOY

These patients are always somewhat in danger of being in a catastrophic condition—which I shall discuss later—as a result of not being able to find the right solution to a problem put before them. They are often afraid that they may not be able to react correctly, and that they will be in a catastrophic condition. Therefore, when they believe they have the right answer, they answer as quickly as possible. Because of impairment of abstraction, they are not able to deliberate; they try to do what they can do

as quickly as possible because every retardation increases the tension which they experience when they are not able to answer. The quick response is an effect of their *strong necessity to release tension;* they are forced to release tension because they cannot handle it any other way. They cannot bear anything that presupposes deliberation, considering the future, and so on, all of which are related to abstraction.

This difference in behavior between these patients and more normal people throws light on the nature of the *trend to release tension*. These patients must, so to speak, follow the "pleasure principle." This phenomenon is one *expression of the abnormal concreteness* which is a counterpart to the impairment of abstraction. The *trend to release tension appears to be an expression of pathology*—the effect of a protective mechanism to prevent catastrophic condition. To normal behavior belong deliberation and retardation; but in addition there is the ability to speed up an activity or a part of it to correspond to the requirements of the task, or at least part of the requirements, so that its performance guarantees self-realization. Sometimes the ability to bear tension and even to enjoy it are also a part of this normal behavior. In contrast, the patients that I am talking about are only able to experience the pleasure of release of tension; they never appear to enjoy anything—a fact which is often clearly revealed by the expression on their faces. This becomes understandable if we consider that immediate reality is transcended in any kind of joy and that joy is a capacity we owe to the abstract attitude, especially that part of it concerned with possibility. Thus brain-injured patients who are impaired in this attitude cannot experience joy. Experience with brain-injured patients teaches us that we have to distinguish between *pleasure by release of tension*, and the active *feeling of enjoyment* and freedom so characteristic of joy. Pleasure through release of tension is the agreeable feeling which we experience on returning to a state of equilibrium after it has been disturbed—the passive feeling of being freed from distress. Pleasure lasts only a short time till a new situation stimulates new activity; we then try to get rid of the tension of the new situation which acts to shorten the span of

---

[12] See K. Goldstein, "On Emotions: Considerations from the Organismic Point of View," *Journal of Psychology*, 1951, 31, 37–49.

pleasure. In contrast, we try to extend joy. This explains the different speeds of joy and pleasure. Because of the capacity for joy, we can experience the possibility of the indefinite continuation of a situation. The two emotions of joy and pleasure play essentially different roles in regard to self-realization; they belong to different performances or different parts of a performance; they belong to different moods. Pleasure may be a necessary state of respite. But it is a phenomenon of standstill; it is akin to death. It separates us from the world and the other individuals in it; it is equilibrium, quietness. In joy there is disequilibrium. But it is a productive disequilibrium, leading toward fruitful activity and a particular kind of self-realization. This difference in approach between the normal person and the brain-injured patient is mirrored in the essentially different behavior of the latter and the different world in which he lives. The different significance of the two emotional states in his total behavior is related to their time difference.

Edith Jacobson,[13] in the outline of her paper presented to the Psychoanalytic Association, speaks about the speed factor in psychic discharge processes and comes to the conclusion that discharge is not the only process which produces pleasure—that we have to distinguish between different qualities of pleasure in terms of the slow rising and the quick falling of tension. That is very much in accordance with my conclusions derived from experience with brain-injured patients. If one distinguishes two forms of pleasure, one should, for clarity's sake, use different names for them; I think that my use of pleasure and joy fits the two experiences. But I would not like to call them both discharge processes: the one is a discharge process; the other one a very active phenomenon related to the highest form of mental activity—abstraction. From this it becomes clear why they have such an essentially different significance in the totality of performance: the one is an equalization process which prepares the organism for new

activity; the other one is an activity of highest value for self-realization. They belong together just as in general equalization process and activity belong together. Therefore they cannot be understood as isolated phenomena.

THE PHENOMENON OF WITTICISM

From this viewpoint of the emotions of brain-injured patients, the phenomenon of witticism appears in a new aspect. We can see that even though a patient makes witty remarks, he is not able to grasp the character of situations which produce humor in an average normal individual. Whether or not some situation appears humorous depends upon whether it can be grasped in a concrete way which is suited to producing the emotion of humor. In accordance with the impairment of his ability for abstraction, such a patient perceives many humorous pictures in a realistic way, which does not evoke the expected humor. But of course any of us who might at a given time perceive a humorous picture in a realistic way would respond similarly. On the other hand a patient may make a witty remark in relation to a situation which is not considered humorous by us, because he has experienced the situation in another way. Thus we should not speak of witticism as a special characteristic of these patients. It is but one expression of the change in their personality structure in the same way that their inability to understand jokes under other conditions expresses this change. Indeed, these patients are in general dull because of their limited experience, and their witticisms are superficial and shallow in comparison with those of normal people.

FRIENDSHIP AND LOVE

The drive towards the release of tension, which I have already mentioned, is one of the causes of the strange behavior of these patients in friendship and love situations. They need close relationships to other people and they try to maintain such relationships at all cost; at the same time such relationships are easily terminated suddenly if the bearing of tension is necessary for the maintenance of the relationship.

The following example is illustrative: A pa-

---

[13]Edith Jacobson, "The Speed Pace in Psychic Discharge Processes and Its Influence on the Pleasure-Unpleasure Qualities of Affects," paper read before the Amer. Psychoanal. Assn., Atlantic City, May, 1952.

tient of mine, Mr. A, was for years a close friend of another patient, Mr. X. One day Mr. X went to a movie with a third man. Mr. X did not take Mr. A along because Mr. A had seen the picture before and did not want to see it a second time. When Mr. X came back, my patient was in a state of great excitement and refused to speak to him. Mr. A could not be quieted by any explanations; he was told that his friend had not meant to offend him, and that the friendship had not changed, but these explanations made no impression. From that time on, Mr. A was the enemy of his old friend, Mr. X. He was only aware that his friend was the companion of another man, and he felt himself slighted. This experience produced a great tension in him. He regarded his friend as the cause of this bad condition and reacted to him in a way that is readily understandable in terms of his inability to bear tension and to put himself in the place of somebody else.

Another patient never seemed to be concerned about his family. He never spoke of his wife or children and was unresponsive when we questioned him about them. When we suggested to him that he should write to his family, he was utterly indifferent. He appeared to lack all feeling in this respect. At times he visited his home in another town, according to an established practice, and stayed there several days. We learned that while he was at home, he conducted himself in the same way that any man would in the bosom of his family. He was kind and affectionate to his wife and children and interested in their affairs insofar as his abilities would permit. Upon his return to the hospital from such a visit, he would smile in an embarrassed way and give evasive answers when he was asked about his family; he seemed utterly estranged from his home situation. Unquestionably the peculiar behavior of this man was not really the effect of deterioration of his character on the emotional and moral side; rather, his behavior was the result of the fact that he could not summon up the home situation when he was not actually there.

Lack of imagination, which is so apparent in this example, makes such patients incapable of experiencing any expectation of the future. This lack is apparent, for instance, in the behavior of a male patient toward a woman whom he later married.[14] When he was with the girl, he seemed to behave in a friendly, affectionate way and to be very fond of the girl. But when he was separated from her, he did not care about her at all; he would not seek her out and certainly did not desire to have a love relationship with her. When he was questioned, his answers indicated that he did not even understand what sexual desire meant. But in addition he had forgotten about the girl. When he met her again and she spoke to him, he was able immediately to enter into the previous relation. He was as affectionate as before. When she induced him to go to bed with her and embraced him, he performed an apparently normal act of sexual intercourse with satisfaction for both. She had the feeling that he loved her. She became pregnant, and they were married.

CHANGE IN LANGUAGE

Of particular significance in these patients is the change in their language because of their lack of abstract attitude.[15] Their words lose the character of meaning. Words are not usable in those situations in which they must represent a concept. Therefore the patients are not able to find the proper words in such situations. Thus, for instance, patients are not able to name concrete objects, since as shown by investigation, naming presupposes an abstract attitude and the abstract use of words. These patients have not lost the sound complex; but they cannot use it as a sign for a concept. On other occasions, the sound complex may be uttered; but it is only used at those times as a simple association to a given object, as a property of the object, such as color and form, and not as representative of a concept. If a patient has been particularly gifted in language before his brain is damaged and has retained many such associations or can acquire associations as a substitute for naming something, then he may utter the right word through association, so that an ob-

---

[14]K. Goldstein and J. I. Steinfeld, "The Conditioning of Sexual Behavior by Visual Agnosia," *Bull. Forest Sanit.*, Vol. 1, No. 2 (1942), pp. 37–45.
[15]See K. Goldstein, *Language and Language Disturbances* (New York: Grune & Stratton, 1918), p. 56.

server is not able to distinguish between his uttering the sound complex and giving a name to something; only through analysis can one make this distinction.[16] Thus we can easily overlook the patient's defect by arriving at a conclusion only on the basis of this capacity for a positive effect. In the same way we can be deceived by a negative effect which may only be an expression, for instance, of the patient's fear that he will use the wrong word. I have used the term *fallacy of effect* to describe the uncertain and ambiguous character of a conclusion which is based only upon a patient's effective performance. This term applies not only to language but to all performances of the patients. It is the source of one of the most fatal mistakes which can be made in interpretation of phenomena observed in organic patients; incidentally, it is a mistake which can be made also in functional cases.

FRONTAL LOBOTOMY

In reference to the fallacy of effect, I want to stress how easily one can be deceived about the mental condition of patients who have undergone frontal lobotomy. The results of the usual intelligence test, evaluated statistically, may not reveal any definite deviation from the norm; yet the patient can have an impairment of abstraction that will become obvious through tests which take into consideration the fallacy of effect.[17] My experience with frontal lobotomy patients and my evaluation of the literature on frontal lobotomy leave no doubt in my mind that at least many of these patients show impairment of abstract capacity, although perhaps not to such a degree as do patients with gross damage of the brain. Because of the fallacy of effect, which tends to overlook the defect in abstraction, the reports of the relatives that the lobotomized patient behaves well in every-

day life are often evaluated incorrectly by the doctor.[18] In the sheltered, simple life that these patients have with their families, the patients are not often confronted with tasks which require abstract reasoning; thus the family is likely to overlook their more subtle deviations from the norm. Sometimes peculiarities of the patient are reported which definitely point to a defect in abstraction, which is more serious than it is often evaluated: for instance, a patient who in general seems to live in a normal way does not have any relationship with even the closest members of his family and manifests no interest in his children; another patient exists in a vacuum so that no friendship is possible with him.

A woman patient after lobotomy still knows how to set a table for guests, and how to act as a perfect hostess. Before lobotomy, she was always a careful housewife, deciding everything down to the last detail; but now she does not care how the house is run, she never enters the kitchen, and the housekeeper does all the managing, even the shopping. She still reads a great number of books, but she does not understand the contents as well as before.

A skilled mechanic, who is still considered an excellent craftsman, is able to work in a routine way; but he has lost the ability to undertake complicated jobs, has stopped studying, and seems to have resigned himself to being a routine worker, apparently all this is an effect of the loss of his capacity for abstraction, which is so necessary for all initiative and for creative endeavor. Thus we see that even when the behavior of the patients appears not to be overtly disturbed, it differs essentially from normal behavior—in the particular way which is characteristic of impairment in abstract attitude. Freeman,[19] who was originally so enthusiastically in favor of the operation, has become more cautious about its damage to the higher mental functions. He writes:

The patients with frontal lobotomy show always some lack of personality depth; impulse, intelligence,

---

[16]*Ibid.*, p. 61.

[17]Thirty years ago we constructed special tests when we were faced with the problem of re-educating brain-injured soldiers. (See K. Goldstein and A. Gelb, "Ueber Farbennamenamnesie," *Psychol. Forsch.* 1924, *6*, 127). These tests, which were introduced in America by Scheerer and myself (reference footnote 11), proved to be particularly useful not only for studying the problem of abstraction in patients, but also for the correct organization of treatment.

[18]See K. Goldstein, "Frontal Lobotomy and Impairment of Abstract Attitude," *Journal of Nervous and Mental Disease*, 1949, *110*, 93–111.

[19]W. Freeman and J. Watts, *Psychosurgery*, (2d ed.; Springfield, Ill., Thomas), 1950.

temperament are disturbed; the creative capacity undergoes reduction—the spiritual life in general was affected. They are largely indifferent to the opinions and feelings of others.

He apparently discovered the same personality changes in his patients as those which we have described as characteristic of the behavior of patients with impaired capacity for abstraction. Thus we should be very careful in judging personality change following frontal lobotomy. Although I would not deny the usefulness of the operation in some cases, I would like to say, as I have before, that the possibility of an impairment of abstraction should always be taken into consideration before the operation is undertaken.

I would now like to present a survey of the various situations in which the patient is unable to perform. He fails when he has: (1) to assume a mental set voluntarily or to take initiative (for instance, he may even be able to perform well in giving a series of numbers, once someone else has presented the first number, but he cannot begin the activity); (2) to shift voluntarily from one aspect of a situation to another, making a choice; (3) to account to himself for his actions or to verbalize the account; (4) to keep in mind simultaneously various aspects of a situation or to react to two stimuli which do not belong intrinsically together; (5) to grasp the essence of a given whole, or to break up a given whole into parts, isolating the parts voluntarily and combining them into wholes; (6) to abstract common properties, to plan ahead ideationally, to assume an attitude toward a situation which is only possible, and to think or perform symbolically; (7) to do something which necessitates detaching the ego from the outer word or from inner experiences.

All these and other terms which one may use to describe the behavior of the patients basically mean the same. We speak usually, in brief, of an *impairment of abstract attitude*. I hope that it has become clear that the use of this term does not refer to a theoretical interpretation but to the real behavior of the human being and that it is suitable for describing both normal and pathological personality.

In brief, the patients are changed with respect to the most characteristic properties of the human being. They have lost initiative and the capacity to look forward to something and to make plans and decisions; they lack phantasy and inspiration; their perceptions, thoughts, and ideas are reduced; they have lost the capacity for real contact with others, and they are therefore incapable of real friendship, love, and social relations. One could say they have no real ego and no real world. That they behave in an abnormally concrete way and that they are driven to get rid of tensions are only expressions of the same defect. When such patients are able to complete a task in a concrete way, they may—with regard to the effect of their activity—not appear very abnormal. But closer examination shows that they are abnormally rigid, stereotyped, and compulsive, and abnormally bound to stimuli from without and within.

To avoid any misunderstanding, I would like to stress that the defect in patients with brain damage does not always have to manifest itself in the same way—not even in all frontal lobe lesions. To what degree impairment of abstraction appears depends upon the extensiveness, the intensity, and the nature of the lesion. To evaluate the relationship between a patient's behavior and his defect, we have to consider further that personal experience plays a role in determining whether a patient can solve a problem or not. One patient reacts well—at least at face value—when he is given a task, although another patient has failed the same task; to the first patient the task represents a concrete situation; for the second patient it is an abstract situation. But in both cases, the defect will always be revealed by further examination.

CATASTROPHIC CONDITIONS

Impairment of abstraction is not the only factor which produces deviations in the behavior of patients, as I have stated before. Another very important factor is the occurrence of a catastrophic condition.[20] When a patient is not able to fulfill a task set before him, this condition is a frequent occurrence. A patient may look animated, calm, in a good mood, well-poised,

---

[20]Goldstein, *The Organism, op. cit.,* pp. 35 ff.

collected, and cooperative when he is confronted with tasks he can fulfill; the same patient may appear dazed, become agitated, change color, start to fumble, become unfriendly, evasive, and even aggressive when he is not able to fulfill the task. His overt behavior appears very much the same as a person in a state of anxiety. I have called the state of the patient in the situation of success, *ordered condition;* the state in the situation of failure, *disordered or catastrophic condition.*

In the catastrophic condition the patient not only is incapable of performing a task which exceeds his impaired capacity, but he also fails, for a longer or shorter period, in performances which he is able to carry out in the ordered state. For a varying period of time, the organism's reactions are in great disorder or are impeded altogether. We are able to study this condition particularly well in these patients, since we can produce it experimentally by demanding from the patient something which we know he will not be able to do, because of his defect. Now, as we have said, impairment of abstraction makes it impossible for a patient to account to himself for his acts. He is quite unable to realize his failure and why he fails. Thus we can assume that catastrophic condition is not a reaction of the patient to failure, but rather belongs intrinsically to the situation of the organism in failing. For the normal person, failure in the performance of a nonimportant task would be merely something disagreeable; for the brain-injured person, however, as observation shows, any failure means the impossibility of self-realization and of existence. The occurrence of catastrophic condition is not limited therefore to special tasks; any task can place the patient in this situation, since the patient's self-realization is endangered so easily. Thus the same task produces anxiety at one time, and not at another.

ANXIETY

The conditions under which anxiety occurs in brain-injured patients correspond to the conditions for its occurrence in normal people in that what produces anxiety is not the failure itself, but the resultant danger to the person's exist-ence. I would like to add that the danger need not always be real; it is sufficient if the person imagines that the condition is such that he will not be able to realize himself. For instance, a person may be in distress because he is not able to answer questions in an examination. If the outcome of the examination is not particularly important, then the normal person will take it calmly even though he may feel somewhat upset; because it is not a dangerous situation for him, he will face the situation and try to come to terms with it as well as he can by using his wits, and in this way he will bring it to a more or less successful solution. The situation becomes totally different, however, if passing the examination is of great consequence in the person's life; not passing the examination may, for instance, endanger his professional career or the possibility of marrying the person he loves. When self-realization is seriously in danger, catastrophe may occur together with severe anxiety; when this occurs, it is impossible for the person to answer even those questions which, under other circumstances, he could solve without difficulty.

I would like to clarify one point here—namely, that anxiety represents an emotional state which does not refer to any object. Certainly the occurrence of anxiety is connected with an outer or inner event. The organism, shaken by a catastrophic shock, exists in relation to a definitive reality; and the basic phenomenon of anxiety, which is the occurrence of disordered behavior, is understandable only in terms of this relationship to reality. But anxiety does not originate from the experiencing of this relationship. The brain-injured patient could not experience anxiety, if it were necessary for him to experience this relationship to reality. He is certainly not aware of this objective reality; he experiences only the shock, only anxiety. And this, of course holds true for anxiety in general. Observations of many patients confirm the interpretation of anxiety by philosophers, such as Pascal and Kierkegaard, and by psychologists who have dealt with anxiety—namely, that the source of anxiety is the inner experience of not being confronted with anything or of being confronted with nothingness.

In making such a statement, one must distinguish sharply between *anxiety* and *fear*— another emotional state which is very often confused with anxiety.[21] Superficially, fear may have many of the characteristics of anxiety, but intrinsically it is different. In the state of fear we have an object before us, we can meet that object, we can attempt to remove it, or we can flee from it. We are conscious of ourselves, as well as of the object; we can deliberate as to how we shall behave toward it, and we can look at the cause of the fear, which actually lies before us. Anxiety, on the other hand, gets at us from the back, so to speak. The only thing we can do is to attempt to flee from it, but without knowing what direction to take, since we experience it as coming from no particular place. We are dealing, as I have shown explicitly elsewhere, with qualitative differences, with different attitudes toward the world. Fear is related, in our experience, to an object; anxiety is not—it is only an inner state.

What is characteristic of the object of fear? Is it something inherent in the object itself, at all times? Of course not. At one time an object may arouse only interest, or be met with indifference; but at another time it may evoke the greatest fear. In other words, fear must be the result of a specific relationship between organism and object. What leads to fear is nothing but the experience of the possibility of the onset of anxiety. What we fear is the impending anxiety, which we experience in relation to some objects. Since a person in a state of fear is not yet in a state of anxiety but only envisions it—that is, he only fears that anxiety may befall him— he is not so disturbed in his judgment of the outer world as the person in a state of anxiety. Rather, driven as he is by the tendency to avoid the onset of anxiety, he attempts to establish special contact with the outer world. He tries to recognize the situation as clearly as possible and to react to it in an appropriate manner. Fear is conditioned by, and directed against, very definite aspects of the environment. These

have to be recognized and, if possible, removed. Fear sharpens the senses, whereas anxiety renders them unusable. Fear drives to action; anxiety paralyzes.

From these explanations it is obvious that in order to feel anxiety it is not necessary to be able to give oneself an account of one's acts; to feel fear, however, presupposes that capacity. From this it becomes clear that our patients do not behave like people in a state of fear—that is, they do not intentionally try to avoid situations from which anxiety may arise. They cannot do that because of the defect of abstraction. Also from our observation of the patients we can assume that they do not experience fear and that they only have the experience of anxiety.

Anxiety, a catastrophic condition in which self-realization is not possible, may be produced by a variety of events, all of which have in common the following: There is a discrepancy between the individual's capacities and the demands made on him, and this discrepancy makes self-realization impossible. This may be due to external or internal conditions, physical or psychological. It is this discrepancy to which we are referring when we speak of "conflicts." Thus we can observe anxiety in infants, in whom such a discrepancy must occur frequently, particularly since their abstract attitude is not yet developed or not fully. We also see anxiety in brain-injured people, in whom impairment of abstraction produces the same discrepancy. In normal people, anxiety appears when the demands of the world are too much above the capacity of the individual, when social and economic situations are too stressful, or when religious conflicts arise. Finally we see anxiety in people with neuroses and psychoses which are based on unsolvable and unbearable inner conflicts.

THE PROTECTIVE MECHANISMS

The last group of symptoms to be observed in brain-injured patients are the behavior changes which make it possible for the patient to get rid of the catastrophic condition—of anxiety.[22] The

---

[21]See K. Goldstein, "Zum Problem der Angst," *Allg. ürztl. Ztschr. f. Psychotherap, u. psych. Hygiene,* 1929, 2, 409–437. Also, Goldstein, *The Organism, op. cit.,* p. 293.

[22]Goldstein, *The Organism, op. cit.,* p. 40 ff.

observation of this phenomenon in these patients is of special interest since it can teach us how an organism can get rid of anxiety without being aware of its origin and without being able to avoid the anxiety voluntarily. After a certain time these patients show a diminution of disorder and of catastrophic reactions (anxiety) even though the defect caused by the damage to the brain still exists. This, of course, can occur only if the patient is no longer exposed to tasks he cannot cope with. This diminution is achieved by definite changes in the behavior of the patients: They are withdrawn, so that a number of stimuli, including dangerous ones, do not reach them. They usually stay alone; either they do not like company or they want to be only with people whom they know well. They like to be in a familiar room in which everything is organized in a definite way. They show extreme orderliness in every respect; everything has to be done exactly at an appointed time—whether it is breakfast, dinner, or a walk. They show excessive and fanatical orderliness in arranging their belongings; each item of their wardrobe must be in a definite place—that is, in a place where it can be gotten hold of quickly, without the necessity of a choice, which they are unable to make. Although it is a very primitive order indeed, they stick fanatically to it; it is the only way to exist. Any change results in a state of very great excitement. They themselves cannot voluntarily arrange things in a definite way. The orderliness is maintained simply because the patients try to stick to those arrangements which they can handle. This sticking to that which they can cope with is characteristic for their behavior; thus any behavior change can be understood only in terms of this characteristic behavior.

An illustration of this characteristic behavior is the fact that they always try to keep themselves busy with things that they are able to do as a protection against things that they cannot cope with. The activities which engross them need not be of great value in themselves. Their usefulness consists apparently in the fact that they protect the patient. Thus a patient does not like to be interrupted in an activity. For instance, although a patient may behave well in a conversation with someone he knows and likes, he does not like to be suddenly addressed by someone else.

We very often observe that a patient is totally unaware of his defect—such as hemiplegia or hemianopsia—and of the difference between his state prior to the development of the symptoms and his present state. This is strikingly illustrated by the fact that the disturbances of these patients play a very small part in their complaints. We are not dealing simply with a subjective lack of awareness, for the defects are effectively excluded from awareness, one might say. This is shown by the fact that they produce very little disturbance—apparently as the result of compensation. This exclusion from awareness seems to occur particularly when the degree of functional defect in performance is extreme. We can say that defects are shut out from the life of the organism when they would seriously impair any of its essential functions and when a defect can be compensated for by other activities at least to the extent that self-realization is not essentially disturbed.

One can easily get the impression that a patient tries to deny the experience of the functional disturbance because he is afraid that he will get into a catastrophic condition if he becomes aware of his defect. As a matter of fact, a patient may get into a catastrophic condition when we make him aware of his defect, or when the particular situation does not make possible an adequate compensation. Sometimes this happens—and this is especially interesting—when the underlying pathological condition improves and with that the function.

A patient of mine who became totally blind by a suicidal gunshot through the chiasma opticum behaved as if he were not aware of his blindness; the defect was compensated for very well by his use of his other senses, his motor skill, and his knowledge and intelligence. He was usually in a good mood; he never spoke of his defect, and he resisted all attempts to draw his attention to it. After a certain time, the condition improved; but at the same time he realized that he could not recognize objects through his vision. He was shocked and became deeply depressed. When he was asked why he was depressed, he said, "I cannot see." We might assume that in the beginning the patient denied the defect intentionally because he could not bear it. But why then did he not deny it when he began to see? Or we might assume that in the beginning he did not deny his blindness, but that in total blindness an adjustment occurred in terms of a change of behavior for which vision was not necessary; and because of this it was not necessary for him to realize his blindness. The moment he was able to see, he became aware of his defect and was no longer able to eliminate it. The exclusion of the blindness defect from awareness could thus be considered a secondary effect of the adjustment. But in this patient who was mentally undisturbed a more voluntary denial cannot be overlooked. A voluntary denial is not possible in patients with impairment of abstraction as in brain-injured patients. Here the unawareness of the defect can only be a secondary effect—an effect of the same behavior, which we have described before, by which the brain-injured person is protected against catastrophes which may occur because of his defect. As we have said, the patient, driven by the trend to realize himself as well as possible, sticks to what he is able to do; this shows in his whole behavior. From this point of view, the patient's lack of awareness of his defect, as well as his peculiarities in general, becomes understandable· For instance, in these terms, it is understandable why an aphasic patient utters a word which is only on the normal fringe of the word that he needs; for the word that he needs to use is a word that he cannot say at all or can say only in such a way that he could not be understood and would as a result be in distress.[23] Thus a patient may repeat "church" instead of "God," "father" instead of "mother," and so on; he considers his reaction correct, at least as long as no one makes him aware of the fact that his reaction is wrong. This same kind of reaction occurs in disturbances of recognition, of feelings, and so on.

One is inclined to consider the use of wrong words or disturbances of recognition, actions, and feelings as due to a special pathology; but that is not their origin. Since these disturbances are reactions which represent all that the individual is able to execute, he recognizes them as fulfillment of the task; in this way, these reactions fulfill this need to such a degree that no catastrophe occurs. Thus the protection appears as a passive effect of an active "correct" procedure and could not be correctly termed denial, which refers to a more intentional activity, "conscious" or "unconscious."

This theory on the origin of the protective behavior in organic patients deserves consideration, particularly because the phenomena observed in organic patients shows such a similarity to that observed in neurotics. One could even use psychoanalytic terms for the different forms of behavior in organic patients. For instance, one might use the same terms that Anna Freud[24] uses to characterize various defense mechanisms against anxiety. Both neurotic and organic patients show a definite similarity in behavior structure and in the purpose served by that structure. In organic patients, however, I prefer to speak of protective mechanisms instead of defense mechanisms; the latter refers to a more voluntary act, which organic patients certainly cannot perform, as we have discussed earlier. In neurotics, the development of defense mechanisms generally does not occur so passively through organismic adjustment, as does the development of protective mechanisms in the organic patients; this is in general the distinction between the two. It seems to me that this distinction is not true in the case of neurotic children, however; some of these children seem to develop protective mechanisms in a passive way, similar to organic patients. Such mechanisms can perhaps be found in other neurotics. Thus, in interpreting these mechanisms, one should take into account the possibility of confusing the neurotic patient with the organic patient.

I would like to add a last word with regard to the restrictions of the personality and of the world of these patients which is brought about by this protective behavior. The restrictions are not as disturbing in the brain-injured patients as is the effect of defense mechanisms in neuroses. In a neurotic, defense mechanisms rep-

---

[23]Goldstein, *Language and Language Disturbances, op. cit.*, p. 226.

[24]A. Freud, *The Ego and the Mechanisms of Defense* (New York: International University Press, 1946).

resent a characteristic part of the disturbances he is suffering from; but the organic patient does not become aware of the restriction since his protective mechanisms allow for some ordered form of behavior and for the experience of some kind of self-realization—which is true, of course, only as long as the environment is so organized by the people around him that no tasks arise that he cannot fulfill and as long as the protecting behavior changes are not hindered. This is the only way the brain-damaged person can exist. The patient cannot bear conflict—that is, anxiety, restriction, or suffering. In this respect he differs essentially from the neurotic who is more or less able to bear conflict. This is the main difference which demands a different procedure in treatment; in many respects, however, treatment can be set up in much the same way for both.[25] In treating these patients, it is more important to deal with the possible occurrence of catastrophe rather than with the impairment of abstraction, for my observations of a great many patients for over ten years indicate

that the impairment of abstraction cannot be alleviated unless the brain damage from which it originated is eliminated. There is no functional restitution of this capacity by compensation through other parts of the brain. Improvement of performances can be achieved only by the building up of substitute performances by the use of the part of concrete behavior which is preserved; but this is only possible by a definite arrangement of the environment.

I am well aware that my description of the personality change in brain damage is somewhat sketchy. The immense material and the problems involved, so manifold and complex, make a more satisfactory presentation in such a brief time impossible. I hope that I have been successful in outlining, to the best of my ability, the essential phenomena and problems of these patients. In addition, I trust that I have shown how much we can learn from these observations for our concept of the structure of the personality, both normal and pathological, and for the treatment of brain-damaged patients and also, I hope, of patients with so-called psychogenic disorders.

[25]See K. Goldstein, "The Idea of Disease and Therapy," *Review of Religion*, 1949, *14*, 229–240.

51.

WILDER PENFIELD

MEMORY MECHANISMS AND EPILEPSY

> The stream of consciousness in the human brain can be electrically reactivated.
> WILDER PENFIELD

There is an area of the surface of the human brain where local electrical stimulation can call back a sequence of past experience. An epileptic irritation in this area may do the same. It is as though a wire recorder, or a strip of cinematographic film with sound track, had been set in motion within the brain. The sights and sounds,

and the thoughts, of a former day pass through the man's mind again.

The purpose of this article is to describe, for readers from various disciplines of science, the area of the cerebral cortex from which this neuron record of the past can be activated and to suggest what normal contribution it may make to cerebral function.

The human brain is the master organ of the human race. It differs from the brains of other mammals particularly in the greater extent of its cerebral cortex. The gray matter, or cortex, that covers the two cerebral hemispheres of the

From Wilder Penfield, "The interpretive cortex." *Science*, 1959, *129*, 1719–1725. Reprinted by permission.

brain of man is so vast in nerve cell population that it could never have been contained within the human skull if it were not folded upon itself, and refolded, so as to form a very large number of fissures and convolutions (Figure 7.1). The fissures are so deep and so devious that by far the greatest portion of this ganglionic carpet (about 65 percent) is hidden in them, below the surface (Figure 7.2).

The portion that is labeled "interpretive" in Figures 7.1 and 7.3 covers a part of both temporal lobes. It is from these two homologous areas, and from nowhere else, that electrical stimulation has occasionally produced physical responses which may be divided into (i) experiential responses and (ii) interpretive responses.

EXPERIENTIAL RESPONSES

Occasionally during the course of a neurosurgical operation under local anesthesia, gentle electrical stimulation in this temporal area, right or left, has caused the conscious patient to be aware of some previous experience.[1] The experience seems to be picked out at random from his own past. But it comes back to him in great detail. He is suddenly aware again of those things to which he paid attention in that distant interval of time. This recollection of an experiential sequence stops suddenly when the electrical current is switched off or when the electrode is removed from contact with the

---

[1]W. Penfield, *Journal of Mental Science*, 1955, *101*, 451.

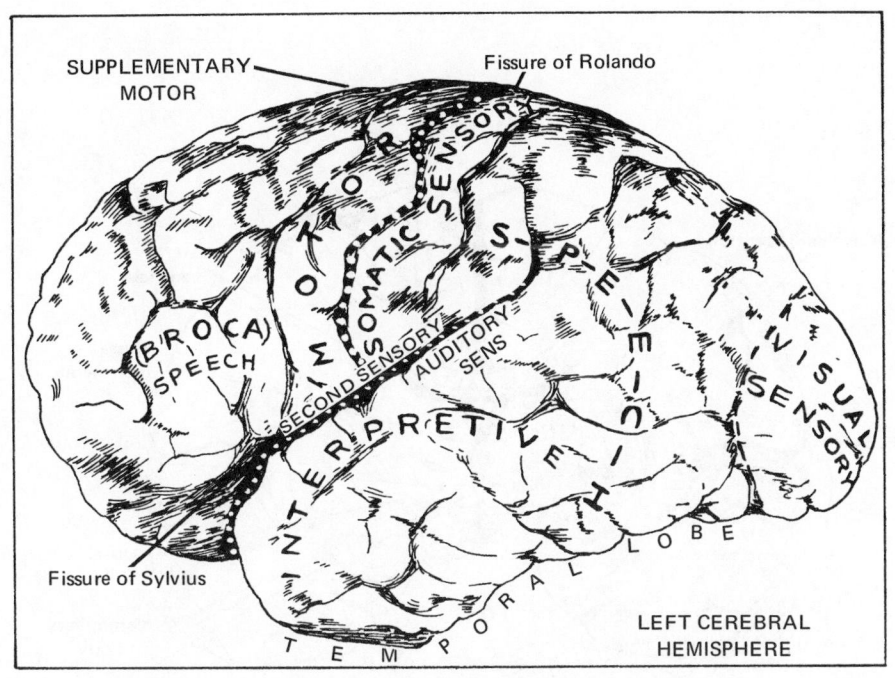

FIGURE 7.1. Photograph of the left hemisphere of a human brain. The frontal lobe is on the left, the occipital lobe on the right. The major motor and sensory areas are indicated, as well as the speech areas and the interpretive area. W. Penfield and L. Roberts, *Speech and Brain Mechanisms* (Princeton, N.J.: Princeton University Press, 1959).

FIGURE 7.2. Drawing of a cross section of the left cerebral hemisphere, G. Jelgersma, *Atlas Anatomicum cerebri humani* (Amsterdam: Schiltama and Holkema). The white matter is stained black and the gray matter is unstained. The major convolutions of the cerebral cortex and the subcortical masses of gray matter can be identified by reference to the diagram below. (Bottom) Drawing of the cross section shown at right, above, with additions. The surfaces and convolutions of the temporal lobe are identified, and the relationship of one hemisphere to the other and the relationship of the hemispheres to the brain stem and cerebellum are shown.

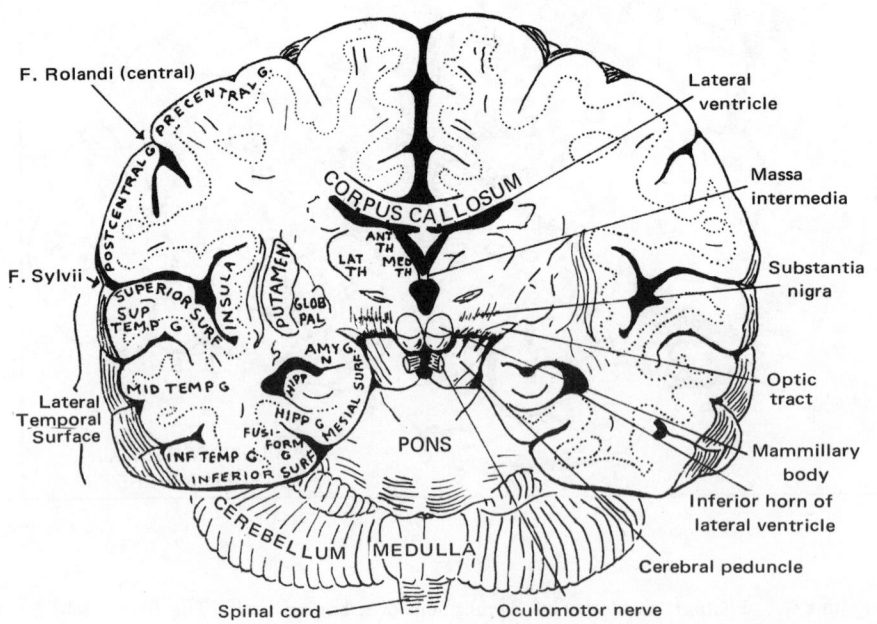

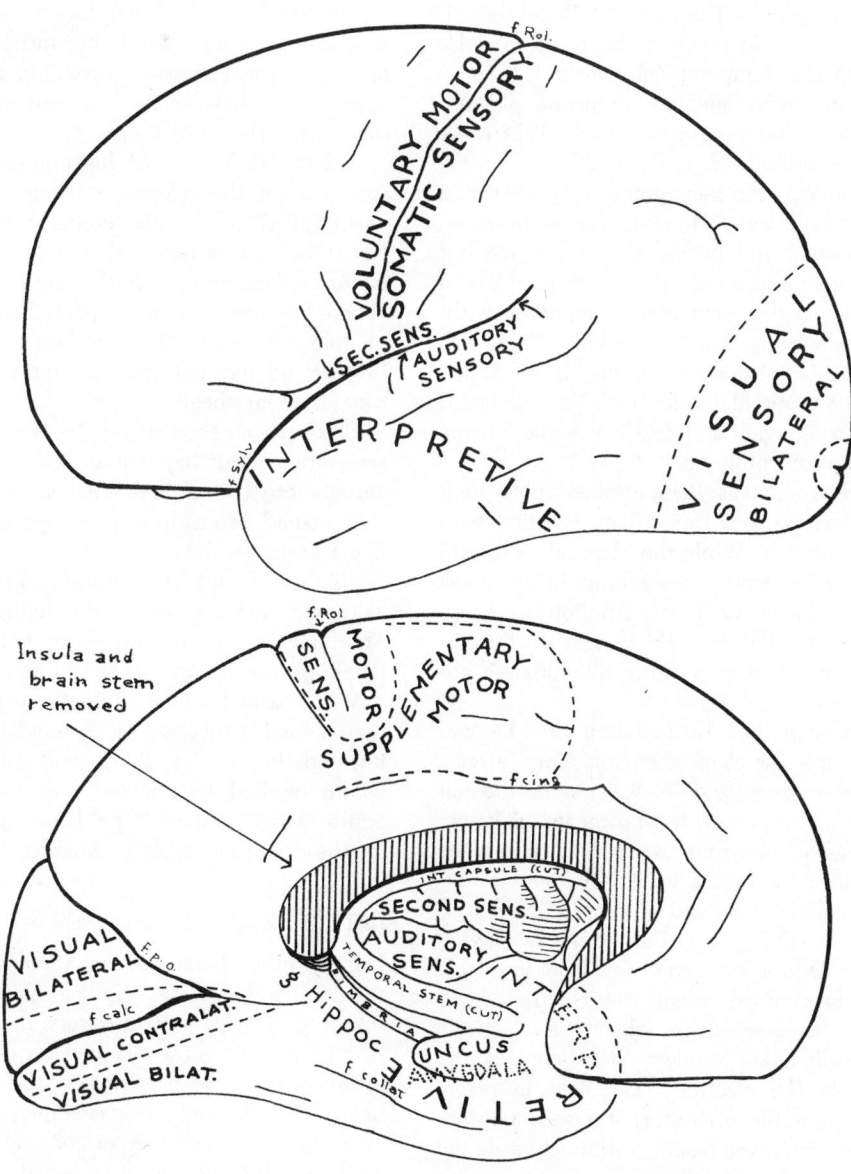

FIGURE 7.3. The left cerebral hemisphere; the lateral surface is shown above and the mesial surface below. In the lower drawing the brain stem with the island of Reil has been removed to show the inner banks of the fissure of Sylvius and the superior surface of the temporal lobe. The interpretive cortex extends from the lateral to the superior surface of the temporal lobe. W. Penfield and L. Roberts, *Speech and Brain Mechanisms* (Princeton, N.J.: Princeton University Press, 1959).

cortex. This phenomenon we have chosen to call an experiential response to stimulation.

Case Examples.[2] The patient S.Be. observed, when the electrode touched the temporal lobe (right superior temporal convolution), "There was a piano over there and someone playing. I could hear the song you know." When the cortex was stimulated again without warning, at approximately the same point, the patient had a different experience. He said: "Someone speaking to another, and he mentioned a name but I could not understand it . . . It was like a dream." Again the point was restimulated without his knowledge. He said quietly: "Yes, 'Oh Marie, Oh Marie'! Someone is singing it." When the point was stimulated a fourth time he heard the same song again and said it was the "theme song of a radio program."

The electrode was then applied to a point 4 centimeters farther forward on the first temporal convolution. While the electrode was still in place, S.Be. said: "Something brings back a memory. I can see Seven-Up Bottling Company—Harrison Bakery." He was evidently seeing two of Montreal's large illuminated advertisements.

The surgeon then warned him that he was about to apply the electrode again. Then, after a pause, the surgeon said "Now," but he did not stimulate. (The patient has no means of knowing when the electrode is applied, unless he is told, since the cortex itself is without sensation.) The patient replied promptly, "Nothing."

A woman (D.F.)[3] heard an orchestra playing an air while the electrode was held in place. The music stopped when the electrode was removed. It came again when the electrode was reapplied. On request, she hummed the tune, while the electrode was held in place, accompanying the orchestra. It was a popular song. Over and over again, restimulation at the same spot produced the same song. The music

seemed always to begin at the same place and to progress at the normally expected tempo. All efforts to mislead her failed. She believed that a gramophone was being turned on in the operating room on each occasion, and she asserted her belief stoutly in a conversation some days after the operation.

A boy (R.W.) heard his mother talking to someone on the telephone when an electrode was applied to his right temporal cortex. When the stimulus was repeated without warning, he heard his mother again in the same conversation. When the stimulus was repeated after a lapse of time, he said, "My mother is telling my brother he has got his coat on backwards. I can just hear them."

The surgeon then asked the boy whether he remembered this happening. "Oh yes," he said, "just before I came here." Asked again whether this seemed like a dream, he replied: "No, it is like I go into a daze."

J.T. cried out in astonishment when the electrode was applied to the temporal cortex; "Yes doctor, yes doctor. Now I hear people laughing—my friends in South Africa!"

When asked about this, he explained the reason for his surprise. He seemed to be laughing with his cousins, Bessie and Ann Wheilow, whom he had left behind him on a farm in South Africa, although he knew he was now on the operating table in Montreal.

INTERPRETIVE RESPONSES

On the other hand, similar stimulation in this same general area may produce quite a different response. The patient discovers, on stimulation, that he has somehow changed his own interpretation of what he is seeing at the moment, or hearing or thinking. For example, he may exclaim that his present experience seems familiar, as though he had seen it or heard it or thought it before. He realizes that this must be a false interpretation. Or, on the contrary, these things may seem suddenly strange, absurd. Sights or sounds may seem distant and small, or they may come unexpectedly close and seem loud or large. He may feel suddenly afraid, as though his environment were threatening him, and he is possessed by a nameless dread or panic.

[2]These patients, designated by the same initials, have been described in previous publications in much greater detail. An index of patients (designated by initials) may be found in any of my books.
[3]This case is reported in detail in W. Penfield and H. Jasper, *Epilepsy and the Functional Anatomy of the Human Brain* (Boston: Little, Brown, 1954) [published in abridged form in Russian (translation by N. P. Graschenkov and G. Smirnov) by the Soviet Academy of Sciences, 1958].

Another patient may say he feels lonely or aloof, or as though he were observing himself at a distance.

Under normal circumstances anyone may make such interpretations of the present, and these interpretations serve him as guides to action or reaction. If the interpretations are accurate guides, they must be based upon previous comparable experience. It is conceivable, therefore, that the recall mechanism which is activated by the electrode during an experiential response and the mechanism activated in an interpretive response may be parts of a common inclusive mechanism of reflex recognition or interpretation.

No special function had been previously assigned by neurologists to the area in each temporal lobe that is marked "interpretive" in Figures 7.1 and 7.3, though some clinicians have suggested it might have to do with the recall of music. The term *interpretive cortex*, therefore, is no more than slang to be employed for the purposes of discussion. The terms *motor cortex, sensory cortex,* and *speech cortex* began as slang phrases and have served such a purpose. But such phrases must not be understood to signify independence of action of separated units in the case of any of these areas. Localization of function in the cerebral cortex means no more than specialization of function as compared with other cortical regions, not separation from the integrated action of the brain.

Before considering the interpretive cortex further, we may turn briefly to the motor and sensory areas and the speech areas of the cortex. After considering the effects of electrical stimulation there, we should be better able to understand the results of stimulation in the temporal lobes.

SPECIALIZATION OF FUNCTION IN THE CORTEX

Evidence for some degree of localization within the brain was recognized early in the 19th century by Flourens. He concluded from experiment that functional subdivision of "the organ of the mind" was possible. The forebrain,[4]

he said [cerebral hemispheres and higher brain stem (Figure 7.4)] had to do with thought and will power, while the cerebellum was involved in the coordination of movement.

In 1861, Paul Broca showed that a man with a relatively small area of destruction in a certain part of the left hemisphere alone might lose only the power of speech. It was soon realized that this was the speech area of man's dominant (left) hemisphere. In 1870, Fritsch and Hitzig applied an electric current to the exposed cortex of one hemisphere of a lightly anesthetized dog and caused the legs of the opposite side to move. Thus, an area of cortex called motor was discovered.

After that, localization of function became a research target for many clinicians and experimentalists. It was soon evident that in the case of man, the precentral gyrus (Figure 7.5) in each hemisphere was related to voluntary control of the contralateral limbs and that there was an analogous area of motor cortex in the frontal lobes of animals. It appeared also that other separate areas of cortex (Figures 7.1 and 7.5) in each hemisphere were dedicated to sensation (one, for visual sensation, others for auditory, olfactory, and discriminative somatic sensation, respectively).

It was demonstrated, too, that from the "motor cortex" there was an efferent bundle of nerve fibers (the pyramidal tract) that ran down through the lower brain stem and the spinal cord to be relayed on out to the muscles. Through this efferent pathway, voluntary control of these muscles was actually carried out. It was evident, too, that there were separate sensory tracts carrying nerve impulses in the other direction, from the principal organs of special sense (eye, ear, nose, and skin and muscle) into separate sensory areas of the cortex.

These areas, motor and sensory, have been called "projection areas." They play a role in the projection of nerve currents to the cortex from the periphery of the body, and from the cortex to the periphery. This makes possible (sensory) awareness of environment and pro-

---

[4]The forebrain, or prosencephalon, properly includes the diencephalon and the telencephalon or higher brain stem, and hemispheres. Flourens probably had cerebral hemispheres in mind as distinguished from cerebellum.

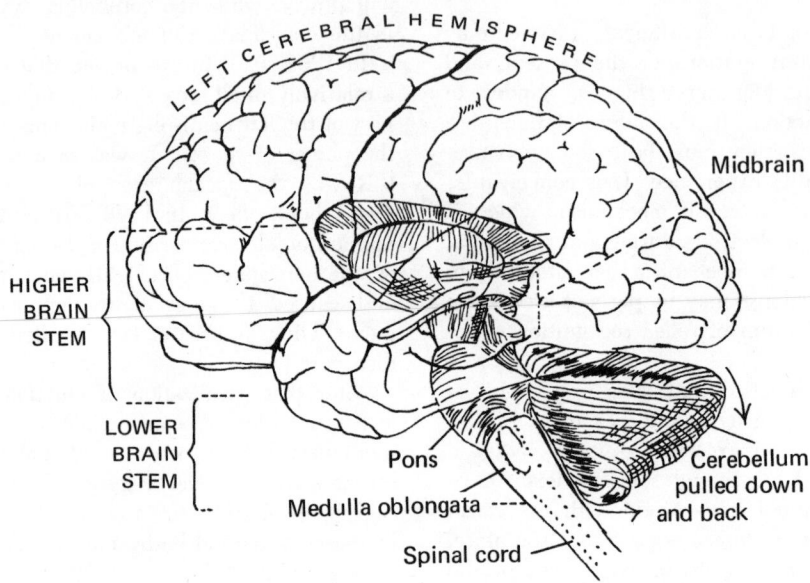

FIGURE 7.4. Drawing of the left cerebral hemisphere, showing the higher brain stem, including the thalamus, within and the lower brain stem and spinal cord emerging below. The cerebellum is shown, attached to the lower brain stem. W. Penfield and L. Roberts, *Speech and Brain Mechanisms* (Princeton, N.J.: Princeton University Press, 1959).

vides the individual with a means of outward (motor) expression. The motor cortex has a specialized use during voluntary action, and each of the several sensory areas has a specialized use, when the individual is seeing, hearing, smelling, or feeling.

TRAVELING POTENTIALS

The action of the living brain depends upon the movement, within it, of "transient electrical potentials traveling the fibers of the nervous system." This was Sherrington's phrase. Within the vast circuits of this master organ, potentials travel, here and there and yonder, like meteors that streak across the sky at night and line the firmament with trails of light. When the meteors pass, the paths of luminescence still glow a little while, then fade and are gone. The changing patterns of these paths of passing energy make possible the changing content of the mind. The

patterns are never quite the same, and so it is with the content of the mind.

Specialized areas in the cortex are at times active and again relatively quiet. But, when a man is awake, there is always some central integration and coordination of the traveling potentials. There must be activity within the brain stem and some areas of the cortex. This is centrencephalic integration.[5]

SENSORY, MOTOR, AND PSYCHICAL RESPONSES TO CORTICAL STIMULATION

My purpose in writing this article is to discuss in simple words (free of technical terms) the

[5]"Within the brain, a central transactional core has been identified between the strictly sensory or motor systems of classical neurology. This central reticular mechanism has been found capable of grading the activity of most other parts of the brain." H. Magoun, *The Waking Brain* (Springfield, Ill.: Charles C Thomas, 1958).

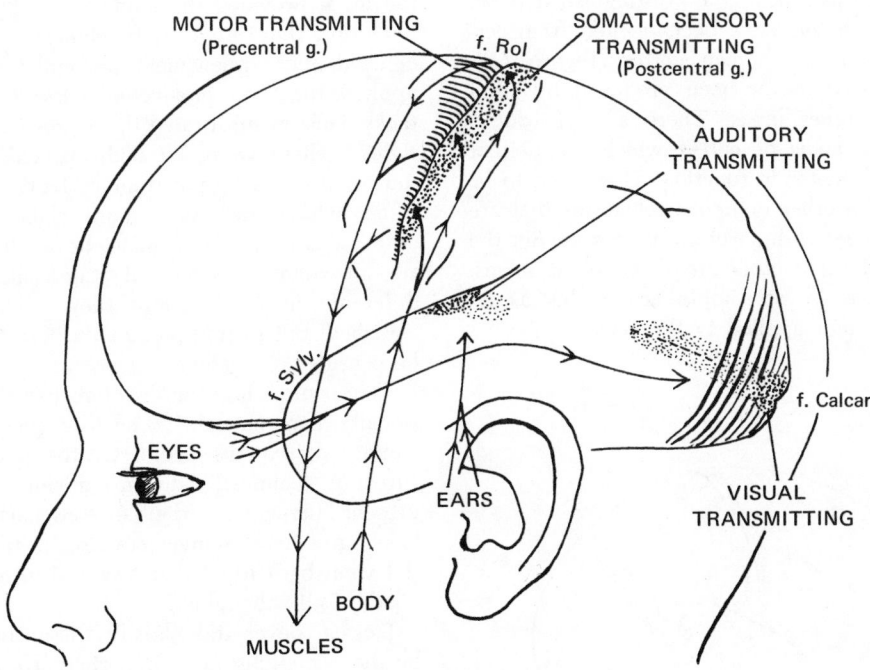

FIGURE 7.5. Sensory and motor projection areas. The sensory areas are stippled, and the afferent pathways to them from eyes, ears, and body are indicated by entering arrows. The motor cortex is indicated by parallel lines, and the efferent corticospinal tract is indicated by emerging arrows. W. Penfield and L. Roberts, *Speech and Brain Mechanisms* (Princeton, N.J.: Princeton University Press, 1959).

meaning of the "psychical" responses which appear only on stimulation of the so-called interpretive cortex. But before considering these responses let us consider the motor and sensory activity of the cortex for a moment.

When the streams of electrical potentials that pass normally through the various areas of sensory cortex are examined electrically, they do not seem to differ from each other except in pattern and timing. The essential difference is to be found in the fact that the visual stream passes to the visual cortex and then to one subcortical target and the auditory stream passes through the auditory cortex and then on to another subcortical target.

When the surgeon stimulates the intact sensory cortex he must be sending a current along the next "piece of road" to a subcortical destination. This electrode (delivering, for example, 60

"waves" per second of 2-millisecond duration and 1-volt intensity) produces no more than elementary sight when applied to visual cortex. The patient reports colors, lights, and shadows that move and take on crude outlines. The same electrode, applied to auditory cortex, causes him to hear a ringing or hissing or thumping sound. When applied to postcentral gyrus it produces tingling or a false sense of movement.

Thus, sensation is produced by the passage inward of electrical potentials. And when the electrode is applied to the motor cortex, movement is produced by passage of potentials outward to the muscles. In each case positive response is produced by conduction in the direction of normal physiological flow—that is, by dromic conduction.[6]

---

[6]W. Penfield, *The Excitable Cortex in Conscious Man* (Springfield, Ill.: Charles C Thomas, 1958).

Responses to electrical stimulation that may be called "psychical," as distinguished from sensory or motor, have been elicited from certain areas of the human cortex (Figure 7.6). But they have never been produced by stimulation in other areas. There are, of course, other large areas of cortex which are neither sensory nor motor in function. They seem to be employed in other neuron mechanisms that are also associated with psychical processes. But the function of these other areas cannot, it seems, be activated by so simple a stimulus as an electric current applied to the cortex.

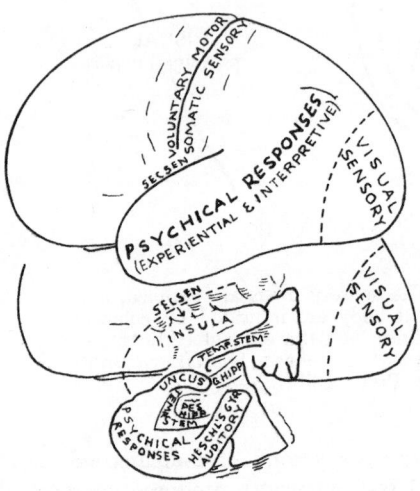

FIGURE 7.6. The left cerebral hemisphere is shown with the temporal lobe cut across and turned down. The areas of cortex from which psychical responses have been elicited are indicated. [Penfield (*1*)]

DREAMY STATES OF EPILEPSY

"Epilepsy" may be defined in Jackson's words, as "the name for occasional, sudden, excessive, rapid and local discharges of grey matter." Our aim in the operations under discussion was to remove the gray matter responsible for epileptic attacks if that gray matter could be spared. When the stimulating electrode repro-

duced the psychical phenomenon that initiated the fit, it provided the guidance sought.[7]

During the 19th century clinicians had recognized these phenomena as epileptic. They applied the term *intellectual aura* to such attacks. Jackson substituted the expression *dreamy states*.[8] These were, he said, "psychical states during the onset of certain epileptic seizures, states which are much more elaborate than crude sensations." And again, he wrote, "These are all voluminous mental states and yet of different kinds; no doubt they ought to be classified, but for my present purpose they may be considered together."

"The state," he said, "is often like that occasionally experienced by healthy people as a feeling of 'reminiscence.' " Or the patient has "dreamy feelings," "dreams mixing up with present thoughts," "double consciousness," a "feeling of being somewhere else," a feeling "as if I went back to all that occurred in my childhood," "silly thoughts."

Jackson never did classify these states, but he did something more important. He localized the area of cortex from which epileptic discharge would produce dreamy states. His localization was in the anterior and deep portions of the temporal lobes, the same area that is labeled "interpretative" cortex in Figure 7.3.

Case Example. Brief reference may be made to a specific case. The patient had seizures, and stimulation produced responses which were first recognized as psychical.

In 1936, a girl of 16 (J.V.) was admitted to the Montreal Neurological Institute complaining of epileptic attacks, each of which was ushered in by the same hallucination. It was a little dream, she said, in which an experience from early childhood was reenacted, always the same train of events. She would then cry out with fear and run to her mother. Occasionally this was followed immediately by a major convulsive seizure.

---

[7]It did more than this; it produced illusions or hallucinations that had never been experienced by the patient during a seizure.

[8]J. Taylor (Ed.), *Selected Writings of John Hughlings Jackson*, Vol. 1, *On Epilepsy and Epileptiform Convulsions* (London: Hodder and Stoughton, 1931).

At operation, under local anesthesia, we tried to set off the dream by a gentle electrical stimulus in the right temporal lobe. The attempt was successful. The dream was produced by the electrode. Stimulation at other points on the temporal cortex produced sudden fear without the dream. At still other points, stimulation caused her to say that she saw "someone coming toward me." At another point, stimulation caused her to say she heard the voices of her mother and her brothers.[9]

This suggested a new order of cortical response to electrical stimulation. When the neighboring visual sensory area of the cortex is stimulated, any patient may report seeing stars of light or moving colors or black outlines but never "someone coming toward me." Stimulation of the auditory sensory cortex may cause any patient to report that he hears ringing, buzzing, blowing, or thumping sounds, perhaps, but never voices that speak. Stimulation in the areas of sensory cortex can call forth nothing more than the elements of visual or auditory or tactile sensation, never happenings that might have been previously experienced.

During the 23 years that have followed, although practically all areas of the cerebral cortex have been stimulated and studied in more than 1,000 craniotomies, performed under local anesthesia, psychical responses of the experiential or interpretive variety have been produced only from the temporal cortex in the general areas that are marked "psychical responses" in Figure 7.3.[10, 11]

---

[9]Twenty-one years later this young woman, who is the daughter of a physician, was present at a meeting of the National Academy of Sciences in New York while her case was discussed. She could still recall the operation and the nature of the "dreams" that had preceded her seizures. W. Penfield, *Proceedings of the National Academy of Science, U. S.,* 1958, *44,* 51.

[10]In a recent review of the series my associate, Dr. Phanor Perot, has found and summarized 35 out of 384 temporal lobe cases in which stimulation produced experiential responses. All such responses were elicited in the temporal cortex. In a study of 214 consecutive operations for temporal lobe epilepsy, my associate Sean Mullan found 70 cases in which interpretive illusion occurred in the minor seizures before operation, or in which an interpretive response was produced by stimulation during operation. In most cases it occurred both before and during operation.

CLASSIFICATION

It seems reasonable to subdivide psychical responses and psychical seizures (epileptic dreamy states) in the same way, classifying them as "interpretive" or "experiential." Interpretive psychical responses are those involving interpretations of the present experience, or emotions related to it; experiential psychical responses are reenactments of past experiences. Interpretive seizures are those accompanied by auras and illusions; experiential seizures are those accompanied by auras and hallucinations.

The interpretive responses and seizures may be divided into groups[11a] of which the commonest are as follows: (i) recognition, the illusion that things seen and heard and thought are familiar (*déjà vu* phenomenon); (ii) visual illusion, the illusion that things seen are changing—for example, coming nearer, growing larger (macropsia); (iii) auditory illusion, the illusion that things heard are changing—for example, coming near, going away, changing tempo; (iv) illusional emotion, the emotion of fear or, less often, loneliness, sorrow, or disgust.

Experiential phenomena (hallucinations) are an awareness of experiences from the past that come into the mind without complete loss of awareness of the present.

DISCUSSION

What, then, is the function of the interpretive cortex? This is a physiological question that follows the foregoing observations naturally.

An electrode, delivering, for example, 60 electrical pulses per second to the surface of the motor cortex, causes a man to make crude movements. When applied to the various sensory areas of the cortex, it causes him to have crude sensations of sight or sound or body feeling. This indicates only that these areas have something to do with the complicated mechanism of voluntary action or conscious sensation. It does not reveal what contribution the cortex may make, or in what way it may contribute to skill in making voluntary movement or qualify the incoming sensory streams.

---

[11]S. Mullan and W. Penfield, A.M.A. *Archive of Neurological Psychiatry,* 1959, *81,* 269.
[11a]*Ibid.*

In the case of the interpretive cortex, the observations are similar. We may say that the interpretive cortex has something to do with a mechanism that can reactivate the vivid record of the past. It has also something to do with a mechanism that can present to consciousness a reflex interpretation of the present. To conclude that here is the mechanism of memory would be an unjustified assumption. It would be too simple.

What a man remembers when he makes a voluntary effort is apt to be a generalization. If this were not so, he might be hopelessly lost in detail. On the other hand, the experiential responses described above are detailed reenactments of a single experience. Such experiences soon slip beyond the range of voluntary recall. A man may summon to mind a song at will. He hears it then in his mind, not all at once but advancing phrase by phrase. He may sing it or play it too, and one would call this memory.

But if a patient hears music in response to the electrode, he hears it in one particular strip of time. That time runs forward again at the original tempo, and he hears the orchestration, or he sees the player at a piano "over there." These are details he would have thought forgotten.

A vast amount of work remains to be done before the mechanism of memory, and how and where the recording takes place, are understood. This record is not laid down in the interpretive cortex, but it is kept in a part of the brain that is intimately connected with it.

Removal of large areas of interpretive cortex, even when carried out on both sides, may result in mild complaints of memory defect, but it does not abolish the capacity to remember recent events. On the other hand, surgical removals that result in bilateral interference with the underlying hippocampal zone do make the recording of recent events impossible, while distant memory is still preserved. [12, 13]

The importance of the hippocampal area for memory was pointed out long ago in a forgotten publication by the Russian neurologist Bechterew.[14] The year before publication Bechterew had demonstrated the case before the St. Petersburg Clinic for Nervous and Mental Diseases. The man on whom Bechterew reported had "extraordinary weakness of memory, falsifications of memory and great apathy." These defects were shown at autopsy to be secondary to lesions of the mesial surface of the cortex of both temporal lobes. The English neurologists Glees and Griffith[15] reported similar defects, a half century later, in a patient who had symmetrical lesions of the hippocampus and of hippocampal and fusiform gyri on both sides.

The way in which the interpretive cortex seems to be used may be suggested by an example: After years of absence you meet, by chance, a man whose very existence you had forgotten. On seeing him, you may be struck by a sudden sense of familiarity, even before you have time to "think." A signal seems to flash up in consciousness to tell you that you've seen that man before. You watch him as he smiles and moves and speaks. The sense of familiarity grows stronger. Then you remember him. You may even recall that his name was Jones. The sight and the sound of the man has given you an instant access, through some reflex, to the records of the past in which this man has played some part. The opening of this forgotten file was subconscious. It was not a voluntary act. You would have known him even against your will. Although Jones was a forgotten man a moment before, now you can summon the record in such detail that you remark at once the slowness of his gait or a new line about the mouth.

If Jones had been a source of danger to you, you might have felt fear as well as familiarity before you had time to consider the man. Thus, the signal of fear as well as the signal of familiarity may come to one as the result of subconscious comparison of present with similar past experience.

---

[12]This area is marked "Hipp" and "Hipp. G" in Figure 7.2 (bottom) and "g. Hippoc." and "amygdala" in Figure 7.3.

[13]W. Penfield and B. Milner, *A.M.A. Archive of Neurological Psychiatry*, 1958, 79, 475.

[14]W. V. Bechterew, "Demonstration eines Gehirns mit Zerstörung der vorderen und inneren Theile der Hirnrinde beider Schläfenlappen," *Neurol. Zentralbl. Leipzig*, 1900, 19, 990. My attention was called to this case recently by Dr. Peter Gloor of Montreal.

[15]P. Glees and H. B. Griffith, *Monatsschrift für Psychiatrie und Neurologie*, 1952, 123, 193.

One more example may be given from common experience. A sudden increase in the size of objects seen and in sounds heard may mean the rapid approach of something that calls for instant avoidance action. These are signals that, because of previous experience, we sometimes act upon with little consideration.

SUMMARY

The interpretive cortex has in it a mechanism for instant reactivation of the detailed record of the past. It has a mechanism also for the production of interpretive signals. Such signals could only be significant if past records are scanned and relevant experiences are selected for comparison with present experience. This is a subconscious process. But it may well be that this scanning of past experience and selection from it also renders the relevant past available for conscious consideration as well. Thus, the individual may refer to the record as he employs other circuits of the brain.

Access to the record of the past seems to be as readily available from the temporal cortex of one side as from that of the other. Auditory illusions (or interpretations of the distance, loudness, or tempo of sounds) have been produced by stimulation of the temporal cortex of either side. The same is true of illusional emotions, such as fear and disgust.

But, on the contrary, visual illusions (interpretations of the distance, dimension, erectness, and tempo of things seen) are only produced by stimulation of the temporal cortex on the nondominant (normally, right) side of the brain. Illusions of recognition, such as familiarity or strangeness, were also elicited only from the nondominant side, except in one case.

CONCLUSION

"Consciousness," to quote William James,[16] "is never quite the same in successive moments of time. It is a stream forever flowing, forever changing." The stream of changing states of mind that James described so well does flow through each man's waking hours until the

time when he falls asleep to wake up no more. But the stream, unlike a river, leaves a record in the living brain.

Transient electrical potentials move with it through the circuits of the nervous system, leaving a path that can be followed again. The pattern of this pathway, from neuron to neuron along each nerve-cell body and fiber and junction, is the recorded pattern of each man's past. That complicated record is held there in temporal sequence through the principle of durable facilitation of conduction and connection.

A steady stream of electrical pulses applied through an electrode to some point in the interpretive cortex causes a stream of excitation to flow from the cortex to the place where past experience is recorded. This stream of excitation acts as a key to the past. It can enter the pathway of recorded consciousness at any random point, from childhood on through adult life. But having entered, the experience moves forward without interference from other experiences. And when the electrode is withdrawn there is a likelihood, which lasts for seconds or minutes, that the stream of excitation will enter the pathway again at the same moment of past time, even if the electrode is reapplied at neighboring points.[17]

Finally, an electric current applied to the surface of what may be called the interpretive cortex of a conscious man (i) may cause the stream of former consciousness to flow again or (ii) may give him an interpretation of the present that is unexpected and involuntary. Therefore, it is concluded that, under normal

[16]W. James, *The Principles of Psychology* (New York: Henry Holt, 1910).

[17]Thus, it is apparent that the beam of excitation that emanates from the interpretive cortex and seems to scan the record of the past is subject to the principles of transient facilitation already demonstrated for the anthropoid motor cortex [A. S. F. Grünbaum and C. Sherrington, *Proceedings of the Royal Society* (London) 1901, 72B, 152. T. Graham Brown and C. S. Sherrington, *Proceedings of the Royal Society* (London), 1912, 85B, 250.] Similarly subject to the principles of facilitation are the motor and the sensory cortex of man [W. Penfield and K. Welch, *Journal of Physiology* (London), 1949, 109, 358.] The patient D.F. heard the same orchestra playing the same music in the operating room more than 20 times when the electrode was reapplied to the superior surface of the temporal lobe. Each time the music began in the verse of a popular song. It proceeded to the chorus, if the electrode was kept in place.

circumstances, this area of cortex must make some functional contribution to reflex comparison of the present with related past experience. It contributes to reflex interpretation or perception of the present.

The combination and comparison of present experience with similar past experience must call for remarkable scanning of the past and classification of similarities. What contribution this area of the temporal cortex may make to the whole process is not clear. The term *interpretive cortex* will serve for identification until students of human physiology can shed more light on these fascinating findings.

52.

SEYMOUR B. SARASON AND JOHN DORIS

MENTAL DEFICIENCY

CYTOGENETICS OF DOWN'S SYNDROME

By Penrose's account the suspicion had existed some time before its proof that a chromosomal aberration might be implicated in the pathology of mongolism. As early as 1932 Waardenburg had suggested that an excess or a deficiency of chromosomes might be the cause of the disorder. Chromosomal aberrations were known to exist in other species, where they were observed to be accompanied by profound and pervasive effects on the organism. Mongolism was a congenital disorder involving multiple organ systems yet its incidence was not compatible with any model of Mendelian genetics or theory of prenatal trauma; thus the hypothesis of chromosomal error had a certain plausibility. Unfortunately, at the time, cytological techniques were not up to an adequate testing of this hypothesis. Mittwoch in 1952 attempted a chromosomal count on the cells of a mongol patient but the results were consistent with the then accepted assumption that the normal chromosomal count in man was 48 chromosomes in the somatic cells and 24 chromosomes in the mature sex cells. Therefore there seemed to be no reason to assume that the mongol's chromosomal count was any different than that of normal individuals (Penrose, 1962).

However, during the 1950's cytological techniques for preparing satisfactory material for chromosomal analysis improved. In 1956 Tjio and Levan, using some modification of these newer techniques, found that chromosomal counts for cells prepared from four human embryos indicated that 46 and not 48 was the normal chromosomal complement for somatic cells.

In their technique, tissue cultures from the embryos were treated with colchicine which stopped cell division at a point where the chromosomes—ordinarily invisible in the resting cell—can be made visible. Other technical treatment of the preparation was necessary in order to insure that the chromosomes for any one cell would be spread out sufficiently well to permit accurate counting. The chromosomes so spread out are seen to differ in size and configuration in such fashion that classificatory systems can be devised. Twenty-two of the chromosomes can be paired off with an identical looking mate. These are known as autosomes. The remaining pair of chromosomes are known as the sex chromosomes since they determine the sex of the individual. In the human female the sex chromosomes, like the autosome pairs, are of the same size and shape. In the male, the sex chromosomes are of unequal size. One, the larger, is identical to the sex chromosomes of the female and it is known as the X chromosome. The other smaller sex chromosome in the male is the Y chromosome.

In the Denver classificatory system, the chromosomes are arranged in seven groups according to their size and to the position of the centromeres. The centromere is a specialized region of the chromosome with staining properties different from the rest of the chromosome. Within some of these groups the individual chromosomes are also easily distinguished. In others the size and configuration of the group members does not permit discrimination by visual examination. Thus Group 1–3 is a group of large chromosomes with approximately median centromeres in which the three pairs of homologous chromosomes in the group are distinguishable from each other by size and configuration. Group 4–5 includes two chromosome pairs difficult to distinguish from one another. Group 6–12 also includes the X chromosome. This group presents greatest difficulty in discriminating the individual members. Group 13–15 are medium sized chromosomes with nearly terminal centromeres. The remaining groups decreasing in size are 16–18, 19–20, and 21–22. The Y chromosome is similiar in appearance to the very short chromosomes of Group 21–22 (Report of a Study Group, 1960).

Following Tjio and Levan's determination of 46 as the diploid chromosome number in man, confirmation occurred in several other laboratories. The question of a chromosomal aberration in mongolism was now reopened.

In 1959, Lejeune and his coworkers (Lejeune, Gautier, and Turpin, 1959) reported chromosomal analyses on tissue cultures obtained from nine mongoloid children which indicated the presence of 47 chromosomes. The extra chromosome was a small one with the centromere located near the end. Lejeune and his coworkers advanced the hypothesis that this extra chromosome was a product of nondisjunction during the reduction division that occurs in the maturation of the sex cells. They further noted that in the fruit fly, *Drosophila,* nondisjunction is greatly influenced by maternal aging. Such a mechanism would then account for the increase in frequency of mongolism as a function of the advanced age of the mother.

Other investigators quickly confirmed Le-

jeune's findings and it was determined that the small extra chromosome would correspond to number 21 in the Denver classification system (Polani, 1963).

The etiology of Down's syndrome was then postulated to result from an error in the reduction division that occurs in the maturation of the ovum or egg cell. In the maturation of an egg cell a specialized cell called an oöcyte undergoes two successive cell divisions to produce the mature egg cell and three polar bodies. The result of this complicated process is to reduce the chromosomal number of 46 existing in the oöcyte to the 23 existing in the mature egg cell. Thus the oöcyte, like the somatic cells, contains 23 pairs of chromosomes for a total of 46. The germ cell, in this case the egg, has only one representative of each pair for a total of 23. In the maturation of the sperm a similar process of two successive divisions occurs starting with a spermatocyte and ending in four sperms. Again, during the process the chromosomal count is halved, but unlike the process in the maturation of the egg when only one of the final cells, the ovum, can participate in fertilization, all four sperm cells are capable of participating in fertilization.

In the case of Down's syndrome it is assumed that an error in reduction division occurs so that the ovum instead of possessing the normal complement of 23 chromosomes, contains 24 the number 21 being in duplicate. If such an ovum is fertilized by a normal sperm with 23 chromosomes, the resulting zygote and the individual developing from it will be characterized by 47 chromosomes.

It is of course possible that the extra chromosome will be contributed by the sperm cell rather than the egg, but the strong correlation between maternal age and the occurrence of Down's syndrome makes it likely that in the usual case the egg bears the extra chromosome.

* * *

SEX-CHROMOSOME ANOMALIES

In the same year that the abnormal chromosome count in mongolism was reported in the literature there also appeared reports of abnormal chromosome counts in patients with certain forms of gonadal dysgenesis.

Jacobs and Strong (1959) reported the case

of an apparent male with small testes, enlarged breasts, poor facial-hair growth, and a high-pitched voice. Tissue obtained by a sternal marrow puncture was cultured and examined for its chromosomal complement, with the result that the individual was discovered to have 47 chromosomes. The extra chromosome was assumed, on the basis of size and shape, to be an *X* chromosome and the patient was considered to be of an *XXY* chromosome constitution rather than the *XY* constitution of the normal male.

The patient of Jacobs and Strong is representative of a group exhibiting Klinefelter's syndrome. Patients with this syndrome develop fairly normally until puberty at which time the abnormalities of the primary and secondary sexual characteristics become apparent. Testes are atrophied and there is some degree of feminization such as scant facial hair, high-pitched voice, and breast development. In the many chromosomal studies that have been done on Klinefelter's syndrome since the Jacobs and Strong report more than one type of anomaly involving the sex chromosomes have been found. Thus some patients show a constitution of *XXXY*, *XXXXY*, or *XXYY*. But in all chromosomal anomalies accompanying Klinefelter's syndrome there is more than one *X* and at least one *Y*.

The intellectual range of this group of patients is wide, varying from severe defect to above average. There is the usual problem of sampling because the more severely affected—either physically or intellectually—are more likely to come to the attention of the clinician. However, in the main, these individuals do not show severe degrees of mental defect and are likely to be in the educable class if they are retarded. Penrose (1962) estimates that the majority of individuals with Klinefelter's syndrome are probably intellectually normal.

Sex-chromosome anomalies also exist in females with gonadal dysgenesis, the first reported case involving the chromosomal analysis of a patient with Turner's syndrome (Ford *et al.*, 1959). Turner's syndrome is characterized by retardation in growth and in sexual development, accompanied by assorted congenital anomalies which may or may not be present in any given case. These include digital anomalies, imperfect extension of the elbows, cardiac malformations, and the presence of a band of tissue alongside the neck (described as a webbed neck). Ford's patient at the age of 14 was short (51″) and without secondary sex characteristics. In addition she was retarded at school. On chromosomal analysis she was found to have only 45 chromosomes with the missing chromosome assumed to be an *X*. The chromosome constitution was designated as *X0*, the *0* being used to denote the absence of the second sex chromosome.

The majority of Turner's-syndrome patients are intellectually normal; when retardation is present it is not severe. Polani (1960) feels that subnormality is more likely to be present in those patients that display the webbing of the neck, but even in this group it would not appear to exceed 25 percent of the cases.

Other sex-chromosome anomalies in the female may involve an excess number of *X* chromosomes. Penrose (1962) describes the triple-*X* female as similar to the normal female though in some instances menstruation may be delayed or absent. Intellectually, however, they tend to be subnormal, usually in the educable range. Cases of females with four *X* chromosomes have also been reported, again with no notable physical defect but with intellectual retardation.

REFERENCES

FORD, C. E., JONES, K. W., POLANI, P. E., DEALMEIDA, J. C., & BRIGGS, J. H. A sex-chromosome anomaly in a case of gonadal dysgenesis. *Lancet,* 1959, *1,* 711–713.

JACOBS, P., & STRONG, J. A. A case of human intersexuality having a possible XXY sex-determining mechanism. *Nature,* 1959, *183,* 302–303.

LEJEUNE, J., GAUTIER, M., & TURPIN, R. Study of the somatic chromosomes of nine mongoloid idiot children, 1959. In S. H. Boyer, *Papers on human genetics.* Englewood Cliffs, N. J.: Prentice-Hall 1963.

PENROSE, L. S. *The biology of mental defect.* (Rev. ed.) New York: Grune & Stratton, 1962.

POLANI, P. E. Chromosomal factors in certain types of educational subnormality. In P. W. Bowman and H. V. Mautner, *Mental retardation.* New York: Grune & Stratton, 1960.

POLANI, P. E. Cytogenetics of Down's syndrome (mongolism). *Pediatric Clinics of North America,* 1963, *10,* 423–448.

REPORT OF A STUDY GROUP. A proposed standard system on nomenclature of human mitotic chromosomes. *American Journal of Human Genetics,* 1960, *12,* 384–388.

CHAPTER VIII

Psychopaths, Addicts, Sexual Deviates, and Other Conduct Disorders

(A) PSYCHOPATHY AND SOCIOPATHY

PSYCHOPATHY AS A PSYCHOLOGICAL CONCEPT is a controversial one, not even found in the *Diagnostic and Statistical Manual: Mental Disorders* of the American Psychiatric Association (1965), though it lists sociopathic personality with a subhead "antisocial reaction" which "includes cases previously classified as 'constitutional psychopathic state' and 'psychopathic personality.' As defined here the term is more limited, as well as more specific in its application" (p. 38). Mathis (1968) and his associates identified the term as obsolete, and replaced it by "character and behavioral disorders."

McCord and McCord define the psychopath as an "asocial, aggressive, highly impulsive person, who feels little or no guilt and is unable to form lasting bonds of affection with other human beings" (1964, p. 3). Maher summarizes the primary psychopath as having a "behavior pattern marked by poor acquisition of a conditioned response to noxious stimulation, poor development of adaptive response in an avoidance learning task, little sign of any manifest anxiety, poor or shortened future time perspective, and a history of antisocial behavior" (1966, pp. 221–222).

In a study conducted by Albert, Brigante, and Chase (1959), these researchers concluded from an analysis involving 70 articles and books that there is considerable consensus regarding the concept, with disagreement entailing etiology of psychopathy.

Cleckley, who favors the term "psychopath" and uses it interchangeably with "sociopath," hypothesizes that it is a serious and "subtle disorder at deep levels disturbing the integration and normal appreciation of experience and resulting in pathology that might, in analogy with Henry Head's classifications of the aphasias, be described as semantic" (1964, p. 424). Cleckley's (1959, 1964) diagnostic criteria of psychopathic states include: unexplained failure; undisturbed technical intelligence; absence of neurotic anxiety; persistent and inadequately motivated antisocial behavior; irresponsibility; peculiar inability to distinguish between truth and falsehood; inability to accept blame; failure to learn by experience; incapacity for love; inappropriate or fantastic reactions to alcohol; lack of insight; shallow and impersonal responses to sexual life; persistent pattern of self-defeat; and the rare execution of suicides. Maher (1966) characterizes psychopaths by (1) impulsive antisocial behavior; (2) inability for forming lasting, genuine emotional attachments; and (3) vanity concerning appearance, social importance, etc.

Frankenstein (1959) cites 11 criteria of psychopathy under a dichotomous division of extraversion and introversion, with the morally indolent psychopath common to both groups. The other five characterizing the extravert are: (1) brutal destructiveness; (2) egocentric incorporation of the nonego, owing to the need to regain security and a fear of the void; (3) oscillating psychopathy (with contradictory reality elements); (4) shallow-attachment variety of oscillation; and (5) imposter and swindler type. Characteristics of the introvert are: (1) explosiveness (fantasies of destructive mastery over a hostile world); (2) paranoid who sees his identity as a negated one; (3) drifting psychopath (addict, sex pervert); (4) unstable psychopath (imitates another's behavior); and (5) owner of absolute truth (eccentricity, peculiar saint).

Buss (1966) ascribes three characteristics to the psychopathic personality: (1) a hollow, isolated person; (2) lacking any fundamental identity of his own; and (3) inability to bind time. Concerning the problem of time in relation to psychopathy, Siegman (1961), and Brock and Del Giudice (1963) found a shorter time perspective among delinquents, suggesting an inability of psychopaths to adapt behavior in the light of future adverse consequences. The question arises as to their time perspective respecting the future.

In a British study conducted by Craft (1965), he found the following clinical features of psychopathy, with the only negative ones being the "absence of psychosis" and "severe dullness:" (1) emotional instability;

need to act impulsively (thus preventing the psychopaths the time or opportunity of considering the consequences of their actions); (2) love-lessness; inability to feel affection for another; to think in terms of another, self-centeredness, coldness, hostility, and desire for destructiveness ter-minating in (3) antisocial behavior that is not deterred by (4) shame, guilt, or punishment (qualities lacking in psychopaths); and (5) ration-ality remaining intact. Craft inferred a concomitant relationship existing between the severity of personality disturbance and the frequency of early adverse childhood influences, i.e., an adverse parental relationship.

Primary psychopaths are often distinguished from neurotics by their lack of anxiety, while some authorities recognize *secondary psychopaths* who do show some manifestations of anxiety, hence complicate their condition with neurosis. Measuring anxiety by the Taylor Manifest Anxiety Scale, Fairweather (1954) found that psychopaths obtained the lowest scores. Using the Heineman (1953) form of the Taylor Manifest Anxiety Scale, Lykken (1957) obtained an AI (Anxiety Index) calculated by Welsh's (1952) formula of 49 psychopaths identified by Cleckley's criteria, and discovered that primary psychopaths displayed less anxiety while the neurotic psychopaths showed significantly higher scores on the Taylor Anxiety Scale and Welsh Anxiety Scale. In the employment of the Psy-chopathic Deviate Scale of the Minnesota Multiphase Personality Inven-tory, Hetherington and Klinger (1964) found psychopathy to be asso-ciated with "deficient passive avoidance" learning under punishment, i.e., psychopathic subjects learned at slower rates when punished for incorrect responses, but at the same rate when rewarded for correct ones.

In her study regarding conscience in the psychopath, Greenacre ascer-tained a faulty structural development of the conscience of psychopaths or those personalities "characterized by impulsiveness and marked irre-sponsibility, intense but labile emotional states, and generally quixotic and superficial love relationships" (1945, p. 495). She does not find them to be deliberate offenders, but rather persons who lie and steal impulsive-ly, particularly when under pressure.

Stern (1964) differentiates between sociopathy and "character neu-rosis"; while both come into conflict with their society, the latter (on the increase) are neurotics who "manifest themselves mainly in patho-logical distortions of patterns of behavior and conduct" (p. 134). He also recognizes a subtype of sociopath, the psychopath who is "morally color-blind." Approaching the subject matter from the standpoint of a clinician, Schneider, however, rejects the prevailing view that psychopathy is a study of the asocial or delinquent personality. Psychopaths are those individuals "who either suffer personally because of their own abnor-mality or make the community suffer because of it" (1958, p. 3).

According to Maher's (1966) subcultural hypothesis of criminal behavior, criminality has been acquired through a subculture, one of criminal environment in which the criminal is not a psychological deviant per se, since he is the product of reinforcements conducive to his subculture. Accordingly he should be regarded as subcultural rather than criminal. Related to Maher's hypothesis is "differential association" of Sutherland and Cressey (1960) that relates criminality to frequency, priority, duration, and intensity of association with other criminals.

Employing a learning theory approach to psychopathy, Eysenck recommends the treatment of "children with a sufficient degree of severity to achieve conditioning required by society, but not to treat them so severely that they fall prey to neurotic disorders" (1964, p. 159), the introverted child requiring less severe discipline than the extravert.

(B) ADDICTION
ALCOHOLISM: DEFINITION AND RESEARCH

The American Medical Association's *Manual on Alcoholism* defines alcoholism as *"an illness characterized by preoccupation with alcohol and loss of control over its consumption such as to lead usually to intoxication if drinking is begun; by chronicity; by progression; and by tendency toward relapse. It is typically associated with physical disability and impaired emotional, occupational, and/or social adjustments as a direct consequence of persistent and excessive use"* (1967, p. 6). Keller's definition of alcoholism is "a chronic disease manifested by repeated implicative drinking so as to cause injury to the drinker's health or to his social or economic functioning" (1960, p. 133).

The etiology of alcoholism is unknown, but consensus favors a multiple-cause theory (Alexander, 1963), linking it to one or a number of the following possibilities: biological, psychological, and social factors, with the psychological considered as of primary importance. As a progressive disease that is chronic in nature, alcoholism is associated with liver, kidney, stomach, nervous, and mental disorders, including brain damage. Alcohol, as a drug, with its direct action "on the individual nerve cell seems to be narcotic in nature with consequent depression of its function" (Courville, 1966, p. 85). The narcotic effects compare with those of anoxia, the need for oxygen. But according to Forbes and Duncan (1957), alcohol is also a stressing agent.

According to the U. S. Department of Health, Education, and Welfare (1966), using the Jellinek Estimation Formula, 4½ percent of Americans 21 years of age and over are alcoholic. Holmes, reporting for the National Council on Alcoholism, Inc. (1962), estimates 258,000 alcoholics in New York City. Lindesmith (1968), citing statistics from the Federal Bureau of Investigation in the *Uniform Crime Reports* for the year 1966, notes that drug arrests have increased from 3,400 in 1947 to 60,000 in 1966.

The addictive alcoholics, those persons psychologically and physically dependent upon alcohol as a drug, represent a large percentage of alcoholics according to Catanzaro (1968); the same is true of nonaddictive alcoholics, i.e., those dependent upon alcohol as a drug psychologically but who lack a physical dependence and experience no withdrawal symptoms. With time, however, they too may become addictive alcoholics.

Bowman and Jellinek (1942) also have drawn distinctions between primary and secondary addiction, secondary addiction being the physical dependence upon the drug, while primary addiction is considered as the immediate, psychological dependence devoid of the physiological component. Thompson (1956) rejects the concept of primary alcoholism. Furthermore, Jellinek (1960) identifies four species of alcoholism: (*a*) *alpha*, the "purely psychological *continual* dependence or reliance upon the effect of alcohol to relieve bodily or emotional pain"; (*b*) *beta*, that form of alcoholism resulting in polyneuropathy, gastritis and cirrhosis of the liver, yet without physical or psychological alcoholic dependence; (*c*) *gamma*, that species of alcoholism wherein is found: "(1) acquired increased tissue tolerance to alcohol, (2) adaptive cell metabolism . . ., (3) withdrawal symptoms and 'craving,' i.e., physical dependence, and (4) loss of control" (1960, p 37); (*d*) *delta*, the inability to abstain added to the previous three species of alcoholism.

In an earlier study on alcoholism, Jellinek (1952) cites four phases of alcohol addiction: (1) *prealcoholic symptomatic phase:* social drinking experienced as a rewarding relief of tension; (2) *prodromal phase:* characterized by blackouts, alcoholic palimpsests, surreptitious drinking, preoccupation with alcohol, avid drinking, guilt feelings associated with drink-induced behavior, heavy drinking; (3) *crucial phase:* identified by loss of control (or physical need) of the drug, rationalization of behavior, loss of self-esteem, grandiose behavior, withdrawal from society, aggressive behavior, persistent remorse, periods of total abstinence, changing patterns of drink, dropping of friends and jobs, loss of outside interests, reinterpretation of interpersonal relations, self-pity, change of family habits, resentment, neglect of proper nutrition, decrease in sexual desire, alcoholic jealousy, habitual matutinal drinking, intensive evening drinking; and (4) *chronic phase:* ethical deterioration, thought impairment, alcoholic psychoses, drinking with social inferiors, resorting to substitutes (bay rum, rubbing alcohol), loss of tolerance for alcohol, fears (indefinable), tremors, psychomotor inhibition, obsessive drinking, development of vague religious ideas, failure of the rationalization system.

Researching alcoholic psychoses in New York state, Malzberg (1960) found it rare in the under 20-year-old bracket, and rising in males to a rate of first admissions of 27.8 at ages 45 to 49; for females to 8.9 at ages 40 to 44. The male rate (11.6) not only exceeds the female (3.3) rate of first admissions, but also increases with age. Education is also a factor, rates being highest for those lacking any education (14.4) or with only a secondary education (14.5), and lowest for the college educated (4.0).

On a twin study project regarding heredity factors underlying the use of alcohol, Partanen and his associates found that "normal drinking as well as abstinence and heavy use show considerable heredity variation. . . . On the other hand, the social consequences and arrests for drunkenness . . . do not show any hereditary determination" (1966, p. 19).

In the classic experiments of the influence of alcohol on experimentally induced neuroses in cats, Masserman and Yum (1946) report a preference for alcohol in drinking water by neurotic cats. To varying degrees, adaptive patterns were disintegrated, especially the more recent and complex one, whereas normal cats on recovery from intoxication showed complete functional restitution with but little alcoholic habituation and no preference for the drug, the inference of the experiments being that under conflict situations, alcohol has a drive reducing effect, alleviating the drive of anxiety.

Experimenting on the effect of stress on the consumption of alcohol and reserpine on rats, Casey's (1960) findings supported those of Masserman and Yum. Casey favors a "reinforcement theory interpretation in terms of a stress produced anxiety drive which is reduced by the effect of consumed alcohol, thereby reinforcing alcohol-drinking behavior" (1960, pp. 213–214). With the continued absence of stress, behavior (based on the drive of anxiety) is eventually extinguished.

PERSONALITY OF ALCOHOLICS

In her research on alcoholic personalities from the orientation of intelligence, Pollmer (1965) found the lower the intelligence of a given group of alcoholics, the more numerous were their stable personality characteristics, the same holding true of parental home environment. "The higher the intelligence of subjects, the more pronounced and, compared to the total environment, the more exclusively similar their problem areas seemed to be. . . . The lower the intelligence of subjects, the more their total home environments seemed to be alike, and the more diffuse the border of their particular problem area" (1965, p. 154). Furthermore, alcoholics of higher intelligence had a higher rate of cure as well as treatment of a relatively shorter duration. Morever, they blamed others for their predicament.

Fox (1967) notes that alcoholism tends to run in families, with 52 percent of alcoholics with at least one parent an alcoholic. She thinks this fact may reflect an inadequate family life with poor models with whom to identify. In his study of the alcoholic personality, Tähkä (1966) found that subjects' mothers had a tendency to insecurity concerning their roles as women, and married men over whom they could feel superior. They narcissistically used their sons by way of overcompensation for inferiority regarding their sex. Subjects were submissive to and ambivalently dependent upon the mother who was the dominant parent.

On a comparison of male with female cases of alcoholism, Karpman (1957) noted that males report alcohol as a secondary factor (emotional maladjustment being the primary) while females attribute their alcoholism to external circumstances, unaware of their emotional maladjustment. Hence the male's insight as to his alcoholic problem is markedly greater than the female's. Females deplore their weakness in succumbing to alcohol, while men accept their weakness. Women compensate for this deficiency by resorting to culture and aesthetic interests.

THERAPY

As yet, no cure of alcoholism is known though a variety of approaches are helpful. Among some common ones are: (1) *disulfiram* (Antabuse) and calcium carbimide (Temposil), drugs which interfere with alcohol metabolism, making the individual sick; (2) *hypnosis,* used to alter attitude toward alcohol; (3) *conditioned reflex therapy,* used to create an aversion to drink; (4) *Alcoholics Anonymous,* a social-spiritual approach; (5) *group therapy* and *psychodrama,* for gaining self-insight; (6) *psychoanalysis and psychotherapy (individual),* valuable only after sobriety for gaining a better perspective of self; (7) *team psychotherapy and counseling* entailing psychologists, psychiatrists, psychiatric social workers, and clergy working conjointly where possible; and (8) *"halfway"* houses.

In addition to endorsing Alcoholics Anonymous as a successful mode of therapy, Williams (1959) recommends a nutritional approach to therapy, one consisting of good amounts of high quality protein (plus vitamins and minerals but avoidance of refined foods) so that the alcoholic's improved physical condition will enhance his ability to cope with the problem of abstinence. Tracing alcoholism to the immaturity of personality, Thompson sees Alcoholics Anonymous as an excellent vehicle for building character in the alcoholic. Even Cain, whose hostile attitude toward A.A. is uninhibited, recommends: "To *anyone* who is having trouble with alcohol I say: try A.A. first; it's the answer for most people" (1964, p. 72).

The most desirable approach to alcoholism is preventive treatment (Block, 1967); however, in the case of alcoholism, when signs of diagnostic significance manifest themselves, the disorder is already in an advanced state. According to Hayman (1966), only 5 to 10 percent of alcoholics are in a psychiatric condition that is amenable to recovery. Conducting experimental research on 178 alcoholic patients at Winter VA Hospital, Wallerstein and his colleagues (1957) report that Antabuse precipitated psychotic reactions in borderline schizophrenia and depressed patients, whereas the same type patients benefited from milieu therapy owing to increased personal relationships with their therapists. Although the schizoid type responded to hypnotherapy, he failed to improve on hospital discharge. For the masochistic individual, conditioned reflex therapy was contraindicated, while the oppressed patient responded to it. Mullan and Sanguiliano (1966) found the most satisfactory therapy to consist of a separate treatment unit, group treatment, vocational counseling, and rehabilitation.

Following the lead of Hollingshead and Redlich (1958), Schmidt and his collaborators (1968) corroborate the findings of the former in regard to alcoholics, their hypothesis being that a patient's "social class is related to all aspects of treatment for alcoholics, that is, to sources of referral, diagnoses, prognoses, and types and duration of treatment including treatment personnel involved" (1968, p. 19).

THEORIES OF ALCOHOLISM AND DRUG ADDICTION

Levy (1958), whose neo-Freudian views identify the function of alcohol as residing in its toxic effect, theorizes that it consists of "discharge" and "narcotizing" functions, and the toxic effects possess symbolic meaning. The list of functions are: (1) *discharge* (cathartic value; blocks anxiety, guilt, and shame); (2) *narcotizing* (sleep value in dealing with tensions); (3) *symbolic*; (4) *infantomimetic* (orally gratifying); (5) *masochistic*; (6) *hostility* (release of rage); (7) *homosexuality* (discharge, sublimation, and denial of homosexual strivings); (8) *identification* and *identity* (parental identification).

Button (1956) proceeding also from neo-Freudian principles, seeks to isolate dynamic variables peculiar to alcoholics, and presents a schematic outline giving a theoretical basis of the genesis and development of alcoholism.

Conger (1951) and Kingham (1958) developed learning theory approaches to alcoholism. The former, applying Dollard and Miller views on drive and reinforcement, concluded that the alleviation of anxiety through alcohol consumption acts as a reinforcement and eventually becomes habit forming. The latter hypothesizes that alcoholism develops from predisposing conditions: (1) desire to escape reality; (2) uncontrollable blitz drinking pattern; and (3) drive-cue-response-reinforcement learning paradigm enacted with the "blitz drinking pattern reducing the disturbance in psychological homeostasis." More than resolving unconscious conflicts is needed for successful treatment; total abstinence is necessary to extinguish the blitz drinking pattern.

Storm and Smart (1965), building on the findings of Overton (1964) and Otis (1964) that animals acquiring habits when drugged fail to show a transfer to a nondrugged state (the inverse also being true), verified this hypothesis in reference to alcohol. They found that the longer the span of intoxication, the greater the dissociation (difference) between the intoxicated and sober condition. Accordingly, the sober-state learned behavior fails to generalize to states of inebriation. Thus learning theory rather than physiological response accounts for loss of control and "blackouts" (dissociation). These findings imply that "if dissociation is important, then treatment should be given to alcoholics while alcohol is present in the organism and be directed to conditioning the patient to respond to the cues of increased intoxication by not drinking" (p. 115).

According to Hebb (1966), addiction is theorized as an *artificial hunger* and as a *homeostatic process* that occurs in two stages: an intermediate stage of "physiological dependence," followed by "addiction proper." The two may occur concurrently, but usually happen consecutively. The first stage, the physiological modification of physical tissues, leads to the need for the drug in order to maintain stable, homeostatic functioning; while the second results from a learning process.

Devoting many years to the study of opiate addiction, Lindesmith (1965, 1968) defines addiction as "that behavior which is distinguished primarily by an intense, conscious desire for the drug, and by a tendency to relapse, evidently caused by the persistence of attitudes established in the early stages of addiction" (1968, p. 64). Lindesmith attributes drug addiction, not to the pleasure or euphoria derived from the use of it, but from the recognition and identification of it with withdrawal distress. Relief from withdrawal distress (once physical distress has been established) accounts for addiction.

Convinced of multiple causality in drug addiction, Ausubel (1958, 1961) hypothesizes that both internal factors such as hereditary susceptibility and external factors such as the social environment conducive to the use of the drug and its availability explain narcotic addiction.

Inasmuch as physiological addiction and withdrawal symptoms can be readily eliminated by a hospital stay for a relatively brief period of time, and inasmuch as addicts return to the drug soon on release from a hospital cure of physical dependence, more than an explanation of physical addiction is necessary. Two important types of addiction are (1) maturational deficiency, the failure of the personality to mature and actualize himself (motivationally, vocationally, etc.); and (2) reactive addiction, the need for an outlet (especially to rebel and defy the norms of conventional society). A third or miscellaneous type is an escape from anxiety or depression.

(C) SEXUAL DEVIANCE
THE PROBLEM OF DEFINING SEXUAL PERVERSION

Sexual deviance does not admit of a simple definition, inasmuch as what one society would allow as normal, another may condemn as a perversion. For example, in the American society mouth to mouth kissing is considered quite normal, even with persons with whom one is hardly acquainted. But when the Thonga first observed kissing among the Europeans, they ridiculed them saying: "Look at them—they eat each other's saliva and dirt" (Ford & Beach, 1951, p. 49).

The problem of defining sexual perversion is clearly seen in the matter of voyeurism. In the *Psychiatric Dictionary* of Hinsie and Shatsky (1953), "voyeur" is defined as "sexual pervert. . . . One who obtains sexual gratification by looking at the genitals of another. . . . A scopophiliac" (p. 549). They define scopophilia as "sexual pleasure derived from contemplation or looking" (p. 476). According to this definition (which is widely used) virtually all persons are sexual perverts. In the light of such encompassing definitions, Gebhard and his colleagues comment:

Thus, a lounger on the street watching passing girls, or a person watching a strip-tease act could qualify as a voyeur, or so could the peruser of "cheesecake" magazines. One might say that a peeper is a voyeur who has no legal right to be at the location from whence he observes, but even this definition is imperfect since a man has a right to be on a public street at night, but is liable to arrest if he stands on the sidewalk looking into the window of the adjacent apartment house. . . . All males have voyeuristic and peeping tendencies (1965, pp. 358–359).

Another problem confronting psychopathologists regarding sexual normality and deviation is the social strictures prohibiting experimentation with humans. Recently, however, Masters and Johnson (1966) were remarkably successful in conducting experiments on human sexual activity.

HOMOSEXUALITY

Of the great variety of sexual offenses, more attention and research has been allocated in recent years to homosexuality than any other form of deviation.

Buss (1966), differentiating between two types of homosexuality, seems to imply that one is normal and the second a deviation. The first, "appropriate sexual activity," is "sexual behavior consistent with the gender of the participant," that is, the male plays the role normally undertaken by males in heterosexual activity; but in the second, "sexual inversion," the male homosexual assumes the female role, and this is considered the more abnormal. Neustatter (1968) draws a distinction between psychopathic homosexuals and those that are not; the psychopathic are identified by the lack of a sense of conscience or scruples regarding their behavior.

According to Bergler (1956), there are "statistically induced homosexuals," those who read books citing the widespread practice of homosexuality, thus assume it to be normal and yield to experimentation. Although there are healthy heterosexuals, Bergler claims that there are "no healthy homosexuals."

Neither Kinsey and his associates (1948, 1953) nor Allen (1958) found glandular factors accounting for homosexuality. Allen is adamant in his stand regarding the absence of discernible differences in physique between homo- and heterosexuals. Despite the increase in premarital, extramarital, and masturbatory sex practices in individuals born subsequent to 1920, Kinsey found no increase in homosexuality in comparing the 1920 plus figures with those prior to the year 1910. Although homosexuality is not on the increase, the Committee on Public Health of the New York Academy of Medicine (1964) has found it to be "more open and obtrusive." The Committee cites two goals of present-day homosexuals: (1) acceptance, rather than mere toleration; and (2) to be regarded as desirable, noble, and a preferable way of life, rather than merely an acceptable mode of existence. Suggs (1966), in an elaborate study of Marquesan sexual behavior, reports that homosexuality is rare among them and considered unnatural.

Studies on homosexuality by Westwood (1960) revealed the following sequence: from 13 to 15 years of age sexual play among boys was a matter of curiosity rather than "homosexuality," followed by an experimental phase and a latent period; from 16 to 19 years of age was a time of conflict of guilt and shame coupled with a determined effort to resist homosexual feelings; and by the early twenties the homosexual finds self-acceptance and pursues his unmistakable homosexual inclinations.

Concluding from a limited sampling, Schofield (1965a) suggests that

1 in 7 boys succumbs to homosexuality, but only 1 in 10 girls. He also found that one third of the boys are introduced to heterosexual intercourse by a partner older than himself, as against two thirds of the girls. A hearsay report is recorded by Ellis to the effect that "a Catholic confessor, a friend tells me, informed him that for one man who acknowledges homosexual practices there are three women" (1963, p. 195).

THEORIES OF HOMOSEXUALITY

Viewing homosexuality from a genetic orientation, Kallmann (1952a, 1952b, 1953) found post-adolescent overt homosexual behavior in the entire series of 44 one-egg pairs of twins. More than merely being concordant, the majority of the one-egg pairs displayed a tendency toward similarity in the roles they assumed in their individual sexual activities in addition to their femininity both as to appearance and behavior. Kallmann found in identical twins twice the incidence of homosexuality than that which occurred in the two-egg group.

Theorizing as to the etiology of sexuality, Ollendorff (1966) asserts that homosexuality is found only in "sex-negating societies," and absent in sex-permissive ones, or at the most is regarded as a childish deviation which has no place in the normal sexually mature personality.

The causes of homosexuality, as induced in childhood by the sex-negating patterns of upbringing, grow to promote a fixed neurotic illness in the predisposed, especially by the mass occurrence of mutual masturbation and homosexual play in adolescence. . . . Homosexuality is a neurotic illness of great strength caused by two factors: a predisposed neurotic personality and the impact of sex-negating and prohibitive elements of conventional upbringing (1966, p. 116–117).

He believes that overt or constitutional homosexuals number approximately 3 percent of the male population.

According to psychoanalytic theory, Freud (1946) assumed a polymorphous perversity in childhood that may (through improper psychosexual development) reach a stage of arrested development—homosexuality. Stekel (1948) conjectures that homosexuality results when a child experiences a deep sense of rejection by the parent of the opposite sex so that the parent of the same sex wins his love and affection.

Kurt Adler (1967), following in the tradition of his father, postulates that a person's style of life determines his sexual behavior. Impaired "gender-identity" or "gender-role" in childhood issues in a "fear of the opposite sex, or fear of inadequacy in one's proper sex role, or both" (1967, p. 77), hence is responsible for homosexuality.

A theory resulting from the research of homosexuals convicted of the crime was advanced by Schofield (1965b). Although homosexuality affects personality development slightly, the attitude of nonhomosexuals toward the homosexual produces a stress that does have profound effects upon the homosexual, resulting in "character deterioration," preventing suitable social integration. While some homosexuals can cope with society's hostility, others, becoming social casualties, end in prisons or clinics. Accordingly, not homosexuality per se, but accompanying social pressures associated with it create the attending psychopathological consequences.

53.

Davɪᴅ T. Lʏᴋᴋᴇɴ

ANXIETY IN PSYCHOPATHS (SOCIOPATHS)

The concept of the psychopathic personality includes so heterogeneous a group of behavior disorders as to be at least two steps removed from the level of useful psychiatric diagnosis. Sociopathic personality is a more recent designation (1) which refers to a subgroup of these disorders in which the pathognomic characteristics are impulsiveness, antisocial tendencies, immorality, and a seemingly self-destructive failure to modify this pattern of behavior in spite of repeated painful consequences. This category may be regarded as a genus composed of phenotypically similar, but etiologically distinct, subtypes such as the dissocial and the neurotic sociopaths.

A third species has been described (3, 12, 13, 14, 17), which may be called *primary sociopathy,* in which neither neurotic motivations, hereditary taint, nor dissocial nurture seem to be determining factors. Cleckley (3) has reported the chief clinical characteristic of this group as a lack of the normal affective accompaniments of experience. If this observation is correct, it would point the way toward accurate diagnostic isolation of primary sociopathy as well as guiding research into the question of its etiology. Classification according to the presence or absence of defective emotional reactivity, therefore, satisfies one criterion of useful diagnosis in that it shows promise of relationship to the as yet unknown origins of the disorders to be distinguished.

The other requirement for useful diagnosis is that the criteria of classification must be objective. Clinical assessment of the "normality of the affective accompaniments of experience" is subjective and unreliable. In consequence,

From David T. Lykken, "A study of anxiety in the sociopathic personality," *Journal of Abnormal and Social Psychology, 55,* 1957, 6–10.

© 1957 by the American Psychological Association, reproduced by permission.

Cleckley's work has had as yet little real impact on psychiatric practice. By expressing this putative defect of the primary sociopath in terms of the anxiety construct of experimental psychology (18, 19, 20, 21, 22), it becomes susceptible to quantification and empirical test.

An experimental hypothesis may now be formulated. Among persons conventionally diagnosed as psychopathic personality, those who closely resemble the syndrome described by Cleckley are (*a*) clearly defective as compared to normals in their ability to develop (i.e., *condition*) anxiety, in the sense of an anticipatory emotional response to warning signals previously associated with nociceptive stimulation. Persons with such a defect would also be expected to show (*b*) abnormally little *manifest anxiety* in life situations normally conducive to this response, and to be (*c*) relatively incapable of *avoidance learning* under circumstances where such learning can only be effected through the mediation of the anxiety response.

METHOD

Tʜᴇ Sᴀᴍᴘʟᴇ

The extreme heterogeneity, even on the crudest descriptive level, of persons diagnosed as psychopathic personalities in various clinical or institutional settings complicated the selection of an appropriate experimental sample. The institution psychologists were given a list of 14 criteria drawn from Cleckley (3, pp. 355–392) and were asked to compare against these criteria those inmates diagnosed as psychopathic personality. Inmates who, in their opinion, best fitted the Cleckley prototype were listed as candidates for experimental Group I, the primary sociopathic group. Inmates who they felt did *not* meet the criteria in important respects were listed as candidates for experimental Group

II, designated as the neurotic sociopathic group. In this selection process, the psychologists were asked to reaffirm the original diagnosis, discarding from consideration for either group those inmates who, in their present opinion, would not be diagnosed as psychopathic personality at all.

A control Group III of 15 "normals," roughly comparable in age, intelligence, and socioeconomic background, was selected from the University General College and a local high school.

Group I, composed of 12 males and 7 females, had a mean age of 21.6 years ($SD = 4.3$), and a mean IQ of 109.2 ($SD = 10.7$). Group II included 13 males and 7 females, had a mean age of 24.5 years ($SD = 5.4$), and a mean IQ of 104.5 ($SD = 8.8$). For the 10 male and 5 female normals, the mean age was 19.07 ($SD = 3.2$), and the mean IQ 100.4 ($SD = 10.2$). None of these group differences were significant.

THE MEASURES AND TESTING PROCEDURE

It was necessary to do the testing at the several institutions under varying conditions. In all cases, however, the apparatus was arranged on a large table, the experimenter on one side and the subject (S) seated comfortably opposite. The S was told that he was assisting in a psychological experiment having no bearing on his personal record and that his performance would be treated with strict anonymity. An attempt was made throughout to keep the testing on an informal basis.

As an indicant of manifest anxiety as referred to in hypothesis b, an "Anxiety Scale" was constructed expressly for this study to supplement the Taylor scale and Anxiety Index which appear to be more strongly loaded on a factor of neurotic self-description. In this new scale, each of the thirty-three items involves two statements of activities or occurrences, matched for general unpleasantness or undesirability according to a modified Thurstone scaling procedure utilizing 15 college student judges. One activity of each pair is unpleasant, presumably because of its frightening or embarrassing character (e.g., "making a parachute jump" or "knocking over a glass in a restaurant"). The paired activity is intended to be onerous but not frightening

(e.g., "digging a big rubbish pit" or "cleaning up a spilled bottle of syrup"). The S is required to choose that member of each pair which he would prefer as a lesser of evils. The degree to which the "frightening" alternatives are rejected is interpreted as an index of the extent to which anxiety determines behavior choices within the range of life situations sampled by this test.

The booklet form of the MMPI was used and the answer sheets scored and K-corrected in the usual way (10). The Anxiety Index, or AI, was calculated according to the formula given by Welsh (23). The Heineman form (11) of the Taylor scale was given and scored by subtracting the number of "anxiety" items rejected as "least applies to me" from the number endorsed as "most applies to me."

An avoidance learning test was given to determine whether there were group differences in capacity to learn on the basis of anxiety reduction (hypothesis c). It involved an elaborate, electrically operated mental maze which the S was given 20 trials to learn (the "manifest task"). At each of the 20 choice points in this maze, choice of one of the 4 possible alternatives (always an error alternative) gave an electric shock. It was intended that social and ego rewards should reinforce performance in the manifest task. Performance on the "latent task," which was to avoid the shocked alternatives—to err instead on the unshocked alternatives—was presumably reinforced only through anxiety reduction.

The measure of anxiety conditionability (hypothesis a) employed the GSR as the dependent variable. A shocking electrode was attached to S's nondominant hand, the GSR electrodes being already in place on the dominant hand. The S was told that after the blindfold had been replaced, he was to sit as quietly as possible for the next 30 to 40 minutes, during which time he would periodically hear a buzzer (which was then demonstrated) and occasionally receive a brief electric shock. When the S was seated comfortably and relaxed insofar as possible, the recording apparatus was started and the conditioning series (CS) begun.

Two buzzers were used which were distinguishably different in timbre rather than in pitch, the difference being one not easily labeled (to minimize verbal mediation of a discrimination between them). Buzzer No. 1 was used as the CS and was the only one reinforced; buzzer No. 2 was used to test for generalization effects. In all cases, stimuli of the conditioning series were presented as soon as GSR activity from preceding stimuli had subsided, the intertrial interval being therefore not constant within or between Ss, but averaging between 20 and 60 seconds. (This method of stimulus timing automatically eliminates temporal conditioning.) When turned on, the buzzers sounded for a period of 5 seconds, controlled by an automatic timer.

The reinforcing stimulus or UnCS was an electric shock from a 700-volt AC supply through two 68,000-ohm series resistors, presented automatically for about 100 milliseconds just before the termination of the CS (buzzer No. 1). The shock was applied between an electrode on the palm of one hand and the GSR *ground* electrode on the palmar tip of the middle finger of the opposite hand. The shock sensation was felt mainly on the richly innervated finger tip and was a decidedly unpleasant stimulus, producing in most cases a pronounced startle reaction and in all cases a strong GSR.

The sequence of trials or stimulus presentations was as follows:

1. To permit the adaptation of unconditioned GSR, to the buzzers themselves, stimuli were first presented without shock reinforcement for a total of 10 trials in the order 2, 1, 2, 1 S, 2, 2, 1, 1, 1, 1. A single preliminary shock was given in the series at the point S, separated by at least 30 seconds from the buzzers occurring before and after it.

2. Seven consecutive shock-reinforced presentations of the CS were given as the conditioning series, followed by four more reinforcements interspersed with four unreinforced trials with buzzer No. 2 in the order 1, 1, 1, 1, 1, 1, 1, 2, 1, 2, 2, 1, 2, 1, 1.

3. A total of 24 extinction trials was then given, the two buzzer stimuli being presented in the order 1, 2, 1, 1, 2, 1, 2, 1, 2, 1, 1, 1, 1, 2, 2, 1, 2, 1, 1, 2, 1, 1, 1. Considering only the CS buzzer No. 1, the series therefore consisted of 6 prereinforcement trials, 11 reinforced conditioning trials, and 16 extinction trials.

Skin resistance was measured by a modification of a circuit suggested by Flanders (6) which passed an electronically regulated constant DC current of 40 microamperes through S. The electrodes were curved discs of Monel metal, 15 mm. in diameter, applied to the palmar surface of the distal phalange of the first, second, and third fingers of the same hand. The skin surface was first scrubbed with alcohol and then coated with Sanborn electrode paste. The exosomatic current was applied between the first and third fingers, which were also connected to the push-pull input grids of a Sanborn Model 126 DC amplifier, driving a Sanborn Model 127 recording milliameter. The electrode on the second finger was connected to amplifier and external ground. The instrument was calibrated before each use and provided a linear record of resistance and resistance change, accurate to less than ±50 ohms.

All GSRs were recorded in terms of resistance change. A variety of transformations was then applied and tested against the usual criteria of normality of distribution, correlation with basal resistance, and homogeneity of variance across people with respect to several test stimuli (2, 8, 9, 16). The result of this analysis was that each resistance change was expressed as the logarithm of the ratio of the change to the mean resistance change produced by the first six electric shocks. This unit expresses the galvanic CR as a proportion of the individual's UnCR and, for a conditioning study, seems quite appropriate for individual comparisons.

Three GSR indices were derived from the protocols of the conditioning series: (*a*) GSR Reactivity, which is the mean GSR to the CS during the fourth through seventh conditioning trials; (*b*) GSR Conditioning, which is equal to (*a*) minus the mean GSR to the last three preconditioning trials and the last three extinction trials (this index measures essentially the slope of the conditioning curve or the increment actually produced by the reinforced trials); (*c*) GSR Generalization, the ratio of the mean GSR to buzzer No. 2 during early extinction trials 18, 20, 21, 23 to the mean GSR to buzzer No. 1 during trials 17, 19, 22, 24.

The testing sequence was as follows: (*a*) Anxiety scale; (*b*) GSR Conditioning series; (*c*) Avoidance Learning test; (*d*) MMPI (given during the week following the foregoing individual testing); (*e*) Taylor Manifest Anxiety Scale, forced-choice form given later with the MMPI.

RESULTS AND DISCUSSION

Scores on all measures were converted for easier comparison to a standard score form with each distribution having a grand mean of 500 and a standard deviation of 100. Group means on all measures, together with significance test results, are given in Table 8.1.

TABLE 8.1
GROUP MEANS ON ALL MEASURES: SIGNIFICANCE TESTS*

Measure	Group			d-Test
	I	II	III	prob.†
Taylor Scale	471	556	462	.01
Anxiety Index	472	557	464	.01
Anxiety Scale	470	511	529	.05
MMPI *Pd*-Scale	532	547	395	.05
Avoidance Learning ..	461	501	558	.01
GSR Reactivity	498	494	534	.05
GSR Conditioning ...	478	483	551	.05
Generalization	473	542	490	—

*All measures converted to a scale having an over-all mean of 500 and SD of 100.

†Probabilities given are for significance of largest difference [e.g., III–I for GSR Conditioning]. Significance test was Festinger's distribution-free 'd' test (5).

It would clearly be too much to expect of the judgments based upon the Cleckley criteria that they should have perfectly separated the psychopathic sample into a "primary" species in Group I, and a neurotic or dissocial species in Group II. That the separation was reasonably good, however, is supported by the finding that Group II scored significantly higher than the normals on the Taylor scale, a great deal of evidence having accumulated (4, 7, 15) to indicate that this scale is primarily a measure of neurotic maladjustment or neuroticism rather than of anxiety level or anxiety reactivity *per se*. On the MMPI Anxiety Index, which like the Taylor scale is unquestionably polydimensional with a heavy loading on neuroticism, Group II again has the highest mean, with Group I again only slightly higher than Group III.

In contrast, the Anxiety scale, which was designed for this study and which is not loaded on neuroticism and only negligibly correlated with the Taylor scale or the AI, separated the groups in a different order. On this test, the primary types of Group I show the least anxiety reactivity, significantly less than the normals, with Group II falling in between but rather nearer to the Group III mean. This result appears to support hypothesis *b* of this study, that the subset of primary sociopaths shows abnormally little manifest anxiety, i.e., anxiety reactivity to the real-life anxiety stimuli referred to in the questionnaire.

Both sociopathic groups scored significantly higher than the normals on the *Pd* scale of the MMPI, but this measure, which differentiates at the phenotypic or genus level, does not distinguish between the types or species of sociopathy represented in Groups I and II.

Schedule difficulties unfortunately led to a reduction in the number of Ss to whom the avoidance learning test could be given. With nearly half of the total group, the available testing time was too short to cover all of the procedures; in such cases the avoidance test, requiring nearly an hour to give, was passed over. Even on the residual sample of 34 Ss, however, rather clear-cut differences exist. As a crude, overall index of avoidance learning, the avoidance scores (shock errors divided by unshocked errors) were averaged for all but the first of the 20 trials; this is the basis of the mean scores entered under "avoidance" in Table 8.1. The distribution was reversed to make high values represent greater avoidance of the shock. It is impossible, of course, to summarize adequately a complex learning process by a single numerical index of this sort, but in spite of these limitations, it is striking that Group I (primaries) shows the least avoidance as expected, Group II (neurotics) next, and Group III (normals) the most. The Group I versus Group III, and Group II versus Group III differences are significant by Festinger's *d*-test (5), and the actual distribution of scores shows the groups to be remarkably well separated (only 17 per cent overlap between Groups I and III). This result supports hypothesis *c* of this study, that the primary sociopath demonstrates defective avoidance learning.

RESULTS OF THE GSR CONDITIONING SERIES

Of all the tests employed here, principal emphasis should be laid on GSR conditioning. The various difficulties attending the interpretation of GSR data are well known, but one fact stands out with relative certainty: given certain necessary conditions, if an S does *not* produce a GSR to a stimulus, one can be sure that he has not "reacted emotionally" to that stimulus.

The two numerical indices which were derived as alternative ways of representing in a single value the conditioning indicated by the GSR protocols (anticipatory GSR to the buzzer after several pairings with shock) have already been described. As shown in Table 8.1, the group means are in the expected order on both indicants, with Group I significantly lower than Group III on GSR Reactivity and GSR Conditioning (.05 level, *d*-test).

A somewhat more meaningful comparison is obtained by contrasting the reactivity by trials for the three groups. Group I shows the least GSR reaction to CS in 14 out of the 16 double trials. Group II is significantly higher (.02 level) than Group I at the end of the extinction trials. The positions of Group II and Group III interchange during the series with Group II beginning to show greater reactivity during the extinction trials, suggesting a perseveration (failure of extinction) of the anxiety response in the neurotic group. This trend was tested for statistical reliability by correlating the differences between Group II and Group III with the ordinal position in the conditioning series at which the difference was taken. The quadrant sign test (24) shows this association to be significant at the .01 level: This result supports hypothesis *a* of this study, that the primary sociopath is defective in his ability to condition the anxiety response.

The generalization scores were leptokurtically distributed, the group differences being determined by a few deviant Ss. Group II shows the highest mean generalization score, but the differences are not significant.

SUMMARY

Forty-nine diagnosed psychopaths were divided into two groups according to the descriptive criteria of Cleckley. Fifteen normals served as controls. A battery of tests related to anxiety reactivity or anxiety conditionability were administered. As compared with normals, the Cleckley, or "primary" sociopaths, showed significantly less "anxiety" on a questionnaire device, less GSR reactivity to a "conditioned" stimulus associated with shock, and less avoidance of punished responses on a test of avoidance learning. The "neurotic" sociopaths scored significantly higher on the Taylor Anxiety Scale and on the Welsh Anxiety Index.

REFERENCES

1. AMERICAN PSYCHIATRIC ASSOCIATION. *Diagnostic and statistical manual: mental disorders.* Washington, D.C.: A.P.A., 1952.
2. BITTERMAN M. E., & HOLTZMAN, W. H. Development of psychiatric screening of flying personnel. III. Conditioning and extinction of the GSR in relation to clinical evidence of anxiety. *USAF School of Aviation Medicine,* 1952, Proj. No. 21-37-002, Rep. No. 3, N. 232 p.
3. CLECKLEY, H. *The mask of sanity.* (2nd ed.) St. Louis: C. V. Mosby, 1950.
4. ERIKSEN, C. W., & DAVIDS, A. The meaning and clinical validity of the Taylor Anxiety Scale and the hysteria-psychasthenia scales from the MMPI. *Journal of Abnormal and Social Psychology,* 1955, *50,* 135–137.
5. FESTINGER, L. The significance of the difference between means without reference to the frequency distribution function. *Psychometrika,* 1945, *11,* 97–105.
6. FLANDERS, N. A. A circuit for the continuous measurement of palmar resistance. *American Journal of Psychology,* 1953, *66,* 295–299.
7. FRANKS, C. Conditioning and personality: a study of normal and neurotic subjects. *Journal of Abnormal and Social Psychology,* 1956, *52,* 143–150.
8. HAGGARD, E. A. Experimental studies in affective processes. II. On the quantification and evaluation of "measured" changes in skin resistance. *Journal of Experimental Psychology,* 1945, *33,* 45–56.
9. HAGGARD, E. A. On the application of analysis of variance to GSR data. I. The selection of an appropriate measure. *Journal of Experimental Psychology,* 1949, *39,* 378–392.
10. HATHAWAY, S. R. *Supplementary manual for the MMPI. Part I, The K scale and its use.* New York: Psychological Corp., 1946.
11. HEINEMAN, C. E. A forced choice form of the

Taylor Anxiety Scale. *Journal of Consulting Psychology*, 1953, *17*, 447–454.

12. KARPMAN, B. Psychopathic types: the symptomatic and the ideopathic. *Journal of Criminal Psychopathology*, 1941, *3*, 112–124.

13. KARPMAN, B. The myth of the psychopathic personality. *American Journal of Psychiatry*, 1948, *104*, 523–534.

14. KARPMAN, B. Conscience in the psychopath: another version. *American Journal of Orthopsychiatry*, 1948, *18*, 455–491.

15. KERRICK, JEAN S. Some correlates of the Taylor Manifest Anxiety Scale. *Journal of Abnormal Social Psychology*, 1955, *50*, 75–77.

16. LACEY, O. L., & SIEGEL, P. S. An analysis of the unit of measurement of the galvanic skin responses. *Journal of Experimental Psychology*, 1949, *39*, 122–123.

17. LIPMAN, H. S. Psychopathic behavior in infants and children: a critical survey of existing concepts. *American Journal of Orthopsychiatry*, 1951, *21*, 227–231.

18. MAY, M. A. Experimentally acquired drives. *Journal of Experimental Psychology*, 1948, *38*, 66–77.

19. MILLER, N. E. Studies of fear as an acquirable drive. I. Fear as motivation and fear-reduction as reinforcement in the learning of new responses. *Journal of Experimental Psychology*, 1948, *38*, 89–101.

20. MILLER, N. E. Learnable drives and rewards. In S. S. Stevens (Ed.), *Handbook of experimental psychology*. New York: Wiley, 1951. Pp. 435–472.

21. MOWRER, O. H. A stimulus-response analysis of anxiety. *Psychological Review*, 1939, *46*, 553–565.

22. MOWRER, O. H. Anxiety reduction and learning *Journal of Experimental Psychology*, 1940, *27*, 497–516.

23. WELSH, G. S. An anxiety index and an internalization ratio for the MMPI. *Journal of Consulting Psychology*, 1952, *16*, 65–72.

24. WILCOXON, F. *Some rapid approximate statistical procedures*. New York: American Cyanamid Co., 1949.

54.

HERVEY M. CLECKLEY

CHARACTERISTICS OF PSYCHOPATHY

We shall list the characteristic points that have emerged. . . .

1. Superficial charm and good "intelligence"

2. Absence of delusions and other signs of irrational thinking

3. Absence of "nervousness" or psychoneurotic manifestations

4. Unreliability

5. Untruthfulness and insincerity

6. Lack of remorse or shame

7. Inadequately motivated antisocial behavior

8. Poor judgment and failure to learn by experience

9. Pathologic egocentricity and incapacity for love

10. General poverty in major affective reactions

11. Specific loss of insight

12. Unresponsiveness in general interpersonal relations

13. Fantastic and uninviting behavior with drink and sometimes without

14. Suicide rarely carried out

15. Sex life impersonal, trivial, and poorly integrated

16. Failure to follow any life plan

From Hervey Cleckley, *The Mask of Sanity.* (4th ed.) St. Louis: C. V. Mosby, 1964. Pp. 362–363. Reprinted by permission.

PSYCHOPATHIC PERSONALITY

CHARACTERISTICS OF THE PSYCHOPATH

The psychopath does not give the impression, even on careful examination of being mentally ill, handicapped, or emotionally disturbed. Nor does he, typically, show any attitude or outlook that would indicate he lacked conscience or had chosen rebellious or antisocial aims. His reasoning is excellent. What he tells of his allegiances, aims, and understanding indicates that he is normal, reliable, and utterly sincere. Despite this, his past conduct and what will emerge in the future are very likely to bear out the truth of Lindner's statement that here we encounter "the most expensive and most destructive of all known forms of aberrant behavior."

The typical psychopath is a person who appears to have at least average, and often unusual, ability and who seems to be clearly aware of the amenities and to affirm the moral code. Frequently he demonstrates superior intelligence and other assets and is likely to succeed brilliantly for a time in work, in studies, and in all his human relations. But inevitably, and repeatedly, he fails, losing his job, alienating his friends, perhaps losing his wife, and children. It is difficult to account for these failures. Seldom can one find adequate motivation to explain why a person has, in the midst of success, grossly shirked his immediate responsibilities, and perhaps abandoned his work, at the behest of impulses that seem to the observer no more compelling than a trivial whim. However effective he may show himself to be over a limited period, when given sufficient time, he proves himself inadequate. His failures deprive him of what he tells us are his chief objectives and also bring hardship, shame, and disaster to his wife, children, parents, and all those closely connected with him (Cleckley 1941).

In addition to such relatively passive types of failure most fully developed psychopaths also commit aggressive antisocial acts. They forge checks, swindle, steal repeatedly, lightly indulge in bigamy, and show little or no compunction about their sexual behavior, regardless of the consequences. Some psychopaths who have attracted wide public attention committed murder or other shocking felonies, usually with little or no provocation, often without comprehensible motivation (Cleckley 1941). The majority, despite many conflicts with the law, appear to avoid crimes sufficiently grave to result in their removal from society for long prison terms. The psychopath may repeatedly receive punishment that would be likely to cause an ordinary person to mend his ways. But he appears to learn nothing important from experience. He is quite familiar with the correct ethical criteria, claims allegiance to such criteria, and can formulate in words excellent rules and plans for himself to follow. He does not seem to be lying as simply as the ordinary liar, whose motives are usually comprehensible. Sometimes the psychopath does not seem to be aware that he is lying or even to grasp emotionally the essence of falsehood and how falsehood differs from truth. Sometimes such people seem to mean for the moment to do what they promise so convincingly, but the resolution passes almost as the words are spoken.

The psychopath expresses normal reactions (love, loyalty, gratitude, etc.) with a most impressive appearance of sincerity and depth, but the emotional ties and the attitudes he professes fail to deter him from deeds that continually contradict his verbal claims. There appears to be in him a strange lack of insight or, perhaps more accurately, a total lack of one of the dimensions that constitute insight. After innumerable lies that he knows have been detected, he still speaks confidently of giving his word of honor, apparently assured that this will settle the issue immediately and absolutely. Although he may demonstrate, over considerable

Reprinted from *International Encyclopedia of Social Sciences*, Vol. 13, pp. 113–114; 118. New York: The Macmillan Company and The Free Press, 1968.

periods, adequate general abilities, or even extraordinary talent, he always throws away what he has gained, what he insists are his chief objectives. No adequate motivation can be found or even imagined to account for his conduct. Conceivable temptations are often extremely trivial, but they inevitably evoke actions that lead to the loss of fortune and the respect of friends, the destruction of marriage, and imprisonment or confinement in a psychiatric institution. The psychopath seems to be almost totally immune to real remorse or deep feelings of guilt or shame.

Etiology: Masked personality disorder. Is there some defect or disorder within the psychopath that causes him to lack the capacity to feel guilt? If so, this hypothetical deficiency seems also to interfere with his reacting to, and pursuing consistently, the normal goals of life. And he seems to lack the ability to participate adequately in the major emotional experiences of life.

The typical psychopath's excellent intellectual abilities and his freedom from the manifestations of ordinary psychiatric disorder make it difficult to believe that deep within him may be concealed a deficiency that leads not to conflict or unconscious guilt but, instead, makes him incapable of feeling normal remorse and of appreciating adequately the major emotional experiences of human life (Cleckley 1941).

The outer characteristics of the psychopath strongly indicate warmth of feeling, kindness, sincerity, pride, courage, a deep sense of honor, and genuine capacities for love and loyalty. Such an outer appearance could be the result of excellent peripheral function in the organism, which gives strong and convincing promise of robust health within and makes it difficult to suspect that there may be a central and very serious inner defect. The psychopath's conduct, however, is consistent with a serious defect in the very qualities for which his superficial aspect and verbal performance give such rich promise. The peripheral mechanisms, one might say, of his functional entity are undamaged and operate well. They demonstrate technical intelligence and convincingly mimic the expression of normal inner experience. But the implied inner experience, the glowingly promised emotional participation in life, is not there.

If we compare speech disorders with personality disorders, an analogy emerges that may be helpful in conveying this concept. When the outer physiologic apparatus involved in the production of speech is damaged, the disability is overt, and its cause is usually easy to understand. When the tongue is mutilated or its motor nerve damaged, there is likely to be gross difficulty in enunciating words and perhaps even in moving the tongue itself. Efforts to speak may give rise only to inarticulate sounds that communicate nothing. The inner use of language, however, and its meaning to the person who has suffered the injury, is preserved intact. In contrast with dysarthria, in which the peripheral apparatus of speech is affected, let us consider the aphasias which are caused by lesions more centrally located in the brain. In these the outer mechanisms of speech are preserved.

Let us consider particularly semantic aphasia as described by Henry Head (1926). In this very deep-seated disorder of speech, words are clearly and accurately enunciated, and often complete and grammatical sentences are fluently spoken. These utterances, however, have little or no meaning. They are not related, within the person, to ideas or feelings that they seem to indicate and seem intended to convey. The words of this ostensible communication are, in a very important sense, not really words but only a mimicry of words, produced mechanically by the peripheral mechanisms of speech that have become isolated from the inner source that gives rise to thought, feeling, and intention. Despite this more or less reflex simulation of real speech, a deep loss has occurred that prevents the person from using language inwardly to think.

If the psychopath has a profound and centrally located defect that prevents him from participating significantly in man's deepest fulfillments and joys, is it not possible that this inability to participate might contribute to restlessness and boredom? And might this not in turn prompt him to indulge in unprofitable or damaging indiscretions and destructive behavior that would not be particularly tempting to others who are devoting their attention to major goals and responding to major fulfillments? This hypothesis—of an extremely serious central pathology or a biological deficit concealed by mis-leading peripheral functions, by what one might call an impressive "mask of sanity"—cannot be established by objective evidence at present but is, in many important respects, consistent with the psychopath's behavior (Cleckley 1941).

55.

ALFRED R. LINDESMITH

ADDICTION AS COGNITION OF WITHDRAWAL DISTRESS

The nature of the process in which addiction is established may perhaps be most effectively presented by describing a few selected instances which exemplify it in an especially clear-cut manner. The first of these cases is quoted from an article by L. L. Stanley;[1] the second and third are based upon interviews that I conducted.

The assumption underlying the analysis of the nature of the addiction process presented in this chapter is that the special and extraordinary craving of the addict is derived in a learning process from the repetition of a certain kind of experience with the drug which all addicts have. The point of this discussion therefore is to isolate and describe this experience from which the "hook" in addiction is derived. The three accounts that follow should be considered, not as three unique historical accounts of how addiction was established several decades ago, but rather as especially critical instances from which it may be possible to infer what the universal features are in the acquisition of the pattern of behavior that addiction constitutes.

"*Case 1.* In 1899 I went to the Philippine Islands with the Third Infantry, landing in Manila in March. Along about the end of my service I developed dysentery and as a result became so weak that from 140 pounds I went down to 100 pounds. I would report at the sickline and the doctors would give me C and O (camphor and opium) pills. These pills I took for four months until the time of my discharge in 1900. Returning from Manila on the *Sherman*, I was so weak that I had to go to bed. I felt miserable, and the steward accused me of being an opium smoker. At this time I did not know anything about the habit, and did not know what made me so restless and nervous. After my discharge I could not sleep. I met an ex-soldier who said, 'I know what's the matter with you. You've been up against the pipe. You'd better start to shoot it.' Before this, though, he had given me laudanum and yenshee, which relieved my habit. I bought a gun and began to use two one-fourth grain tablets three times a day. I used more and more until I was using thirty grains a day."

Case 2. Before 1910, Mr. R. became acquainted with a number of persons who were using heroin nasally. At this time heroin was cheap and not regarded as habit-forming. He had once tried cocaine and found it unpleasant but observed that heroin seemed to have different effects, transforming a weak and miserable man into a normally alert one. He tried it once and liked it, and, inasmuch as it was cheap, he bought a dime's worth and kept it in his room. Every now and then, whenever it occurred to him or when he felt particularly downcast, he

Reprinted from Alfred Lindesmith, *Addiction and opiates* (Chicago: Aldine Publishing, 1968); Copyright © 1947, 1968 by Alfred R. Lindesmith. Reproduced by permission.
[1]L. L. Stanley, "Drug Addictions," *Journal of Criminal Law and Criminology*, 1919–20, 10, 65.

used a little. At first he used it only every few weeks or so, but gradually he began to take it more and more frequently, until, after five years of intermittent use, he had gone from once a month use to once a week, to once a day, and finally to several times a day. He did not realize that he was in any danger of acquiring a habit even when he used it every day. In the morning he took a sniff before he went to work, to arouse himself. Then, toward the latter part of the afternoon, when he noticed a let-down feeling, which he attributed to the blazing sun under which he was forced to work, he found that a sniff of heroin, which he now carried about with him, enabled him to finish out the day's work in a satisfactory state of mind and body. He had no idea that he was hooked.

Somewhat later, while Mr. R was on his way to Chicago, he made plans to be picked up by a friend in Joliet, but when his friend failed to appear he became worried, since he did not have sufficient funds to pay his fare. Having exhausted his heroin supply, he threw away the empty box and did not think of buying another. Gradually he noticed that he did not feel well; his eyes and nose were running and he yawned incessantly. He began to wonder if he was getting the flu. He walked into a restaurant, for he suddenly realized that he had not eaten for a long time, but the sight of food repelled him and he left without eating.

At the corner drug store he might have purchased all the heroin he needed for only a dime, but it did not occur to him to do so. Instead, he attempted to obtain money from a stranger whom he accosted and to whom he explained his condition, but he was turned down. This affected him so much that he could not accost another prospect.

By catching a ride on a train, he finally got into Chicago that night, and early the next morning, feeling more miserable than ever, he visited a friend, who was still in bed. As he sat talking, he noticed a box of heroin tablets on the dresser. Quite naturally, without altering the tone of his voice or interrupting the conversation, he reached for the familiar box and mechanically broke up a tablet of heroin and sniffed it. In a few minutes the entire aspect of the world changed, and in a flash he realized that this was what "dope fiends" experienced and that he was addicted. All his distress and misery vanished and then, feeling hungry, he went out and ate heartily. Mr. R. attributed great importance to this critical experience, saying that if, instead of coming to Chicago and meeting a heroin user, he had been taken to a farm, he might have suffered a few days and then recovered rapidly and never have been the worse for it. He believes that he would never have become a "dope fiend" under such circumstances.

Case 3. Dr. H., a physician, was given morphine liberally and regularly for months, when he was undergoing an appendectomy and two subsequent operations resulting from complications. For a time he was not expected to live, but as he recovered the dosage of morphine was gradually reduced and finally withdrawn. He knew that he had received morphine, but during the gradual withdrawal he attributed those symptoms of distress which he noted to the after-effects of the operations and to the processes of convalescence. During the next five years he went on with his practice, without craving the drug, and nothing whatever was amiss with his mental state. He had seen drug addicts in the course of his medical practice and felt a horror of them. He believed that he would certainly shoot himself in preference to being one. This attitude remained absolutely unaltered by the hospital experience just described. Several years later Dr. H. contracted gallstone trouble and was advised that an operation would probably be necessary. With his previous operations still fresh in his mind, he wished to avoid another, if at all possible, and was told that it might conceivably not be required; in this case it would be necessary for him to take opiates for his attacks. He did not like the idea of using narcotics, but was more afraid of an operation, so he resorted to them to ease his pain. He now required them more and more frequently, both because the attacks came oftener and because he gradually used the drug for less severe pains. Being permitted to administer the opiates himself, he finally "caught himself" taking injections every day, even when he had no pain. During the process his horror of drug addiction disappeared, and he began to read all the books he could find on the subject. He still believed he was an exception to the rule and would be able to quit easily. He realized *in retrospect* that he had experienced withdrawal symptoms several years before and had failed to recognize them. His efforts to cure himself soon ended, and a year later he acceded to his wife's request to enter a sanitarium. Upon discharge, after three years, he did not feel right without the drug. He is still an addict; he has lost his practice, money, and family, and uses the drug whenever he is out of jail.

In all three of these instances it is striking that there is no evidence of craving for the drug and of the other changes in attitude that characterize addiction appearing solely as a consequence of physical dependence. It is also evident that mere knowledge of the drug is not a critical factor since the third case involved a doctor who became physically dependent upon morphine on two separate occasions, knowing in each instance that he was receiving morphine, but not becoming addicted until the second. Neither can it be said that the transition from merely taking drugs to becoming addicted occurs when the individual ceases having the drugs given to him and begins to administer them to himself. Case 2 contradicts this idea, since the person involved administered the drug to himself for a substantial period without developing the craving. It will be pointed out later that addiction is sometimes established in persons who never administer the drug to themselves.

What these three cases do suggest is that a critical and universal feature of addiction is the recognition and proper identification of the withdrawal distress, given the fact of physical dependence. It was inferred that the experience from which the addict learns to crave the drug is that of the relief or avoidance of withdrawal distress when the latter is understood for what it is. The "hook" in opiates is thus conceived, not as something inherent in the pharmacological action of the drug or as the consequence of the sheer biological facts of physical dependence and relief of withdrawal, but as a product of learning in a situation involving biological events as they appear to or are interpreted by the subject. Addiction is not established in an instant of time, as these three cases might suggest, but is acquired over a period of time from the repetition of the relief of withdrawal. Recognition of the nature and significance of the withdrawal symptoms does sometimes occur as a flash of sudden insight, but in other instances it dawns upon the beginner gradually. In any case, the cognitive experience alone is not sufficient by itself to generate addiction and does not do so, for example, if use of the drug is discontinued at once or if recognition comes long after the withdrawal distress has vanished. Both the cognitive and the biological elements in the situation are indispensable features of the total experience, and both must be present as the repetition of the experience establishes the behavioral and attitudinal patterns of opiate addiction.

The above paragraph states the core of the theoretical conclusion of this study. According to it, the hook in addiction arises, not from the euphoria which the drug initially produces, but from the beginner's realization that the discomfort and misery of withdrawal is caused by the absence of the drug and can be dispelled almost magically by another dose of it. The repetition of this experience functions as a conditioning process of the type known to psychologists as "negative reinforcement," which quickly establishes in the beginner the fatal craving for the drug. The beginning phase of the process involves an *escape* experience, but as addiction progresses and the addict learns to anticipate withdrawal it becomes, to a large extent, an *avoidance* experience as the user tries to space his shots so as to prevent withdrawal distress rather than to relieve it. The cognitive feature of the experience which is the source of addiction is an essential aspect of it, since addiction evidently does not occur when a person who is physically dependent on opiates fails to understand the withdrawal symptoms.

56.

DAVID P. AUSUBEL

A PSYCHOSOCIAL THEORY OF NARCOTIC ADDICTION

Addiction to narcotic drugs is one of the most serious but least understood medico-social problems of our time. The grievous lack of public enlightenment about this problem reflects in part its inherent complexity as well as the paucity of definite research findings dealing with physiological, psychological, and social aspects of addiction. But an even more important cause, perhaps, of both lay and professional misunderstanding of the drug addiction problem is the continuous stream of lurid and sensational misinformation about this topic which appears in the various mass media.

THE ADDICT'S VIEW

Let us examine first the addict's own view of the cause of drug addiction. According to him, all human beings are equally susceptible to addiction. The unlucky victim need only have the misfortune to be introduced to the drug as a result of abnormal curiosity, chance encounters with addicts and narcotic peddlers, or prolonged illness. Then, once he is caught in the "iron grip" of physical dependence on the drug he is allegedly powerless to help himself. He is obligated to continue using more narcotics "just to stay normal," that is, to avoid the "unbearable" symptoms that ensue when the drug is discontinued.

This dangerously distorted account of the causes of drug addiction is a great comfort to the addict. It puts his illness in the most favorable possible light and also absolves him of all reponsibility. Unfortunately, however, he has not only successfully deluded himself, but has also managed, with the unwitting co-operation of the mass media, to foist his understandably

From David P. Ausubel, "Causes and types of narcotic addiction: A psychosocial view." *Psychiatric Quarterly*, 1961, *35*, 523–531. Reprinted by permission of *Psychiatric Quarterly*, Utica, N.Y.

biased view on a credulous American public. Physical dependence and withdrawal symptoms are genuine physiological phenomena, and association with confirmed addicts or drug peddlers *is* the typical way in which candidate addicts are introduced to narcotics. But neither factor explains *why* an individual becomes a drug addict.

PHYSICAL DEPENDENCE

How credible is the physical dependence explanation? In the first place, although the symptoms of withdrawal are distressing, they are generally no worse than a bad case of gastrointestinal influenza, and, in any event, largely disappear within 10 days. Thus, unless other potent satisfactions were derived from the narcotic habit, it is difficult to believe that any individual would be willing to pay the fantastic price of the drug and risk imprisonment and social ostracism merely to avoid a moderately severe 10-day illness. Second, every year thousands of persons with serious fractures, burns and surgical conditions receive opiates long enough to develop physiological dependence, but are nevertheless able to break this dependence quite easily. Third, the dosage of morphine (or equivalent) required to prevent withdrawal symptoms is never more than one to two grains daily. Hence, why will drug addicts take up to 20 grains a day if they take the drug, as they claim to, "just to feel normal"? Fourth, withdrawal symptoms can be adequately prevented and relieved if morphine is taken hypodermically. Therefore, why will addicts run the risk of thrombophlebitis and septicemia by injecting the drug "main-line"—or directly into their veins —with crude, homemade syringes? The answer to both third and fourth questions is that the large dose and the "main-line" route increase the "kick" or euphoric effect. Fifth, new, synthetic opiate-like drugs have been developed which have all of the analgesic and euphoric properties of opiates, but for which withdrawal symptoms are minimal. Nevertheless, the evidence is conclusive that addiction develops just as rapidly for these drugs as for other opiates.[1]

Last, if physical dependence were a significant causal factor in drug addiction, how could we explain the fact that at least 75 per cent of all addicts discharged from federal hospitals start using the drug almost immediately after release?[2] By the time of release, it is at least a year since physical dependence was broken. If addicts are really so terrified by withdrawal symptoms, why should they start developing the habit all over again after suffering the symptoms once and then escaping their clutches?

MULTIPLE CAUSALITY IN DISEASE

Generally speaking, research on drug addiction has been hampered by the same type of faulty thinking that has plagued the investigation of the causes of such other complex disorders as cancer, tuberculosis and juvenile delinquency. This is the error of assuming that since the disorder in questions *appears* to be identical in all individuals, it must necessarily have the same *single* cause in all instances. Actually, there are many different kinds of drug addicts, and the causes of drug addiction are multiple and additive in their impact rather than mutually exclusive.

As in most other diseases, the causes of drug addiction include both *internal* factors originating within the affected individual (e.g., hereditary susceptibility) and *external* factors originating within the environment. Each type of factor may be further categorized with respect to whether its impact occurs immediately prior to, and is essential for, the appearance of the disease (*precipitating*), or is operative over a longer period of time and merely contributory (*predisposing*). In tuberculosis, for example, hereditary susceptibility to the inroads of tubercle bacilli is the predisposing internal

cause, and temporary lowering of general resistance (as in overexertion or exposure to extremes of temperature) is the precipitating internal cause. Comparable external causes would include overcrowded living conditions, on the one hand, and actual exposure to an adequately large dose of tubercle bacilli, on the other.

It makes little sense, therefore, to talk about *the* cause of tuberculosis. Exposure to a reasonably large dose of virulent organisms is a necessary causal factor but is rarely a sufficient cause in the absence of particular hereditary susceptibility to tuberculosis, depressed standards of living, and transitory lapses in general resistance to disease. In any given case, one particular factor may overshadow all others and thus provide a spurious appearance of single causality; but this neither guarantees that this same factor will be equally prominent in other cases nor excludes the operation of other factors in the same case. All we can say in this regard is that if any one of the relevant causes is especially salient, the other contributory factors are less necessary to bring about the disease. If one individual, for example, by virtue of his heredity, happened to be highly susceptible to tuberculosis, whereas his neighbor happened to be highly resistant to this disease, the former would obviously succumb to a much smaller dose of tubercle bacilli than would be necessary to strike down the latter. It also follows that both the severity of the disease and the outlook for recovery would vary in accordance with the relative prominence of the various causal factors.

MULTIPLE CAUSALITY IN DRUG ADDICTION

The causal picture in drug addiction is quite analogous to that just described for tuberculosis. Availability of narcotics (that is, exposure to addicts and drug peddlers, or, in the case of physicians and others, even more direct access to the drug) is the *external precipitating* factor. No matter how great an individual's susceptibility, he obviously cannot become a drug addict unless he has regular access to narcotics. The factor of relative availability explains why the rate of addiction is so much higher in slum areas and among members of the medical and

---

[1] A. Wikler, *Opiate Addiction.* (Springfield, Ill.: Charles C Thomas, 1953), p. 50.

[2] M. J. Pescor, "Follow-up study of treated narcotic drug addicts." *Public Health Report*, Supplement No. 170, 1943.

allied professions than in middle-class neighborhoods and among other occupational groups. To account for the higher Puerto Rican addiction rate in comparably exposed Negro and Puerto Rican sections of New York City's Harlem slum area,[3] and for the much higher addiction rate in China than in Japan,[4] one must invoke a major predisposing factor, also of environmental origin, namely, degree of community or cultural tolerance for the practice.

But *external* factors alone cannot explain all of the known facts about the incidence and distribution of drug addiction. In a given slum area of uniformly high exposure to and tolerance for the drug addiction habit, why is the practice limited to a relatively small minority of the residents, and why do male adolescents constitute such a disproportionately large percentage of the affected group? Why do some addicts originate in middle-class neighborhoods despite little exposure to narcotics and strong community disapproval of the habit? To explain these facts, we must turn to the important internal factor of differential susceptibility. In the same sense that individuals are not equally susceptible to tuberculosis, they are not equally susceptible to drug addiction.

TYPE OF ADDICTION

Maturational Deficiency. The most serious, and prognostically least hopeful, variety of drug addiction occurs among individuals who fail to undergo adult personality maturation, that is who fail to develop the long-term drives and corresponding motivational traits characteristic of normally mature adults in our society. Such motivationally immature persons are typically passive, dependent, irresponsible, lacking in perseverance and self-discipline, and pre-occupied with achieving immediate, pleasurable self-gratification. They are unconcerned about marriage, raising a family, socially useful employment, vocational achievement, financial in-

dependence, and constructive service to the community.[5] The euphoria (objectively unwarranted feelings of ecstasy, well-being and self-confidence) induced by narcotics has uniquely efficient adjustive value for them. It provides immediate and effortless pleasure and dulls their self-critical faculties, thereby enabling them to feel supremely contented with their immature and inadequate adjustment to life's problems. Hence, since few other adjustive mechanisms are able to compete with drugs in attractiveness to persons possessing this type of personality structure, the disorder tends to be chronic, and the outlook for recovery is poor.

What are the sources of the motivational immaturity that constitutes the internal predisposing factor in drug addiction? Apart from hereditary proclivities toward such personality traits as passivity, self-indulgence, and excessive need for pleasurable self-gratification, the principal causes of motivational immaturity are particular kinds of unsatisfactory parent-child relationships. Considerations of space do not permit a full discussion of this topic. But examination of the kinds of relationships that drug addicts as children and adolescents have had with their parents reveals several typical patterns: (1) the extremely *overprotecting* parent, who shields the child from all independent experience and all possibility of failure so that he never gets the opportunity to set mature goals for himself or to act independently; (2) the extremely *underdominating* parent, who makes no demands on the child for mature behavior and leads him to believe that he is a specially privileged person whose needs will always be satisfied by others; and (3) the extremely *overdominating* parent, who imposes excessively high goals on the child, thereby inviting complete sabotage of the goals of adult maturation as soon as the child can escape from parental control.[6]

REACTIVE ADDICTION

Reactive addiction is the most common type of addiction found in the United States today,

---

[3]Committee on Public Health Relations, New York Academy of Medicine, *Conference on Drug Addiction among Adolescents.* (New York: Blakiston, 1953), p. 64.

[4]F. T. Merrill, *Japan and the Opium Menace.* (New York: Institute of Pacific Relations, and the Foreign Policy Association, 1942).

[5]M. J. Pescor, "A statistical analysis of the clinical records of hospitalized drug addicts," *Public Health Report,* Supplement No. 143, 1938.

[6]D. P. Ausubel, *Drug Addiction: Physiological, Psychological and Sociological Aspects.* (New York: Random House, 1958), pp. 43–44.

having increased spectacularly since the end of World War II. It is a transitory, developmental phenomenon, occurring principally among slum-dwelling adolescents with essentially normal personalities. The adjustive value of drugs for these individuals is simply that they provide an outlet both for the exaggerated rebellious ness and defiance of conventional norms (which is not uncommon among American adolescents generally), and for the particular aggressive attitudes associated with membership in an underprivileged and often ethnically stigmatized segment of the urban population. These precipitating internal factors are further compounded by such external factors as the ready availability of drugs, high community tolerance for addiction, and coercive pressures from addict associates in the closely-knit predatory gangs of the urban slum. Dabbling or experimenting with drugs has no unique adjustive value for the tensions and attitudes operative in this context. It is just one of many possible nonspecific ways of expressing aggression, hostility, nonconformity, and identification with deviant age-mates. Like juvenile delinquency, therefore, this type of addiction gradually diminishes and is eventually discarded by most of the reactive drug users, with the approach of adult life, as normally mature family and vocational interests assert themselves and as adolescent identification with deviant norms correspondingly declines.

A difficult problem in differential diagnosis is posed by the fact that the motivationally immature type of addict is found most commonly (although by no means as exclusively as is the reactive type of addict) among adolescent and young adult males in urban slum areas. This is hardly surprising, when one considers that motivational immaturity is no more rare in such areas than elsewhere, and that the actual development of addiction in highly susceptible individuals is further abetted by adolescent stresses, gang influences, racial and social class tensions, social demoralization, high availability of narcotics, and high community tolerance for the drug habit. How then does one distinguish between these two basically different types of addicts, both of whom are often represented in the same gang?

Data collected by the Research Center for Human Relations of New York University[7] suggest several feasible criteria for differential diagnosis. Motivationally immature addicts tend to use narcotics more regularly, in larger quantities, and more for their adjustive values than "for kicks." They also tend to manifest more serious and deep-seated personality problems, to be peripheral rather than active members of delinquent gangs, and to participate more in the remunerative, criminal ventures of the gangs than in their athletic, heterosexual and gang warfare activities. Reactive users, on the other hand, are typically week-end "joy-poppers" who much more rarely take the drug regularly enough or in sufficient quantity to develop physical dependence. They are more likely to be delinquent before addiction, to come from the economically more depressed homes in the neighborhood, and to use drugs either to conform to age-mate standards or as just another nonspecific means of expressing antisocial attitudes. After the age of 18, the reactive drug user tends to abandon both his active, predatory gang interests and his casual use of drugs in favor of more mature, conventional concerns with vocation and family; but the motivationally immature habitual user retreats further from normal adult adjustment into drug-induced euphoria.

MISCELLANEOUS VARIETIES OF DRUG ADDICTION

A relatively rare form of narcotic addiction is found sometimes among individuals suffering from neurotic anxiety and depression. These addicts, usually professional persons who have easy access to the drug, tend to use small, stabilized doses of opiates for the *sedative* rather than euphoric effects. Possessing strong achievement drives and normally mature motivational traits, they value the drug solely for its anxiety-reducing properties and for its ability to soften the unreasonably harsh and critical view that anxious and depressed individuals take of themselves. But since many other adjustive mechan-

---

[7]Research Center for Human Relations of New York University, *Personal Background of Drug Users, Delinquents, and Controls,* Report No. II (New York, 1957).

isms (e.g., rationalization, compensation, delusion, fantasy, phobia, compulsion) are available, and since the barbiturates and tranquilizers are, in any case, both more efficient and legally accessible for the desired purposes, this type of addiction is becoming increasingly more rare. Drug addiction also occurs occasionally among certain vicious, remorseless criminals, the aggressive antisocial psychopaths, who use the addiction habit merely as a nonspecific means of expressing hostile and destructive personality trends.

SUMMARY

The addict's dependence on continued use of narcotics to avoid withdrawal symptoms is not a significant factor in causing drug addiction, even though the drug addict has been amazingly successful in deluding both himself and the American public into believing that it is the primary causal consideration. Physical dependence cannot account convincingly for the surplus dosage and intravenous route habitually taken by the confirmed addict, or for the latter's willingness to risk social ostracism and incarceration just to avoid a moderately severe 10-day illness. Neither does it adequately explain the recurrence of addiction long after physical dependence is lost, nor the strong addicting-potential of new opiate-like drugs which give rise to only minimal degrees of physical dependence, nor the ease with which normal persons are able to overcome the physical dependence on narcotics which they may inadvertently acquire during the course of prolonged illness. All of these facts suggest that susceptibility to drug addiction is variable rather than uniform, and that addicts use opiates primarily for their euphoric properties.

The causes of drug addiction are both multiple and additive in their impact. As in most other diseases, they include factors originating both within the person (internal) and within his environment (external), and each category in turn may be further divided into predisposing and precipitating causes. The major external and necessary precipitating factor is the ready availability of the drug, a factor which is reinforced by the predisposing environmental factor of high community or cultural tolerance for the practice. These external factors are sufficient to induce the disorder in individuals who are highly susceptible to addiction.

Susceptibility to drug addiction (the internal factor) is largely a reflection of the relatively great adjustive value which narcotic drugs possess for potential addicts. This adjustive value is most specific and efficient in the case of those individuals for whom the euphoric properties of opiates are most attractive. These are persons who manifest the internal predisposing factor (failure to develop the drives and motivational traits characteristic of normally mature persons in our society). This internal predisposing factor (motivational immaturity) is itself largely an outcome of particular kinds of unsatisfactory parent-child relationships, as well as partly a reflection of various temperamental traits of hereditary origin.

Susceptibility to drug addiction is less marked when the euphoric effects of opiates have less specific and efficient adjustive potential. This occurs when the susceptibility reflects internal precipitating factors of a more transitory nature, such as adolescent revolt against conventional norms, gang pressures, and attitudes associated with residence in a socially demoralized urban slum or membership in a racial minority group.

On the basis of the relative prominence of these various causal factors, it is both possible and diagnostically important to distinguish between two major and essentially different types of drug addicts. In instances where increased susceptibility to addiction is indicative of long-standing motivational immaturity (the internal predisposing factor), the highly specific and efficient adjustive value of the drug makes for a chronic type of disorder with a very poor prognosis. Where external causal factors are more prominent and internal factors are of a more temporary (precipitating) nature, the adjustive value of the drug is less specific and efficient, and the resulting (reactive) type of addiction accordingly tends to be a transitory aberration similar to juvenile delinquency. Both types of addiction, however, the motivationally immature as well as the reactive, are found most commonly among adolescent males in the urban slums. This is because motivational immaturity occurs just as frequently there as elsewhere, and because all of the other internal and external causal factors (the various developmental and social stresses, the high availability of the drug, the high community tolerance) tend to converge on teen-age boys who reside in such areas.

57.

Donald Olding Hebb

ADDICTION AS ARTIFICIAL HUNGER AND A HOMEOSTATIC PROCESS

The various addictions of this society, to caffeine, nicotine or alcohol as well as to less frequently used drugs such as morphine or cocaine, are commonly referred to as "habits." They are not merely bad habits, however, like eating with one's knife, or mispronouncing some word. "Habit" implies learning, and this is certainly involved in addiction as it is in hunger; but like hunger, the addiction has the further effect of maintaining the level of a specific substance in the blood stream. In short, an addiction is a homeostatic process, even though the presence of the drug in the blood stream was not originally necessary, or biologically desirable. Once the addiction is well established the drug becomes necessary to stable neural functioning, and lack of it can be very strongly motivating.

There are two stages in the establishment of morphine addiction and presumably of others also: an intermediate stage of physiological dependence, and addiction proper. When young chimpanzees were given injections of morphine daily by S. D. S. Spragg, physiological dependence developed in five or six weeks. Now when the animal was not given his injection he showed the typical signs of physiological disturbance with restlessness, yawning, scratching and so forth; these are called withdrawal symptoms. The chimpanzee was clearly "unhappy" but at this intermediate stage had not yet learned that it was the injection that made him comfortable again. If it was omitted, he did nothing about it.

The experiment required one to three months of further injections before addiction proper occurred. Then the animal would try hard to get the injection, dragging the experimenter to where the drug and hypodermic needle were kept, taking out the needle from its case and handing it to the experimenter, and so on. At this stage, the chimpanzee would do anything in its power to get the injection, and now the need of the drug had become powerfully motivating.

In human beings who know that they are taking a drug, and know that it is the drug that produces the feeling of well-being, the intermediate stage and true addiction may coincide. Essentially, however, the two stages represent different kinds of process, the first being some physiological modification of bodily tissues, so that they now require the presence of the drug for "normal" (i.e., reasonably stable) functioning. Without it, there is irritability, restlessness, and disturbance of work habits and social behavior. The second is a learning process.

There is a good deal of evidence to indicate that there are considerable constitutional differences, from one person to another, which determine susceptibility to addiction. It is often thought that alcoholism, for example, is simply an attempt to escape from personal troubles, or is due to some form of neurosis. This may

From Donald Olding Hebb, *A textbook of psychology*. Philadelphia: W. B. Saunders, 1966. Pp. 221–223. Reprinted by permission.

be partly true, but there are some neurotics who fail to solve their problems in this way, and despite using alcohol do not become alcoholics. Others with little emotional excuse become addicted at once. It seems clear that emotional difficulties are often the decisive factor that turns the susceptible person into an alcoholic; but it also seems that physiological susceptibility is not the same for all persons. For some, *alcohol is a deadly poison* because of its capacity for rapidly making, in these persons, a homeostatic modification which is in effect irreversible and which thereafter is likely to dominate behavior, with personally and socially disastrous consequences. This is not true for others, and *if* the student is going to drink it is of the greatest practical importance to find out in which class he belongs before he gets finally caught. It is at least a danger sign if alcohol immediately gives great pleasure.

58.

Elvin Morton Jellinek

PHASES OF ALCOHOL ADDICTION

In 1946 E. M. Jellinek, on the basis of a questionnaire study of members of Alcoholics Anonymous, first formulated his concept of phases in the drinking history of alcoholics. With the original publication[1] of this concept Jellinek outlined a more detailed questionnaire, which in the intervening years has been administered to some 2,000 alcoholics. The elaboration of the phases concept resulting from analysis of these additional materials has been presented by Jellinek in lectures at the Yale Summer School of Alcohol Studies (July 1951 and July 1952) and at the European Seminar on Alcoholism (Copenhagen, October 1951). The summary of these lectures, as published under the auspices of the Alcoholism Subcommittee of the World Health Organization,[2] is reproduced here in full.

Reprinted by permission from *Quarterly Journal of Studies on Alcohol*, 13, 673–684, 1952. Copyright by Journal of Studies on Alcohol, Inc., New Brunswick, N.J.

[1]E. M. Jellinek, Phases in the drinking history of alcoholics. Analysis of a survey conducted by the official organ of Alcoholics Anonymous, (Memoirs of the Section of Studies on Alcohol, Yale University, No. 5). *Quart. J. Stud. Alc.*, 7, 1–88, 1946. Published also as a monograph (Hillhouse Press, New Haven, 1946) under the same title; the monograph is now out of print.
[2]Expert Committee on Mental Health, Alcoholism Subcommittee, Second Report. Annex 2, *The*

INTRODUCTION

Only certain forms of excessive drinking—those which in the present report are designated as alcoholism—are accessible to medical-psychiatric treatment. The other forms of excessive drinking, too, present more or less serious problems, but they can be managed only on the level of applied sociology, including law enforcement. Nevertheless, the medical profession may have an advisory role in the handling of these latter problems and must take an interest in them from the viewpoint of preventive medicine.

The conditions which have been briefly defined by the Subcommittee as alcoholism are described in the following pages in greater detail, in order to delimit more definitely those excessive drinkers whose rehabilitation primarily requires medical-psychiatric treatment.

Furthermore, such detailed description may serve to forestall a certain potential danger which attaches to the disease conception of alcoholism, or more precisely of addictive drinking.

With the exception of specialists in alcoholism, the broader medical profession and representa-

Phases of Alcohol Addiction. World Hlth. Org. techn. Rep. Ser., No. 48, Aug. 1952.

tives of the biological and social sciences and the lay public use the term "alcoholism" as a designation for any form of excessive drinking instead of as a label for a limited and well-defined area of excessive drinking behaviors. Automatically, the disease conception of alcoholism becomes extended to all excessive drinking irrespective of whether or not there is any physical or psychological pathology involved in the drinking behavior.

Such an unwarranted extension of the disease conception can only be harmful, because sooner or later the misapplication will reflect on the legitimate use too and, more importantly, will tend to weaken the ethical basis of social sanctions against drunkenness.

The Disease Conception of Alcohol Addiction

The Subcommittee has distinguished two categories of alcoholics, namely, "alcohol addicts" and "habitual symptomatic excessive drinkers." For brevity's sake the latter will be referred to as nonaddictive alcoholics. Strictly speaking, the disease conception attaches to the alcohol addicts only, but not to the habitual symptomatic excessive drinkers.

In both groups the excessive drinking is symptomatic of underlying psychological or social pathology, but in one group after several years of excessive drinking "loss of control" over the alcoholic intake occurs, while in the other group this phenomenon never develops. The group with the "loss of control" is designated as "alcohol addicts." (There are other differences between these two groups and these will be seen in the course of the description of the "phases.")

The disease conception of alcohol addiction does not apply to the excessive drinking, but solely to the "loss of control" which occurs in only one group of alcoholics and then only after many years of excessive drinking. There is no intention to deny that the nonaddictive alcoholic is a sick person; but his ailment is not the excessive drinking, but rather the psychological or social difficulties from which alcohol intoxication gives temporary surcease.

The "loss of control" is a disease condition per se which results from a process that superimposes itself upon those abnormal psychological conditions of which excessive drinking is a symptom. The fact that many excessive drinkers drink as much as or more than the addict for 30 or 40 years without developing loss of control indicates that in the group of "alcohol addicts" a superimposed process must occur.

Whether this superimposed process is of a psychopathological nature or whether some physical pathology is involved cannot be stated as yet with any degree of assurance, the claims of various investigators notwithstanding. Nor is it possible to go beyond conjecture concerning the question whether the "loss of control" originates in a predisposing factor (psychological or physical), or whether it is a factor acquired in the course of prolonged excessive drinking.

The fact that this "loss of control" does not occur in a large group of excessive drinkers would point towards a predisposing X factor in the addictive alcoholics. On the other hand this explanation is not indispensable as the difference between addictive and nonaddictive alcoholics could be a matter of acquired modes of living—for instance, a difference in acquired nutritional habits.

The Meaning of Symptomatic Drinking

The use of alcoholic beverages by society has primarily a symbolic meaning, and secondarily it achieves "function." Cultures which accept this custom differ in the nature and degree of the "functions" which they regard as legitimate. The differences in these "functions" are determined by the general pattern of the culture, e.g., the need for the release and for the special control of aggression, the need and the ways and means of achieving identification, the nature and intensity of anxieties and the modus for their relief, and so forth. The more the original symbolic character of the custom is preserved, the less room will be granted by the culture to the "functions" of drinking.

Any drinking within the accepted ways is symptomatic of the culture of which the drinker is a member. Within that frame of cultural symptomatology there may be in addition individual symptoms expressed in the act of drinking. The fact that a given individual drinks a glass of beer with his meal may be the symptom of the culture which accepts such a use as a refreshment, or as a "nutritional supplement." That this individual drinks at this given moment may be a symptom of his fatigue, or his elation or some other mood, and thus an individual symptom, but if his culture accepts the use for these purposes it is at the same time a cultural symptom.

In this sense even the small or moderate use of alcoholic beverages is symptomatic, and it may be said that all drinkers are culturally symptomatic drinkers or, at least, started as such.

The vast majority of the users of alcoholic beverages stay within the limits of the culturally accepted drinking behaviors and drink predominantly as an expression of their culture, and while an individual expression may be present in these behaviors its role remains insignificant.

For the purpose of the present discussion the expression "symptomatic drinking" will be limited to the predominant use of alcoholic beverages for the relief of major individual stresses.

A certain unknown proportion of these users of alcoholic beverages, perhaps 20 per cent, are occasionally inclined to take advantage of the "functions" of alcohol which they have experienced in the course of its "cultural use." At least at times, the individual motivation becomes predominant and on those occasions alcohol loses its character as an ingredient of a beverage and is used as a drug.

The "occasional symptomatic excessive drinker" tends to take care of the stresses and strains of living in socially accepted—i.e., "normal"—ways, and his drinking is most of the time within the cultural pattern. After a long accumulation of stresses, however, or because of some particularly heavy stress, his tolerance for tension is lowered and he takes recourse to heroic relief of his symptoms through alcoholic intoxication.[3] Under these circumstances the "relief" may take on an explosive character, and thus the occasional symptomatic excessive drinker may create serious problems. No psychological abnormality can be claimed for this type of drinker, although he does not represent a well-integrated personality.

[3]This group does not include the regular "periodic alcoholics."

Nevertheless, within the group of apparent "occasional symptomatic excessive drinkers" there is a certain proportion of definitely deviating personalities who after a shorter or longer period of occasional symptomatic relief take recourse to a constant alcoholic relief, and drinking becomes with them a "mode of living." These are the "alcoholics" of whom again a certain proportion suffer "loss of control," i.e., become "addictive alcoholics."

The proportion of alcoholics (addictive and nonaddictive) varies from country to country, but does not seem to exceed in any country 5 per cent or 6 per cent of all users of alcoholic beverages. The ratio of addictive to nonaddictive alcoholics is unknown.

THE CHART OF ALCOHOL ADDICTION

The course of alcohol addiction is represented graphically in Figure 8.1. The diagram is based on an analysis of more than two thousand drinking histories of male alcohol addicts. Not all symptoms shown in the diagram occur necessarily in all alcohol addicts, nor do they occur in every addict in the same sequence. The "phases" and the sequences of symptoms within the phases are characteristic, however, of the great majority of alcohol addicts and represent what may be called the average trend.

For alcoholic women the "phases" are not as clear-cut as in men and the development is frequently more rapid.

The "phases" vary in their duration according to individual characteristics and environmental factors. The "lengths" of the different phases on the diagram do not indicate differences in duration, but are determined by the number of symptoms which have to be shown in any given phase.

The chart of the phases of alcohol addiction serves as the basis of description, and the differences between addictive and nonaddictive alcoholics are indicated in the text.

THE PREALCOHOLIC SYMPTOMATIC PHASE

The very beginning of the use of alcoholic beverages is always socially motivated in the prospective addictive and nonaddictive alcoholic. In contrast to the average social drinker, how-

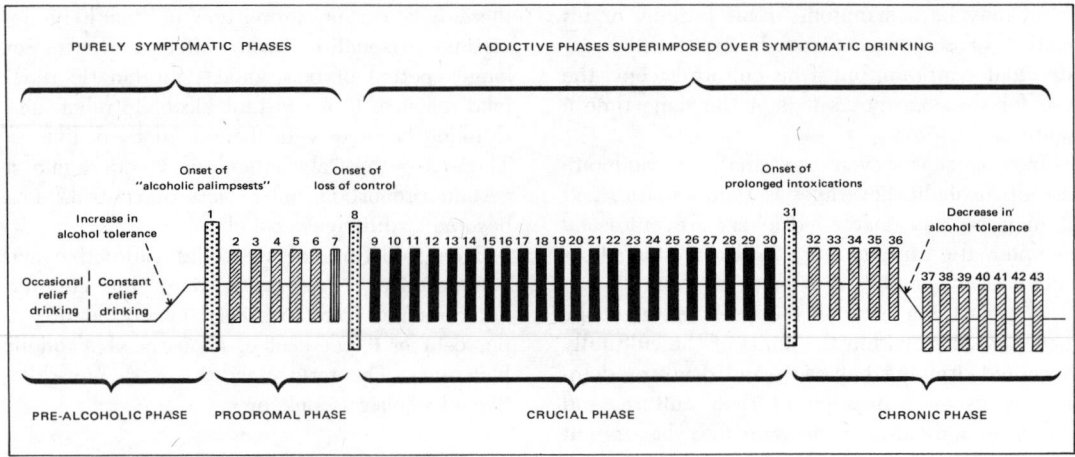

FIGURE 8.1. *The Phases of Alcohol Addiction.* The large bars denote the onset of major symptoms which initiate phases. The short bars denote the onset of symptoms within a phase. Reference to the numbering of the symptoms is made in the text.

ever, the prospective alcoholic (together with the occasional symptomatic excessive drinker) soon experiences a rewarding relief in the drinking situation. The relief is strongly marked in his case because either his tensions are much greater than in other members of his social circle, or he has not learned to handle those tensions as others do.

Initially this drinker ascribes his relief to the situation rather than to the drinking and he seeks therefore those situations in which incidental drinking will occur. Sooner or later, of course, he becomes aware of the contingency between relief and drinking.

In the beginning he seeks this relief occasionally only, but in the course of 6 months to 2 years his tolerance for tension decreases to such a degree that he takes recourse to alcoholic relief practically daily.

Nevertheless his drinking does not result in overt intoxication, but he reaches toward the evening a stage of surcease from emotional stress. Even in the absence of intoxication this involves fairly heavy drinking, particularly in comparison to the use of alcoholic beverages by other members of his circle. The drinking is,

nevertheless, not conspicuous either to his associates or to himself.

After a certain time an increase in alcohol tolerance may be noticed, i.e., the drinker requires a somewhat larger amount of alcohol than formerly in order to reach the desired stage of sedation.

This type of drinking behavior may last from several months to 2 years according to circumstances and may be designated as the prealcoholic phase, which is divided into stages of occasional relief-drinking and constant relief-drinking.

THE PRODROMAL PHASE

The sudden onset of a behavior resembling the "blackouts" in anoxemia marks the beginning of the prodromal phase of alcohol addiction. The drinker who may have had not more than 50 to 60 g. of absolute alcohol and who is not showing any signs of intoxication may carry on a reasonable conversation or may go through quite elaborate activities without a trace of memory the next day, although sometimes one or two minor details may be hazily remembered. This amnesia, which is not connected with loss of consciousness, has been called by Bonhoeffer the "alcoholic palimpsests," with reference to old Roman manuscripts superimposed over an incompletely erased manuscript.

"*Alcoholic palimpsests*" (*1*)[4] may occur on rare occasions in an average drinker when he drinks intoxicating amounts in a state of physical or emotional exhaustion. Nonaddictive alcoholics, of course, also may experience "palimpsests," but infrequently and only following rather marked intoxication. Thus, the frequency of "palimpsests" and their occurrence after medium alcohol intake are characteristic of the prospective alcohol addict.

This would suggest heightened susceptibility to alcohol in the prospective addict. Such a susceptibility may be psychologically or physiologically determined. The analogy with the "blackouts" of anoxemia is tempting. Of course, an insufficient oxygen supply cannot be assumed, but a malutilization of oxygen may be involved. The present status of the knowledge of alcoholism does not permit of more than vague conjectures which, nevertheless, may constitute bases for experimental hypotheses.

The onset of "alcoholic palimpsests" is followed (in some instances preceded) by the onset of drinking behaviors which indicate that, for this drinker, beer, wine and spirits have practically ceased to be beverages and have become sources of a drug which he "needs." Some of these behaviors imply that this drinker has some vague realization that he drinks differently from others.

Surreptitious drinking (*2*) is one of these behaviors. At social gatherings the drinker seeks occasions for having a few drinks unknown to others, as he fears that if it were known that he drinks more than the others he would be misjudged: those to whom drinking is only a custom or a small pleasure would not understand that because he is different from them alcohol is for him a necessity, although he is not a drunkard.

Preoccupation with alcohol (*3*) is further evidence of this "need." When he prepares to go to a social gathering his first thought is whether

there will be sufficient alcohol for his requirements, and he has several drinks in anticipation of a possible shortage.

Because of this increasing dependence upon alcohol, the onset of *avid drinking* (*4*) (gulping of the first or first two drinks) occurs at this time.

As the drinker realizes, at least vaguely, that his drinking is outside of the ordinary, he develops *guilt feelings about his drinking behavior* (*5*) and because of this he begins to *avoid reference to alcohol* (*6*) in conversation.

These behaviors, together with an *increasing frequency of "alcoholic palimpsests"* (*7*), foreshadow the development of alcohol addiction; they are premonitory signs, and this period may be called the prodromal phase of alcohol addiction.

The consumption of alcoholic beverages in the prodromal phase is "heavy," but not conspicuous, as it does not lead to marked, overt intoxications. The effect is that the prospective addict reaches towards evening a state which may be designated as emotional anesthesia. Nevertheless, this condition requires drinking well . beyond the ordinary usage. The drinking is on a level which may begin to interfere with metabolic and nervous processes as evidenced by the frequent "alcoholic palimpsests."

The "covering-up" which is shown by the drinker in this stage is the first sign that his drinking might separate him from society, although initially the drinking may have served as a technique to overcome some lack of social integration.

As in the prodromal phase rationalizations of the drinking behavior are not strong and there is some insight as well as fear of possible consequences, it is feasible to intercept incipient alcohol addiction at this stage. In the United States of America, the publicity given to the prodromal symptoms begins to bring prospective alcoholics to clinics as well as to groups of Alcoholics Anonymous.

It goes without saying that even at this stage the only possible modus for this type of drinker is total abstinence.

The prodromal period may last anywhere from 6 months to 4 or 5 years according to the physical and psychological make-up of the

---

[4]The italicized figures in parentheses following the designations of the individual symptoms represent their order as given in Figure 8.1.

drinker, his family ties, vocational relations, general interests, and so forth. The prodromal phase ends and the crucial or acute phase begins with the onset of loss of control, which is the critical symptom of alcohol addiction.

THE CRUCIAL PHASE

Loss of control (8) means that any drinking of alcohol starts a chain reaction which is felt by the drinker as a physical demand for alcohol. This state, possibly a conversion phenomenon, may take hours or weeks for its full development; it lasts until the drinker is too intoxicated or too sick to ingest more alcohol. The physical discomfort following this drinking behavior is contrary to the object of the drinker, which is merely to feel "different." As a matter of fact, the bout may not even be started by any individual need of the moment, but by a "social drink."

After recovery from the intoxication, it is not the "loss of control"—i.e., the physical demand, apparent or real—which leads to a new bout after several days or several weeks; the renewal of drinking is set off by the original psychological conflicts or by a simple social situation which involves drinking.

The "loss of control" is effective after the individual has started drinking, but it does not give rise to the beginning of a new drinking bout. The drinker has lost the ability to control the quantity once he has started, but he still can control whether he will drink on any given occasion or not. This is evidenced in the fact that after the onset of "loss of control" the drinker can go through a period of voluntary abstinence ("going on the water wagon").

The question of why the drinker returns to drinking after repeated disastrous experiences is often raised. Although he will not admit it, the alcohol addict believes that he has lost his will power and that he can and must regain it. He is not aware that he has undergone a process which makes it impossible for him to control his alcohol intake. To "master his will" becomes a matter of the greatest importance to him. When tensions rise, "a drink" is the natural remedy for him and he is convinced that this time it will be one or two drinks only.

Practically simultaneously with the onset of

"loss of control" the alcohol addict begins to *rationalize his drinking behavior* (9): he produces the well-known alcoholic "alibis." He finds explanations which convince him that he did not lose control, but that he had a good reason to get intoxicated and that in the absence of such reasons he is able to handle alcohol as well as anybody else. These rationalizations are needed primarily for himself and only secondarily for his family and associates. The rationalizations make it possible for him to continue with his drinking, and this is of the greatest importance to him as he knows no alternative for handling his problems.

This is the beginning of an entire "system of rationalizations" which progressively spreads to every aspect of his life. While this system largely originates in inner needs, it also serves to counter *social pressures* (10) which arise at the time of the "loss of control." At this time, of course, the drinking behavior becomes conspicuous, and the parents, wife, friends and employer may begin to reprove and warn the drinker.

In spite of all the rationalizations there is a marked loss of self-esteem, and this of course demands compensations which in a certain sense are also rationalizations. One way of compensation is the *grandiose behavior* (11) which the addict begins to display at this time. Extravagant expenditures and grandiloquence convince him that he is not as bad as he had thought at times.

The rationalization system gives rise to another system, namely the "system of isolation." The rationalizations quite naturally lead to the idea that the fault lies not within himself but in others, and this results in a progressive withdrawal from the social environment. The first sign of this attitude is a *marked aggressive behavior* (12).

Inevitably, this latter behavior generates guilt. While even in the prodromal period remorse about the drinking arose from time to time, now *persistent remorse* (13) arises, and this added tension is a further source of drinking.

In compliance with social pressures the addict now goes on *periods of total abstinence* (14). There is, however, another modus of control of drinking which arises out of the rationalizations of the addict. He believes that his trouble arises from his not drinking the right kind of beverages or not in the right way. He now attempts to control his troubles by *changing the pattern of his drinking (15)*, by setting up rules about not drinking before a certain hour of the day, in certain places only, and so forth.

The strain of the struggle increases his hostility towards his environment and he begins to *drop friends (16)* and *quit jobs (17)*. It goes without saying that some associates drop him and that he loses some jobs, but more frequently he takes the initiative as an anticipatory defence.

The isolation becomes more pronounced as his entire *behavior becomes alcohol-centered (18)*, i.e., he begins to be concerned about how activities might interfere with his drinking instead of how his drinking may affect his activities. This, of course, involves a more marked egocentric outlook which leads to more rationalizations and more isolation. There ensues a *loss of outside interests (19)* and a *reinterpretation of interpersonal relations (20)* coupled with *marked self-pity (21)*. The isolation and rationalizations have increased by this time in intensity and find their expression either in contemplated or actual *geographic escape (22)*.

Under the impact of these events, a *change in family habits (23)* occurs. The wife and children, who may have had good social activities, may withdraw for fear of embarrassment or, quite contrarily, they may suddenly begin intensive outside activities in order to escape from the home environment. This and other events lead to the onset of *unreasonable resentments (24)* in the alcohol addict.

The predominance of concern with alcohol induces the addict to *protect his supply (25)*, i.e., to lay in a large stock of alcoholic beverages, hidden in the most unthought-of places. A fear of being deprived of the most necessary substance for his living is expressed in this behavior.

Neglect of proper nutrition (26) aggravates the beginnings of the effects of heavy drinking on the organism, and frequently the *first hospitalization (27)* for some alcoholic complaint occurs at this time.

One of the frequent organic effects is a *decrease of the sexual drive (28)* which in-

creases hostility towards the wife and is rationalized into her extramarital sex activities, which gives rise to the well-known *alcoholic jealousy (29)*.

By this time remorse, resentment, struggle between alcoholic needs and duties, loss of self-esteem, and doubts and false reassurance have so disorganized the addict that he cannot start the day without steadying himself with alcohol immediately after arising or even before getting out of bed. This is the beginning of *regular matutinal drinking (30)*, which previously had occurred on rare occasions only.

This behavior terminates the crucial phase and foreshadows the beginnings of the chronic phase.

During the crucial phase intoxication is the rule, but it is limited to the evening hours. For the most part of this phase drinking begins sometime in the afternoon and by the evening intoxication is reached. It should be noted that the "physical demand" involved in the "loss of control" results in continual rather than continuous drinking. Particularly the "matutinal drink" which occurs toward the end of the crucial phase shows the continual pattern. The first drink at rising, let us say at 7 A.M., is followed by another drink at 10 or 11 A.M., and another drink around 1 P.M., while the more intensive drinking hardly starts before 5 P.M.

Throughout, the crucial phase presents a great struggle of the addict against the complete loss of social footing. Occasionally the aftereffects of the evening's intoxication cause some loss of time, but generally the addict succeeds in looking after his job, although he neglects his family. He makes a particularly strong effort to avoid intoxication during the day. Progressively, however, his social motivations weaken more and more, and the "morning drink" jeopardizes his effort to comply with his vocational duties as this effort involves a conscious resistance against the apparent or real "physical demand" for alcohol.

The onset of the "loss of control" is the beginning of the "disease process" of alcohol addiction which is superimposed over the excessive symptomatic drinking. Progressively, this disease process undermines the morale and the physical resistance of the addict.

THE CHRONIC PHASE

The increasingly dominating role of alcohol, and the struggle against the "demand" set up by matutinal drinking, at last break down the resistance of the addict and he finds himself for the first time intoxicated in the daytime and on a weekday and continues in that state for several days until he is entirely incapacitated. This is the onset of *prolonged intoxications* (31), referred to in the vernacular as "benders."

This latter drink behavior meets with such unanimous social rejection that it involves a grave social risk. Only an originally psychopathic personality or a person who has later in life undergone a psychopathological process would expose himself to that risk.

These long-drawn-out bouts commonly bring about *marked ethical deterioration* (32) and *impairment of thinking* (33) which, however, are not irreversible. True *alcoholic psychoses* (34) may occur at this time, but in not more than 10 per cent of all alcoholics.

The loss of morale is so heightened that the addict *drinks with persons far below his social level* (35) in preference to his usual associates—perhaps as an opportunity to appear superior—and, if nothing else is available, he will *take recourse to "technical products"* (36) such as bay rum or rubbing alcohol.

A *loss of alcohol tolerance* (37) is commonly noted at this time. Half of the previously required amount of alcohol may be sufficient to bring about a stuporous state.

Indefinable fears (38) and *tremors* (39) become persistent. Sporadically these symptoms occur also during the crucial phase, but in the chronic phase they are present as soon as alcohol disappears from the organism. In consequence the addict "controls" the symptoms through alcohol. The same is true of *psychomotor inhibition* (40), the inability to initiate a simple mechanical act—such as winding a watch—in the absence of alcohol.

The need to control these symptoms of drinking exceeds the need of relieving the original underlying symptoms of the personality conflict, and the *drinking takes on an obsessive character* (41).

In many addicts, approximately 60 per cent, some *vague religious desires develop* (42) as the rationalizations become weaker. Finally, in the course of the frequently prolonged intoxications, the rationalizations become so frequently and so mercilessly tested against reality that the entire *rationalization system fails* (43) and the addict admits defeat. He now becomes spontaneously accessible to treatment. Nevertheless, his obsessive drinking continues as he does not see a way out.

Formerly it was thought that the addict must reach this stage of utter defeat in order to be treated successfully. Clinical experience has shown, however, that this "defeat" can be induced long before it would occur of itself and that even incipient alcoholism can be intercepted. As the latter can be easily recognized it is possible to tackle the problem from the preventive angle.

THE "ALCOHOLIC PERSONALITY"

The aggressions, feelings of guilt, remorse, resentments, withdrawal, etc., which develop in the phases of alcohol addiction, are largely consequences of the excessive drinking, but at the same time they constitute sources of more excessive drinking.

In addition to relieving, through alcohol, symptoms of an underlying personality conflict, the addict now tends to relieve, through further drinking, the stresses created by his drinking behavior.

By and large, these reactions to excessive drinking—which have quite a neurotic appearance—give the impression of an "alcoholic personality," although they are secondary behaviors superimposed over a large variety of personality types which have a few traits in common, in particular a low capacity for coping with tensions. There does not emerge, however, any specific personality trait or physical characteristic which inevitably would lead to excessive symptomatic drinking. Apart from psychological and possibly physical liabilities, there must be a constellation of social and economic factors which facilitate the development of addictive and nonaddictive alcoholism in a susceptible terrain.

THE NONADDICTIVE ALCOHOLIC

Some differences between the nonaddictive alcoholic and the alcohol addict have been stated passim. These differences may be recapitulated and elaborated, and additional differential features may be considered.

The main difference may be readily visualized by erasing the large bars of the diagram (see Figure 8.1). This results in a diagram which suggests a progressive exacerbation of the use of alcohol for symptom relief and of the social and health consequences incumbent upon such use, but without any clear-cut phases.

The prealcoholic phase is the same for the nonaddictive alcoholic as for the alcohol addict, i.e., he progresses from occasional to constant relief of individual symptoms through alcohol.

The behaviors which denote that alcohol has become a drug rather than an ingredient of a beverage (symptoms 2 to 6) occur also in the nonaddictive drinker, but, as mentioned before, the "alcoholic palimpsests" occur rarely and only after overt intoxication.

"Loss of control" is not experienced by the nonaddictive alcoholic; and this is the main differentiating criterion between the two categories of alcoholics. Initially, of course, it could not be said whether the drinker had yet reached the crucial phase, but after 10 or 12 years of heavy drinking without "loss of control," while symptoms 2 to 6 were persistent and "palimpsests" were rare and did not occur after medium alcohol intake, the differential diagnosis is rather safe.

The absence of "loss of control" has many involvements. First of all, as there is no inability to stop drinking within a given situation there is no need to rationalize the inability. Nevertheless, rationalizations are developed for justifying the excessive use of alcohol and some neglect of the family attendant upon such use. Likewise, there is no need to change the pattern of drinking, which in the addict is an attempt to overcome the "loss of control." Periods of total abstinence, however, occur as a response to social pressure.

On the other hand, there is the same tendency toward isolation as in the addict, but the social repercussions are much less marked as the nonaddictive alcoholic can avoid drunken behavior whenever the social situation requires it.

The effects of prolonged heavy drinking on the organism may occur in the nonaddictive alcoholic too; even delirium tremens may develop. The libido may be diminished and "alcoholic jealousy" may result.

Generally, there is a tendency toward a progressive dominance of alcohol resulting in greater psychological and bodily effects. In the absence of any grave initial psychopathy, however, the symptoms of the chronic phase as seen in addicts do not develop in the nonaddictive alcoholic. In the presence of grave underlying psychopathies a deteriorative process is speeded up by habitual alcoholic excess, and such a nonaddictive drinker may slide to the bottom of society.

TYPES OF ALCOHOLISM

Alpha alcoholism represents a *purely* psychological *continual* dependence or reliance upon the effect of alcohol to relieve bodily or emotional pain. The drinking is "undisciplined" in the sense that it contravenes such rules as so-

ciety tacitly agrees upon—such as time, occasion, locale, amount and effect of drinking—*but does not lead to "loss of control"* or *"inability to abstain."* The damage caused by this species of alcoholism may be restricted to the disturbance of interpersonal relations. There may also be interference with the family budget, occasional absenteeism from work and decreased productiv-

From Elvin Morton Jellinek, *The disease concept of alcoholism.* New Haven: Hillhouse Press, 1960. Pp. 36–39. Reprinted by permission.

ity, and some of the nutritional deficiencies of alcoholism, but not the disturbances due to withdrawal of alcohol. *Nor are there any signs of a progressive process.*

The relief of bodily pain or emotional disturbance implies an underlying illness and thus the "undisciplined" use of alcoholic beverages may be regarded as a symptom of the pathological conditions which it relieves. This species of alcoholism cannot be regarded as an illness per se.

Of course, it is quite possible that in many instances alpha alcoholism may develop into gamma alcoholism, i.e., that it may often be a developmental stage. On the other hand, it is well known that this species of alcoholism may be seen in a drinking career of 30 or 40 years without any signs of progression. When we speak here of alpha alcoholism we mean this latter "pure culture" but not the developmental stage of gamma alcoholism.

Alpha alcoholism as described here is sometimes called problem drinking, but that expression just as frequently includes physical dependence upon alcohol. The terms problem drinking and problem drinker will not be used in the present study.

Beta alcoholism is that species of alcoholism in which such alcoholic complications as polyneuropathy, gastritis and cirrhosis of the liver may occur without either physical or psychological dependence upon alcohol. The incentive to the heavy drinking that leads to such complications may be the custom of a certain social group in conjuction with poor nutritional habits. The damage in this instance is of course the nutritional deficiency diseases, but impaired family budget and lowered productivity as well as a curtailed life span may also occur. Withdrawal symptoms, on the other hand, do not emerge.

Beta alcoholism too may develop into gamma or delta alcoholism, but such a transition is less likely than in the instance of alpha alcoholism.

Gamma alcoholism means that species of alcoholism in which (*1*) acquired increased tissue tolerance to alcohol, (*2*) adaptive cell metabolism (see below), (*3*) withdrawal symptoms and "craving," i.e., physical dependence, and (*4*) loss of control are involved. In gamma

alcoholism there is a definite progression from psychological to physical dependence and marked behavior changes such as have been described previously (Jellinek, 1946 and 1952). Alpha and beta alcoholism, as already noted, may develop under given conditions into gamma alcoholism.

This species produces the greatest and most serious kinds of damage. The loss of control, of course, impairs interpersonal relations to the highest degree. The damage to health in general and to financial and social standing are also more prominent than in other species of alcoholism.

Gamma alcoholism is apparently (but not with certainty) the *predominating* species of alcoholism in the United States and Canada, as well as in other Anglo-Saxon countries. It is what members of Alcoholics Anonymous recognize as alcoholism to the exclusion of all other species. Of course they use loss of control and "craving" as the criteria par excellence but these necessarily involve the other characteristics of gamma alcoholism mentioned above. As I have said before, Alcoholics Anonymous have naturally created the picture of alcoholism in their own image, although at least 10 to 15 per cent of their membership are probably specimens of alpha alcoholism who conform in their language to the A.A. standards. I base this statement on the fact that in a sample of slightly over 2,000 A.A. members I have found 13 per cent who never experienced loss of control. More likely than not only a small percentage of those with alpha alcoholism would seek the help of Alcoholics Anonymous, and almost none of those with beta alcoholism. The latter may be seen most frequently in general hospitals.

In spite of the respect and admiration to which Alcoholics Anonymous have a claim on account of their great achievements, there is every reason why the student of alcoholism should emancipate himself from accepting the exclusiveness of the picture of alcoholism as propounded by Alcoholics Anonymous.

Delta alcoholism shows the first three characteristics of gamma alcoholism as well as a less marked form of the fourth characteristic— that is, instead of loss of control there is inability to abstain. In contrast to gamma alcoholism, there is no ability to "go on the water wagon" for even a day or two without the manifestation of withdrawal symptoms; the ability to control the amount of intake on any given occasion, however, remains intact. The incentive to high intake may be found in the general acceptance of the society to which the drinker belongs, while pre-alcoholic psychological vulnerability, more often than not, may be of a low degree. This species of alcoholism and its underlying drinking pattern have been sufficiently described in connection with the *predominant* species of alcoholism ("inveterate drinking") in France and some other countries with a large wine consumption. For reasons discussed in that chapter, delta alcoholism would rarely be seen in Alcoholics Anonymous, since the alcoholic afflicted with this species of alcoholism does not go through the distressing social and psychological experiences of the gamma alcoholic and manifests only a few of the behavior changes of the latter.

There are, of course, many other species of alcoholism—if it is defined as any drinking that causes any damage—and all the remaining 19 letters of the Greek and if necessary other alphabets are available for labeling them.

Among these other species is periodic alcoholism, which in Europe and Latin America is designated as dipsomania, a term in disuse in North America. We may denote it as *Epsilon alcoholism* but it will be neither described nor defined here, as it seems to be the least known species of alcoholism. In the course of their periodic bouts, epsilon alcoholics may cause serious damage. I should like to point out that in the last 20 or 25 years a phenomenon which

may be called pseudoperiodic alcoholism has turned up. It would appear that some gamma alcoholics who have not benefited to the full extent from the A.A. program or from therapy in clinics or by private psychiatrists are able to resist drinking for 3, 6 or 12 months, but then find no other solution than intoxication, after which they remorsefully return to "sobriety."

Other species of alcoholism (accepting the criterion of damage through drinking) are, of course, "explosive drinking" as well as what the French call "alcoolisation," i.e., the undermining of health and curtailing of the life span (to the exclusion of other "alcoholic complications" and physical or psychological dependence). Then there is the excessive weekend drinking which follows a cultural pattern and causes damage through rowdiness, absenteeism and impairment of the family budget. Still other species cause damage, for instance, "fiesta drinking" and occasional drinking that causes accidents. I do not propose to list, describe or discuss all these species of alcoholism, but should like to point out that the student of the problems of alcohol cannot afford to overlook these behaviors, whether or not he is inclined to designate them as species of alcoholism.

REFERENCES

Jellinek, E. M. Phases in the drinking history of alcoholics. *Quarterly Journal of Studies on Alcohol*, 1946, 7, 1–88.

Jellinek, E. M. Phases of alcohol addiction. *Quarterly Journal of Studies on Alcohol*, 1952, 13, 673–684.

59.

ALFRED C. KINSEY, WARDELL B. POMEROY, AND CLYDE E. MARTIN

THE HETEROSEXUAL–HOMOSEXUAL BALANCE

The histories which have been available in the present study make it apparent that the heterosexuality of many individuals is not an all-or-none proposition. It is true that there are persons in the population whose histories are exclusively heterosexual, both in regard to their overt experience and in regard to their psychic reactions. And there are individuals in the population whose histories are exclusively homosexual, both in experience and in psychic reactions. But the record also shows that there is a considerable portion of the population whose members have combined, within their individual histories, both homosexual and heterosexual experience and/or psychic responses. There are some whose heterosexual experiences predominate, there are some whose homosexual experiences predominate, there are some who have had quite equal amounts of both types of experience.

Some of the males who are involved in one type of relation at one period in their lives, may have only the other type of relation at some later period. There may be considerable fluctuation of patterns from time to time. Some males may be involved in both heterosexual and homosexual activities within the same period of time. For instance, there are some who engage in both heterosexual and homosexual activities in the same year, or in the same month or week, or even in the same day. There are not a few individuals who engage in group activities in which they may make simultaneous contact with partners of both sexes.

Males do not represent two discrete populations, heterosexual and homosexual. The world is not to be divided into sheep and goats. Not all things are black nor all things white. It is a fundamental of taxonomy that nature rarely deals with discrete categories. Only the human mind invents categories and tries to force facts into separated pigeon-holes. The living world is a continuum in each and every one of its aspects. The sooner we learn this concerning human sexual behavior the sooner we shall reach a sound understanding of the realities of sex.

While emphasizing the continuity of the gradations between exclusively heterosexual and exclusively homosexual histories, it has seemed desirable to develop some sort of classification which could be based on the relative amounts of heterosexual and of homosexual experience or response in each history. Such a heterosexual-homosexual rating scale is shown in Figure 8.2. An individual may be assigned a position on this scale, for each age period in his life, in accordance with the following definitions of the various points on the scale:

0. Individuals are rated as *0's* if they make no physical contacts which result in erotic arousal or orgasm, and make no psychic responses to individuals of their own sex. Their socio-sexual contacts and responses are exclusively with individuals of the opposite sex.

1. Individuals are rated as *1's* if they have only incidental homosexual contacts which have involved physical or psychic response, or incidental psychic responses without physical contact. The great preponderance of their socio-sexual experience and reactions is directed toward individuals of the opposite sex. Such homosexual experiences as these individuals have may occur only a single time or two, or at least infrequently in comparison to the amount of their heterosexual experience. Their homosexual experiences never involve as specific psychic reactions as they make to heterosexual stimuli. Sometimes the homosexual activities in which they engage may be inspired by curiosity, or may be more or less forced upon them by other individuals, perhaps when they are asleep or when they are drunk, or under some other peculiar circumstance.

2. Individuals are rated as *2's* if they have more than incidental homosexual experience, and/or if they respond rather definitely to homosexual stimuli. Their heterosexual experiences and/or reactions still

From Alfred C. Kinsey, Wardell B. Pomeroy, and Clyde E. Martin, *Sexual behavior in the human male.* Philadelphia: W. B. Saunders, 1948. Pp. 638–639, 641, 647, 650–651. Reprinted by permission.

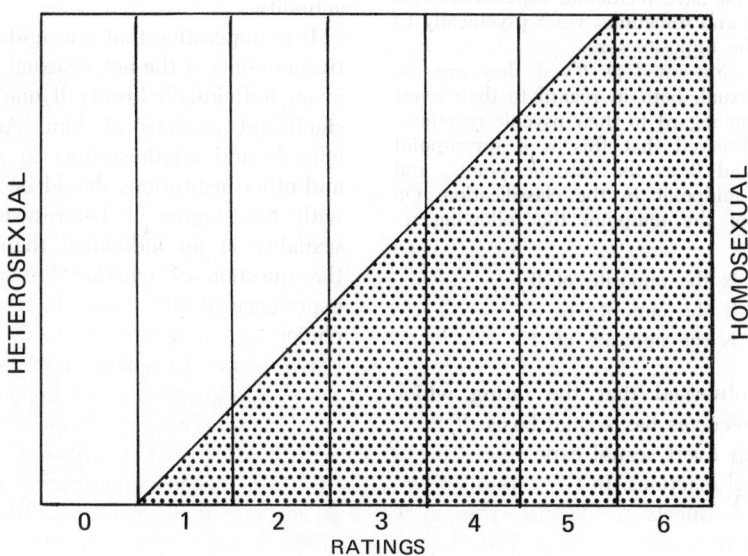

FIGURE 8.2. Heterosexual-homosexual rating scale

Based on both psychologic reactions and over experience, individuals rate as follows:

0. Exclusively heterosexual with no homosexual
1. Predominantly heterosexual, only incidentally homosexual
2. Predominantly heterosexual, but more than incidentally homosexual
3. Equally heterosexual and homosexual
4. Predominantly homosexual, but more than incidentally heterosexual
5. Predominantly homosexual, but incidentally heterosexual
6. Exclusively homosexual

surpass their homosexual experiences and/or reactions. These individuals may have only a small amount of homosexual experience or they may have a considerable amount of it, but in every case it is surpassed by the amount of heterosexual experience that they have within the same period of time. They usually recognize their quite specific arousal by homosexual stimuli, but their responses to the opposite sex are still stronger. A few of these individuals may even have all of their overt experience in the homosexual, but their psychic reactions to persons of the opposite sex indicate that they are still predominantly heterosexual. This latter situation is most often found among younger males who have not yet ventured to have actual intercourse with girls, while their orientation is definitely heterosexual. On the other hand, there are some males who should be rated as 2's because of their strong reactions to individuals of their own sex, even though they have never had overt relations with them.

3. Individuals who are rated *3's* stand midway

on the heterosexual-homosexual scale. They are about equally homosexual and heterosexual in their overt experience and/or their psychic reactions. In general, they accept and equally enjoy both types of contacts, and have no strong preferences for one or the other. Some persons are rated 3's, even though they may have a larger amount of experience of one sort, because they respond psychically to partners of both sexes, and it is only a matter of circumstance that brings them into more frequent contact with one of the sexes. Such a situation is not unusual among single males, for male contacts are often more available to them than female contacts. Married males, on the other hand, find it simpler to secure a sexual outlet through intercourse with their wives, even though some of them may be as interested in males as they are in females.

4. Individuals are rated as *4's* if they have more overt activity and/or psychic reactions in the homosexual, while still maintaining a fair amount of heterosexual activity and/or responding rather definitely to heterosexual stimuli.

5. Individuals are rated 5's if they are almost entirely homosexual in their overt activities and/or reactions. They do have incidental experience with the opposite sex and sometimes react psychically to individuals of the opposite sex.

6. Individual's are rated as 6's if they are exclusively homosexual, both in regard to their overt experience and in regard to their psychic reactions.

It will be observed that this is a seven-point scale, with 0 and 6 as the extreme points, and with 3 as the midpoint in the classification. On opposite sides of the midpoint the following relations hold:

> 0 is the opposite of 6
>
> 1 is the opposite of 5
>
> 2 is the opposite of 4

It will be observed that the rating which an individual receives has a dual basis. It takes into account his overt sexual experience and/or his psychosexual reactions. In the majority of instances the two aspects of the history parallel, but sometimes they are not in accord. In the latter case, the rating of an individual must be based upon an evaluation of the relative importance of the overt and the psychic in his history.

In each classification there are persons who have had no experience or a minimum of overt sexual experience, but in the same classification there may also be persons who have had hundreds of sexual contacts. In every case, however, all of the individuals in each classification show the same balance between the heterosexual and homosexual elements in their histories. The position of an individual on this scale is always based upon the relation of the heterosexual to the homosexual in his history, rather than upon the actual amount of overt experience or psychic reaction.

Finally, it should be emphasized again that the reality is a continuum, with individuals in the population occupying not only the seven categories which are recognized here, but every graduation between each of the categories, as well. Nevertheless, it does no great injustice to the fact to group the population as indicated above.

From all of this, it should be evident that one is not warranted in recognizing merely two types of individuals, heterosexual and homo-sexual, and that the characterization of the homosexual as a third sex fails to describe any actuality.

It is imperative that one understand the relative amounts of the heterosexual and homosexual in an individual's history if one is to make any significant analysis of him. Army and Navy officials and administrators in schools, prisons, and other institutions should be more concerned with the degree of heterosexuality or homosexuality in an individual than they are with the question of whether he has ever had an experience of either sort. It is obvious that the clinician must determine the balance that exists between the heterosexual and homosexual experience and reactions of his patient, before he can begin to help him. Even courts of law might well consider the totality of the individual's history, before passing judgment on the particular instance that has brought him into the hands of the law.

Everywhere in our society there is a tendency to consider an individual "homosexual" if he is known to have had a single experience with another individual of his own sex. Under the law an individual may receive the same penalty for a single homosexual experience that he would for a continuous record of experiences. In penal and mental institutions a male is likely to be rated "homosexual" if he is discovered to have had a single contact with another male. In society at large, a male who has worked out a highly successful marital adjustment is likely to be rated "homosexual" if the community learns about a single contact that he has had with another male. All such misjudgments are the product of the tendency to categorize sexual activities under only two heads, and of a failure to recognize the endless gradations that actually exist.

From all of this, it becomes obvious that any question as to the number of persons in the world who are homosexual and the number who are heterosexual is unanswerable. It is only possible to record the number of those who belong to each of the positions on such a heterosexual-homosexual scale as is given above. Summarizing our data on the incidence of overt homosexual experience in the white male population and the distribution of various degrees of heterosexual-homosexual balance in that population the following generalizations may be made:

37 per cent of the total male population has *at least some overt homosexual experience* to the point of orgasm between adolescence and old age. This accounts for nearly 2 males out of every 5 that one may meet.

50 per cent of the males *who remain single until age 35* have had overt homosexual experience to the point of orgasm, since the onset of adolescence.

58 per cent of the males who belong to the group that goes into *high school* but not beyond, *50 per cent of the grade school level,* and *47 per cent of the college level* have had homosexual experience to the point of orgasm if they remain single to the age of 35.

63 per cent of all males *never have overt* homosexual experience to the point of orgasm after the onset of adolescence.

50 per cent of all males (approximately) *have neither overt nor psychic* experience in the homosexual after the onset of adolescence.

13 per cent of the males (approximately) *react erotically* to other males *without having overt* homosexual contacts after the onset of adolescence.

30 per cent of all males *have at least incidental homosexual experience* or reactions (*i.e.,* rate 1 to 6) over at least a three-year period between the ages of 16 and 55. This accounts for one male out of every three in the population who is past the early years of adolescence.

25 per cent of the male population *has more than incidental homosexual experience* or reactions (*i.e.,* rates 2–6) for at least three years between the ages of 16 and 55. In terms of averages, one male out of approximately every four has had or will have such distinct and continued homosexual experience.

18 per cent of the males have at least *as much of the homosexual as the heterosexual* in their histories (*i.e.,* rate 3–6) for at least three years between the ages of 16 and 55. This is more than one in six of the white male population.

13 per cent of the population *has more of the homosexual than the heterosexual* (*i.e.,* rates 4–6) for at least three years between the ages of 16 and 55. This is one in eight of the white male population.

10 per cent of the males are *more or less exclusively homosexual* (*i.e.,* rate 5 or 6) for at least three years between the ages of 16 and 55. This is one male in ten in the white male population.

8 per cent of the males are *exclusively homosexual* (*i.e.,* rate a 6) for at least three years between the ages of 16 and 55. This is one male in every 13.

4 per cent of the white males are *exclusively homosexual throughout their lives,* after the onset of adolescence.

60.

KURT A. ADLER

HOMOSEXUALITY FROM THE STANDPOINT OF INDIVIDUAL PSYCHOLOGY

The history of homosexuality, interesting as it may be, is beyond the scope of this paper. I only wish to stress that most historical analogies to today's homosexuality are invalid, because the social scene and the social forces prevalent at any other time are so different from what they are today.

I shall also not go into refutations of organic and endocrine theories of homosexuality, since I deem it unnecessary for this audience.

From a sociological aspect, it seems clear that homosexuality brings' an additional dimension of strife and hostility into the community not only because of its divisive, separatist and isolationist aspects, but also because within the homosexual group itself, fellowship and social

From Kurt A. Adler,"Life style, gender role, and the symptom of homosexuality."*Journal of Individual Psychology,* 1967, 23, 67–78. Paper read at the Tenth International Congress of Individual Psychology, Salzburg, September 1–4, 1966. Reprinted by permission.

interest are at an extremely low level. As Adler pointed out, the sexual problem is a social problem; it cannot be solved by an egotist, or one who is indifferent to mankind.

Sexuality is very generally considered a social issue, because the form it takes determines to a large extent the mode by which people live with each other and by which their children will live; in addition, it involves the obvious question of procreation, and economic, philosophical, moral, and religious issues. Most people therefore reject homosexuality and feel revolted by it—although the human tendency to depreciate others in order to feel superior oneself, unfortunately enters their judgment and dilutes the validity of their attitude.

This view is, however, quite different from that found in Freudian literature which maintains that revulsion against homosexuality only betrays a defense and battle against one's own secret homosexual drives and desires. Should this statement be valid it would follow logically that a revulsion against sex with chickens, for instance, would only betray a defense and battle against one's own drive and desire for sex with chickens. The only difference between the two statements is that the latter has so far not been needed to support a theory of psychosexual development that includes a chicken stage, while the former was needed in support of the Freudian theory of psychosexual development that included a homosexual stage.

SEXUAL FUNCTION AND LIFE STYLE

The facts of life, however, are that human beings are endowed with sexual organs and sexual functions, among the many other organs and functions they possess, and that it greatly depends on the individuals' goals and styles of life, how they will use their sexual and other organs and functions. This means that people's thoughts and feelings about themselves, others, and their relationships with others will determine the use of their organs and functions, including the sexual ones.

This fact may be seen by every therapist in his daily practice. He observes in his patients —both homosexual and heterosexual—that they use their sexual organs and functions for domina-

tion, humiliation, revenge, making money, evading other responsibilities, a sense of victory, etc. It is then always our task as therapists to help the patient change or modify his thoughts and feelings about himself, others, and his relationships with others, generally and sexually, so that friendship rather than hostility, cooperation rather than competition, trust rather than suspicion, equality rather than domination and exploitation, closeness rather than distance, become more prominent in his thinking, feeling, and acting.

Our experience has taught us that life is primarily social; and that mental health, satisfaction, and a genuine self-esteem, are only derived from a mode of thinking, feeling, and acting where self-interest is to the highest possible degree in accord with the common, human, or social interest. It is not a question of the patient repressing asocial or antisocial wishes or drives, but of realizing, emotionally and intellectually, that his private interest is most effectively served when it is integrated with, and runs parallel to, the common interest. It is probably no accident that this maxim is also the basis for all true morality.

All human functions are first developed for the satisfaction of self-interest, private bodily needs—or drives, if you will—and are then modified or supplanted by more social forms of expression, though always according to the individual's goals and style of life.

The sexual function, too, developing from its infantile precursors, such as tickling sensations, tumescence, and semiorgastic feelings, enters its first functional stage, pollution and masturbation, in the service of pure self-interest. There is no oral, anal, Oedipal, phallic, or homosexual stage in Adlerian psychosexual development. The mature heterosexual stage develops from the pollutional and masturbatory stage, if a sufficient amount of social interest, courage, and ability to cooperate is present. All sexual failures are due to a lack of social interest and ability to cooperate, and are therefore all considered masturbatory in nature, be they homosexual or heterosexual, fetishistic, sado-masochistic, or of any other form.

Since the sexual function arrives at its first functional stage so much later in life than the other functions, i.e., at puberty, its forms and uses by the individual are influenced in their development by a fixed and socialized style of life. The hiding of masturbatory activities, the presence of people in the sexual dreams and fantasies, reveal the social influences on this otherwise self-serving activity. All character traits and attitudes mold the feeling, thinking, and use of this function. In no way can it be considered autonomous. The total personality uses all functions in line with its goal and the developed unique style of life.

DEVELOPMENT OF GENDER ROLE

A development in childhood along the opposite gender role[1] is guided by the goals and attitudes of the child; this begins at an age when sexuality plays no part at all. The only issue for the child is how he considers and feels about the social role of a man or a woman, and which of his parents he should emulate. Uncertainty or doubt about the sex to which he belongs, is easily induced in a child by such statements as: "She looks like a boy," or "He is pretty, like a girl." The child's uncertainty and confusion is then further abetted when people who make such perverted statements also treat the child as if he were of the other sex. In such cases, as you see, it is the face, not the sexual organs, that brings the earliest confusion about his gender role into the child's mind. Such early confusion is probably necessary for any further opposite gender development which facilitates the eventual development of homosexuality. On the other

---

[1]The term "gender role" is attributed by Stoller (5, p. 198) to Money *et al.*, from whom he quotes the following definition: "By the term, gender role, we mean all those things that a person says or does to disclose himself or herself as having the status of boy or man, girl or woman, respectively. It includes, but is not restricted to sexuality in the sense of eroticism. A gender role is not established at birth, but is built up cumulatively through experiences encountered and transacted through casual and unplanned learning, through explicit instruction and inculcation, and through spontaneous putting two and two together to make four and sometimes, erroneously, five" (3).

Regarding the term "gender," Stoller says further: It "connotes psychological aspects of behavior related to masculinity and femininity . . . 'Sex' is biological, 'gender' social. . . . sex and gender may be independent of each other" (5, p. 197).

hand, it is hard to see how a child who is absolutely certain about his sex, can develop even the idea of training for the opposite role— although presumably anything is possible.

Since the child uses his parents as his guiding picture, and constructs his life plan in such a way as to overcome the discrepancy between himself and his parents, it is only natural that using his meager experience and feeble judgment, he will attempt to arrive at a position of superiority, whatever that may mean to him. Where a father, for instance, plays a subordinate role and occupies a humiliating position to a domineering mother, a boy may easily decide that there is no advantage in becoming a man, and that a man can never equal a woman in power and pre-eminence. But, a boy may become equally disenchanted by an overly domineering father who stresses his own omnipotence, thus discouraging the boy from all hope of ever becoming a man like his father. In his hopelessness, frustration, and rage, he may well hit on the brilliant strategy of defeating such a father, who always admonishes him depreciatingly "to be a man," by training himself to become anything *but* a man, whatever the cost to himself. The same, of course, holds true for girls in their respective situations.

In general then, it is the role of the man and the role of the woman that attract or frighten the child into denying his own anatomical sex and training for the opposite role. Only much later, in prepuberty and puberty, is the actual sexual function included and integrated with this now already fixed pattern of denial of one's own sex and training for the opposite role. And only then do we find erotic dreams and fantasies of the same sex and actual homosexual activities.

Sexual activities with the same sex, however, in prepuberty and puberty, do not by themselves indicate homosexuality. In this masturbatory stage, the reasons for choosing the same sex rather than the opposite sex can be manifold. It may occur because it is easier for members of the same sex to be undisturbed and undetected by watchful adults; it may be because threats of punishment for activity with the other sex are too great. Then, also, sexual activity is new for this group; they feel untrained and unsure about it; and some might more easily expose their lack of knowledge to equal novices than to members of the other sex whose sophistication they may overestimate. Some are introduced by others on a dare, or are led by their desire to be in the "in-group." Of course, some in these groups are individuals who have for a long time trained entirely along homosexual lines; but for the others it constitutes only training for future heterosexual relations.

Even individuals who have trained themselves since early childhood to deny their own gender role and have trained intensely for the opposite role may, possibly due to more favorable and encouraging influences later on, exclude the actual sexual function from the role of the opposite gender. They may develop entirely along heterosexual lines, including their erotic dreams and fantasies. We do see people who betray quite clearly, in demeanor and expressive movements, that their early training had been for the opposite gender role, but who have not become homosexuals, certainly not in the sexual sense. As surprising as this outcome seems, it does happen. All we can say is that such individuals have overcome or aborted their early development along opposite-gender lines. They are not even latent homosexuals, if this term has any meaning. I have never seen any one of them turn to homosexuality, even after great disappointment or humiliation by the opposite sex.

His own estimation of his body in comparison with other children, may urge a child into giving up developing his own gender role. But this also happens only if he has been confused about his gender. A frail or clumsy body in a boy, or a weaker constitution, aside from adding to the feeling of inadequacy generally, may serve to convince him that he can never become a real man. As he stops participating and training with other boys, he may concentrate on activities that are considered "feminine" instead, and the distance from other boys becomes increasingly hopeless to bridge. Also such things as ungainly birthmarks, supranumerary nipples, too thin legs or arms, facial asymetries, the size and shape of the genitals, or for that matter any defect or deficiency, may affirm to the child, that he will remain irrevocably inferior to members of his own sex and never make the grade with the other sex. Here, of course, the trouble

is the child's total social atmosphere, which is steeped in a psychology of possession instead of a psychology of use. By this I mean, that the value system by which the child grows up is one in which the possession of money, beauty, a family tree, a large penis, or a high IQ is given priority over the much more important question of how all these are used.

But none of these conditions will inevitably cause a child to develop the opposite gender role or homosexuality. We can find scores of men and women with misshapen sex organs, distorted facial features and hunchbacks, as well as those with domineering mothers or overpompous fathers, who nevertheless develop entirely their own gender role and find their way to heterosexuality without any remarkable difficulties.

In a very illuminating paper on this subject R. J. Stoller (6) reported a study of two boys born without penises. He found that, since the parents never doubted the maleness of the boys, neither did the boys; they developed entirely in a masculine way, although aware of their anatomical defects. Stoller concluded, that the penis, while contributing to the sense of maleness, is not essential to it; and that the certainty of the sex to which one belongs is firmly fixed between the ages of 3 and 5, and therefore long before the Freudian, so-called phallic stage. We can only wonder about the fate of the castration complex and penis envy now.

A CASE

The sibling relations must also not be forgotten, when one searches for factors which may have discouraged a child from pursuing his proper gender role. One boy's earliest memory was that his twin sister, in their double perambulator, used to crawl over to his side and beat him. We know, of course, that a memory may not correspond to the facts; however, in any case this was his estimation of his sister, of himself and of the relationship between them. His features and body build were very delicate. His mother was extremely domineering. Being disenchanted with her athletic and masculine daughter, she treated the son like a girl. His father played a subordinate role. The patient came to me at the age of 28. After four years of psychoanalysis, five times a week, his psychoanalyst had declared him unanalyzable and transferred him to a colleague for supportive treatment. When the latter became sick, I inherited the patient. He had been a promiscuous homosexual since the age of 18, and had never even dated a girl, which, with such an earliest memory, we can well understand. Aside from establishing a friendly, trusting relationship, which he needed very badly, I directed his treatment mainly at his false notions about his irrevocable inferiorities, generally and sexually, in comparison to other men, and at his firm conviction of the superiority of women. He had greatly reduced his homosexual activities by the sixth month of treatment, had started to work, and even cagily dated some girls.

Then he had the following dream: "I was trying to prove that somebody was a bigamist. Nobody wanted to believe me, but I felt I had to prove it. I was on a train and was wearing two coats; one under the other. I pulled them apart, to show them as proof. The men around me got very angry and wanted to throw me off the train; but I resisted them successfully. Then I woke up." The patient said he felt anxious and fearful only when the men tried to throw him off the train, but felt triumphant, when he managed not to be thrown off. He did not understand the dream. When the interpretation was given to him that he was contemplating a bisexual (bigamist) solution to his problem, was afraid the homosexual group would not stand for it and throw him out, yet feels he can pull off this trick and succeed, he admitted that these had been exactly his thoughts and endeavors in the past month.

The patient soon stopped homosexual activities with but a few exceptions, and went out with girls and even necked with them. (Many homosexual patients become asexual before they switch to heterosexuality.) He moved away from his mother and became moderately successful as an artist. He then said he wanted a very feminine girl.

How much he was still afraid of women, and how much homosexuality still served him as an escape hatch from them, is shown in a dream he had after 14 months of treatment. "I was on a train, standing outside on the platform. An-

other train came in the same direction; it was on fire; it looked like a meteor. I jumped inside my train, as the other train passed. After it had gone, I came out on the platform again. Two policemen looked at me with suspicion; but then they left, and I woke up." He said he had had strong fear when the other train came.

He interpreted his dream himself, with very little help on my part. "The other train is heterosexuality. I am afraid as it approaches me, and jump into my train, homosexuality, where I had only been an outsider, a bystander before. As soon as the threat of heterosexuality passes, I get out of homosexuality and am an onlooker of it again. I avoid heterosexuality by going for a moment, as long as it threatens, into homosexuality. The policemen are my guilt and fear of homosexuality and its activities."

Not all homosexuals, however, have trained in their childhood for the opposite, or have denied their own, gender role, although I believe there must have been some confusion about their sex identity. They may be so frightened in puberty of women and heterosexuality, that they decide on an escape into homosexuality. Such a solution is strongly suggested by the mere fact that if one excludes *one* sex as a possible solution, this leaves only the *other* sex (as long as one is sufficiently socially inclined to insist on human beings). This statement, by the way, is very effective in the treatment of homosexuals, when they insist that they are so attracted by their own sex and wonder why this should be so.

HOMOSEXUALITY AS PART OF A SYNDROME

So far I have stressed that men and women who develop along homosexual lines do so, each for his own reason; each uses homosexuality to safeguard his personality ideal, in pursuit of his unique goal. Yet there are certain types of homosexuals who, with exceptions of course, have specific traits in common. I should like to point out in the following that what they really have in common is the particular neurosis, psychosis or personality disorder of which their homosexuality is a symptom.

Sociopathy. One example of such a type are the male homosexual prostitutes. I have found most of them to be bisexual in their activities.

Their erotic fantasies and daydreams are of money, an easy life, and exploitation of people. Many of them would prostitute themselves equally with women, had they the opportunity. Some are not homosexual at all, despite their homosexual activities. Reiss (4) has described a group of delinquent youths, who go through a period of allowing themselves to be used for money by adult fellators, but who neither define themselves as homosexuals, nor continue their homosexual relationships as they move into adulthood.

The treatment of homosexual prostitutes has to be directed primarily at prostitution and their whole hostile, sociopathic world outlook, their lack of self-confidence and fear of responsibility. To direct treatment at their homosexuality would make no sense at all, even in those who have developed along purely homosexual lines.

Schizoid Personality. Another type are those men who are caught in homosexual activities in public washrooms, in parks, etc., and are sent for treatment by the court, as a condition for probation (at least in New York). Many of them at first complain loudly about the unfairness of being persecuted for their "natural," "biological" nature. I tell them quite sharply, that they are not entitled to any complaint on that account, because, had they been apprehended in a public washroom in sexual activities with a woman, the judge would have been much more severe with them. This point is usually effective; they become more willing to listen.

Their treatment has to be directed at their inability to form meaningful relations, their promiscuity, their lack of self-esteem generally and sexually and, of course, their gross lack of social interest. They are usually diagnosed as schizoid personalities, if not as schizophrenics. Most of them quit treatment as soon as the court permits, though sometimes, if you can form a good enough relationship with them before that happens, they continue it.

It is interesting to note that homosexuals as well as schizoids and schizophrenics so frequently say they feel irrevocably different from other people and have felt so since early childhood.

Compulsion Neurosis. There is, however, another group of men, who show quite similar outward manifestations, in that they also seek out public washrooms for promiscuous homosexual relations; but they are rarely caught, and they come to treatment on their own volition. Their chief complaint is their inability to resist or control their impulses for homosexual adventures. They are usually married, have children, and are often in high social positions. To all outward appearances, they have at least fairly satisfactory relations with their wives. Their erotic fantasies and daydreams are mostly of women, but sometimes of men. On careful examination of the events that preceded each irresistible homosexual impulse, one will always find a real or imagined rejection by a woman, usually the wife. One university professor would regularly seek out a homosexual washroom adventure whenever his wife, because of menstruation, a cystitis, a fight they had had, or for whatever reason would not or could not have intercourse with him. It also happened twice after his mother, who lived in another town, had criticized him in a letter.

His treatment was mainly directed at his lack of self-confidence as a man, his fear of authority, his notion of the superiority of women and their rejecting attitude toward men, his passive-aggressive revenge against women, and his cowardly evasion of responsibility for his actions by invoking irresistable impulses, or compulsions, to replace volition. Unless these men are caught, their wives never know of these activities. To cure them of their homosexual activities is not too difficult or lengthy, but the treatment of their compulsion neurosis is another matter.

The question of homosexuality has been discussed by many authors. Erwin O. Krausz, an Adlerian, considers it a compulsion neurosis, whereas Otto Fenichel, a Freudian, considers it an impulse neurosis. From the Adlerian point of view of goal-directedness and the use of safeguarding devices, we can, I believe, easily see that just as the phobic will say, "I cannot," when he lacks the courage to say, "I don't want to," so the compulsive will say, "I must," when he lacks the courage to say, "I want to." Both are attempting to avoid responsibility for their action or inaction, to safeguard their goals or protect them from defeat.

The homosexual's actions are designed to

protect him from anticipated failure with the other sex and in competition with the same sex. He has a particularly great need to substitute compulsion for volition because he has to deny such obvious facts as his anatomical sex, defy the judgment of the entire community, set himself in opposition to common and social sense, and live as an outcast by choice. For such irrational and asocial attitudes and actions it is of course much more comfortable to have the excuse of compulsion, than to take the responsibility of intention and volition. Furthermore it would seem quite obvious that obsessive concentration of thoughts and feelings is necessary for the intensive self-training in homosexuality, in opposition to the total social scene surrounding him. In fact, a disproportionately large number of homosexuals manifest rather severe obsessive-compulsive traits, which can nearly always be traced to childhood.

Furtiveness, suspicion and paranoid attitudes are characteristic of some homosexuals. We can easily understand this. All people who isolate themselves from the community, fear and feel hostile towards others, and do not feel at home on this earth, are likely to show suspicion and paranoid attitudes. Homosexuals on the whole certainly belong in this group.

It would appear then that homosexuality can be a symptom of any neurosis, psychosis, or personality disorder. The obsessive-compulsive homosexual will elevate his homosexuality to great importance and be obsessively pre-occupied with it, so that thoughts and feelings about the other sex are totally excluded. The revulsion of some other homosexuals against the opposite sex will have a definitely phobic flavor. Psychotic homosexuals may paint anything in their minds, from the vagina dentata to the phallic dagger, in order to stress to themseves the dangers of heterosexuality, and thus evade it. And sociopathic homosexuals may simply expound on the lesser responsibility and the greater freedom that homosexuality offers as compared to heterosexuality.

The neurosis of which homosexuality is a part and symptom may be mild or severe; and the homosexuals themselves may be active or passive people. No two homosexuals are alike.

CONCLUSION

In concluding we should like to point out that in 1917 Adler (1, p. 5) wrote: "Homosexuality, by itself, has many meanings, and can be comprehended in its significance only with regard to time and the individual." (*Die Homosexualität ist an sich vieldeutig, und kann in ihrer Bedeutung nur zeitlich und individuell erfasst werden.*) Writing in 1965, Judd Marmor said of homosexuality very similarly: "We are probably dealing with a condition that is not only multiply determined by psychodynamic, sociocultural, biological, and situational factors but also reflects the significance of subtle temporal, qualitative, and quantitative variables" (2, p. 5).

In the present paper we stated the general view that it is not sexuality which determines the personality, but rather that the total personality, the style of life, determines the form of sexual as well as other behavior. What is specific about the homosexual symptom, aside from a prolonged uncertainty as to gender identity in childhood, is fear of the opposite sex, or fear of inadequacy in one's proper sex role, or both. This may have started in childhood with aversion against one's own gender role, and with emulation of the opposite role, or, less frequently, in puberty when sexuality became a problem. We should like to note that Marmor essentially concurs in this when he states that for homosexuality actually to occur there must be "impaired gender-identity" and "a fear of intimate contact with members of the opposite sex." To this he adds as a third, ecological condition, the opportunity for homosexual behavior (2, p. 5).

The type of excuse homosexuals use to establish their distance from the opposite sex and to deny their own sex depends not on their homosexuality as such, but on the type of neurosis, psychosis or personality disorder from which they are suffering. The fact that they are ready in their way of living to accept the necessity of putting themselves outside the mainstream of mankind shows their private logic in opposition to common logic and common sense, shows their attitude to mankind as negativistic and hostile or irresponsible. In sexuality, as in all other tasks of life, the crucial issue is to bring self-interest into agreement with the common, human interest; to bring closeness, sexual gratification, and family life into line with social interest, namely with the heterosexuality of the community of man.

REFERENCES

1. ADLER, A. *Das Problem der Homosexualität.* Leipzig: Hirzel, 1930.
2. MARMOR, J. (Ed.) *Sexual inversion.* New York: Basic Books, 1965.
3. MONEY, J., HAMPSON, JOAN G., & HAMPSON, J. L. Hermaphroditism: recommendations concerning assignment of sex, change of sex, and psychological management. *Bulletin of Johns Hopkins Hospital,* 1955, 97, 284–300.
4. REISS, A. J., JR. The social integration of queers and peers. *Social Problems,* 1961, 9, 102–120.
5. STOLLER, R. J. Passing and the continuum of gender identity. In J. Marmor (Ed.), *Sexual inversion.* New York: Basic Books, 1965. Pp. 190–210.
6. STOLLER, R. J. The sense of maleness. *Psychoanalytical Quarterly,* 1965, 34, 207–218.

CHAPTER IX

Psychotherapy

Reviewing the effectiveness of psychotherapy, which they identify as a "heterogeneous collection of ingredients or psychological conditions that produce varying degrees of both positive and deteriorative personality change in patients," Truax and Carkhuff (1967, p. 21) concluded that while certain unspecified types of psychotherapy are effective, that under particular unspecified conditions, "therapy and control patients show equivalent average outcomes, but those treated by psychotherapy show greater variability in outcome than those in control conditions" (1967, p. 21). They draw the further inference that ineffective psychotherapists result from the majority of approaches currently employed in training. Psychotherapy must be more than merely two individuals affecting each other (Beier, 1966); it must yield sources of gain (Berenson & Carkhuff, 1967), though occasionally this is not the case. Psychotherapy must channel a person's behavior into more constructive patterns (Hadley, 1958).

Since the discovery of psychoanalysis by Freud, the field of psychotherapy has developed fruitfully in a variety of directions. In addition to psychotherapy, and allied to it, are the physical or physiodynamic therapies, including shock therapies, psychosurgery, and drug therapy.

PHYSIODYNAMIC THERAPIES

Malarial Treatment of General Paresis. In 1887, Wagner-Jauregg (1968) accidentally discovered the therapeutic effects of malaria on general paresis, and in 1917 injected the blood of a malarial patient into that of one suffering from syphilitic infection, and consequently hit upon malarial therapy.

Electroshock Therapy. Cerletti (1950, 1954, 1968) reported that he and his associate L. Bini in 1937 successfully treated a schizophrenic patient by applying a 60-cycle alternating current to produce convulsion by electrodes placed on the patient's head. On the conclusion of EST, the schizophrenic whose only speech previously was gibberishness "sat up of his own accord, looked about him calmly with a vague smile, as though asking what was expected of him. I asked him; 'What has been happening to you?' He answered with no more gibberish: 'I don't know; perhaps I have been asleep" (Cerletti, 1968, pp. 363–364).

Insulin Shock Therapy. In a series of articles in the *Wiener medizinische Wochenschrift* in 1934 to 1935, Sakel (1938) reported that his success with insulin shock therapy with schizophrenics began as early as 1927. "The main therapeutic principle lay in the inducement of a pathophysiological condition of insulin hypoglycemia with one of two clinical manifestations, comahybernation ǒr convulsion. These conditions I term 'shock'" (1954, p. 264). Sakel's method underwent three phases: adaptation; shock; and polarization. He claimed as high as 86 percent success with cases of schizophrenia that had not been ill over a year.

Metrazol Convulsive Therapy and Carbon Dioxide Therapy. A convulsive treatment with the intravenous use of metrazol was developed by Meduna (1936, 1954) and introduced in 1934. The convulsive reaction to metrazol is comparable to that of epilepsy (grand mal). A brief coma, following convulsion, is accompanied by an improvement in respiration and relaxation, with a gradual clearing in consciousness. Meduna deduced the existence of a "biologic antagonism between the schizophrenic and the epileptic process" (Meduna, 1968, p. 367), because of the rarity of epileptic convulsions in schizophrenia.

Later, Meduna (1954) developed a carbon dioxide psychotherapy for use with neurotics. Essentially it is a desensitization process whereby through repeated inhalations of CO_2 "for a protracted period of time, the patient regains a normal homeostatic balance; and his excitability to old and new pathogenic influences becomes so lowered that the particular influences cease to be pathogenic" (1948). Loss of consciousness usually occurs before 20 to 25 respirations of CO_2, during which time psychomotor excitement is perceptible as well as sensory and other phenomena. Three types of abreaction may take place: "conscious realistic, conscious allegoric, and unconscious realistic . . . explained by *inhibition of cortical inhibitory functions*" (1958, p. 86). Unless considerable improvement occurs by 20 to 30 treatments, this form of therapy is of no avail.

Psychosurgery: Prefrontal Leucotomy and Prefrontal Lobotomy. Following Fulton and Jacobsen's (1935) successful experimental surgery on the frontal brain region of monkeys, alleviating anxiety and frustration, Moniz (1954) developed bilateral prefrontal leucotomy, the severance of the association tracts joining the prefrontal brain areas and the thalamic centers by drilling holes on either side of the forehead through the skull and cutting the cores in brain tissue. Moniz believed that the operation, first performed on December 27, 1935, would cause new synaptic paths, and accordingly new behavior patterns. He felt that disordered behavior of established "synaptic relations must be altered, and the paths in which the impulses revolve in constant passage must be modified, so that the ideas which are connected with them will be modified and the thought will take another course" (1968, p. 376).

The psychosurgery of the Portuguese psychiatrist, Moniz, reached a second stage of sophistication in 1942 in the United States with the efforts of Freeman and Watts (1950) and their technique of prefrontal lobotomy. Though Freeman (1962) claims a renewed interest in psychosurgery developing in England, this surgical technique is rapidly reaching a point of historical value only. The white matter of the prefrontal lobes is reached by an instrument capable of severing the nerve paths connecting the prefrontal areas and the nuclei of the thalamus.

The white matter in the frontal lobes is cut approximately in the plane of the coronal suture. A burr hole is made through or near the suture line and with a long cannula the sphenoidal ridge is identified. With the coronal suture and the sphenoidal ridge as landmarks, the nerve pathways can be sectioned in the desired plane. The lobotomy may be performed with a blunt knife-like instrument or with a special leucotome (Freeman & Watts, 1968, p. 378).

Sleep Therapy, Narcoanalysis, Hypnoanalysis, and Autogenic Training. Drug-induced narcosis accompanied with psychotherapy and abreaction in the drugged state produced by sodium pentothal and sodium amytal were techniques developed by Grinker and Spiegel (1945) in World War II, and by Horsley (1943) in Great Britain. The drugs, augmenting abreaction, served to release intense guilt feelings as well as hostility and fear. As early as 1931 Horsley discovered the effectiveness of nembutal as a psychotherapeutic agent. Grinker and Spiegel, who refer to their systems as narcosynthesis, claim that it is more than a

process of recapture by the ego of alienated ideas and emotions. It is also the synthesis of related feelings that have been separated by the process of dissociation. Thus, under pentothal, hostility and fear may be recombined as derivatives of the reaction to the same stress. The patient becomes aware that his anger is due to his being left unprotected in a fearful situation (1945, p. 393).

Jacobson's (1938) *progressive relaxation,* and the *autogenic training* of Schultz and Luthe (1959) are attempts at a synthesis of physiologic processes with psychotherapy. Combining hypnosis with their system, Schultz and Luthe developed six steps as the core of autogenic training: "heaviness and warmth in the extremities, regulation of cardiac activity and respiration, abdominal warmth and cooling of the forehead" (1959, p. 1). In addition, there are "autogenic standard exercises," such as, training postures, verbal formulae, meditative exercises, organ-specific exercises, intentional formulae. Organ-specific exercises and intentional formulae are adjuncts of the standard exercises, used as supplements to them.

Hypnoanalysis finds its strongest protagonist in Wolberg (1964, 1966) who contends that all persons are capable of being hypnotized, though his success is limited to 90 percent, with a correlation existing between a person's suggestibility and his hypnotic susceptibility. Neurotics respond to hypnotic therapy, but those with character disorders do not, and psychotics cannot be significantly aided by this mode of therapy. At best, hypnosis is a tool.

Sleep therapy, a form of treatment currently employed in the Soviet Union rather than in the United States, is used for both schizophrenics and neurotics. Andreev (1960) reports that the most effective results ensue from sleep that is closest to natural rather than narcotic induced. Hypnosis, conditioned reflex, and at times minute doses of hypnotic **drug** may be used toward this end. With neurotics, psychotherapy is an indispensable accompaniment, since sleep's value is only "restorative and protective in character."

GROUP PSYCHOTHERAPY

The *raison d'être* of group psychotherapy is that the group itself is virtually the therapeutic agent, and not (as so many persons mistakenly believe) that it simply alleviates the congestion of patients waiting for a psychotherapeutic session (Mullan & Rosenbaum, 1962).

Analytic Group Psychotherapy. Utilizing many psychoanalytic principles, Slavson (1964, 1965a, 1965b) developed a variety of group techniques: (*a*) In *play group psychotherapy*, primarily for children from 7 to 12 years of age, the children act out through free activity their impulses, fantasies, tensions, and conflicts in respect to their surrounding environment, both the social and physical. (*b*) In *activity-interview group psychotherapy*, for those in their latency period, the psychotherapist interprets, poses leading questions, and allows the members of the group to do likewise to the end that insight and understanding are achieved. (*c*) In *interview group psychotherapy*, for adolescents and adults, the setting transpires around a circular table. The participants are encouraged to speak freely, assured that their utterances are held in strictest confidence. The group functions on its own initiative. The psychodynamics operative in these three types of analytic groups are relationship or transference, catharsis, insight, ego strengthening, reality testing, and sublimation. Another variation is *para-analytic group psychotherapy* which consists of "the fusing of analytic group psychotherapy with guidance, counseling, advice and 'teaching,' as indicated" (1965b, p. 328).

Group Focal-Conflict Theory and Other Systems. Foulkes (1948), and in collaboration with Anthony (1957), regarding the group as a "dynamic field of experience" and the analyst as a participant-observer, strove for spontaneous contributions from members of the group. *Bion* (1961), influenced by Melanie Klein, viewed the group as a series of emotional states or as cultures, with its members reacting to or accepting the cultures as they move along a series of valences from one emotional culture to others. The therapist's task is the interpretation of the group's behavior as a unit. Interested in Bion's system, *Thelen* (Stock & Thelen, 1958) studied group interaction in terms of its emotion factors, functional process, and relationship between individual and group. Prompted by these studies, a *group focal-conflict theory of psychotherapy* was developed by three of Thelen's students (Whitaker, Stock & Lieberman, 1964) based on French's ideas (1952–1954).

Psychodrama. Group psychotherapy (1953, 1966a), especially in the form of psychodrama (1946, 1966b, 1969), has been developed by Moreno to whom therapy must be "living and doing." Motivated by spontaneity and creativity to combat anxiety, the patient acts out on a stage, living space, situations personally meaningful to him. Aided by therapists who function as directors and auxiliary egos who confront patients with significant stimulus conditions, the patient through role-playing gains insight respecting his conflict, and emotional release through catharsis.

Transactional Analysis. Utilizing the ideas of psychoanalysis, especially those of Eduardo Weiss and Paul Federn's ego psychology, Berne (1961, 1963, 1964) offered his version which he terms transactional analysis, that is, the analysis of single transactions (a unit of social action) of interpersonal relationships or various ego states. "The objective of transactional analysis in group therapy is to carry each patient through the progressive stages of structural analysis, trnsactional anlysis proper, game analysis, and script analysis, until he attains social control" (1961, p. 165). Structural analysis, the analysis of ego states, makes for reality testing, thus leading to transactional analysis, the goal of which is social control or controlling one's own tendency to manipulate others destructively and responding without insight. Archaic ego states are segregated, while archaic conflicts and distortions are resolved.

Milieu Therapy: The Therapeutic Community. Drawing upon the social
and cultural atmosphere itself as a therapeutic agent, Jones (1953, 1956,
1962) developed (and Rapoport [1960, 1968] articulated) the concept
of a therapeutic community. Milieu therapy, a form of social psychiatry,
employs the following concepts and tactics: (1) the holistic view wherein the entire hospital is considered a therapeutic community, a wholesome society with which patients would choose to identify; (3) permissiveness in contrast to the traditional restrictive environment of mental institutions; (3) patient participation in the conduct and affairs
of their institutions; (4) broadening the base of therapy by extending
the range of activities, relationships, and environment; and (5) rehabilitation through rehearsing social roles in a hospital whose social
setting and operation is a replica of the world at large, hence creating
a therapeutic atmosphere.

Kraft (1966) cites seven difficulties facing the therapeutic community;
(1) the lack of clear, conceptual model; (2) ill-defined boundaries and
roles of the professional which make for diminution of professional
identity; (3) group responsibility deteriorating into a state of "no responsibility"; (4) the possibility of lack of personal attention; (5) the
values of the therapeutic community possibly being inappropriate in
society at large; (6) difficulties of program evaluation and research; and
(7) the unavailability of staff especially trained for the therapeutic
community.

Conjoint Family Therapy. A form of therapy closely related to group
therapy, conjoint family therapy, consists of treating the patient in conjunction with "other members of his family together as a functioning
natural group" (Jackson & Weakland, 1961, p. 30). The underlying
theory is that the therapist is dealing with a "sick family," not merely
a "sick patient" (Jackson, 1967). A novel variation of Jackson's system
is that of Satir (1967) who places the accent on psychological health rather
than psychopathology by calling for well-family checkups as a preventive
measure.

In Great Britain, *family psychiatry* developed by Howells (1962, 1963,
1968b, 1968c), has as its goal the production of an "emotionally healthy
family," since the family members sent for referral are merely an indicator
of that family's psychopathology. Family psychotherapy may employ the
following techniques: (1) individual therapy; (2) didactic therapy (joint
therapy); family group therapy (conjoint family therapy); and nonfamily
group therapy.

Numerous other forms of group therapies exist both in fact and in
theory, such as: Daytop Lodge, group therapy for drug addicts (Shelly
& Bassin, 1965); the new group therapy (Mowrer, 1964) consisting of

laymen operations, numbering about 265 throughout the country, and affiliated with the American Conference of Therapeutic Self-Help Clubs; multiple impact therapy, and many others.

PSYCHOANALYTIC AND RELATED THERAPIES

More than an understanding of psychopathological phenomena, Freud's (1916–17) major contribution was a psychotherapeutic system free from the use of drugs and other physiological devices. Freud traced, as the root of mental disorder, faulty libidinal development which makes for arrested personality development, fixation, and regression. Unearthing and accepting the contents of the unconscious through dream analysis and interpretation (Freud, 1900), and through recall by free association issuing in abreaction with its accompanying cathartic effect (Breuer & Freud, 1895), Freud found it to lead to a satisfactory transference relationship with the therapist, delivering one from neurosis, provided that successful personality development (integration of id, ego, and superego; and a strong ego) is achieved through psychoanalysis (Freud, 1940).

Variations from Freudian Psychoanalysis. Numerous variations of the Freudian system are prevalent today: Stekel's (1950) short-term *active analytic psychotherapy* deemphasizes the patient's past, while accenting the personality of the analyst, intuitive listening, and intuitive analysis. Ferenczi's (1950, 1952) *active therapy* or *relaxation therapy,* one of permissiveness, allows the patient to play games and talk as if he were a child. Believing in the curative effect of love and permissiveness, the therapist provides both love and acceptance. By active therapy Ferenczi "meant the use of prohibitions and commands by an analyst for the purpose of mobilizing the patient's resistances and affects" (Bernstein, 1965, p. 1185).

Reich's (1948, 1949) *orgastic psychotherapy, orgone therapy,* and *character analysis* attempt to combat character resistances, a patient's characterological "armor." Mental illness stems from sexual repression, and therapy must "enable the human animal to accept nature within himself" and enjoy it, for "psychic health depends upon orgastic potency." Orgastic impotence, the damming up of biological energy is the source of irrational behavior. The objective of analytic therapy is to establish orgastic potency or "the ability to discharge an amount of sexual energy equal to that accumulated" (1948, p. 67).

Rank's (1945, 1968, 1969) *will therapy,* emphasizing the role of choice or will, is predicated on: "(a) the therapeutic situation being a present experience instead of a mere reliving of the past as in psychoanalysis;

(*b*) the nonsexual nature of the transference relationship which he regarded as a reinstituting of the maternal tie; and (*c*) the establishment of a therapeutic control by setting a time for the termination of treatment" (Sahakian, 1969a, p. 118).

According to Federn's (1952) *ego psychology therapy,* neurosis is regarded as a loss of cathexis, whereas psychosis is a disease of the ego. Psychotherapy's aim is the restoration of the lost cathexis to the psychotic ego, but a reduction of hypercathexis to the neurotic ego. In psychosis the weakened ego, experiencing a loss of ego boundary, must have as its therapeutic goal, re-repression.

Klein (1948b, 1960) adds the following modifications to Freudian analysis: the ego's existence originating at birth; and good and bad emotions stemming from the infant's relationship with his mother, who constitutes the external world. Introjection and projection, two processes appearing with the development of the infantile ego, are fundamental to the infant's outlook on the world. Healthy development enhances reality testing, while anxiety, guilt, and destructive impulses split the ego in a paranoid-schizoid state, eventuating in depression. The *object relations theory of personality* developed by Fairbairn (1952) shows the influence of his British compatriot Klein. Bad infant experiences cause splitting of the ego that at birth is a unity. The psyche's primary life drive, the libido, makes for good ego relations and growth, but with the loss of ego unity, ego splitting occurs.

The *Chicago School,* championed by Alexander and French (1946), sought corrective emotion experiences, interpretation of resistances, examination of character or total behavior of the patient; and a flexibility respecting the frequency of interview, the use of the couch, and interruptions in the therapeutic relationship.

The *direct analysis* technique of Rosen (1953) calls for therapist-participation in the patient's psychosis or world of fantasy as a figure in the psychosis by accepting his psychotic reality, thereby accompanying or assisting him in returning to reality. Utilizing the "governing principle" (therapist as a "loving, omnipotent protector and provider for the patient") and direct interpretation, insight (a vital ingredient for recovery) is achieved. Other tactics employed in direct analysis are: attacking the patient's mother; promising help, care, and cure; informing the patient of his insanity; enhancing positive transference; feigning sexual seduction; attacking the superego parental image; adopting the patient; entering into the psychosis; agreeing with megalomanic claims; love toward the patient; and interpreting delusions (English, 1961).

Other forms of psychotherapy are Deutsch's (Deutsch & Murphy, 1955) *sector therapy* wherein association with key words and phrases, taken from the patient's autobiographical social history, offer understanding of symptoms and conflicts; and Karpman's (1957) *direct psychotherapy,* adopting a similar technique.

Jung's (1966, 1969) *analytical psychotherapy,* a dialectical procedure containing the individuation process, endeavors to integrate the patient to wholeness by coordinating conscious and unconscious mind into a unity, a transcendent function.

Variations of Freudian Psychoanalysis: The Cultural School. Adler's (1929, 1939) *individual psychology* applied a therapy of social usefulness, creative selfhood, self-transcendence, and broadening of the patient's social interest, thereby eliminating inferiority feelings, egoism, and social indigency. The therapist, conveying a social feeling (transference) to his patient, who assumes a face-to-face position with him, cultivates altruism in his patient as well as a renewal of a role or position in society.

Sullivan's (1953, 1954, 1964) *interpersonal theory of psychiatry* depicts the therapist as a participant observer engaged in an interpersonal relationship with his patient. The dissipation of anxiety, tension, or the establishment of a sense of equilibrium, euphoria, or security is the goal of therapy. The processes of socialization issue in satisfactions or fulfillment of needs, and as such are conducive to becoming a person. Empathy, emotional communication, or contagion is at the disposal of the therapist for an effective (or damaging) psychiatric interview.

A synthesis of Sullivan's interpersonal approach and Freud's concepts was developed by Fromm-Reichmann (1943, 1950), the outcome being *intensive psychotherapy.* Its goal is "gaining insight into an understanding of the unconscious roots of patients' problems, the genetics and dynamics, on the part of both patient and psychiatrist, whereby such understanding and insight may frequently promote changes in the dynamic structure of the patient's personality" (1950, p. x).

Horney's (1950) *character analysis therapy,* like Sullivan's, strives for the diminution of anxiety, reducing it to levels that will free the neurotic from his behavior patterns, thereby restoring his autonomy. Neurotic self-idealization must yield to self-actualization, and the ideal self (pride-system) to the real self.

EXISTENTIAL, PHENOMENOLOGICAL, AND RELATED PSYCHOTHERAPIES

Existential psychologists trace their philosophical antecedents to the thought of Heidegger (1962) and Kierkegaard (1941a, 1941b, 1941c, 1957), while phenomenological psychologists are in closer affiliation with

Scheler (1966), Husserl (1931), and Brentano (1874, 1968). Key emphases in the thinking of existentialists are the priority of man's existence over his essence; the power of man to respond with deliberation, decision, or choice; man viewed as in the process of becoming human; man's psychological dimension, i.e., self-awareness; a person's becoming a person by encounter with others; and man as a being-in-the-world, that is, only man potentially has a world whereas other beings merely have an environment.

The three existential anxieties (anxiety of having to die, the anxiety of having to become guilty, and the anxiety of lacking a meaning in life [Tillich, 1961]) have their corresponding neurotic anxieties; but unlike neurotic anxieties, no psychotherapist can remove existential or ontological anxieties. Frankl's (1967a, 1967b) *logotherapy*, predicated on man's will to meaning (1969), developed a psychotherapeutic technique to combat existential or noögenic neurosis, that is, a neurosis generated by meaninglessness in one's life rather than a sexual neurosis.

Another existential psychotherapist treating neurosis is May (1959, 1967; May, Angel, & Ellenberger, 1958). Salient features of his system include: presence; transference as "an event occurring in a real relationship between two people"; the aim of therapy being the patient's experiencing his existence as real; commitment, i.e., a decisive orientation toward life or existence since insight follows decision; being as indivisible, that is, the conscious and unconscious are one.

Binswanger (1956, 1958a, 1958b, 1963) incorporates five major principles in his existential-analytic system: (1) the investigation of the patient's life history as a modification of his total structure as a being-in-the-world; (2) viewing the patient as failing in the realization of the fullness of his humanity (and seeing that he "experiences" it as such); (3) standing on the plane of common existence or the same plane with his patient, an *encounter* of relatedness and love, of "being-with-others in genuine presence"; (4) interpretation of dreams in the light of the whole man in a specific world and specific mode of existence; (5) "opening up to the sick fellow man an understanding of the structure of human existence, and [allowing] him to find his way back from his neurotic or psychotic, lost, erring, perforated or twisted mode of existence and world, into the freedom of being able to utilize his own capacities for existence" (1956, p. 148).

A synthesis of psychoanalysis and Daseinsanalysis was sought by Boss (1963), but with time Daseinsanalysis became liberated from psychoanalysis (Condrau & Boss, 1968). Daseinsanalysis is a psychotherapeutic theory that relies considerably upon the philosophical premises of Kierkegaard (1941a, 1941b, 1941c) and Heidegger (1962), especially the concepts of "therapeutic intervention" and of "anticipatory care" derived from the latter. A system that is based on the analysis of Dasein and of comprehending man as a "being-in-the-world," becomes the vehicle by which a therapist will adequately understand the "being-human."

Those psychotherapists leaning toward the phenomenological approach for understanding personality both neurotic and normal are Frankl (Fabry, 1968) and Rogers (1951, 1965). Ansbacher (1965) regards contemporary Adlerian or individual psychology as phenomenological. Kantor and Herron (1966) apply Frankl's *logotherapy* to schizophrenia. Logotherapy has several important and strikingly new features to commend it: (1) will to meaning, i.e., search for life's unique meanings, an effective objective in both existential neurosis (Frankl, 1959) and schizophrenia (Kantor & Herron, 1966); (2) paradoxical intention, a desirable technique for treating phobias and obsessional neurosis (comparable to Dunlap's [1932] method of negative practice); (3) de-reflection, a valuable method in somatic preoccupations, functional sexual disturbances, and insomnia (Kaczanowski, 1967); and (4) a psychotherapy for treating suffering by offering values and meaningfulness to be found therein (Weisskopf-Joelson, 1955; Frankl, 1961).

Nondirective counseling or the *client-centered therapy* of Rogers (1942, 1951, 1959), a nonauthoritarian approach based on client permissiveness, moves from the client's state of incongruence or anxiety to congruence, insight, self-scrutiny, positive self-regard, and self-actualization. This is accomplished with the assistance of the therapist whose empathetic understanding, positive regard for, and congruent relationship with the client functions as a catalyst in the reorganization of the self-structure of the client in his achievement of reintegration and maturity. Accurate empathetic understanding is the primary task of the therapist. Concentration is upon the client's phenomenological experiences, the world as he perceives it, rather than upon objective factual data. Man, innately good with a self-actualizing tendency or behavior that is purposive and goal-directed, effects changes in his personality himself by self-discovery, with the therapist establishing conditions under which the client can be effective in growing to a fully functioning person from one with merely the "existing capacity" of a "fully competent individual."

Laing (1965) sought a synthesis of the existential-phenomenological as a foundation for understanding psychosis, interpreting psychotherapy as *"an obstinate attempt of two people to recover the wholeness of being human through the relationship* between them" (1967, p. 53).

The *psychotherapy of Zen*, examined by Watts (1961) and Fromm (1963) attempts attainment of *satori* (enlightenment) by searching or "seeing" within one's being in order to achieve freedom, and the liberation of stored energies requiring channelization and activity, thereby preventing one from crippling mental disorders and enhancing one's faculty for happiness and love (Suzuki, 1949).

BEHAVIOR THERAPIES AND RELATED
LEARNING THEORY TECHNIQUES

Despite their current popularity, behavior therapies are not new, dating back to the rise of learning theory. Occasionally learning theory (classical conditioning of Pavlov [1927]; instrumental learning theory of Thorndike [1911]; and Hull's theory [1943]) is synthesized with Freudian concepts to produce a psychotherapeutic system as Dollard and Miller (1950) achieved, but ordinarily the behavior therapies are free from or even antagonistic (Salter, 1949) to psychoanalysis. Behavior therapy has been used interchangeably with conditioning therapy and learning theory therapy (Wolpe, Salter & Reyna, 1964).

Shoben (1948, 1949), constructing a learning theory therapy premised on Mowrer's (1947, 1953) two-factor learning theory, proposes three processes:

first, the lifting of repression and development of insight through the symbolic reinstating of the stimuli for anxiety; second, the diminution of anxiety by counter-conditioning through the attachment of the stimuli for anxiety to the comfort reaction made to the therapeutic relationship; and third, the process of reeducation through the therapist's helping the patient to formulate rational goals and behavioral methods for attaining them (1949, p. 390).

Behavior therapies are committed to the view that neurosis is merely a habit requiring attention (Dollard & Miller, 1950; Eysenck & Rachman, 1965; Schaefer & Martin, 1969; Wolpe, 1969a, 1969b). What distinguishes neurotic habits from others is their resistance to extinction despite their disvalue from the standpoint of reward or unadaptiveness (Wolpe & Lazarus, 1966), hence resulting in a neurotic paradox (Mowrer, 1950). Behavior therapy's aim, according to Wolpe's (1958, 1969) *psychotherapy by reciprocal inhibition,* is the alteration or removal of habits considered undesirable by counterconditioning, positive reconditioning, and experimental extinction. By systematic desensitization, a piecemeal erosion of neurotic anxiety-response habits, anxiety-evoking stimuli are diminished through training in relaxation and the construction of anxiety hierarchies.

Mowrer evaluates three basic types of behavior therapy: Type-I, Wolpe's, traces neurosis to the traumatic learning of unrealistic fears, and eliminates them by

associating, in imagination, the thing or situation feared with a relaxed state. . . . In Type-II, Skinnerian behavior therapy, the assumption is not that the individual has learned false fears but that he has *failed to learn* effective and socially acceptable overt behavior; and change is sought through altered "reinforcement contingencies," namely, the structure of rewards and punishments, in the subject's environment. In Type III (integrity) therapy the assumption is that the subject has mistakenly ("stupidly") decided that deception, denial, "phoniness" is a good personal strategy; and here the greatest "help" another can give is to encourage, persuade, "inspire" . . . that person, by means of "sharing" and "modeling," to try honesty and openness as an alternative personal strategy (Mowrer, 1966, p. 455–456).

Integrity therapy, endorsed by Mowrer and inherent in existential psychotherapy, is enunciated by Drakeford (1967).

Social learning theorists regard abnormal behavior "not as a symptom of a hidden illness but as a problem of 'social learning,' and can be treated directly by methods that are derived from principles of learning" (Bandura, 1967, p. 78). According to Rotter, maladaptive behavior arises when an individual's expectations of achieving desirable gratification are low, i.e., "when freedom of movement is low and need value is high" (1964, p. 82), resulting in avoidance learning or the frustration of failing to achieve one's goals. Social learning therapy employs flexible techniques suitable for the particular patient in question, and the cultivation of problem-solving skills, especially offering alternative courses for the patient's achievement of goals. The therapist, assuming an active role, interprets so that optimal behavior is acquired through reinforcement and reward, and valuable and satisfying life goals are achieved. Furthermore, social, physical, vocational, and environmental changes are effected as a way of altering personality. The therapist, however, possesses no special characteristic (Rotter, 1954) except to be warmly concerned or interested and to guide the learning process.

Today, considerable varieties of psychotherapy related to learning theory are prevalent. Among them are: an *assertioned-structured therapy* based on interference theory developed by Phillips (1956) and revised with the assistance of Weiner (1966), the goal of which is behavior alteration by restructuring the patient's behavior on a suitable set of probabilities and assumptions; *constructive alternativism psychotherapy* based on the personal construct psychology of Kelly (1955, 1969) which has the client experiment with new constructs as if he were playing a role, the therapist's responsibility being that of exchanging undesirable constructs for wholesome new ones; the *reinforcement theory* of Pepinsky and Pepinsky (1954), based on a modified Hullian learning theory, attempts the reduction of anxiety as an undesirable drive that deters the patient from eliciting fitting responses, and prediction of behavioral changes expected to occur under given conditions of treatment. Reduction of anxiety augments discriminatory ability regarding anxiety-arousing stimuli, as well as other behavioral changes such as the acquisition of new and suitable patterns of stimulus-response. In recent years, Bandura (1968a, 1969), has been espousing a modeling theory of psychotherapy, a technique utilizing "observational learning," by which new response patterns are established through modeling, emotional responses through vicarious conditioning, and extinction established vicariously. Behavior patterns are modified through observing the behavior of others. "Performance of observationally learned responses is largely regulated by reinforcing outcomes that may be externally applied, self-administered, or vicariously experienced" (Bandura, 1969, p. 202). Emotional behavior is vicariously extinguished through modeling therapy by exposing the observer to feared objects without their producing adverse effects. After the client's observation of another he undergoes the feared experience without unpleasant effects.

Beier's (1966) *silent language psychotherapy,* a synthesis of the Freudian unconscious with Skinner's principle of reinforcement by reward, aims at the social reinforcement of unconscious processes.

RATIONAL AND NONRATIONAL PSYCHOTHERAPIES

Ellis (1958, 1962, 1967) developed a rational therapy, termed *rational-emotive psychotherapy.* Believing that neurotic behavior is prompted from emotions based on irrational philosophies, the therapist must restructure his patient's thoughts rationally so that rational behavior patterns may ensue. It is a therapy reserved for a patient who is reasonably free from psychosis.

Turning to the other side of the coin, Whitaker and Malone (1953; Malone, Whitaker, Warkentin, & Felder, 1961) developed an *experiential* or *nonrational psychotherapy* emphasizing the patient's feeling of experience rather than his intellect. Proper unconscious functioning is scored in the sense that certain of man's makeup was intended by nature to operate below the level of awareness, such as the heart's operation, and when physical and psychic functions intended for subconscious operation are constantly held in awareness, then they fail to behave normally. Hence, re-repression is an important objective in therapy, in addition to personal growth, and autonomous choice spontaneously and unconsciously executed.

Whitaker and his associates (1956) have introduced a system of *multiple therapy,* entailing two or more psychotherapists comprising a therapeutic team that interviews the patient jointly from the initial contact to the termination of treatment, with each therapist utilizing his own preferred technique. Though costly, it is valuable particularly in difficult cases.

A system termed *reality therapy* has been developed by Glasser, which he defined as "a therapy that leads all patients toward reality, toward grappling successfully with the tangible and intangible aspects of the real world . . . a therapy toward reality" (1965, p. 6). Reality therapy strives for the fulfillment of the individual's needs in the real world, as well as the acceptance of the real world. It entails an intense personal involvement, responsible modes of behavior, and learning more desirable modes of behavior in addition to confronting reality. Drakeford (1967), summarizing his *integrity therapy*, adds the need for confession to what Mowrer terms the "three R's" of Glasser's therapy; responsibility, reality, right and wrong.

Another form of rational therapy, *philosophical psychotherapy* (Sahakian, 1969c), seeks to alter attitudes and behavior patterns by restructuring a person's beliefs and intellectual outlook (*Weltanschauung*) on life. A person copes with emotional problems by an appropriate philosophical attitude capable of coloring or reshaping his emotional tenor, thereby releasing much of its pressure.

HOLISTIC AND GESTALT PSYCHOTHERAPIES

Gestalt therapy, espoused by Perls (1966a, 1966b; Perls, Hefferline & Goodman, 1965), attempts a process of integration by supporting the patient's genuine interests, needs, desires, and the achievement of maturity through a "transition from environmental support to self-support" (1966b), thereby developing his own potential, while increasing his frustration tolerance.

Goldstein (1959) also has offered an organismic psychotherapy constructed upon the principles of gestalt psychology, and aiming at self-realization by enabling the patient to make right choices, despite conflicts with fear, by the therapist's creation of an environment conducive to an experience of communion and transference.

Psychobiologic therapy, the system of Meyer (1948, 1951), attempts to treat the patient as a whole in action, both mind and body. However, the patient is not regarded as diseased, but poorly adjusted. Therapy, a cooperative endeavor, utilizes specificity or the patient's personal history in order to investigate irrational and immature behavior patterns so as to replace them with objective and realistic responses to life that are within one's reach of choices and resources.

In addition to the types of psychotherapy discussed, there are numerous others treating specialized areas or types of individuals, such as, psychotherapy with children (Hammer & Kaplan, 1967); pastoral psychotherapy, counseling by trained clergy (Clinebell, 1966); counseling juvenile delinquents (Slavson, 1965a); psychotherapy via psychopharmacology (Wortis, 1962); poetry therapy (Leedy, 1969); and Daytop Lodge approach to drug addiction (Shelly & Bassin, 1965).

61.

CARL R. ROGERS

CLIENT-CENTERED THERAPY

A. CONDITIONS OF THE THERAPEUTIC PROCESS

For therapy to occur it is necessary that these conditions exist.

1. That two persons are in *contact*.

2. That the first person, whom we shall term the client, is in a state of *incongruence*, being *vulnerable*, or *anxious*.

3. That the second person, whom we shall term the therapist, is *congruent* in the *relationship*.

4. That the therapist is *experiencing unconditional positive regard* toward the client.

5. That the therapist is *experiencing* an *empathic* understanding of the client's *internal frame of reference*.

6. That the client *perceives*, at least to a minimal degree, conditions 4 and 5, the *unconditional positive regard* of the therapist for him, and the *empathic* understanding of the therapist.

❂   ❂   ❂

B. THE PROCESS OF THERAPY

When the preceding conditions exist and continue, a process is set in motion which has these characteristic directions:

1. The client is increasingly free in expressing his *feelings*, through verbal and/or motor channels.

2. His expressed feelings increasingly have reference to the *self*, rather than nonself.

3. He increasingly differentiates and discriminates the objects of his *feelings* and *perceptions*, including his environment, other persons, his

From Carl R. Rogers, "A theory of therapy, personality, and interpersonal relationships, as developed in the client-centered framework." In S. Koch (Ed.) *Psychology: A study of a science.* Vol. 3. *Formulations of the person and the social context.* New York: McGraw-Hill, 1959. Pp. 213, 216, 218–9. Reprinted by permission.

self, his *experiences,* and the interrelationships of these. He becomes less *intensional* and more *extensional* in his *perceptions,* or to put it in other terms, his experiences are more *accurately symbolized.*

4. His expressed *feelings* increasingly have reference to the *incongruity* between certain of his *experiences* and his *concept of self.*

5. He comes to experience in awareness the threat of such *incongruence.*

    a. This *experience of threat* is possible only because of the continued *unconditional positive regard* of the therapist, which is extended to *incongruence* as much as to *congruence,* to *anxiety* as much as to absence of *anxiety.*

6. He *experiences* fully, in *awareness,* feelings which have in the past been *denied to awareness,* or *distorted in awareness.*

7. His *concept of self* becomes reorganized to assimilate and include these *experiences* which have previously been *distorted in* or *denied to awareness.*

8. As this reorganization of the *self-structure* continues, his *concept* of *self* becomes increasingly *congruent* with his *experience;* the *self* now including *experiences* which previously would have been too *threatening* to be in *awareness.*

    a. A corollary tendency is toward fewer perceptual *distortions in awareness,* or *denials to awareness,* since there are fewer *experiences* which can be *threatening.* In other words, *defensiveness* is decreased.

9. He becomes increasingly able to *experience,* without a feeling of *threat,* the therapist's *unconditional positive regard.*

10. He increasingly feels an *unconditional positive self-regard.*

11. He increasingly *experiences* himself as the *locus of evaluation.*

12. He reacts to *experience* less in terms of

his *conditions of worth* and more in terms of an *organismic valuing process.*

* * *

C. OUTCOMES IN PERSONALITY AND BEHAVIOR

There is no clear distinction between process and outcome. Items of process are simply differentiated aspects of outcome. Hence the statements which follow could have been included under process. For reasons of convenience in understanding, there have been grouped here those changes which are customarily associated with the terms outcomes, or results, or are observed outside of the therapeutic relationship. These are the changes which are hypothesized as being relatively permanent:

1. The client is more *congruent,* more *open to his experience,* less *defensive.*

2. He is consequently more realistic, objective, *extensional* in his *perceptions.*

3. He is consequently more effective in problem solving.

4. His *psychological adjustment* is improved, being closer to the optimum.

   a. This is owing to, and is a continuation of, the changes in *self-structure* described in *B*7 and *B*8.

5. As a result of the increased *congruence* of *self* and *experience* (*C*4 above) his *vulnerability* to *threat* is reduced.

6. As a consequence of *C*2 above, his perception of his *ideal self* is more realistic, more achievable.

7. As a consequence of the changes in *C*4 and *C*5 his *self* is more *congruent* with his *ideal self.*

8. As a consequence of the increased *congruence* of *self* and *ideal self* (*C*6) and the greater *congruence* of *self* and *experience,* tension of all types is reduced—physiological tension, psychological tension, and the specific type of psychological tension defined as *anxiety.*

9. He has an increased degree of *positive self-regard.*

10. He *perceives* the *locus of evaluation* and the locus of choice as residing within himself.

   a. As a consequence of *C*9 and *C*10 he feels more confident and more self-directing.

   b. As a consequence of *C*1 and *C*10 his values are determined by an *organismic valuing process.*

11. As a consequence of *C*1, and *C*2, he *perceives* others more realistically and accurately.

12. He *experiences* more *acceptance* of others, as a consequence of less need for distortion of his perceptions of them.

13. His behavior changes in various ways.

   a. Since the proportion of *experience* assimilated into the *self-structure* is increased, the proportion of behaviors which can be "owned" as belonging to the *self* is increased.

   b. Conversely, the proportion of behaviors which are disowned as *self-experiences,* felt to be "not myself," is decreased.

   c. Hence his behavior is *perceived* as being more within his control.

14. His behavior is perceived by others as more socialized, more *mature.*

15. As a consequence of *C*1, 2, 3, his behavior is more creative, more uniquely adaptive to each new situation and each new problem, more fully expressive of his own purposes and values.

62.

Joseph Wolpe

BEHAVIOR THERAPY

PSYCHOTHERAPY BY RECIPROCAL INHIBITION

The aim of behavior is always to change habits judged undesirable. The achievement of this aim depends on the application of one or more of three categories of conditioning operations.

1. Counterconditioning

A basic premise about neuroses is that they are persistent unadaptive learned habits of reaction. . . . Almost universally, anxiety is a prominent constituent of neurotic reaction; and since anxiety involves a primitive (subcortical) level of neural organization, its unlearning can be procured only through processes that involve this primitive level. Neurotic anxiety cannot be overcome purely by intellectual action—logical argument, rational insight—except in the special case where it stems entirely from misconceptions. . . .

The elimination of anxiety response habits is usually accomplished by the inhibition of anxiety by a competing response. The formal process is the development of conditioned inhibition through reciprocal inhibition (Wolpe, 1954). *If a response inhibitory of anxiety can be made to occur in the presence of anxiety-evoking stimuli it will weaken the bond between these stimuli and the anxiety.* In human neuroses, a considerable number of responses which empirically inhibit anxiety have been successfully used to overcome neurotic anxiety-response habits as well as other neurotic habits. For example, assertive responses . . . are used to overcome neurotic anxieties that inhibit effective action towards those persons with whom the patient has to interact. The essence of the therapist's

From Joseph Wolpe, *The practice of behavior therapy.* New York: Pergamon Press, 1969. Pp. 14–17, 100–101, 107–110, 121–123. Reprinted by permission.

role is to encourage the outward expression, under all reasonable circumstances, of the feelings and action tendencies previously inhibited by anxiety. Each act of assertion to some extent reciprocally inhibits the concurrent anxiety and slightly weakens the anxiety response habit. The reduction of anxiety drive is the main reinforcing agent of this habit change. Similarly, relaxation responses can be employed to bring about systematic decrements of anxiety response patterns to many classes of stimuli. . . .

The reciprocal inhibition principle also comes into play in overcoming responses other than anxiety. It is the basis of the conditioned inhibition of obsessional and compulsive habits by aversion therapy. . . . In this a painful faradic shock or similar stimulus inhibits the undesired behavior, with the result that conditioned inhibition of the latter is established, and accumulates with repetition. There are also many instances of positive conditioning which *ipso facto* include the conditioned inhibition of previous habits of response to the antecedent stimuli concerned. For example, when assertive behavior is instigated, while the expression of "positive" feelings produces conditioned inhibition of anxiety, the motor actions involved in such expression inhibit and consequently displace the previous motor habit. It should be noted that here the reinforcement comprises the various "rewarding" consequences of the new response.

2. Positive Reconditioning

The conditioning of new motor habits or ways of thinking may accompany the overcoming of unadaptive autonomic responses, as in the example just given. But frequently new habits of action or of thought are needed in contexts that do not involve anxiety. An instance of this is the conditioning treatment of enuresis nocturna. By arranging for the patient to be awakened by an alarm as soon as the first drop of urine is excreted during sleep, the waking reaction is conditioned to the imminence of urination, and this subsequently leads to the development of an inhibition of the tendency to urinate in response to bladder stimulation during sleep (Gwynne Jones, 1960, Lovibond, 1963). A further example is the conditioning of effective study habits in individuals who have unproductive habits and fritter away their time when they should be working (Sulzer, 1965).

Successful conditioning of new habits always involves the use of "rewards" of one kind or another. It sometimes suffices to supply these on an *ad hoc* basis, but in recent years there has been increasing formal use of Skinner's (1953) operant conditioning principles to remove and replace undesirable habits. In order to establish a new behavior pattern in a particular situation, the desired response has to be elicited and each time rewarded, while the undesired behavior is consistently not rewarded and even punished. For example, anorexia nervosa has been successfully treated by making social rewards such as the use of a radio or the granting of companionship contingent on eating, withdrawing these rewards when the patient fails to eat (Bachrach, Erwin and Mohr, 1965). Various types of behavior in schizophrenics have been treated on the same principle (Lindsley, 1956, Williams, 1959, Ayllon, 1963, Davison, 1964) and major and lasting changes of behavior have been produced, even in patients who had been hospitalized for years. . . .

3. Experimental Extinction

This is the progressive weakening of a habit through the repeated nonreinforcement of the responses that manifest it. Thus, behavior that depends on food reinforcement becomes progressively weaker if its occurences are not followed by food. The same is usually true of avoidance behavior if it is not reinforced by an occasional shock. The very evocation of the response has effects that are self-weakening (whether or not it should ultimately be proved that this depends on the fatigue-associated reactive inhibition mechanism proposed by Hull (1943).

Therapeutic techniques based on the extinction mechanism, introduced a quarter of a century ago by Dunlap (1932) under the name "negative practice," have in recent years again been employed in the treatment of such motor habits as tics (e.g. Yates, 1958). In correlation with a very large number of unreinforced trials spontaneous evocations of the undesired movement are progressively lessened.

❊   ❊   ❊

THE TECHNIQUE OF SYSTEMATIC DESENSITIZATION

The problems posed by the patient are carefully considered by the therapist, and if changed behavior is required in social, sexual or other life situations, this will usually be given attention first. If systematic desensitization is also indicated, it is started as soon as possible in parallel with whatever measures have been instituted in life situations. The technique involves three separate sets of operations:

1. Training in deep muscle relaxation;
2. The construction of anxiety hierarchies;
3. Counterposing relaxation and anxiety-evoking stimuli from the hierarchies.

I. Training in Relaxation

The method of relaxation taught is essentially that of Jacobson (1938), but instruction is completed in the course of about six interviews, in marked contrast to Jacobson's very prolonged training schedules. The patient is asked to practice at home for two fifteen-minute periods a day.

In introducing the subject of relaxation, I tell the patient (who has usually already gained a general idea of the nature of conditioning therapy) that relaxation is just one of the methods in our armamentarium for combating anxiety. I continue as follows:

Even the ordinary relaxing that occurs when one lies down often produces quite a noticeable calming effect. It has been found that there is a definite relationship between the extent of muscle relaxation and the production of emotional changes opposite to anxiety. I am going to teach you how to relax far beyond the usual point, and with practice you will be able to 'switch on' at will very considerable emotional effects of an 'anti-anxiety' kind.

There is no established sequence for training the various muscle groups in relaxation, but whatever sequence is adopted should be systematic. My own practice is to start with the arms because they are convenient for purposes of demonstration and easy to check on. The head region is next because the most marked anxiety-inhibiting effects are usually obtained by relaxations there.

*   *   *

2. THE CONSTRUCTION OF HIERARCHIES

An anxiety hierarchy is a list of stimuli on a common theme ranked in descending order according to the amount of anxiety they evoke. In some anxiety neuroses the rank order of the stimuli is an exceedingly difficult matter. . . .

The theme, or common core, of a neurosis is usually derived from extrinsic stimulus situations disturbing to the patient—like spiders or criticisms; but sometimes the core subsists in response-produced stimuli. A variety of physically disparate stimulus situations may all induce a common response. For example, a case of claustrophobia (Wolpe, 1961) had the same kind of trapped feeling when she had irremovable nail polish on her fingers or was wearing a tight ring as when she was physically confined. Such commonality of response is the basis of secondary generalization (Hull, 1943, p. 191).

Hierarchy construction usually begins at about the same time as relaxation training, and is subject to alterations or additions at any time. It is important to note that both the gathering of data and its subsequent organizing are done in an ordinary conversational way and *not under relaxation*, since the patient's *ordinary* responses to stimuli are what the therapist needs to know.

The raw data from which the hierarchies are constructed come from four main sources: (a) the patient's history . . . ; (b) responses to the Willoughby Questionnaire, which reveals anxieties mainly in certain interpersonal contexts: (c) a Fear Survey Schedule (Wolpe & Lang, 1964) . . . and (d) special probings into all possible situations in which the patient feels

unadaptive anxiety. It frequently helps to assign the patient the homework task of listing all situations, thoughts, or feelings that he finds disturbing, fearful, embarrassing, or in any other way distressing.

When all the identified sources of neurotic disturbance have been listed, the therapist classifies them into themes. Usually there is more than one theme. In most cases these are fairly obvious, but there are many exceptions. For example, a fear of going to movies, parties and other public situations may suggest a claustrophobia and yet really be a basic fear of scrutiny. Frequently, fear and avoidance of social occasions turns out to be based on fear of criticism or of rejection; or the fear may be a function of the mere physical presence of people, varying with the number to whom the patient is exposed. One patient's ostensible fear of social situations was really a conditioned anxiety response to the smell of food in public places. A good example of the importance of correct identification of relevant sources of anxiety is to be found in a previously reported case (Wolpe, 1958, p. 152) where a man's impotence turned out to be due to anxiety not related to any aspect of the sexual situation as such, but to the idea of trauma. In the context of an attempt at defloration, anxiety had been conditioned to the sexual act. In this instance the strategy of treatment was shifted by this revelation from *in vivo* use of the sexual response to systematic desensitization to tissue damage.

It is not necessary for the patient actually to have experienced each situation that is to be included in a hierarchy. The question posed is, "If you were today confronted by such and such a situation, *would you expect* to be anxious?" To answer this question he has to *imagine* the situation concerned, and it is generally almost as easy to imagine a supposed event as one that has at some time occurred. The temporal setting of an imagined stimulus configuration scarcely affects the responses to it. A man with a phobia for dogs will usually have about as much anxiety at the idea of meeting a bulldog on the way home tomorrow as at recalling an actual encounter with this breed of dog.

The following list of fears from a recent patient will be used to illustrate some of the intricacies of hierarchy construction. This list is reproduced exactly as the patient presented it.

Raw List of Fears

1. High Altitudes	11. Fire
2. Elevators	12. Fainting
3. Crowded Places	13. Falling Back
4. Church	14. Injections
5. Darkness—Movies, etc.	15. Medications
6. Being Alone	16. Fear of the Unknown
7. Marital Relations (pregnancy)	17. Losing My Mind
8. Walking any Distance	18. Locked Doors
9. Death	19. Amusement Park Rides
10. Accidents	20. Steep Stairways

With the help of a little clarification from the patient the items were sorted into categories, thus:

A. Acrophobia

1. High Altitudes	20. Steep Stairways
19. Amusement Park Rides	

B. Claustrophobia

2. Elevators	5. Movies (darkness factor)
3. Crowded Places	
4. Church	18. Locked Doors

C. Agoraphobia

6. Being Alone	8. Walking any Distance (alone)

D. Illness and its Associations

12. Fainting	14. Injections
13. Falling Back	15. Medication

E. Basically Objective Fears

7. Marital Relations (pregnancy)	11. Fire
9. Death	16. Fear of the Unknown
10. Accidents	17. Losing My Mind

3. DESENSITIZATION PROCEDURE: COUNTERACTING ANXIETY BY RELAXATION

The stage is now set for the conventional desensitization procedure—the patient having attained a capacity to calm himself by relaxation, and the therapist having established appropriate hierarchies. It is natural to hope for a smooth therapeutic passage, and such is often the case but there are many difficulties that may encum-ber the path. I shall first describe the technique and the characteristic course of the uncomplicated process of desensitization.

The assessment of a patient's ability to relax depends partly upon his reports of the degree of calmness that relaxing brings about in him, and partly upon impressions gained from observing him. By the second or third lesson, most patients report calmness, ease, tranquility or sleepiness. A few experience little or no change of feeling. It would, of course, be a boon to have objective indicators to determine degree of relaxation. Jacobson (1939, 1964) has used the electromyogram, but mainly as a corroborative measure. It is too laborious for routine use. Meanwhile, fortunately, the reports of patients usually serve as a sufficiently reliable guide to their emotional state, especially with the help of the subjective anxiety scale (see above). Quite a number of patients, especially those who have little or no current anxiety, report a positive feeling of calm after only one or two sessions of relaxation training. In some fortunate individuals there appears to be a kind of relaxation-radiation zone (usually in the arms or face); and these report a diffuse spread of relaxation to many regions with correlated growth of calmness when the radiation zone is relaxed. If the hierarchies are ready early it is my practice to start desensitization with those who can attain distinct emotional calm before concluding the relaxation training (though this is continued during subsequent interviews).

In embarking upon a desensitization program it is of course highly desirable for the patient to achieve a positive feeling of calm, i.e. a negative of anxiety; but it is *not* mandatory and one is always well satisfied with zero subjective units of disturbance (*suds*). In a fair number who have considerable levels of current anxiety [whether or not this is pervasive ('free-floating') anxiety], it has been found that a substantial lowering of the level—say, from 50 to 15 *suds*—may afford a sufficiently low anxiety baseline for successful desensitization. Apparently, an anxiety-inhibiting 'dynamism' can inhibit small quanta of intercurrent anxiety even when it does not fully overcome current anxiety. Desensitizing effects are only rarely obtainable with levels in excess of 25 *suds;* and in some individuals a zero level is a *sine qua non.*

REFERENCES

AYLLON, T. Intensive treatment of psychotic behavior by stimulus satiation and food reinforcement. *Behaviour Research and Therapy,* 1963, *1,* 53.

BACHRACH, A. J., ERWIN, W. J., & MOHR, J. P. The control of eating behavior in an anorexic by operant conditioning techniques. In L. Ullman and L. Krasner (Eds.), *Case studies in behavior modification.* New York: Holt, Rinehart, and Winston, 1965.

DAVISON, G. C. A social learning therapy programme with an autistic child. *Behaviour Research and Therapy,* 1964, *2,* 149.

DUNLAP, K. *Habits: their making and unmaking.* New York: Liveright, 1932.

HULL, C. L. *Principles of behavior.* New York: Appleton-Century, 1943.

JACOBSON, E. *Progressive relaxation.* Chicago: University of Chicago Press, 1938.

JACOBSON, E. Variation of blood pressure with skeletal muscle tension and relaxation. *Annals of Internal Medicine,* 1939, *12,* 1194.

JACOBSON, E. Variation of pulse rate with skeletal muscle tension and relaxation. *Annals of Internal Medicine,* 1940, *13,* 1619.

LINDSLEY, O. R. Operant conditioning methods applied to research in chronic schizophrenia. *Psychiatric Research Reports,* 1956, *5,* 118.

LOVIBOND, S. H. The mechanism of conditioning treatment of enuresis. *Behaviour Research and Therapy,* 1963, *1,* 17.

SKINNER, B. F. *Science and human behavior.* New York, Macmillan & Co., 1953.

SULZER, E. S. Behavior modification in psychiatric adult patients. In L. Ullman and L. Krasner (Eds.), *Case studies in behavior modification,* New York, Holt, Rinehart, and Winston, 1965.

WILLIAMS, C. D. The elimination of tantrum behavior by extinction procedures, case report. *Journal of Abnormal and Social Psychology,* 1959, *59,* 269.

WOLPE, J. Reciprocal inhibition as the main basis of psychotherapeutic effects. *Archives of Neurology and Psychiatry,* 1954, *72,* 205.

WOLPE, J. *Psychotherapy by reciprocal inhibition.* Stanford: Stanford University Press, 1958.

WOLPE, J. The systematic desensitization treatment of neuroses. *Journal of Nervous and Mental Disease,* 1961, *112,* 189.

WOLPE, J., & LANG, P. J. A fear survey schedule for use in behavior therapy. *Behaviour Research and Therapy,* 1964, *2,* 27.

YATES, A. J. The application of learning theory to the treatment of tics. *Journal of Abnormal and Social Psychology,* 1958, *56,* 175.

63.

JULIAN B. ROTTER

SOCIAL LEARNING PSYCHOTHERAPY

SOCIAL LEARNING THEORY

Another approach utilizing psychological needs is that of social learning theory, developed by the writer, his colleagues, and students. This is a somewhat different view of psychological needs from that of Murray, relying heavily on learning theory to account for the development and change in psychological needs.

According to social learning theory, man's behavior is determined by his goals. Behavior

From Julian B. Rotter, *Clinical psychology.* Pp. 56–59, 82–87. © 1964. Reprinted by permission of Prentice-Hall, Inc., Englewood Cliffs, New Jersey.

is always directional. An individual responds with those behaviors that he has learned will lead to the greatest satisfaction in a given situation. Each person gradually associates certain goal objects and internal conditions with unlearned or inborn satisfactions. For example, first the mother's feeding satisfies the infant; then the presence of the mother herself becomes pleasurable; then the individual may strive to do things of which the mother approves, until finally even in the absence of the mother, he takes satisfaction in the accomplishment of tasks once associated with her approval. As differentiated from the unlearned or biologically based satisfactions of the organism, the psychological motives are the result of experience rather than instinct.

Gradually a set of differentiated motives, or needs, develops in each individual, varying from very specific to very general. The more specific the category of behaviors and goals included in the need, the more possible it is to predict the strength of one from another. The more general, broad, or inclusive the concept, the less accurate the prediction of one behavior from another.

From this point of view a need has three essential components. One of these is the set of behaviors directed toward the same goal (or to similar or related ones); an example is the set of behaviors used by a person to get others to take care of him. These behaviors are called *need potentials;* the term refers to their potential strength, that is, the likelihood that they will be used in certain given situations.

The second major component is the expectancies that certain behaviors will lead to satisfactions or goals that a person values. An individual may have learned many ways of getting others to take care of him as a child, but at the present time he may have little expectation that they will lead to satisfaction. For example, crying will bring an infant care and help, but a ten- or twelve-year-old boy using the same technique may find himself being rejected by his father as "a sissy." The average level of the expectations that the behaviors one has learned to rely upon to achieve certain satisfactions will actually lead to those satisfactions is referred to as *freedom of movement.*

The third general component of needs is the value (*need value*) attached to the goals themselves—that is, the degree to which an individual prefers one set of satisfactions to another. For example, given the same opportunity to obtain two satisfactions, one individual prefers to do something others will admire him for (recognition need) and another prefers to do something that will make others like him (love and affection need).

Another major aspect of social learning theory is the weight it gives to the psychological situation of the individual both in understanding and predicting his behavior. In contrast with trait or faculty approaches, or in fact any personality approach that places all the stress on internal states, this view, because of its basic learning theory assumptions, emphasizes that an individual learns through past experiences that some satisfactions are more likely in some situations than in others. Individual differences exist not only in the strength of different needs but in the way the same situation is perceived. An individual's reactions to different situations depend on his own past experience, which therefore constitutes an important aspect of individual differences. The psychological situation, then, provides the cues for a person's expectancies that his behaviors will lead to desired outcomes.

Frequently when an individual places high value on some set of goals, such as the desire for recognition or the desire to be taken care of, he may at the same time have low expectations for achieving these goals. That is, he may have learned to anticipate punishment, failure, or rejection when he attempts to achieve these desires (for example, the child who constantly obtains poor or failing grades in school). When this occurs, the person usually learns other behaviors to avoid the punishments themselves. Sometimes he tries to obtain the satisfactions by "irreal" ways, such as by daydreaming or symbolic techniques that represent to him, but to no one else, the obtaining of the satisfaction. These avoidance and irreal behaviors are *learned* and constitute what are usually regarded as the symptoms of abnormal behavior. In this view, then, abnormal behavior is not disease or disorder or breakdown but a meaningful attempt to avoid certain punishments or to obtain certain gratifications on an irreal level.

For illustrative purposes, six very broad needs, which attempt to include most learned psychological behavior, are listed below with their definitions. Actually, these terms are so broad as to permit of only limited prediction, and more specific concepts are generally more useful. For example, the need for recognition and status can be easily broken down to the more specific levels of social activities, occupational or intellectual activities, and physical or athletic skills.

1. *Recognition-Status.* The need to excel, to

be considered competent, good or better than others in school, occupation, profession, athletics, social position, physical appeal, or play. That is, the need to obtain high position in a socially valued competitive scale.

2. *Dominance.* The need to control the actions of other people, including family and friends; to be in a position of power, to have others follow one's own ideas and desires.

3. *Independence.* The need to make one's own decisions, to rely on oneself, to develop the skills necessary to obtain satisfaction and reach goals without the help of others.

4. *Protection-Dependency.* The need to have another person or persons prevent frustration, provide protection and security, and help obtain other desired goals.

5. *Love and Affection.* The need for acceptance and liking by other people, to have their warm regard, interest, concern, and devotion.

6. *Physical Comfort.* The need for physical satisfactions that have become associated with security and a state of well-being, the avoidance of pain and the desire for bodily pleasures.

To sum up, the potentiality of a given behavior or set of behaviors to occur in some specific situation is dependent on an individual's expectancy that the behavior will lead to a particular goal or satisfaction, the value that satisfaction has for him, and the relative strength of other behavior potentials in the same situation. It is assumed that often the individual is unaware of the goals (or meaning) of his behavior and of the expectancies of achieving these goals.

It can be seen that the understanding and prediction of individual behavior in complex social situations is extremely difficult, requiring intensive study and much information. One particular implication of social learning theory of special importance for the procedures of assessing personality is that the situation of testing, itself, has an effect on behavior that must be taken into account before predictions from the test to other kinds of situations can be made.

From the point of view of social learning theory, in diagnosing personality not only must the individual's behavior (need potential) be assessed, but also his expectations and the values he places on different goals. It is important to know how these expectations change from situation to situation and how the obtaining of one set of satisfactions runs into conflict with another. Finally, for purposes of psychological treatment, it is frequently important to know how the expectations and values were acquired to know how best to change them.

* * *

SOCIAL LEARNING PSYCHOTHERAPY

One of the major contributions of American psychology has been an extensive development of learning theory. As a natural consequence, important attempts to apply learning theory to the problems of psychotherapy have been made by John Dollard and Neal Miller and by Hobart Mowrer. The learning model they used stemmed primarily from studies of subhuman species in highly controlled, relatively simple laboratory experiments. The following section deals with the application of learning theory to psychotherapy based on the social learning theory of the author described earlier. This theory is based on research with humans in relatively complex social interactions.

From this point of view, the problems of psychotherapy are problems of how to effect changes in behavior through the interaction of one person with another. That is, they are problems in human learning in a social situation.

It will be recalled that according to social learning theory the strength (or the potential of occurrence) of goal-directed behavior depends on a person's expectancy that the behavior will lead to a desired outcome as well as on the value of that outcome for him. The likelihood for a set of related behaviors to occur in a given set of situations is called *need potential.* The expectancies that these behaviors will lead to a set of goals, reinforcements, or rewards is called *freedom of movement,* and the value importance or preference value of the reinforcements is referred to as *need value.* In order to understand, in general terms, the application of social learning theory to psychotherapy, we must examine some additional concepts.

When freedom of movement is low and need

value is high—in other words, when an individual has a low expectation of obtaining certain gratifications that he desires—then defensive or maladaptive behavior frequently arises. Instead of learning how to achieve his goals, he learns how to avoid, or defend himself against, the failure and the frustration of not achieving his goals, or he may attempt to reach the goals by "irreal" ways.

Low freedom of movement may result from his lack of knowledge or ability to acquire adequate behaviors to reach his goals. (For example, the college boy from a small town who greatly desires social acceptance from girls, is not shy, but doesn't know the accepted manner of approach for the new social group he has joined.) Low freedom of movement may also be a consequence of the nature of the goal itself, which may frequently result in strong punishments in a specific society. (For example, some people have a strong desire to avoid responsibility and attempt to make others responsible for their actions. In order to accomplish this, they must avoid the adult role in many situations, and by so doing they frequently make people angry with them because of their need to blame others.) A mistaken expectancy for failure may result from the generalization of experiences of frustration in one life area to another. For example, a child who learns that he cannot be good in athletics because of a partial leg paralysis may generalize these feelings of inadequacy to other areas and feel that because he cannot play as well as other children, the other children do not like him. Another example would be that of a child who does poorly in school and feels, because he finds it difficult to make grades that his parents and teachers find acceptable, that the other children will likewise reject him because he is a "dumbell."

That such generalizations take place is shown in a study by Vaughn Crandall. Crandall developed a way of measuring freedom of movement from stories told to pictures of the thematic apperception type (see Chapter 4). He developed two equivalent sets of nine pictures each to measure freedom of movement in three need areas. Each need area was represented by three pictures. One of these was recognition for physical skill (athletic coordination), one was

recognition for academic skill, and the third was need for love or affection from the opposite sex. Crandall gave one set of pictures to a group of 30 male subjects and then asked them to do a series of difficult, if not impossible, coordination tasks at which they all failed. After this he gave them the second series of nine pictures in order to measure changes in freedom of movement that took place in all three need areas when the subjects were frustrated only in the need area of recognition for athletic skills. Stories were noted by judges for freedom of movement on a scale of 0 to 7. A control group of 36 subjects did not have the failure experience following the first set of pictures, but after spending an equal amount of time in "neutral" activity, they also told stories to the second series. Figure 9.1 shows the results of this study.

Note the amount of lowering of freedom of movement in the three need areas for the frustrated group as compared to the control group.

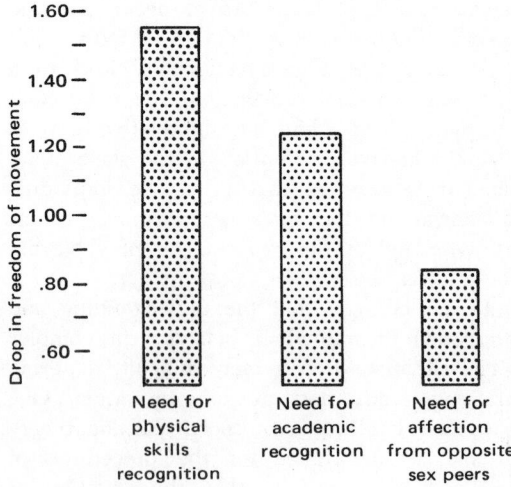

FIGURE 9.1. Difference in the amount of lowering of freedom of movement in Crandall's experimental subjects compared to his control subjects. (From data reported by Vaughn J. Crandall. An investigation of the specificity of reinforcement of induced frustration, *J. soc. Psychol.*, 1955, *41*, pp. 311–318.)

Clearly the expectancy for failure as a result of frustration increased for the experimental subjects significantly in the area of recognition for physical skills. It is also increased significantly, but not as much, in the somewhat related area of recognition for academic skills, and increased, but still less, in the more unrelated area of gratification from opposite-sex peers. But since the frustration was only in physical skills, the study demonstrates how expectancies for failure may generalize from one need to other needs.

Low freedom of movement may also result from "mistaken" evaluations of the present because of early experience. (For example, a girl whose sister was prettier and so was made much of by their father grows up to think of herself as "ugly" and expects that no boy could like her, though she is, in fact, an attractive girl by most standards.) In summary, then, for a given person, sometimes lack of knowledge of the necessary behaviors, sometimes the nature of his goals, and sometimes "erroneous" expectations are the primary source of difficulty. This concept of low freedom of movement, or anticipation of failure and punishment, overlaps to some extent with the construct of "anxiety" used in other approaches.

One important aspect of low freedom of movement relates to the concept of *minimal goal level*. In any given situation the possible outcomes of behavior can be ordered on a scale from a very high positive reinforcement, or reward, to a very high negative reinforcement, or punishment. The theoretical point at which, in this ordering, the outcome changes from positive to negative is called the minimal goal level. Such a concept can be applied either to a series of goals of the same class (for example, school grades, A, B, C, D, E) or to any combination of outcomes possible in a given situation or set of situations. An individual may have low freedom of movement, even though from the viewpoint of others he often appears to succeed, because his reinforcements are usually below his own minimal goal level. An example of high minimal goals is the student who is unhappy and upset because he has received one B grade along with three A's. Another example is the girl with very high goals for social status who is ashamed to be seen with a boy who is not a member of the "best" campus fraternity. Such internalized high minimal goals are frequently involved in problems of low freedom of movement. It should be stressed that the goals can be of any kind: moral, ethical, achieving, sexual, affectional, dominating, dependent, and so on. In social learning theory, any functionally related set of reinforcements towards which an individual strives is the basis for assuming a need and for which a need potential, freedom of movement, and need value can be determined.

In order to increase a patient's freedom of movement for goals he values highly, one possible approach is to change the importance to him of the goals themselves. This might be necessary for a person who has two or more goals of high value that conflict so that the satisfaction of one involves the frustration of the other. An example is the person with strong desires for masculinity and dependency in the same situation. Another instance would be a patient whose goals, such as the desire to control and dominate others, lead to conflict with others' needs and eventuate in both immediate and delayed punishment. A third instance is the individual whose goals are unrealistically high, such as a man who regards any indication of fear in himself as proof that he is not sufficiently masculine and goes to extreme lengths to avoid any "proof" of his lack of masculinity.

As noted above, in some instances, although a patient's goals are realistic enough and appropriate enough for his social group and although his expectancies are based accurately on present situations, his problem may lie in having learned inadequate pathways to achieve these goals. Here the problem might be regarded as pedagogical. Frequently, a clinician must teach a patient the idea of searching for alternative ways of reaching goals both as a general technique of dealing with problems and as a method of achieving specific satisfactions in current life situations. The assumption that once a person is free from internal disorganization, conflict, or repression, he will automatically be able to find adequate ways to reach his goals, does not appear to be substantiated.

In predicting behavior, social learning theory emphasizes the importance of the psychological situation in addition to internal states. The individual who may be dominating, inconsiderate, and grasping for power at work, may be submissive at home and affectionate towards his family. The mild-mannered, seemingly retiring and shy professor frequently turns into a highly vocal participant and aggressive spectator at a football game. The child who has learned that he can "get away with anything at home" may be quite conforming at school, once he has learned that he will be disciplined for unacceptable behavior in that setting. Similarly, the child who gives no trouble in the warm affectionate atmosphere of the home may be sullen and hostile in a school situation where he feels he is being ignored and treated unfairly. From this point of view, personality is not merely composed of characteristics entirely within the individual, rather it is a potential to respond in a given way to a given situation. The general tendency to neglect the importance of the situation stems from the old disease-entity approach to personality which assumed that the crucial determiner of behavior was some internal condition that would be present regardless of the specific situation in which the person found himself. The specific social situation apparently does not seriously affect the progress of measles, and it was assumed that psychic disorders or mental disorders were of a similar nature.

Two implications of emphasizing the psychological situation in determining behavior are: (1) That the clinician should make a greater attempt to develop the patient's understanding and discrimination of different situations, including a better understanding of other people; and (2) that he should make more use of environmental control, that is, manipulations of the individual's surroundings, to effect changes in his behavior.

It can be seen from the foregoing paragraphs that there are many possibilities for changing behavior. A person can learn new behaviors or increase the potential of old behaviors in specific situations. He may learn general methods of solving problems, he may change old expectancies or change the value he places on certain goals, he may reduce his minimal goals, or he may acquire a better understanding of what behavior is appropriate for different situations.

Although it is not possible in this brief survey to describe how these different changes are accomplished, it is possible to summarize some of the major characteristics of the application of social learning theory to psychotherapy.

Since patients come into therapy with many different motives and many different past experiences, it is generally assumed that the conditions for optimal learning will vary considerably from patient to patient. One characteristic of therapy derived from a social learning point of view is that the technique must be suited to the patient. This requires the therapist to have great flexibility in his methods, since there is no single special technique that can be applied to all cases. Since it is true that some therapists are more effective with particular methods and less so with others, it is hoped that eventually patients can be matched systematically to therapists. Until then, psychotherapists will usually work with the kinds of cases and the kinds of methods with which they are most effective.

Another general characteristic of social learning theory is its problem-solving orientation towards the patient's difficulties. Patients can frequently be understood in terms of their failure to meet the challenges of making an adjustment in their society and to make use of their own potentials or assets. Consequently, the theory emphasizes the development of problem-solving skills, such as those of looking for alternative ways of reaching goals, analyzing the consequences of behavior, understanding the motives of others, and trying to analyze how one situation differs from others.

Since the therapist perceives his function partly as that of guiding the learning process—not only are there inadequate behaviors and attitudes to be weakened or eliminated but also more satisfying and constructive alternatives to be learned—the tendency in social learning theory is for a highly active role on the part of the therapist. He is more active in making interpretations to patients, in directly reinforcing or rewarding particular kinds of optimal behavior, and in helping the patient find new alternatives to deal with problems. In order to do all this successfully, it is necessary that the patient trust him and accept his objectivity in the situation. Consequently, the good therapist is "warm" and communicates to his patients his concern and interest in them.

In the changing of the nature or value of life goals, the therapist must consider how these goals relate to future satisfactions. A patient may obtain gratifications in his current life from his ability to dominate a marital partner or his children but not recognize that the long-term consequences of such behavior will involve serious frustrations. One characteristic of a social learning theory is that it not only emphasizes insight into one's own motives as they have been developed from past experience, but also insight into the motives of others and insight into the long-term consequences of one's own behavior.

Finally, the therapist with a social learning orientation tends to make greater use of environmental change in order to effect personality change. In the face-to-face treatment of either children or adults, he may accomplish this by changing attitudes of others who live with the patient—by treating or occasionally consulting with marital partners, parents, or others. He may accomplish it by altering the individual's environment—by changing schools, or jobs, or play or social groups. Of course, such changes with children are usually accomplished through consultation with parents and teachers. With adults they are accomplished through direct discussion about the advisability and consequences of their making such attempts to change their own environmental conditions.

Most broadly considered, social learning theory implies that psychotherapy is a social interaction. The therapist helps the patient achieve a more satisfactory and constructive interrelationship with his social environment. The laws and principles that govern behavior in other interpersonal situations apply as well to the therapy situation.

Although the author obviously feels that social learning theory holds great promise for the future in the development of more effective and scientifically grounded approaches to psychological treatment, it should be noted that there is still much work to be done before the optimal conditions for learning for different individuals can be readily determined. Much of what social learning theory has to contribute to this field is its orientation, which points the way to future research and development.

64.

ALBERT BANDURA

MODELLING THERAPY

One of the fundamental means by which human behaviour is acquired and modified is through modelling or vicarious processes. Research conducted within the broad framework of social learning theory (Bandura, 1965; Bandura and Walters, 1963) provides considerable evidence that virtually all learning phenomena that result from direct experiences can occur vicariously, as a function of observing other people's behaviour and its consequences for them. Thus, for example, persons can acquire complex response patterns through exposure to the performances of exemplary models; emotional responses can be conditioned, through observation, by witnessing the affective reactions of others undergoing painful or pleasurable experiences; fearful and avoidant responsivity can be extinguished vicariously through observing modelled approach behaviour toward feared objects without any

From Albert Bandura,"Modelling approaches to the modification of phobic disorders."In Ruth Porter (Ed.), *The role of learning in psychotherapy.* London: J. & A. Churchill, 1968. Pp. 201–217. Reprinted by permission.

adverse consequences happening to the performer; inhibitions can be induced by witnessing the behaviour of others being punished; and, finally, the expression of well-learned responses can be enhanced and socially regulated through the actions of influential models. Modelling procedures are, therefore, ideally suited for effecting diverse changes in psychological functioning.

A comprehensive review of the numerous psychotherapeutic applications of modelling approaches is beyond the scope of this paper. Instead attention will be focused mainly on a series of experiments designed both to establish the efficacy of modelling procedures for treating phobic conditions, and to delineate some of the variables governing the process of vicarious extinction. The findings derived from this programme of research will be discussed at length, followed by some speculations on the probable mechanisms through which vicarious extinction effects are produced.

New therapeutic approaches are traditionally promoted enthusiastically and it is not until after the methods have been applied clinically for some time by a coterie of advocates that objective tests of efficacy are conducted. Usually the methods are unceremoniously retired by subsequent controlled studies. Workers in psychotherapy have, therefore, come to view any new therapeutic approach as a passing fad. When laboratory tests of efficacy precede clinical application, new methods are subjected to close scrutiny at each stage of development, and those that evolve are likely to produce outcomes sufficiently favourable to weather the test of time.

All the studies reported in this paper employ essentially the same basic experimental design. Subjects are first given an objective test of avoidance behaviour in which they are asked to perform progressively more threatening interactions with a phobic object. Those who are sufficiently fearful to qualify for the project are then assigned, on the basis of the severity of their avoidance behaviour, to various treatment conditions.

Evidence that deviant behaviour can be modified by a particular method is of limited therapeutic significance unless it can be demonstrated that established response patterns generalize to stimuli beyond those encountered in treatment,

and that induced changes endure after the formal therapeutic conditions have been discontinued. Therefore the administration of tests for avoidance behaviour toward different phobic objects is repeated after the subjects have completed the treatment programme, to measure transfer effects. The assessment procedures are repeated after one month to determine how well the behavioural changes have been maintained.

Since the absence of anticipated aversive consequences is a requisite for fear extinction, the modelling displays most likely to have strong effects on phobic observers are those in which performances that the observers regard as hazardous are repeatedly shown to be safe in a variety of threatening circumstances. But the presentation of modelled approach responses toward the most aversive situations at the outset is apt to generate in observers high levels of emotional arousal that can impede vicarious extinction. The efficacy of modelling procedures may, therefore, partly depend on the manner in which the modelled performances are presented.

Avoidance responses can be extinguished with minimal distress if subjects are exposed to a graduated sequence of modelling activities beginning with displays that have low arousal value. After emotional reactions to attenuated threats have been extinguished, progressively more aversive modelling cues, which are weakened by generalization of anxiety extinction from preceding displays, are gradually introduced and neutralized. Stimulus graduation is not a necessary condition for vicarious extinction, but it permits greater control over the change process and elicits less anxiety than approaches with repeated exposure to modelling events having high threat value.

VICARIOUS EXTINCTION OF PHOBIC BEHAVIOUR

Our initial study (Bandura, Grusec and Menlove, 1967) was a stringent test of the degree to which strong avoidance behaviour can be extinguished through modelling procedures. We also investigated whether the induction of positive affective responses in observers during exposure to modelling cues that potentially are threatening expedites vicarious extinction.

Young children, who exhibited a strong fear of dogs, were assigned to one of four treatment conditions. One group participated in eight brief sessions during which they observed a fearless peer-model exhibit progressively more fear-arousing interactions with a dog. For these children, the modelled approach behaviour was presented within a highly positive party context designed to counteract anxiety reactions. When the jovial party was well under way, a dauntless four-year-old boy entered the room with a dog in tow, and performed pre-arranged sequences of interactions with the dog for approximately three minutes during each session. The fear-provoking properties of the modelled displays were gradually increased from session to session by varying simultaneously the physical restraints on the dog, the directness and intimacy of the modelled approach responses, and the duration of interaction between the model and the dog.

A second group of children observed the same graduated performances, but in a neutral context. In the two treatment conditions described, the stimulus complex contained both modelling cues and repeated observation of the phobic stimulus. Therefore, in order to evaluate the effects of exposure to a feared animal alone, a third group of children observed the dog in the positive context but without the model. A fourth group participated in the positive activities but was never exposed to either the dog or the modelled displays.

Children's phobic behaviour toward two different dogs was measured separately, after the treatment programme and again a month later. The avoidance test consisted of a graded sequence of interactions with the dog. The children were asked, for example, to approach and pet the dog, to release it from a playpen, remove its leash, feed it with dog biscuits, and spend a fixed period of time alone in the room with the animal. The final and most difficult set of tasks required the children to climb into the playpen with the dog and, after having locked the gate, to pet it and remain alone with it under these confining fear-arousing conditions.

As shown in Figure 9.2, the modelling treatment produced stable and generalized reduc-

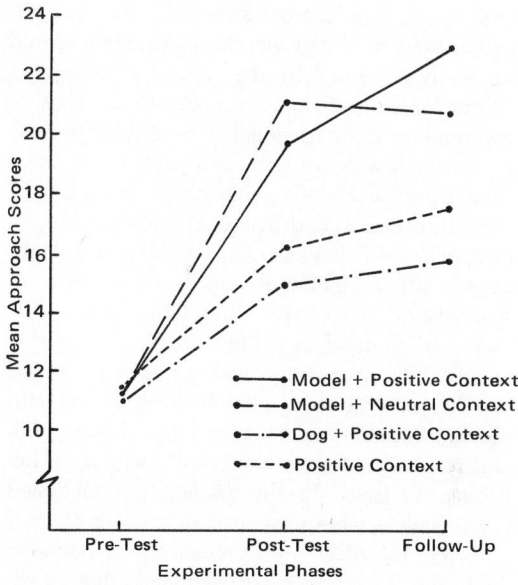

FIGURE 9.2. Mean approach scores achieved by children with dog phobias in each of the treatment conditions on three different periods of assessment. (From Bandura, Grusec and Menlove, 1967; by permission of the American Psychological Association.)

tion in avoidance behaviour. The two groups of children who had observed the peer-model interact without anxiety with the dog displayed significantly greater approach behaviour toward both the experimental and an unfamiliar animal than children in the third and fourth groups (exposure to the dog alone and control conditions with neither dog nor model), who did not differ from each other. The positive context, however, did not contribute much to the favourable outcomes obtained. A more stringent criterion of therapeutic efficacy is the percentage of participants who could manage the final set of tasks. That is, the majority (67 per cent) of children receiving the modelling treatment were eventually able to remain alone in the room and confined with the dog in the playpen; in contrast, this terminal task was attained by relatively few children in the two control conditions.

VICARIOUS EXTINCTION AS A FUNCTION OF MULTIPLE MODELLING

One would expect, from knowledge of generalization processes, that vicarious extinction would be partly governed by the variety of modelling stimulus elements that are neutralized. That is, exposure to multiple models who exhibit fearless behaviour toward variant forms of phobic object should produce relatively thorough extinction of arousal reactions, and hence, extensive reduction in avoidance behaviour. On the other hand observers whose emotional responsiveness to a restricted set of aversive modelling elements is extinguished tend to achieve weaker extinction effects. This proposition was tested in a second experiment (Bandura and Menlove, 1968) employing the same assessment methodology with children who displayed severe avoidance behaviour to dogs. In this project the modelled performances were presented in a series of brief cine-films in order to test the efficacy of symbolic modelling techniques, which lend themselves readily to psychotherapeutic applications.

One group of children, who participated in a single modelling treatment, observed a fearless male model display the same progressively more fear-arousing interactions with a dog as in the preceding experiment. The second group of children, receiving multiple modelling treatments, observed several different girls and boys of varying ages interacting positively with various breeds of dogs of different sizes. The size and fearsomeness of the dogs were progressively increased from small dogs that were not threatening in appearance to massive animals that were. Children assigned to a control group were shown cine-films without dogs.

As in the previous experiment, children who observed approach behaviour modelled without any adverse consequences to the performer displayed enduring and generalized reduction in avoidance behaviour, whereas the controls did not show such changes (Figure 9.3). Comparison of the performance of the most difficult terminal tasks by children presented with the single modelling display and those who witnessed the multiple modelling, showed that the latter treatment is more effective in completely eliminating phobic behaviour. As a further test

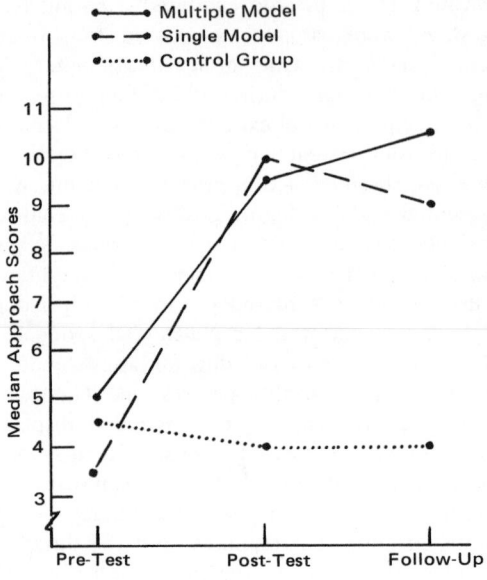

FIGURE 9.3. Median approach scores obtained by children with dog phobias in each of three conditions at different phases of the experiment. (From Bandura and Menlove, 1968; by permission of the American Psychological Association.)

of the therapeutic value of symbolic modelling, the control group of children were given the multiple modelling treatment after the main experiment had been completed. These children, whose avoidance behaviour remained unchanged in several tests conducted during the control period, displayed, after the treatment, a sharp increase in their ability to approach dogs.

Comparison of the results of the two experiments suggests that symbolic modelling is less powerful than live demonstrations of essentially the same behaviour. Although the single modelling treatment effected significant reductions in children's avoidance responses, it did not sufficiently weaken their fears to enable them to carry out the most frightening terminal approach behaviour (being confined with the dog in the playpen). But the diminished efficacy of symbolic modelling can be offset by a broader sampling of models and aversive stimulus objects. Children who received this diverse modelling treatment not only showed continued improvement in approach behaviour between posttest and follow-up periods, but also achieved terminal performances at rates comparable to equally severely phobic children who, in the previous experiment, had observed fearless behaviour by a single real-life model.

The potency of modelling influences in the transmission of anxiety responses is widely acknowledged, but the therapeutic value of these influences has sometimes been questioned (Jersild and Holmes, 1935) on the grounds that fears persist even though modelling frequently occurs under ordinary conditions of life. The effectiveness of any principle of learning depends not only on its validity but also on the manner in which it is implemented. Inconsistent, haphazard and inadequately sequenced learning experiences will produce disappointing results regardless of the cogency of the principle supposedly guiding the treatment programme.

In many instances weak fears are undoubtedly extinguished, or substantially reduced, through fortuitous naturalistic modelling. But carefully planned modelling experiences are essential for the modification of more tenacious phobias. There is some evidence (Bandura and Menlove, 1968) that parents of children who exhibit severe fearfulness make no attempt to overcome their children's fears because they (the parents) suffer from similar fears. Consequently they seldom model fearlessness and, on the rare occasion when they do so, the modelling endeavours do not consist of the carefully graded presentation of threatening stimuli without which this method is not only likely to be ineffective, but may actually exacerbate anxiety reactions. A not uncommon domestic modelling scene, for example, is one in which a parent is busily petting a dog that is jumping about, while simultaneously bidding the child, who is clinging fearfully, to touch the bounding animal. By contrast, the modelling treatments, in addition to utilizing the principle of graduation to reduce anxiety arousal, involved concentrated exposures to modelling displays under protected observation conditions, and extensive variations of the characteristics of the model, the intimacy of approach behaviour,

and the aversive properties of the feared object. Had the modelling sequences been presented in a widely dispersed and haphazard fashion, and restricted to the more reserved petting responses by adults (whom children are likely to discriminate as better able to protect themselves), the vicarious extinction outcomes might have been relatively weak and unpredictable.

In addition to exposure variables, qualitative aspects of the modelled behaviour are likely to exercise some degree of control over vicarious extinction outcomes. It has been shown in studies of vicarious emotional conditioning (Bandura and Rosenthal, 1966; Berger, 1962) that negative affection expressions by models can serve as powerful arousal cues for observers. One would expect modelled approach responses accompanied by positive affective expressions to engender less anxiety arousal and, hence, faster extinction than if the model showed fearful reactions while performing the same behaviour. Parental modelling efforts intended to overcome children's fears are frequently nullified when parents suffer similar apprehensions and force themselves into tense contact with the feared objects. In the present experiments the models frequently expressed pleasant emotional reactions as they performed approach responses in a relaxed manner.

COMPARATIVE EFFICACY OF MODELLING AND DESENSITIZATION TREATMENT APPROACHES

Our third project (Bandura, Blanchard and Ritter, 1968) used an elaborate experimental design that assessed the comparative efficacy of modelling and desensitization treatment approaches for producing affective, behavioural and attitudinal changes. The participants were adolescents and adults with snake phobias that unnecessarily restricted their psychological functioning in various ways. This type of behaviour disorder was selected for study partly because snake phobias have been frequently employed in evaluating the potency of different forms of behavioural therapy and substantial data have been accumulated on the results (Davison, 1968; Lang, Lazovik and Reynolds, 1965; Schubot, 1966). Apart from the comparative data, this paradigm is well suited for laboratory investigations of extinction processes because avoidance behaviour can be effectively measured and extra-experimental encounters with snakes that might confound the effects of treatment rarely occur or can be easily controlled.

In the initial phase of the experiment the participants were given a behavioural test that measured the strength of their avoidance of snakes. They also completed a comprehensive fear inventory to determine whether the elimination of anxieties about snakes is associated with concomitant changes in other areas of anxiety. Attitudinal ratings on several scales describing various encounters with snakes, and on evaluative dimensions of the semantic differential technique, were also obtained. The latter measures were included to furnish the data on the inadequately explored attitudinal effects of behavioural changes induced through social-learning methods. The attitude scales were always given before and after the snake-avoidance test to permit evaluation of the reciprocal interaction between attitudinal and behavioural changes.

The cases were individually matched according to their avoidance behaviour, and assigned to one of four conditions. One group participated in a self-regulated symbolic modelling treatment in which the clients observed a graduated film depicting young children, adolescents and adults engaging in progressively more fear-provoking interactions with a large king snake. To increase the therapeutic power of this method two other features were added. First, clients were taught to induce and to maintain anxiety-inhibiting relaxation throughout the period of exposure. A self-managed modelling treatment should permit greater control over extinction outcomes than one in which a person is exposed to a sequence of aversive modelling cues without regard to his anxiety reactions. Therefore the rate of presentation of the modelling stimuli was regulated by the client through a projector equipped with remote-control starting and reversing devices. Clients were instructed to stop the film whenever a particular modelled performance proved anxiety-provoking, to reverse the film to the beginning of the aversive sequence, and to reinduce deep relaxation. They then re-viewed the threatening scene repeatedly

in this manner until it was completely neutralized before proceeding to the next item in the graduated sequence. After the clients became skilled in the stimulus presentation and self-induction of relaxation, the therapist absented himself from the situation so that the clients themselves conducted their own treatment until their anxieties to the depicted scene were thoroughly extinguished.

The second group of clients received a live-modelling-guided participation form of treatment in which, after observing intimate snake-interaction behaviour repeatedly modelled by the therapist, they were aided, through demonstration, to perform progressively more approach responses toward a snake. At each step the therapist himself performed fearless behaviour, and gradually led the clients into touching, stroking, and then holding the middle of the snake's body with gloved and then bare hands, while he held the snake by the head and tail. When clients no longer felt any apprehension about touching the snake under these secure conditions, anxieties about contact with the snake's head area and entwining tail were extinguished. The therapist again performed the tasks fearlessly, and then he and the client performed the responses jointly; as clients became less fearful the therapist gradually reduced his participation and control over the snake until eventually the clients were able to hold the snake in their laps without assistance, to let the snake loose in the room and retrieve it, and to let it crawl freely over their bodies. Progress through the graded approach tasks was paced according to the clients' apprehensiveness. When they reported being able to perform one activity with little or no fear, they were eased into a more difficult interaction.

Clients assigned to the third group received the standard form of counter-conditioning therapy devised by Wolpe (1958). In this procedure deep relaxation was successively paired with imaginal representations of snake scenes arranged in order of increasing aversiveness. As in the other conditions, treatment was continued until the clients' anxiety reactions were totally extinguished or the maximum time (6 hours) allotted for treatment (not counting relaxation training) was completed. The maximum contact with snakes, either live or in symbolic form, was thus equated across treatments.

Clients assigned to the control group participated in the behavioural and attitudinal assessments without receiving any intervening treatment. This group was included primarily to furnish a control for changes resulting from repeated measurements. A relationship pseudotherapy was not used because several previous investigations have shown that snake avoidance behaviour is unaffected by such experiences. In addition, the controls were subsequently used to test a variation of the symbolic modelling treatment. To evaluate the reliability of treatment outcomes the procedures were administered by two therapists, one female and the other male, with different personality characteristics.

After the treatment series was completed the assessment procedures were readministered to all subjects. The behavioural test, using two snakes of strikingly different colours, consisted of series of tasks requiring subjects to approach, look at, touch and hold a snake with gloved and bare hands; to remove the snake from its cage, let it loose in the room, and then replace it in the cage; to hold it within five inches of their faces; and, finally, to tolerate the snake in their laps while they held their hands passively at their sides. Immediately before and during the performance of each task clients rated the intensity of their fear on a ten-interval scale to provide a measure of affective changes associated with the different methods of treatment.

BEHAVIOURAL CHANGES

The results of the behavioural test, summarized graphically in Figure 9.4, show that the control subjects are essentially unchanged in avoidance behaviour; symbolic modelling and desensitization treatments substantially reduced phobic behaviour; while live modelling combined with guided participation proved to be an unusually powerful treatment and eliminated snake phobias in virtually all subjects (92 per cent).

AFFECTIVE CHANGES

The modelling procedures not only extinguished strong, long-standing avoidance behaviour, but also effectively neutralized the anxiety-arousing

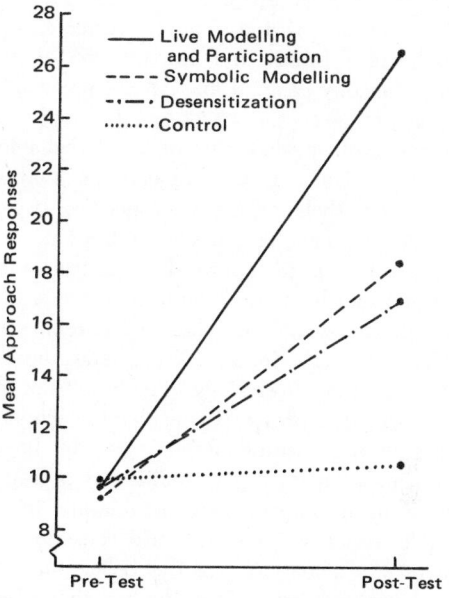

FIGURE 9.4. Mean number of approach responses performed by clients with snake phobias, who received either systematic desensitization, symbolic modelling, live modelling combined with guided performance, or no treatment. Each of the groups contains 12 subjects. (From Bandura, Blanchard and Ritter, 1968.)

properties of the phobic stimuli. Both of the modelling treatments achieved marked decrements in anticipatory and performance anxiety. Although subjects who had received desensitization treatment also experienced less emotional arousal while approaching the snakes in the various ways described, their fear was significantly less reduced than the fear shown by subjects in the modelling conditions.

ATTITUDINAL CHANGES

Because cognitive and attitudinal changes have been systematically assessed in applications of behavioural therapies, it has been generally assumed that these types of approaches alter behaviours only. One can distinguish between three basic strategies of attitude change. The *information-oriented* approach attempts to modify the subjects' attitudes by altering their beliefs about the attitude object through various forms of persuasive interpretation. This method produces changes in attitudes but generally has little effect on overt actions (Festinger, 1964; Fleischmann, Harris and Burtt, 1955; Levitt, 1965; Maccoby *et al.*, 1962). A second general strategy involves an *affect-oriented* approach wherein both evaluations of, and behaviour toward, particular attitude objects are modified by altering their affective properties, usually through vicarious or direct conditioning procedures. The third approach, which is often used in social learning (Bandura, 1969) and in experimental social psychology (Brehm and Cohen, 1962; Festinger, 1957), relies upon a *behaviour-oriented* strategy. The results of this procedure have provided considerable evidence that enduring attitudinal changes can be induced most effectively by getting a person to engage in new behaviour in relation to the attitude object without untoward consequences. The relative superiority of the behavioural approach probably stems from the fact that a basic change in behaviour and the resultant experiential feedback provide an objective and genuine basis for new evaluations.

The results of the present experiment show that applications of social learning therapies have important attitudinal consequences. Both symbolic modelling and desensitization, which primarily involve extinction of the negative affect aroused by aversive stimuli, produced favourable changes in attitudes toward snakes. Consistent with theoretical expectation, the treatment condition that reduced the anxiety-arousing properties of snakes and enabled subjects to engage in intimate interactions with snakes effected the greatest attitudinal changes.

POSITIVE TRANSFERS OF ANXIETY DECREMENTS

The difference between psychodynamic and social-learning approaches to psychotherapy is often misconstrued as the difference between treatment of causes and of symptoms. But one cannot eliminate behaviour as such, except perhaps through direct removal of the requisite neurophysiological systems. Response patterns can be modified only by altering the conditions that regulate their occurrence. Psychodynamic and social-learning therapies are, therefore, equally concerned with modifying the "causes" of deviant behaviour; however, these theories differ (often radically) in what they regard these determinants to be—a crucial difference which, in turn, influences the types of psychological events favoured in the respective treatments. It would be more accurate and advantageous to redefine the cause-symptom treatment controversy as being primarily concerned with the question of whether a particular form of therapy chooses to modify conditions that, in reality, exercise strong, weak, or no significant control over the behaviour in question. One would predict from this point of view that favourable changes induced in one area of behaviour will tend to set in motion beneficial changes in related areas of psychological functioning.

Analysis of the fear inventory scores in our studies does indeed reveal some degree of reduction of fear towards situations beyond the specifically treated phobia, the decrements being roughly proportional to the potency of the treatments employed. Untreated controls showed no changes in either the number or intensity of their fears; desensitization produced a decrease only in the severity of fears towards other animals; and symbolic modelling was accompanied by a reduction in the number of animal fears and a general diminution in the intensity of anxiety in several other areas of functioning. Live modelling combined with participation, on the other hand, effected widespread reductions of fear in relation to a variety of threats involving both interpersonal and nonsocial events.

The positive transfer obtained in this study probably reflects the operation of at least two somewhat different processes. The first involves generalization of extinction effects from treated stimuli to related sources of anxiety. The second entails positive reinforcement of a sense of capability through success, which mitigates emotional responses to potentially threatening situations. In a follow-up questionnaire most of the clients reported that, having successfully overcome a phobia that had plagued them for most of their lives, they felt increased confidence that they could cope effectively with other fear-provoking events.

Under conditions where a given treatment procedure exercises weak behavioural control, many other variables (such as the personality characteristics of the therapists, attributes of the clients and minor technical variations) will emerge as influential determinants of change. But if a method is sufficiently powerful it should be able to override such influences. To demonstrate that in the cases that showed only partial improvement the major deficits resided in the method rather than in the client, all subjects who failed to achieve terminal performances, including the controls, were subsequently treated with the live modelling and guided participation techniques. Snake phobia was thoroughly extinguished in all these subjects, within a few brief sessions, regardless of their age, sex, anxiety proneness and the severity of the avoidance behaviour. Moreover, this supplementary treatment produced further reductions in fearfulness toward both the phobic stimuli and other types of threats, and additional attitudinal changes.

A one-month follow-up assessment revealed that the beneficial changes produced in behaviour, attitudes and emotional responsiveness were effectively maintained. The clients also gave evidence that the behavioural improvements had generalized to real-life situations. They were able to participate in recreational activities such as camping, hiking and gardening which they formerly avoided because of their dread of snakes; they no longer experienced marked distress when unexpectedly confronted with snakes in the course of their social or occupational activities; and they were able to handle harmless snakes, and a few even served as model therapists for their own children and faint-hearted friends. These favourable outcomes illustrate the need for new psychological facilities that offer brief and highly efficacious treatments for specific types of behaviour dysfunction. Vast numbers of people, who otherwise endure unnecessary restrictions in certain areas of their lives, could benefit from such services.

Ritter (1968) has achieved a uniform degree of success with group modelling procedures in children with snake phobias. Groups of children participated in two 35-minute sessions in which they either merely observed several fearless children exhibit intimate interactions with a snake, or received a modelling-guided participation form of treatment during which the therapist displayed positive responses toward the snake and then gradually eased the children into performing the feared behaviour. Snake phobias were completely extinguished in 53 per cent of the children by modelling alone and in 80 per cent of the children after modelling combined with guided participation. The results of these projects indicate that a powerful form of therapy is one in which therapeutic agents themselves model the desired behaviour and arrange optimum conditions for clients to engage in similar activities until they can perform the behaviour skilfully and fearlessly. The therapeutic outcomes associated with this approach are sufficiently promising to warrant its further extension to other types of anxieties and phobias.

In a recently completed experiment O'Connor (1968) employed symbolic modelling in treating pre-school children who showed extreme social withdrawal, a behaviour disorder that reflects both deficits in social skills and fear of close interpersonal contacts. One-half of this group of children were shown a control film, while a matched group of isolates observed a talkie depicting timid children initially watching ongoing social activities at a distance but eventually joining and interacting with the children, with evident positive consequences. In a behavioural assessment conducted immediately after the treatment session the controls remained markedly withdrawn, whereas children who had received the symbolic modelling showed a fivefold increase in social interaction.

Within the modelling-guided participation treatment there are three processes operative that might contribute in varying degrees to such striking psychological changes. These are observation of fearless behaviour being modelled without any unfavorable consequences, incidental information received regarding the feared objects, and direct personal interactions with threatening objects, without adverse effects. In an experiment aimed at isolating the relative influence of these component variables, Blanchard (1968) matched subjects in terms of their snake-avoidance behaviour and assigned them to one of four conditions. One subject in each quartet received the standard procedure, which includes the benefits of modelling, incidental information and guided interaction with a snake. A second subject simultaneously observed the modelling sessions and listened to the verbal interchanges thus being exposed to both modelling and information influences. The third subject received only the modelling component, while the fourth, who merely participated in the testing procedures, experienced none of the constituent influences. Modelling accounted for a major part of the psychological changes, and guided participation also contributed a significant increment, particularly to approach behaviour and fear reduction. On the other hand, informational influences had no effects on either attitudes, emotional arousal or approach behaviour.

MECHANISMS UNDERLYING VICARIOUS EXTINCTION

Research is also needed to clarify the mechanisms through which modelling combined with guided participation achieves such uniformly powerful extinction effects. The findings of the studies described, particularly those based on a paradigm of non-response extinction, can perhaps be best explained in terms of a dual-process theory of avoidance behaviour (Rescorla and Solomon, 1967). According to this view, conditioned aversive stimuli evoke emotional arousal which has both autonomic and central components. It is further assumed that these arousal processes, especially those involving central systems, exert some degree of mediating control over instrumental avoidance responses. The influential role of arousal mediators is most clearly demonstrated by experiments in which avoidance responses to a given stimulus are established through prior classical pairings of that stimulus with aversive experiences. The skeletal muscles of the experimental animals are immobilized by curare to prevent avoidance responses from being conditioned directly to the external stimuli (Rescorla and Solomon, 1967; Solomon and Turner, 1962).

It follows from the dual-process theory that if the arousal capacity of a phobic stimulus is extinguished, then both the motivation and one set of controlling stimuli for avoidance behaviour

are removed. Neutralization of an aversive stimulus through classical extinction procedures alone markedly facilitates subsequent elimination of avoidance behaviour (Black, 1958). It has been further shown (Bandura, Blanchard and Ritter, 1968) that emotional arousal can be effectively extinguished on a vicarious basis when observers merely witness models exhibiting approach responses toward feared objects without experiencing any adverse consequences. The more thoroughly emotional arousal to threatening stimuli is vicariously extinguished the greater is the reduction in avoidance behaviour (Blanchard, 1968). In accordance with these findings, the process of change associated with the powerful procedure involving modelling combined with guided participation may be conceptualized as follows. Repeated modelling of approach responses decreases the arousal potential of aversive stimuli below the threshold for activating avoidance responses, thus enabling subjects to engage, albeit somewhat anxiously, in approach behaviour. The favourable outcomes resulting from direct contact with threatening events further extinguish any residual anxiety and avoidance tendencies. Without the benefit of previous vicarious extinction the reinstatement of severely inhibited behaviour generally requires a tedious and protracted treatment programme. After approach behaviour towards formerly avoided objects has been fully restored the resultant new experiences give rise to substantial reorganization of attitudes.

SUMMARY

This paper is principally concerned with modelling processes whereby phobic behaviour is successfully extinguished through observation of modelling approach behaviour without adverse consequences accruing to the fearless performers. Results of several laboratory investigations reveal that live modelling combined with guided participation is an unusually powerful treatment that effects stable and generalized extinction of phobic behaviour in virtually all cases. Moreover, modelling procedures, both singly and in combination with guided performance, produce a marked reduction in emotional responsivity, substantial attitudinal changes, and anxiety decrements in areas of functioning beyond the specifically treated phobia.

A major factor in modelling procedures that expedites behavioural changes is assumed to be vicarious extinction of arousal reactions to aversive stimuli below the level for activating avoidance responses; this extinction thus enables the clients to approach the phobic objects. Direct contact with threats that are no longer objectively justified provides a variety of new experiences which, if favourable, further extinguish residual anxiety and augment attitudinal changes.

Laboratory findings suggest that a powerful form of therapy is one in which therapeutic agents themselves model the desired behaviour and arrange optimal conditions for clients to engage in similar activities until they can perform the behaviour skilfully and fearlessly.

REFERENCES

BANDURA, A. In L. Berkowitz (Ed.), *Advances in experimental social psychology.* New York: Academic Press, 1965. Pp. 1–55.

BANDURA, A. *Principles of behavioral modification.* New York: Holt, Rinehart & Winston, 1969.

BANDURA, A., BLANCHARD, E. B., & RITTER, B. J. The relative efficacy of desensitization and modelling therapeutic approaches for inducing behavioral, affective and attitudinal changes. Unpublished manuscript, Stanford University, 1968.

BANDURA, A., GRUSEC, J. E., & MENLOVE, F. L. *Journal of Personality and Social Psychology,* 1967, *5,* 16–23.

BANDURA, A., & MENLOVE, F. L. *Journal of Personality and Social Psychology,* 1968, *8,* 99–108.

BANDURA, A., & ROSENTHAL, T. L. *Journal of Personality and Social Psychology,* 1966, *3,* 54–62.

BANDURA, A., & WALTERS, R. H. *Social learning and personality development.* New York: Holt, Rinehart & Winston, 1963.

BERGER, S. M. *Psychological Review,* 1962, *69,* 450–466.

BLACK, A. H. *Journal of Comparative and Physiological Psychology,* 1958, *51,* 519–524.

BLANCHARD, E. B. Doctoral thesis, Stanford University, Faculty of Arts and Science, 1968.

BREHM, J. W., & COHEN, A. R. *Explorations in cognitive dissonance.* New York: Wiley, 1962.

DAVISON, G. C. *Journal of Abnormal Psychology,* 1968, *73,* 91–99.

FESTINGER, L. *A theory of cognitive dissonance.* Evanston, Ill.: Row and Peterson, 1957.

FESTINGER, L. *Public Opinion Quarterly,* 1964, *28,* 404–417.

FLEISHMANN, E., HARRIS, E., & BURTT, H. *Leadership and supervision in industry.* Columbus, Ohio: Ohio State University Bureau of Educational Research, 1955.

JERSILD, A. T., & HOLMES, F. B. *Journal of Psychology,* 1935, *1,* 75–104.

LANG, P. J., LAZOVIK, A. D., & REYNOLDS, D. J. *Journal of Abnormal Psychology,* 1965, 70, 395–402.

LEVITT, T. *Industrial purchasing behavior.* Cambridge, Mass.: Harvard University Press, 1965.

MACCOBY, N., ROMNEY, A. K., ADAMS, J. S., & MACCOBY, E. E. *"Critical periods" in seeking and accepting information.* Stanford: Stanford University Institute for Communication Research, 1962.

O'CONNOR, R. D. Modification of social withdrawal through symbolic modelling. Unpublished manuscript, Stanford University, 1968.

RESCORLA, R. A., & SOLOMON, R. L. *Psychological Review,* 1967, *74,* 151–182.

RITTER, B. J. *Behavior Research Therapy,* 1968, *6,* 1–6.

SCHUBOT, E. D. Doctoral thesis, Stanford University, Faculty of Arts and Science, 1966.

SOLOMON, R. L., & TURNER, L. H. *Psychological Review,* 1962, *69,* 202–219.

WOLPE, J. *Psychotherapy by reciprocal inhibition.* Stanford: Stanford University Press, 1958.

65.

ALBERT ELLIS

RATIONAL PSYCHOTHERAPY

The central theme of this paper is that psycho-therapists can help their clients to live the most self-fulfilling, creative, and emotionally satisfying lives by teaching these clients to organize and discipline their thinking. Does this mean that *all* human emotion and creativity can or should be controlled by reason and intellect? Not exactly.

The human being may be said to possess four basic processes—perception, movement, thinking, and emotion—all of which are integrally interrelated. Thus, thinking, aside from consisting of bioelectric changes in the brain cells, and in addition to comprising remembering, learning, problem-solving, and similar psychological processes, also is, and to some extent has to be, sensory, motor, and emotional behavior (1, 4). Instead, then, of saying, "Jones thinks about this puzzle," we should more accurately say, "Jones perceives-moves-feels-THINKS about this puzzle." Because, however, Jones' activity in relation to the puzzle may be *largely* focussed upon solving it, and only *incidentally* on seeing, manipulating, and emoting about it, we may perhaps justifiably emphasize only his thinking.

Emotion, like thinking and the sensori-motor processes, we may define as an exceptionally complex state of human reaction which is integrally related to all the other perception and response processes. It is not *one* thing, but a combination and holistic integration of several seemingly diverse, yet actually closely related, phenomena (1).

Normally, emotion arises from direct stimulation of the cells in the hypothalamus and autonomic nervous system (e.g., by electrical or chemical stimulation) or from indirect excitation via

sensori-motor, cognitive, and other conative processes. It may theoretically be controlled, therefore, in four major ways. If one is highly excitable and wishes to calm down, one may (*a*) take electroshock or drug treatments; (*b*) use soothing baths or relaxation techniques; (*c*) seek someone one loves and quiet down for his sake; or (*d*) reason oneself into a state of calmness by showing oneself how silly it is for one to remain excited.

Although biophysical, sensori-motor, and emotive techniques are all legitimate methods of controlling emotional disturbances, they will not be considered in this paper, and only the rational technique will be emphasized. Rational psychotherapy is based on the assumption that thought and emotion are not two entirely different processes, but that they significantly overlap in many respects and that therefore disordered emotions can often (though not always) be ameliorated by changing one's thinking.

A large part of what we call emotion, in other words, is nothing more or less than a certain kind—a biased, prejudiced, or strongly evaluative kind—of thinking. What we usually label as thinking is a relatively calm and dispassionate appraisal (or organized perception) of a given situation, an objective comparison of many of the elements in this situation, and a coming to some conclusion as a result of this comparing or discriminating process (4). Thus, a thinking person may observe a piece of bread, see that one part of it is mouldy, remember that eating this kind of mould previously made him ill, and therefore cut off the mouldy part and eat the non-mouldy section of the bread.

An emoting individual, on the other hand, will tend to observe the same piece of bread, and remember so violently or prejudicedly his previous experience with the mouldy part, that he will quickly throw away the whole piece of bread and therefore go hungry. Because the

From Albert Ellis,"Rational psychotherapy." *The Journal of General Psychology,* 1958, 59, 35–49. Paper presented at the session on "Recent Innovations in Psychotherapeutic Strategy" at the American Psychological Association Convention, August 31, 1956. Reprinted by permission.

thinking person is relatively calm, he uses the maximum information available to him—namely, that mouldy bread is bad but non-mouldy bread is good. Because the emotional person is relatively excited, he may use only part of the available information—namely, that mouldy bread is bad.

It is hypothesized, then, that thinking and emoting are closely interrelated and at times differ mainly in that thinking is a more tranquil, less somatically involved (or, at least, perceived), and less activity-directed mode of discrimination than is emotion. It is also hypothesized that among adult humans raised in a social culture thinking and emoting are so closely interrelated that they usually accompany each other, act in a circular cause-and-effect relationship, and in certain (though hardly all) respects are essentially the *same thing,* so that one's thinking *becomes* one's emotion and emotion *becomes* one's thought. It is finally hypothesized that since man is a uniquely sign-, symbol-, and language-creating animal, both thinking and emoting tend to take the form of self-talk or internalized sentences; and that, for all practical purposes, the sentences that human beings keep telling themselves *are* or *become* their thoughts and emotions.

This is not to say that emotion can under *no* circumstances exist without thought. It probably can; but it then tends to exist momentarily, and not to be sustained. An individual, for instance, steps on your toe, and you spontaneously, immediately become angry. Or you hear a piece of music and you instantly begin to feel warm and excited. Or you learn that a close friend has died and you quickly begin to feel sad. Under these circumstances, you may feel emotional without doing any concomitant thinking. Perhaps, however, you do, with split-second rapidity, start thinking "This person who stepped on my toe is a blackguard!" or "This music is wonderful!" or "Oh, how awful it is that my friend died!"

In any event, assuming that you don't, at the very beginning, have any conscious or unconscious thought accompanying your emotion, it appears to be difficult to *sustain* an emotional outburst without bolstering it by repeated ideas. For unless you keep telling yourself on the

order of "This person who stepped on my toe is a blackguard!" or "How could he do a horrible thing like that to me!" the pain of having your toe stepped on will soon die, and your immediate reaction will die with the pain. Of course, you can keep getting your toe stepped on, and the continuing pain may sustain your anger. But assuming that your physical sensation stops, your emotional feeling, in order to last, normally has to be bolstered by some kind of thinking.

We say "normally" because it is theoretically possible for your emotional circuits, once they have been made to reverberate by some physical or psychological stimulus, to keep reverberating under their own power. It is also theoretically possible for drugs or electrical impulses to keep acting directly on your hypothalamus and autonomic nervous system and thereby to keep you emotionally aroused. Usually, however, these types of continued direct stimulation of the emotion-producing centers do not seem to be important and are limited largely to pathological conditions.

It would appear, then, that positive human emotions, such as feelings of love or elation, are often associated with or result from thoughts, or internalized sentences, stated in some form or variation of the phrase "This is good!" and that negative human emotions, such as feelings of anger or depression, are frequently associated with or result from thoughts or sentences which are stated in some form of variation of the phrase "This is bad!" Without an adult human being's employing, on some conscious or unconscious level, such thoughts and sentences, much of his emoting would simply not exist.

If the hypothesis that sustained human emotion often results from or is directly associated with human thinking and self-verbalization is true, then important corollaries about the origin and perpetuation of states of emotional disturbance, or neurosis, may be drawn. For neurosis would appear to be disordered, over- or under-intensified, uncontrollable emotion; and this would seem to be the result of (and, in a sense, the very same thing as) illogical, unrealistic, irrational, inflexible, and childish thinking.

That neurotic or emotionally disturbed behavior is illogical and irrational would seem to be almost definitional. For if we define it otherwise, and label as neurotic *all* incompetent and ineffectual behavior, we will be including actions of *truly* stupid and incompetent individuals —for example, those who are mentally deficient or brain injured. The concept of neurosis only becomes meaningful, therefore, when we assume that the disturbed individual is *not* deficient or impaired but that he is theoretically capable of behaving in a more mature, more controlled, more flexible manner than he actually behaves. If, however, a neurotic is essentially an individual who acts significantly below his own potential level of behaving, or who defeats his own ends though he is theoretically capable of achieving them, it would appear that he behaves in an illogical, irrational, unrealistic way. Neurosis, in other words, consists of stupid behavior by a non-stupid person.

Assuming that emotionally disturbed individuals act in irrational, illogical ways, the questions which are therapeutically relevant are: (*a*) How do they originally get to be illogical? (*b*) How do they keep perpetuating their irrational thinking? (*c*) How can they be helped to be less illogical, less neurotic?

Unfortunately, most of the good thinking that has been done in regard to therapy during the past 60 years, especially by Sigmund Freud and his chief followers (5, 6, 7), has concerned itself with the first of these questions rather than the second and the third. The assumption has often been made that if psychotherapists discover and effectively communicate to their clients the main reasons why these clients originally became disturbed, they will thereby also discover how their neuroses are being perpetuated and how they can be helped to overcome them. This is a dubious assumption.

Knowing exactly how an individual originally learned to behave illogically by no means necessarily informs us precisely how he *maintains* his illogical behavior, nor what he should do to change it. This is particularly true because people are often, perhaps usually, afflicted with *secondary* as well as *primary* neuroses, and the two may significantly differ. Thus, an individual may originally become disturbed because he discovers that he has strong death wishes against his father and (quite illogically) thinks he

should be blamed and punished for having these wishes. Consequently, he may develop some neurotic symptom, such as a phobia against dogs because, let us say, dogs remind him of his father, who is an ardent hunter.

Later on, this individual may grow to love or be indifferent to his father; or his father may die and be no more of a problem to him. His fear of dogs, however, may remain: not because, as some theorists would insist, they still remind him of his old death wishes against his father, but because he now hates himself so violently for *having* the original neurotic symptom—for behaving, to his mind, so stupidly and illogically in relation to dogs—that every time he thinks of dogs his self-hatred and fear of failure so severely upset him that he cannot reason clearly and cannot combat his illogical fear.

In terms of self-verbalization, this neurotic individual is first saying to himself: "I hate my father—and this is awful!" But he ends up by saying: "I have an irrational fear of dogs—and this is awful!" Even though both sets of self-verbalizations are neuroticizing, and his secondary neurosis may be as bad as or worse than his primary one, the two can hardly be said to be the same. Consequently, exploring and explaining to this individual—or helping him gain insight into—the origins of his primary neurosis will not necessarily help him to understand and overcome his perpetuating or secondary neurotic reactions.

If the hypotheses so far stated have some validity, the psychotherapist's main goals should be those of demonstrating to clients that their self-verbalizations have been and still are the prime source of their emotional disturbances. Clients must be shown that their internalized sentences are illogical and unrealistic at certain critical points and that they now have the ability to control their emotions by telling themselves more rational and less self-defeating sentences.

More precisely: the effective therapist should continually keep unmasking his client's past and, especially, his present illogical thinking or self-defeating verbalizations by (*a*) bringing them to his attention or consciousness; (*b*) showing the client how they are causing and maintaining his disturbance and unhappiness; (*c*) demonstrating exactly what the illogical links in his internalized sentences are; and (*d*) teaching him how to re-think and re-verbalize these (and other similar) sentences in a more logical, self-helping way. Moreover, before the end of the therapeutic relationship, the therapist should not only deal concretely with the client's specific illogical thinking, but should demonstrate to this client what, *in general,* are the main irrational ideas that human beings are prone to follow and what more rational philosophies of living may usually be substituted for them. Otherwise, the client who is released from one specific set of illogical notions may well wind up by falling victim to another set.

It is hypothesized, in other words, that human beings are the kind of animals who, when raised in any society similar to our own, tend to fall victim to several major fallacious ideas; to keep reindoctrinating themselves over and over again with these ideas in an unthinking, autosuggestive manner; and consequently to keep actualizing them in overt behavior. Most of these irrational ideas are, as the Freudians have very adequately pointed out, instilled by the individual's parents during his childhood, and are tenaciously clung to because of his attachment to these parents and because the ideas were ingrained, or imprinted, or conditioned before later and more rational modes of thinking were given a chance to gain a foothold. Most of them, however, as the Freudians have not always been careful to note, are also instilled by the individual's general culture, and particularly by the media of mass communication in this culture.

What are some of the major illogical ideas or philosophies which, when originally held and later perpetuated by men and women in our civilization, inevitably lead to self-defeat and neurosis? Limitations of space preclude our examining all these major ideas, including their more significant corollaries; therefore, only a few of them will be listed. The illogicality of some of these ideas will also, for the present, have to be taken somewhere on faith, since there again is no space to outline the many reasons *why* they are irrational. Anyway, here, where angels fear to tread, goes the psychological theoretician!

1. The idea that it is a dire necessity for an adult to be loved or approved by everyone for everything he does—instead of his concentrating on his own self-respect, on winning approval for necessary purposes (such as job advancement), and on loving rather than being loved.

2. The idea that certain acts are wrong, or wicked, or villainous, and that people who perform such acts should be severely punished—instead of the idea that certain acts are inappropriate or antisocial, and that people who perform such acts are invariably stupid, ignorant, or emotionally disturbed.

3. The idea that it is terrible, horrible, and catastrophic when things are not the way one would like them to be—instead of the idea that it is too bad when things are not the way one would like them to be, and one should certainly try to change or control conditions so that they become more satisfactory, but that if changing or controlling uncomfortable situations is impossible, one had better become resigned to their existence and stop telling oneself how awful they are.

4. The idea that much human unhappiness is externally caused and is forced on one by outside people and events—instead of the idea that virtually all human unhappiness is caused or sustained by the view one takes of things rather than the things themselves.

5. The idea that if something is or may be dangerous or fearsome one should be terribly concerned about it—instead of the idea that if something is or may be dangerous or fearsome one should frankly face it and try to render it non-dangerous and, when that is impossible, think of other things and stop telling oneself what a terrible situation one is or may be in.

6. The idea that it is easier to avoid than to face life difficulties and self-responsibilities —instead of the idea that the so-called easy way is invariably the much harder way in the long run and that the only way to solve difficult problems is to face them squarely.

7. The idea that one needs something other or stronger or greater than oneself on which to rely—instead of the idea that it is usually far better to stand on one's own feet and gain faith in oneself and one's ability to meet difficult circumstances of living.

8. The idea that one should be thoroughly

competent, adequate, intelligent, and achieving in all possible respects—instead of the idea that one should *do* rather than always try to do *well* and that one should accept oneself as a quite imperfect creature, who has general human limitations and specific fallibilities.

9. The idea that because something once strongly affected one's life, it should indefinitely affect it—instead of the idea that one should learn from one's past experiences but not be overly-attached to or prejudiced by them.

10. The idea that it is vitally important to our existence what other people do, and that we should make great efforts to change them in the direction we would like them to be—instead of the idea that other people's deficiencies are largely *their* problems and that putting pressure on them to change is usually least likely to help them do so.

11. The idea that human happiness can be achieved by inertia and inaction—instead of the idea that humans tend to be happiest when they are actively and vitally absorbed in creative pursuits, or when they are devoting themselves to people or projects outside themselves.

12. The idea that one has virtually no control over one's emotions and that one cannot help feeling certain things—instead of the idea that one has enormous control over one's emotions if one chooses to work at controlling them and to practice saying the right kinds of sentences to onself.

It is the central theme of this paper that it is the foregoing kinds of illogical ideas, and many corollaries which we have no space to delineate, which are the basic causes of most emotional disturbances or neuroses. For once one believes the kind of nonsense included in these notions, one will inevitably tend to become inhibited, hostile, defensive, guilty, anxious, ineffective, inert, uncontrolled, or unhappy. If, on the other hand, one could become thoroughly released from all these fundamental kinds of illogical thinking, it would be exceptionally difficult for one to become too emotionally upset, or at least to sustain one's disturbance for very long.

Does this mean that all the other so-called basic causes of neurosis, such as the Oedipus complex or severe maternal rejection in childhood, are invalid, and that the Freudian and other psychodynamic thinkers of the last 60 years have been barking up the wrong tree? Not at all. It only means, if the main hypotheses of this paper are correct, that these psychodynamic thinkers have been emphasizing secondary causes or results of emotional disturbances rather than truly prime causes.

Let us take, for example, an individual who acquires, when he is young, a full-blown Oedipus complex: that is to say, he lusts after his mother, hates his father, is guilty about his sex desires for his mother, and is afraid that his father is going to castrate him. This person, when he is a child, will presumably be disturbed. But, if he is raised so that he acquires none of the basic illogical ideas we have been discussing, it will be virtually impossible for him to *remain* disturbed.

For, as an adult, this individual will not be too concerned if his parents or others do not approve of his actions, since he will be more interested in his *own* self-respect than in *their* approval. He will not believe that his lust for his mother is wicked or villainous, but will accept it as a normal part of being a limited human whose sex desires may easily be indiscriminate. He will realize that the actual danger of his father castrating him is exceptionally slight. He will not feel that because he was once afraid of his Oedipal feelings he should forever remain so. If he still feels it would be improper for him to have sex relations with his mother, instead of castigating himself for even thinking of having such relations he will merely resolve not to carry his desires into practice and will stick determinedly to his resolve. If, by any chance, he weakens and actually has incestuous relations, he will again refuse to castigate himself mercilessly for being weak but will keep showing himself how self-defeating his behavior is and will actively work and practice at changing it.

Under these circumstances, if this individual has a truly logical and rational approach to life in general, and to the problem of Oedipal feelings, in particular, how can he possibly *remain* disturbed about his Oedipal attachment?

Take, by way of further illustration, the case of an individual who, as a child, is continually criticized by his parents, who consequently feels himself loathesome and inadequate, who refuses to take chances at failing at difficult tasks, and who therefore comes to hate himself more. Such a person will be, of course, seriously neurotic. But how would it be possible for him to *sustain* his neurosis if he began to think in a truly logical manner about himself and his behavior?

For, if this individual does use a consistent rational approach to his own behavior, he will stop caring particularly what others think of him and will start primarily caring what he thinks of himself. Consequently, he will stop avoiding difficult tasks and, instead of punishing himself for being incompetent when he makes a mistake, will say to himself something like: "Now this is not the right way to do things; let me stop and figure out a better way." Or: "There's no doubt that I made a mistake this time; now let me see how I can benefit from making it."

This individual, furthermore, will if he is thinking straight, not blame his defeats on external events, but will realize that he himself is causing them by his illogical or impractical behavior. He will not believe that it is easier to avoid facing difficult things, but will realize that the so-called easy way is always, actually, the harder and more idiotic one. He will not think that he needs something greater or stronger than himself to help him, but will independently buckle down to difficult tasks himself. He will not feel that because he once defeated himself by avoiding doing things the hard way that he must always do so.

How, with this kind of logical thinking, could an originally disturbed person possibly maintain and continually revivify his neurosis? He just couldn't. Similarly, the spoiled brat, the worrywart, the ego-maniac, the autistic stay-at-home —all of these disturbed individuals would have the devil of a time indefinitely prolonging their neuroses if they did not continue to believe utter nonsense: namely, the kinds of basic irrational postulates previously listed.

Neurosis, then, usually seems to originate in and be perpetuated by some fundamentally unsound, irrational ideas. The individual comes to believe in some unrealistic, impossible, often perfectionistic goals—especially the goals that he

should always be approved by everyone, should do everything perfectly well, and should never be frustrated in any of his desires—and then, in spite of considerable contradictory evidence, refuses to give up his original illogical beliefs.

Some of the neurotic's philosophies, such as the idea that he should be loved and approved by everyone, are not entirely inappropriate to his childhood state; but all of them are quite inappropriate to average adulthood. Most of his irrational ideas are specifically taught him by his parents and his culture; and most of them also seem to be held by the great majority of adults in our society—who theoretically should have been but actually never were weaned from them as they chronologically matured. It must consequently be admitted that the neurotic individual we are considering is often statistically normal; or that ours is a generally neuroticizing culture, in which most people are more or less emotionally disturbed because they are raised to believe, and then to internalize and to keep reinfecting themselves with, arrant nonsense which must inevitably lead them to become ineffective, self-defeating, and unhappy. Nonetheless: it is not absolutely *necessary* that human beings believe the irrational notions which, in point of fact, most of them seem to believe today; and the task of psychotherapy is to get them to disbelieve their illogical ideas, to change their self-sabotaging attitudes.

This, precisely, is the task which the rational psychotherapist sets himself. Like other therapists, he frequently resorts to the usual techniques of therapy which the present author has outlined elsewhere (2, 3), including the techniques of relationship, expressive-emotive, supportive, and insight-interpretive therapy. But he views these techniques, as they are commonly employed, as kinds of preliminary strategies whose main functions are to gain rapport with the client, to let him express himself fully, to show him that he is a worthwhile human being who has the ability to change, and to demonstrate how he originally became disturbed.

The rational therapist, in other words, believes that most of the usual therapeutic techniques wittingly or unwittingly show the client *that* he is illogical and how he *originally* became so. They often fail to show him, however, how he is presently *maintaining* his illogical thinking, and precisely what he must do to change it by building general rational philosophies of living and by applying these to practical problems of everyday life. Where most therapists directly or indirectly show the client that he is behaving illogically, the rational therapist goes beyond this point to make a forthright, unequivocal *attack* on the client's general and specific irrational ideas and to try to *induce* him to adopt more rational ones in their place.

Rational psychotherapy makes a concerted attack on the disturbed individual's irrational positions in two main ways: (*a*) the therapist serves as a frank counter-propagandist who directly contradicts and denies the self-defeating propaganda and superstitions which the client has originally learned and which he is now self-propagandistically perpetuating. (*b*) The therapist encourages, persuades, cajoles, and at times commands the client to partake of some kind of activity which itself will act as a forceful counter-propagandist agency against the nonsense he believes. Both these main therapeutic activities are consciously performed with one main goal in mind: namely, that of finally getting the client to internalize a rational philosophy of living just as he originally learned and internalized the illogical propaganda and superstitions of his parents and his culture.

The rational therapist, then, assumes that the client somehow imbibed illogical ideas or irrational modes of thinking and that, without so doing, he could hardly be as disturbed as he is. It is the therapist's function not merely to show the client that he has these ideas or thinking processes but to persuade him to change and substitute for them more rational ideas and thought processes. If, because the client is exceptionally disturbed when he first comes to therapy, he must first be approached in a rather cautious, supportive, permissive, and warm manner, and must sometimes be allowed to ventilate his feeling in free association, abreaction, role playing, and other expressive techniques, that may be all to the good. But the therapist does not delude himself that these relationship-building and expressive-emotive techniques in most instances really get to the core of the client's illogical thinking and induce him to think in a more rational manner.

Occasionally, this is true: since the client may come to see, through relationship and emotive-expressive methods, that he *is* acting illogically, and he may therefore resolve to change and actually do so. More often than not, however, his illogical thinking will be so ingrained from constant self-repetitions, and will be so inculcated in motor pathways (or habit patterns) by the time he comes for therapy, that simply showing him, even by direct interpretation, *that* he is illogical will not greatly help. He will often say to the therapist: "All right, now I understand that I have castration fears and that they are illogical. But I *still* feel afraid of my father."

The therapist, therefore, must keep pounding away, time and again, at the illogical ideas which underlie the client's fears. He must show the client that he is afraid, really, not of his father, but of being blamed, of being disapproved, of being unloved, of being imperfect, of being a failure. And such fears are thoroughly irrational because (*a*) being disapproved is not half so terrible as one *thinks* it is; because (*b*) no one can be thoroughly blameless or perfect; because (*c*) people who worry about being blamed or disapproved essentially are putting themselves at the mercy of the opinion of *others*, over whom they have no real control; because (*d*) being blamed or disapproved has nothing essentially to do with one's *own* opinion of oneself; etc.

If the therapist, moreover, merely tackles the individual's castration fears, and shows how ridiculous *they* are, what is to prevent this individual's showing up, a year or two later, with some *other* illogical fear—such as the fear that he is sexually impotent? But if the therapist tackles the client's *basic* irrational thinking, which underlies *all* kinds of fear he may have, it is going to be most difficult for this client to turn up with a new neurotic symptom some months or years hence. For once an individual truly surrenders ideas of perfectionism, of the horror of failing at something, of the dire need to be approved by others, of the opinion that the world owes him a living, and so on, what else is there for him to be fearful of or disturbed about?

To give some idea of precisely how the rational therapist works, a case summary will now be presented. A client came in one day and said he was depressed but did not know why. A little questioning showed that he had been putting off the inventory-keeping he was required to do as part of his job as an apprentice glass-staining artist. The therapist immediately began showing him that his depression was related to his resenting having to keep inventory and that this resentment was illogical for several reasons:

(*a*) The client very much wanted to learn the art of glass-staining and could only learn it by having the kind of job he had. His sole logical choice, therefore, was between graciously accepting this job, in spite of the inventory-keeping, or giving up trying to be a glass-stainer. By resenting the clerical work and avoiding it, he was choosing neither of these two logical alternatives, and was only getting himself into difficulty.

(*b*) By blaming the inventory-keeping, and his boss for making him perform it, the client was being irrational since, assuming that the boss was wrong about making him do this clerical work, the boss would have to be wrong out of some combination of stupidity, ignorance, or emotional disturbance; and it is silly and pointless blaming people for being stupid, ignorant, or disturbed. Besides, maybe the boss was quite right, from his own standpoint, about making the client keep the inventory.

(*c*) Whether the boss was right or wrong, resenting him for his stand was hardly going to make him change it; and the resentment felt by the client was hardly going to do him, the client, any good or make him feel better. The saner attitude for him to take, then, was that it was too bad that inventory-keeping was part of his job, but that's the way it was, and there was no point in resenting the way things were when they could not, for the moment, be changed.

(*d*) Assuming that the inventory-keeping was irksome, there was no sense in making it still *more* annoying by the client's continually telling himself how awful it was. Nor was there any point in shirking this clerical work, since he

eventually would have to do it anyway and he might as well get this unpleasant task out of the way quickly. Even more important: by shirking a task that he knew that, eventually, he just had to do, he would lose respect for himself and his loss of self-respect would be far worse than the slight, rather childish satisfaction he might receive from trying to sabotage his boss's desires.

While showing this client how illogical was his thinking and consequent behavior, the therapist specifically made him aware that he must be telling himself sentences like these: "My boss makes me do inventory-keeping. I do not like this. . . . There is no reason why I have to do it. . . . He is therefore a blackguard for making me do it. . . . So I'll fool him and avoid doing it. . . . And then I'll be happier." But these sentences were so palpably foolish that the client could not really believe them, and began to finish them off with sentences like: "I'm not really fooling my boss, because he sees what I'm doing. . . . So I'm not solving my problem this way. . . . So I really should stop this nonsense and get the inventory-keeping done. . . . But I'll be damned if I'll do it for him!" . . . . However, if I don't do it, I'll be fired. . . . But I still don't want to do it for him! . . . . I guess I've got to, though. . . . Oh, why must I always be persecuted like this? . . . And must I keep getting myself into such a mess? . . . I guess I'm just no good. . . . And people are against me. . . . Oh, what's the use?"

Whereupon, employing these illogical kinds of sentences, the client was becoming depressed, avoiding doing the inventory-keeping, and then becoming more resentful and depressed. Instead, the therapist pointed out, he could tell himself quite different sentences, on this order: "Keeping inventory is a bore. . . . But it is presently an essential part of my job. . . . And I also may learn something useful by it. . . . Therefore, I had better go about this task as best I may and thereby get what *I* want out of this job."

The therapist also emphasized that whenever the client found himself intensely angry, guilty, or depressed, there was little doubt that he was then thinking illogically, and that he should immediately question himself as to what was the irrational element in his thinking, and set about replacing it with a more logical element or chain of sentences.

The therapist then used the client's current dilemma—that of avoiding inventory-keeping—as an illustration of his general neurosis, which in his case largely took the form of severe alcoholic tendencies. He was shown that his alcoholic trends, too, were a resultant of his trying to do things the easy way, and of poor thinking preluding his avoidance of self-responsibilities. He was impressed with the fact that, as long as he kept thinking illogically about relatvely small things, such as the inventory-keeping, he would also tend to think equally illogically about more important aspects, such as the alcoholism.

Several previous incidents of illogical thinking leading to emotional upheaval in the client's life were then reviewed, and some general principles of irrational thought discussed. Thus, the general principle of blamelessness was raised and the client was shown precisely why it is illogical to blame anyone for anything. The general principle of inevitability was brought up and he was shown that when a frustrating or unpleasant event is inevitable, it is only logical to accept it uncomplainingly instead of dwelling on its unpleasant aspects. The general principle of self-respect was discussed, with the therapist demonstrating that liking oneself is far more important than resentfully trying to harm others.

In this matter, by attempting to show or teach the client some of the general rules of logical living, the therapist tried to go beyond his immediate problem and to help provide him with a generalized mode of thinking or problem solving that would enable him to deal effectively with almost any future similar situation that might arise.

The rational therapist, then, is a frank propagandist who believes wholeheartedly in a most rigorous application of the rules of logic, of straight thinking, and of scientific method to everyday life, and who ruthlessly uncovers every vestige of irrational thinking in the client's experience and energetically urges him into more rational channels. In so doing, the rational therapist does not ignore or eradicate the client's emotions; on the contrary, he considers them most seriously, and helps change them, when they are disordered and self-defeating, through the same means by which they commonly arise in the first place—that is, by thinking and acting. Through exerting consistent interpretive and philosophic pressure on the client to change his thinking or his self-verbalizations and to change his experiences or his actions, the rational therapist gives a specific impetus to the client's movement toward mental health without which it is not impossible, but quite unlikely, that he will move very far.

Can therapy be effectively done, then, with *all* clients mainly through logical analysis and reconstruction? Alas, no. For one thing, many clients are not bright enough to follow a rigorously rational analysis. For another thing, some individuals are so emotionally aberrated by the time they come for help that they are, at least temporarily, in no position to comprehend and follow logical procedures. Still other clients are too old and inflexible; too young and impressionable; too philosophically prejudiced against logic and reason; too organically or biophysically deficient; or too something else to accept, at least at the start of therapy, rational analysis.

In consequence, the therapist who *only* employs logical reconstruction in his therapeutic armamentarium is not likely to get too far with many of those who seek his help. It is vitally important, therefore, that any therapist who has a basically rational approach to the problem of helping his clients overcome their neuroses also be quite eclectic in his use of supplementary, less direct, and somewhat less rational techniques.

Admitting, then, that rational psychotherapy is not effective with all types of clients, and that it is most helpful when used in conjunction with, or subsequent to, other widely employed therapeutic techniques, I would like to conclude with two challenging hypotheses: (a) that psychotherapy which includes a high dosage of rational analysis and reconstruction, as briefly outlined in this paper, will prove to be more effective with more types of clients than any of the non-rational or semi-rational therapies now being widely employed; and (b) that a considerable amount of—or, at least, proportion of—rational psychotherapy will prove to be virtually the only type of treatment that helps to undermine the basic neuroses (as distinguished from the superficial neurotic symptoms) of many clients, and particularly of many with whom other types of therapy have always been shown to be ineffective.

REFERENCES

1. COBB, S. *Emotions and clinical medicine.* New York: Norton, 1950.
2. ELLIS, A. New approaches to psychotherapy techniques. *Journal of Clinical Psychology, Monograph Supplement*, No. 11. Brandon, Vermont: *Journal of Clinical Psychology*, 1955.
3. ELLIS, A. Psychotherapy techniques for use with psychotics. *American Journal of Psychotherapy*, 1955, 9, 452–476.
4. ELLIS, A. An operational reformation of some of the basic principles of psychoanalysis. *Psychoanalytic Review*, 1956, 43, 163–180.
5. FENICHEL, O. *The psychoanalytic theory of neurosis.* New York: Norton, 1945.
6. FREUD, S. *Basic Writings.* New York: Modern Library, 1938.
7. FREUD, S. *Collected Papers.* London: Hogarth Press, 1924–1950.

66.

GION CONDRAU AND MEDARD BOSS

DASEINSANALYSIS

The assumption of an unconscious became necessary for psychoanalytical theory so that within it hidden forces and energies could be subordinated to psychic phenomena and "explained" on the basis of such phenomena. As opposed to this, Daseinsanalysis is phenomenologically oriented; it is not concerned with "explaining," with a deduction of Something from something Else, but with laying clear, revealing. Daseinsanalysis does not seek to prove anything at all, but "merely" tries to show and understand the immediately perceptible phenomenon in its full meaning-content. The natural scientific deductive demonstration is a progression from one to the other, in a continuous causal sequence. From the standpoint of interpretative understanding, what is involved is unmediated (immediate) grasping of the whole that is to be understood. Thus it can be said that where we are after the understanding of a "meaning," the classical natural scientific and mathematical procedures of

deduction and induction are henceforth out of the 'question. While psychoanalysis inquires about the play of forces lying at the basis of the neurosis, and the causes to be assumed behind its appearances, Daseinsanalysis searches for the meaning or meaning-content of the pathological behaviour.

The choice of the illness or the form of the neurosis is, then, in short, dependent on the intensity with which specific world-relationships are admitted or warded off. The case is quite different concerning the choice of organ. Here the decisive role is not played by the degree of knowing admission or rejection of conflict-fraught phenomena, but by the given special meaning-content of the affected organ. The symbolic thinking prevalent in the doctrine of psychoanalysis is responsible for the introduction of the concept of the organ idiom into medicine, taking for granted that this idiom, this code, is not immediately understandable, but has to be deciphered first, like the symbolic language of dreams. The stomach ulcer was interpreted as "hunger for a sense of security"; asthma signified symbolically anxiety in the face of loss of sense of security and defiance; the

From Gion Condrau and Medard Boss, Existential analysis. In John G. Howells (Ed.) *Modern perspectives in world psychiatry.* Edinburgh & London: Oliver & Boyd, 1968. Pp. 488–518. This selection from pp. 505–518. Reprinted by permission.

asthma attack became an outcry against the mother or a cry for her. However, the exact observation and elucidation of the psychosomatic illnesses confirmed neither a symbolic nor a conflictual organ specificity. Rather, the choice of organ is determined from the given special type of disturbed vital relation. We can acquire a better understanding of the patient suffering from heart or stomach trouble only if we know how the heart or the stomach figure physically in the milieu of a given life.

To be sure, a physical organ does not accompany, for instance, every "psychic" quality, every mood, vicariously jumping in and announcing in its organic idiom, as it were, the "situs" or the essential nature of the illness. Rather, both the heart and the sex organs can express the bodily aspect of love. The heart, however, is also the seat of hate, sorrow, anxiety, courage or timidity. In a state of joyful expectancy it beats faster, in a state of fright it almost stops. In still another way the stomach is related to the situation in which food is taken in and digested, which for the man with an ulcer means that he is always trying to cope with more than is in keeping with his existential possibilities. Many other examples could be given; such a medical-psychological understanding of human illness is applicable to the entire field of medicine.

While the existence (*Existieren*) of neurotics and psychosomatic patients is to a great extent accessible to a human understanding and does not appear entirely alien even to the layman, the relationship to the world of mentally disturbed persons, especially that of schizophrenics, is often judged to be empathically inaccessible and deranged, infantile or retrograde. Scientific pathology is lacking of an understanding of psychoses and is content to classify them according to symptoms and types of development, to study their causes and laws. Freudian theory is based on the hypothesis that a mental illness is a consequence of a predominance of the "id," by which the "ego" would be compelled to retreat "from a portion of reality." A psychosis is said to deny reality and to seek to take its place. While a neurosis represents the conflict between the ego and the id, a psychosis signifies the analogous outcome of such a disturbance in the relations between ego and external world.

By contrast, Daseinsanalysis stresses the point that failure is unavoidable in any attempt to understand the optical and auditory hallucinations of the schizophrenic as mere sensory delusions without any reality-value or even as results of metabolic changes, and indeed all psychological attempts at explanation are bound to fail. The patients themselves are convinced that the reality of their experiences is quite different in nature. Being-human in the true sense of the word includes the appropriation of all the potentialities of behaviour, and opening-up to what confronts one, which is given to man as such and constitutes his essence. Frequently, the radically rejected potentialities of relation and development that have not yet been appropriated, along with the human and environmental phenomena appearing in their light, as well as the corresponding, and merely instilled, defensive behaviour, can only be perceived from an uncanny, alien "realm of spirits," in the shape of precisely those phenomena which psychiatry is accustomed to call "hallucinations." Everything that the patients refuse to face stares at them now as "hallucinatory," monstrous, visages and pries into their most hidden selves (3). The potentialities of development of the sensuous-erotic life, for instance, can only be lived out by the patients in the shape of psychotic "sensory delusions," which always indicates an especially intensive, indeed complete "self-closure" and "not-letting-oneself-be-used" when confronted by these phenomena (4).

Both the exponents of a "somatogenesis" and the interpreters of "psychogenesis" are guilty of a decisive self-misunderstanding when they seek to understand the nature of schizophrenia, one group making organic findings into a "foundation" of psychiatry and the other making its psychodynamic considerations into a "depth" psychology. Wanting to regard any sort of somatic processes as the basis of any kind of perceiving-understanding human mode of behaviour in the only really fundamental sense—that one sees the latter as caused, or derived from the former, or the former as being manifested in the latter—is to go astray in the abyss of a kind of intellectual magic and to assume an inconceivable transformation of material things into meaning-perceiving intellectual acts.

But, again, the psychogenetic, psychodynamic, depth-psychological approaches can not penetrate into the real depths of phenomena, because they themselves stop at the shallow level of vague, never ascertainable assumptions of psychic structures and of forces lying behind the observed phenomena (5). On the other hand, in the schizophrenic break-down man is usually so overwhelmed and swamped by alien-seeming external factors that, wholly sacrificed to the excess of new contents of awareness, he is caught and totally subjugated by them. Such a happening leads to a break-down and tearing-open of a self-being that had always been dependent, precarious, and hardly viable. Such a complete subjection of the existence (Dasein) to something perceived amounts, however, to a proximity to the latter, a proximity which out of itself condenses the perceived meaning-content into the appearance of a sensorily present phenomenon. For this reason, it is observed that schizophrenic patients become increasingly helpless when they are confronted by what they perceive and this reveals itself to them in ever more corporeal shape and becomes a direct physical threat. At first such a thing can occur as a compulsive having-to-think of something. Soon, however, it emerges in the shape of delusions and hallucinations. The transition from a relatively reserved, intellectual, representational, recalling, imagining visualization of something into its hallucinatory, oppressive, palpable, sensuous-perceptible being-present, corresponds to the given stage of break-down of an existence in the face of an emergent meaning-content. The excessively great, but also unfree proximity of a hallucinatory visibility and audibility makes clearly understandable the immediate, unquestionable knowledge of the full meaning of what is seen and heard. A corresponding, if only transitory, immediate certainty can also be observed in the intensive "emotionalism" of normal people.

An insight into this profound complexity of a "schizophrenic symptom" prevents us at the same time, however, from cherishing the deceptive hope of ever being able to explain it "genetically," and to think of it as caused by organic cerebral processes, somatic disturbances or by psychic, environmental impressions. At best, we shall be able to take the individual somatic and psychic findings, ascertained before or during schizophrenic hallucinations, as the possible means which attune a person to this or that world-situation, that is always a co-constituent of his existence (Dasein), and hold on to it there, in certain circumstances, in a way that is pathologically restrictive or liberating.

THE IMPACT OF EXISTENTIAL ANALYSIS ON PSYCHOTHERAPY

There is no doubt that daseinsanalytical interpretation is not only compelling us to undertake theoretical modifications of our theory of illness, but is also of decisive significance for psychotherapeutic practice. At first, it seemed as if Daseinsanalysis differed from psychoanalysis only, or mainly, on the theoretical plane; however, it has become increasingly clear that theory and practice can never be wholly separated. Thus, for practical psychotherapy, it is not a matter of indifference what anthropological theory lies at the basis of a treatment.

An example may be adduced in support of what has been said above: a young bookkeeper suffered from an intense case of writer's cramp, which threatened his whole future career. Every time he attempted to write his right hand became painfully cramped. His writing became so illegible that after a short time the patient was obliged to give up this work. The writing inhibition of this patient made its first appearance while he was in school, when he was seeking in secret to copy a test. During puberty, and again a few years later, the symptom became more obvious in connection with an incipient acquaintance with a girl.

Psychoanalysis, according to Freud, sees in writer's cramp, as in every sort of inhibition, a functional restriction of the ego, an excessive eroticization of the organs used, in this case, for the function of writing. He writes: "We have, quite generally speaking, arrived at the insight that the ego function of an organ is damaged when its sexual significance increases. It then behaves, if we may venture a rather scurrilous comparison, like a cook who does not care to work at the stove any longer because the master of the house has become her lover.

If writing, which consists in letting fluid run out of a tube on to a piece of white paper, has assumed the symbolic significance of coitus . . . ," [it] becomes inhibited, "because it is as if one would carry out the prohibited sexual act. The ego renounces these functions incumbent on it in order not to be obliged to proceed to yet another repression, in order to evade a conflict with the id."

For our patient this, then, would mean that the right hand, required for writing, abdicated its ego function owing to its charging with sexual libido. At this juncture we merely point out the dubiousness of an interpretation of writing as a symbol of sexual union. Interpretations of symbols are a part of the psychoanalytical basic premise, according to which our main attention is to be devoted not to the phenomenon, but to drives "assumed" to be behind phenomena. Perhaps, however, one is required to ascribe to a thing an additional symbolic content only where one has already essentially restricted its full meaningful and referential relations. In the case of our patient, we learn immediately that when he writes he gets a cramp in the hand. At first we see no sign of any sexual charging; we see nothing of a renouncing ego and nothing of a symbol. If we want to get at the phenomenon of writer's cramp, we have to try to understand the meaningful content of this symptom. In this quest we are assisted by the three indications constituting his "illness" that are offered by the patient: the writing, the hand, the cramp.

Accordingly we shall first have to concern ourselves with the meaning-content of writing, if we want to grasp the meaning of writer's cramp. Writing signifies informing, making known, getting in touch. Informing means that I am sharing something with another person. This "something" is a part of me, I share myself with another, or I share myself with another in respect of a matter. Information means accordingly being-open primordially for another, for a fellow human being. What is written is, in addition, a firmly laid down announcement of something. In writing man reveals himself in a definitive, largely irreversible fashion. He sets forth his position; he commits himself. While the spoken word can be forgotten or taken back, what is written is binding. It can no longer be denied, reinterpreted, altered. "Let me have that in writing" is what people demand of one another, whenever they want to nail down a statement, and make it stick. The significance of writing as information, announcement, has even been experimentally confirmed, by demonstrating that writing movements of those suffering from writer's cramp have been executed without effort when the patients were under the impression the writing instrument was not making any mark (6).

The fact that the symptom of cramp manifested itself precisely in the *hand* is explained, no doubt, by the fact that writing is a function of the hand. But the meaning-content of the hand is not exhausted in the function of merely writing. The hand is also used for all sorts of other actions—it grasps, it seizes, with it we hold on to things, it furnishes us with support, it is indispensable for life. The hand can strike out in hate, it can stroke tenderly in a mood of love. We speak of the strong hand of a father and the tender hand of a mother, of the generous hand of the benefactor, of the corrective hand of the educator. In writer's cramp the hand is inhibited, its free capacity to play is restricted, hampered. In this disturbance there is immediately revealed, however, the constriction of the world-openness of the patient, that world-openness of which the hand is part. This constriction of the world-openness is experienced as *cramp*. When we said every world-relation was always attuned, that means here: the world-relation of interpersonal being-open is attuned in the sense of cramp. The cramp is the opposite of freedom. Cramp means tension, compulsion, unfreedom. The cramped person surrounds himself with an armour, he is not emotionally open to things, but sealed, encapsulated. Our patient spoke very significantly of a "confected shape" into which he had been squeezed.

The human shape of the patient was so rigidified that he was able to live his life only in a very deficient form of being-together, in the solitude of one exiled and isolated, like the existence (Dasein) of a sado-masochistic patient suffering from a cramped defensive state of mind described by Boss (1). Like this patient our cramped writer was "squeezed into a purely personal egoistic standpoint and constrained to merely utilitarian actions, cut off both from his environment and from the inner world of his feelings, and from the ground of his existence (Dasein)." (1) He was separated from the world of his own feelings, in order to allow himself to be determined by the world of things, professional advancement, money (a book-keeper!) Characteristic of him was anxiety in the face of loving attitudes, the onset of feeling into his intellectualistic world. Feelings, human sensitivity and capacity to love were present, to be sure, somewhere in the patient, but immured within him.

This cramped state of our patient included a catastrophic relation to the *body*. Everything concerning the creatureliness of the patient had, from childhood been outlawed as sinful by a puritanical upbringing that was hostile to the instinctual life. A brutal, alcoholic father and a soft, weak mother, who gave him no feeling of security, had seen to it that the patient never got to know about the realm of interpersonal love and of the body.

The patient went through an analysis lasting two and a half years. Externally this analysis did not differ essentially from a classical psychoanalysis, in that the patient—as in psychoanalysis—was asked to lie down on a couch and to tell everything that came into his mind at that moment. At first the therapist confined himself to listening to him in that state of free-hovering attentiveness recommended by Freud and to drawing his attention to inner resistances wherever these appeared. He came regularly to his sessions, three times a week, with neither the number of sessions nor the frequency representing a daseinsanalytical deviation from the procedure followed in psychoanalysis. In both cases rules should not be rigid but adapted to circumstances and to individual patients.

It is occasionally asserted that daseinsanalytical psychotherapy is not technically different from Freudian psychoanalysis. For example, Rollo May (8) writes that Medard Boss is "a thorough-going Freudian in his technique, using couch, free association, and the other methods of classical psychoanalysis." This is correct only to the extent that "technique" is understood

solely as the external procedure of analysis. However, in so far as one also counts as part of the method the behaviour of the analyst, the technique of dream interpretation, permitting and denying, the processing of the material, Daseinsanalysis can surely no longer be put on the same footing with psychoanalysis. It is equally wrong to state that "therapists with the existential viewpoint can and do belong to different schools of practice." To be sure, Daseinsanalysis does not claim to be a school of its own; it seeks to induce the leading schools of therapy to come to terms with their own principles. In point of fact, however, all psychotherapeutical approaches which do so, and really go into the essential nature of man and his illness, are obliged not only to drop their theoretical ballast, but in most cases to alter their practice in accordance with the new understanding.

Space does not allow to present a complete survey of the technique of daseinsanalytical psychotherapy. Thus, only two deviations from Freudian psychoanalysis will be mentioned: namely, the treatment of "acting out" and the interpretation of dreams.

In the treatment Daseinsanalysis can do more than interpret the acting out of the patients as behaviour indicating resistance, as psychoanalytical theory does. Freud still thought that in the analysis the patients would try "to act something, to repeat in life what they ought only to remember, to reproduce as psychic material and to retain on the psychic plane." But, Daseinsanalysis sees the "acting out" of the patient not simply as resistance to memories, but understands in it the same immediate and genuine appearance of newly emerging possibilities of relation that is found in intellectual thought. What is involved here is not necessarily a wanting to "repress" memories. Rather, in many cases, the analysand in his acting out dares to take his first step towards his own unfolding. In other words: he catches up with a possibility of behaviour that was previously not permitted and never got to be lived out. The result is that the admitting, granting of the acting out, can be therapeutically most beneficial.

The analytical self-opening of a neurotically

constricted patient becomes possible only when the doctor permits the patient to enter into those modes of behaviour in which the latter actually finds himself. These modes of behaviour, in the case of patients who are seriously ill, are not the conceptual, intellectual-linguistic possibilities of relating possessed by normal adults. For this reason, as in the relationship between the infant and his mother, an authentic interpersonal relation corresponding truly to the natural constitution of the patient can often emerge only in a wordless gesture language, perhaps at times exclusively in a permissive silence and simple presence-there (Dasein). In the psychotherapeutic treatment of small children it is not possible to dispense with allowing the patient to act-out, and the same applies to daseinsanalytical treatment, seeing that the neurotic by his nature has remained, to a great extent, at the developmental stage of the infant. For the same reason Daseinsanalysis treats with causal-genetic explanations and deductions following from the psychoanalytical "Why?", in order to replace this question with the provocative question "Really why not?" The "Why" question demands too much of the analysand, while with the permissive "Why not" question it is made possible, often for the first time, for the patient to rid himself in the analysis of at least certain inhibitions imposed on him by the external world. Of course we take for granted the fact that such a permissive approach presupposes in the analyst himself a high degree of maturity and sense of responsibility, and obliges him never to slip himself into the unfreedom of childish or compulsively egoistic behaviour.

Daseinsanalysis is distinguished from *Freudian* conceptions in the interpretation of *dreams* just as clearly as in the handling of the transference and the acting-out. Daseinsanalysis speaks of "interpretation" ("*Auslegung*") of dreams and by that means "interpreting" in the sense of "grasping the meaning of the immediately emerged dream phenomena." When psychoanalysis speaks of dream interpretation, it means an "explanation," a reduction to something else of hidden meaning supposed to be behind what is presented. Such "explanation" presupposes that the "meaning" of the dream does not reveal itself as such, but remains at first veiled, and

has to be deciphered like a secret script. *Freud,* however, supplies no justification for such a procedure. The whole assumption of the so-called psychoanalytical dream-distortion serves only the purpose of making dreams correspond to a pre-conceived theory. But, existential analysis maintains that dreams are not to be regarded as some sort of objects detached from a person, nor can they be compared with other objects fashioned by a person. Rather, a human being, whether dreaming or waking, always remains in some sort of percipient state regarding the things and fellow human beings confronting him. For this reason, the daseinsanalytical-phenomenological interpretation of dreams speaks neither of "latent dream ideas," nor of a "dream censorship," nor does it speak of symbols or dream figments. Also, it recognizes no justification for distinguishing dream interpretations on an "object relation" from those on a "subject relation," nor does it believe in the theory of the dream as a wish fulfilment. If we judge our dreams not from an external, alien standpoint, but we allow the dream phenomena to be simply in their immediate givenness, it is obvious that what we dream is perceived neither as images nor as symbols. We experience what confronts us in dreaming as real entities: a thing as a real thing, an animal as a real animal, a human being as a real human being, a ghost as a real ghost. In our dreams we are in a world just as authentic and palpable as that of our waking life, and in both worlds we live out our existence (Dasein) in our relations and in our behaviour towards the things and fellow human beings confronting us (2).

THE SIGNIFICANCE OF EXISTENTIALISM AND EXISTENTIAL ANALYSIS FOR PSYCHIATRY

Insights into the nature of human existence can become a major foundation of psychiatry in its efforts to liberate patients from the bonds of their psychotic, neurotic and psychosomatic symptoms. We even maintain that without such knowledge no psychotherapist will succeed at all.

Another question affecting psychotherapeutic practice in detail is in what way we can induce our patients to share in the insight into their human nature, which would allow them to overcome anxiety and oppressive guilt. To be sure, we shall never get anywhere with an intellectual appeal to reason and understanding, or with invocations of the modern slogan word "existence." That would mean a step backward to the psychotherapy of Freud's time. After all, it is not our patients' heads and intellects that are sealed up and cut off by anxiety, but rather their hearts. Therefore, all words, even the cleverest, remain for them mere sound and fury signifying nothing.

As psychotherapists we have to abstain from influencing our patients by maxims and dogmas. Our function is a modest one, the removing here and there of a little stone, of an obstacle. The highest aim of psychotherapy is and remains to enable our patients to a being-able-to-love-and-trust, which can overcome all oppressive anxiety and guilt, as mere misunderstandings cleared away. Such trust can and may be regarded as the most mature kind of human love. However, our mentally and emotionally disturbed patients can get to this point only by means of a human maturing process. Normally, this would happen if the corporeal concrete experience of a sufficient never-failing maternal love were present. Our patients would not become ill if they had not lacked this. But this harmful missing out never depends solely on mothers, but just as much on the widely varying needs for love in the children. In psychotherapy the rule is to allow the patient to make up for the loss of the indispensable maternal love that was adapted to the nature of the child. The psychoanalytical situation is the arena of selfless authentic love, and from here the patient can gradually emerge out of childish reserve into ever more mature possibilities of love, and this can occur spontaneously, in so far as the patient is furnished by nature with the corresponding potentialities of development. For this purpose the psychotherapist is bound to credit the spiritual or religious experiences of his patients that come up in the treatments with the same primordial quality, authenticity and reality, as the phenomena of the so-called instinctual sphere. He must be on his guard against demoting these things, for the sake of

a prejudice of the secondary psychoanalytical theory, to the status of merely derived products of sublimation of libido.

But not only in theory and practice can one distinguish between Daseinsanalysis and psychoanalysis. The therapeutic goal too requires correction. To Freud man's nature originates from a pleasure-ego, wants to satisfy sexual instincts and preserve itself. He believed that early, primitive man, and especially children exemplified the more or less unadulterated, primary, guiltless "naturalness" of man—a naturalness obligated only to the "pleasure principle." Modification of the pleasure principle is forced on man by the external world; but this modification is called the "reality principle," which is secondary, according to Freud. It occurs because the individual would perish (and would be unable to have any kind of satisfaction) if he did not consider the given realities of the external world. One part of this adaptation to external reality is the child's acceptance of the moral demands his parents make on him. Eventually, the superior force of external reality results in the child's psychic incorporation of these and other demands and prohibitions which originally come from outside. The final result of this theory is Freud's "Super-Ego," or conscience. Once the super-ego has been formed, it becomes a source of guilt feelings. Hence, man experiences feelings of guilt every time he violates, or intends to violate, one of the seven commandments. Characteristically enough, Freud in all his papers never spoke of guilt as such, but only of guilt feelings. He expected psychoanalysis to liberate the patient from neurotic thralldom and allow him to return to his "original naturalness." So he would no longer be inhibited by feelings of guilt, but would have the guarantee of guiltless enjoyment.

In contrast to Freud, Existential Analysis is accepting guilt feelings, not only as secondary, externally determined ones which can be removed by psychoanalysis. From the standpoint of analysis of Dasein, man is primarily guilty. His primary guilt commences at birth. For it is then that he begins to be in debt to his Dasein, by not being able to carry out all the possibilities of life. Man remains guilty in this sense, i.e., indebted to all the demands that his future keeps in store for him until his last breath. Also, as we have pointed out, every act, every decision, every choice, involves the rejection of all other possibilities which also belong to a human being at a given moment. In this twofold sense, he must always remain behind, so to speak. This is as much a part of fundamental human nature as the other *existentialia*. Man's existential guilt consists in his failing to carry out the mandate to fulfil all his possibilities. Man is aware of existential guilt when he hears the never-ending call of his conscience. This essential inevitable being-in-debt is guilt, and not merely a subjective feeling of guilt, which is disguised in a neurotic way. Because of existential being-in-debt (experienced as guilt), even the most skilfully conducted psychoanalysis cannot free man of guilt. Actually, not one single analysand could be found who has been transformed into a really guiltless person by psychoanalytic treatment. The worst result an analysis could accomplish in this regard would be to deafen a patient to the pangs of his conscience, and this would not be to his advantage. Being liberated from guilt by psychoanalysis is an antiquated myth.

Psychotherapy, however, can accomplish something else. It can elucidate the past, present and future of a patient's life to the point where he becomes thoroughly aware of his existential being-in-debt. This enables him to acknowledge his debt, to say "yes" to it and take it upon himself. He becomes aware of his possibilities by listening to the call of his conscience; he can take over responsibility and stand by himself.

Once a person has been freed from his essential and existential being-in-debt, he no longer experiences neurotic feelings of guilt. The latter did not originate in himself, but derived from a foreign and crippling mentality which his educators forced upon him. He had to live up to modes of life which were alien to him, but he could not shake them off. Such neurotic feelings of guilt continually increase existential guilt as well, since they result in a steadily increasing debt in regard to a fulfilment of one's own existence. As a result, the call of conscience becomes increasingly persistent. But the patient, caught in acquired moralistic concepts, misunderstands this voice as a demand to follow even

more rigidly this mode of living. Only analysis can break this vicious circle.

If a patient reaches the goal of Daseinsanalysis, that is, if he freely accepts his debt to his existence, he reaches at the same time the goal Freud had in mind—full capacity for work and enjoyment. But he will no longer use these capacities in the service of egotistic power—or pleasure—tendencies. Rather he will let all his possibilities of relating to the world be used as the luminated realm into which all he encounters may come to its fulfilment.

CONCLUSION

Since the existential analytical conception of illness is based on a totally different anthropological concept from the one underlying psychoanalysis, its aims must also be different. The essential significance of the analysis of Dasein of Martin Heidegger for psychiatry does not consist solely in the clarification of merely theoretical or technical details and individual problems. More important than this, and something that only renders possible this kind of understanding, are two fundamental aids offered to the doctor by analysis of Dasein.

Heidegger in *Sein und Zeit* (*Being and Time*) (7) describes two possibilities of behaviour, which may serve as invaluable guidance for the psychotherapist's attitude to his patients, when he speaks of "intervening" and of "anticipating" care. Intervening care is acting for the other. The latter steps back, in order to take up what has been done for him as something ready-made and available, or he dispenses with it entirely. In such care the other can become dependent and dominated, be this dominance tacit or not, and concealed from the dominated one or not. This intervening, solicitous care determines the being-together to a great extent, and it affects mainly the treatment of what is present at that moment. In contrast to this, is the possibility of a type of care which does not intervene so much for the other but anticipates him in his ability-to-be, does not relieve him of concern, but in fact gives it back to him. This type of care helps the other to become free for his concern.

If the psychotherapist takes to heart these statements of Heidegger as to how he ought to behave towards his patients, he has already gained the decisive point of view underlying a truly effective therapeutic intervention. Above all, however, the doctor regains a new respect for everything confronting him by absorbing the discoveries of the analysis of Dasein. He also becomes spontaneously aware of the reality presenting itself to him. In an age of radical reduction of all things to the level of calculable elementary particles and quanta of energy, there is special need for an understanding of the "Being-in-the-world."

REFERENCES

1. Boss, M. *Sinn und Gehalt der sexuellen Perversionen.* 2. Aufl. Bern und Stuttgart: Huber, 1952.

2. Boss, M. *Der Traum und seine Auslegung.* Bern and Stuttgart: Huber, 1953.

3. Boss, M. Martin Heidegger und die Aerzte. In *Martin Heidegger-Festschrift.* Pfullingen: Neske, 1959.

4. Boss, M. Psychotherapeutischer Beitrag zur Schizophrenielehre. *Congress Report,* II International Congress of Psychiatry, Zurich, 1959.

5. Boss, M. Gedanken über eine schizophrene Halluzination. *Schweizer Archiv für Neurologie, Neurochirurgie und Psychiatrie,* 1963, 91.

6. CONDRAU, G. *Die Daseinsanalyse von Medard Boss und ihre Bedeutung für die Psychiatrie.* Bern und Stuttgart: Huber, 1965.

7. HEIDEGGER, M. *Sein und Zeit.* 8 Aufl. Tübingen: Niemeyer, 1957.

8. MAY, R. The existential approach. In S. Arieti (Ed.), 1960. *American handbook of psychiatry,* Vol. 2. New York: Basic Books, 1959.

67.

VIKTOR E. FRANKL

LOGOTHERAPY

It is the contention of some authors that in existential psychiatry, logotherapy is the only school which has evolved psychotherapeutic techniques. Man's primary concern is to find and fulfill meaning and purpose in life. Today, however, ever more patients relate the feeling of a profound meaninglessness. In logotherapy, this inner void is referred to as the "existential vacuum." According to existential analysis (*Existenzanalyse*) which underlies logotherapy, there are two specifically human phenomena, the "capacity of self-transcendence" and the "capacity of self-detachment." They are mobilized by two logotherapeutic techniques, "de-reflection" and "paradoxical intention," respectively. Both lend themselves particularly to the short-term treatment of sexual as well as obsessive-compulsive and phobic neuroses, especially in cases in which the anticipatory anxiety mechanism is involved.

Most of the authors agree in that logotherapy falls under the category of existential psychiatry. Pertinent statements have been made by Allport

[1], Ungersma [2], Tweedie [3, 4], Leslie [5], Kaczanowski [6], Crumbaugh [7] and Pervin [8]. In fact, as early as in the thirties I coined the word *Existenzanalyse* as an alternative name for logotherapy. Later on, when American authors started publishing in the field of logotherapy they introduced the term "existential analysis" [9] as a translation of *Existenzanalyse.* Unfortunately, other authors did the same with the word *Daseinsanalyse*—a term which, in the forties, had been selected by Ludwig Binswanger, to denote his own teachings, and henceforth existential analysis became quite an ambiguous word. In order not to add to the confusion which had been aroused by this state of affairs, I decided to refrain more and more from using the term existential analysis in so far as my publications in English were concerned—at the risk, to be sure, to speak of logotherapy even in a context where no therapy in the strict and proper sense of the word was involved. What I

From Viktor E.. Frankl, "Logotherapy." *Israel Annals of Psychiatry and Related Disciplines,* 1967, 5, 142-155. Reprinted by permission.

call medical ministry [10], e.g., forms an important aspect of the practice of logotherapy but is indicated precisely in those cases where actual therapy is impossible—simply because the patient is confronted and facing an incurable disease. To be sure, in the widest possible sense logotherapy is treatment even then; it is treatment of the patient's attitude toward his unchangeable fate.

Logotherapy goes beyond *Daseinsanalyse* or, to adopt the translation by Scher, ontoanalysis in that it is not only concerned with ontos or being, but also with logos or meaning. This may well account for the fact that logotherapy is more than mere analysis, namely, as the very name indicates, therapy. In a personal conversation Ludwig Binswanger felt that, as compared with ontoanalysis, logotherapy was more activistic, and even more, that logotherapy could lend itself as the therapeutic supplement to ontoanalysis.

Logotherapy has not only been subsumed under the heading existential psychiatry but also has been acclaimed, within this province, as the only school which has succeeded in developing what one might be justified in calling a technique. This at least is the contention of such authors as Ungersma [2], Tweedie [3, 4], Leslie [5], Kaczanowski [40, 6] and Crumbaugh [7]. This does not imply that we logotherapists are too proud of this fact. For long we have come to realize that what counts and matters in therapy is not techniques but rather the human relation between doctor and patient, or the personal and existential encounter.

By way of a deliberate oversimplification for didactic purposes one could define logotherapy by the literal translation as healing through meaning [11]. What in logotherapy is called the will to meaning [1] indeed occupies a central place in the system. It refers to the fact which reveals itself to a phenomenological analysis, namely, that man is basically striving to find and fulfill meaning and purpose in life.

Today, the will to meaning is often frustrated. In logotherapy, one speaks of existential frustration. Patients who fall into this diagnostic category usually complain of a sense of futility and meaninglessness or emptiness and void. In logotherapy, this condition is termed "existential vacuum." As to its etiology it seems to me to be due to the following facts. First, in contrast to an animal, no drives and instincts tell man what he must do. Second, in contrast to former times, no conventions, traditions and values tell him what he should do. Soon, one may predict, he will not even know what he basically wishes to do. All the more he simply will wish to do what other people do, or he just will do what other people want him to do. That is to say, he will fall prey to conformism or totalitarianism, respectively, the first being representative for the West, the second being representative for the East.

The existential vacuum constitutes the mass neurosis of our age. In a recent publication, a Czechoslovakian psychiatrist, Stanislav Kratochvil [12], has pointed out that existential frustration makes itself felt even in Communist countries.

In cases in which existential frustration produces neurotic symptoms, one is dealing with a new type of neurosis which I call "noogenic neurosis." It goes to the credit of Crumbaugh to have developed a special test diagnostically to differentiate the noogenic neurosis from the conventional neuroses. After publishing the results obtained by his Purpose-in-life Test (PIL) together with Maholick [13] he delivered an amplified version before the annual meeting of The American Psychological Association, the data having been based on a total of 1,151 subjects. Crumbaugh arrived at the conclusion that "noogenic neurosis exists apart from the conventional diagnostic categories" and is not "identical with any of the conventional diagnostic syndromes." It represents "a new clinical syndrome which cannot be adequately comprehended under any of the classical descriptions. Present results lend support" and are "favorable to Frankl's concepts of noogenic neurosis and existential vacuum. The low correlation between the PIL and educational level implies on the one hand that purposeful, meaningful lives are not limited to those with educational opportunity, and on the other that education alone by no means assures the attainment of meaning in life." [14]

Along with the empirical corroboration and confirmation of logotherapeutic concepts as furnished by Crumbaugh statistical research has been conducted referring to the frequency of noogenic neurosis. Werner [15] in London, Langen and Volhard [16] in Tübingen, Prill [17] in Würzburg, and Niebauer [18, p. 753] in Vienna agree in so far as they estimate that about 20 per cent of the neuroses one encounters are noogenic in nature.

It goes without saying that meaning and purpose in life cannot be prescribed like a drug. It is not the job of a doctor to *give* meaning to the patient's life. But it may well be his task, through an existential analysis, to enable the patient to *find* meaning in life. Again it was Crumbaugh and Maholick [19] who, to my knowledge for the first time, have pointed to the fact that finding meaning in a situation has something to do with a Gestalt perception. This assumption is confirmed by Wertheimer [20], who explicitly states that a quality of "requiredness" is inherent in the situation and, what is even more, "the demands and 'requirements'" of the situation are "objective qualities."

According to logotherapeutic teachings, meaning is not really lacking in any life situation. This is due to the fact that even the negative aspects of human existence such as suffering, guilt, and death can still be turned into something positive, provided that they are faced with the right attitude. Needless to say, meaning can be found only in unavoidable suffering whereas accepting avoidable pain would form some sort of masochism rather than heroism. As a matter of fact, unavoidable suffering is inherent in the human condition and the therapist should take heed not to reinforce the patient's evasive denial of this existential fact.

Alongside the will to meaning stands the will to power and what one could call the will to pleasure. In the final analysis, the direct intention of pleasure or the pursuit of happiness as it usually is referred to, defeats and thwarts itself. The more an individual aims at pleasure the more he misses the aim. In logotherapy we speak in this context of hyperintention.

Along with this pathogenic phenomenon and associated with it we may observe and meet another one, i.e., what in logotherapy is called hyperreflection. Hyperreflection means excessive attention. Spontaneity and activity are impeded and inhibited if too much made a target of attention. Consider the centipede who, as a story has it, was asked by his enemy in which sequence he moved his legs. The effect was that the centipede payed attention to the problem, and by so doing was incapacitated to move his legs at all. He is said to have died from starvation. Should we say that he died from fatal hyperreflection?

In logotherapy hyperreflection is counteracted by dereflection. One of those domains in which this technique is applied is that of sexual neuroses, be it frigidity or impotence. Sexual performance or experience are strangled to the same extent to which they are made either an object of attention or an objective of intention. As far as frigidity is concerned, the reader is referred to an instructive and illustrative case I have included in my book, *Man's Search for Meaning* [1, pp. 194 f.]. In cases of impotence, hyperintention is frequently due to the fact that the patient approaches sexual intercourse as something which is demanded of him. I have elaborated on this aspect of the etiology of impotence elsewhere (21, pp. 159 ff.). A logotherapeutic technique has been developed in order to remove the demand quality the patient attaches and attributes to sexual intercourse. I have discussed this technique in a paper at a symposium on logotherapy in London [22]. Yet the logotherapeutic treatment of sexual neurosis is applicable regardless of whether or not one adopts the logotherapeutic theory. In the Neurological Department of the Poliklinik Hospital in Vienna, I have entrusted an outpatient ward for patients with sexual neuroses to a psychoanalytically trained physician who uses in the given setting the logotherapeutic rather than the psychoanalytic technique.

Whereas dereflection is part and parcel of the logotherapeutic treatment of sexual neurosis there is another logotherapeutic technique which lends itself to the short-term treatment of obsessive-compulsive and phobic patients. This technique is called paradoxical intention. I have described it as early as 1946 in my book, *The Doctor and the Soul* [10], and in a paper [23] reprinted in another of my books [24].

To put it in a nutshell, paradoxical intention

means that the patient is encouraged to do, or wish to happen, the very things he fears. In order to understand the therapeutic efficiency of this technique we must consider the phenomenon called "anticipatory anxiety." By this I mean the response and reaction to an event in terms of the fearful expectation of the recurrence of the event. However, fear tends to make come true precisely that which one is afraid of and in the same vein anticipatory anxiety triggers off what the patient so fearfully expects to happen. Thus a vicious circle is established. A symptom evokes a phobia and the phobia provokes the symptom. The recurrence of the symptom then reinforces the phobia.

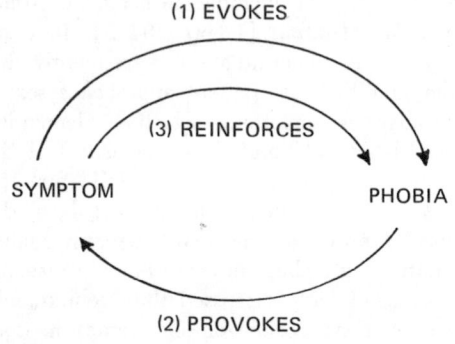

The patient is caught in a cocoon. A circle formation is built up or, as we might say as well, a feedback mechanism is established. How can we break up the vicious circle? It can be managed in two ways, first by pharmacotherapy and second by psychotherapy, unless we decide to combine both. This is necessary in severe cases.

It is possible even to start with pharmacotherapy. This holds for those cases with agoraphobic symptoms in which hyperthyroidism is an underlying factor [25], or cases of claustrophobia which I could trace to latent tetany [26]. One should bear in mind, however, that the organic factor involved in such cases provides no more than a mere inclination to anxiety while the full-fledged anxiety neurosis does not develop unless the anticipatory anxiety mech-

anism comes into play. Therefore, to unhinge the circle one must attack it on the psychic pole as well as on the organic pole. And the first is precisely the job done by paradoxical intention.

What then is going on when paradoxical intention is applied? Encouraging the patient to do, or wish to happen, the very things he fears entails and engenders an inversion of intention. The pathogenic fear is replaced by a paradoxical wish. By the same token, however, the wind is taken out of the sails of anticipatory anxiety.

The intention of a phobic individual is to escape and avoid those situations which arouse fear and anxiety. In logotherapy, we speak of flight from fear. We may observe it in those cases, e.g., in which anxiety itself is the target of fear. In these cases the patient himself speaks of "fear of fear." He really fears the potential effects of fear, be it a faint, a coronary or a stroke.

According to logotherapeutic findings and teachings, flight from fear is a pathogenic pattern [28]. More specifically it is the phobic pattern. But the development of a phobia can be obviated by confronting one with the situation he begins to fear.

Alongside flight from fear there are two more pathogenic patterns, namely, fight for pleasure and fight against obsessions and compulsions. Fight for pleasure is identical with hyperintention of pleasure, that is to say, one of the major factors underlying sexual neuroses. Fight against obsessions and compulsions in turn is the pathogenic pattern underlying obsessive-compulsive neuroses. Obsessive-compulsive neurotics are plagued by the idea that they might commit suicide or even homicide or that the strange thoughts which haunt them might be signs of imminent, if not present, psychosis. In other words, they fear the potential effects or the potential cause of the strange thoughts. The phobic individual fears the potential effects of fear, I have said, and this "fear of fear" prompts him to set out on his flight from fear. This phobic pattern is paralleled by the obsessive-compulsive pattern. The obsessive-compulsive neurotics also display fear. But they do not exhibit "fear of fear" but rather fear of themselves, and their response and reaction to this fear is fight against obsessions and compulsions rather than flight from fear. But the more the patients fight their obsessions and compulsions the stronger these symptoms become. In other words, alongside the circle formation built up by anticipatory anxiety in phobic cases, there is another feedback mechanism which we may encounter in the obsessive-compulsive neurotics. Pressure induces counterpressure, and counterpressure, in turn, increases pressure. Conversely, if one succeeds in making the patient stop fighting his obsessions and compulsions—and this may well be accomplished by paradoxical intention—these symptoms soon diminish and finally atrophy.

Having discussed the theory let us turn to the practice of paradoxical intention. Let us take up a case report:

The patient refused to leave his house because every time he did he had attacks of fear that he would collapse on the street. Every time he did leave his house he returned after a few steps. He ran away from his fear. Admitted to my department, a thorough checkup made certain that there was nothing wrong with his heart. One of the doctors told him that. Then he suggested the patient should go out on the street and try to get a heart attack. He told him, "Tell yourself that yesterday you had two heart attacks, and today you have time to get three—it's still early in the morning. Tell yourself that you will have a nice, fat coronary, and a stroke to boot." For the first time the patient was able to break through his cocoon in which he had enclosed himself.

Another instance of paradoxical intention is the following case history that Gerz [29] presented:

It concerns a fifty-six-year-old lawyer, who was married and the father of an eighteen-year-old son. His neurosis began seventeen years ago, when he was still in private practice. "All of a sudden, out of a clear blue sky, an awful obsession came into my mind that I had defrauded the government by underestimating my income tax by some three hundred dollars, even though I made it out as honestly as I knew how. I began to worry that it might be several hundred dollars more. Try as I might, I could not get these ideas out of my head." The patient imagined himself being prosecuted for fraud, going to jail, receiving newspaper publicity, and finally losing his job. He was hospitalized at a private sanitarium, receiving psychotherapy and twenty-five treatments with electro-convulsive ther-

apy, without improvement. Meanwhile he had to give up his law practice and to take a job as a court clerk. Further obsessions developed. They shifted from day to day, and week to week. He developed the habit of checking and rechecking things, such as the wheels of his car and things he did at his office. He became obsessed about his insurance policies, fearing that perhaps one had expired or that one did not include the protection he wanted. It was at this time that he bought special insurance from Lloyds, because he feared he might make a mistake in court and be sued. He felt compelled to check and recheck everything, including his various insurance policies locked in a special steel box in a safe at home. The policies themselves were in envelopes secured by a number of strings. His fear of being sued was so great that off and on he had to go through the involved procedure of taking out his policies and making sure he was insured properly; and when he finally had put them back into the steel box in the safe, he wondered whether he had really checked everything. He had to repeat this process over and over until he finally "felt certain" that he was "safe." In court he became so completely incapacitated that he needed to be hospitalized. It was at this time that Dr. Gerz began treating him with paradoxical intention. He was in logotherapy for four months three times weekly, and was instructed to use the following "paradoxical intentions": "I don't give a damn any more. Hell, who wants to be a perfectionist? I hope I get sued very soon, the sooner the better." Dr. Gerz instructed him to try "to get sued three times a day and get his money's worth from Lloyds of London!" He was told to wish that he would make many, many mistakes, really mess up his work, and show his secretaries that he was the greatest "mistake maker" in the world. No doubt, Dr. Gerz's complete lack of anxiety could be adopted by the patient, as a humourous situation was created and as Dr. Gerz kept telling the patient on each visit: "For heaven's sake, are you still around! I've been looking through the newspapers hoping to read about the big scandalous lawsuit.", At these comments the patient would burst into laughter, and he finally adopted the attitude of: "To hell with everything. I don't care if I make mistakes; I don't give a damn what happens. Let 'em sue me." He would laugh and say: "My insurance companies will go bankrupt." About a year after therapy began, he said: "This formula has worked a miracle for me. Dr. Gerz has made a new person out of me in four months. I occasionally get a worry, but now I am able to cope with it. I know how to handle it."

Weisskopf-Joelson [30] makes the following statement:

"I have made use of 'paradoxical intention' with many of my patients, including myself, and I have found it very effective. For example, a university student complained about being anxious with regard to an oral report to be given—let us say—on Friday. I advised him to take his appointment calendar and to write on every page of the week, with large letters, the word 'ANXIETY.' As it were—I asked him to plan for an anxious week. He was much relieved after doing this because now he was suffering from anxiety only, but not from anxiety about anxiety."

In recent years many reports were published on the use of paradoxical intention. In addition to David (Buenos Aires), mention may be made of the associates of Ernst Kretschmer (Tübingen), Langen and Volhard, Prill (Gynecological University Clinic of Würzburg), and Rehder (Hamburg). At the Fourth International Congress for Psychotherapy (1958), Ledermann declared: "The results (of logotherapy) are not to be denied. I have found the method helpful in cases of obsessional neurosis." Frick (Bolzano, Italy) goes still further by stating that there are cases of severe obsessive-compulsive neurosis in which a logotherapeutic procedure is the "only therapeutic way," and refers to some cases in which electro-shock therapy had failed and logotherapy alone proved successful. Lopez-Ibor (Madrid) makes a similar statement. In addition to my associates, Kocourek and Niebauer, N. Toll reports that she has been using it successfully for over six years. Bazzi (Rome) has even worked out special indications in which paradoxical intention should be applied and those in which the autogenic training method of Schultz is indicated [31].

There is evidence that paradoxical intention even works in chronic cases [32]. For example, in the German *Encyclopaedia of Psychotherapy* [18, p. 757] the case of a sixty-five-year-old woman is described who for 60 years had suffered from a hand-washing compulsion. A member of my staff successfully applied the paradoxical intention technique in this case.

J. Lehembre has tried paradoxical intention on children, at the Departments of Psychiatry and Pediatrics of the Universities of Utrecht and Nijmegen. He has been successful in most of the cases. In his report [33] he makes the point that only in a single case symptom substitution has been observed.

Jasper's dictum, "in philosophy, being new speaks against being true," may also hold for psychotherapy. Unwillingly and unwittingly, paradoxical intention has certainly been used all along. With regard to unwilling use, an example was reported to me by the Head of the Department of Psychiatry at the University of Mainz in West-Germany. When he was in Junior High School his class was to present a play. One of the characters was a stutterer and so they gave this role to a student who actually stuttered. Soon, however, he had to give up the role because it turned out that when standing on the stage he was completely unable to stutter. He had to be replaced by another boy.

With regard to unwitting use, an instance of paradoxical intention is the following:

One of my American students who had to take his exams from me and in this setting was to explain paradoxical intention resorted to the following autobiographical account: "My stomach used to growl in company of others. The more I tried to keep it from happening, the more it growled. Soon started to take it for granted that it would be with me rest of my life. Began to live with it—laughed with others about it. Soon it disappeared."

In this context, I should like to place emphasis on the fact that my student adopted a humorous attitude toward a symptom. In fact, paradoxical intention should always be formulated in as humorous a manner as possible. Humor is indeed a definitely human phenomenon; after all, no beast is capable of laughing. What is even more important, humor allows man to create a perspective, to put a distance between himself and whatever may confront him. By the same token, humor allows man to detach himself and thereby to attain the fullest possible control over himself. To make use of the human capacity of self-detachment is what paradoxical intention basically achieves. Keeping this in mind, it seems no longer true that we do not yet take humor earnestly and seriously enough (*dass wir den Humor noch nicht ernst genug nehmen*) as Konrad Lorenz [34, p. 411] contends in his most recent book.

What comes to mind, however, is a question which once was raised by Gordon W. Allport after I had read a paper at Harvard University. It is the question whether or not that sound sense of humor which is inherent in the technique of paradoxical intention is equally available in each and every patient. I insisted that in principle each and every human being by virtue of his humanness is capable of detaching himself from himself and laughing about himself. But there are certainly quantitative differences in the degree to which the human capacity for self-detachment and the sound sense of humor[1] can be mobilized. An example of a low degree is the following:

I had a man in my Department, a guard in a museum who could not stay on his job because he suffered from deadly fears that someone would steal a painting. During a round I made with my staff, I tried paradoxical intention with him: "Tell yourself they stole a Rembrandt yesterday and today they would steal a Rembrandt and a Van Gogh." He just stared at me and said, "But, Herr Professor, that's against the law!" This man simply was too feebleminded to understand the meaning of paradoxical intention.

In this respect paradoxical intention or for that matter logotherapy is not an exception. It is the rule that psychotherapy—each and every method of psychotherapy—is not applicable to each patient with the same degree of success. Even more, not every doctor is capable of handling each and every method of psychotherapy with the same degree of skill. That is why I am used to comparing the method of choice in a given case with an equation with 2 unknowns:

$$\Psi = x + y$$

The first unknown represents the unique personality of the patient. The second unknown represents the unique personality of the doctor. Both have to be taken into account if in a given case the method of psychotherapy is to be chosen. What holds for psychotherapy is also true of logotherapy.

Logotherapy is no panacea. For this if for

no other reason it is justified to combine logotherapy with other methods as it has been propounded, among others, by Ledermann (hypnosis [35]), Bazzi (relaxation training after Schultz [31]), Kvilhaugh (behavior therapy [36]), Vorbusch [37], Kratochvil (activation training after Bojanovsky and Chloupkova) and also Gerz (pharmacotherapy [38]).

On the other hand, the remarkable results obtained by paradoxical intention cannot be explained merely in terms of suggestion. Actually, our patients often set out to use paradoxical intention with a strong conviction that it simply cannot work and yet they finally succeed. In other words, they do succeed not because, but rather in spite, of suggestion. Benedikt [39] subjected his patients to test batteries in order to evaluate their susceptibility with respect to suggestion. It turned out that these patients were even less susceptible to suggestion than the average. But paradoxical intention was successful in these cases.

Gerz [29, 32] and Tweedie [4, 5] have proved that paradoxical intention must not be confounded with persuasion. However, it is my contention that in some cases paradoxical intention cannot be launched without being preceded by persuasion. That is particularly true of obsessions with blasphemy, for the treatment of which a special logotherapeutic technique has been devised [21, p. 239].

Most of the authors who have practiced paradoxical intention and published their work agree that it is a short term procedure. The assumption, however, "that the durability of results corresponds to the length of therapy" is one of "the illusions of Freudian orthodoxy," to quote Gutheil [41]. It is also "a completely baseless assertion," to cite the grand old man of German psychotherapy, J. H. Schultz [42], "that symptom removal must be followed by substitute symptoms." Weisskopf-Joelson [43, 44], has expressed the same view. "Psychoanalytically oriented therapists," she says, "might argue no real improvement can be achieved with methods such as logotherapy, since the pathology in 'deeper' layers remains untouched, while the therapist limits himself to the strengthening or erecting of defenses. Such conclusions are not free of danger. They may keep us from the awareness

[1]Speaking of humor I am justified in defining paradoxical intention in terms of a joke: A boy who came to school late offered as an excuse to the teacher the fact that the icy streets were so slippery that whenever he moved one step forward he slipped two steps back again. Thereupon the teacher retorted: But now I have caught you in a lie—if this had been true, you never could have succeeded in arriving at school," whereupon the boy replied: "Why not? I just turned around and went home." Wasn't this paradoxical intention? Wasn't the boy successful through an inversion of the original intention?

of major sources of mental health because these sources do not fit into a specific theoretical framework. We must not forget that such concepts as 'defenses,' 'deeper layers,' and 'adequate functioning on a superficial level with underlying pathology' are theoretical concepts rather than empirical observations." By contrast the results obtained by paradoxical intention do deserve to be qualified as empirical observations. G. Golloway contends that paradoxical intention does not resolve the "underlying conflict." But this "does not detract from paradoxical intention as a successful technique. It is no insult to surgery that it does not cure the diseased gall bladder it removes. The patient is better off."

For this reason many psychoanalysts have been using the paradoxical intention technique successfully. Some workers in the field try to explain this success and specifically to explain it in psychodynamic terms [24, 32]. To cite another instance, Müller-Hegemann [45] (Leipzig) interprets paradoxical intention in terms of a "neurophysiologically oriented approach." Anyway, he "has observed favorable results in the last years in patients suffering from phobias" and therefore considers paradoxical intention "to have much merit." Again, it should be noted that even doctors who adhere to theories different from the one which underlies logotherapy include paradoxical intention in their armamentarium [49, 50].

Attempts have been made to clarify the indications for logotherapy. For example, Gerz feels that paradoxical intention is a specific and effective treatment of phobic and obsessive-compulsive conditions. It "lends itself in the acute cases to short-term therapy." [29]

With respect to statistics Gerz reported: "88.2% of all patients recovered or made considerable improvement. Most of these cases suffered from their illness up to 24 years." [29] "Those who have been sick for several years need up to 12 months of biweekly sessions to bring about recovery. Most acute cases who are sick for a few weeks or months respond to paradoxical intention within about 4 to 12 sessions." [32]

To be sure, "it is understandable that the psychiatrist with many years of psychoanalytic training might tend to be prejudiced and to reject paradoxical intention without having tried it." [32] However, even if much of the resistance to paradoxical intention or for that matter logotherapy were not due to financial but rather emotional grounds such as the adherence and obedience to a sect, the sectarian is admonished by Freud that "reverence before the greatness of a genius is certainly a great thing. But our reverence before facts should exceed it." [46]

As compared with the indications for logotherapy, it is even more important to delineate where paradoxical intention is counterindicated. It is strictly counterindicated in psychotic depressions. For such patients a special logotherapeutic technique is reserved whose guiding principle is the decrease of that burden of guilt feelings on the part of the patient which is due to his tendency to self-accusations [21, pp. 261 ff.]. It would be a misconception of existential psychiatry to interpret these self-accusations as indicating that a patient suffering from endogenous depression not only feels guilty, but really is guilty, "existentially guilty," and hence depressed. This would amount to mistaking an effect for the cause. Even more, such an interpretation would reinforce the patient's guilt feelings to the extent that his suicide might well be the result. Incidentally, logotherapy offers a special test to evaluate the suicide risk in a given case [21, p. 262].

As far as schizophrenic patients are concerned, logotherapy is far from providing a causal treatment. As a psychotherapeutic adjunct, however, the aforementioned logotherapeutic technique called dereflection is also recommended for such patients [21, p. 260, pp. 264 f.]. The volume, *Modern Psychotherapeutic Practice* [47], includes some tape-recorded sessions with schizophrenic patients to demonstrate the way in which dereflection can be utilized [51].

Burton [48] recently stated that "the last 50 years of therapeutic psychiatry have made a fetish of the deep personal history of the patient. Freud's startling cures of supposed unremitting hysterias led us to seek a similar traumatic experience in every patient and to reify insight as curative, something we are only now recovering from." But even if one assumes that neuroses or even psychoses are caused by what is supposed to cause them in terms of psychodynamic hypotheses, logotherapy would still be indicated in terms of a noncausal treatment [43, 44]. For one must consider the fact that as long as there is an existential vacuum in the patient, the symptoms will rush into it. That is why the "logotherapeutic encounter," as Crumbaugh [7] contends, "continues beyond where most therapies, especially analytically oriented methods, stop: it holds that unless purposeful goals and commitment to them are attained, therapy will have been for naught as the pathological etiology will remain and the symptom will later return."

It is the contention of some authors that in existential psychiatry, logotherapy is the only school which has evolved psychotherapeutic techniques. Even more, it has been said that logotherapy adds a new dimension to psychotherapy; more specifically, that it adds to it the dimension of the distinctively human phenomena. In fact, two specifically human phenomena, the capacity of self-transcendence and the capacity of self-detachment, are mobilized by two logotherapeutic techniques, dereflection and paradoxical intention, respectively. Petrilowitsch (Mainz) ascribes the surprising and astonishing results obtained by the two logotherapeutic techniques to the fact that logotherapy does not remain and stay in the dimension of neurosis, i.e., in the dimension of dynamics or conditioning processes. In contrast to behavior therapy, e.g., logotherapy is not satisfied with reconditioning but opens the dimension of the very humanness of man and draws upon the resources which are available in the humanitas of the homo patiens.

The findings of the pioneering schools are not annulled by logotherapy but rather overarched by it. This equally holds for scientific approaches such as Watsonian behaviorism, Pavlovian reflexology, Freudian psychoanalysis and Adlerian psychology. Now the findings of these schools are seen in the light of a higher, the human, dimension. They are not nullified by logotherapy but rather reinterpreted and reevaluated by it —or, as the Norwegian psychotherapist Bjarne Kvilhaugh [36] put it—they are rehumanized by logotherapy.

REFERENCES

1. FRANKL, V. E. Preface by Gordon W. Allport. *Man's search for meaning: An introduction to logotherapy.* New York: Washington Square Press, 1963.
2. UNGERSMA, A. J. *The search for meaning: A new approach to psychotherapy and pastoral psychology.* Philadelphia: The Westminster Press, 1961.
3. TWEEDIE, D. F. *Logotherapy and the Christian faith: An evaluation of Frankl's existential approach to psychotherapy.* Grand Rapids: Baker Book House, 1965.
4. TWEEDIE, D. F. *The Christian and the couch: An introduction to Christian logotherapy.* Grand Rapids: Baker Book House, 1963.
5. LESLIE, R. C. *Jesus and logotherapy: The ministry of Jesus as interpreted through the psychotherapy of Viktor Frankl.* New York: Abingdon Press, 1965.
6. KACZANOWSKI, G. In Arthur Burton, *Modern psychotherapeutic practice: Innovations in technique.* Palo Alto: Science and Behavior Books, 1965.
7. CRUMBAUGH, J. C. The application of logotherapy. *Journal of Existentialism,* 1965, 5, 403–12. PERVIN, L. A. Existentialism, psychology, and psychotherapy. *American Psychologist,* 1960, 15, 305–9.
9. POLAK, P. Frankl's existential analysis. *American Journal of Psychotherapy,* 1949, 3, 517.
10. FRANKL, V. E. *Ärztliche Seelsorge: Grundlagen der Logotherapie und Existenzanalyse.* (7th exp. ed.) Vienna: Deuticke, 1966.
11. FABRY, J. B. *The pursuit of meaning: Logotherapy applied to life.* Boston: Beacon Press, 1968.
12. KRATOCHVIL, S. Ka psychoterapii existencialni frustrace. *Ceskoslovenska Psychiatrie,* 1961, 57, 186.
13. CRUMBAUGH, J. C., & MAHOLICK, L. T. An experimental study in existentialism: The psychometric approach to Frankl's concept of noogenic neurosis. *Journal of Clinical Psychology,* 1964, 20, 200.
14. CRUMBAUGH, J. C. Cross-validation of purpose-in-life test based on Frankl's concepts. *Journal of Individual Psychology,* 1968, 24, 74.
15. WERNER, T. A. Opening paper read before the Symposium on Logotherapy, International Congress of Psychotherapy, Vienna, 1961.
16. VOLHARD, R., & LANGEN, D. Mehrdimensionale Psychotherapie. *Zeitschrift für Psychotherapie und Medizinische Psychologie,* 1953, 3, 1.
17. PRILL, H. J. Organneurose und Konstitution bei chronisch-funktionellen Unterleibsbeschwerden der Frau. *Zeitschrift für Psychotherapie und Medizinische Psychologie,* 1955, 5, 215.
18. KOCOUREK, K., NIEBAUER, E., & POLAK, P. Ergebnisse der klinischen Anwendung der Logo-

therapie. In V. E. Frankl, V. E. von Gebsattel, and J. H. Schulz (Eds.)*Handbuch der Neurosenlehre und Psychotherapie*, Vol. 3. Munich-Berlin: Urban & Schwarzenberg, 1959.

19. CRUMBAUGH, J. C., & MAHOLICK, L. T. The case for Frankl's "Will to Meaning." *Journal of Existential Psychiatry*, 1963, *4*, 43.

20. WERTHEIMER, M. Some problems in the theory of ethics. In M. Henle (Ed.) *Documents of gestalt psychology*. Berkeley: University of California Press, 1961.

21. FRANKL, V. E. *The doctor and the soul: From psychotherapy to logotherapy*, (2d. exp. ed.) New York: Knopf, 1965.

22. FRANKL, V. E. Logotherapy and existential analysis: A review. *American Journal of Psychotherapy*, 1966, *20*, 252.

23. FRANKL, V. E. Paradoxical intention: A logotherapeutic technique. *American Journal of Psychotherapy*, 1960, *14*, 520.

24. FRANKL, V. E. *Psychotherapy and existentialism: Selected papers on logotherapy*. New York: Washington Square Press, 1967.

25. FRANKL, V. E. Psychische Symptome und neurotische Reaktionen bei Hyperthyreose. *Medizinische Klinik*, 1956, *51*, 1139.

26. FRANKL, V. E. Über somatogene pseudoneurosen. *Wiener Klinische Wochenschrift*, 1956, *68*, 280.

28. FRANKL, V. E. Angst und Zwang. Zur Kenntnis pathogener Reaktionsmuster. *Acta Psychother.*, 1953, *1*, 111.

29. GERZ, H. O. Experience with the logotherapeutic technique of paradoxical intention in the treatment of phobic and obsessive-compulsive patients. *American Journal of Psychiatry*, 1966, *123*, 548.

30. WEISSKOPF-JOELSON, E. The present crisis in psychotherapy. *The Journal of Psychology*, 1968, *69*, 107.

31. BAZZI, T. Considerations sur les limitations et les contraindications de la logotherapie. Paper read before the Fourth International Congress of Psychotherapy in Barcelona, Spain, 1958.

32. GERZ, H. O. The treatment of the phobic and the obsessive-compulsive patient using paradoxical intention sec. Viktor E. Frankl. *Journal of Neuropsychiatry*, 1962, *3*, 375.

33. LEHEMBRE, J. L'intention paradoxale, procedé de psychotherapie. *Acta Neurologica et Psychiatrica Belgica*, 1964, *64*, 725.

34. LORENZ, K. *Das sogenannte Böse*. Vienna: Borotha-Schoeler, 1963.

35. LEDERMANN, F. K. Clinical applications of ex-istential psychotherapy. *Journal of Existential Psychiatry*, 1962, *3*, 45.

36. KVILHAUGH, B. Klinische Erfahrungen mit der logotherapeutischen Technik der paradoxen Intention beziehungsweise deren Kombination mit anderen Behandlungsmethoden (Bericht über 40 Fälle). Paper read before the Austrian Medical Society of Psychotherapy, Vienna, July 18, 1963.

37. VORBUSCH, H. J. Die Behandlung schwerer Schlafstörungen mit der paradoxen Intention. Paper read before the Austrian Medical Society of Psychotherapy, Vienna, June 1, 1965.

38. GERZ, H. O. Severe depressive and anxiety states. *Mind*, 1963, *1*, 235.

39. BENEDIKT, F. Zur Therapie angst- und zwangs-neurotischer Symptome mit Hilfe der "paradoxen Intention" und "Dereflexion" nach V. E. Frankl. *Dissertation*. University of Munich Medical School, 1966.

40. KACZANOWSKI, G. Frankl's logotherapy. *American Journal of Psychiatry*, 1960, *117*, 563.

41. GUTHEIL, E. A. Proceedings of the Association for the Advancement of Psychotherapy. *American Journal of Psychotherapy*, 1956, *10*, 134.

42. SCHULTZ, J. H. Analytische und organismische Psychotherapie. *Acta Psychotherapeutica Psychosomatica et Orthopaedagogica*, 1953, *1*, 33.

43. WEISSKOPF-JOELSON, E. Some comments on a Viennese school of psychiatry. *Journal of Abnormal and Social Psychology*, 1955, *51*, 701.

44. WEISSKOPF-JOELSON, E. Logotherapy and existential analysis. *Acta Psychotherapeutica Psychosomatica et Orthopaedagogica*, 1958, *6*, 193.

45. MULLER-HEGEMANN, D. Methodological approaches in psychotherapy. *American Journal of Psychotherapy*, 1963, *17*, 554.

46. FREUD, S. Über Forel: Der Hypnotismus, seine Bedeutung und seine Handhabung. *Wiener medizinische Wochenschrift*, 1889, *34*, 1098.

47. FRANKL, V. E. Fragments from the logotherapeutic treatment of four cases. In Arthur Burton, *Modern psychotherapeutic practice: Innovations in technique*. Palo Alto: Science and Behavior Books, 1965.

48. BURTON, A. Beyond the transference. *Psychotherapy: Theory, Research, & Practice*, 1964, *1*, 49.

49. VICTOR, R. G., & KRUG, C. M. *Paradoxical intention. American Journal of Psychotherapy*, 1967, *21*, 808.

50. HAVENS, L. Paradoxical intention. *Psychiatry & Social Science Review*, 1968, *2*, 16.

51. FRANKL, V. E. *The will to meaning: Foundations and applications of logotherapy*. New York: The New American Library, 1970.

68.

William S. Sahakian

PHILOSOPHICAL PSYCHOTHERAPY

As in ancient times a person's anxiety was dissipated by changing his philosophical *Weltanschauung,* so in several present-day psychotherapeutic systems philosophy is employed toward the end of curing the patient. Particularly is this true of Frankl's logotherapy (7, 8), Adler's style of life (2) and social interest therapy (3), and Ellis' rational-emotive psychotherapy (5). But elements of philosophical indoctrination may be found in numerous other systems, including Freud, Jung, and Meyer, just to mention a few.

Philosophical psychotherapy may require other therapeutic techniques to supplement it, but it is an unusually effective complement to nearly all systems, of which we have recently presented almost two dozen (9). The value of philosophical psychotherapy can be readily seen and appreciated by those who are aware of the importance of changing a patient's attitude, under the assumption that "the conscious as well as the unconscious is determined by subjective values and interests" (4, p. 9). One of the most efficient methods of altering a person's psychological posture is by changing his philosophical outlook. One may even go so far as to assert that in certain instances a symptom is produced or controlled or eliminated by a change in a patient's philosophical attitude. One's beliefs play an important role in reinforcing or eliminating symptoms.

The present paper deals with the application of Stoic philosophy to psychotherapy. According to the psychology of the Stoics (6), what cannot be changed should be accepted or else treated with philosophical indifference. A fact which is not accepted by a person may cause him great distress; that is, if he is confronted with a problem or situation that he cannot

change but nevertheless strives doggedly to dispel, he will merely succeed in intensifying the emotional tension and stress, causing him more misery than the problem that he is seeking to resolve. Emotional exhaustion compounded by a sense of defeat or despair in combatting one's psychological disturbances is often more distressing than the original ailment. It is in these cases that philosophical psychotherapy is definitely indicated: Instead of removing the object of complaint of a person, you alter his philosophical attitude or posture.

To appreciate the degree to which this thesis is true, it would be helpful to consider some case studies.

CASE 1

A woman in her fifties, after having undergone brain surgery, complained of headaches localized behind the left ear. After careful examination, her physicians concluded that the operation was quite successful and that they could find nothing physically wrong with her, and recommended that she see the clinic's psychiatrist. Some months later, when she came to my attention, she had had no less than a dozen visits with the clinic's psychiatrist but to no avail.

Knowing that she had competent psychiatric care, I decided to proceed along another approach, namely philosophical psychotherapy. On the conclusion of a brief introductory chat, enabling us to become better acquainted with each other, I explored her attitude regarding her ailment by engaging in the following dialogue with her:

"Is the pain severe?"
"Yes, at times."
"Is it endurable?"
"Not at times, and I think that it is getting worse."
"Is it very painful at this moment?"
"Excruciating!"

From William S. Sahakian," Stoic philosophical psychotherapy." *Journal of Individual Psychology,* 1969, 25, 32–35.

"Do you feel that the pain will become so intense that it will drive you out of your mind?"

"How did you know that? That is precisely what terrifies me; I am afraid that I am going insane, that is, the pain will get worse until I lose my mind."

At this point it was decided to employ Stoic psychotherapy. The patient would be offered the choice of accepting her condition laden with pain, instead of fighting it, which she had been doing up to now. What she did not realize was that she was suffering from a dual pain, one which she had localized in the brain, and the other, the strain of emotional tension. Apparently, the latter was the less endurable of the two and had a concomitant aggravating effect upon the former.

The dialogue with the patient continued:

"Why do you want to get rid of the pain?"

"Nobody wants pain," she said looking at me as if I were rather peculiar for asking such an asinine question.

"If you could feel confident that no matter how severe the pain in your head becomes it will, nevertheless, not drive you to 'insanity' as you put it, do you think it would then be possible for you to endure the headache?"

"Why? Won't it?"

"But do think that you could endure it?"

"Yes, I'm sure that I can."

"What if I were to tell you that your headache will never cause 'insanity'; and if you were ever to become 'insane,' it would not be from your head pain?"

"Is that true?"

"Actually, a person becomes adapted to pain."

"Truly?"

"It is true."

Then smilingly she said: "I don't think that you will believe it but the pain in my head has subsided considerably, and I know that I can endure it."

When the tension that she had suffered was alleviated, she accepted her condition and was reasonably content, which indicates that it was not the head pain (regardless of whether it was psychological, psychosomatic, or otherwise) that distressed her, but the strenuous emotional confrontation with what she thought was a grave problem. Note that the symptom had "subsided considerably" through this dialectical method.

CASE 2

This second case is that of a man in his late thirties complaining of neurotic symptoms though he had been to a number of psychiatrists. When he came to me it was uncertain whether he expected a miracle or was just shopping for another psychotherapist. It was quite obvious in this case that, owing to the failure of a number of psychiatrists, Stoic philosophical psychotherapy might possibly succeed where the other methods had failed. At least it was worth the attempt. He had a number of persistent neurotic symptoms with which he was wrestling, with the hope of conquering them. Instead of gaining any control over them, he had become worse by succumbing to despair and by depleting himself emotionally. It became quite clear that the tense, emotional strain exerted in combatting his neurosis was more painfully distressing than the neurosis itself. After some time, our session took the following dialectical course:

"You have told me of some of your neurotic symptoms and you say that you want me to help you to eradicate them. Why?"

"What do you mean, 'Why?' Any normal person would want to get rid of them. They are tormenting problems and disturb me terribly. They have made me miserable for a long time."

"Have you ever tried to live with them; accept them? Some crippled people have learned to live with their ailment. They do not spend every hour of their waking day or an entire lifetime striving to gain mastery over their problem. They accept their plight and learn to live with it, as do many other people who are handicapped victims. Some persons with the loss of an arm or with a heart condition learn to live within the limitations of their handicap; they do not waste their time and exhaust themselves vainly combatting their problem. Is it not possible for you also to do something comparable?"

After staring at me with a meaningless look for almost a minute, the patient's eyes and face lit up, and he smiled broadly (a smile that never left his face for the remainder of the session) and said: "Why didn't the other psychotherapists tell me this long ago? Of course I can accept it and live with it. In fact, I feel better already. It is most ironic that I should come to a therapist, requesting that he cure me, and then have him tell me to keep my problem."

Two weeks later I saw this man, and with a similar smile and sense of relief he reported that he was "all better." Six months later, he was still content. The goal of Stoic psychotherapy is not happiness, but tranquility. In Stoic tranquility, there is neither anguish nor joy (10).

CONCLUSION

Actually, what is most distressing to many neurotics is the emotional stress exerted to combat their problem, creating an emotional exhaustion, a state of doubt and insecurity, that readily stimulates or triggers anxiety at the slightest provocation. What needs to be accomplished in these cases is the removal of the super-imposed emotional stress that comes with the fighting of the symptoms and not the symptoms *per se.*

Stoic psychotherapy may work here. The emotional block is removed by eliminating the driving force, namely, the unrelenting determination to control neurotic symptoms. Eliminate the tension created by the determination to gain mastery over the symptoms and the symptoms themselves may dissipate. If you cannot remove the problem, then change the attitude that is assumed toward it, and you will discover that you may have effectively dealt with two problems: the original neurosis and the distressing emotional tension expended in wresting it.

In closing we should like to point out that the motto of the "Introduction" of Adler's *The Neurotic Constitution* is a quotation from a leading Stoic, Seneca: "Everything depends on one's opinion. . . . We suffer according to our opinion. One is as miserable as one believes oneself to be.—*Epist.* 78, 13" (1).

REFERENCES

1. ADLER, A. *The neurotic constitution.* New York: Dodd, Mead, 1926.
2. ADLER, A. *The science of living* (1929). Garden City, N. Y.: Doubleday Anchor Books, 1969.
3. ADLER, A. *Social interest: a challenge to mankind* (1933). New York: Capricorn, 1964.
4. ANSBACHER, H. L., & ANSBACHER, ROWENA R. (Eds.) *The individual psychology of Alfred Adler.* New York: Basic Books, 1956.
5. ELLIS, A. *Reason and emotion in psychotherapy.* New York: Lyle Stuart, 1962.
6. EPICTETUS. *Discourses.* Oxford: Clarendon, 1916.
7. FRANKL, V. E. *Man's search for meaning: an introduction to logotherapy.* Boston: Beacon, 1962.
8. FRANKL, V. E. *Psychotherapy and existentialism: Selected papers on logotherapy.* New York: Washington Square, 1967.
9. SAHAKIAN, W. S. (Ed.) *Psychotherapy and counseling: studies in technique.* Chicago: Rand McNally, 1969.
10. SIMPSON, H. N. *Stoic apologetics.* 440 Linden Ave., Oak Park, Ill. 60302: Author, 1966.

69.

J. L. MORENO

PSYCHODRAMA

The growing demand for skilled workers in psy-

From J. L. Moreno (in collaboration with Zerka T. Moreno), *Psychodrama.* Vol. 3. *Action Therapy & Principles of Practise.* Beacon, N.Y.: Beacon House, 1969. Pp. 233–246. The sections "Telic Sensitivity and Sensitivity Training" and "Encounter and Encounter Groups" are new sections added by Dr. and Mrs. Moreno. Reprinted by permission.

chodrama has awakened us to the need to structure a comprehensive statement of fundamental rules[1] in the practice of this method, and a brief survey and explanation of the numerous ver-

[1]See J. L. Moreno, Chapter on Psychodrama, *American Handbook of Psychiatry* (New York: Basic Books, 1959).

sions of psychodramatic intervention. Other surveys of methods have described some of these,[2] but a number of basic rules to serve as guidelines for the practitioner are vital.

RULES

I

"The subject (patient, client, protagonist) acts out his conflicts, instead of talking about them."

To this end, a special vehicle or psychodrama stage may be used, though the process may have to take place in any informal room or space whenever no such specially designed vehicle is available. Ideally, the special vehicle makes for more intense involvement. The process requires further a director (or chief therapist), and at least one trained auxiliary ego (though the director may be forced to act also as an auxiliary ego where no one is available). Maximum learning is achieved whenever such trained assistant-therapist-actors are used.

It should be borne in mind that psychodrama may be applied as a method of individual treatment—one patient with one director and auxiliary ego, or one patient and the director. Where it is applied as a method of group treatment, other patients in the group may very well serve as auxiliary egos for one another. In this fashion even individual-centered sessions involve in action other members of the group, who, in turn, derive therapeutic benefit from this auxiliary ego function. This further intensifies the learning of all those present.

II

"The subject or patient acts 'in the here and now,' regardless of when the actual incident took place or may take place, past, present or future, or when the imagined incident was fantasied, or when the crucial situation out of which this present enactment arose, occurred."

This is also true of situations which have not and may not ever take place. One of the notable experiences in psychodrama is the ineffectual, weak, incomplete and distorted fashion

in which recall and re-enactment are produced. This has been experimentally verified by the immediate re-enactment of scenes which took place only five minutes earlier, using the identical persons involved in the original scene. Both verbal and action recall, as well as interpersonal perception were impossible to reproduce, even though all actual partners tried systematically and honestly to recapture "what actually happened."

The subject speaks and acts "in the present," and not in the past, because the past is related to memory and speaking in the past tense removes the subject from the immediacy of experience, turns him into a spectator or a storyteller rather than an actor.

The inability to recall perfectly indicates that such recall is a practical impossibility, absolute recall does not exist and correct reproduction is a hardly attainable ideal. Furthermore, spontaneity and "presentness" are subjugated to correct reproduction and thus disappears. To release spontaneity and increase presentness in the here and now, the protagonist is specifically instructed to make time his servant, not his master, to "act as if this is happening to you *now*, so that you can feel, perceive and act as if this were happening to you for the first time."

III

"The subject must act out 'his truth,' as he feels and perceives it, in a completely subjective manner (no matter how distorted this appears to the spectator)."

The warming up process can not proceed properly unless we accept the patient with all his subjectivity. Enactment comes first, retraining comes later. We must give him the satisfaction of act completion first, before considering re-training for behavior changes.

IV

"The patient is encouraged to maximize all expression, action, and verbal communication, rather than to reduce it."

To this end, delusions, hallucinations, soliloquies, thoughts, fantasies, projections, are all allowed to be a part of the production. Again, restraint has to come after expression, though it should never be overlooked. Without, however,

[2]Zerka T. Moreno, A Survey of Psychodramatic Techniques, *Group Psychotherapy*, Vol. XII, 1959.

getting expression in toto, restraint can at best be only partial.

V

"The warming up process proceeds from the periphery to the center."

The director will, therefore, not begin with the most traumatic events in the patient's life. The commencement is on a more superficial level, allowing the self-involvement of the patient to carry him more deeply towards the core. The director's skills will be expressed in the construction of the scenes and the choice of persons or objects needed to assist the patient in his warming up.

VI

"Whenever possible, the protagonist will pick the time, the place, the scene, the auxiliary ego he requires in the production of his psychodrama."

The director serves as dramaturg in assisting the protagonist. The director and protagonist are partners; at one moment the director may be more active, but the protagonist always reserves the right to decline the enactment of, or to change a scene. Furthermore, when the interaction between patient and director becomes negative, the patient resisting the director as well as the process, the director may: (1) ask the patient to designate another director—if more than one are present; or (2) ask the patient to sit down and watch a mirror production of himself by auxiliary ego or egos; or (3) turn the direction over to the patient himself, who may then involve others in the group as auxiliary egos; or (4) ask the patient to choose another scene; or (5) explain to the patient why he chose a particular scene and, even though it may not be carried out now, the patient should understand his rationale in making the choice; or (6) return to such an enactment at a later time if he continues to believe the patient needs this; or (7) insist upon its enactment if he believes that the benefits to be derived thereby for the patient are greater than his resistance.

VII

"Psychodrama is just as much a method of restraint as it is a method of expression."

The repressiveness of our culture has attached to "expression per se" a value which is often beyond its actual reward. In such methods as role reversal, or enactment of roles which require restraint, retraining and/or reconditioning of excitability lies a greatly underestimated and disregarded application of psychodrama.

One thinks here especially of the chronic bad actor in life, the delinquent or psychopath, whose ability for self-restraint has not been strengthened by his warming up to stresses in life.

VIII

"The patient is permitted to be as unspontaneous or inexpressive as he is at this time."

This may seem to be a contradiction to the Fourth Imperative above, but only apparently so. Thus "maximizing of expression" may also refer to the patient's inability to express, his withdrawal, his submerged anger, etc. First we must accept this inability, and assist him to accept himself; gradually we try to release him from his own bonds by various methods as asides or soliloquies, the use of the double, etc.

The fact that a patient lacks in spontaneity is not a block to psychodramatic production. That is the reason for the existence of auxiliary egos who are trained to support, assist and strengthen the patient. Thus, also, have developed techniques as the soliloquy, the double, the mirror, role reversal, etc. The person who is unable to be spontaneous as himself, in his own roles, may become extremely spontaneous in role reversal as his wife, father, baby, pet dog, etc. His expressiveness will grow as his spontaneity increases. Expressiveness at any price is not necessarily spontaneous. It may be a cover-up for genuine feelings, as for instance, by producing a steady flow of words and actions. A patient may be entirely spontaneous, for instance, while sitting quietly in a chair, or observing others around him.

IX

"Interpretation and insight-giving in psychodrama is of a different nature from the verbal types of psychotherapy."

In psychodrama we speak of action insight, action learning, or action catharsis. It is an integrative process brought about by the synthesis of numerous techniques at the height of the protagonist's warm up. Psychodrama is actually the most interpretative method there is, but the director acts upon his interpretations in the construction of the scenes. Verbal interpretation may either be essential, or entirely omitted at the discretion of the director. Because his interpretation is in the act, it is frequently redundant.

X

"Even when interpretation is given, action is primary. There can be no interpretation without previous action."

Interpretation may be questioned, rejected or totally ineffective. The action speaks for itself. Furthermore, interpretation is colored by the orientation of the individual therapist. Thus, a Freudian will interpret from a different framework than an Adlerian, Jungian, Horneyan, etc. But that does not in any way change the value of the production itself. It merely puts interpretation into a lesser rung of importance. At times, indeed, interpretation may be destructive rather than constructive; it may be that what the patient requires is not analysis, but emotional identification.

XI

"Warming up to psychodrama may proceed differently from culture to culture and appropriate changes in the application of the method have to be made."

It may be impossible to start a psychodrama in the Congo by verbal exchange; it may be necessary to start with singing and dancing. What may be a suitable warm up in Manhattan may fall flat in Tokyo. Cultural adaptations must be made. The important thing is not how to begin but what we begin.

XII

"Psychodrama sessions consist of three portions: the warm up, the action portion and the post-action sharing by the group."

Disturbances in any one of these areas reflect upon the total process. However, "sharing" may at times be of a nonverbal nature, a silence pregnant with emotion is often the most suitable way of sharing with a protagonist, or going out to coffee together, or making plans to meet again, or whatever.

XIII

"The protagonist should never be left with the impression that he is all alone with this type of problem in this group."

The director must draw from the group, in the post-action discussion phase, identifications with the subject. This will establish anchorages in the group for mutually satisfying relations among group members, increase cohesion and broaden interpersonal perceptions.

When there is no one in the audience who openly identifies with the subject, the protagonist feels denuded, robbed of that most sacred part of himself, his private psyche. Then it is the task of the director to reveal himself as not merely in sympathy with the protagonist, but as being or having been similarly burdened. It is not analysis which is indicated here, but love and sharing of the self. The only way to repay a person for giving of himself is in kind. This will frequently warm up other persons in the audience to come forward in a similar manner, thus involving the audience in a genuine warming up which once more includes the protagonist, and helps to establish closure.

XIV

"The protagonist must learn to take the role of all those with whom he is meaningfully related, to experience those persons in his social atom, their relationship to him and to one another."

Taking this step further still, the patient must learn to "become" in psychodrama that which he sees, feels, hears, smells, dreams, loves, hates, fears, rejects, is rejected by, is attracted to, is wanted by, wants to avoid, wants to become, fears to become, fears not to become, etc.

The patient has "taken unto himself" with greater or lesser success, those persons, situations, experiences and perceptions from which he is now suffering. In order to overcome the distortions and manifestations of imbalance, he has to re-integrate them on a new level. Role reversal is one of methods par excellence in achieving this, so that he can re-integrate, redigest and grow beyond those experiences which are of negative impact, free himself and become more spontaneous along positive lines.

XV

"The director must trust the psychodrama method as the final arbiter and guide in the therapeutic process."

This imperative is so universal that it finds confirmation among psychodramatic director-therapists. When the warm up of the director is objective, the spontaneity of his presence and availability to the needs of the patient and the group, or, conversely stated, when there is no anxiety in his performance, then the psychodramatic method becomes a flexible, all embracing medium leading systematically to the heart of the patient's suffering, enabling the director, the protagonist, the auxiliary egos and the group members to become a cohesive force, welded into maximizing emotional learning.

TECHNIQUES

SOLILOQUY

A monologue of the protagonist *in situ*, for example, the patient is preparing to go to bed, combing her hair, speaks to herself: "Why don't I cut my hair short again? It is such a nuisance, this long hair. On the other hand, it really suits me better this way and I don't look like everybody else."

THERAPEUTIC SOLILOQUY

The portrayal by side dialogues and side actions, of hidden thoughts and feelings, parallel with overt thoughts and actions.

Patient is confronting her superior, who has called her on the carpet for participating in civil rights demonstrations. The auxiliary ego as the superior, asks her to account for her whereabouts the previous evening. Patient tells her she went to visit a sick friend. Auxiliary ego states she has evidence that this is not the truth. Director stops the overt action, asks patient to express how she feels, explains that "her superior" won't hear her and will not react, since she could not have known what was going on inside of her in the real situation. Patient

states: "I really *did* go to that demonstration; she can't really do anything to me because I have tenure, but she can make it unpleasant for me." Director: "What do you want to do?" Patient: "Give her a raspberry, but of course, I can't." Director: "Here you can." Patient belches lustily. Director asks her now to continue the scene as it was and end it on the reality level.

SELF-PRESENTATION

The protagonist presents himself, his own mother, his own father, his brother, his favorite professor, etc. He acts all these roles himself, in complete subjectiveness, as he experiences and perceives them.

SELF-REALIZATION

Protagonist enacts, with the aid of a few auxiliary egos, the plan of his life, no matter how remote this may be from his present situation. For instance, he is actually an accountant, but for a long time he has been going to singing lessons, hoping to try out for a part in summer stock in musical comedy, planning eventually to make this his life's work. Alternatives may be explored: success of this venture, possible failure, the return to his old livelihood, or preparing for still another one, etc.

TELIC SENSITIVITY AND SENSITIVITY TRAINING

"Telic sensitivity may be described as some real process in one person's life situation which is sensitive and corresponds to some real process in another person's life situation. There are numerous degrees, positive and negative, of these 'inter-personal sensitivities.' "[3] To speak of sensitivity training in a general, non-defined manner, is to overlook this telic basis for sensitivity.

A feeling complex which goes out from a person does not run wildly into space, but goes to a certain other person and that other person, in turn, does not accept this passively like a robot, but responds actively with another feeling complex. One tele may become interlocked with another tele, a pair-relation being formed.

Sensitivity training, so commonly practiced today, clearly derives from this kind of inter-personal approach, albeit in a watered-down

[3] See J. L. Moreno, *Sociometry* (Beacon House, 1937), Vol. I, Pp. 9–80, 372–74.

form. In the original application the subject is faced with persons and situations which have meaning for him. Without such motivation, the proper warm-up can not be achieved and sensitivity training, hit or miss, bastardizes the method and reduces its validity.

Encounter and Encounter Groups

Encounter[4] is the English translation of the German *Begegnung*, a concept introduced by Moreno in 1914. In therapy as well as in life, it spells out a meeting of two human beings, I and Thou, in their genuine humanness, revealing themselves to one another and learning to look at each other intimately, without fear of shame, recrimination or rejection. From this concept and the motto used by psychodramatists for over fifty years, "A meeting of two, eye to eye, face to face," Moreno developed the idea of the "Encounter Group,"[5] which may not exactly be a therapy group, nor a training group, nor will it resemble groups as they occur in life itself, rather it represents an existential form of experiencing one another's personalities in the here-and-now, with all that this implies of past, present and future, of faults, failings and also of positive worth. This may be done by looking intently at one another, by bodily contact, touching, dancing, clinging, caressing, walking, often through non-verbal ways of interacting.

Hallucinatory Psychodrama

The patient enacts the hallucinations and delusions he is at present experiencing (though they may not be so designated by the director). Patient portrays the voices he hears, the sounds emanating from the chair he sits on, the visions he has when the trees outside his window turn into monsters which pursue him. Auxiliary egos are called to enact the various phenomena expressed by the patient, to involve him in interaction with them, so as to put them to a reality test.

---

[4]Paul E. Johnson, *Psychology and Religion* (Nashville: Abingdon Press, 1959).

[5]See J. L. Moreno's reply to Robert R. Blake in *Group Training vs. Group Therapy*, Sociometry Monograph No. 35 (Beacon House, 1958).

Double

The patient portrays himself, an auxiliary ego is asked also to represent the patient, to "establish identity with the patient," to move, act, behave like the patient. The patient is preparing to get up in the morning, he is in bed. The auxiliary ego lies down on the stage alongside of him, taking the same bodily posture. The double may start speaking: "What is the use of waking up? I have nothing to live for." Patient: "Yes, that is true, I have no reason for living." Auxiliary ego: "But I am a very talented artist, there have been times when life has been very satisfying." Patient: "Yes, but it seems a long time ago." Auxiliary ego: "Maybe I can get up and start to paint again." Patient: "Well, let's try and get up first, anyway, and see what will happen." Both patient and auxiliary ego get up, go through the motions of washing, shaving, brushing teeth, all along moving together as if they were one. The auxiliary ego becomes the link through which the patient may try to reach out into the real world.

Multiple Double

The protagonist is on the stage with several doubles of himself, each portraying another part of the patient, one as he is now, another as he was five years ago, a third as he was when at three years of age he first heard that his mother had died, another how he may be twenty years hence. The multiple representations of the patient are simultaneously present and act in sequence, one continuing where the other left off.

Mirror

When the patient is unable to represent himself, in word or action, an auxiliary ego is placed on the action portion of the psychodramatic space. The patient or patients remain seated in the group portion. The auxiliary ego re-enacts the patient, copying his behavior and trying to express his feelings in word and movement, showing the patient or patients "as if in a mirror" how other people experience him.

The mirror may be exaggerated, employing techniques of deliberate distortion in order to arouse the patient to come forth and change from a passive spectator into an active participant, an actor, to correct what he feels is not the right enactment and interpretation of himself.

ROLE-REVERSAL

The patient, in an inter-personal situation, for instance, with his mother, "steps into his mother's shoes" while the mother steps into those of her son. The mother may be the real mother, as is done in psychodrama in situ,[6] or may be represented by an auxiliary ego. In role reversal, the son is now enacting his mother, the mother enacting the son. Distortions of inter-personal perception can be brought to the surface, explored and corrected in action. The son, who is still himself, must now warm up to how his mother may be feeling and perceiving himself, the mother, now the son, goes through the same process.

A mother of an eight-year-old girl, after showing how they argue for ten minutes every morning during the winter as to what clothing the child should wear to school, is asked after their own roles have become clear, to take the role of Kay; Kay is asked to take the role of her mother. They are instructed to change place in space, to assume the role of the other, the posture and position each had.

Kay stretches a foot in the role of her mother, shows authority and certainty, whereas in her own role her anxiety was very evident. Mother now has to subdue her ebullience and restrain herself to be her somewhat withdrawn daughter. Both open their eyes wide at the image each holds before the other. Mother remarks when this scene is ended: "Am I really as aggressive as Kay portrayed me? My poor Kay!"

FUTURE PROJECTION

The patient portrays in action how he thinks his future will shape itself. He picks the point in time—or is assisted by the director to do so—the place and the people, if any, whom he expects to be involved with at that time.

The patient is studying to be an English

[6]J. L. and Z. T. Moreno, "The Discovery of the Spontaneous Man," *Psychodrama* (Beacon House, 1959), Vol. II.

major and has his bachelor's degree; he has been working on his M.A. for almost eight years, is unable to complete it. The future projection shows him three years hence, teaching his first course in English at the university. The entire audience is his class; he is asked to face them and inspire them with the beauty of the English language. "My name is Mr. Johnson; it is a very ordinary and yet beautiful name. I should like to welcome you here today, by asking you all to introduce yourselves to one another. But remember, that name stands for you. Try to present it in such a way that it sings, that it reaches out to the other as if to say 'here I am, who are you?'"

DREAM PRESENTATION

The patient enacts a dream, instead of telling it. He takes the position he usually has in bed, when sleeping; before lying down and taking the position of the sleeper, he warms up to the setting separately. The director asks him when and where he had this dream, to describe the room, the location and size of the bed, the color of his pajamas, whether he wears top and bottom, or sleeps in the nude, whether he sleeps alone, with the light on or off, with windows open or closed, and how long it normally takes him to fall asleep.

The patient is asked, in the lying down position, to breathe deeply and evenly, as he does in sleep, to move in bed as he does ordinarily while asleep, and lastly, to relax and let himself drift off. The final instructions of the director are: "Try, without telling me about it, to visualize in your mind the beginning, the middle, and the end. Do you see it? Just answer yes or no."

When the patient has fixed the various images somewhat in his mind's eye, the director asks: "Where are you in the dream? Do you see yourself? Yes? Then step out of the dream. What are you doing, walking, swimming, sitting, running, what?" Patient: "I do not see myself, I am in the dream." Director: "You are acting, doing something?" Patient: "Yes, I am flying, over the rooftops of houses." Director: "Do you see the rooftops? Get up and start to take a position resembling flying, here, stand on top of this table." Patient climbs on table, leans forward somewhat. "Yes, I see the rooftops, in fact, I'm hardly able to fly over them, sometimes it seems I'm going to crash into them." Director: "Where are these buildings and what are they?" Patient: "This is a residential section, in fact, as I realize now, this is the suburb where I live!" Director: "Do you see your house?" Patient: "No, but I seem to sense this is my section." Director: "Are you the only one who is flying? Are you alone?" Patient: "No, I am carrying a bundle in my arms." Director: "In both arms, or only in one? Look at your arms." Patient looks down at his arms which appear to be carrying something, then drops his left arm, says: "My right arm." Director: "What is in the bundle, do you know its contents?" Patient: (Looking intently at his right arm, crooked around an object, amazed): "It's a baby." Director: "Whose?" Patient: "My parents'; it's my baby sister, we are 18 years apart in age." Director motions to an auxiliary ego to come upon the stage to represent the baby. The baby is asked to kneel in such a way that the top of her head is approximately at the height of his right elbow, and the director asks the protagonist to hold her as best he can. Director: "What are you doing there, flying with her?" Patient: "I am carrying her with me through life, protecting her from harm, but I'm not very sure that I am able to do this; I seem to have trouble keeping her aloft with me." Director: "Are you afraid?" Patient: "Afraid, but also very angry." Director: "Angry at whom? The baby?" Patient: "No, at fate. Why should I be saddled with this responsibility? She is my parents' child, not mine." Director: "In the actual dream, do you speak to your baby sister?" Patient: "No." Director: "Well, here you can." (This is a psychodramatic extension of the dream.) To auxiliary ego baby: "Talk to your older brother." Baby (auxiliary ego): "I am a bit scared flying this high. Do you hold me carefully?" Patient: "I am doing my best, but you are very heavy." Baby: "You won't drop me, will you?" Patient: "I can't, though frankly, I'd like to." Baby: "Why? Are you angry at me for being here with you?" Patient: "Not at you, but after all, I'm not ready for such responsibility yet, I'm just starting college, and you're just a tiny infant." Baby: "I like you, you

are my big, strong brother." Director: "What happens next in the dream?" Patient: "I clutch her and the dream just fades off." Director: "You do not see any conclusive ending? Concentrate for a moment." Patient: "No, I just wake up in a cold sweat." Director dismisses auxiliary ego, returns patient to the position of the sleeper, back in bed. Director: "You wake up in a cold sweat." Patient: "Yes, I'm thoroughly soaked."

RE-TRAINING OF THE DREAM

Director: "Sounds like a very frightening dream. Obviously, you wish it had not ended this way." Patient: "I even wish it had never started!" Director: "Yes, of course. You see, in psychodrama, we can 'change the dream.' When you are there, at night, things happen to you which appear to be out of your control. But, after all, it is you who produced the dream, because of your fears and anxieties. We believe that if we can help you to change your dream pattern, to train your unconscious, so to speak, the next time when you are dreaming, your dreams will change in character, you will be in better control. Now, let's see how you wish to change your dream." Patient: "I don't want to have this dream at all." Director: "Yes, I can see that, but what would you like to do instead?" Patient: "I would want to have a good talk with my parents." Director: "Fine, let's have a good talk with your parents. Get up, and pick a mother and father from the group, two auxiliary egos to represent them. Patient does so, and sets up the livingroom of their house. Patient now confronts his parents: "Gee Mom, Dad, I know you have both been very ill in the past year, and, being the oldest son, I feel terribly burdened by the responsibility of the two younger kids, especially about Alice. Timmy is already older and not quite such a problem, but Alice is just a little infant." Director: "Tell them as brutally as possible what is on your mind; after all, these are not your 'real' parents, merely stand-ins. They will not be hurt by anything you say or feel or do." Patient: (blurts out) "Why the devil did you have to go and have a menopause baby? Don't you think you have enough complications? Mother works, the housekeeper is terrible, she doesn't even speak English, is my kid sister going to learn broken English? And don't you care what she eats? That dope can't even cook, all the kid gets is cereals and mashed banana." Now mother and father respond, try to soothe the patient, he role reverses with them, and finally, feels more reassured that his parents still have the major responsibility for the child.

This is the unique contribution of psychodrama to dream therapy, to go into enactment over and beyond the actual dream, including actual and latent material, but even more, to retrain the dreamer rather than to interpret. Interpretation is in the act itself.

THERAPEUTIC COMMUNITY

This is a community in which disputes and conflicts between individuals and groups are settled under the rule of therapy instead of the rule of law. The entire population, patients and staff alike, are responsible for the welfare of every other person, participate in the therapeutic process and have equal status.

ADJUNCTIVE METHODS

HYPNODRAMA

Hypnosis is induced on the psychodrama stage portion. The hypnotizant is free to act, to move about, and is given auxiliary egos to help portray his drama. Hypnodrama is a merging of hypnotherapy with psychodrama.

PSYCHODRAMATIC SHOCK

The patient is asked to throw himself back into the hallucinatory experience while it is still vivid. He does not describe it, he must act. He puts his body into the position in which it was then, in the space he was in, at the time of day or night when this actually occurred. He may select a staff member to recreate the hallucinatory involvement.[7]

The patient may show resistance against being placed again into the horrifying experience from which he has just emerged. His natural bent is to forget, not to talk about it and to leave it behind. He is full of fears that his newfound

freedom may be shattered. The mere recall frightens him, and the idea of enactment still more. The psychodramatic director explains that it is to learn control, not a mere reliving, that this reenactment will help him build resources against recurrence.

Once the patient has warmed himself up again into the psychotic state, and has thoroughly enacted it, the director stops him, to assist the patient in the realization that he can construct his own inner controls.

IMPROVISATION FOR PERSONALITY ASSESSMENT

The subject is brought into the psychodrama theater or the life situation without any prior preparation. The director has structured the situation in advance with the aid of auxiliary egos. The subject is then asked to warm up to the situation as he would do if it were actually happening to him.

The subject is told he is in his car, driving on the highway. He is alone. Suddenly he hears a siren and a police car comes alongside, then ahead of him. The policeman stops him, walks over to him, demands to see his license and gives him a tonguelashing because he was driving 20 miles over the speed limit. He gives him a ticket for speeding.

Or: the subject enters a cafeteria. An auxiliary ego, obviously the worse for indulgence in alcohol, approaches him and asks for money.

Numerous sets of standard situations have been devised and they enable the director and group members to get a profile of the action potential of the individual which paper and pencil tests are unable to uncover.[8]

DIDACTIC PSYCHODRAMA AND ROLE PLAYING

Used as a teaching method, auxiliary egos, nurses, social workers, psychologists, psychiatrists, are taking the role of a patient, in a situation of everyday occurrence for instance, the patient who refuses to obey rules as they are applied in the hospital or clinic setting. The students learn to take both roles, those of a patient, as well as their own professional role. The training situations are structured according to typical conflicts with which they are familiar,

---

[7]J. L. Moreno, "Psychodramatic Shock Therapy," *Psychodrama and Group Psychotherapy* Monograph No. 5. (Beacon, N.Y.: Beacon House, 1939).

[8]Office of Strategic Services, *Assessment of Men* (New York: Rinehart, 1947).

or which they are likely to face in their professional roles. Several versions of how to deal with the obstreperous patient can be represented by various students. The patient is usually portrayed by an auxiliary ego, a staff member, so that real patients need not be involved.

Another teaching application is to have staff members sit in on actual patient sessions, becoming involved as seems necessary. In this event, the patient represents himself, the staff members themselves. Role reversal between staff member and patient will intensify learning, with each getting a new perception of their relationship and of the responsibility in being a staff member, and the agony of being a patient.

PSYCHODRAMA COMBINED WITH NARCOSYNTHESIS, LSD, ETC.

Under the influence of drugs, the patient relives certain experiences or, after having undergone drug therapy, needs to integrate his melodrama as it unfolded inside of him, while he was unable to communicate those experiences.

There are two variables, the drug, for instance Pentothal Sodium, and the enactment of the inner worlds. The question here is which variable contributes what to the treatment.

FAMILY PSYCHODRAMA AND FAMILY THERAPY

Husband and wife, mother and child, are treated as a combine rather than alone, often facing one another and not separate, because separate from one another they may not have any tangible mental ailment.[9]

In the course of this approach the family members may reverse roles, double for each other, and in general, serve as each other's auxiliary ego.

SUMMARY

The important question which remains to be answered is the scientific evaluation of psychodrama. Does psychodrama, with or without group psychotherapy, beyond the subjective reports of therapists and their patients, produce behavior change? According to John Mann[10] forty-one studies have substantiated that fundamental changes in behavior take place.

[9]J. L. Moreno, *Group Psychotherapy, A Symposium* (Beacon, N.Y.: Beacon House, 1945), p. 316. J. L., Z. T. and J. D. Moreno, *The First Psychodramatic Family* (Beacon, N.Y.: Beacon House, 1964).

[10]John Mann, "Evaluation of Group Psychotherapy," *International Handbook of Group Psychotherapy*, Ed. J. L. Moreno (New York: Philosophical Library, 1965).

70.

ROBERT W. WHITE

FIVE BASIC PROCESSES IN PSYCHOTHERAPY

We are now in a position to try to discern the fundamental processes that are at work in psychotherapy. Nothing that we have studied violates the general principle that the essence of therapy is a corrective emotional experience which opens the way to changes in feeling and behavior. No one today will raise the flag for bare intellectual understanding as a means of

treatment. Our search for basic processes therefore resolves itself into an attempt to isolate the measures taken to favor corrective emotional experiences.

It seems possible to name five processes which pretty well cover the action that goes on in psychotherapy.

1. *Therapeutic Relationship.* First there is the creation of a unique situation and a unique personal relationship. There are four important aspects of the therapeutic situation. (*a*) The

therapist is *expert,* in the sense that he possesses special training, experience, and knowledge about maladjusted and disordered behavior. (*b*) The therapist is *permissive,* in the sense that he serves only the interests of health and makes no censorious judgments upon the patient's acts or feelings. (*c*) The therapist is *interested and friendly,* communicating in this way a certain warmth that makes the relationship more personal than is ordinarily the case in a professional consultation. (*d*) The therapist is a *source of encouragement.* While it is necessary to avoid all false reassurance, the effect of his presence is to increase courage. The patient dares to express feelings and relax defenses because of his strengthening alliance with the therapist. It is within the shelter of this relationship that corrective emotional experience begins to take place.

2. *Expression of Feelings.* Steps are taken to encourage the patient to express his feelings. This may be done by asking questions, by taking a case history, or by encouraging the patient to give his own story. From non-directive counseling, however, we learned that feelings come to expression more readily when the patient rather than the therapist leads the way in the conversation. In this chapter we have also studied a technical device for increasing the expression of feelings. *Free association* is intended to remove superficial resistances and bring into prominence the emotional patterns that stand in need of correction.

3. *Pointing out of Feelings.* The action of the therapist upon what the patient expresses consists essentially of pointing out the feelings. In this way the patient becomes more fully aware of his feelings; he develops insight and is thus better able to profit by further experiences in which he is moved by the same feelings. We have examined two forms of the pointing out procedure. (*a*) *Recognition of feeling,* the process neatly isolated by Rogers, consists of paraphrasing what the patient says in such a way as to emphasize its feeling implications. The therapist sets the focus of interest on feeling and brings about a greater expression of feeling than is usual for the patient. The changes that ensue from this free expression in the presence of the therapist constitute in

themselves a corrective emotional experience. (*b*) *Interpretation,* the cornerstone of psychoanalytic procedure may be regarded as a more active form of recognition. Instead of recognizing the patient's feelings as they are expressed, the therapist recognizes feelings before they are expressed or when they are still being expressed in disguised ways—at all events, before the patient himself has recognized them. When suitably timed this procedure also results in corrective emotional experience.

4. *Transference.* The initial therapeutic relationship can readily become colored by chillike attitudes in the patient. The importance of the treatment is so great, and the emotions involved so strong, that the patient can hardly avoid developing certain feelings that have little to do with the actual situation and much to do with his own past. The transference of childlike feelings into the therapeutic relationship can be either discouraged or encouraged by the therapist. If the patient is allowed to develop the same emotional conflicts in relation to the therapist that he had with parental and other important figures in early life, a situation is created that is peculiarly favorable for interpretation. The *transference neurosis,* as developed in Freudian psychoanalysis, is a state of very real emotion, but the experience becomes corrective only when through interpretation the patient realizes the inappropriate character of his feelings and reappraises the archaic dangers from which they spring.

5. *New Behavior.* As treatment progresses, the patient begins to behave in new ways outside the therapeutic relationship. He starts to replace his rooted maladjustive patterns with better adjusted forms of behavior. To the extent that these new actions are successful and prove rewarding, they constitute corrective emotional experience. The possibility of dissolving the therapeutic relationship can be gauged from the success and stability of the patient's new behavior. A variety of attitudes can be taken toward what the patient does in his actual life, ranging all the way from simple recognition through encouragement to persuasion and direction. We saw that the client-centered counselor never explicitly urged any line of new conduct upon his client but was quick to recog-

nize it when it occurred, thus strengthening it by implicit subsequent approval. Standard psychoanalysis also steers away from explicit direction, preferring to work out the transference relation thoroughly before the patient tries his wings in new ventures. Psychoanalytically oriented psychotherapy is more apt to be flexible on this matter, but not to the point of bluntly urging the patient to behave differently and change his attitudes.

The reluctance of psychotherapists to exert a direct pressure of this kind should not blind us to the presence of a certain indirect pressure. Jerome Frank argues that in all methods of psychotherapy there is an inescapable element of persuasion.[1] Even if nothing is said about new behavior, something is inevitably implied. The therapist may sedulously avoid comments of a censorious nature and try to keep his own preferences and ideals out of the conversation; but it is clear that in the end he is against the irrational anxieties, defensiveness, and symptoms that make for neurosis, and in favor of a more free and healthful pattern of life. Patient and therapist alike know that change is desirable; the whole point of their relation is to produce it. Thus it is likely that a subtle kind of persuasion plays its part in the process of psychotherapy, but the work we have thus far studied suggests that better results are obtained when this is kept out of the foreground.

CHOICE OF PATIENTS FOR PSYCHOTHERAPY

As a practical matter it has long been recognized that some patients are more suitable than others for psychotherapy. Although corrective emotional experience and subsequent relearning do not seem to imply any special kind of talent, therapists have learned that in any given case of psychogenic disorder it is wise to try to estimate the patient's chances of developing and profiting by such experiences. Obviously the presence of important organic difficulties and instabilities makes psychological treatment problematical and suggests that if used at all it

should be combined with supportive and somatic measures. The real circumstances surrounding the patient also have to be carefully assessed. He may be burdened by inescapable responsibilities which contribute heavily to his trouble. Ideally the patient should be in a position to change those circumstances in his life that tend to reinforce neurotic patterns of behavior and to oppose new ones. On this account it is generally true that youth is an advantage, though advanced age is not an absolute contra-indication. In private practice there is also the question of ability to pay, and here and in public clinics the patient may find it difficult to set aside the necessary time. All of these considerations, however, lie outside the psychological sphere. Are there any strictly psychological dimensions to the problem of selecting patients?

There seems to be substantial agreement among different workers concerning three such dimensions.

1. First there is the question of motivation or need. As Rogers expresses it, the patient must be "under a degree of tension, arising from incompatible personal desires or from the conflict of social and environmental demands with individual needs."[2] Discomfort and tension must be great enough to overbalance the stress that inevitably arises during treatment. When patients seek help of their own accord, this first condition is usually met, but when they have been sent for treatment the therapist must judge carefully whether their own motives will become enlisted. Psychotherapy is a learning situation, and the factor of motivation cannot be neglected.

2. Intelligence cannot be ruled out, inasmuch as psychotherapy proceeds through the medium of conversation and requires a coherent reporting and synthesizing of one's experience. Feeblemindedness would bar psychotherapy, and there is considerable doubt about the dull-normal range.

3. An elusive factor variously known as adaptability, ego potentiality, and capacity to cope with life must be weighed as well as possible in estimating the chances for success.

---

[1] J. D. Frank, *Persuasion and Healing: A Comparative Study of Psychotherapy* (Baltimore: Johns Hopkins Press, 1961).

[2] C. R. Rogers, *Counseling and Psychotherapy.* Boston: Houghton Mifflin, 1942. P. 76.

Hendrick refers to this factor as "strength of character" or, more precisely, "the capacity to endure an excess of emotional tension, to strive for reasonable goals in spite of inner difficulties which tempt one to accept the decision, 'I am just made that way,' as an excuse for withdrawing from struggle." He adds, "The patient's capacity to fight the neurosis is a great asset, and it varies as greatly among individuals as does the degree of neurosis itself."[3] Obviously it is no mean task to estimate such a capacity beforehand.

[3] I. Hendrick. *Facts and Theories of Psychoanalysis* (2nd ed.) New York: Alfred A. Knopf, 1939. Pp. 240–241.

CHAPTER X

Social Psychopathology

SOCIAL PSYCHOPATHOLOGY, a young study yet in its infancy, has been gaining attention among psychopathologists in recent years partly due to the strides made by the milieu psychotherapists, partly owing to advances achieved by social psychopathologists dealing with statistics on social class and mental illness, and partly attributable to other factors, including sociopsychological hypotheses or theories of schizophrenia and studies in sociopathy. Inasmuch as the chapter on psychotherapy contained a discussion of the psychotherapeutic community (milieu therapy), that topic will be dispensed with in this chapter.

Some researchers regard the community or society as well as individuals as being mentally ill. Frank (1936) sees the society as the patient and claims a growing realization "that our culture is sick, mentally disordered and in need of treatment"; while Halliday (1945a, 1948) postulates mental disorder as an index of the psychological health of a community, attributing the rising incidence of psychosomatic illness to "a response to noxious psychological factors of environment" (1938, p. 13). Fromm, too, viewing psychopathology from a social orientation, seeks to establish a "sane society" in the form of his proposed humanistic communitarian socialism (1955). He explains the psychosis of totalitarian movements in terms of man's craving to escape from his earlier won freedom that failed to afford the autonomy to construct a "meaningful life based on reason and love" (1941). Supplanting the Freudian concept of libidinal development, Fromm prefers a development of the "evolution of character in interpersonal terms" (1947), one of "humanistic psychoanalysis," the fundamental premise being "that the basic passions of man are not rooted in his instinctive needs, but in the specific conditions of human existence, in the need to find a new relatedness to man and nature after having lost the primary relatedness of the pre-human stage" (1955, p. viii). Fromm underscores the danger of alienation owing to its dehumanizing effect (1965). He develops his thought further by showing that man has the capacity to love (1956) as well as the capacity to destroy (1964), the former being a "syndrome of growth" or the love of life, independence, and conquest over narcissism, and the latter being a "syndrome of decay," or the love of death, malignant narcissism, and incestuous symbiosis.

In his experimental research, Calhoun (1962) encountered what he termed *behavioral sink*, a social psychopathological phenomenon occurring among populations of his domesticated albino rats in which their normal social behavioral patterns were disrupted, with pansexuality, "pathological togetherness," and disorganization dominant.

SOCIAL CLASS AND PSYCHOPATHOLOGY

Sociocultural factors in psychopathology received a potent impact with the publication of *Social Class and Mental Illness* by Hollingshead and Redlich (1958), a study revealing the commensurate relationship between the lower social class and a corresponding higher rate of psychosis among them. An inverse relationship was found to exist between neurotic and psychotic among the upper and lower classes, so that neurosis declined from the higher to the lower classes while psychosis increased. Their research concluded that mental illness is correlated to social class, that the social position and status of the mentally-ill patient affects his treatment for his disorder because the treatment varies according to his respective class status, that specific classes exhibit specific types of psychopathology, and that social reaction to the presence of mental illness differs according to each class.

In a study dealing with social class and alcoholism, Schmidt and his group (1968) found facts corroborating the Hollingshead and Redlich study. They concluded that "class differences make it more likely that mental illness will develop in lower class persons, that it will last longer, and that it will be less adequately treated. Furthermore, for those lower class patients who come to the treatment agency, mental illness is like only one of a number of disturbances" (1968, p. 9).

In another study of schizophrenics of lower socioeconomic status in Puerto Rico by Hollingshead and Rogler (1962), mental illness was for the families of the ill studied virtually a way of life or part of their lives, and "eighty-five per cent of the sick families report a mentally ill member in either the husbands' or wives' family of orientation, while only fifty-five per cent of the well families report a mentally ill member in either the parental or the sibling generation" (1962, p. 394).

Freeman and Simmons (1959, 1963), studying social class and post-hospital levels of performance, found that a critical factor that affects the course of the patient's posthospital experience consists of the values of, the part played by, or the attitude of the family members regarding tolerance of deviant behavior. They claim their findings support their hypothesis of a direct relationship existing between the patient's post-hospital performance levels and the social class status of his family. "Tolerance of deviance on the part of family members has been posited as a key factor in the prolonged community tenure of former patients who function at inadequate levels" (Simmons & Freeman, 1959, p. 233).

In a subsequent study, Freeman and Simmons (1961) found that on the whole recent innovations endorsed in hospital regime and release practices failed to be accompanied by appropriate programs effective in extending the therapeutic process (as a treatment base) to the community and family of the patient. They suspect the reason may be that community agencies, owing to their exhausted resources, do not encourage former psychotics' participation in these programs; or that the patients' low socioeconomic status is a deterrent from seeking professional help in their respective communities. It is possible that the rehospitalization rate is low among these former patients because of their lack of contact with professionals and their relative nonidentity in larger communities.

SOCIALLY SHARED PSYCHOPATHOLOGY

In a study on the sharing of disordered functioning by psychotics who are close associates, Gruenberg (1957) concluded: (1) social groupings do occur among mentally ill persons; (2) people can be bound together in groups owing to disordered functioning; (3) unusual health, rather than mental disorder, may be implied by one's alienation from his close associates; (4) ideas, attitudes, feelings, activities, and defense mechanisms are shared rather than the diagnostic groupings common among psychiatrists; (5) shared disordered functioning is more common among women; (6) leaders tend to be more seriously disordered; and (7) group size varies from a couple to a nation; mutual contact is unnecessary when the group shares the same mass media of communication.

In examining shared neurosis in a cultural and familial context, Cleveland and Longaker (1957) found neurotic patterning to be partially "reaction to cultural process through which family members experience their basic introduction to culturally-defined paths of behavior" (1957, p. 194). The neurotic is seen as an exaggeration of disparagement, a common maladjustive mode of our culture. Through the socialization process, especially via the family, cultural value conflicts and ambiguities confront the individual early in life, setting a fertile field for neurotic growth.

Clausen (1957) traces shared mental illness of adolescents through common drug use, the practice of which enhances group cohesiveness, bolsters solidarity, possibly serving as a symbol of "consensual pattern," and thereby augmenting the individual's sense of group membership.

SOCIOCULTURAL CRITERION OF PSYCHOPATHOLOGY

Concluding from an examination of rare, unclassifiable, collective, and exotic psychotic syndromes that occur only in specific cultures and among certain groups while being absent in other societies, Arieti and Meth (1959) believe there is strong evidence for sociocultural etiology of mental disorder.

Mead (1967) carries this mode of reasoning one step further, questioning whether psychotic syndromes are significant only in respect to cultural norms in vogue in a given society. She cites the case of a colleague, an anthropologist, who was about to be attacked by a native with a spear readied to strike. While the children climbed trees, and shouted: "Don't hurt him; he'll be all right tomorrow;" the man's sister was summoned to calm the person temporarily mad. Rather than the attacker's behavior being considered deviant, "the only unusual element in this situation was the anthropologist, who hadn't climbed a tree in time," comments Mead.

The underlying philosophical rationale of the therapeutic community of Jones (1962, 1966) is that a sick society made one of its members ill, and it requires a wholesome therapeutic society to restore him to mental health. Jackson and Weakland (1961) find the mentally ill patient as a victim of a smaller society, that of a sick family.

Laing (1965, 1967) also considers psychosis as socioculturally designated, for he cites certain persons as "radically unsound," dangerous to self and others, but who socially are not regarded as psychotic, insane, or as persons fit for committal to a "madhouse." He observes:

A man who prefers to be dead rather than Red is normal. A man who says he has lost his soul is mad. A man who says that men are machines may be a great scientist. A man who says he *is* a machine is "depersonalized" in psychiatric jargon. A man who says that Negroes are an inferior race may be widely respected. A man who says his whiteness is a form of cancer is certifiable.

A little girl of seventeen in a mental hospital told me she was terrified because the Atom Bomb was inside her. That is a delusion. The statesmen of the world who boast and threaten that they have Doomsday weapons are far more dangerous, and far more estranged from "reality" than many of the people on whom the label "psychotic" is affixed. (1955, pp. 11–12).

The growing consensus of mental illness as social deviation is also shared by Szasz (1963) who tacitly endorses Lemert's (1951) position of mental illness as "sociopathic behavior." Primary and secondary forms of socially deviant behavior are distinguishable, the latter form being intolerable to society. Goffman (1961) notes that imprisonment and confinement to a mental institution are quite alike, accordingly mental hospitalization serves as a form of social control as if mental disorder is a form of crime rather than an illness. "Instead of recognizing the deviant as an individual different from those who judge him, but nevertheless worthy of their respect, he is first discredited as a self-responsible human being, and then subjected to humiliating punishment defined and disguised as treatment" (Szasz, 1963, p. 108).

Social learning theorists would also view maladaptive behavior in sociocultural terms. Bandura (1968b) repudiates psychodynamic formulations of mental disorder for an explanation of deviant behavior under the aegis of social learning principles.

Considering the arbitrary and relativistic nature of the social judgment and definition of deviance, the main value of the normal-abnormal dichotomy is in guiding the sociolegal actions of societal agents concerned with the maintenance of an efficiently functioning society. This dichotomy, however, has little theoretical significance since there is no evidence that the behaviors so dichotomized are either qualitatively different or under the control of fundamentally different variables (1968, p. 335).

Phillips (1968) entertains the thought that in technologically backward societies it may be that what in our society would be designated psychosis is normal for them because their entire society is in a state of immaturity. Consequently, in the rural society of Brazil it is normal to talk to God. Owing to belief in magical devices and supernaturalism, a person with certain psychotic symptoms (for Western society) would not be deviant in unsophisticated cultures. With the more advanced societies, there is a higher level of sophistication of personality development. In the estimation of Maher, mental deficiency is a phenomenon reached by culturally derived criteria:

What constitutes mentally retarded behavior depends to a large extent upon the society which happens to be making the judgment. An individual who does not create a problem for others in his social environment and who manages to become self-supporting is usually not defined as mentally retarded no matter what his test IQ may be. Mental retardation is primarily a socially defined phenomenon, and it is in large part meaningless to speak of mental retardation without this criterion in mind. (1963, p. 238).

71.

Maxwell Jones

THE THERAPEUTIC COMMUNITY: MILIEU THERAPY

The decentralization of large state hospitals into small, semi-autonomous units serving discrete geographical areas may prove to have many benefits for patient management and treatment. The improvement of communications both intra and extramurally, manifested by the establishment of closer ties between patients, staff and relatives, and with outside agencies, can be seen as advantageous. The smaller treatment units also allow for easier examination and modification of roles, role-relationships and the over-all culture on the unit.

This process can be developed further and a very different picture emerges when the above trends are developed and the sociocultural process becomes an integral part of treatment. The resultant picture is often called a therapeutic community or the process described as milieu therapy. I have elsewhere (21) described a therapeutic community as distinctive among other comparable treatment centers in the way the institution's total resources, both staff and patients, are self-consciously pooled in furthering treatment. This implies, above all, a change in the usual status of patients. In collaboration with the staff, they now become active participants in the therapy of themselves and other patients and in other aspects of the over-all hospital work—in contrast to their relatively more passive, recipient role in conventional treatment regimes.

SOCIAL STRUCTURE

The social structure of a therapeutic community is characteristically different from the more traditional hospital ward or decentralized unit. The term implies that the whole community of staff and patients is involved at least partly in treatment and administration. The extent to which this is practicable or desirable will depend on many variables including the attitude of the leader and the other staff, the type of patients being treated, and the sanctions afforded by higher authority. The emphasis on free communication in and between both staff and patient groups and on permissive attitudes which encourage free expression of feeling imply a democratic equalitarian rather than a traditional hierarchical social organization (68).

Staff and patient roles and role-relationships are the subject of frequent examination and discussion. This is devised to increase the effectiveness of roles and sharpen the community's perception of them. Thus, it may be felt that a nurse's role is clarified and rendered more effective if she ceases to wear a uniform. It may take months of study and discussion to decide that, say, a nurse requires on an average four months on a ward before she feels secure enough to discard her uniform. To share this discussion with the patients is to increase their awareness of the difficulties of a nursing role and may modify their relationship to the nurses. The aim is to achieve sufficient role flexibility so that the role at any one time reflects the expectations of behavior of both staff and patients collectively.

The examination and clarification of roles inevitably sharpens the role prescription but may at the same time lead to some role blurring. This is not contradictory. Thus, it may seem appropriate that nurses as well as social workers should visit patients' homes. The former might accompany patients on home visits to help in the rehabilitation process to the outside world and to encourage the family member to attend ward group meetings. The social worker might visit the home with the patient's approval but not in his presence. Her visit might be mainly

From Maxwell Jones, *Social psychiatry: In the community, in hospitals, and in prisons.* Springfield, Ill.: Charles C Thomas, 1962. Pp. 53–71. Reprinted by permission of the author.

to try and engage the family members in treatment which would be complementary to the patient's treatment in hospital.

The over-all culture in a ward or psychiatric unit represents the accumulation through time of the attitudes, beliefs and behavior patterns, common to a large part of the unit. This is arrived at as a result of considerable inquiry into the nature of these attitudes and an attempt is made to modify them to meet the treatment needs of the patients. In this context the term "therapeutic culture" is sometimes perhaps hopefully used. The tendency is for these cultural patterns to be most clearly established in the more stable and permanent members of the community, i.e., the staff.

Examples of such attitudes contributing to a therapeutic culture or treatment ideology would be an emphasis on active rehabilitation, as against "custodialism" and segregation; "democratization" in contrast to the old hierarchies and formalities of status differentiation; "permissiveness" in contrast to the stereotyped patterns of communication and behavior; and "communalism" as opposed to highly specialized therapeutic roles often limited to the doctor (69).

A basic aspect of the social organization of a therapeutic community is the establishment of daily community meetings. By a community meeting, we mean a meeting of the entire patient and staff population who are working together in a single geographical area. My colleagues and I have found it practicable to hold meetings of this kind with as many as eighty patients and twenty to thirty staff. It is our opinion that the upper limit for the establishment of a therapeutic community in the sense that the term is used here is around 100 patients. The term group therapy as opposed to community therapy is used in the more conventional sense. A relatively small group of patients who are treated by their own doctor or therapist in a group setting will often represent a subgroup of the total community who have been selected on clinical grounds, age, intelligence, motivation, et cetera. In my experience, it is desirable for community meetings to be followed by group meetings. In the community meetings, the tensions in the ward or unit at a particular time

will be ventilated and will activate a great deal of material within the individual patient. Many of the tensions cannot easily be worked through in a community meeting but if this is followed by a group meeting, it would seem to act as a useful stimulus to communication in the smaller meeting.

THE COMMUNITY MEETING

A ward or treatment unit of, say, eighty or ninety patients have to live together and, although of course they split off into small subgroups or even withdraw to a relatively isolated position, the patients must inevitably interact with each other in varying degrees. In a community meeting the staff is exposed to some of the social forces which normally operate on the ward. Harry Wilmer (70) has described in great detail ward meetings of this kind involving very disturbed schizophrenic patients.

The first problem to consider is the attitude of the staff. In general, they will view this type of meeting with very mixed feelings. The charge nurse, or charge aide, may see this as depriving her of her cherished exclusive daily interview with the doctor which, in the past, may have done much to relieve her of her own anxieties. In the past she often became "the therapist" of the ward, describing activities of a disturbing kind to the doctor and recommending "treatment" which not infrequently he was only too glad to accept, failing to realize that the "treatment" he was sanctioning was sometimes to relieve the anxiety of the nurse rather than the patient. Thus, the use of shock treatment or sedatives or transfer of patients to another ward has frequently been centralized in the nursing role. The attitudes of other staff members, although obviously important, may never have been examined and the more junior aides especially may have come to feel that they were excluded from much of the interest in the work and that their own status was devalued. However, the establishment of a daily community meeting does very little to improve the situation if the staff, other than the doctor, feel that it is a waste of time and liable to create more, rather than less, disturbance among the patients. The charge nurse or aide may find that she hesitates to say to the whole community what she feels about patient behavior, fearing consciously or unconsciously that some of her prejudices or tendency to have favorites may become apparent to all. Moreover, her authority may be questioned by some of her aides, who may point out the irrationality or inconsistency of some of her decisions. On the other hand, the aides may well feel incapable of communicating in public, fearing ridicule or possibly even later reprisals from their own senior staff.

Perhaps most important, this kind of situation calls for a more responsible role on the part of the nursing staff than they have been used to play. In this context, the aide may talk frequently about her desire for further education and speak resentfully about the poor quality of the inservice training, if any, but the other side of the coin is that frequently she is afraid of change. In fact, she may prefer the passive-dependent role which gives her the relative absence of responsibility and also, of course, an opportunity to grumble quite legitimately about her devalued position. The important point is that no community meeting is likely to be very effective until such time as the unit personnel really believe that it has value, not only for the patients but for themselves.

Clearly the nature of the patient population is extremely important. In a busy admission unit with a rapid turnover of patients, it is difficult to get any continuity of culture. Some patients may begin to appreciate daily meetings just at the time when they have to leave. Many more will probably never see anything in this for them before they leave the ward to return home or are transferred to one of the long-stay wards. Our own experience would indicate that one really needs at least a nucleus of moderately long-stay patients to help the newer patients to perceive the community meeting as a place where they can, from the start, expect to get an answer to some of their difficulties and/or insight into their own behavior. Daily community meetings will tend to produce in both patients and staff an increasing awareness of the nature and predisposing factors behind disturbed behavior. This in turn tends to produce changes in the social structure of the ward so that further disturbances can be in part prevented

and better handled where they occur. It may become clear that patients leave the handling of "incidents" entirely to the nursing staff. At the same time, the nursing staff may be criticized for their actions in these disturbances, some patients feeling that they have been too perfunctory or too rough or used restraints when they were not necessary and so on.

In such a discussion, the likelihood is that many of the patients will bring forward factors about the incident which change its significance for all concerned. They often see where the patient's behavior had been misunderstood by the staff and the tendency is for the patients slowly to become more responsible in relation to the handling and even restraint of their peers. Thus, the passive-dependent attitude which is so often associated with the role of the patient comes to be modified in the direction of more active participation in relation to acting out behavior or other incidents, and becomes much more closely identified with the staff role. Another example of this is the way in which the patients and staff respond to a patient leaving the community meeting. In many instances, the incident passes apparently unnoticed, but if the doctor or other staff member begins to draw attention to the fact that so-and-so leaves at some significant point and suggests that the departure has something to do with the patient's anxiety, then the unit personnel tends to become more sensitive to the meaning of behavior. In time, the patients will probably come to talk about doing something to bring the anxious member back into the community meeting where his anxiety can be examined.

A sharing of responsibility for patient behavior is particularly important in relation to the night staff. Unfortunately, they are frequently the ones who are not present at community meetings or the discussions which should, in our opinion, always follow a community meeting. Communication to them must be through the morning or evening shifts, with overlap. The latter themselves tend to be isolated from the morning teaching programs. The interest of the evening and night shifts can be aroused most effectively by the duty doctor explaining much of the significance of community meetings and telling them how much any written or verbal feedback that they care to offer is appreciated. However, their anxieties about the day staff and their lack of familiarity with the treatment culture may make this difficult. Also, being left alone on the ward with patients about whom they may know very little and who may cause them considerable anxiety often makes them feel that their point of view might be distorted or misunderstood if it is handled by people other than themselves. In rare instances, the night staff or evening shift may be so interested that they choose to stay on or arrive early to participate in the ward community meeting in which case their difficulties can be expressed directly to the patients and staff.

Patient Councils are popular and found in many hospital organizations. The function of these ward councils varies very considerably but in the main, in our experience, they are limited to the handling of practical ward details, such as privileges, arrangements for ward cleaning, rosters, and so on. Nevertheless, they tend through time to assume increasing responsibilities. In our opinion, they should not assume too much responsibility unaided and should be supervised by staff and the content of the discussions in their Council meetings fed back to the community meetings. It seems to us that much good can come from the development of patient responsibility skillfully supervised. Nevertheless, it would be foolish to assume that this kind of development occurs without considerable conflict.

If the Patient Council is allowed to develop responsibilities without having staff to turn to in times of need, and without an adequate "feedback" of their Council meetings, it is more than likely that they will find themselves isolated and resented by their peers. They may come to assume all the characteristics of authority figures and much of the hostility which was previously directed toward the staff is now directed towards them. It is for reasons like this that we feel that the staff should be present at Council meetings and when necessary point out what is happening. A staff member might feel a need to point out that certain decisions ought to be fed through the patient community as a whole before being finalized by the Council. If the Council does not feed back its deliberations and

difficulties to the community meeting, there is a danger that their role may become misunderstood; thus, their peers may come to feel that the Council is no longer made up of members of the patient group but rather by people who are "ganging up" with the staff and are in some kind of alien authoritative relationship with themselves.

In our experience, the Council, and particularly the chairman, may find this difficulty so real that deterioration in his clinical condition may occur. In general, one could say that through time the staff responsibilities can be transferred in part to the patient population and particularly to the Patient Council with real benefit in creating a more varied and responsible role for the patients. At the same time, the general principle could be formulated that the degree of responsibility that the patients can usefully assume is inversely related to the degree of disorganization within a ward. Thus, at times of relatively satisfactory organization, with appropriate leaders within the patient population and free communications, the amount of responsibility which can be safely transferred to the patients is maximal whereas in times of disorganization, when the group ego, if one likes to use the term, is weak, then the staff must assume increasing responsibility for decision-making and the general direction of patient management (71).

THE STAFF MEETING OR "POST MORTEM"

With the increasing interest in the social environment of the patient, the role of the ward psychiatrist becomes more complex. It is not enough to be a competent diagnostician and individual therapist; he must now learn how to recognize and modify the social organization and culture of his ward, as well as the complexities of group treatment. Ideally, this would entail exposure to the teaching of experienced psychiatrists and social scientists. It is rare for a resident to get social science teaching outside a university hospital or clinic. However, the growing interest in the social dimension in mental hospital psychiatry is manifested by books on the social organization of mental hospitals, and the psychiatrist in training is increasingly referring to such studies (64, 63, 62). Nevertheless, it seems to me that whatever training skills are available, the most effective way of teaching this aspect of psychiatry is in the living situation on the ward.

This can best be accomplished by a daily community meeting as already described and lasting about an hour immediately followed by a "post mortem" involving all staff members. This affords an opportunity to examine the response of the various personnel with different skills, expectations, and prejudices, who have been exposed to the same interactional scene in the community meeting. We find that for training purposes a staff meeting or a "post mortem" of this kind should last for about an hour. In this setting, it is possible to discuss the perceptions and feelings of the staff retrospectively in relation to the community meeting and also to examine their interaction during the staff meeting.

Let us assume that all staff who come in contact with the patient in a therapeutic role will be present at both meetings. In the "post mortem," they will, in varying degrees, be able to express both their analysis of certain aspects of the community meeting and their subjective feelings. If we take a frequently recurring problem, such as authority, the aides may perceive this in terms of their own desire to conform to a strict authority system where implementation of the requirements of higher authority are of prime importance. The cleanliness of the ward, the observation of smoking rules, and the avoidance of incidents, are necessary if they are to avoid undue anxiety. In this context, they will tend to express, directly or indirectly, views which support the maintenance of patient discipline. At the other extreme, the doctors, if they have had considerable training and experience in examining the social interaction on a ward, may perceive untidiness or dirt on the ward as symptoms of disorganization among the patients and want to examine this as a form of communication. To do this at all skillfully, the anxieties of the aides will have to be given due consideration, and the realities of their position faced frankly.

In discussion, it may emerge that the aides

are uncomfortable at community meetings, feel that they take up far too much of their time, and are responsible in part for the untidiness of the ward. They may point out that continued disapproval from higher authorities may result in possible loss of employment. The reality of this fear may be reinforced by the fact that their supervisors are themselves not trained in social psychiatry and may apply a value system to their area of responsibility which is at variance with the developing culture on the unit. It may be that a long-term plan involving training seminars with the supervisors will be a necessary adjunct to the effective functioning of the unit if the situation is to be rendered therapeutic. At the same time, it may appear that the anxiety of the aides stems in part from their personality difficulties attributable to their relatively inadequate education and lack of sophistication which hampers them in their role relationship with more highly trained personnel. They may deal with this by denial and rationalization, blaming the frequency of community meetings and lack of discipline for the unsatisfactory state of affairs. A situation of this kind is not infrequent and the mere gain in insight on the part of an aide may not in itself be enough. It may take a long period of education and support, if not of therapy, to tide them over the transition from their previous image of a structured, simplified role to that of a therapeutic one.

What has been said about the role of the aide in a ward problem bearing on authority would apply in different ways to all the roles and role-relationships on the unit.

The charge nurse may have particular difficulties in that, by contrast with the aide, she has a relatively higher status and a professional image which implies knowledge which frequently she does not possess. In the United States, she may have had no formal training in psychiatry other than a short affiliation as a student nurse. Most R.N.'s have been trained in a fairly strict, authoritarian culture and have little experience in the examination of roles and role-relationships, the sharing of responsibility, and the concept of group decisions or group treatment. She may resent both the loss of her relatively exclusive relationship with the doctor and the staff's examination of her handling of patients' problems. In the "post mortem," it may become clear that when she feels threatened by patients, she resorts to devices such as recommending shock treatment, transferring the patient to another ward, or "regressing" to an authoritarian disciplinary role. Like the aide, she, too, has the problem of a nursing authority structure. She is expected to satisfy the needs of personnel who have no direct contact with the ward and who view things from their own particular nursing perspective. Unless nursing supervisors and the higher echelons of nursing can themselves become identified with community programs, then confusion of roles is almost inevitable. The ward views the problems as material for treatment whereas the nursing hierarchy tend to view them as administrative problems, calling for immediate action. One device frequently used by the nursing profession is to transfer a nurse to another ward if there are repeated ward problems. By doing this, of course, nothing is learned from the disturbance on the ward, but, from the point of view of administration, the problem is got rid of by transfer.

I have found it possible, even in a large state hospital, to use situations of this kind as learning experiences for all personnel concerned. The Director of Nursing and her senior colleagues have been extremely willing to participate in seminars involving the ward problems so that even if a nurse has been transferred it is still possible to re-create the situation in retrospect and see what alternative answers could have been found to the problem. Whether this should be done by inviting senior nursing personnel to the unit "post mortem" meeting or whether it calls for a separate administrative learning situation is still, I think, an open question and much would depend upon the circumstances. The essential point is that the unit doctor should be involved so that he is in a position to gain experience in dealing with problems involving extraward personnel and differing role perceptions. Nurses from the Department of Education may, with advantage, also be involved in this kind of learning experience. If they have student nurses on a ward, they tend to teach them in a situation which is removed from the actual ward interaction. If, however, the Nursing Education personnel themselves become involved in community meetings and find a functional role on the ward, they are then in a position to discuss the interactional scene with their students in the staff meeting and in their own teaching seminars. In this way, their own perceptions of what went on and what they would normally teach their students can be examined by other trained personnel and Nursing Education puts itself in the position of having a continuous educational experience, instead of tending to become stereotyped.

Moreover, the staff meeting is an ideal setting in which to work through some of the problems inherent in the role relationships between medical, nursing service, and nursing education personnel. All three have a significant relationship with the student nurse and unless a serious attempt is made to work through this relationship, the student may find herself confused, and, at times, victimized. What she wants above all is someone to turn to when she is in emotional difficulties with her patients. My feeling is that in the kind of program we are discussing, she will be able to turn to the charge nurse, to the Nursing Education supervisor, or to the ward personnel, including the doctor, social worker, psychologist, and so on, all of whom should be in a position to understand certain aspects of the problems of nurse-patient relationships on the ward. This implies a degree of role blurring which is perhaps unusual. At the same time, it implies a degree of sophistication through time of all ward personnel which tends to evolve through daily staff meetings when the problems of treatment, ward management, interpersonal relationships, including staff relationships, are under constant scrutiny and discussion.

What I have said about the roles of the personnel in direct contact with the patient applies equally to the more peripheral roles, including the social worker and psychologist. It seems to me that it is equally important that their relationships with patients, whether as social caseworkers or as therapists or group workers, should be discussed freely with the total unit staff personnel. This implies that roles are constantly being modified and that a psychologist or social worker on Unit A need not necessarily have a similar role on Unit B. In fact, it seems a pity if professional personnel become identified with their own professional subgroup rather than with the Unit on which they are working. All this implies a considerable degree of skill and sophistication on the part of the unit leader who, at the present time, is usually, or perhaps invariably, the psychiatrist. There seems to me no adequate reason why this responsibility should continue to rest with the psychiatrist unless he has the kind of training and skill which we are discussing. This leadership role could reasonably be given to one of the other staff personnel provided, of course, that the purely medical matters were left, as they must be, to the doctor.

In order to become competent in handling the various role-relationships and management problems which we have been discussing, the psychiatrist is forced to attempt to examine the problems of the various personnel and see them from not only his own but from the other points of view. Whether group consensus can be seen as a satisfactory way of resolving problems, if indeed it is ever achieved, is an open question, but the attempt to examine problems in various dimensions is a rich learning experience. Obviously, it is much better if this whole procedure is supervised by a social scientist with experience in psychiatry or a psychiatrist who has considerable experience in group work and the social science field. Such training will help him to make optimal use of his staff and the social environment generally and, where psychiatrists are concerned, will be invaluable preparation for a possible future role as a mental hospital administrator.

COMMUNITY TREATMENT

If one assumes that the patient population has certain treatment potentials which can be developed under constant medical and professional supervision, then one has to set up a structure whereby the patient contribution can be maximized. The immediate objection can be raised that the patients are ill and it is unfair or unrealistic to expect them to help in treatment and make decisions involving a good deal of responsibility; in any case, this is the job that the

staff is paid to do. On the other hand, it can be argued that perhaps the most outstanding characteristic of newly admitted patients is their feeling of depression and despair and, if possible, they must be helped to deal with this. A former colleague, Gil Elles, a psychoanalyst working at the therapeutic community at Henderson Hospital, London (formerly the Social Rehabilitation Unit at Belmont Hospital), described the handling of this problem as follows (72).

The community has developed techniques for dealing with this problem at a conscious level and at the same time has become aware of the unconscious mechanisms which are all the time operating to prevent individual, group, or community from becoming overwhelmed by this despair. In the first instance emphasis is placed on trying to lessen the force of unconscious guilt which drives the psychopath compulsively into trouble again and again, and seriously inhibits his capacity to learn by experience. With the new patient this takes the form of making known to the community his problem so that at the earliest possible moment in treatment he is accepted for what he *is* rather than what he would *like* to be, or what he fears himself to be. In this way, it is hoped that the deep-seated guilt is somewhat diminished and the patient's ego strengths are increased and made more available to him.

In the second place every patient has a dual role both of trying to accept and give treatment. Therefore through the second part of his role his self regard is fortified enabling him to feel less of a failure because he is expected to help and understand others. Thus, in the long run he is able to feel less threatened in admitting some part of his own desperation about himself.

In the third instance and following on from these initial community attitudes despair is limited by improving communication within the individual and between individuals in their various groups. The community has a culture whereby feelings are shared very openly and the reasons for such feelings examined in great detail. To do this the day has to be geared so that every community activity is associated with a long period for discussion about it. Furthermore, the various activity groups are so interrelated that the maximum contact in as many social roles as possible is provided for each patient in the community. In effect this experience tends to build up in each individual a more integrated picture of himself, firstly as seen by others, and finally when accepted by him as part of his own self-evaluation.

What has happened in such situations following admission is that a reduction of the violence and fragmentation of the individual splitting processes has taken place. This means that the despairing patient's urgent need to project wholesale the unacceptable parts of himself—good as well as bad— has been diminished in the first place by the community's attitude of understanding and acceptance. This enables the patient to be aware of new strength so long as he remains a member of the community. By establishing firm bonds through patient-staff and patient-patient interaction which all the while is looked at and discussed a framework is then secondarily built up that is strong enough to carry the weight of a personal depression of a more mature order. Thus some patients for the first time experience both an outer security and an inner despair which allows them to feel and to understand the emotions of remorse and pity, followed by a longing for and a belief in their own ability to repair and restore the fabric of damaged relationships. For such a patient this means that authority figures are gradually perceived as less threatening and other relationships as more lasting. Thus the patient in internalizing a conscience now less punitive can accept both more responsibility and more success.

This question of elaborating the role of a patient to one of therapist is, I think, one of the fundamental tenets of community treatment procedure. This concept is often mistakenly seen as handing over ultimate responsibility to the patients. This, in my opinion, is not practicable and that what one wishes to do is to give the patients the optimal responsibility compatible with their over-all capacity at any one time and that in no sense does the staff or the doctor in charge relinquish his ultimate authority which merely remains latent to be invoked when necessary. It is the application of this principle which calls for considerable experience and skill. As an example, a community may be functioning at a fairly high level of effectiveness and the patients may be able to take over a considerable amount of responsibility and then, on a particular day, four or five of the most responsible and successfully treated members leave to be replaced by four or five new patients who may be in the state of considerable disorganization.

The loss of patient leadership within the ward and the effect of the new intake may be such that the ward functioning is materially altered and the staff have to play a much more active and controlling role than they were previously doing (71). This is not fundamentally different from what happens in an individual or a group treatment session when the lack of ego strength or anxiety level is such that the therapist feels it

necessary to be largely supportive for a time. I am talking about patient responsibility of a higher order than one usually understands by the term "patient government." Patient government is usually restricted to decisions on relatively minor matters of ward organization and activities. What I have in mind is decisions shared with the staff and involving such matters as the discharge of patients or transfer to other wards or what disciplinary action should be taken in the case of deviant behavior. This sharing of serious responsibility with the staff is, I think, one of the most important ways in overcoming the lack of confidence, low self-estimate, and overdependency which all too frequently are characteristic of the psychiatric patient in the hospital ward. This responsibility can also be carried over to the patients' work roles (22).

It is ideal if one can do production work for the community and have patient foremen, timekeepers, et cetera. If one is fortunate enough to have the freedom to build up a therapeutic community from the point of view of the patients' social and treatment needs, then I think one must inevitably end up with a structure which deviates markedly from the more usual pattern in which the organization is essentially staff-centered and often is determined by traditions from the past which have little relevance to current treatment methods and practices. As an example, one finds that in a ward where the patients have a great deal of identification with responsible roles and with treatment, they will come to the aid of the night nurse in the event of disturbed patient behavior, instead of leaving it entirely for the staff to deal with. In this context also, the patients come to feel much more able to bear with highly disturbed behavior among their peers because the community meetings help them to understand the meaning of the disturbed behavior and give them a better idea of how to relate in a helpful and understanding way to the sick member.

The daily examination of behavior and current problems means that the patients become aware of the factors which lie behind behavior and learn a great deal about each other's problems. In any type of hospital, they are forced to relate to other patients and staff at ward level whether they like it or not, and it seems reasonable to try to help them to have a positive role to play and a much better insight into what is going on in themselves and in those around them. In my experience, it is possible to get patients and staff at all levels to appreciate some of the phenomena that occur on the unit and in the daily community meetings. The progress-sion that occurs in these meetings through time has many points in common with ordinary group treatment. In the first instance, the patients in the community meeting tend to look to the staff for leadership and are glad when some general topic is raised which has no personal significance. As time progresses, they begin to talk about some of their deeper feelings and to test out the staff reactions in this direction. As-suming adequate skills on the part of the staff, they become used as transference figures with advantage to the treatment process. The same applies to the transference onto various mem-bers of the patient population.

The concepts of manifest and latent content, the unconscious, and ego defenses come to be understood in much the way that occurs in a small group. It may be necessary to have addi-tional seminars for the aides who are less well-trained than the other staff members and to whom the change of role implicit in this discus-sion is greater than that required of any other staff member. For the staff meeting, concepts like feedback from informal staff-patient groups and difficulties occurring during the night be-tween patients and night staff can be usefully communicated to the group. Ideally, of course, one would hope that nursing personnel rotate so that the night staff have opportunity to par-ticipate in the learning experience afforded to the day staff, more particularly the morning shift.

The meetings I am describing are clearly less specifically therapeutic and more concerned with everyday behavior and ward management than is the typical therapeutic group of six or eight patients of a selected kind. Nevertheless, I think that the community meetings of up to eighty patients and staff have a particular place in institutional therapy, particularly in bringing about the establishment of what one might call a therapeutic culture. By this, I mean that the day-after-day examination of the problems exist-ing on a ward and the consideration of the roles of all staff members and of the patients leads through time to considerable modification of the ward structure. Not only that, but the tradi-tional attitudes and beliefs can come in for scrutiny and we are in a position to ask our-selves why we do what we do when we do. A learning experience of the kind I am describing is far from easy and clearly causes the staff considerable anxiety (20).

Often, the doctors themselves are the people who have had less training than either social workers or psychologists and in any case their training in a general hospital has tended to give them a feeling of considerable authority and even omnipotence. To have their performance in these daily meetings questioned by their juniors and other professional colleagues can be ex-tremely painful but is undoubtedly a valuable learning experience if the personality of the individual allows this to happen. Nevertheless, there are many people who are not suited for this kind of community practice and I think that one has to make this clear from the start. My feeling is that every resident should be afforded the opportunity of learning therapy of this kind but that many of them will not feel comfortable in this type of community situation and will pre-fer to operate in the more traditional, author-itarian role. I see nothing wrong with this as I think that in any case a ward will tend to de-velop along the lines prescribed by the most senior member—that is, at present, the doctor. I would like to think that doctors trained in this way who are able to assimilate this kind of orientation will be well-prepared for future roles as hospital superintendents and to some extent, I think it can be seen as a very valuable training for community psychiatry. My own experience is that the doctor who can relate to his ward personnel and to the patients in an easy and relaxed way and who can listen to their communications is very frequently the doctor, who in outpatient departments or in community psychiatry automatically feels at home meeting the patient in his social setting along with his own family group.

From what has already been said it is clear that training and treatment overlap. In the case of the staff meetings, whether for the total staff or seminars for the less experienced members, many intra-staff difficulties inevitably arise. In general, it is probably wiser to limit examination of these difficulties to situations bearing on the treatment of patients. This makes the discussion relatively objective and the motivation to help the patient at all costs weighs heavily. Thus, in a rivalry situation between two nurses about a patient it would be desirable to uncover or clarify the situation or the patient would almost certainly suffer (73). However, the indications of a covert homosexual problem in a staff member would best be ignored unless it produced obvious difficulties in relationships with the patients. In that case, therapy might well be indicated but should be done by an outside psychiatrist.

The over-all culture of the ward can modify the treatment ideology enormously. Take the question of sedation. Many patients arrive at hospital loaded with sedatives or tranquilizing drugs prescribed by their local doctor. If the culture of the ward is against sedation except under clearly specified conditions, then this may modify the new patient's expectation in a surprisingly short time. The same arguments applies to the establishment of many potentially therapeutic attitudes (e.g., the desirability of invoking the patient's active participation in treatment rather than encouraging a passive-dependent attitude to the hospital).

As has already been pointed out, the development of a therapeutic culture will necessitate frequent, preferably daily, meetings of the entire patient and staff population. In this way the community is faced day in, day out, with the living problems of the patients. These reflect the problems which affected the patients outside and resulted in their hospitalization. By discussing these collectively the staff become involved in some measure with the patients' ward life and are, at the very least, in a better position to modify ward routine, or administrative procedure and so indirectly enhance treatment.

REFERENCES

20. GREENBLATT, M., LEVINSON, D. L., & WILLIAMS, R. H. (Eds.) *The patient and the mental hospital.* Glencoe, Ill.: Free Press, 1957. Chapter 14: The absorption of new doctors into a therapeutic community.
21. JONES, M. Towards a clarification of the therapeutic community concept. *British Journal of Medicine and Psychology,* 1959, 32, 200–205.
22. JONES, M. Social rehabilitation with emphasis on work therapy as a form of group therapy. *British Journal of Medicine and Psychology,* 1960, 33, 67–71.
62. GREENBLATT, M., YORK, R. H., & BROWN, E. L. *From custodial to therapeutic patient care in mental hospitals.* New York: Russell Sage Foundation, 1955.
63. BELKNAP, I. *Human problems of a state mental hospital.* New York: McGraw-Hill, 1956.
64. CAUDILL, W. *The psychiatric hospital as a small society.* Cambridge, Mass.: Harvard University Press, 1958.
68. RAPAPORT, R., & RAPAPORT, R. Permissiveness and treatment in a therapeutic community, *Psychiatry,* 1959, 22, 57–64.
69. RAPAPORT, R. *Community as doctor.* Springfield, Ill.: Charles C Thomas, 1960.
70. WILMER, H. *Social psychiatry in action.* Springfield, Ill.: Charles C Thomas, 1958.
71. PARKER, S. Disorganization on a psychiatric ward. *Psychiatry,* 1959, 22, 65–80.
72. ELLES, G. Research into the aftercare needs of discharged patients. Unpublished paper, 1961.
73. STANTON, A. H., & SCHWARTZ, M. S. *The mental hospital.* New York: Basic Books, 1954.

72.

Don D. Jackson and John H. Weakland

CONJOINT FAMILY THERAPY

The essential point to be gleaned from all these matters of common knowledge is that treatment of a psychiatric patient *necessarily* involves dealing with members of his family, and with family relationships, either directly or indirectly. Clearly, even setting up a rule of excluding the family from the therapy involves handling these matters, and drastically, though perhaps simply. The question at issue, then, is not *whether* the members of a patient's family are to be dealt with, but *how* they are to be dealt with. This paper is concerned with describing our work with conjoint family treatment as a means of dealing with this problem in the case of schizophrenic patients particularly.

THEORETICAL BACKGROUND

To understand our attempts at treating these families and formulating our treatment approach, it is necessary to understand the theory under which we labor, since our present practices and present conceptions have both developed out of the interplay of some very broad original orientations and our groping attempts at treatment of actual families.

At the outset of our program of work with families of schizophrenics our two main concepts were (1) the double bind[1] and (2)

family homeostasis.[2] The concept of family homeostasis arose from observations that psychotherapeutic efforts with one member of a family might be hindered by the behavior of other members, or that another member might become disturbed as the member in treatment improved. These observations, in connection with existing ideas about homeostatic systems generally, suggested that a family forms such a dynamic steady-state system; the characters of the members and the nature of their interaction—including any identified patient and his sick behavior—are such as to maintain a status quo typical of the family, and to react toward the restoration of this status quo in the event of any change, such as is proposed by the treatment of any member.

The double bind concept is grounded in our most basic conception about communication as the chief means of human interaction and influence: that in actual human communication a single and simple message never occurs, but that communication always and necessarily involves a multiplicity of messages, of different levels, at once. These may be conveyed via various channels such as words, tone, and facial expressions, or by the variety of meanings and references of any verbal message in relation to its possible contexts. The relationships among these related messages may be very complex. No two messages, at different levels of communication, can be just the same; however, they may be similar or different, congruent or incongruent. Difference and incongruity appear fundamental to the richness of human communication, as when certain combinations of words and tone define styles of expression, such as irony or humor; however, they also appear fundamental to the origin and character of much psycho-

From Don D. Jackson and John H. Weakland, "Conjoint family therapy: some considerations on theory, technique, and results." *Psychiatry,* 1961, 24, 30–45. This investigation, directed by Gregory Bateson, was supported by Mental Health Project Grant OM-324 from the National Institute of Mental Health, U.S. Public Health Service, by the Veterans Administration Hospital, Palo Alto, and The Mental Research Institute, Palo Alto Medical Research Foundation. Reprinted by special permission of The William Alanson White Psychiatric Foundation, Inc. and the author. The present selection begins with p. 31. Copyright 1961 by The Foundation.

[1]Gregory Bateson, Don D. Jackson, Jay Haley, and John Weakland, "Toward a Theory of Schizophrenia," *Behavioral Science* (1956) 1:251-264.

[2]Don D. Jackson, "The Question of Family Homeostasis," *Psychiatric Quart.,* Suppl. (1959) 31:79-90.

pathology, as in the symptom "inappropriate affect," considered as an evident incongruence between words and tone or expression. Further, the use of double-level messages seems increasingly central to therapy in ways we shall mention later.

The double bind concept refers to a pattern of pairs or sets of messages, at different levels, which are closely related but sharply incongruent, occurring together with other messages which by concealment, denial, or other means seriously hinder the recipient from clearly noticing the incongruence and handling it effectively, as by commenting on it. Instead, he is influenced toward incompatible behavioral responses while enjoined not even to notice either influence or incompatibility. We believe that, within an important relationship, where messages cannot merely be ignored or avoided, the combination of extensive experience of such communication being uttered and the recipient's learning to participate by accepting incongruence without question can be productive of schizophrenic behavior.

It is not hard to note that these two main concepts are both concerned with the description and specification of interaction among actual persons, by various means of communication, at a level of directly observable behavior. This focus implies further an emphasis on what is real and on what is current and continuing to occur. Taken together, these emphases define a broad "communicational" and transactional orientation to the study, understanding, and treatment of human behavior—including that special class most interesting to psychiatrists, symptomatic behavior. This orientation, while related to earlier work, especially Sullivan's, and currently increasing in acceptance, still is considerably different from the strong traditional orientation of psychiatry emphasizing the individual patient and constructs about the unreal or unobservable: fantasies or misperceptions of reality; past, mainly childhood, experience; and intrapsychic organization and content.

In brief, we are much more concerned with influence, interaction, and interrelation between people, immediately observable in the present, than with individual, internal, imaginary, and infantile matters. It is worth making this difference in basic orientation explicit, since to do so helps clarify the nature of our main specific concepts, indicates some important connections between them, and provides a background essential for understanding our whole therapeutic approach—what we do and what we do not do, especially some of our differences from other therapeutic concepts and practices.

The family homeostasis and double bind concepts, with some expansion and modification,[3] continue to be of major significance in our family work. Since these ideas have not always been clearly understood by others, particularly the importance of difference in levels of messages, some more concrete discussion of them seems to be in order here. Some of our critics have felt that the double bind situation is essentially an either-or situation, a damned-if-you-do and damned-if-you-don't predicament, or merely a complicated way of describing ambivalence.[4] The double bind situation is all of these things. But it is more. As an illustration, take the predicament of an innocent person who undergoes a lie detector test. It is common practice in such tests to invoke a standard situation for the establishment of a base line. One such situation is to have the subject draw a card from a deck, look at it, and replace it. He is then told not to reveal which card he drew even should the examiner guess it. When the card drawn is guessed and the subject answers, "No," the squiggles on the tape reveal how much he reacts to a lie. However, a theory merely invoking guilt over the telling of a lie fails to account for some of the complexities in the situation. Most subjects in this situation cannot be confident of innocence because a person cannot know *a priori* what his body will do and thus the subject's literal innocence is no protection against the context being one in which the power rests in the hands of the examiner. Since the examiner has asked him to

---

[3] For instance, John H. Weakland, "The 'Double Bind' Hypothesis of Schizophrenia and Three-Party Interaction," pp. 373–388, in *The Etiology of Schizophrenia*, edited by Don D. Jackson (New York: Basic Books, 1960).

[4] Despite our previous discussion of the "illusion of alternatives" in John H. Weakland and Don D. Jackson, "Patient and Therapist Observations on the Circumstances of a Schizophrenic Episode," *AMA Arch. Neurol. and Psychiat.* (1958) 79:554-574.

lie, is this really a "lie" or is it not the truth—that is, a correct perception of what it takes to make the machine work? The double level situation renders the subject especially vulnerable because if he denies what he totally perceives, he has put into play a self-deception that does not come equipped with clear boundaries. Suppose at the completion of the test, the examiner stated to the subject, "You have been lying." Could the subject be sure that the examiner was referring only to his deliberate "cooperative" lie? Could he be sure that he is not a person who is in a chronic state of not processing all the data available to him and thus subject to self-deception?

THE THERAPEUTIC PROCESS— ARRANGEMENTS AND TECHNIQUES

"The family" we are talking about in practice usually consists of father, mother, and patient. They are seen together once a week for sixty to ninety minutes in a room equipped with a microphone for tape recording and a one-way window for occasional observation and supervision. The meetings may be conducted more frequently than once a week when indicated, but time limitations have not made this possible on a regular basis, and it does not seem essential. Any combination of the basic group's members may be seen as outside necessity—such as trips or illnesses—dictates, or if the therapist feels it is technically wise. We used to be fairly rigid about meeting only if all members could be present. Now, although the general emphasis remains on the whole group, there is variation on this among our several therapists.

The status of the patient's siblings remained obscure for some time and is still only partially settled. We have found them reluctant to be drawn into a potentially unpleasant situation. In retrospect, it appears that we attributed more health to them than they had in fact, and unconsciously went along with their characteristic defense: "This is a situation I am not involved in." For example:

The younger brother of a chronic schizophrenic was visiting this country on vacation from his European job. The therapist had anticipated his arrival by getting him to agree to three family

sessions during his visit, since it appeared likely that he would not be available again during the course of therapy. At the first session, the brother appeared to be everything his parents claimed he was and everything the patient was not. During this session, he maintained a pleasant aloofness and claimed amnesia for any events that the therapist felt had been important in the patient's life. At the end of this session, his mother stated that she knew he would be happy to return, but the therapist, discouraged, made it clear that he realized this was a great imposition on the brother's limited time and, without realizing it, left an excellent opportunity for the brother to back out. However, he did return for the next session, and the several days he had spent with his parents brought to the fore more data than could have been hoped for. He expressed genuine regret at the end of the third session that he could not continue to participate in the family meetings and stated that his life abroad probably protected him from a crack-up.

Currently, we have no hesitation about trying to include one or more siblings in the family sessions if they are living with the parents. If they have established other residences, we generally limit the contact to occasional meetings, usually for our own data needs.

Given this basic group of at least three persons, what is the therapist's orientation toward them and his goal? In other words, how does he envisage the therapeutic process, and how does he structure the situation for the group?

When we started to try family therapy in treating schizophrenia, we assumed from our previous work that the identified patient was on the receiving end of double binds from a parent or parents; and we knew that we needed the parents' cooperation, about which we were uncertain, at least to the extent that they keep coming for a period of time. Accordingly, our initial efforts were crude attempts to protect the patient from his parents and to impress the parents with how much help we might derive from the data that they might furnish about the patient. It rather quickly dawned on us, however, that: First, the patient was not a delicate violet and was quite capable of upsetting his parents and blocking the therapist's ambitions; and, second, the parents were unhappy people who potentially could benefit from psychotherapy.

By now, the ten or so therapists involved in the schizophrenia project appear to be reasonably uniform in their impressions as to why they and the family are in the room. All of the therapists while still inexperienced were patient-oriented, but they quickly achieved the realization that the three persons confronting them are bound together in a mutually destructive way and that the primary symptom presented by all three is a crippling entanglement that from the surface is apparent only in the patient. The parents initially try to preserve this surface view, and hence every initial session is replete with remarks about poor X and his unfortunate illness. Once, however, they respond to the lure of the therapist's curiosity about them, the brittle surface cracks and the utter desolation that can only be experienced by two people living together in apartness begins to ooze from below. It is at this point that the therapist's humane interest can still save the day. It is at this point no longer enough that the parents come for the patient's sake. An abbreviated but typical sequence in early family sessions is as follows:

The patient is a 30-year-old man with some five years of hospital experience who is currently living at home. The parents are disturbed with his inactivity, sloppiness, and delusions. Their attempts to push him into activity or to get him out of the house boomerang and result in unpleasantness not only between them and the patient but sometimes between the parents themselves. In the initial interview, the patient is hugely sloppy, quiet, and makes a point of not appearing involved. The parents are careful to point out their own attainments in contrast to the patient's many faults, which of course are labeled sickness, and there is a sticky back-and-forth exchange between them and the therapist over the details of therapy time—the frequency of sessions and so on.

During the second session, the parents have been thinking about the patient's illness and recall anecdotes from the past having to do with outside events or acts of God that they suggest may have caused it. Typically the schools and school teachers are mentioned as culprits. In this session, the patient demonstrates some of his symptoms with obvious encouragement from the parents.

During the third session, the therapist expresses curiosity about the parents, their background, how they met, and their early marriage. He introduces these topics deliberately, at the suggestion of his supervisor. Although the parents start out initially to report factually, there appears to be more tension in the air. Finally, well along in the session, the mother says to the father, "Why don't you tell the doctor about New York?" Her reference is to a not completely estimable escapade on the father's part, and he responds with an unhappy but gallant attempt to face the music. But the focus does not stay on the parents and off the patient for long. In the course of recounting this episode, it is stated that the patient was living with the father temporarily. This is quite correct, but largely irrelevant. The son was only about ten at the time and his staying in one city with the father temporarily, while the mother remained in another, was the parents' arrangement and indeed one related to their problem being discussed. But once the son is mentioned, the parents are soon off again on his difficulties and the father is off the hook.

During the fourth session, the therapist attempts to clarify the experience alluded to in the previous session and to discuss further some aspects of the parents' marriage. During this session, the patient appears interested and laughs heartily on several occasions when the father is willing to make himself the butt of a particular story. There is more of a feeling that, however unhappy they are, these people do share something together.

In the next session, the father appears alone. The mother is said to be down with some vague illness, and the patient is waiting in the car. The father has come in only to tell the therapist that they won't be arriving that evening. However, he stays to chat and, to the therapist's surprise, writes on a matchbook cover (presumably so it won't be overheard by the tape recorder) that he and his wife are having terrible fights. He then retrieves and destroys the matchbook cover. The father is almost totally unable to break down and to allow the therapist to sympathize with him over his marital discord; nevertheless, a breach has been made, and subsequent sessions reveal that the mother was not ill but that there had been a family quarrel before the session and she had refused to come. This leads to further consideration of their difficulties as well as those of the patient.

This example illustrates some of the typical characteristics of our families and typical responses they show to the situation posed by initially entering into therapy together. We may explicitly summarize some of these before going on to list and illustrate certain standard initial moves we have developed to deal with the problems these features pose, and then to consider the further course of therapy similarly.

In most of the families we have seen, perhaps especially in middle-class ones, the mother appears as the prime mover about therapy, with the emphasis on her concern for her child; many mothers also appear as "lay experts" on schizophrenia and its treatment on the basis of long experience with their child's illness, often plus reading up on the subject. In some cases the father is more in the foreground, but on closer inspection he seems usually to be so largely as a spokesman or front man for the mother. Often it is found that the father is physically absent from the family a lot, as by being very much occupied with his business. In fact, in many of the families it seems that the members hardly ever get together except in the therapy room, although they have little independent life as individuals either.

The father and mother both center their initial discussion on the subject of their child, especially on his illness; this might seem natural in the circumstances, except that this focus is extreme while at the same time it often centers on minor aspects of the illness, such as details of the patient's dress and manners. The parents are able to get together and agree fairly well when the patient's illness is thus the topic of discussion, although they may both speak of this in a disjointed or incongruent way—that is, at one moment they may insist that the patient is too sick to be held responsible for anything, and the next complain in extreme ways about his irresponsible misbehavior, making this abrupt transition without giving the cues or structuring that ordinarily accompany such a shift. Yet this area of agreement stands out, especially as it soon becomes evident that these two people can agree very little on any other matter. The patient, meanwhile, is appearing helpless and hopeless, yet by withdrawal or acting-up is influencing everyone and upsetting the therapy situation in part. It is thus very easy to see from these early sessions why observers without further experience would naturally tend to draw big distinctions between the "sick" patient and the "well" parents and siblings. Yet, on closer and more extended contact with these families, we have been struck by the observation not only that the parents also have considerable personal difficulties, but that their difficulties are apt to be fundamentally like those the patient exhibits via his symptomatology.[5]

A number of problems connected with these

characteristics tend to arise very quickly in the therapy. The parents keep their discussion centered on the patient and by this avoid talking of themselves and their relationship. The patient often helps them in this by some kind of overt "goofing up" or going too far which aids in keeping him labeled as *the* patient; this may occur especially at points when the parents do happen to approach some topic that is hot for them, and so strongly that even the therapist is likely to turn on the patient, away from the parents, without quite noticing what he is doing.

If the therapist does attempt to put the focus on the family, or to define the parents as equally patients with their child, certain other difficulties are expectable. Either the mother or the father may move to involve the therapist in individual and private communication, by phone calls or before or after the family session. Fathers tend to avoid involvement in the family therapy by distancing devices; sometimes actual absences from meetings, sometimes withdrawal by silence, or intellectualization under the label of "objectivity." Mothers seem to feel more guilty about their possible relationship to the child's illness, and they tend to be correspondingly active in one way or another. In some cases, there is danger that the mother will be so concerned as to terminate therapy very rapidly once the "family therapy" idea really is clear. In others, sessions may continue but be dominated by the mother, who may take over the therapist's position by endorsing everything he says, by being more expert and scientific than he, usually with biological and chemical theories of schizophrenia which deny her guilt, or even in a few cases by taking blame on herself so strongly and indiscriminately that examining actual family interactions again is badly hampered. Indeed, such examination is difficult at best, since it is a real project to get clarity about anything with these families; the statements of the various members do not agree, and each tends to be vague and shifting, or to bury everything in details, or both. Of particular importance is the fact that the family members present their behavior in terms of responses to outside situations, so that it is difficult even for the

[5]Don D. Jackson and John H. Weakland, "Schizophrenic Symptoms and Family Interaction," *AMA Arch. Gen. Psychiatry* (1959) 1:618–621.

therapist to keep in mind and in view how much they are responding to each other, and to begin to clarify this with them.

FRAMING OF THE THERAPY

If such typical initial problems are not dealt with adequately, they are likely to become acute or chronic, ending the therapy quickly or leading into a repetitive stalemate similar to the family's usual circle of interactions, only with the therapist drawn in as one more player in this game with no winners. On the other hand, effective dealing with these initial problems is correspondingly valuable. As we see it, "patient management" in family therapy, which includes management of all the family members involved in the therapeutic situation, is a central part of therapy, and by no means only superficial in its effects. Thus, the standard procedures we have evolved to utilize in the initial family sessions represent much more than merely a means of avoiding limited particular difficulties. They involve a framing of the therapy as a whole, a setting-up of continuing broad standards and expectations. Also, the means by which the therapist does this framing are illustrative of much about our over-all technical orientation and practice.

In the initial session, the therapist customarily expresses a philosophy of "We are here to work together on better understanding one another so that you all can get more out of your family life." Such a statement implies that the parents are as much involved in the family unhappiness, specified or unspecified, as the patient, and also that they equally have something to gain from therapy. This replaces our former tendency to open the initial interview by asking what they would like to get out of the sessions, an approach that resulted in the standard answer, "Nothing is wrong except poor Bill," or whoever the identified patient happened to be. Such mention of "working on understanding" also implicitly focuses on communication as deeply involved in their difficult relationships and as a means of therapy. These are similar implications in our usual handling of the problem of private communication. Formerly, it was customary for the therapist to receive a phone call from one or both parents during the early weeks of therapy asking if the patient shouldn't be put on tranquilizers or shouldn't be getting more exercise, and so on. Then the therapist would feel awkward about bringing this up at the next family meeting and awkward if he did not bring it up because it implied a conspiracy with one or the other of the parents. Now, in the initial session, the therapist casually announces that all parties are privileged to all information about contacts with the therapist; and, like most rules that are brought up matter-of-factly, this is accepted.

Alternatively, the therapist may sometimes handle similar matters less by implication and more by making fairly explicit statements, while attaching to these a prefabricated framing interpretation. For example, he may state that all families develop habitual patterns of communication, including some avoidances by which the family members protect each other, and therefore part of the therapist's job is to clarify these patterns and avoidances when they stand in the way of resolving important blocks between the family members; it is the therapist's responsibility to them all—while treating them impartially, although naturally each of them will feel at times he is not doing so—not to let the solution of such problems be missed even by such protective tendencies. Thus the family is given credit for their good intentions, while the therapist's position of stirring things up at times is defined as a positive duty for their benefit. Also the therapist will point out that they must have some important relationship with each other, regardless of their difficulties, since they have stayed together for a long time; in addition, they really know each other better than anyone else, including the therapist, can, and thus they are the best possible therapists for each other. This framing places responsibility for helpful participation on all the family members equally, which both calls on the more withdrawn ones to take more part and undercuts the usual tendency of some one family member to take over the situation from the therapist.

The members of our group also tend to be active in similar ways in connection with many of the more specific issues that arise initially.

For example, we commonly avoid some dreary time-wasting by politely interrupting the parents' attempts to focus exclusively on the patient's illness. In addition, we tend to discipline the patient if he attempts to utilize the "I am the sick one so I am not responsible" ploy, as the following example shows.

The therapist was questioning the parents in the initial session about their living. The mother was uneasy, apparently about her alcoholism which had not yet been disclosed. At this point, the schizophrenic son broke in to announce how much he had benefited from shock therapy in the hospital. Immediately both parents discussed this with him, and the father asked if he wished more. The mother stated that maybe he needed tranquilizers and then thought to ask him if he was currently taking them, to which the patient replied, "No." At this juncture, the therapist broke in to ask the patient in a rather commanding tone, "Bob, you're not on shock therapy now? Right?" The patient replied that he was not. The therapist added, "And you said you were not on drugs." Again the patient acknowledged that this was true. The therapist continued, "So it's fortunate then that you are *you* this morning here with us. In other words, you and mom and dad and I are all responsible for what we say and *that makes it easier to understand each other.*"

The patient's rescue operations which dig his own hole deeper are usually an issue in the first few minutes of the initial session. The therapist's criticism or irritation at these attempts implies not only that this kind of thing is not acceptable, but also that the patient can do better. This attitude is in contrast to that of the parents, who usually will drop whatever they are engaged in and follow up the patient's intervention like a hound dog in pursuit. (However, an alternative approach that is sometimes feasible is to accept this line of joint interest in the patient's symptoms but to press the inquiry in such a way as to include more of the family circumstances surrounding symptomatic behavior and their relevance to it.) Another matter that comes up in the first session is the question of what to do if someone in the family is absent from one of the sessions. It may seem to be borrowing trouble to anticipate such a happening, but experience has taught us that the multitudinous excuses proffered for someone's not appearing would delight a sage truant officer. It seems more efficacious to announce to the family that there will be times when they

do not wish to come and that such absence is a rather powerful lever to use against the therapist and against family members; or to announce that they are likely to feel reluctant to come just when important progress is occurring. Such announcements also emphasize our philosophy that family members do have a great effect on each other and that there is no such thing as not commenting even if the "No comment" is attempted through silence or through a nonappearance.

In summary, a few principal means that the therapist may use—separately, jointly, or alternatively, according to taste and circumstances—in handling the typical problems arising at the start of family therapy might be listed as follows. First, there is a certain place for being very clear, direct, and explicit. This is comparatively limited, applying mostly to practical details such as the schedule of meetings; unless the therapist is quite clear and definite, even such a simple matter can set off a long, inconclusive discussion. Second comes the making of certain matter-of-fact statements whereby the important messages are conveyed implicitly. Third comes the making of statements about some aspect of the therapy which are accompanied by some comment that serves to anticipate and disarm resistance—for example, "I intend to be impartial, though each of you will surely doubt that I am at times." This may be carried all the way to an "inversion of meaning" statement such as "There will be times, just as real progress is being made, when you will feel like not coming to the meetings."

From the discussion so far it must now be evident that active intervention in and management of family interaction has an important place in our initial work; and, indeed, this holds true of the further course of family therapy also. This active orientation, however, grew out of our experience and was not a predisposition except that experience in treating individual schizophrenics presses one toward an active and varied style of therapy. Nevertheless, in beginning our work with families, we were concerned lest activity on the part of the therapist would obscure family operations and dim the light of our research. Actually, it has been so difficult to keep the sicker families involved, to produce shifts and not mere repetitions of the standard patterns characteristic of any one family, that we are no longer so concerned about the therapist remaining a flyspeck by his own design and efforts, and more concerned with avoiding being put into such a useless position by the family.

If it is kept in mind that families have horizontal as well as vertical layers, then the pattern of response to the therapist's intervention can simply be viewed as a further unfolding of the range of this particular family's transactions. By vertical, we mean going back in time; by horizontal, we mean layers of complexity of communications or, as they might be called, layers of defense in concentric circles. One of the things that the tyro therapist must experience is that he will have to deal with the same problem over and over again in different forms and guises, as the following example suggests.

Initially, the father of a paranoid patient complained to the therapist of his son's obesity and requested a diet for him. He and his wife expressed futility about "doing anything with him." They occasionally took action of an interesting sort, considering their son's suspicious nature; for example, the father sneaked out early one morning to tell the milkman that he was to ignore any requests for ice cream. The therapist held fast to his recommendation that the patient would change himself when he was ready, and several sessions later the patient announced that he had lost some weight. As the therapist tried to congratulate him, the mother cut in to discuss her own weight problem, and the father topped her by recounting a rather bizarre episode in which he was found unconscious and taken to a hospital in peril of his life.

This sequence was characteristic for this family. The patient's statements tended to be ignored or rationalized away, the mother usually sounded a serious note about something, and the father topped it by telling something on himself which, while dramatic, inevitably made him out to be slightly foolish. A kind of closure was usually attained at the end of these sequences by the father, mother, and son all chuckling slightly at the father's expense. This sort of closed sequence, however, constitutes the sort of pathological family homeostasis that it is the therapist's business and duty to alter.

FURTHER TECHNICAL MEANS

As family therapy proceeds, we are ordinarily not much concerned with the topics and content of the family discussions, except perhaps when there is evident talking of one matter to avoid something else. Indeed, it may be valuable at times to shift the discussion from a hot topic to a less important one involving the same sort of family alignment and interaction, in the hope that the nature of the interaction can better be seen and some revision inaugurated while dealing with a more minor matter.

Such alteration of self-reinforcing and mutually destructive networks of interaction is the most general goal of our work with families, and our emphasis correspondingly is on means of influencing these patterns rather than on examining their content, or even on describing the pattern as such.

Our experience with this kind of repetitive pattern is that pointing it out to the family does little good. However, its meaning, intent, or focus can be shifted by the therapist's intervention; and after a series of such interventions, the pattern loses some of its highly stereotyped repetitiousness. Various means may be essayed in relation to this formidable task, several of which have already been mentioned. Implication is a powerful tool in the therapist's hands; but making explicit what the family members communicate only implicitly can be equally important. Framing or interpretation of messages—in a communicational, not psychoanalytic, sense of interpretation—is most important, and occurs in many varieties: the therapist may frame his own message, and, equally important, he may reframe and reinterpret the messages of family members. By this means, the positive side of difficult or provocative behavior in the family can be shown, sense made out of craziness, and congruence out of incongruence. Such inverting is a powerful lever for change. Certain sorts of dualistic positive-and-negative messages also are important, such as criticism administered with personal attention for easier swallowing or a strong comment given in a mild tone; in this sort of "quiet bombshell" there is an evident similarity between our communicational orientation and more orthodox psychiatric thought and practice.

We may also give advice. However, our aim in advising is not to tell family members the proper thing to do; rather it is to enable them to accept interest, advice, and help, for they ordinarily are so defensive as to disqualify and reject whatever is offered, even if they have been demanding it. If we can present a little advice in an acceptable way, in accepting it from us as experts, they take a first step toward accepting from each other.

The giving of some rather specific instructions as a technique in therapy illuminates this area still further. We do not expect to achieve change directly by giving instructions on how to behave, and we ordinarily avoid doing so, especially on matters of obvious practical importance—although this is where our advice and instructions are most likely to be solicited. Instead, we are apt to choose an apparently minor manner—which still will be involved in some significant pattern of interaction—and give an instruction to do A, expecting that the person, from our knowledge of his reactions, will in fact do B, which will cause change C in a family relationship. An example may clarify this complicated but significant situation:

The mother of a 15-year-old schizophrenic boy was a very managing woman, taking over everything from her nearly mute son, her rather quiet husband, and also from the struggling therapist. Yet she was very unhappy and anxious. Finally she was able to say one day that she was upset because she felt that her husband was distant; she couldn't get in close touch with him. Yet she felt wrong if she reacted to this, even if only by becoming silently upset. The main emphasis was on the problem of feeling wrong uncontrollably, even when she thought she had some just cause for distress. The therapist then suggested that she could act to resolve this problem of feeling wrong, if she seriously wanted to, by following a simple instruction. After a pause, she agreed. The therapist's instruction was that, during the following week, she should deliberately do something that she considered wrong. The only conditions imposed were that the wrong was not to be a really serious one and was to involve some other family member in some way; other than that she should choose the action. During the next session, she revealed that the daring deed she had committed was subscribing to a book club.

The members of this research group laughed as they heard this section on the tape, thinking how constricted she was to commit such a minor sort of sin. However, they had failed to appreciate the limitations placed on the range of action in this family, because the father, who in the session heard for the first time what she had done, angrily disapproved. Although his reasons were a bit obscure, they appeared to concern the expense involved. In fact, since this was not great, and money was used by the father as a means of control, the mother's independence seems more important. From this episode, the therapist and the group as a whole learned a little more about why this woman had to breathe her sick son's every breath. The fact that she was severely controlling did not mean that she was not similarly controlled by herself and her husband. And if control is this severe, then even the small change of behavior, change of evaluation, and change in relationship with her husband that this act represented, though initiated by the therapist's instruction, may be correspondingly significant.

FAMILY PATHOLOGY AND THERAPY: A THEORETICAL SUMMARY

Perhaps we can now utilize the preceding material to attempt a more condensed and general statement of our ideas on the pathology of these families and its treatment. Even though such a theoretical statement is bound to be oversimplified and incomplete at this stage of our knowledge, it will provide a basis for some comparison between our theoretical and therapeutic slants and those of other workers.

Summing up very broadly then, it appears that these families of schizophrenics are enmeshed in a pathological but very strong homeostatic system of family interaction. That is, regardless of their past history—although that might be enlightening—they are *at present* interacting in ways that are unsatisfying and painful to all, provocative of gross symptomatology in at least one, and yet powerfully self-reinforcing. Their overt behavior may appear varied or even chaotic, but beneath this a pervasive and persistent pattern can be discerned, and one that is quite resistant even to outside therapeutic efforts at change.

How and why is this so? On what basis may such homeostasis be clarified and understood? We may at least begin to do so by using further our basic concepts of the double bind and the still broader concept of the necessary multiplicity of messages, of different levels, in all communication. These ideas, which were helpful in understanding the occurrence of schizophrenic behavior, are also helpful in attacking the more fundamental problem level: Why does pathological behavior or organization persist, even under pressure to change? We have not solved this problem, but we can state a few leading ideas. First, the double bind pattern itself tends to be circular and interactive in a self-perpetuating way, even though we may speak of it carelessly as if it were a one-way matter, with a "binder" acting on a "victim." Actually, if A sends incongruent messages to B, B is very likely to respond with a correspondingly incongruent set of messages in reply. The one main difference likely to exist between their communications only serves to intensify the vicious circularity: If the incongruence between A's messages is concealed and B falls in with this, then the incongruence in B's reply is apt to be correspondingly *exaggerated*, the typical case for schizophrenic utterance. This in turn influences A toward further incongruence, even more concealed or denied, and so on. In three-party situations,[6] essentially the same process may occur. If A and B are parents giving incongruent messages to C, their child, C is likely to respond in a disturbed way with markedly incongruent messages and ones likely to have some reference to the family relationships; at this A and B are very likely to insist more strongly that there are no differences in what they think and say, rather than admitting differences, as we have described earlier.

Second, the existence of a multiplicity of messages obviously offers great possibilities for interaction among family members in which nothing is ever clarified because *both* agreement and disagreement can be avoided. It is possible, with incongruent messages, to agree with another person, yet not agree, by agreeing at one level of message yet disagreeing at another or indicating that it is not really the speaker who is agreeing. And similarly with disagreement; this also can be no-yet-yes. We find that members of families in which there is a schizophrenic are likely to communicate largely by

[6]Discussed in Weakland, *op. cit.*

remarks we may call "disqualifying"—that is, they effectively negate what someone else has said, only in an indirect way, so that statements are not really met. This sort of communication and its paralyzing effects have been particularly striking in some standard interviews that we have given experimentally, since these interviews focused on family organization, leadership, and planning, first by asking the family members to plan something they would like to do together, and then by inquiring who was in charge of the family.

This sort of problem may be seen from a somewhat different angle by considering the two sorts of families of schizophrenics discriminated by Lidz:[7] One ("skew" families) in which harmony is conveyed overtly, but with covert persistent disagreement; the other ("schism" families), in which there is constant overt scrapping yet the family members somehow remain together for many years. Both may be seen as types of pathological organization whose stability is related to the existence of such incongruent double messages about family relationships plus the avoidance of recognition and acknowledgement of such incongruence by family members.

Any move toward change or therapy, finally, immediately encounters difficulties similar to those just mentioned. The members of these families have long been adept at using incongruent messages. Thus, if some change in behavior or family organization is proposed, what is more likely than that it will be met with agreement that is not agreement; with disagreement that is not disagreement; with agreement from one member and disagreement from another, while they insist they are together on the matter, and so on? If a specific change can be brought about in the behavior of some member, it is likely to be negated by a shifting of the general context, by the same person or another: "Yes, my husband is behaving better to me now; but of course that's just because you told him to, not that he cares any more about me." Or a

[7]Theodore Lidz and Stephen Fleck, "Schizophrenia, Human Integration and the Role of Family," pp. 323–345, in *The Etiology of Schizophrenia* (see footnote 3). For other references and more extensive discussion, see Weakland, *op. cit.*, pp. 380–382.

more general shift may be negated by a specific change; or the two parents may both change at once so that they remain on opposite sides of whatever fence divided them, even if reversed from their original stands. All this also throws light on why description or labeling of family behavior is usually ineffective, even where the members themselves appear to grasp it; thus we are more concerned with altering interaction than with "insight."

In other words, these families have a tremendous aptitude for "plus ça change, plus c'est la même chose." It appears increasingly clear to us as we work with them that to be effective we must meet them on their own ground, though with different orientation—toward positive change instead of defensive maintenance of a sick system. That is, the therapist must himself employ dual or multiple messages involving such incongruences as will serve to come to grips with the whole complexity of the messages of the family members he must deal with. A reconsideration of the techniques we have mentioned earlier shows readily enough that for many this is already explicitly so, and it is implicit for most of the others. That is, we have been concerned with using explicit statements that convey concealed and unexpected implicit meanings as well; with using content messages joined with framing statements; with giving instructions whose carrying-out will constitute a further message. We have spoken of this elsewhere, perhaps too narrowly, as the "therapeutic double bind"; the broad principle described here of using multiple—and often incongruent —messages therapeutically, is what needs recognition, and then further investigation.

OURSELVES AND OTHERS: FAMILY THERAPY AS A COMMUNICABLE DISEASE

Except for political rallies, baseball games, and burlesque shows, it is difficult to imagine a situation more capable of arousing enthusiasm among therapists than conjoint family therapy. It is not completely clear to us why this should be, but it does make us cautious about accepting new adherents and we do attempt to review our work with the limited objectivity available to us. There is little question that exposure to con-

joint family therapy alters the psychotherapeutic approach of the exposed, both in his private and research work. Most of those engaged in our family therapy research project have private practices on a part-time basis. It is fascinating and predictable to note that their psychotherapeutic approach undergoes at least the following changes:

(1) The therapist will become more "active" in individual therapy, especially in suggesting the meaning of other people's behavior vis-à-vis the patient.

(2) The therapist will be less interested in diagnosis or the accepted dynamic formulations; he will tend, rather, to describe his patients in terms of an interlocking milieu, consisting mainly of the immediate family situation, but drawing also upon the wider family context and sometimes including ethnic or subcultural factors.

(3) The therapist will greatly increase the number of couples he treats, mostly in the conjoint situation. We believe it is rare for our therapists not to have met the spouses of all their patients.

These tendencies, in other words, parallel several distinctive emphases in the orientation of our family therapy: activity of the therapist rather than passive listening; more concern for alteration of behavior than for "insight"; more intense focus on the present than on the past; and more attention to interaction than to intrapersonal experience.

Perhaps two brief examples will illustrate how the family therapy bug affects its victim:

Example A.—A catatonic young woman was discharged from a Midwestern state hospital because her parents were moving to California. She was referred to one of us for recommendations as to local hospital care. Although the patient was mute and stiff, she appeared evanescently pleased by the suggestion that if she and her parents were willing to start family therapy, we could see how it would work out to have her live at home, with a practical nurse assisting the mother during the daytime. She has remained out of the hospital now for two years and appears to be functioning fairly adequately. Previous to our family work, it would have been unthinkable that such a catatonic patient who did not appear to be in good contact would not be hospitalized.

Example B.—On an emergency home visit, one

of us met a 60-year-old woman who had made a mild suicidal gesture. She appeared to be in a typical agitated depression, and the question seemed to be where to hospitalize her and whether it should be in an institution where she would receive electro-shock therapy. After speaking to her for a few minutes, the psychiatrist asked her daughter with whom she was living to join them; and he noted that, despite a smiling cooperative kindliness, not all was well between daughter and mother. When this was touched on, the daughter mentioned that she had her husband and her own 17-year-old daughter to worry about and perhaps her mother's attitude was a little bit too much. The mother sparked noticeably at this and implied that the daughter didn't have a complete romance with her husband and had in fact invited the mother to live with her partially on this account. The patient was not sent to a hospital but was seen in conjoint therapy with her daughter, son-in-law, and granddaughter. After a very brief time, the blocked communication in the family had noticeably improved and the mother decided she would like to live by herself. In retrospect, it seemed fairly certain that getting the patient's daughter involved after a few minutes of the initial visit, and the orientation of the therapist, altered what would have been fairly standard psychiatric disposition.

TRANSFERENCE, COUNTERTRANSFERENCE, AND INTERACTION

Many analysts have had strong doubts about the idea of family therapy, which are often put on transference and countertransference grounds. Thus the terms "transference and countertransference" are troublesome unless it is kept in mind that they refer strictly to aspects of a very special situation—psychoanalysis. We have no doubt that our therapists have feelings about the family members and vice versa; on the other hand, no clarity is achieved if we label such states of mind transference and counter-transference. There are several reasons for this:

Transference is a manifestation related to the inactivity prescribed for standard psychoanalytic treatment. The patient, on the basis of minimal cues, creates a framework and embroiders it with past personal references. In conjoint psychotherapy, there is a good deal of activity, even if the therapist is only acting as a traffic cop. If skillfully managed, the interaction is largely among family members and not with the therapist. Thus we would consider the proper intervention when a wife is chopping her husband to ribbons, not to be "Look what you're

doing to the poor man," but to ask *him* if she always shows her attachment to him in this way. The wife will be fascinated awaiting his reply and will be busy with her rebuttal.

That is, with so much interaction among the family members, and active therapeutic focus on this, there is no emergence of standard transference phenomena. What we do see can better be labeled parataxic distortions, since the data consist of discrete examples of expectations on the part of a family member that the therapist does or does not fulfill. Some of these instances even seem to be a combination of ignorance and misinformation as to what one can legitimately expect of a therapist, while others appear to result from explanatory concepts that the person brought with him into therapy, such as, "All men are . . . ."

It is difficult to explain the difference between these phenomena in individual and family therapy unless one has observed or participated in both forms of psychotherapy. A statement by a family member, which if it occurred in an individual psychotherapeutic session may be labeled evidence of transference, can have a very different meaning in family therapy. Thus, a comment by the wife that the therapist is the only one who has ever understood her is apt to be an expression of dissatisfaction with her husband, a pointing out of a direction he should take; and before the therapist can label this himself as father transference, the husband's reaction will have to be dealt with, plus one of the children, plus the wife's reaction to her husband's reaction, and so on.

The same difficulties apply to countertransference. If the therapist is active, he becomes aware of his feelings partially through the kind of action he takes, and often not until a supervisory session. An experienced, fairly secure therapist may change the direction of a beginning feeling in himself by taking an action opposite to the feeling. For example, if he finds himself irritated by the mother's quietly nagging, martyred tone, he may turn to the father and ask what he experienced in himself during the time when the wife was speaking. On the surface, it would appear that the therapist simply passes the buck to the father and that this technique might be a fairly destructive one. On the other hand, if it is kept in mind that the father has been having thoughts for years about his wife's attitude, and that now is his chance to express them with the support of another male present, a different face is put on the situation. By the time the husband has made his comments, the therapist may then be in a mood to reaccept the wife and to help find out what she has to complain about. Such interlocking transactions are part of the ordinary family life and have been referred to in papers on everything from pecking order to role playing.

RESULTS

We are not yet in a position to support any claim that family therapy is better or worse than the more usual methods of treating schizophrenics. Insufficient time has elapsed, and unusual and difficult problems of evaluation are posed by our interest not only in the identified patient, but in the parents and siblings and especially in the functioning of the family as a whole, while means for evaluation at this level are largely lacking in psychiatry at present. Thus it is appropriate that the emphasis in this paper has been on our ideas and methods; we have pointed out that family therapy differs from individual therapy, in ways we have tried to outline, and that this difference helps to shape a new orientation in the therapist. We may, however, end by discussing briefly the inconclusive yet promising results of our therapeutic efforts so far.

Various studies have shown that prognosis for recovery from schizophrenia is importantly related to the history of the illness—that is, its duration, amount of hospitalization and other treatment without success, and so on. Therefore, our evaluative scheme for family therapy, with reference to the identified patients, is based on comparing the level of their social adaptation before family therapy and currently, against the background of information on the prior history of their illness. On this basis, our cases can hardly be considered other than difficult ones. We have worked with eighteen families so far. Of the identified schizophrenic patients in these families, eleven were males ranging in age from

13 to 41, and seven were females ranging in age from 14 to 34. Of these eighteen, six had been originally diagnosed as schizophrenic between 10 and 16 years ago, four between 5 and 10 years ago, and eight less than 5 years ago. Perhaps four of these eight were first seen by us as fairly new or acute cases, but fourteen of our eighteen patients could be labeled as already chronic cases when we first saw them. Some had been diagnosed in early childhood, as young as 3 years; the maximum age at first diagnosis was 25. Eleven of these patients had been hospitalized at some time, from a minimum of 2 months up to 6 years maximum, the average being 3 to 4 years. Of the seven patients never hospitalized, probably three or four were clinically sick enough to justify hospitalization and had avoided it only because they were so young or had such passive-withdrawing symptomatology that their behavior could still be tolerated or handled within the home.

Information on prior treatment other than hospitalization, although it is certainly not complete, shows that at least seven patients had received EST, one insulin shock, eight had had tranquilizing drugs, and twelve had received individual psychotherapy ranging from a minimum of 3 sessions to a maximum of 9 years of intermittent examination and treatment. In several cases family members—usually the mother—had also had some individual psychotherapy. In only four instances, all young persons and fresh cases, had there been no therapy before family treatment was started.

At the time of writing, our families had been seen, usually on a once-weekly basis for an hour or an hour and a half, from a minimum of 3 months up to 41 months in one case, the average being about 12 months. Most of our families are still in treatment, although four terminated therapy against our advice.

There were seven patients hospitalized at the outset of family therapy. Of these, one is still in the hospital, three are living at home and able to go out unaccompanied, one is living at home but working, one is living alone and caring for her child though still financially dependent on the parents, and one is living alone, working part-time but financially dependent on her parents. Thus, six of these seven have shown a noticeable improvement in terms of social adaptation and independence. Of the remaining patients, nine were young persons, mostly never hospitalized, who were living with parents and restricted to the home or, if going out, not productive—that is, not working or doing badly in school. All but two of these improved in such degree as starting to school again, changing from failure to passing, starting to work, or at least starting to go out unaccompanied, as did the two remaining patients who had previously been confined to their homes after release from hospitalization.

It is still more difficult to characterize results with the parents and siblings, and with the family as a whole. But, very broadly, it can be said that the other family members generally have improved, though less noticeably than the identified patients. More than half of the fathers were judged improved by their therapists, with the rest showing no distinct change. The picture for the mothers was similar except for two cases where it was judged that the mother was worse. And limited data on siblings showed about evenly divided improvement and no change, excepting again one sibling judged worse.

Finally, though it often appeared a severe course of treatment, all of our therapists seem to have been helped, without exception.

73.

AUGUST B. HOLLINGSHEAD AND FREDRICK C. REDLICH

SOCIAL CLASS AND MENTAL ILLNESS

Americans prefer to avoid the two facts of life studied in this book: social class and mental illness. The very idea of "social class" is inconsistent with the American ideal of a society composed of free and equal individuals, individuals living in a society where they have identical opportunities to realize their inborn potentialities. The acceptance of this facet of the "American Dream" is easy and popular. To suggest that it may be more myth than reality stimulates antagonistic reactions.

Although Americans, by choice, deny the existence of social classes, they are forced to admit the reality of mental illness. Nevertheless, merely the thought of such illness is abhorrent to them. They fear "mental illness," its victims, and those people who cope with them: psychiatrists, clinical psychologists, social workers,

From August B. Hollingshead and Fredrick C. Redlich, *Social class and mental illness: A community study.* New York: John Wiley & Sons, Inc., 1958. Pp. 3–6, 84–85, 94–95, 103–104, 113–114, 198–199, 216–217, 225–229. Reprinted by permission.

psychiatric nurses, and attendants. Even the institutions our society has developed to care for the mentally ill are designated by pejorative terms, such as "bug house," "booby hatch," and "loony bin," and psychiatrists are called "nutcrackers" and "head shrinkers."

Denial of the existence of social classes and derisive dismissal of the mentally ill may salve the consciences of some people. The suggestion that different social classes receive different treatment for mental illness may come as a shock, but to repress facts because they are distasteful and incongruent with cherished values may lead to consequences even more serious than those we are trying to escape by substituting fantasy for reality.

* * *

MENTAL ILLNESS

Our attitudes toward mental illness are also a product of our cultural heritage. Historical evidence indicates that mental "disturbances" have been known in all civilized societies. The severe disturbances of kings, generals, religious leaders, and other personages have been recorded since ancient times. Persons who were not important enough to have their mental aberrations written into the human record undoubtedly also were afflicted, even though their ailments and their numbers have been lost in the mists of time. Although man's mental and emotional maladjustments are not new, the public is more clearly aware of them now than in the past, and responsible leaders have become increasingly concerned with their alleviation.

In the last decade mental illness has been recognized as one of the most serious unsolved health problems facing our society. A few figures will indicate its magnitude. The approximately 750,000 persons who are currently hospitalized in mental institutions occupy some 55 percent of all hospital beds in the United States. Hundreds of thousands of other mentally ill persons are treated by psychiatrists in clinics and in private practice, but the number of hospitalized cases increases year by year. During World War II, 43 percent of all disability discharges (980,000) from the Armed Forces were granted on psychiatric grounds, and 865,000 young men were rejected for psychiatric reasons in Selective Service examinations. Moreover, some 16,000 to 17,000 persons commit suicide each year and, according to the best estimates, there are about 3,800,000 alcoholics in the adult population. We are certain that patients hospitalized in mental institutions in addition to those cared for by psychiatrists in private practice and in clinics represent only a portion of those who are mentally ill. Estimates indicate that there are from seven to eight million other Americans who are less seriously disturbed but who could benefit from psychiatric care if it were available.[1]

SOCIAL CLASS AND MENTAL ILLNESS

Is the presence of mental illness in the population related to class status? Is the treatment received by a mentally ill member of our society an effect of his class position? These questions are crucial to the research reported here. They are even more important from the viewpoint of their scientific meaning and their implications for social policy.

Detailed evidence will be presented in this book to support the answers we have reached. If our answers support American ideals of equality, class status should have no effect upon the distribution of mental illness in the population. Neither should it influence the kind of psychiatric treatment mentally ill patients receive. However, the reader should remember that our ideals and our behavior are two different things.

Both social class and mental illness may be compared to an iceberg; 90 percent of it is concealed below the surface. The submerged portion, though unseen, is the dangerous part. This may be illustrated by recalling what happened when an "unsinkable" trans-Atlantic luxury liner, the *Titanic,* rammed an iceberg on her maiden voyage in 1912. In that crisis, a passenger's class status played a part in the determination of whether he survived or was drowned. The official casualty lists showed that only 4 first class female passengers (3 voluntarily chose to stay on the ship) of a total of 143 were lost. Among the second class passengers, 15 of 93 females drowned; and among the third class, 81 of 179 female passengers went down with the ship. The third class passengers were ordered to remain below deck, some kept there at the point of a gun.[2]

The idea that stratification in our society has any bearing on the diagnosis and treatment of disease runs counter to our cherished beliefs about equality, especially when they are applied to the care of the sick. Physicians share deeply ingrained egalitarian ideals with their fellow citizens, yet they, too, may make subtle, perhaps unconscious, judgments of the differential worth of the members of our society. Physicians, among them psychiatrists, are sensitive to statements that patients may not be treated alike; in fact there is strong resistance in medical circles to the exploration of such questions. But closing our eyes to facts or denying them in anger will

[1]Kenneth Appel, "Present Challenge of Psychiatry," *American Journal of Psychiatry,* Vol. III, No. 1 (July 1954), pp. 1–12; J. M. A. Weiss, "Suicide: An Epidomiological Analysis," *Psychological Quarterly,* Vol. 28 (1954), pp. 225–252.

[2]Walter Lord, *A Night to Remember* (New York: Henry Holt and Company, 1955), p. 107.

help patients no more than the belief that the *Titanic* was "unsinkable" kept the ship afloat after it collided with an iceberg.

CLASS STATUS AND CULTURAL CHARACTERISTICS

CLASS I

Class I is composed of the community's business and professional leaders. Its members live in those areas of the community generally regarded as the "best"; the male heads are college graduates, usually from famous private institutions; their wives have completed from one to four years of college. Incomes are the highest of any stratum, and many families are wealthy; often their wealth is inherited. This is true particularly of a core group of interrelated families who have lived in the area for several generations. Members of the core group are descendants of the pioneers who settled in New England three centuries ago. These families dominate the private clubs that play so prominent a part in this group's use of leisure time. The core group family is stable, secure, and, from the viewpoint of its values, socially responsible for its members and the welfare of the community.

* * *

CLASS II

Almost all adults in the class II stratum have had some formal education beyond high school. The males occupy managerial positions; many are engaged in the lesser ranking professions. The class II members live in one-family houses in the better residential areas. These families are well-to-do, but there is no substantial inherited or acquired wealth. Class II persons are sensitive to status factors perhaps as a consequence of the fact that four in five are upward mobile. The aspirations of these people have taken them away from their parental families and in many cases from their home communities. Upward mobility is closely linked with ethnic heterogeneity and religious affiliation. About one half of the families are Protestants; the remainder are divided rather equally between Roman Catholics and Jews. The nuclear family is composed predominantly of married adults

and their minor children. Only 5 percent of the families with children under 17 years of age are broken or have an aged relative, usually a grandparent, in the home. Family members of all ages are "joiners." Their memberships include neighborhood clique groups, associations for mutual protection against "undesirables," local church organizations, political clubs, fraternal societies, business associations, the Boy Scouts, the Girl Scouts, and Parent Teacher Associations. In addition, about half of these families belong to lesser ranking private clubs in the area.

Tension points in class II generally revolve around the striving for success—economic, educational, and social. The younger adults are oriented toward the future, the time when they will "reach the top." Middle-aged men and women are more aware that they have not quite "made it." Older persons know they will not "make it"; they are resigned to things as they are, but there is an underlying fear that sickness, war, or depression will impair their ability to "hold on."

* * *

CLASS III

Significantly more men and women are dissatisfied with their present living conditions and less optimistic about the future than are the class II's. However, the majority have a positive view of the future. They look forward to the time when the home will be paid for or their income higher, and things will be easier. Some two out of three husbands and wives under 50 years of age believe that their chances of achieving a desired standard of living within the next ten years are "almost certain" or "very good." They expect to double their income within 15 years.

Men and women over 40 years of age are concerned about the maturing of their children, the maintenance of their neighborhood, and their health. Many are disturbed by reports of corruption in business and government, especially at the local level. Others are disturbed by the encroachment of Negroes into their neighborhoods; the feeling that people do not recognize moral responsibilities to their children, their neighbors, and their associates disturbs others;

many middle-aged persons wonder about their "place" in life.

The realization of the gulf between what they think life might be and what it is for them is a point of stress for many beyond the middle years. Years of striving for their ideals has taught them to forego pleasures of the day for spiritual, moral, and social gains of tomorrow. As the years pass, and the realization that hoped-for goals have slipped away, or moved farther into the future, many adults have become re-signed to the realization that they must adjust to things as they are.

* * *

CLASS IV

The modal family may be summarized in general terms. The husband who is 44 and the wife who is 42 years of age are members of an ethnic group—if Italian, second generation; if Irish, third. They were married after an engagement of five months in a Roman Catholic church when the husband was 21 and the wife was 19 years of age. When the couple married, they moved into a "rent" of their own in the dwelling owned by the husband's family. They now live in a two-family home, are satisfied with their housing, but hope to buy a single-family home in the suburbs some day. They have 4 or 5 children; the younger ones are in elementary and high school; the oldest one has finished school and is working on the production line of a local factory, or, if a male, is in the armed services. The husband and father has been working since the age of 17. He worked at his first job for about a year and a half, then changed to one he thought was better; however, he is still a semiskilled worker on a production line. His wife, too, began to work in the factory when she was 17 years of age, but she may have tried sales or clerical jobs as well. She worked at her first job about two years. She was working when she was married and continued to work until her first pregnancy was well advanced.

The recreation of the parents consists of "working around the place," viewing television, occasionally listening to the radio, some reading, and family visiting. The children spend more time with television, the radio, and the movies than do their parents. In addition, they go to local athletic events and visit the amusement park two or three times during the season. The husband belongs to "the union" but no other organization. The wife belongs to no formal organizations, but she is a member of an informal neighborhood women's group.

Their effective family income after withholding taxes, union dues, social security, and hospital insurance is approximately $65 a week, and they are able to save about $5 of it. Their savings are used perodically to pay for emergencies or the purchase of desired consumer goods. At present they feel economically secure, but they are not wholly satisfied with their living conditions; the children are dissatisfied. The parents believe that their marriage has been a "good one" and it has been aided by the cooperation and mutual interest they have held through the years. The parents look forward to a happy future, especially to when they will be able to save enough to buy their "dream house." They believe that their chances of obtaining it are "good" now that the children are "out from underfoot." The husband expects to continue to earn a "good income." He thinks his "best years" will come in his "late fifties" when he will be earning "about $100 a week."

* * *

CLASS V

Occupationally, class V adults are overwhelmingly semiskilled factory hands and unskilled laborers. Educationally, most adults have not completed the elementary grades. Individuals and families are concentrated in the "tenement" and "cold-water flat" areas of New Haven and in semirural "slums" in two of the suburban towns. Immigrants from southern and eastern Europe, their children, grandchildren, and great-grandchildren compose the vast majority of this stratum, but about 4 percent are swamp Yankees; and 25 percent are descendants of the "old immigrants" from northern and western Europe.

Five types of family constellations exist in class V: the nuclear family of father, mother, and children, the three- or four-generation stem family, the broken nuclear family of one parent and minor children, residual families consisting of widows, widowers, or elderly couples whose children have left home, mixed families of one parent, children, roomers and/or boarders, and common-law groups. Forty-one percent of the children under seventeen years of age live in broken homes. There are a few more separated or divorced adults in Class V than there are widows and widowers. Family ties are more brittle in class V than in the higher classes.

Only a small minority of the family members belong to and participate in organized community institutions. Their social life takes place in the household, on the street, or in neighborhood social agencies. Leisure time activities vary with the several age groups, but in all ages they tend to be informal and spontaneous. Reading either for information or pleasure is not a prominent feature of their activities. Television viewing is a major activity at all ages. Out-of-the-home recreations involve commercial amusements or trips to public places. Adolescent boys, in particular, tend to roam the streets and highways in search of adventure. This often brings them into contact with the police and the courts.

The struggle for existence is a meaningful reality to these people. Their level of skill is low, their jobs are poorly paid, and they have no savings to carry them over a crisis. Adults are resentful of the way they have been treated by employers, clergymen, teachers, doctors, police, and other representatives of organized society. They express their resentments freely in the home and in other primary groups. Children hear them, believe them, and react to the targets of the parents' hostility in ways that are generally approved by the parents. This means that the children fit into the mold provided for them by their parents. Their own experiences with representatives of the higher classes reinforce the attitudes they bring into the situation. As a consequence, hostility breeds more hostility; but in order to survive the class V child or adult must repress his feelings and attitudes. These, however, tend to be expressed by acting out against society, members of the

family, or the self. The psychopathological implications of the class V subculture should become clearer as we present data on the psychiatric side of the picture.

* * *

CLASS STATUS AND PREVALENCE OF DISORDERS

The first test of a possible interrelation between class status and mental illness is presented in Table 10.1. A glance at the percentages in Table 10.1 will show that class I has only one third as many patients as might be expected if class I individuals were distributed in the same proportion in the patient population as class I individuals are in the general population. Likewise, class II, III, and IV individuals are under-represented in the patient column, but not to the same extent as class I individuals. On the other hand, the percentage of patients in class V is more than double the percentage of class V individuals in the general population. The distribution of patients in comparison with nonpatients by class is significant.

TABLE 10.1

CLASS STATUS AND THE DISTRIBUTION OF PATIENTS AND NONPATIENTS IN THE POPULATION

Class	Population, %	
	Patients	Nonpatients
I	1.0	3.0
II	7.0	8.4
III	13.7	20.4
IV	40.1	49.8
V	38.2	18.4
$n =$	1891	236,940

$$X^2 = 509.81, 4\ df,\ p < .001$$

This indicates that there is foundation in fact for our assumption that class status is a factor conditioning whether or not a member of the community is a psychiatric patient. However, we are not content to accept the apparent relationship between class status and treatment or nontreatment for a mental disorder without a systematic examination of the influences age, sex, religion, and marital status may have on the data. If it should occur that, when these factors are included in the analysis, the significant association between class status and the prevalence of treated disorders in the population shown in Table 10.1 disappears, then we should modify the theoretical position posited in this research. If, however, the inclusion of these factors does not efface the differences between class status and the prevalence of patients in the different classes, then we may conclude *Hypothesis 1* is tenable. Control of the five factors, in addition to class, will tell us whether the relationship we have found between class status and mental illness can be attributed to these factors.

* * *

The series of analyses we have presented in this chapter have been focused on a step-by-step examination of the tenability of the first hypothesis around which this research was designed. This hypothesis was premised on the assumption that the prevalence of psychiatric patients in the population of the community studies is related significantly to social class. The search for a clear-cut answer to this proposition was carried through six progressively more difficult steps. The first involved a direct comparison of the patients with the general population. This comparison revealed three things:

(1) A definite association exists between class position and being a psychiatric patient.

(2) The lower the class, the greater the proportion of patients in the population.

(3) The greatest difference is between classes IV and V in that class V has a much higher ratio of patients to population than class IV.

To assure ourselves that the strong association between class status and mental illness is not produced by variables other than class, the data were analyzed, in the second step, with selected factors controlled—sex, age, race, religion, and marital status. When each of these factors was held constant, the association between class status and mental illness reappeared. We next held two factors constant, and the association of mental illness with class continued to reappear with one exception: No significant difference was found between mental disorder

and class position for individuals aged 15 through 24. The fourth analytical step entailed holding three factors constant. Once again the association between class and the prevalence of mental illness reappeared with few exceptions. The fifth step was taken when the previously demonstrated relationship between class and the prevalence of mental illness was viewed in terms of rates. The sixth step was taken when the components in prevalence were analyzed by class: incidence, re-entry into treatment, and continuous treatment. The rates for each of these components in the general picture of treated mental illness are linked in significant ways to class status.

The several procedures followed enable us to conclude that *Hypothesis 1* is true. Stated in different terms, a distinct inverse relationship does exist between social class and mental illness. The linkage between class status and the distribution of patients in the population follows a characteristic pattern; class V, almost invariably, contributes many more patients than its proportion of the population warrants. Among the higher classes there is a more proportionate relationship between the number of psychiatric patients and the number of individuals in the population.

* * *

CLASS POSITION AND TYPES OF MENTAL ILLNESS

CLASS STATUS AND THE NEUROSES

We are now ready to present the crucial *internal* test we made of the proposition that class status is related to neurotic illnesses. The data essential for the examination of this proposition are summarized in Table 10.2.

The data in Table 10.2 demonstrate that a significant relationship does exist between class position and the kind of diagnoses psychiatrists place upon their patients. Anti-social and immaturity reactions are concentrated in classes III and V, whereas phobic and anxiety reactions cluster in class IV. Character neuroses focus in classes I and II; relatively few character neuroses are found in classes IV and V. The depressive reactions are scattered, but classes

TABLE 10.2

PERCENTAGE OF PATIENTS IN EACH DIAGNOSIS CATEGORY OF NEUROSIS—BY CLASS
(Age and Sex Adjusted)

Diagnostic Category of Neurosis	Class			
	I-II	III	IV	V
Antisocial and immaturity reactions	21	32	23	37
Phobic-anxiety reactions	16	18	30	16
Character neuroses	36	23	13	16
Depressive reactions	12	12	10	8
Psychosomatic reactions	7	9	13	11
Obsessive-compulsive reactions	7	5	5	0
Hysterical reactions	1	1	6	12
$n =$	98	119	182	65

$$X^2 = 53.62, \; df \; 18, \; p < .001$$

I and II have 50 percent more depressives than class V.

Psychosomatic reactions, by way of contrast, are related inversely to class. The class IV's and the class V's somatize their complaints to a greater extent than class I, II, and III patients. On the other hand, obsessive-compulsive reactions are directly related to class position. The obsessive-compulsives are concentrated in classes I and II. The gradient for hysterical patients runs in the opposite direction; in this illness there is an extreme concentration in class V.

* * *

CLASS POSITION AND THE PSYCHOSES

Now that we have described the five diagnostic categories established for the psychoses, we are ready to test the applicability of *Hypothesis 2*

to these several mental disorders. The essential data for this examination are summarized in Table 10.3.

The figures given in Table 10.3 reveal a significant association between the five types of psychotic disorders and class status. The effective disorders are linked directly to class position: The higher the class, the larger the proportion of patients who are affective psychotics. The proportion of affective psychotics in classes I and II is three times greater than in class V, but the percentage is the same in class III and class IV. The alcoholic and addictive psychotics show few class differences except in class IV where the percentage is only half that in classes I and II and class V. The organics exhibit a reverse of the distribution observed among the affective psychotics. Only 5 percent of the class I and II patients have an organic disorder,

TABLE 10.3

PERCENTAGE OF PATIENTS IN EACH DIAGNOSTIC CATEGORY OF PSYCHOSIS—BY CLASS
(Age and Sex Adjusted)

Diagnostic Category	Class			
	I-II	III	IV	V
Affective psychoses	21	14	14	7
Psychoses resulting from alcoholism and drug addiction	8	10	4	8
Organic psychoses	5	8	9	16
Schizophrenic psychoses	55	57	61	58
Senile psychoses	11	11	12	11
$n =$	53	142	584	672

$$X^2 = 48.23, \; df \; 12, \; p < .001$$

whereas 16 percent of the class V's suffer from one. The schizophrenic and senile psychotics show *no* appreciable percentage differences from class to class. We believe that this is a very important finding. In all classes schizophrenics make up well over half the patients. The senile psychotics represent a relatively small proportion, but this proportion is also constant from class to class.

In all classes schizophrenia is the predominant psychotic disorder. The next most frequent group is the affective one, but it tends to be concentrated more highly in classes I and II than in the other strata. The two functional psychotic groups, affectives and schizophrenics, make up well over two thirds of the patients in the four higher classes; but in class V these disorders total only 65 percent of the patients.

74.

HOWARD E. FREEMAN AND OZZIE G. SIMMONS

POSTHOSPITAL PERFORMANCE AND PSYCHIATRIC REHABILITATION

The concept of differential tolerance of deviant behavior that was adopted as the point of departure in this study maintained that the posthospital experience of mental patients could best be understood by reference to certain characteristics of family settings and family members. As formulated at the outset of the investigation, the notion of differential tolerance had considerable heuristic value in the identification of correlates of posthospital performance. This notion provided only limited understanding, however, of the patients' success or failure in remaining in the community. Therefore, we have had to revise our conceptual position. Here we shall consider further our revised position. We believe that our interpretations of the findings of this study have implications both for the treatment of mental patients and for sociological research on deviant behavior.

FAMILY SETTINGS, FAMILY MEMBERS, AND POSTHOSPITAL EXPERIENCE

This study was designed on the basis of results

From Howard E. Freeman and Ozzie G. Simmons, *The mental patient comes home*. New York: John Wiley & Sons, Inc., 1963. Pp. 196–217. Reprinted by permission.

obtained in two previous investigations. In these earlier studies we considered, for the most part, only "successful" patients and were primarily concerned with the issue of instrumental performance. The present study, like our previous efforts, points unequivocally to an association between the level of instrumental performance of the patient after hospitalization and characteristics of his family setting and family members.

The further examination of the same variables in the present study, however, neither permits the prediction of the success or failure of the patient to remain in the community nor supports our original position that instrumental performance and community tenure are necessarily related aspects of the posthospital experience of the patient. As we indicated in discussing the first of our predictor variables—family type—the concept of tolerance of deviance continues to have utility but only as an explanation for conforming social behavior and not for success and failure.

It is clear that two of the assumptions made on the basis of the earlier studies were incorrect. The *first* of these assumptions was that the rehospitalization of the patient typically is associated with inadequate instrumental performance. As our results indicate, as well as those obtained in a similar investigation by an Ohio State group, inadequate instrumental performance by itself does not account for rehospitalization.[1] Most typically, relatives' reports of reasons for rehospitalization specify bizarre behavior. Also, we know that the place of residence of the patients in the study group is remarkably stable. Our findings strongly suggest that inadequate instrumental performance usually does not result in rehospitalization of the patient or his ejection from the family network to other settings within the community. Rather, it would appear that the reactions to inadequate performance, if there are any, take place within the familial network and that the sanctions imposed are mainly attitudinal. We shall enlarge upon this point further when we discuss the implications of our study for social research.

The *second* assumption, which now seems erroneous, was to regard the posthospital period as a discrete time span in the life experience of the patient. In part, at least, this was derived from the prevailing stereotype—which we also held—that there are clearly distinguishable boundaries between the patient's pre-, in-, and posthospital careers. As one of the consequences of new hospital treatment programs and of the advent of tranquilizing drugs, hospitalizations have become quite short—a matter of months. Another consequence has been to open the hospital doors in a real sense. The patient's return to the community is typically preceded by leaves, passes, and off-ground privileges. Return to the community is not an "event" in the same sense that it is for the prisoner or for the patient hospitalized for an acute physical illness. Consequently, "recidivism" may not have any substantial relationship to the gross characteristics we measured of the patient's posthospital setting or of his significant others, since these are not likely to be different from those that prevailed in the prehospital period.

These observations immediately raise questions about the applicability of the concept of deviant behavior for understanding at least certain aspects of psychiatric rehabilitation as well as about its relevance for the current assumptions held by sociologists who are working in the field of "social psychiatry." In considering our results, we find that there are at least three alternatives—equally plausible and perhaps interrelated—for explaining the lack of relationship between community tenure and performance levels:

1. Reactions of primary group members to behavior typically associated with hospitalization— viz., of the bizarre type—are relatively uniform. That is, regardless of differences in the social, cultural, and social-psychological characteristics of primary group members, their reactions to bizarre behavior are essentially the same.
2. The genesis of behavior that is typically associated with hospitalization is not strategically affected by the relatively static social characteristics of the family or the gross interpersonal attributes of family members.
3. The ideologies of current treatment programs and their value positions result in diagnostic practices that make the selection of a study group of former patients and the implementation of any definitions of rehabilitation essentially arbitrary and possibly extrinsic to the real condition of the patients.

UNIFORMITY OF RESPONSE

The social scientist and the psychiatrist interested in cultural differences have emphasized the variations in the manifestations of mental illness from one community to the next and in the range of reactions of community members to atypical modes of interpersonal behavior.[2] It may be, however, that we have overemphasized the differences which actually exist, at least in the contemporary urban community.[3] It could be that rehospitalization, in particular, occurs in the face of behavior that community members regard, with reasonable uniformity, as requiring the action of a formal treatment or social control agent—the hospital. Our study

---

[1]Benjamin Pasamanick, Simon Dinitz, and Mark Lefton, "Psychiatric Orientation and Its Relation to Diagnosis and Treatment in a Mental Hospital," *American Journal of Psychiatry, 116* (August 1959), pp. 127-132.

[2]Charles C. Hughes, Marc-Adelard Tremblay, Robert N. Rapoport, and Alexander H. Leighton, *People of Cove and Woodlot* (New York: Basic Books, 1960).
[3]Stephen A. Richardson, Norman Goodman, Albert H. Hastorf, and Sanford Dornbusch, "Cultural Uniformity in Reaction to Physical Disabilities," *American Sociological Review, 26* (April 1961), pp. 241-247.

group of patients and their families was drawn from a single metropolitan area. Although it is a locale with considerable diversity and the study group represents a considerable range of variation in social class status, religious and ethnic backgrounds, and life experiences, there are also certain common factors. For example, despite variations in educational background, virtually everyone in the study group has had sufficient education to be sensitive to the messages transmitted by the mass media and has had opportunities to be exposed to the "mental hygiene" movement conducted by television, magazines, and newspapers. Also, the very fact that patients were once hospitalized, in comparison with those who have never received formal treatment, may well be the key "cutting point" with respect to social differences in the reaction to bizarre behavior.[4] Unlike work and social participation, the extreme forms of symptomatic behavior, which are the main reasons reported for rehospitalization of the patient, may constitute a range of behavior about which there is widespread agreement regarding the action that must be taken, *once relatives have been through the experience of hospitalizing a family member.*

It should be noted, in this respect, that despite the emphasis on social and cultural factors in mental illness research, the identification of sociological correlates of rehospitalization has been rare. A major exception is social class, but there is good reason, as we have indicated in examining our findings on social class, to question the relationships found between this variable and rehospitalization. Although the relatives interviewed did show a range of variation in their apparent willingness to contact the hospital, this scale does not correlate well with success or failure. This does not mean that class differences or other social factors are not related to different *expressed* attitudes about rehospitalization. It seems probable that there are, how-

ever, a number of areas in which attitudinal expression varies considerably but behavior is relatively uniform in the face of an actual event.

Of course the notion of uniformity of response may be too simple; one alternative is that there are contradictory mechanisms operating that result in similar reactions of family members. For example, it may be that certain families move to rehospitalize the patient even though he may exhibit less bizarre behavior than would elicit this response in other families. On the other hand, it may be that severity of symptoms is also differentially distributed and that the two phenomena operate so as to obscure each other.

In any case, the notion of differential tolerance can have only limited applicability in explaining patients' success and failure. Moreover, families able to tolerate extreme forms of symptomatic behavior may never refer patients to practitioners or hospitals. The lack of relationship between sociocultural characteristics and community tenure may be associated with the selection process of who gets hospitalized or receives professional treatment in the first place. Families most tolerant of symptomatic behavior may never get the mentally ill person involved in the pathways to professional treatment.

GENESIS OF BEHAVIOR

Thus far, we have been concerned with the reactions of the patient's family members but have not considered the issue of the genesis of the types of behavior that lead to rehospitalization. As we have noted, our findings are not clear on the relationships of social factors to the symptomatic expressions of mental illness. We assumed that these relationships would be maximized by selection of a study group limited to functional disorders. Even if reactions to bizarre behavior were uniform, differential rehospitalization rates might be expected if social factors were pervasive in symptomatic expressions of mental illness (except, as we have suggested, if the two sets of forces contradicted each other). The current emphasis on social deviance assumes that mental health, adjustment, rehabilitation, and similar rubrics have come to designate a single entity, and that the patient's interpersonal behavior and his medical condition are only minimally differentiated. Both

---

[4] We are aware of studies which suggest that symptomatic expressions of illness are mediated by culture. Not only has the study group of relatives been exposed to a common learning experience, hospitalization, but the selection procedures—e.g., all patients were native born—and the common features of socialization in an urban setting may override any ethnic differences.

interpersonal behavior and symptomatology are looked upon as manifestations of "social deviance," especially, but not only, when the physician cannot identify a definite organic basis for the condition.

We should note, at this point, that the patients in the study group, in general, were not carefully screened as to whether or not they are part of the group who may in fact have organic disorders. Except for those patients who have extended contact with private physicians or treatment experience in teaching or private hospitals, few mental patients, particularly in the large state hospitals, receive exhaustive neurophysical work-ups. Patients in our study group, drawn from large mental hospitals like the bulk of the study groups of most other social psychiatric investigations, may have been designated "functional" as a result of diagnoses made without a thorough medical history and physical examination. Conversely, patients may have been excluded from the study group because they were inappropriately identified as organic cases.

In our analysis, we found no relationship between reports of symptomatic behavior and either sociocultural or interpersonal variables. Socially deviant behavior and illness as manifested in symptoms may not be either the same or even parallel phenomena. If so, variables predictive of social deviance may have little to do with illness. The course of the illness itself may not be related primarily to the setting the patient returns to after hospitalization or to characteristics of his family associates.

IDEOLOGY OF TREATMENT PROGRAMS

There is no need to document the dramatic changes that have occurred in the inhospital treatment of patients during the last 10 to 15 years. Social psychiatrists, social scientists, as well as lay and professional community mental health workers have had their impact on inhospital treatment programs and on discharge planning and decisions regarding the appropriateness of discharge, as have new therapies, particularly the utilization of tranquilizing drugs. It is evident, moreover, that a number of situational factors enter into decisions regarding each patient. In the first place, there are different pressures to return patients to the community because of the need for bed space, budget limitations, and personnel problems. Also, there is little uniformity in discharge procedures. As we have pointed out, we had to impose a particular definition of "left bed" because patients in various hospitals and wards and under the supervision of different physicians are returned to the community in different ways. Trial visits, extended leaves, and so on, provide alternative ways that some hospital personnel believe are appropriate for testing the patient's readiness to return to the community; others do not think it appropriate to adopt these practices. A key factor, also, in the length of the patient's stay in the hospital is whether or not he is legally committed or voluntarily admitted to the hospital.

There are differential external pressures associated with the discharge of particular patients. For examp' , married patients often have shorter hospital stays than single patients. Marital status may be associated with the illness condition of the patient and this is why these correlations are found. On the other hand, there may be greater pressure to release a particular patient from the hospital if the husband is coping with the care of the children, or if the wife depends for income upon the return of her husband to the community. A variety of external pressures may result in different criteria being employed in the discharge of different groups. Having a job or being able to take care of the home may be much ore important than evaluation of psychiatric status for married patients in comparison with single patients. In brief, we are arguing that social factors may be correlated with success or failure, but that such relationships cannot be identified as long as they are obscured by the vagaries of hospital experience and the prevailing inconsistencies in release practices.

With these alternatives in mind, we shall explicate a modified view of differential tolerance of deviance, and shall speculate about the role of social factors in the rehabilitation of the patient. Our first premise is that rehabilitation must not be regarded as unidimensional. We can identify at least two dimensions, one of which is instrumental performance, the other symptomatic expressions of illness. A second premise that follows is that the patient's actions should be viewed not only as deviant social behavior but as *both* a reaction to the norms of the community and to illness. Finally, we assume that there may be degrees of uniformity in the response of family associates to the behavior of patients and that the variation in response may be greater to deviance on the social than on the illness dimension.

LIFE EXPERIENCE, DEVIANCE, AND MENTAL ILLNESS

Consistent with the premises offered, we shall examine first the issue of instrumental performance. It is virtually indisputable that the degree of conformity of an individual to the norms of the community is dependent upon his interaction with primary group associates and that in this respect the members of his family setting are key figures. In child-rearing, expectations of conformity are expressed and communicated, to a large degree, by means of a reward and punishment system—one that includes a variety of verbal and physical coercive measures as punishments, as well as material and psychological rewards. In adult life, of course, some of the same coercive elements remain, as in industrial work groups and street corner gangs.[5] In childhood and adulthood, however, obtaining effective social control and enforcing conformity with community standards do not require, in the usual case, imposition of external controls but rest on the assumption of shared expectation systems.[6]

One of our stages of rehabilitation, that of meeting the normative standards of instrumental performance, appears to be a consequence of such shared expectations. We started with the assumption that performance that did not meet expectations would result in exclusion, that is, inadequate performance in the face of high normative standards would invoke rehospitalization. We failed to take sufficiently into account, however, that the return of the patient to his

family does not constitute an interpersonal situation in which group members are experimenting and innovating with different means of making known their expectations and standards of conduct. Rather, it is a relatively stabilized system in which the already established shared expectations of family members constitute the main, if not the only, means of control, at least for adult members of the unit.

In part, of course, expectations of adult performance differ, depending upon the position of the individual in the family. For example, expectations of spouses, by virtue of their role as marriage partners, are higher. It is, of course, the degree of exposure of the family members to the relevant value system of the larger community that determines their levels of expectations with respect to the behavior of the persons in their family settings. Consequently, the types of characteristics that we have found to be associated with performance levels are probably reflections of a larger system, that is, the differential commitment to and internalization of the normative patterns that serve as models in urban communities. This is the explanation we offered in describing the relationship between performance levels and scores on a test that measures verbal skills. It may be that the key is not differential internalization but rather the variations in the ability and skill of the relative in communicating his expectations to the patient. Again, the types of variables found associated with performance levels appear to "make sense" when looked upon in the light of this interpretation.

Whatever the relative importance of these characteristics as reflectors of internalization of norms or as indicators of manipulative interpersonal skills, our results indicate that in the posthospital situation conformity to shared expectations is *not* obtained by an active process in which family members continually engage in an assessment of alternatives, including rehospitalization. Rather, it is a passive situation in which the performance level of the family member is virtually prescribed at any point in time. There are no real choices; conformity with the expectations of one's familial associates is the only alternative.

Our data regarding posthospital expectations

---

[5] George C. Homans, *The Human Group* (New York: Harcourt, Brace and Company, 1950).

[6] Richard T. LaPiere, *A Theory of Social Control* (New York: McGraw-Hill Book Company, 1954).

suggest that there were no marked shifts in the expectation system of family members occurring during the hospital period. If there were, this would be reflected in the posthospital period by some degree of innovation and experimentation with active means for enforcing more adequate instrumental performance, in which rehospitalization would figure as one such means. Relatives have little contact with hospital personnel of a sort that might induce marked shifts in their expectations, and there is no evidence of posthospital contact with other professional persons at a level that might instigate change in relatives' expectation systems. Moreover, the philosophy of some contemporary mental health practitioners, who preach "tolerance" because they believe it leads to less stress for the patient and consequently less bizarre behavior, may actually support rather than discourage the maintenance of expectations incongruent with the norms of the community.

Apart from family members, the patient's own expectations regarding his performance may receive negative reinforcement by virtue of the emphasis that may be accorded gradual transition to the community in such treatment activities as day and night hospitals and in-hospital work programs. We have suggested that the interpersonal process which determines the patient's conformity to norms of instrumental performance places him in a role that is more passive than active, but this does not mean that his situation is static. Interpersonal factors that do influence the expectation system—if they are truly important at the level of familial relationships between adult members—may have the effect of *lowering* rather than raising the shared expectations of family and patient. In part, this is because both the practitioner and the patient's family link rehabilitation with regard to performance levels to the control of symptomatic behavior. Most simply put, symptomatic behavior is frequently regarded as the reaction that the patient manifests when he is unable to cope with the expectations and demands of those with whom he interacts. Treatment programs often seek to limit the demands imposed upon patients to those with which he is "ready" to cope. On this basis, patients who manifest symptomatic behavior or whose life history includes episodes of severe bizarreness are typically believed to be highly vulnerable to the stress of high expectations. Our data fail to support this notion that symptomatic behavior of the patient is related directly to the expectations of those with whom he interacts. Indeed, in our data, there is a correlation between expectations and symptomatology, but in the opposite direction: high expectations are associated with an absence of symptomatology.[7]

We have noted that there is a significant correlation between reports of symptomatic behavior and instrumental performance, and family members may no longer concern themselves with the patient's instrumental performance if he is exhibiting certain kinds of symptomatic behavior. But repeated experiences with symptomatic behavior may result either in direct reduction in the level of familial expectations, or have an impact on the "set" of individual family members, that is, on certain personality and other attributes associated with social potency of family members; or, in fact, both may occur.

Along these lines, we should note that marriage is one of the strategic points in the life experience of the individual when it is possible for a shift to occur in the demands placed on him. Marriage is probably the most marked point where the mental illness history of the patient, in the sense of manifestations of symptomatic behavior, influences rehabilitation with regard to instrumental performance. Undoubtedly, the patient limits his chances for marriage—particularly in the case of the male—with the recurrence of symptomatic behavior, and consequently minimizes the hope of moving to a setting where the shared expectation system is more likely to be in the direction of adequate instrumental performance.

We have, of course, used an absolute standard of rehabilitation in considering performance levels. Comparison of shifts in the pre- and posthospital performance of the patients sug-

---

[7] It may well be that high expectations actually are associated with symptom remission. Carstairs has noted, for example, that even "recovered" patients relapse when denied opportunities for employment. See G. Morris Carstairs, "The Social Limits of Eccentricity: An English Study," in Marvin K. Opler (ed.), *Culture and Mental Health* (New York: The Macmillan Company, 1959), chap. 16.

gests however, that a relative definition of rehabilitation with respect to instrumental performance, if implemented, would not change the findings. Dramatic improvement in patients' instrumental performance levels after hospitalization, when compared with the prehospital period, are exceptional.

We wish to consider further the point we are making about the relative continuity of performance levels between the pre- and posthospital period, and about hospitalization itself as rarely being a discrete segment of the life experience of the patient. First, however, we shall discuss the meaning of this position with regard to success or failure. As repeatedly noted, we find no relationships between success and our sociocultural variables. We have no adequate information in this study on the regularity or intensity with which patients manifest symptomatic behavior, except for relatives' responses in such evaluative terms as "frequently" and "occasionally." Patients are likely to manifest bizarre behavior episodically rather than consistently. In the face of this, one alternative already mentioned is that families are rather uniformly distributed in their degree of tolerance of symptomatic behavior regardless of their sociocultural differences. Another possibility, as noted, is that the genesis of these symptomatic behaviors may be organic or psychodynamic, and thus the patient may not appreciably respond to interpersonal control as it is exerted by family members.

It also would be most useful if we had data on the factors that affect the decision made by hospital personnel to release the patient. What we do find in the hospital records and in reports from relatives is that concern with symptomatic behavior is associated with rehospitalization. But what leads to release? We think that a different set of indicators is used, namely: How well can the patient "adjust" to the community? We do not have direct evidence of this, but certainly the current emphasis in most hospitals on the rehabilitation of the patient reflects our view.[8] The patients in our study group do not

resemble those with chronic illness, at least if length of hospitalization is any indicator of chronicity. Rather, the patients studied, who probably are representative of the bulk of persons hospitalized and subsequently returned to the community, are individuals whose psychiatric status is not the only consideration at time of release. Hospital personnel, of course, are concerned with whether or not the patient is likely to become "dangerous" either to himself or to others in the community, but where resocialization is the prevailing orientation in determining release, adjustment with regard to the level of instrumental performance may be accorded more importance than psychiatric status.

The remission of illness, as perceived by the physician on the basis of symptoms, is not the only rationale for the release of patients in our study group. Sociological and situational factors play a part, and perhaps the strategic part, in the release process.[9] Since the factors affecting outcome are not uniform and we do not know enough to identify and control them, our study is not one in which the significance of social factors in the etiology of mental illness can be assessed. We do not have a systematic sample of persons with the same degree of mental illness, and sociological and situational factors may override medical considerations in decisions for release. This problem pervades the entire literature on the relationship of social factors to the etiology and prognosis of mental illness. Each time a study is done, the sampling variations may result in systematic biases, and so we are left with the inconclusive result that sociocultural factors may or may not be determinants of bizarre behavior. Moreover, there is no clear-cut evidence that the sociocultural characteristics of patients and family members play the strategic role in the rehospitalization process or that the differential pressures and stresses families place upon patients have a substantial influence on the inception of behavior that typically leads

[8]David Landy and Harry Raulet, "The Hospital Work Program," in Benjamin Pasamanick (ed.), *Rehabilitation of the Mentally Ill* (Washington, D.C.: American Association for the Advancement of Science, 1959), pp. 71–87.

[9]Ozzie G. Simmons, James A. Davis, and Katherine Spencer, "Interpersonal Strains in Release from a Mental Hospital," *Social Problems*, 4 (July 1956), pp. 21–28; and Howard E. Freeman and Ozzie G. Simmons, "Consensus and Coalition in the Release of Mental Patients: A Research Note," *Human Organization*, 20 (Summer 1961), pp. 89–91.

to rehospitalization. At this point, then, it is probably just as valid to look upon the rehabilitation of the patient *with regard to success or failure* as essentially an issue of the control of symptomatic manifestations of illness and not of instrumental behavior.

IMPLICATIONS FOR PROGRAM DEVELOPMENT

As we observed in beginning this report, research on former mental patients is a consequence of innovations in treatment practices. The need and continued quest for further changes in treatment programs are apparent in the final report of the Joint Commission on Mental Illness and Health.[10]

While this research does not provide us with a basis for recommending extensive modification of current psychiatric practices, our findings do need to be taken into account in program development and in experimental and demonstration studies.

Hospital personnel are often faced with the problem of conflicting obligations in according relative priority to the issues of instrumental performance, on the one hand, and remission of symptoms on the other. This conflict is, of course, not unique to the mental health practitioner but occurs in virtually all the practice of medicine. Perhaps the point may be made most easily by an analogy. The physician treating a patient with a stomach ulcer may advise him to leave his job and take an extended rest or vacation. Although this may indeed be indicated medically, it can result in economic deprivation for the patient and his family and a corresponding change in their style of living. In the actual case, the physician is likely to compromise on a recommendation which takes into account both the patient's medical and social needs. We contend that this conflict is even more likely to occur in current mental hospital programs and release practices.

A predominant orientation of hospital personnel is to treat symptomatology, and the ques-

tion of social needs is handled by reinterpreting inadequate instrumental behavior as an integral part of the illness condition. Such behavior, however, is in significant part a function of life-long socialization experience and analytically distinct from illness. In the psychiatric profession, treatment based on "insight," if the practitioner is psychodynamically oriented, or on drugs and shock therapy, if he is more physiologically oriented, is not necessarily aimed at inducing changes in performance potential. Few physicians would contend, let us say, that shock treatment is conducive to better work performance, or drugs to greater social participation, and most psychiatrists would not feel comfortable in using measures of instrumental performance to assess the outcome of their therapeutic endeavors. But they would contend, or at least it is often implied, that improvement in the patient, as measured by their psychiatric criteria, eventuates in more effective instrumental performance. According to our findings, however, this is questionable.

One position mental-health practitioners could adopt is to limit their goals to remission of psychiatric symptoms and to exclude from their purview any concern with levels of instrumental performance. Medical practitioners are confronted, however, in the treatment of all illnesses –physical as well as mental–with the realities of the "sociological" demands of their patients and patients' families. Getting well in the medical sense is, of course, of interest to the patient and his family, but illness and wellness in their eyes are likely to be regarded as primarily affecting the prerequisites for instrumental activity. This is one factor that may account for the intrusion of concern with instrumental performance into the goal orientation of the hospital.

If, however, the mental hospital is to play a major role in social control as well as in the treatment of illness, then, with respect to the value accorded instrumental performance in our society, the key emphasis must be placed on modifying the patient's expectation system in the direction of greater conformity to the normative demands of the larger community. The risks in doing this would be great, if in fact such attempts at modifying expectations had direct consequences for the patient's psychiatric

10Joint Commission on Mental Illness and Health. *Action for Mental Health,* Final report of the Joint Commission on Mental Illness and Health (New York: Basic Books, 1961), p. 16.

state. Our findings suggest that this linkage is minimal, however, and that current notions of permissiveness and reduction of stress need to be re-examined, both with respect to hospital and posthospital programs.[11] This orientation can be quite compatible with the conception of the hospital as dedicated to humanitarian therapeutic care, and would not require a return to traditional custodial care.

If conformity to normative demands is to be achieved, the transitional programs now in such vogue as bridges between hospital and community in the rehabilitation process may require substantial re-orientation. For example, one risk incurred in those half-way houses which advocate gradualism is that they may constitute, as a consequence, "low expectation" settings. Programs that serve transitional functions may be needed, but are likely to be effective only to the extent that they consistently orient toward instrumental performance the patient who can potentially respond to such expectations. Low expectations simply support socially deviant instrumental performance and reinforce the patient's failure to perform in ways defined by the instrumental role expectations of the larger society.

Perhaps even more important than a transitional program, which can serve only a relatively small proportion of former patients, is one that can provide permanent posthospital settings for patients as alternatives to the ones from which they were hospitalized. If modification of patients' low expectations is the desired goal, perhaps the only feasible approach is to relocate them into residential settings that are oriented to higher levels of instrumental performance than those from which they came. There is little point in raising the patient's self-expectations during hospital treatment with regard to instrumental performance levels if he is returned to a family that does not expect him to

perform instrumentally. Organizing transitional programs oriented to high expectations and shifting patients into new settings in the posthospital period would, of course, impose heavy responsibilities on the hospital. As our findings indicate, the patient's relationship with the hospital is minimal once he leaves his bed. If hospitals are to take the role of agents of social control, they will have to develop and maintain extensive procedures for follow-up relationships with former patients.

It is not, of course, the hospital's responsibility alone to carry forward such a modified program. Not only is there minimal posthospital contact between hospital and patient, but he is similarly ignored by community agencies as well. The point we are making is not unique to mental patients, but applies generally to the set of conditions that the community seems to impose on all persons defined as markedly deviant. The same issues are involved in returning the delinquent, the criminal, and other deviants to their previous environment, and are equally problematic for the former patient. If we are correct in our interpretation that the primary means of social control for the patient are his own expectation system and those of his significant others, then effective social control calls for radical alteration of the low-level patient's life situation, including detachment from settings that only reinforce low expectations.

This interpretation also raises some points about the strategy currently employed in the allocation of the hospital's resources for different kinds of patients. From the point of view of potential instrumental performance, most effort is currently expended on those patients who have the highest self-expectations and come from family settings with the highest expectations. From the standpoint of social control, there is little need to devote major attention to those patients whose prehospital careers and community settings suggest that they are likely to resume adequate levels of instrumental performance. Moreover, it may actually be a disservice to involve them in follow-up relations with those hospital or community agencies whose present orientations are toward reduction of stress which might lower rather than raise the patient's

[11]In this respect, we can refer to the findings presented in Chapter 9 on expectations and rehospitalization as well as to unreported correlations on expectations of symptomatology. We do have, of course, a problem in our data in that we cannot be sure which variables are antecedent and which consequent; but the correlations are quite clear. If anything, high expectations are associated with low symptomatology.

expectations. The more logical approach in such cases would be to adopt the physician's orientation to acute disease, namely, that when the condition has been treated, the patient's relationships with medical personnel should be severed.[12] The notion of regarding all the mentally ill as chronically ill needs also to be reconsidered. A number of attempts to differentiate between the acute patient and the chronic patient have been reported in the literature.[13] Although this is often highly recommended as a diagnostic procedure, any such categorization of patients is attempted only rarely in developing posthospital treatment programs. In sum, we would suggest that if the hospital assumes responsibility as an agent of social control, its resources should be diverted mainly to those whose return to the community would be to settings highly tolerant of deviant instrumental performance, and all available effort should be applied toward redirecting such patients into settings more in accord with the prevailing community norms.

If the emphasis is to be on social control, however, it must be acknowledged that this can be achieved only with great difficulty and extensive reorientation of both administrators and practitioners in institutions.[14] If our findings on families have relevance for professional-patient relations as well, a critical message to be communicated is that expectations of instrumental performance constitute the key orientation in interpersonal relations between staff and patients.[15] Furthermore, the hospital would have to place its exclusive emphasis on the return of patients to either productive non-kin settings or families with high expectation systems. Moreover, if community agencies are to play a more

substantial part in after-care programs, they would not only have to step up their activity, but would have to modify many of the basic orientations of their current programs from ideals of tolerance to the value and merit of conformity to the normative standards of the community.

Taking Albee's findings regarding the shortage of personnel in the mental-health field, perhaps the mental health professions cannot afford to act as agents of social control.[16] There may be little justification in setting goals of social control for the mental hospital, and for the course of its future development. In this context, we would suggest, on the basis of our findings, that there is considerable justification for minimizing the duration of hospital stay. If the position is taken that the goal of hospitalization is social control, a substantial new program development is indicated. If the goal is simply that of remission of psychiatric symptoms, however, this requires much less of a program than is often advocated as ideally needed.

In seeking to clarify the dual orientation that most hospital practitioners now hold, we submit that, if the hospital is concerned solely with the treatment of psychiatric symptoms, practitioners must forget the rationale that treatment directed at symptom remission also maximizes the performance potential of the patient. If symptom remission is the only goal of the hospital, it seems clear that the alternative is to provide, in the community, other persons whose primary responsibility is the movement of patients toward higher instrumental performance in accordance with the community's norms. The present concern with the problem of mental illness is, of course, twofold. In the first place, there is truly the illness problem and a professional group dedicated to its treatment. But there is the other issue, that of large numbers of persons who fail to contribute to the productivity of the larger community and who represent, because of their limited contribution, a serious social problem as well.

In view of the substantial discrepancy between the community's standards regarding the productivity of the individual and the low

[12]This may be an overstatement; in the same sense that the diabetic may need minimal medical supervision, so some former mental patients may need chemotherapeutic control.

[13]Edward Zigler and Leslie Phillips, "Psychiatric Diagnosis: A Critique," *Journal of Abnormal and Social Psychology*, 63 (November 1961), pp. 607–618.

[14]Erving Goffman, "Some Characteristics of Total Institutions," *Asylums* (Garden City, New York: Doubleday and Company, 1962).

[15]One might even wish to go so far in treatment programs as to demand high instrumental performance as a prerequisite for seeking residence in halfway houses or help with intrapsychic problems.

[16]George W. Albee, *Mental Health Manpower Trends* (New York: Basic Books, 1959).

levels that characterize the instrumental performance of so many former mental patients, the community is confronted with a social problem in which the issue of instrumental performance and its social control is to be judged by policy rather than by psychiatric criteria. It is for this reason that we are concerned with clarification of the distinction between the need for treatment of mental illness, on the one hand, and the need for promoting conformity to the community's standards regarding instrumental role performance on the other. In the present state of affairs, responsibility for meeting both these needs is left to the mental-health practitioner, even though he may be explicitly concerned only with the need for treatment of illness.[17] Nevertheless, when statements are made that one out of every seven men was judged to be mentally or emotionally incapable of serving effectively in the armed forces, and almost this number cannot support themselves in times of peace, the observation is not based primarily on an image of large numbers of persons being actively ill in the sense of manifesting bizarre behavior but rather of being passive in the face of demands made on them by the larger

community. The cost, in these terms, may be too great a luxury for a reasonable democracy.[18]

IMPLICATIONS FOR SOCIAL RESEARCH

Our experience in this study raises several issues of relevance to the general field of sociology. One is the issue of whether or not social psychiatry, as presently constituted, is most meaningfully oriented as a sociological field of interest. The details of the emergence of social psychiatry as a specialty within sociology have been discussed by Clausen as well as others.[19] It is only fair to state that sociologists in mental illness research have been mainly concerned with either etiology or with the impact of hospital structure and treatment programs on patient care. Sociologists, too, have not been clear about the differences between mental illness as a medical and as a social problem.[20] In working in the mental illness field, they have had to become more than ordinarily specialized in applying their knowledge to the study of problems peculiar to this field and, moreover, have become indoctrinated with many of the ideas, concepts, and criteria of the practicing profession of psychiatry. This was a problem in our study. If we had begun with the conceptual tradition of sociology, rather than that of social psychiatry, we might not have equated deviant behavior with mental illness and not have conceived of rehospitalization as a consequence of differential tolerance of deviant instrumental performance. Indeed, it is a sociological commonplace that in contemporary urban societies exclusion from the family and community is rarely employed as a means of social control.

The point at issue here is that sociological and psychiatric approaches to the field of mental illness are characterized by different points of

[17]Moreover, if we are correct in our interpretation that the control of instrumental performance is mainly vested in primary group members and in shared expectations rather than in behavioral sanctions, then the findings are important for practitioners in fields other than the treatment of mental illness. In specifying the optimal interpersonal conditions for education and for "happy and healthy" marriages, and for group relations in industry, much emphasis has been placed on permissiveness, individualization, and the like. We would contend that in these situations, as well as in family settings, there is every reason to question the utility of these orientations, if high levels of instrumental performance and conformity to the norms are judged to be desirable goals. Again, we are aware of the ideological significance of these remarks, but the literature in the various fields noted does not include studies of an empirical sort that contradict our position that high expectations are associated with high performance. Rather, as Brim notes in discussing child-rearing practices, in the case of emotional characteristics that do not require a maturation base, there is no reason why these social characteristics should appear at all in children, apart from the demands of parents that such behavior or attitudes be developed on the part of the child. (Orville G. Brim, Jr., *Education for Child-Rearing* [New York: Russell Sage Foundation, 1959].)

[18]Eli Ginzberg, James K. Anderson, Sol W. Ginsburg, and John L. Herma, *The Lost Divisions* (New York: Columbia University Press, 1959).

[19]John A. Clausen, *Sociology and the Field of Mental Health* (New York: Russell Sage Foundation, 1956).

[20]Robert A. Nisbet, "The Study of Social Problems," in Robert K. Merton and Robert A. Nisbet (eds.), *Contemporary Social Problems* (New York: Harcourt, Brace and World, Inc., 1961), pp. 3–18.

view. Theory in sociology must be empirically based, if it is to be minimally acceptable to sociologists. There is some question, however, as to whether psychiatry, at present, requires this criterion in the conceptualization and organization of its data. The orientations of the psychiatrist may serve his own professional goals as a practitioner, but we must question their promise as a frame of reference for sociological contributions to the field of mental illness. Sociologists working in this field, including ourselves, have made the mistake of accepting too readily some of the concepts of psychiatry about which psychiatrists themselves are still unclear and in disagreement.[21]

What if social psychiatry, as currently constituted, does not have a proper object of study? In the extreme, what if the etiology of mental illness is, in fact, relatively independent of sociocultural factors? This does not obviate the need for social research on mental patients, but rather places the objectives of such research in another perspective, one that focuses primarily on gaining an understanding of social behavior and not of what makes people sick. Assumption of such a position would considerably enhance sociological contributions to mental illness research, since it would place the focus of investigation squarely on the mental patient as a social problem, even though his mental illness may not be primarily a sociological phenomenon. In brief, the issue of the interdependence between the illness and social problems should not be taken as a given, but as an empirical question for investigation.

In discussing the implications of our data, we may seem to have placed the principal burden on the psychiatrist for the confusion regarding instrumental performance and symptomatic behavior. We would contend, however, that many of the current notions held by sociologists working within a social deviance frame of reference have also contributed to the present status of social psychiatry. Deviance usually is assessed with reference to some criterion of how persons should act in given situations at given times; it refers to the failure of individuals to behave in ways normatively expected of them. The emphasis in the study of deviant behavior is not only on deviance itself but also on identification of aggregates of social deviants. Establishing criteria for identifying these aggregates requires moving beyond the discrepancy between the individual's behavior and the society's norms. It is necessary to be as specific about responses to deviance as about deviance *per se*.[22] Social deviants, as aggregates, cannot be sufficiently identified by their non-conformity alone but rather by the responses of community members to their behavior. It is the range of these responses that becomes the principal focus for the study of the social roles in particular aggregates.

We have no quarrel with the current emphasis among sociologists on these aggregates of social deviants. There are any number of justifiable reasons for their study, and it may be that the emphasis upon such groups is what distinguishes the field of deviant behavior from general sociology, since so much of the general field is concerned with deviance from social norms.[23] Furthermore, as classification schemes of social deviance suggest, there is no question but that mental illness is clearly a phenomenon that places individuals in an aggregate whose identity is dependent not only on their behavior but also on the responses of community members to their acts. The point to be emphasized, however, is that membership in such an aggregate does not restrict the individual to being deviant only in ways that evoke a response from community members that identifies him as mentally ill. To be specific, inadequate instrumental performance may not connote "sickness" among former mental patients any more than it does among other community members. We would contend that the distinguishing characteristic of a mental patient is his symptomatology; it is

[21]Cf. Bertram Schaffner, "Summary," in Vera Rubin (ed.), *Culture, Society, and Health* (New York: Annals of the New York Academy of Sciences, *84*, December 1960), p. 1029.

[22]See, for example, along these lines the comments in Robert K. Merton, "Social Conformity, Deviation, and Opportunity Structures: A Comment on the Contributions of Dubin and Cloward," *American Sociological Review*, 24 (April 1959), pp. 147–189.

[23]Edwin Lemert, *Social Pathology* (New York: McGraw-Hill Book Company, 1951).

symptomatic behavior that evokes a response from community members, at least on the formal level. When the sociologist is concerned with aggregates of social deviants other than mental patients, does he seek to account for deviance in the same terms as he does in considering mental patients? In brief, why attempt to explain inadequate instrumental performance differently for mental patients than for everyone else in the community?

The separation of the deviance that identifies mental patients as members of this particular aggregate from other deviance is difficult because symptomatic behavior cuts across the range of social roles of the individual. Nevertheless, this analytic distinction is essential for understanding interpersonal relations between deviants and their associates and the social control problems of aggregates of deviants. For mental patients, the aggregate consists of individuals whose symptomatology and the responses of community members to it are such that their instrumental role behavior as members of the community is highly visible. One of the consequences, as we have observed, is that practitioners view as identical the control of their illness and the control of their instrumental performance. Nevertheless, as our data indicate, these are neither identical nor mutually dependent issues in the relationships between former patients and their significant associates. In order to understand the posthospital fate of the mental patient, it is essential that the analytic distinction between illness behavior and instrumental behavior be kept clear, and that the issues related to the illness not be confused with those related to inadequate instrumental role performance.

The point needs to be extended further. There is some tendency to explain even the behavioral area in which social deviants conform by reference to their membership in the particular aggregate. This explanation is invoked frequently for mental patients because symptomatology cuts across role performance. In an earlier study, we pointed this out in an analysis of the residential mobility inclinations of families of mental patients. As we reported in that study, the residential mobility inclinatons of these families are closely associated with changes in housing needs and life cycle stage and *not* with pathology and maladjustment.[24] In the same way that the practitioner has confused the issues of illness and instrumental behavior, the sociologist has sometimes been misled in his attempts to identify the distinguishing qualities of deviants with reference to their aggregates.

These observations lead us to some final comments regarding a modified strategy for research in the field of deviant behavior. There are three issues crucial to the study of aggregates of social deviants, and these may have little relationship to one another.

1. Is the genesis of the deviance related to aspects of the social structure?
2. Are the responses of community members to the members of the aggregate of deviants associated with social structural variables?
3. Is the efficacy of means of social control associated with the social structure?

There is the further question, apart from these three, of whether or not *other* deviant behavior on the part of members of such aggregates is linked to or intensified by the type of deviance that identifies them as members of the aggregate. The major modification that is needed in research strategy is to avoid the ready assumption that *all* four of these questions must necessarily be answered in the affirmative in order to demonstrate the worth of sociology. At present there is a tendency to look to the social structure as often as possible to explain the genesis of deviant behavior, the reactions of community members to the deviance, and the efficacy of means of controlling the deviance. In research on mental illness, the psychodynamically oriented sociologist and the mental-health practitioner have provided each other with mutual support in viewing aggregates of deviants in this way. There are, we think, certain aggregates, such as "gang delinquents," where a fairly convincing argument can be made for the impact of social structure on the genesis of, reaction to, and control of deviance. But what is the evidence for the view that mental illness is in this same category? The sociologist is aware that many

[24]Howard E. Freeman, Ozzie G. Simmons, and Bernard J. Bergen, "Residential Mobility Inclinations among Families of Mental Patients," *Social Forces*, 38 (May 1960), pp. 320–324.

aggregates—such as the blind—are not related in all those respects to social structure, but nevertheless constitute proper objects of study for the field of sociology of deviance. In our view, the point of departure for the sociology of deviant behavior should not be the deviant alone but also the responses of community members to deviance. It is by linking up deviance, defined as departure from the norm, to response to deviance that the analytic distinction may be made between those aspects of an individual's non-conforming behavior that identify him as a member of a specific aggregate, and other aspects that are not related to aggregate membership and to the social control functions of community members. The issue of response to deviant behavior as the departure point of analysis of aggregates of deviants would permit an approach to the problems of genesis of deviance and of the efficacy of social control on a more specific level.

There may be alternative interpretations of many of our specific findings that are as convincing as those we have presented. In view of our results, however, it is difficult to hold to the assumption that social structural variables are *always strategically* related to the whole range of deviant behavior, including mental illness. Our study is not the only attempt to demonstrate the pervasive impact of social structure on deviant behavior that has met with limited success. The more profitable course may be to develop conceptual foci for research which take as their departure point the degree of independence, rather than of dependence, between social structure and deviant behavior.

References to Introductions

ABRAHAM, K. Notes on the psychoanalytic investigation and treatment of manic-depressive insanity and allied conditions (1911). In *Selected papers of Karl Abraham.* New York: Basic Books, 1953.

ABRAHAM, K. The first pregenital stage of the libido (1916). In *Selected papers of Karl Abraham.* New York: Basic Books, 1953.

ABRAHAM, K. A short study of the development of the libido viewed in the light of mental disorders (1924). In *Selected papers of Karl Abraham.* New York: Basic Books, 1953.

ADLER, A. *The neurotic constitution.* New York: Dodd & Mead, 1926.

ADLER, A. *The practice and theory of individual psychology.* New York: Harcourt, Brace, 1927; London: Routledge & Kegan Paul, 1929.

ADLER, A. *Social interest: A challenge to mankind.* London: Faber & Faber, 1938; New York: Putnam's, 1939.

ADLER, A. *The science of living.* New York: Anchor, 1969.

ADLER, K. A. Depression in the light of individual psychology. *Journal of Individual Psychology,* 1961, *17,* 56–67.

ADLER, K. A. Life style, gender role, and the symptom of homosexuality. *Journal of Individual Psychology,* 1967, *23,* 67–78.

ALBEE, G. W. *Mental health manpower trends.* New York: Basic Books, 1959.

ALBERT, R. S., BRIGANTE, T. R., & CHASE, M. The psychopathic personality: A content analysis of the concept. *Journal of General Psychology,* 1959, *60,* 17–28.

ALEXANDER, F. Psychological aspects of medicine. *Psychosomatic Medicine,* 1939, *1,* 7–18. (a)

ALEXANDER, F. Emotional factors in essential hypertension. *Psychosomatic Medicine*, 1939, *1*, 173–198. (b)

ALEXANDER, F. Fundamental concepts of psychosomatic research: Psychogenesis, conversion, specificity. *Psychosomatic Medicine*, 1943, 5, 205–210.

ALEXANDER, F. *Psychosomatic medicine.* New York: Norton, 1950.

ALEXANDER, F. Panel: Experimental study of psychophysiological correlations. Paper delivered at the Annual Meeting of the American Psychosomatic Society, Atlantic City, N.J., May, 1959.

ALEXANDER, F. The development of psychosomatic medicine. *Psychosomatic Medicine*, 1962, *24*, 13–23.

ALEXANDER, F. Alcohol and behavior disorder-alcoholism. In S. P. Lucia (Ed.), *Alcohol and civilization.* New York: McGraw-Hill, 1963.

ALEXANDER, F., FLAGG, G. W., FOSTER, S., CLEMENS, T., & BLAHD, E. Experimental studies of emotional stress: I. Hyterthyroidism. *Psychosomatic Medicine*, 1961, *23*, 104–114.

ALEXANDER, F., & FRENCH, T. M. *Psychoanalytic therapy.* New York: Ronald Press, 1946.

ALEXANDER, F., & SZASZ, T. S. The psychosomatic approach in medicine. In F. Alexander and H. Ross (Eds.), *Dynamic psychiatry.* Chicago: University of Chicago Press, 1952.

ALLEN, C. *Homosexuality.* London: Staples Press, 1958.

ALLINSMITH, W., & GOETHALS, G. W. Cultural factors in mental health: Anthropological perspective. *Review of Educational Research*, 1950, *26*, 429–450.

ALLPORT, G. W. *Personality: A psychological interpretation.* New York: Holt, 1937.

ALLPORT, G. W. *Pattern and growth in personality.* New York: Holt, Rinehart & Winston, 1961.

AMERICAN MEDICAL ASSOCIATION. Committee on Alcoholism. *Manual on alcoholism.* Chicago: AMA, 1967.

AMERICAN PSYCHIATRIC ASSOCIATION. Diagnostic and statistical manual: Mental disorders, with special supplement on plans for revision (special printing). Washington, D.C.: APA, 1965.

ANDREEV, B. V. *Sleep therapy in the neuroses.* New York: Consultants Bureau, 1960.

ANGYAL, A. *Neurosis and treatment: A holistic theory.* New York: John Wiley, 1965.

ANSBACHER, H. L. The structure of individual psychology. In B. B. Wolman (Ed.), *Scientific psychology.* New York: Basic Books, 1965.

ARBUCKLE, D. S. (Ed.) *Counseling and psychotherapy: An overview.* New York: McGraw-Hill, 1967.

ARIETI, S. *Interpretation of schizophrenia.* New York: Robert Brunner, 1955.

ARIETI, S. Schizophrenia: The manifest symptomatology, the psychodynamic and formal mechanisms. In S. Arieti (Ed.), *American handbook of psychiatry,* Vol. 1. New York: Basic Books, 1959.

ARIETI, S. *American handbook of psychiatry.* New York: Basic Books, 1959–1966. 3 vols.

ARIETI, S. Etiological considerations of schizophrenia. In S. C. Scher and H. R. Davis (Eds.), *The out-patient treatment of schizophrenia.* New York: Grune & Stratton, 1960.

ARIETI, S. *The intrapsychic self: Feeling, cognition, and creativity in health and mental illness.* New York: Basic Books, 1967.

ARIETI, S., & METH, J. M. Rare, unclassifiable, collective, and exotic psychotic syndromes. In S. Arieti (Ed.), *American handbook of psychiatry.* Vol. 1. New York: Basic Books, 1959.

ARTISS, K. L. *Milieu therapy in schizophrenia.* New York: Grune & Stratton, 1962.

ASTRUP, C. *Schizophrenia: Conditional reflex studies.* Springfield, Ill.: Charles C Thomas, 1962.

ASTRUP, C., & NOREIK, K. *Functional Psychoses: Diagnostic and prognostic models.* Springfield, Ill.: Charles C Thomas, 1966.

AUERBACK, A. (Ed.) *Schizophrenia: An integrated approach.* New York: Ronald Press, 1959.

AUSUBEL, D. P. *Drug addiction: Physiological, psychological, and sociological aspects.* New York: Random House, 1958.

AUSUBEL, D. P. Causes and types of narcotic addiction: A psychosocial view. *Psychiatric Quarterly,* 1961, 35, 523–531.

BANDURA, A. Behavioral psychotherapy. *Scientific American,* 1967, *216,* 78–86.

BANDURA, A. Modelling approaches to the modification of phobic disorders. In R. Porter (Ed.), *The role of learning in psychotherapy.* London: J. & A. Churchill, 1968. (a)

BANDURA, A. A social learning interpretation of psychological dysfunctions. In P. London and D. Rosenhan (Eds.), *Foundations of abnormal psychology.* New York: Holt, Rinehart & Winston, 1968. (b)

BANDURA, W. *Principles of behavior modification.* New York: Holt, Rinehart and Winston, 1969.

BARKER, J. C. The medical aspects of sexual perversion. In W. A. R. Thomson (Ed.), *Sex and its problems.* Edinburgh: Livingstone, 1968.

BARRON, F. Toward a positive definition of psychological health. Paper read before the American Psychological Association, 1955.

BATESON, G., JACKSON, D. D., HALEY, J., & WEAKLAND, J. Toward a theory of schizophrenia. *Behavioral Science,* 1956, *1,* 251–264.

BECK, A. T. Thinking and depression. *Archives of General Psychiatry,* 1963, *9,* 324–333.

BECK, A. T. Thinking and depression: II. Theory and therapy. *Archives of General Psychiatry,* 1964, *10,* 561–571.

BECK, A. T. *Depression: Clinical, experimental, and theoretical aspects.* New York: Harper & Row, 1967.

BECK, A. T., SETHI, B. B., & TUTHILL, R. W. Childhood bereavement and adult depression. *Archives of General Psychiatry,* 1963, *9,* 295–302.

BECK, S. J. *Psychological processes in the schizophrenic adaptation.* New York: Grune & Stratton, 1965.

BECKER, W. C. The process-reactive distinction: A key to the problem of schizophrenia. *Journal of Nervous and Mental Disease,* 1959, *129,* 442–449.

BEIER, E. G. *The silent language of psychotherapy: Social reinforcement of unconscious processes.* Chicago: Aldine, 1966.

BELLAK, L. A multiple-factor psychosomatic theory of schizophrenia. *Psychiatric Quarterly,* 1949, *23,* 738–755.

BELLAK, L. Toward a unified theory of schizophrenia: An elaboration of the multiple-factor psychosomatic theory of schizophrenia. *Journal of Nervous and Mental Disease,* 1955, *12,* 60–66.

BELLAK, L. *et al. Manic-depressive psychosis and allied conditions.* New York: Grune & Stratton, 1952.

BENDER, L. Childhood schizophrenia. *American Journal of Orthopsychiatry,* 1947, *17,* 40–56.

BENDER, L. Childhood schizophrenia. *Psychiatric Quarterly,* 1953, *27,* 663–687. (a)

BENDER, L. Evidences from studies of childhood schizophrenia. *Archives of Neurology and Psychiatry,* 1953, *70,* 535. (b)

BENDER, L. Twenty years of clinical research on schizophrenic children, with special reference to those under six years of age. In G. Caplan (Ed.), *Emotional problems of early childhood.* New York: Basic Books, 1955.

BENEDEK, T. F. Sexual functions in women and their disturbance. In S. Arieti (Ed.), *American handbook of psychiatry.* New York: Basic Books, 1959.

BENEDICT, P. K., & JACKS, I. Mental illness in primitive societies. *Psychiatry,* 1954, *17,* 337–389.

BERENSON, B. G., & CARKHUFF, R. R. (Eds.), *Sources of gain in counseling and psychotherapy: Readings and commentary.* New York: Holt, Rinehart & Winston, 1967.

BERGLER, E. *Homosexuality: Disease or way of life?* New York: Hill & Wang, 1956.

BERNE, E. *Transactional analysis in psychotherapy: A systematic individual and social psychiatry.* New York: Grove Press, 1961.

BERNE, E. *The structure and dynamics of organizations and groups.* New York: Lippincott, 1963.

BERNE, E. *Games people play: The psychology of human relationships.* New York: Grove Press, 1964.

BERNSTEIN, A. The psychoanalytic technique. In B. B. Wolman (Ed.), *Handbook of clinical psychology.* New York: McGraw-Hill, 1965.

BETTELHEIM, B. Joey: A "mechanical boy." *Scientific American,* 1959, *200,* 116–127.

BIBRING, E. The mechanism of depression. In P. Greenacre (Ed.), *Affective disorders.* New York: International Universities, 1953.

BINSWANGER, L. Existential analysis and psychotherapy. In Frieda Fromm-Reichmann and J. L. Moreno (Eds.), *Progress in psychotherapy.* New York: Grune & Stratton, 1956.

BINSWANGER, L. The existential analysis school of thought. In R. May, E. Angel, and H. F. Ellenberger (Eds.), *Existence: A new dimension in psychiatry and psychology.* New York: Basic Books, 1958. (a)

BINSWANGER, L. The case of Ellen West. In R. May, E. Angel, and H. F. Ellenberger (Eds.), *Existence: A new dimension in psychiatry and psychology.* New York: Basic Books, 1958. (b)

BINSWANGER, L. *Being-in-the-world.* New York: Basic Books, 1963.

BION, W. R. Differentiation of the psychotic from the non-psychotic personalities. *International Journal of Psychoanalysis,* 1957, *38,* 266–275.

BION, W. R. *Experiences in groups.* New York: Basic Books, 1961.

BLEULER, E. *The theory of schizophrenic negativism.* New York: Journal of Nervous and Mental Disease Publishing, 1912.

BLEULER, E. *Dementia praecox or the group of schizophrenias.* New York: International Universities Press, 1950.

BLISS, E. L. (Ed.) *Roots of behavior.* New York: Hoeber, 1962.

BLOCK, M. A. Opportunities and limitations in the treatment of alcoholics by the internist. In J. Hirsh (Ed.), *Opportunities in the treatment of alcoholics.* Springfield, Ill.: Charles C Thomas, 1967.

Böök, J. A. A genetic and neuropsychiatric investigation of a North Swedish population: I. Psychoses. *Acta Genetica et Statistica Medica,* 1953, *4,* 1–100. (a)

Böök, J. A. Schizophrenia as a gene mutation. *Acta Genetica et Statistica Medica,* 1953, *4,* 133–139. (b)

Böök, J. A. Genetical etiology in mental illness. *Millbank Memorial Fund Quarterly,* 1960, *38,* 193–212.

Böök, J. A., Fraccaro, M., & Lindsten, J. Cytogenetical observations in mongolism. *Acta Paedopsychiatrica,* 1959, *48,* 453–468.

Borgatta, E. F. & Lambert, W. W. (Eds.) *Handbook of personality theory and research.* Chicago: Rand McNally, 1968.

Boss, M. The conception of man in natural science and daseinsanalysis. *Comprehensive Psychiatry,* 1962, *3,* 193–214.

Boss, M. *Psychoanalysis and daseinsanalysis.* New York: Basic Books, 1963.

Bosselman, B. C. *Neurosis and psychosis.* Springfield, Ill.: Charles C Thomas, 1964.

Bowman, K. M., & Jellinek, E. M. Alcohol addiction and its treatment. In E. M. Jellinek (Ed.), *Alcohol and chronic alcoholism,* New Haven: Yale University Press, 1942.

Bowman, K. M., & Rose, M. In A. Auerback (Ed.), *Schizophrenia: An integrated approach.* New York: Ronald Press, 1959.

Bragg, R. L. Risk of admission to mental hospital following hysterectomy or cholecystectomy. *American Journal of Public Health,* 1965, *55,* 1403–1410.

Brattemo, C. *Studies in metaphoric verbal behavior in patients with a psychiatric diagnosis of schizophrenia.* Stockholm: Skandinaviska Testförlaget, 1968.

Brentano, F. *Psychologie vom empirischen Standpunkte.* Leipzig: Duncker und Humblot, 1874. Found translated in W. S. Sahakian (Ed.), *History of psychology: A source book in systematic psychology.* Itasca, Ill.: F. E. Peacock Publishers, Inc., 1968.

Brentano, F. Act psychology. In W. S. Sahakian (Ed.), *History of psychology: A source book in systematic psychology.* Itasca, Ill.: F. E. Peacock Publishers, Inc., 1968.

Breuer, J., & Freud, S. *Studies on hysteria.* London: Hogarth (1895) 1955.

Broadbent, D. E. *Perception and communication.* London: Pergamon Press, 1958.

Brock, H., & Del Giudice, C. Stealing and temporal orientation. *Journal of Abnormal and Social Psychology,* 1963, *66,* 91–94.

Brown, G. W., Bone, M., Dalison, B., Wing, J. K. *Schizophrenia and social care: A comparative follow-up study of 339 schizophrenic patients.* London: Oxford University Press, 1966.

Buss, A. H. Two anxiety factors in psychiatric patients. *Journal of Abnormal Psychology,* 1962, *65,* 426–427.

Buss, A. H. *Psychopathology.* New York: Wiley, 1966.

Button, A. D. The genesis and development of alcoholism: An empirically based schema. *Quarterly Journal of Studies on Alcohol,* 1956, *17,* 671–675.

BYRNE, D. The repression-sensitization scale: Rationale, reliability and validity. *Journal of Personality,* 1961, *29,* 334–349.

BYRNE, D. Repression-sensitization as a dimension of personality. In B. A. Maher (Ed.), *Progress in experimental personality research.* Vol. 1. New York: Academic, 1964.

BYRNE, D., GOLIGHTLY, C., & SHEFFIELD, J. The repression-sensitization scale as a measure of adjustment: Relationship with the *CPI. Journal of Consulting Psychology,* 1965, *29,* 586–589.

CAIN, A. H. *The cured alcoholic: New conceptions in alcoholism treatment and research.* New York: John Day Co., 1964.

CALHOUN, J. B. A "behavioral sink." In E. L. Bliss (Ed.), *Roots of behavior.* New York: Hoeber, 1962.

CAMERON, N. *Personality development and psychopathology: A dynamic approach.* Boston: Houghton Mifflin, 1963.

CAMPBELL, J. D. *Manic-depressive disease.* Philadelphia: Lippincott, 1953.

CASEY, A. The effect of stress on the consumption of alcohol and reserpine. *Quarterly Journal of Studies on Alcoholism,* 1960, *21,* 208–215.

CATANZARO, R. J. (Ed.) *Alcoholism: The total treatment approach.* Springfield, Ill.: Charles C Thomas, 1968.

CATTELL, R. B. *Personality and motivation: Structure and measurement.* New York: World Book, 1957.

CATTELL, R. B. Advances in the measurement of neuroticism and anxiety in a conceptual framework of unitary-trait theory. *Annals of the New York Academy of Science,* 1962, *93,* 815–839.

CATTELL, R. B. The nature and measurement of anxiety. *Scientific American,* 1963, *208,* 96–104.

CATTELL, R. B. *The scientific analysis of personality.* Baltimore: Penguin Books, 1965.

CATTELL, R. B. (Ed.) *Handbook of multivariate experimental psychology.* Chicago: Rand McNally, 1966.

CATTELL, R. B., & SCHEIER, I. H. *The meaning and measurement of neuroticism and anxiety.* New York: Ronald Press, 1961.

CERLETTI, U. Old and new information about electroshock. *American Journal of Psychiatry,* 1950, *107,* 87–91.

CERLETTI, U. Electroshock therapy. *Journal of Clinical and Experimental Psychopathology & Quarterly Review of Psychiatry and Neurology,* 1954, *15,* 191–217.

CERLETTI, U. Electroshock therapy. In W. S. Sahakian (Ed.), *History of psychology: A source book in systematic psychology.* Itasca, Ill.: F. E. Peacock Publishers, Inc., 1968.

CHAPMAN, L. J., & CHAPMAN, J. P. Interpretation of words in schizophrenia. *Journal of Personality and Social Psychology*, 1965, *1*, 135–146.

CLAUSEN, J. A. Social patterns, personality, and adolescent drug use. In A. H. Leighton, J. A. Clausen, and R. N. Wilson (Eds.), *Explorations in social psychiatry*. New York: Basic Books, 1957.

CLECKLEY, H. M. Psychopathic states. In S. Arieti (Ed.), *American handbook of psychiatry*. New York: Basic Books, 1959.

CLECKLEY, H. M. *The mask of sanity* (4th ed.) St. Louis: C. V. Mosby, 1964.

CLEVELAND, E. J., & LONGAKER, D. W. Neurotic patterns in the family. In A. H. Leighton, J. A. Clausen, and R. N. Wilson (Eds.), *Explorations in social psychiatry*. New York: Basic Books, 1957.

CLINEBELL, H. J. *Basic types of pastoral counseling*. Nashville, Tenn.: Abingdon, 1966.

COLE, J. O., & WITTENBORN, J. R. (Eds.) *Pharmacotherapy of depression*. Springfield, Ill.: Charles C Thomas, 1966.

COLEMAN, J. C. *Abnormal psychology and modern life*. (3rd ed.) Chicago: Scott, Foresman, 1964.

COMMITTEE ON NOMENCLATURE AND STATISTICS OF THE AMERICAN PSYCHIATRIC ASSOCIATION. *Diagnostic and statistical manual: Mental disorders with special supplement on plans for revision*. Washington, D.C.: APA, 1965.

CONDRAU, G., & BOSS, M. *Existential analysis*. In J. G. Howells (Ed.) *Modern perspectives in world psychiatry*. Edinburgh: Oliver & Boyd, 1968.

CONGER, J. J. The effects of alcohol on conflict behavior in the albino rat. *Quarterly Journal of Studies on Alcohol*, 1951, *12*, 1–29.

COURVILLE, C. B. *Effect of alcohol on the nervous system of man*. Los Angeles: San Lucas Press, 1966.

CRAFT, J. *Ten studies into psychopathic personalities*. Bristol: John Wright, 1965.

CRAIG, W. J. Objective measures of thinking integrated with psychiatric symptoms. *Psychological Reports*, 1965, *16*, 539–546.

DANA, R. H. *Foundations of clinical psychology: Problems of personality and adjustment*. Princeton, N.J.: Van Nostrand, 1966.

DAVIES, E. B. (Ed.) *Depression*. Cambridge: Cambridge University Press, 1964.

DESLAURIERS, A. M. *The experience of reality in childhood schizophrenia*. New York: International Universities, 1962.

DEUTSCH, F. The choice of organ in organ neurosis. *International Journal of Psychoanalysis*, 1939, *20*, 252–262.

DEUTSCH, F., & MURPHY, W. F. *The clinical interview.* New York: International Universities, 1955.

DOLLARD, J., & MILLER, N. E. *Personality and psychotherapy.* New York: McGraw-Hill, 1950.

DOUST, J. W. L. Psychiatric aspects of somatic immunity. *British Journal of Social Medicine,* 1952, 6, 49–67. (a)

DOUST, J. W. L. Dysplastic growth differentials in patients with psychiatric disorders. *British Journal of Social Medicine,* 1952, 6, 169–177. (b)

DRAKEFORD, J. W. *Integrity therapy.* Nashville, Tenn.: Broadman, 1967.

DRAPER, G., DUPERTIUS, C. W., & CAUGHEY, J. L. *Human constitution in clinical medicine.* New York: Hoeber, 1944.

DUBLIN, L. I. *Suicide: A sociological and statistical study.* New York: Ronald Press, 1963.

DUNAIF, S. L., & HOCH, P. Pseudopsychopathic schizophrenia. In P. H. Hoch and J. Zubin (Eds.), *Psychiatry and the law.* New York: Grune & Stratton, 1955.

DUNBAR, F. The relationship between anxiety states and organic disease. *Clinics,* 1942, 1, 879–908.

DUNBAR, F. *Psychosomatic diagnosis.* New York: Hoeber-Harper, 1943.

DUNBAR, F. *Emotions and bodily changes: A survey of literature on psychosomatic interrelationships 1910–1953* (4th ed.) New York: Columbia University Press, 1954.

DUNBAR, F. *Psychiatry in the medical specialties.* New York: McGraw-Hill, 1959.

DUNLAP, K. *Habits: Their making and unmaking.* New York: Liveright, 1932.

DURELL, J., & SCHILDKRAUT, J. J. Biochemical studies of the schizophrenic and affective disorders. In S. Arieti (Ed.), *American handbook of psychiatry.* New York: Basic Books, 1966.

ELLIS, A. Rational psychotherapy. *Journal of General Psychology,* 1958, 59, 35–49.

ELLIS, A. *Reason and emotion in psychotherapy.* New York: Lyle Stuart, 1962.

ELLIS, A. Rational-emotive psychotherapy. In D. S. Arbuckle (Ed.), *Counseling and psychotherapy: An overview.* New York: McGraw-Hill, 1967.

ELLIS, H. *Studies in the psychology of sex.* Vol. 2. New York: Random House, 1936.

ELLIS, N. R. (Ed.) *Handbook of mental deficiency.* New York: McGraw-Hill, 1963.

ENGEL, G. L. The psychoanalytic approach to psychosomatic medicine.

In J. Marmor (Ed.), *Modern psychoanalysis: New directions and perspectives.* New York: Basic Books, 1968.

ENGLISH, O. S. Clinical observations on direct analysis. In O. S. English *et al.* (Eds.), *Direct analysis and schizophrenia: Clinical observations and evaluations.* New York: Grune & Stratton, 1961.

ENOCH, M. D., TRETHOWAN, W. H., & BARKER, J. C. *Some uncommon psychiatric syndromes.* Bristol: John Wright, 1967.

ERIKSEN, C. W. The case for perceptual defense. *Psychological Review,* 1954, *61,* 175–182.

EYSENCK, H. J. Criterion analysis—An application of the hypothetico-deductive method to factor analysis. *Psychological Review,* 1950, 57, 38–53.

EYSENCK, H. J. *The scientific study of personality.* London: Routledge & Kegan Paul, 1952. Selections found in W. S. Sahakian, *Psychology of personality: Readings in theory.* Chicago: Rand McNally, 1965.

EYSENCK, H. J. *Dynamics of anxiety and hysteria.* London: Routledge & Kegan Paul, 1957.

EYSENCK, H. J. *The scientific study of personality.* London: Routledge and Kegan Paul, 1952.

EYSENCK, H. J. Learning theory and behavior therapy. *Journal of Mental Science,* 1959, *105,* 61–75.

EYSENCK, H. J. (Ed.) *Handbook of abnormal psychology.* London: Sir Isaac Pitman, 1960.

EYSENCK, H. J. *Handbook of abnormal psychology: An experimental approach.* New York: Basic Books, 1961.

EYSENCK, H. J. *Crime and personality.* London: Routledge & Kegan Paul, 1964.

EYSENCK, H. J. Criterion analysis—An application of the hypothetico-deductive method to factor analysis. *Psychological Review,* 1950, 57, 39–44. An abridged form found in W. S. Sahakian, *Psychology of personality: Readings in theory.* Chicago: Rand McNally, 1965.

EYSENCK, H. J., & RACHMAN, S. *The Causes and cures of neurosis: An introduction to modern behaviour therapy based on learning theory and the principles of conditioning.* San Diego: Robert A. Knapp, 1965.

FABRY, J. B. *The pursuit of meaning: Logotherapy applied to life.* Boston: Beacon, 1968.

FAIRBAIRN, R. *Object-relations theory of the personality.* New York: Basic Books, 1952.

FAIRWEATHER, G. The effect of selected incentive conditions on the performance of psychopathic, normal and neurotic criminals in a serial rote learning situation. Unpublished doctoral dissertation, University of Illinois, 1954.

FEDERN, P. Psychoanalysis of psychoses. In P. Federn (Ed.), *Ego psychology and the psychoses*. New York: Basic Books (1943), 1952.

FEDERN, P. Mental hygiene of the ego in schizophrenia. In P. Federn (Ed.), *Ego psychology and the psychoses*. New York: Basic Books (1948), 1952.

FEDERN, P. The ego in schizophrenia. In P. Federn (Ed.), *Ego psychology and the psychoses.* New York: Basic Books (1949), 1952.

FEDERN, P. (Ed.) *Ego psychology and the psychoses.* New York: Basic Books, 1952.

FENICHEL, O. *The psychoanalytic theory of neurosis.* New York: Norton, 1945.

FERENCZI, S. *Sex in psychoanalysis.* New York: Basic Books, 1950.

FERENCZI S. *Further contributions to the theory and technique of psychoanalysis.* New York: Basic Books, 1952.

FISH, F. J. *Schizophrenia.* Bristol: John Wright, 1962.

FORBES, J. C., & DUNCAN, G. M. Effect of vitamin intake on adrenal cholesterol after acute alcoholic intoxication in rats. In H. E. Himwich (Ed.), *Alcohol: Basic aspects and treatment.* Washington, D.C.: American Association for the Advancement of Science, 1957.

FORD, C. S., & BEACH, F. A. *Patterns of sexual behavior.* New York: Harper & Row, 1951.

FOULKES, S. H. *An introduction to group-analytic psychotherapy.* London: Heinemann, 1948.

FOULKES, S. H. & ANTHONY, E. J. *Group psychotherapy.* London: Penguin Books, 1957.

FOX, R. Introduction. In R. P. Maickel, *Biochemical factors in alcoholism.* Oxford: Pergamon Press, 1967.

FRANK, L. K. Society as the patient. *American Journal of Sociology,* 1936, *42,* 335–344.

FRANKENSTEIN, C. *Psychopathy: A comparative analysis of clinical pictures.* New York: Grune & Stratton, 1959.

FRANKL, V. E. Collective neurosis of the present day. *Internationales Journal für prophylaktische Medizin und Sozialhygiene,* 1958, *2,* 1–5. (a)

FRANKL, V. E. On logotherapy and existential analysis. *American Journal of Psychoanalysis,* 1958, *18,* 28–37.

FRANKL, V. E. The spiritual dimension in existential analysis and logotherapy. *Journal of Individual Psychology,* 1959, *15,* 157–165.

FRANKL, V. E. Paradoxical intention: A logotherapeutic technique. *American Journal of Psychotherapy,* 1960, *14,* 520–535.

FRANKL, V. E. Logotherapy and the challenge of suffering. *Review of Existential Psychology and Psychiatry,* 1961, *1,* 3–7.

FRANKL, V. E. Psychiatry and man's quest for meaning. *Journal of Religion and Health*, 1962, *1*, 93–103. (a)

FRANKL, V. E. *Man's search for meaning: An introduction to logotherapy* (Rev. ed.) Boston: Beacon, 1962. (b)

FRANKL, V. E. *The doctor and the soul: From psychotherapy to logotherapy* (Rev. ed.) New York: Knopf, 1966. (a)

FRANKL, V. E. Logotherapy and existential analysis—A review. *American Journal of Psychotherapy*, 1966, *20*, 252–260. (b)

FRANKL, V. E. *Psychotherapy and existentialism.* New York: Washington Square, 1967. (a)

FRANKL, V. E. Logotherapy. *Israel Annals of Psychiatry and Related Disciplines*, 1967, *5*, 142–155 (b)

FRANKL, V. E. *The will to meaning.* New York: World Publishing, 1969.

FRAZIER, S. H., & CARR, A. C. *Introduction to psychopathology.* New York: Macmillan, 1964.

FREEMAN, H. E., & SIMMONS, O. G. Social class and post-hospital performance levels. *American Sociological Review*, 1959, *24*, 345–351.

FREEMAN, H. E., & SIMMONS, O. G. Treatment experiences of mental patients and their families. *American Journal of Public Health*, 1961, *51*, 1266–1273.

FREEMAN, H. E., & SIMMONS, O. G. *The mental patient comes home.* New York: John Wiley, 1963.

FREEMAN, T. *Studies on psychosis: Descriptive, psychoanalytical and psychological aspects.* London: Tavistock, 1965.

FREEMAN, W. Psychosurgery. *American Journal of Psychiatry*, 1962, *119*, 621–628.

FREEMAN, W., & WATTS, J. W. *Psychosurgery: In the treatment of mental disorders and intractable pain.* Springfield, Ill.: Charles C Thomas, 1950.

FREEMAN, W., & WATTS, J. W. Prefrontal lobotomy. In W. S. Sahakian (Ed.), *History of psychology: A source book in systematic psychology.* Itasca, Ill.: F. E. Peacock Publishers, Inc., 1968.

FRENCH, T. M. *The integration of behavior.* Chicago: University of Chicago Press, 1952–54. 2 vols.

FREUD, S. Psychoanalytic notes upon an autobiographical account of a case of paranoia. *Collected Papers.* London: Hogarth (1911), 1925.

FREUD, S. *A general introduction to psycho-analysis.* New York: Liveright (1916–17), 1935.

FREUD, S. *The ego and the id.* London: Hogarth (1923), 1960.

FREUD, S. *Collected papers.* London: Hogarth, 1946.

FREUD, S. *The unconscious.* In S. Freud, *Collected papers.* London, Hogarth (1915), 1947.

FREUD, S. Metaphysical supplement to the theory of dreams. In S. Freud, *Collected papers*. London: Hogarth (1916), 1947.

FREUD, S. Neurosis and psychosis. In S. Freud, *Collected papers*. London: Hogarth (1924), 1947.

FREUD, S. Mourning and melancholia. In S. Freud, *Collected papers*. London: Hogarth (1917), 1950.

FREUD, S. *The interpretation of dreams*. In standard edition of the complete psychological works of Sigmund Freud. London: Hogarth, (1900), 1953. Vols. IV, V.

FREUD, S. *The collected papers of Sigmund Freud*. New York: Basic Books, 1959.

FREUD, S. *The ego and the id*. New York: Norton (1923), 1960.

FREUD, S. *New introductory lectures on psycho-analysis*. London: Hogarth, 1961.

FREUD, S. *An outline of psychoanalysis*. New York: Norton (1940), 1963. (a)

FREUD, S. *A general introduction to psycho-analysis*. London: George Allen & Unwin, 1963. (b)

FROMM, E. *Escape from freedom*. New York: Norton, 1941.

FROMM, E. *Man for himself: An inquiry into the psychology of ethics*. New York: Holt, Rinehart & Winston, 1947.

FROMM, E. *The sane society*. New York: Holt, 1955.

FROMM, E. *The art of loving*. New York: Harper & Row, 1956.

FROMM, E. Psychoanalysis and Zen Buddhism. In D. T. Suzuki, E. Fromm, and R. DeMartino. *Zen Buddhism and psychoanalysis*. New York: Grove Press, 1963.

FROMM, E. *The heart of man*. New York: Harper & Row, 1964.

FROMM, E. (Ed.) *Socialist humanism: An international Symposium*. New York: Doubleday, 1965.

FROMM-REICHMANN, F. Psychoanalytic psychotherapy with psychotics: The influence of the modifications in technique on present trends in psychoanalysis. *Psychiatry*, 1943, 6, 277–279.

FROMM-REICHMANN, F. Recent advances in psychoanalysis. *Journal of the American Medical Women's Association*, 1949, 4, 320–326.

FROMM-REICHMANN, F. *Principles of intensive psychotherapy*. Chicago: University of Chicago Press, 1950.

FROMM-REICHMANN, F., & MORENO, J. L. (Eds.) *Progress in psychotherapy*. New York: Grune & Stratton, 1956.

FULLER, J. L., & THOMPSON, W. R. *Behavior genetics*. New York: Wiley, 1960.

FULTON, J. F., & JACOBSEN, C. E. The function of frontal lobes, a comparative study in monkeys, chimpanzees and man. *Abstracts of the Second International Neurological Congress,* London, 1935.

GARMA, A. Gastric neurosis. *International Journal of Psychoanalysis,* 1950, *31,* 53–72. (a)

GARMA, A. On the pathogenesis of peptic ulcer. *International Journal of Psychoanalysis,* 1950, *31,* 53–72. (b)

GARMEZY, N. Process and reactive schizophrenia. In M. M. Katz, J. O. Cole and W. E. Barton (Eds.), *The role and methodology of classification in psychiatry and psychopathology.* Chevy Chase, Md.: National Institute of Mental Health, 1968.

GARMEZY, N., & RODNICK, E. H. Premorbid adjustment performance in schizophrenia: Implications for interpreting heterogeneity in schizophrenia. *Journal of Nervous and Mental Disease,* 1959, *129,* 450–466.

GEBHARD, P. H., GAGNON, J. H., POMEROY, W. B., & CHRISTENSON, C. V. *Sex offenders: An analysis of types.* New York: Harper & Row, 1965.

GERSHON, S., HOLMBERG, G., MATTSON, N., & MARSHALL, A. Imipramine hydrochloride, autonomic and psychological functions. *Archives of General Psychiatry,* 1962, *6,* 112–117.

GESELL, A., & ILG, F. L. *Child development.* New York: Harper & Row, 1949.

GLASSER, W. *Reality therapy: A new approach to psychiatry.* New York: Harper & Row, 1965.

GOFFMAN, E. *Asylums: Essays on the social situation of mental patients and other inmates.* New York: Doubleday, 1961.

GOLDFARB, W. *Childhood schizophrenia.* Cambridge, Mass.: Harvard University Press, 1961.

GOLDSTEIN, K. *The organism.* New York: American Book, 1939.

GOLDSTEIN, K. *Human nature in the light of psychopathology.* Cambridge, Mass.: Harvard University Press, 1940.

GOLDSTEIN, K. The effect of brain damage on the personality. *Psychiatry,* 1952, *15,* 245–260.

GOLDSTEIN, K. The organismic approach. In S. Arieti (Ed.), *American handbook of psychiatry.* New York: Basic Books, 1959.

GOTTESMAN, I. I., & SHIELDS, J. Schizophrenia in twins: 16 years' consecutive admissions to a psychiatric clinic. *British Journal of Psychiatry,* 1966, *112,* 809–818.

GRACE, W. J., & GRAHAM, D. T. Relationship of specific attitudes and emotions to certain bodily diseases. *Psychosomatic Medicine,* 1952, *14,* 243–251.

GRAHAM, D. T., GRAHAM, F. K., & KABLER, J. D. Experimental production of predicted physiological differences by suggestion of attitude. Paper presented at American Psychosomatic Society meetings, 1960.

GRAHAM, D. T., KABLER, J. D. & GRAHAM, F. K. Physiological responses to the suggestion of attitudes specific for hives and hypertension. *Psychosomatic Medicine*, 1962, *24*, 159–169.

GRAHAM, D. T., LUNDY, R. M., BENJAMIN, L. S., KABLER, J. D., LEWIS, W. C., KUNISH, N. O. & GRAHAM, F. K. Specific attitudes in initial interviews with patients having different "psychosomatic" diseases. *Psychosomatic Medicine*, 1962, *24*, 257–266.

GRAHAM, D. T., STERN, J. A., & WINOKUR, G. Experimental investigation of the specificity of attitude hypothesis in psychosomatic disease. *Psychosomatic Medicine*, 1958, *20*, 446–457.

GREENACRE, P. Conscience in the psychopath. *American Journal of Orthopsychiatry*, 1945, *15*, 495–509.

GREENBLATT, M., GROSSER, G. H., & WECHSLER, H. Differential response of hospitalized depressed patients to somatic therapy. *American Journal of Psychiatry*, 1964, *120*, 935–943.

GREGORY, I. Genetic factors in schizophrenia. *American Journal of Psychiatry*, 1960, *116*, 961–972.

GREGORY, I. *Fundamentals of psychiatry*. Philadelphia: Saunders, 1968.

GREINER, A. C., & NICOLSON, G. A. Schizophrenia: Melanosis. *Lancet*, 1965, *2*, 1165–1167.

GRINKER, R. R. *Psychosomatic research*. New York: Norton, 1953.

GRINKER, R. R. The phenomena of depressions. In *Third World Congress of Psychiatry, Proceedings*. Montreal, Can.: University of Toronto Press, 1961, *1*, 160–164.

GRINKER, R. R., MILLER, J., SABSHIN, M., NUNN, R., & NUNNALLY, J. C. *The phenomena of depressions*. New York: Hoeber, 1961.

GRINKER, R. R., & NUNNALLY, J. C. The phenomena of depressions. In M. M. Katz, J. O. Cole and W. E. Barton (Eds.) *The role and methodology of classification in psychiatry and psychopathology*. Chevy Chase, Md.: National Institute of Mental Health, 1968.

GRINKER, R. R., & SPIEGEL, J. P. *War neuroses*. New York: Blakiston, 1945.

GRINKER, R. R., WERBLE, B., & DRYE, R. C. *The borderline syndrome: A behavioral study of ego-functions*. New York: Basic Books, 1968.

GROEN, J. J. Psychosomatic disturbances as a form of substituted behaviour. *Journal of Psychosomatic Research*, 1957, *2*, 85–96.

GROEN, J. J. *Psychosomatic research*. Oxford: Pergamon, 1964.

GROEN, J. J., & WELNER, A. The biological basis of psychosomatic medicine. *Israel Annals of Psychiatry and Related Disciplines*, 1966, *4*, 136–147.

GRUENBERG, E. M. Socially shared psychopathology. In A. H. Leighton, J. A. Clausen, and R. N. Wilson (Eds.), *Explorations in social psychiatry*. New York: Basic Books, 1957.

GUERTIN, W. H. An inverted factor analytic study of schizophrenia. *Journal of Consulting Psychology,* 1952, *16,* 371–375.

GUERTIN, W. H. Medical and statistical-psychological models for research in schizophrenia. *Behavioral Science,* 1961, *6,* 200–204. (a)

GUERTIN, W. H. Empirical syndrome groupings of schizophrenia hospital admissions. *Journal of Clinical Psychology,* 1961, *17,* 268–275. (b)

GUTHEIL, E. A. Sexual dysfunctions in men. In S. Arieti (Ed.), *American handbook of psychiatry.* New York: Basic Books, 1959.

HADLEY, J. M. *Clinical and counseling psychology.* New York: Knopf, 1958.

HALLIDAY, J. L. The rising incidence of psychosomatic illness. *British Medical Journal,* 1938, 2, 11–14.

HALLIDAY, J. L. Principles of etiology. *British Journal of Medicine and Psychology,* 1943, *19,* 367–380. (a)

HALLIDAY, J. L. Concept of psychosomatic affection. *Lancet,* 1943, *245,* 692–696. (b)

HALLIDAY, J. L. The incidence of psychosomatic affections in Britain. *Psychosomatic Medicine,* 1945, *7,* 135–146. (a)

HALLIDAY, J. L. Significance of "the concept of a psychosomatic affection." *Psychosomatic Medicine,* 1945, *7,* 240–245. (b)

HALLIDAY, J. L. *Psychosocial medicine: A study of the sick society.* New York: Norton, 1948.

HAMILTON, M. The assessment of anxiety states by rating. *British Journal of Medicine and Psychology,* 1959, *32,* 50–59.

HAMMER, M., & KAPLAN, A. M. *The practice of psychotherapy with children.* Homewood, Ill.: Dorsey, 1967.

HAYMAN, M. *Alcoholism: Mechanism and management.* Springfield, Ill.: Charles C Thomas, 1966.

HEATH, R. G. A biochemical hypothesis on the etiology of schizophrenia. In D. D. Jackson (Ed.), *The etiology of schizophrenia.* New York: Basic Books, 1960.

HEATH, R. G. Schizophrenia: Biochemical and physiologic aberrations. *International Journal of Neuropsychiatry,* 1966, *2,* 597–610.

HEATH, R. G. Catatonia induced in monkeys by antibrain antibody. *American Journal of Psychiatry,* 1967, *123,* 1499-1504.

HEATH, R. H. (Ed.) *Serological fractions in schizophrenia.* New York: Hoeber Medical Division, Harper & Row, 1963.

HEBB, D. O. *A textbook of psychology* (2nd ed.) Philadelphia: W. B. Saunders, 1966.

HEIDEGGER, M. *Being and time.* New York: Harper & Row, 1962.

HEINEMAN, C. E. A forced choice form of the Taylor Anxiety Scale. *Journal of Consulting Psychology,* 1953, *17,* 447–454.

HETHERINGTON, E., & KLINGER, E. Psychopathy and punishment. *Journal of Abnormal and Social Psychology*, 1964, *69*, 113–115.

HIMWICH, H. E. *Alcoholism: Basic aspects and treatment.* Washington, D.C.: American Association for the Advancement of Science, 1957.

HINSIE, L. E., & SHATSKY, J. *Psychiatric dictionary: With encyclopedic treatment of modern terms* (2nd ed.) New York: Oxford University Press, 1953.

HIRSCH, J. *Opportunities in the treatment of alcoholics.* Springfield, Ill.: Charles C Thomas, 1967.

HOCH, P. H., & POLATIN, P. Pseudoneurotic forms of schizophrenia. *Psychiatric Quarterly*, 1949, *23*, 248–276.

HODERN, A., BURT, C. G., & HOLT, N. F. *Depressive states: A pharmatherapeutic study.* Springfield, Ill.: Charles C Thomas, 1965.

HOFFER, A. *Niacin therapy in psychiatry.* Springfield, Ill.: Charles C Thomas, 1962.

HOFFER, A., & OSMOND, H. *The chemical basis of clinical psychiatry.* Springfield, Ill.: Charles C Thomas, 1960.

HOFFER, A., & OSMOND, H. *How to live with schizophrenia.* New Hyde Park, N.Y.: University Books, 1966.

HOFFER, A., OSMOND, H., CALLBECK, M. J., & KAHAN, I. Treatment of schizophrenia with nicotinic acid and nicotinamide. *Journal of Clinical and Experimental Psychopathology & Quarterly Review of Psychiatry and Neurology*, 1957, *18*, 131–158.

HOFFER, A., OSMOND, H., & SMYTHIES, J. Schizophrenia: A new approach, II. Result of a year's research. *Journal of Mental Science*, 1954, *100*, 29–45.

HOLLINGSHEAD, A. B., & REDLICH, F. C. *Social class and mental illness: A community study.* New York: Wiley, 1958.

HOLLINGSHEAD, A. B., & ROGLER, L. H. Lower socioeconomic status and mental illness. *Sociology and Social Research*, 1962, *46*, 387–396.

HORNEY, K. *The neurotic personality of our time.* New York: Norton, 1937.

HORNEY, K. *Self-analysis.* New York: Norton, 1942.

HORNEY, K. *Our inner conflicts.* New York: Holt, 1945.

HORNEY, K. *Neurosis and human growth.* New York: Norton, 1950.

HORSLEY, J. S. *Narco-analysis.* New York: Oxford University Press, 1943.

HOSKINS, R. G. *The biology of schizophrenia.* New York: Norton, 1946.

HOSKINS, R. G. Hormone therapy. *Journal of Clinical Psychopathology & Quarterly Review of Psychiatry and Neurology*, 1954, *14*, 363–372.

HOWELLS, J. G. The nuclear family as the functional unit in psychiatry. *Journal of Mental Science*, 1962, *108*, 675–684.

HOWELLS, J. G. *Family psychiatry.* Edinburgh: Oliver & Boyd, 1963.

HOWELLS, J. G. (Ed.) *Modern perspectives in world psychiatry.* Edinburgh: Oliver & Boyd, 1968. (a)

HOWELLS, J. G. *Theory and practice of family psychiatry.* Edinburgh: Oliver & Boyd, 1968. (b)

HOWELLS, J. G. Family psychiatry. In J. G. Howells (Ed.), *Modern perspectives in world psychiatry.* Edinburgh: Oliver & Boyd, 1968. (c)

HULL, C. L. *Principles of behavior.* New York: Appleton-Century-Crofts, 1943.

HUSSERL, E. *Ideas: General introduction to pure phenomenology.* New York: Macmillan, 1931.

JACKSON, D. D. Aspects of conjoint family therapy. In G. H. Zuk and I. Boszormenyi-Nagy (Eds.), *Family therapy and disturbed families.* Palo Alto, Calif.: Science and Behavior Books, 1967.

JACKSON, D. D., & WEAKLAND, J. H. Conjoint family therapy: Some considerations on theory, technique, and results. *Psychiatry,* 1961, *24,* 30–45.

JACOBS, P. A., BAIKIE, A. G., COURT BROWN, W. M., & STRONG, J. A. The somatic chromosomes in mongolism. *Lancet,* 1959, *1,* 710.

JACOBSON, E. *Progressive relaxation.* Chicago: University of Chicago Press, 1938.

JACOBSON, E. Contributions to the metapsychology of cyclothymic depression. In P. Greenacre (Ed.), *Affective disorders.* New York: International Universities, 1953.

JACOBSON, E. Transference problems in the psychoanalytic treatment of severely depressive patients. *Journal of the American Psychoanalytic Association,* 1954, *2,* 595–606.

JAHODA, M. *Current concepts of positive mental health.* New York: Basic Books, 1958.

JASPERS, K. *General psychopathology.* Chicago: University of Chicago Press, 1963.

JELLINEK, E. M. Phases of alcohol addiction. *Quarterly Journal of Studies on Alcohol,* 1952, *13,* 673–674.

JELLINEK, E. M. *The disease concept of alcoholism.* New Haven: Hillhouse Press, 1960.

JENNINGS, A. N. Depressive and deprivation reactions in early childhood. In D. Maddison and G. M. Duncan (Eds.), *Aspects of depressive illness.* Edinburgh: Livingstone, 1965.

JONES, M. *Social psychiatry: A study of therapeutic communities.* London: Tavistock, 1952.

JONES, M. *The therapeutic community: A new treatment method in psychiatry.* New York: Basic Books, 1953.

JONES, M. The concept of a therapeutic community. *American Journal of Psychiatry*, 1956, *112*, 647–650.

JONES M. *Social psychiatry: In the community, in hospitals, and in prisons.* Springfield, Ill.: Charles C Thomas, 1962.

JONES, M. Group work in mental hospitals. *British Journal of Psychiatry*, 1966, *112*, 1007–1011.

JUNG, C. G. *Psychological types.* New York: Harcourt, Brace, 1924.

JUNG, C. G. *Contributions to analytical psychology.* New York: Harcourt, Brace, 1928.

JUNG, C. G. *Two essays on analytical psychology.* New York: Bollingen, 1953.

JUNG, C. G. The practice of psychotherapy. In C. G. Jung, *The collected works of C. G. Jung,* 16, New York: Bollingen, 1966.

JUNG, C. G. Analytic psychotherapy. In W. S. Sahakian (Ed.), *Psychotherapy and counseling: Studies in technique.* Chicago: Rand McNally, 1969.

KACZANOWSKI, G. K. Logotherapy—A new psychotherapeutic tool. *Psychosomatics*, 1967, 8, 158–161.

KALLMANN, F. J. *The genetics of schizophrenia.* New York: J. J. Augustin, 1938.

KALLMANN, F. J. The genetic theory of schizophrenia—An analysis of 691 twin index families. *American Journal of Psychiatry*, 1946, *103*, 309–322.

KALLMANN, F. J. Comparative twin study on the genetic aspects of male homosexuality. *Journal of Nervous and Mental Disease*, 1952, *115*, 283–298. (a)

KALLMANN, F. J. Twin and sibship study of overt male homosexuality. *American Journal of Human Genetics*, 1952, *4*, 136–146. (b)

KALLMANN, F. J. *Heredity in mental health and disorder.* New York: Norton, 1953.

KALLMANN, F. J. The genetics of mental illness. In S. Arieti (Ed.), *American handbook of psychiatry.* New York: Basic Books, 1959.

KALLMANN, F. J. Genetic factors in the etiology of mental disorders. *American Journal of Orthopsychiatry*, 1961, *31*, 445–451.

KANNER, L. Early infantile autism. *Journal of Pediatrics*, 1944, *25*, 211–217.

KANTOR, R. E., & HERRON, W. G. *Reactive and process schizophrenia.* Palo Alto, Calif.: Science and Behavior Books, 1966.

KANTOR, R. E., WALLNER, J. M., & WINDER, C. L. Process and reactive schizophrenia. *Journal of Consulting Psychology*, 1953, *17*, 157–162.

KARPMAN, B. *The hangover: A critical study in the psychodynamics of alcoholism.* Springfield, Ill.: Charles C Thomas, 1957.

KATZ, L. N. Newer concepts in relation to hypertension. *California Medicine,* 1962, *97,* 201–205

KEISER, L. *The traumatic neurosis.* Philadelphia: Lippincott, 1968.

KELLER, M. Definition of alcoholism. *Quarterly Journal of Alcoholism,* 1960, *21,* 125–134.

KELLY, G. A. *The psychology of personal constructs.* New York: Norton, 1955. 2 vols.

KELLY, G. A. *Selected Papers of . . . .* New York: Wiley, 1969.

KENDELL, R. E. *The classification of depressive illnesses.* London: Oxford University Press, 1968.

KETY, S. S. Biochemical theories of schizophrenia. *Science,* 1959, *129,* 1528–1532, 1590–1596.

KETY, S. S. Recent biochemical theories of schizophrenia. In D. D. Jackson (Ed.), *The etiology of schizophrenia.* New York: Basic Books, 1960.

KETY, S. S. Biochemical theories of schizophrenia. *International Journal of Psychiatry,* 1965. *1,* 409–466.

KETY, S. S. Biochemical hypotheses and studies. In L. Bellak and L. Loeb (Eds.), *The schizophrenic syndrome.* New York: Grune & Stratton, 1969.

KIERKEGAARD, S. *Concluding unscientific postscript.* Princeton, N. J.: Princeton University Press, 1941. (a)

KIERKEGAARD, S. *Fear and trembling,* Princeton, N.J.: Princeton University Press, 1941. (b)

KIERKEGAARD. S. *Sickness unto death.* Princeton, N.J.: Princeton University Press, 1941. (c)

KIERKEGAARD, S. *The concept of dread.* Princeton, N. J.: Princeton University Press, 1957.

KILOH, L. G., BALL, J. R. B., & GARSIDE, R. F. Prognostic factors in treatment of depressive states with imipramine. *British Medical Journal,* 1962, *1,* 1225–1227.

KILOH L. G., & GARSIDE, R. F. The independence of neurotic depression and endogenous depression. *British Journal of Psychiatry,* 1963, *109,* 451–463.

KING, G. F. Differential autonomic responsiveness in the process-reactive classification of schizophrenia. *Journal of Abnormal and Social Psychology,* 1958, *56,* 160–164.

KINGHAM, R. J. Alcoholism and reinforcement theory of learning. *Quarterly Journal of Studies on Alcohol,* 1958, *19,* 320–330.

KINSEY, A. C., POMEROY, W. B., & MARTIN, C. E. *Sexual behavior in the human male.* Philadelphia: Saunders, 1948.

KINSEY, A. C., POMEROY, W. B., MARTIN, C. E., & GEBHARD, P. *Sexual behavior in the human female.* Philadelphia: Saunders, 1953.

KIMBLE, G. A., & GARMEZY, N. *Principles of general psychology.* New York: Ronald Press, 1968.

KLEIN, M. A contribution to the psychogenesis of manic-depressive states. *Contributions to psycho-analysis, 1921–1945.* London: Hogarth (1934), 1948. (a)

KLEIN, M. *Contributions to psycho-analysis, 1921–1945.* London: Hogarth, 1948. (b)

KLEIN, M. *The psychoanalysis of children.* New York: Grove Press, 1960.

KNUTSON, A. L. New perspectives regarding positive mental health. *American Psychologist,* 1963, *18,* 300–306.

KOLB, L. C. *Noyes' modern clinical psychiatry.* Philadelphia: Saunders, 1968.

KRAFT, A. M. The therapeutic community. In S. Arieti (Ed.), *American handbook of psychiatry.* New York: Basic Books, 1966.

KRAINES, S. H. *Mental depressions and their treatment.* New York: Macmillan, 1957. (a)

KRAINES, S. H. The physiological basis of the manic-depressive illness: A theory. *American Journal of Psychiatry,* 1957, *114,* 206–211. (b)

KRAINES, S. H. Manic-depressive syndrome: A diencephalic disease. Paper presented at the Annual Meeting of the American Psychiatric Association. New York, May 6, 1965.

KUBIE, L. S. The fundamental nature of the distinction between normality and neurosis. *Psychoanalytic Quarterly,* 1954, *23,* 167–204.

LADEE, G. A. *Hypochondriacal syndromes.* Amsterdam: Elsevier, 1966.

LAING, R. D. *The divided self: An existential study in sanity and madness.* Baltimore: Penguin Books, 1965.

LAING, R. D. *The politics of experience.* New York: Pantheon, 1967.

LAZARUS, R. S. Is there a mechanism of perceptual defense? A reply to Postman, Bronson and Gropper. *Journal of Abnormal and Social Psychology,* 1954, *49,* 396–398.

LEEDY, J. J. (Ed.) *Poetry therapy.* Philadelphia: Lippincott, 1969.

LEHMANN, H. E. Depression: Categories, mechanisms and phenomena. In J. O. Cole and J. R. Wittenborn (Eds.), *Pharmacotherapy of depression.* Springfield, Ill.: Charles C Thomas, 1966.

LEIGHTON, A. H., CLAUSEN, J. A., & WILSON, R. N. *Explorations in social psychiatry.* New York: Basic Books, 1957.

LEJEUNE, J., GAUTIER, M., & TURPIN, R. Les chromosomes humains en culture de tissus. *Comptes Rendus Hebomadaires des Scéances de l'Académie des Sciences,* 1959, *248,* 602–606. (a)

LEJEUNE, J., TURPIN, R., & GAUTIER, M. Le mongolisme: Premier exemple d'aberation autosomique humaine. *Annales de Génétique,* 1959, *1,* 41–49. (b)

LEMERT, E. *Social pathology: A systematic approach to the theory of sociopathic behavior.* New York: McGraw-Hill, 1951.

LEVY, R. I. The psychodynamic functions of alcohol. *Quarterly Journal of Studies on Alcohol,* 1958, *19,* 649–659.

LIDZ, R. W., & LIDZ, T. The family environment of schizophrenic patients. *American Journal of Psychiatry,* 1949, *106,* 332–245.

LIDZ, T. Psychological aspects of diabetes mellitus. In E. D. Wittkower and R. A. Cleghorn (Eds.), *Recent developments in psychosomatic medicine.* Philadelphia: Lippincott, 1954. (a)

LIDZ, T. The thyroid. In E. D. Wittkower and R. A. Cleghorn (Eds.), *Recent developments in psychosomatic medicine.* Philadelphia: Lippincott, 1954. (b)

LIDZ, T. *The person: His development throughout the life cycle.* New York: Basic Books, 1968.

LIDZ, T., CORNELISON, A. R., TERRY, D., & FLECK, S. The intrafamilial environment of the schizophrenic patient: II. Marital schism and marital skew. *American Journal of Psychiatry,* 1957, *114,* 241–248.

LIDZ, T., CORNELISON, A. R., TERRY, D., & FLECK, S. The intrafamilial environment of the schizophrenic patient: VI. The transmission of irrationality. *Archives of Neurology and Psychiatry,* 1958, 79, 305–316.

LIDZ, T., FLECK, S., ALANEN, Y. O., & CORNELISON, A. Schizophrenic patients and their siblings. *Psychiatry,* 1963, *26,* 1–18.

LIDZ, T. *et al. Schizophrenia and the family.* New York: International Universities, 1965.

LINDESMITH, A. R. Problems in the social psychology of addiction. In D. M. Wilner and G. G. Kassebaum (Eds.), *Narcotics.* New York: Blakiston, 1965.

LINDESMITH, A. R. *Addiction and opiates* (2nd ed.) Chicago: Aldine, 1968.

LONDON, P. The major psychological disorders. In P. London and D. Rosenhan (Eds.), *Foundations of abnormal psychology.* New York: Holt, Rinehart & Winston, 1968.

LONDON, P., & ROSENHAN, D. *Foundations of abnormal psychology.* New York: Holt, Rinehart & Winston, 1968.

LORR, M. Measurement of the major psychotic syndromes. *Annals of the New York Academy of Science,* 1962, *93,* 851–856.

LORR, M. (Ed.) *Explorations in typing psychotics.* Oxford: Pergamon Press, 1966.

LORR, M. Syndromes of deviation. In E. F. Borgatta and W. W. Lambert (Eds.), *Handbook of personality theory and research.* Chicago: Rand McNally, 1968. (a)

LORR, M. A typology for functional psychotics. In M. M. Katz, J. O. Cole and W. E. Barton (Eds.), *The role and methodology of classification in psychiatry and psychopathology.* Chevy Chase, Md.: National Institute of Mental Health, 1968. (b)

LORR, M., KLETT, C. J., & McNAIR, D. M. *Syndromes of psychosis.* New York: Macmillan, 1963.

LORR, M., McNAIR, D. M., KLETT, C. J., & LASKY, J. J. Evidence of ten psychotic syndromes. *Journal of Consulting Psychology,* 1962, *26*, 185–189.

LOURIE, R. S. Suicide and attempted suicide in children and adolescents. In L. Yochelson (Ed.), *Symposium on suicide.* Washington, D.C.: George Washington University School of Medicine, 1965.

LU, YI-CHUANG. Mother-child role relations in schizophrenia: A comparison of schizophrenic patients with nonschizophrenic siblings. *Psychiatry,* 1961, *24*, 133–142.

LU, YI-CHUANG. Contradictory parental expectations in schizophrenia. *American Medical Association Archives of General Psychiatry,* 1962, *6*, 219–234.

LUCIA, S. P. *Alcohol and civilization.* New York: McGraw-Hill, 1963.

LUDWIG, A. O. Rheumatoid arthritis. In E. D. Wittkower and R. A. Cleghorn (Eds.), *Recent developments in psychosomatic medicine.* Philadelphia: Lippincott, 1954.

LYKKEN, D. T. A study of anxiety in the sociopathic personality. *Journal of Abnormal and Social Psychology,* 1957, *55*, 6–10.

MACLEOD, A. W., WITTKOWER, E. D., & MARGOLIN, S. G. Basic concepts of psychosomatic medicine. In E. D. Wittkower and R. A. Cleghorn (Eds.), *Recent developments in psychosomatic medicine.* Philadelphia: Lippincott, 1954.

McCORD, W., & McCORD, J. *The psychopath: An essay on the criminal mind* (Rev. ed.) Princeton, N.J.: Van Nostrand, 1964.

McISAAC, W. M. A biochemical concept of mental disease. *Postgraduate Medicine,* 1961, *20*, 111–118.

McNAIR, D. M., LORR, M., & HEMINGWAY, P. Further evidence for syndrome-based psychotic types. *Archives of General Psychiatry,* 1964, *11*, 368–376.

MADDI, S. R. The existential neurosis. *Journal of Abnormal and Social Psychology,* 1967, *72*, 311–325.

MADDISON, D., & DUNCAN, G. M. *Aspects of depressive illness.* Edinburgh: Livingstone, 1965.

MAHER, B. A. Intelligence and brain damage. In N. R. Ellis (Ed.), *Handbook of mental deficiency.* New York: McGraw-Hill, 1963.

MAHER, B. A. *Principles of psychopathology: An experimental approach.* New York: McGraw-Hill, 1966.

MAICKEL, R. P. *Biochemical factors in alcoholism.* Oxford: Pergamon Press, 1967.

MAHL, G. F. Effect of chronic fear on the gastric secretion of HCl in dogs. *Psychosomatic Medicine,* 1949, *11,* 30–44.

MAHL, G. F. Anxiety, HCl secretion, and peptic ulcer. *Psychosomatic Medicine,* 1950, *12,* 158–169.

MAHL, G. F. Relationship between acute and chronic fear and the gastric acidity and blood sugar levels in *Macaca mulatta* monkeys. *Psychosomatic Medicine,* 1952, *14,* 182–210.

MALIS, G. Y. *Research on the etiology of schizophrenia.* New York: Consultants Bureau, 1961.

MALONE, T. P., WHITAKER, C. A., WARKENTIN, J., & FELDER, R. E. Rational and nonrational psychotherapy. *American Journal of Psychotherapy,* 1961, *15,* 212–220.

MALZBERG, B. *The alcoholic psychoses.* New Haven: Yale Center of Alcohol Studies, 1960.

MARGOLIN, S. G. The behavior of the stomach during psychoanalysis. *Psychoanalytic Quarterly,* 1951, *20,* 349–373.

MARGOLIN, S. G. Genetic and dynamic psychophysiological determinants of pathophysiological processes. In F. Deutsch (Ed.), *The psychosomatic concept in psychoanalysis.* New York: International Universities, 1953.

MARGOLIN, S. G. Psychotherapeutic principles in psychosomatic practice. In E. D. Wittkower and R. A. Cleghorn (Eds.), *Recent developments in psychosomatic medicine.* Philadelphia: Lippincott, 1954.

MASLOW, A. H. *Motivation and personality,* New York: Harper, 1954.

MASLOW, A. H. Neurosis as a failure of personal growth. *Humanitas,* 1967, *3,* 153–169.

MASLOW, A. H. *Toward a psychology of being* (3rd ed.) Princeton, N.J.: Van Nostrand, 1968.

MASLOW, A. H., & MITTELMANN, B. *Principles of abnormal psychology: The dynamics of psychic illness* (Rev. ed.) New York: Harper, 1951.

MASSERMAN, J. H., & YUM, K. S. An analysis of the influence of alcohol on experimental neurosis in cats. *Psychosomatic Medicine,* 1946, *8,* 36–52.

MASTERS, W. H., & JOHNSON, V. E. *Human sexual response.* Boston: Little, Brown, 1966.

MATHIS, J. L., PIERCE, C. M., & PISHKIN, V. *Basic psychiatry: A primer of concepts and terminology.* New York: Appleton-Century-Crofts, 1968.

MAY, R. Contributions of existential psychotherapy. In R. May, E. Angel and H. E. Ellenberger (Eds.), *Existence: A new dimension in psychiatry and psychology.* New York: Basic Books, 1958.

MAY, R. The existential approach. In S. Arieti (Ed.), *American handbook of psychiatry*. New York: Basic Books, 1959.

MAY, R. (Ed.) *Existential psychology* (2nd ed.) New York: Random House, 1969.

MAY, R. *Psychology and the human dilemma*. Princeton, N.J.: Van Nostrand, 1967.

MAY, R., ANGEL, E., & ELLENBERGER, H. F. (Eds.) *Existence: A new dimension in psychiatry and psychology*. New York: Basic Books, 1958.

MEAD, M. The changing world of living. *Diseases of the Nervous System*, 1967, *28* (suppl.) 5–11.

MEDNICK, S. A. A learning theory approach to research in schizophrenia. *Psychological Bulletin*, 1958, *55*, 316–327.

MEDNICK, S. A. Learning theory and schizophrenia: A reply to a comment. *Psychological Bulletin*, 1959, *56*, 315–316.

MEDUNA, L. J. New methods of medical treatment of schizophrenia. *Archives of Neurology and Psychiatry*, 1936, *35*, 361–363.

MEDUNA, L. J. Alteration of neurotic pattern by use of CO_2 inhalations. *Journal of Nervous and Mental Disease*, 1948, *108*, 373–379.

MEDUNA, L. J. *Oneirophrenia: The confusional state*. Urbana, Ill.: University of Illinois Press, 1950.

MEDUNA, L. J. The convulsive treatment: A reappraisal. *Journal of Clinical and Experimental Psychopathology & Quarterly Review of Psychiatry and Neurology*, 1954, *15*, 219–233. (a)

MEDUNA, L. J. The carbon dioxide treatment: A review. *Journal of Clinical and Experimental Psychopathology & Quarterly Review of Psychiatry and Neurology*, 1954, *15*, 235–249. (b)

MEDUNA, L. J. *Carbon dioxide therapy: A neurophysiological treatment of nervous disorders*. Springfield, Ill.: Charles C Thomas, 1958.

MEDUNA, L. J. Metrazol convulsive shock therapy. In W. S. Sahakian (Ed.), *History of psychology: A source book in systematic psychology*. Itasca, Ill.: F. E. Peacock Publishers, Inc., 1968.

MENNINGER, K. Toward a unitary concept of mental illness. In B. H. Hall (Ed.), *A psychiatrist's world*. New York: Viking, 1959.

MENNINGER, K. Concerning the advocacy of a unitary concept of mental illness. In L. Appleby, J. Sher, and J. Cummings (Eds.), *Chronic schizophrenia*. Glencoe, Ill.: Free Press, 1960.

MENNINGER, K. *The vital balance*. New York: Viking, 1963.

MENNINGER, K., ELLENBERGER, H., PRUYSER, P., & MAYMAN, M. The unitary concept of mental illness. *Bulletin of the Menninger Clinic*, 1958, *22*, 4–12.

MEYER, A. *The commonsense psychiatry of* . . . . New York: McGraw-Hill, 1948.

MEYER, A. *Collected papers of . . . .* (Eunice E. Winters, Ed.) Baltimore: Johns Hopkins, 1951.

MILLER, N. E. Liberalization of the basic S-R concepts: Extensions to conflict behavior, motivation and social learning. In S. Koch (Ed.), *Psychology: A study of a science* (Vol. 2) New York: McGraw-Hill, 1959.

MILLER, N. E. Experiments relevant to learning theory and psychopathology. In *Proceedings of the XVIII International Congress of Psychology.* Moscow, 1966. In W. S. Sahakian (Ed.), *Psychopathology today.* Itasca, Ill.: F. E. Peacock Publishers, Inc., 1970.

MITSCHERLICH, M. The psychic state of patients suffering from parkinsonism. In A. Jones and H. Freyberger (Eds.), *Advances in psychosomatic medicine.* New York: Brunner, 1961.

MONIZ, E. How I succeeded in performing the prefrontal leukotomy. *Journal of Clinical Experimental Psychopathology,* 1954, *15,* 373–379.

MONIZ, E. Prefrontal leukotomy. In W. S. Sahakian (Ed.), *History of psychology: A source book in systematic psychology.* Itasca, Ill.: F. E. Peacock Publishers, Inc., 1968.

MORENO, J. L. Who shall survive? *Foundations of sociometry, group psychotherapy and sociodrama.* Beacon, N.Y.: Beacon House, 1953.

MORENO, J. L. *Psychodrama.* Beacon, N.Y.: Beacon House, Vol. I, 1946, II, 1959, III, 1969.

MORENO, J. L. (Ed.) *The international handbook of group psychotherapy.* New York: Philosophical Library, 1966. (a)

MORENO, J. L. Therapeutic aspects of psychodrama. *Psychiatric Opinion,* 1966, 3, 36–42. (b)

MOWRER, O. H. On the dual nature of learning—A reinterpretation of "conditioning" and "problem-solving." *Harvard Educational Review,* 1947, *17,* 102–148.

MOWRER, O. H. Learning theory and the neurotic paradox. *American Journal of Orthopsychiatry,* 1948, *18,* 571–610.

MOWRER, O. H. *Learning theory and personality dynamics.* New York: Ronald Press, 1950.

MOWRER, O. H. Symposium, 1952, the therapeutic process. III. Learning theory and the neurotic fallacy. *American Journal of Orthopsychiatry,* 1952, *22,* 679–689.

MOWRER, O. H. Neurosis, psychotherapy, and two-factor learning theory. In O. H. Mowrer (Ed.), *Psychotherapy: Theory and research.* New York: Ronald Press, 1953.

MOWRER, O. H. "Sin," the lesser of two evils. *American Psychology,* 1960, *15,* 301–304.

MOWRER, O. H. *The crisis in psychiatry and religion.* Princeton, N.J.: Van Nostrand, 1961.

MOWRER, O. H. *The new group therapy.* Princeton, N.J.: Van Nostrand, 1964.

MOWRER, O. H. The behavior therapies, with special reference to modeling and imitation. *American Journal of Psychotherapy,* 1966, *20,* 439–461.

MOWRER, O. H. (Ed.) *Morality and mental health.* Chicago: Rand McNally, 1967. (a)

MOWRER, O. H. Communication, conscience and the unconscious. *Journal of Communication Disorders,* 1967, *1,* 109–135. (b)

MULLAN, H., & ROSENBAUM, M. *Group psychotherapy: Theory and practice.* New York: Free Press, 1962.

MULLAN, H., & SANGUILIANO, I. *Alcoholism: Group psychotherapy and rehabilitation.* Springfield, Ill.: Charles C Thomas, 1966.

NATIONAL COUNCIL ON ALCOHOLISM, INC. *New York City Alcoholism Study.* New York, 1962.

NATIONAL INSTITUTE OF MENTAL HEALTH. *Patients in mental institutions. 1965. Part II. State and county mental hospitals.* Washington, D.C.: U.S. Department of Health, Education and Welfare, 1967.

NEUSTATTER, W. L. The medical aspects of homosexuality. In W. A. R. Thomson (Ed.), *Sex and its problems.* Edinburgh: Livingstone, 1968.

NEW YORK ACADEMY OF MEDICINE, COMMITTEE ON PUBLIC HEALTH. *Homosexuality.* New York: New York Academy of Medicine, 1964.

NINETEENTH WORLD HEALTH ORGANIZATION. *Manual of the international statistical classification of disease, injuries, and causes of death.* Geneva: World Health Organization, 1967.

NOYES, A. P., & KOLB, L. C. *Modern clinical psychiatry* (6th ed.) Philadelphia: Saunders, 1963.

OLLENDORFF, R. H. V. *The juvenile homosexual experience and its effect on adult sexuality.* New York: Julian Press, 1966.

OSMOND, H., & HOFFER, A. Schizophrenia: A new approach. *Journal of Mental Science,* 1959, *105,* 653–673.

OSMOND, H., & HOFFER, A. A comprehensive theory of schizophrenia. *International Journal of Neuropsychiatry,* 1966, *2,* 302–309.

OSMOND, H., & SMYTHIES, J. Schizophrenia: A new approach. *Journal of Mental Science,* 1952, *98,* 309–315.

OTIS, L. S. Dissociation and recovery of a response learned under the influence of chlorpromazine or saline. *Science,* 1964, *143,* 1347–1348.

OVERTON, D. A. State-dependent or "dissociated" learning produced with pentobarbital. *Journal of Comparative and Physiological Psychology.* 1964, *57,* 3–12.

PAFFENBARGER, R. S., & McCABE, L. J. The effect of obstetric prenatal events on risk of mental illness in women of childbearing age. *American Journal of Public Health*, 1966, 56, 400–407.

PARTANEN, J., BRUUN, K., MARKKANEN, T. *Inheritance of drinking behavior: A study on intelligence, personality, and use of alcohol of adult twins.* Vol. 14. Helsinki: Finnish Foundation of Alcohol Studies, 1966.

PAVLOV, I. P. *Conditioned reflexes.* London: Oxford University Press, 1927.

PAYNE, R. W. Cognitive abnormalities. In H. J. Eysenck (Ed.), *Handbook of abnormal psychology.* New York: Basic Books, 1961.

PAYNE, R. W. An object classification test as a measure of overinclusive thinking in schizophrenic patients. *British Journal of Social Clinical Psychology*, 1962, 1, 213–221.

PAYNE, R. W., CAIRD, W. K., & LAVERTY, S. G. Overinclusive thinking and delusions in schizophrenic patients. *Journal of Abnormal and Social Psychology*, 1964, 68, 562–566.

PAYNE, R. W., MATTUSSEK, P., & GEORGE, E. I. An experimental study of schizophrenic thought disorder. *Journal of Mental Sciences*, 1959, 105, 627–652.

PAYNE, R. W., & SLOANE, R. B. Can schizophrenia be defined? *Diseases of the Nervous System*, 1968, 29 (Suppl.), 113–117.

PENFIELD, W. Memory mechanisms. *Archives of Neurology and Psychiatry*, 1952, 67, 178–191.

PENFIELD, W. The interpretive cortex. *Science*, 1959, 129, 1719–1725.

PENFIELD, W., & MILNER, B. Memory deficit produced by bilateral lesions in the hippocampal zone. *A.M.A. Archives of Neurology and Psychiatry*, 1958, 79, 475–497.

PENFIELD, W., & ROBERTS, L. *Speech and brain-mechanisms.* Princeton, N.J.: Princeton University Press, 1959.

PENFIELD, W., & RASMUSSEN, T. *The cerebral cortex of man: A study of the localization of function.* New York: Macmillan, 1950.

PERLS, F. S., HEFFERLINE, R. E., & GOODMAN, P. *Gestalt therapy: Excitement and growth in the human personality.* New York: Dell, 1965.

PERLS, F. S. *Ego, hunger and aggression: A revision of Freud's theory and method.* San Francisco, Calif.: Orbit Graphic Arts, 1966. (a)

PERLS, F. S. Gestalt therapy and human potentialities. In H. A. Otto (Ed.), *Explorations in human potentialities.* Springfield, Ill.: Charles C Thomas, 1966.

PEPINSKY, H. B., & PEPINSKY, P. N. *Counseling: Theory and practice.* New York: Ronald Press, 1954.

PHILIPS, I. (Ed.) *Prevention and treatment of mental retardation.* New York: Basic Books, 1966.

PHILLIPS, E. L. *Psychotherapy: A modern theory and practice.* Englewood Cliffs, N. J.: Prentice-Hall, 1956.

PHILLIPS, E. L., & WIENER, D. N. *Short-term psychotherapy and structured behavior change.* New York: McGraw-Hill, 1966.

PHILLIPS, L. Case history data and prognosis in schizophrenia. *Journal of Nervous and Mental Disease,* 1953, *117,* 515–525.

PHILLIPS, L. A social view of psychopathology. In P. London and D. Rosenhan (Eds.), *Foundations of abnormal psychology.* New York: Holt, Rinehart & Winston, 1968.

PIAGET, J. *Judgment and reasoning in the child.* London: Routledge & Kegan Paul, 1928.

PIAGET, J. *The child's conception of the world.* London: Routledge & Kegan Paul, 1929.

PIAGET, J. *The child's conception of the physical causality.* London: Routledge & Kegan Paul, 1930.

POLLACK, M., KLEIN, D. F., WILLNER, A., BLUMBERG, A., & FINK, M. Imipramine-induced behavioral disorganization in schizophrenic patients: Physiologic and psychologic correlates. In J. Wortis (Ed.), *Recent advances in biological psychiatry.* Vol. 7. New York: Plenum, 1965.

POLLMER, E. *Alcoholic personalities,* New York: Expositional Press, 1965.

POPE, B., & SCOTT, W. H. *Psychological diagnosis in clinical practice.* New York: Oxford University Press, 1967.

RADO, S. The problem of melancholia. *International Journal of Psycho-Analysis,* 1928, *9,* 420–438.

RADO, S. Hedonic control, action-self and the depressive spell. In P. H. Hoch and J. Zubin (Eds.), *Depression.* New York: Grune & Stratton, 1954.

RADO, S. The automatic motivating system of depressive behavior. *Comprehensive Psychiatry,* 1961, *2,* 248–260.

RANK, O. *Will therapy and truth and reality.* New York: Knopf, 1945.

RANK, O. The possibilities of therapy. *Journal of the Otto Rank Association,* 1968, *3,* 26–39.

RANK, O. Will therapy. In W. S. Sahakian (Ed.), *Psychotherapy and counseling: Studies in technique.* Chicago: Rand McNally, 1969.

RAPOPORT, R. N. *Community as doctor: New perspectives on a therapeutic community.* London: Tavistock, 1960.

RAPOPORT, R. N. The therapeutic community. In D. L. Sills (Ed.), *Encyclopedia of the social sciences.* New York: Macmillan & Free Press, 1968.

REDLICH, F. C. The concept of health in psychiatry. In A. H. Leighton,

J. A. Clausen and R. N. Wilson (Eds.), *Explorations in social psychiatry.* New York: Basic Books, 1957.

REDLICH, F. C., & FREEDMAN, D. X. *The theory and practice of psychiatry.* New York: Basic Books, 1966.

REICH, W. *The function of the orgasm: Sex-economic problems of biological energy.* New York: Noonday, 1948.

REICH, W. *Character-analysis.* New York: Noonday, 1949.

ROGERS, C. R. *Counseling and psychotherapy: New concepts in practice.* Boston: Houghton Mifflin, 1942.

ROGERS, C. R. *Client-centered therapy: Its current practice, implications, and theory.* Boston: Houghton Mifflin, 1951.

ROGERS, C. R. Client-centered therapy. In S. Arieti (Ed.), *American handbook of psychiatry.* New York: Basic Books, 1959.

ROGERS, C. R. The therapeutic relationship: Recent theory and research. *Australian Journal of Psychology,* 1965, *17,* 95–108.

ROSEN, E., & GREGORY, I. *Abnormal psychology.* Philadelphia: Saunders, 1965.

ROSEN, J. *Direct analysis: Selected papers.* New York: Grune & Stratton, 1953.

ROSENFELD, H. A. *Psychotic states: A psycho-analytical approach.* New York: International Universities, 1965.

ROSENTHAL, D. (Ed.) *The Genain quadruplets: A case study and theoretical analysis of heredity and environment in schizophrenia.* New York: Basic Books, 1963.

ROTTER, J. B. *Social learning and clinical psychology.* New York: Prentice-Hall, 1954.

ROTTER, J. B. *Clinical psychology.* New York: Prentice-Hall, 1964.

RUESCH, J. The infantile personality—The core problem of psychosomatic medicine. *Psychosomatic Medicine,* 1948, *10,* 134–144.

RUESCH, J., & BATESON, G. *Communication, the social matrix of psychiatry.* New York: Norton, 1951.

RUESCH, J. General theory of communication in psychiatry. In S. Arieti (Ed.), *American handbook of psychiatry.* New York: Basic Books, 1959.

RUSSELL, B. *Principles of mathematics* (2nd ed.) London: George Allen & Unwin, 1937.

SAHAKIAN, W. S. (Ed.) *Psychology of personality: Readings in theory.* Chicago: Rand McNally, 1965.

SAHAKIAN, W. S. (Ed.) *History of psychology: A source book in systematic psychology.* Itasca, Ill.: F. E. Peacock Publishers, Inc., 1968.

SAHAKIAN, W. S. (Ed.) *Psychotherapy and counseling: Studies in technique.* Chicago: Rand McNally, 1969. (a)

SAHAKIAN, W. S. A social learning theory of obsessional neurosis. *Israel Annals of Psychiatry and Related Disciplines*, 1969, 7, 70–75. (b)

SAHAKIAN, W. S. Stoic philosophical psychotherapy. *Journal of Individual Psychology*, 1969, 25, 32–35. (c)

SAKEL, M. The pharmacological shock treatment of schizophrenia. New York: *Journal of Nervous and Mental Disease*, 1938.

SAKEL, M. The classical Sakel shock treatment: A reappraisal. *Journal of Clinical and Experimental Psychopathology & Review of Psychiatry and Neurology*, 1954, 15, 255–316.

SALTER, A. *Conditioned reflex therapy.* New York: Farrar, Straus, 1949.

SAMPSON, H., MESSINGER, S. L., & TOWNE, R. D. *Schizophrenic women: Studies in marital crisis.* New York: Atherton, 1964.

SANDERS, R., SMITH, R. S., & WEINMAN, B. S. *Chronic psychoses and recovery: An experiment in socio-environmental treatment.* San Francisco, Calif.: Jossey-Bass, 1967.

SARASON, S. B. Mental subnormality. In F. C. Redlich and D. X. Freedman, *The theory and practice of psychiatry.* New York: Basic Books, 1966.

SARASON, S. B., & DORIS, J. *Psychological problems in mental deficiency* (4th ed.) New York: Harper & Row, 1969.

SATIR, V. *Conjoint family therapy: A guide to theory and technique.* Palo Alto, Calif.: Science and Behavior Books, 1967.

SCHELER, M. *Der Formalismus in der Ethik und die materiale Wertethik.* Bern: Franke, 1966.

SCHILDKRAUT, J. J. The catecholamine hypothesis of affective disorders: A review of supporting evidence. *American Journal of Psychiatry*, 1965, 122, 509–522.

SCHMIDT, W., SUIART, R. G., & MOSS, M. K. *Social class and the treatment of alcoholism.* Toronto: University of Toronto Press, 1968.

SCHNEIDER, R. *Psychopathic personalities.* Springfield, Ill.: Charles C Thomas, 1958.

SCHOFIELD, M. *The sexual behaviour of young people.* London: Longmans, Green, 1965. (a)

SCHOFIELD, M. *Sociological aspects of homosexuality: A comparative study of three types of homosexuals.* London: Longmans, Green, 1965. (b)

SCHULTZ, J. H., & LUTHE, W. *Autogenic training.* New York: Grune & Stratton, 1959.

SCOTT, W. A. Research definitions of mental health and mental illness. *Psychological Bulletin*, 1958, 55, 29–45.

SCOTT, W. A. Conceptions of normality. In E. F. Borgatta and W. W. Lambert (Eds.), *Handbook of personality theory and research.* Chicago: Rand McNally, 1968.

SEARLES, H. F. Integration and differentiation in schizophrenia. *British Journal of Medical Psychology*, 1959, *32*, 261–281.

SEITZ, P. F. D. Psychological aspects of skin diseases. In E. D. Wittkower and R. A. Cleghorn (Eds.), *Recent developments in psychosomatic medicine*. Philadelphia: Lippincott, 1954.

SELYE, H. The general adaptation syndrome and the diseases of adaptation. *Journal of Allergy*, 1946, *17*, 231–247, 289–323, 358–398.

SELYE, H. Stress and disease. *Science*, 1955, *122*, 625–631.

SELYE, H. *The stress of life*. New York: McGraw-Hill, 1956. (a)

SELYE, H. Stress and psychiatry. *American Journal of Psychiatry*, 1956, *113*, 423–427. (b)

SCHAEFER, H. H., & MARTIN, P. L. *Behavioral therapy*. New York: McGraw-Hill, 1969.

SHAKOW, D. Segmental set: A theory of the formal psychological deficit in schizophrenia. *Archives of General Psychiatry*, 1962, *6*, 17–33.

SHAKOW, D. Psychological deficit in schizophrenia. *Behavioral Sciences*, 1963, *8*, 275–303.

SHELLY, J. A., & BASSIN, A. Daytop Lodge—A new treatment approach for drug addicts. *Correct Psychiatry*, 1965, *11*, 186–195.

SHOBEN, E. J. A learning-theory interpretation of psychotherapy. *Harvard Educational Review*, 1948, *18*, 129–145.

SHOBEN, E. J. Psychotherapy as a problem in learning theory. *Psychological Bulletin*, 1949, *46*, 366–392.

SHOBEN, J. S. Toward a concept of the normal personality. *American Psychologist*, 1957, *12*, 183–189.

SIEGMAN, A. W. The relationship between future time perspective, time estimation and impulse control in a group of young offenders and a control group. *Journal of Consulting Psychology*, 1961, *25*, 470–475.

SILVERMAN, C. *The epidemiology of depression*. Baltimore: Johns Hopkins Press, 1968.

SILVERMAN, H. L. *Psychiatry and psychology: Relationships, intra-relationships, and inter-relationships*. Springfield, Ill.: Charles C Thomas, 1963.

SILVERMAN, S. *Psychological aspects of physical symptoms*. New York: Appleton-Century-Crofts, 1968.

SIMMONS, O. G., & FREEMAN, H. E. Familial expectations and posthospital performance of mental patients. *Human Relations*, 1959, *12*, 233–242.

SLAVSON, S. R. *A textbook in analytic group psychotherapy*. New York: International Universities, 1964.

SLAVSON, S. R. *Reclaiming the delinquent by para-analytic group psychotherapy and the inversion technique*. New York: Free Press, 1965. (a)

SLAVSON, S. R. Para-analytic group psychotherapy: A treatment of choice for adolescents. *Psychotherapy and Psychosomatics*, 1965, *13*, 321–331. (b)

SMYTHIES, J. R. *Schizophrenia: Chemistry, metabolism and treatment.* Springfield, Ill.: Charles C Thomas, 1963.

SMYTHIES, J. R. *Biological psychiatry: A review of recent advances.* London: William Heinemann Medical Books, 1968.

SPENCE, K. W., & FARBER, I. E. Conditioning and extinction as a function of anxiety. *Journal of Experimental Psychology*, 1953, *45*, 116–119.

SPENCE, K. W., & TAYLOR, J. A. Anxiety and the strength of the UCS as determiners of the amount of eyelid conditioning. *Journal of Experimental Psychology*, 1951, *42*, 183–188.

SPENCE, K. W., & TAYLOR, J. A. The relation of conditioned response strength to anxiety in normal, neurotic and psychotic subjects. *Journal of Experimental Psychology*, 1953, *45*, 265–272.

STEKEL, W. *Technique of analytical psychotherapy.* New York: Liveright, 1950.

STEKEL, W. *Homosexuality.* New York: Liveright, 1948.

STERN, P. J. *The abnormal person and his world.* Princeton, N. J.: Van Nostrand, 1964.

STOCK, D., & THELEN, H. *Emotional dynamics and group culture.* New York: New York University Press, 1958.

STOKVIS, B. Results of psychotherapy in psychosomatic diseases. In J. Booij (Ed.), *Psychosomatics.* Amsterdam: Elsevier, 1957.

STORM, T., & SMART, R. G. Dissociation: A possible explanation of some features of alcoholism, and implication for its treatment. *Quarterly Journal of Studies on Alcohol*, 1965, *26*, 111–115.

STRAUSS, E. W. Norm and pathology of I-world relations. *Diseases of the Nervous System*, 1961, *22*, 57–68.

STRAUSS, E. W. *Phenomenological psychology.* New York: Basic Books, 1966.

SUGGS, R. C. *Marquesan sexual behavior.* New York: Harcourt, Brace & World, 1966.

SULLIVAN, H. S. Psychiatry: Introduction to the study of interpersonal relations. *Psychiatry*, 1938, *1*, 121–134.

SULLIVAN, H. S. *Conceptions of modern psychiatry.* New York: Norton, 1947. (a)

SULLIVAN, H. S. Therapeutic investigations in schizophrenia. *Psychiatry*, 1947, *10*, 121–125. (b)

SULLIVAN, H. S. Towards a psychiatry of peoples. *Psychiatry*, 1948, *11*, 105–116.

SULLIVAN, H. S. *The interpersonal theory of psychiatry.* New York: Norton, 1953.

SULLIVAN, H. S. *The psychiatric interview.* New York: Norton, 1954.

SULLIVAN, H. S. *Clinical studies in psychiatry.* New York: Norton, 1956.

SULLIVAN, H. S. *Schizophrenia as a human process.* New York: Norton, 1962.

SULLIVAN, H. S. *The fusion of psychiatry and social science.* New York: Norton, 1964.

SUTHERLAND, E. H., & CRESSEY, D. R. *Principles of criminology* (6th ed.) Philadelphia: Lippincott, 1960.

SUZUKI, D. T. *Introduction to Zen Buddhism.* London: Rider, 1949.

SUZUKI, D. T., FROMM, E., & DeMARTINO, R. *Zen Buddhism and psychoanalysis.* New York: Harper, 1960.

SZASZ, T. S. The problem of psychiatric nosology. *American Journal of Psychiatry,* 1957, *114,* 405–413.

SZASZ, T. S. The myth of mental illness. *American Psychologist,* 1960, *15,* 113–118.

SZASZ, T. S. *The myth of mental illness: Foundations of a theory of personal conduct.* New York: Hoebner-Harper, 1961. (a)

SZASZ, T. S. The uses of naming and the origin of the myth of mental illness. *American Psychologist,* 1961, *61,* 59–65. (b)

SZASZ, T. S. *Law, liberty, and psychiatry: An inquiry into the social uses of mental health practices.* New York: Macmillan, 1963.

TÄHKÄ, V. *The alcoholic personality: A clinical study.* Helsinki: Finnish Foundation for Alcohol Studies, 1966.

TAYLOR, J. A. The relationship of anxiety to the conditioned eyelid response. *Journal of Experimental Psychology,* 1951, *41,* 81–92.

TAYLOR, J. A. A personality scale of manifest anxiety. *Journal of Abnormal and Social Psychology,* 1953, *48,* 285–290.

THOMPSON, G. N. The psychiatry of alcoholism. In G. N. Thompson (Ed), *Alcoholism.* Springfield, Ill.: Charles C Thomas, 1956.

THOMSON, W. A. R. (Ed.), *Sex and its problems.* Edinburgh: Livingstone, 1968.

THORNDIKE, E. L. *Animal intelligence.* New York: Macmillan, 1911.

THORNE, F. C. An existential theory of anxiety. *Journal of Clinical Psychology,* 1963, *19,* 35–43.

THORNE, F. C. An analysis of Szasz "myth of mental illness." *American Journal of Psychiatry,* 1966, *123,* 652–656.

TILLICH, P. Existentialism and psychotherapy. *Review of Existential Psychology and Psychiatry,* 1961, *1.*

TRUAX, C. B., & CARKHUFF, R. R. *Toward effective counseling and psychotherapy: Training and practice.* Chicago: Aldine, 1967.

UHR, L., & MILLER, J. G. *Drugs and behavior.* New York: Wiley, 1960.

ULLMANN, L. P., & KRASNER, L. *A psychological approach to abnormal behavior.* Englewood Cliffs, N.J.: Prentice-Hall, 1969.

U.S. DEPARTMENT OF HEALTH, EDUCATION, AND WELFARE. *Alcoholism.* Washington, D.C.: U.S. Government Printing Office, 1966.

VON DOMARUS, E. The specific laws of logic in schizophrenia. In J. S. Kasanin (Ed.), *Language and thought in schizophrenia.* Berkeley: University of California Press, 1944.

WAGNER-JAUREGG, J. R. Malarial treatment of general paresis. In W. S. Sahakian (Ed.), *History of psychology: A source book in systematic psychology.* Itasca, Ill.: F. E. Peacock Publishers, Inc., 1968.

WALLERSTEIN, R. S. *et al., Hospital treatment of alcoholism: A comparative, experimental study.* New York: Basic Books, 1957.

WATTS, A. W. *Psychotherapy east and west.* New York: Pantheon, 1961.

WATTS, C. A. H. *Depressive disorders in the community.* Bristol: John Wright, 1966.

WEAKLAND, J. H. The "double-bind" hypothesis of schizophrenia and three-party interaction. In D. D. Jackson (Ed.), *The etiology of schizophrenia.* New York: Basic Books, 1960.

WEINER, I. B. *Psychodiagnosis in schizophrenia.* New York: Wiley, 1966.

WEISSKOPF-JOELSON, E. Some comments on a Viennese school of psychiatry. *Journal of Abnormal and Social Psychology,* 1955, *51,* 701–703.

WELSH, G. S. An anxiety index and an internalization ratio for the MMPI. *Journal of Consulting Psychologists,* 1952, *16,* 65–72.

WESTWOOD, G. *A minority: A report on the life of the male homosexual in Great Britain.* London: Longmans, 1960.

WHITAKER, C. A., & MALONE, T. P. *The roots of psychotherapy.* New York: Blakiston, 1953.

WHITAKER, C. A., MALONE, T. P., & WARKENTIN, J. Multiple therapy and psychotherapy. In F. Fromm-Reichmann and J. L. Moreno (Eds.), *Progress in psychotherapy.* New York: Grune & Stratton, 1956.

WHITAKER, C. A., STOCK, D., & LIEBERMAN, M. A. *Psychotherapy through the group process.* Englewood Cliffs, N.J.: Prentice-Hall, 1964.

WHITE, R. W. *The abnormal personality* (3rd ed.) New York: Ronald Press, 1964.

WILLIAMS, R. J. *Alcoholism: The nutritional approach.* Austin, Tex.: University of Texas Press, 1959.

WISHNER, J. Neurosis and tension: An exploratory study of the relationship between physiological and Rorschach measures. *Journal of Abnormal and Social Psychology,* 1953, *48,* 253–260.

WISHNER, J. The concept of efficiency in psychology and psychopathology. *Psychological Review,* 1955, *62,* 69–80.

WITTENBORN, J. R., DEMPSTER, A., MAURER, H., & PLANTE, M. Pretreatment individual difference as potential predictors of response to pharmacotherapy. *Journal of Nervous Disorders*, 1964, *139*, 186–194.

WITTKOWER, E. D., & CLEGHORN, R. A. (Eds.), *Recent developments in psychosomatic medicine*. Philadelphia: Lippincott, 1954.

WOLBERG, L. R. *Hypnoanalysis* (2nd ed.) New York: Grune & Stratton, 1964.

WOLBERG, L. R. *Medical hypnosis* (2nd ed.) New York: Grune & Stratton, 1966.

WOLFF, H. G. Protective reaction patterns and disease. *Annals of Internal Medicine*, 1947, *27*, 944–969.

WOLFF, H. G. Life situations, emotions and bodily disease. In M. L. Reymert (Ed.), *Feelings and emotions*. New York: McGraw-Hill, 1950. (a)

WOLFF, H. G. Life stress and bodily disease—A formulation. *Research Publications of the Association of Nervous and Mental Disease*, 1950, *29*, 1059–1094. (b)

WOLFF, H. G. A concept of disease in man. *Psychosomatic Medicine*, 1962, *24*, 25–30.

WOLMAN, B. B. (Ed.) *Handbook of clinical psychology*. New York: McGraw-Hill, 1965.

WOLMAN, B. B. *Vectoriasis praecox or the group of schizophrenias*. Springfield, Ill.: Charles C Thomas, 1966.

WOLPE, J. *Psychotherapy by reciprocal inhibition*. Stanford, Calif.: Stanford University Press, 1958.

WOLPE, J. *The practice of behavior therapy*. New York: Pergamon, 1969.

WOLPE, J. Conditioning: The basis of modern psychotherapy. In L. D. Eron and R. Callahan (Eds.), *The relation of theory to practice in psychotherapy*. Chicago: Aldine, 1969.

WOLPE, J., & LAZARUS, A. A. *Behavior therapy techniques: A guide to the treatment of neuroses*. New York: Pergamon, 1966.

WOLPE, J., SALTER, A., & REYNA, L. J. (Eds.) *The conditioning therapies: The challenge in psychotherapy*. New York: Holt, Rinehart & Winston, 1964.

WOOLLEY, D. W. Participation of serotonin in mental processes. In M. Rinkel (Ed.), *Chemical concepts of psychosis*. New York: McDowell, Obolensky, 1958. (a)

WOOLLEY, D. W. Serotonin in mental illness. *Research Publications of the Association of Nervous and Mental Disease*, 1958, *36*, 381–400. (b)

WOOLLEY, D. W., & SHAW, E. A biochemical and pharmacological suggestion about certain mental disorders. *Science*, 1954, *119*, 587–588.

WOOLLEY, D. W., & SHAW, E. Some serotoninlike activities of lysergic acid diethylamide. *Science*, 1956, *124*, 121–122.

WORLD HEALTH ORGANIZATION. *Manual of the international statistical classification of disease, injuries, and causes of death.* Geneva: World Health Organization, 1967.

WORTIS, J. Psychopharmacology and physiological treatment. *American Journal of Psychiatry,* 1962, *119,* 621–628.

YALOM, I. D. Plantar warts: A case study. *Journal of Nervous and Mental Disease,* 1964, *138,* 163–171.

ZETZEL, E. R. The predisposition to depression. *Canadian Psychiatric Association Journal,* 1966, *11* (Suppl.), 236–249.

ZUBIN, J., SUTTON, S., SALZINGER, K., BURDOCK, E. I., & PEREZ, D. A biometric approach to prognosis in schizophrenia. In P. H. Hoch and J. Zubin (Eds.), *Comparative epidemiology in the mental disorders.* New York: Grune & Stratton, 1961.

ZUK, G. H., & BOSZORMENYI-NAGY, I. (Eds.) *Family therapy and disturbed families.* Palo Alto, Calif.: Science and Behavior Books, 1967.

Name Index

Subject Index

THE BOOK MANUFACTURE

Psychopathology Today was typeset at Kopecky Typesetting, Inc. Printing and binding were by Kingsport Press, Inc. The internal design was by John Goetz; Charles Kling & Associates designed the cover. The paper is Perkins & Squier's Glatfelter Old Forge. The type in this book is Caledonia with Baskerville display.